Roland E. Larson is Professor of Mathematics at the Behrend College of Pennsylvania State University in Erie. He is a member of NCTM and a highly successful author of many high school and college mathematics textbooks. Several of his D.C. Heath College titles have proven to be top choices for senior high school mathematics courses.

Timothy D. Kanold is Chairman of Mathematics and Science and a teacher at Adlai Stevenson High School in Prairie View, Illinois. He is the 1986 recipient of the Presidential Award for Excellence in Mathematics Teaching, as well as the 1991 recipient of the Outstanding Young Alumni Award from Illinois State University. A member of NCTM, he served on NCTM's *Professional Standards for Teaching Mathematics* Commission and is a member of the Regional Services Committee.

Lee Stiff is an Associate Professor of Mathematics Education in the College of Education and Psychology of North Carolina State University at Raleigh. He has taught mathematics at the high school and middle school levels. He is a member of the NCTM Board of Directors, served on NCTM's *Professional Standards for Teaching Mathematics* Commission, and is a member of the *Committee for a Comprehensive Mathematics Education of Every Child.*

Linda Bailey
Putnam City Schools
Oklahoma City, OK

Pat Beck
Putnam City North High School
Oklahoma City, OK

Lawrence Demetrak
San Marin High School
Novato, CA

Charleen M. DeRidder
Knox County Schools
Knoxville, TN

Melanie Donnell
Russellville High School
Russellville, AR

Joseph P. Dooley
Upper Darby High School
Upper Darby, PA

David J. Enterlin
Upper Darby High School
Upper Darby, PA

M. Jayne Fleener
University of Oklahoma
Norman, OK

Gail Gonyo
Adirondack Community College
Queensbury, NY

Wanda Heflin
Russellville High School
Russellville, AR

Karen Humble
Western Oaks Junior High School
Oklahoma City, OK

Regina D. Kiczek
Ferris High School
Jersey City, NJ

Fran Kormes
Harry S. Truman High School
Levittown, PA

Chicha Lynch
Capuchino High School
San Bruno, CA

Terry McBroom
San Marin High School
Novato, CA

Elizabeth J. Manes
Harry S. Truman High School
Levittown, PA

Deanna Mauldin
Liberty Bell Middle School
Johnson City, TN

Dominic Mendalla
Capuchino High School
San Bruno, CA

Dennis H. Noe
School District of Waukesha
Waukesha, WI

Dean Orfanedes
Capuchino High School
San Bruno, CA

Jennifer J. Penley
Liberty Bell Middle School
Johnson City, TN

Susan Shumate
Edmond Public Schools
Edmond, OK

Sharon Siegel
Dodgen Middle School
Marietta, GA

Linda Tassano
San Marin High School
Novato, CA

John Wellington
Upper Darby High School
Upper Darby, PA

To the Students

Mathematics evolved over the past few thousand years in many stages. *All* the early stages were centered around the use of mathematics to answer questions about real life. This is very much like the way we wrote *Algebra 1*. We centered the concepts around the real-life use of mathematics.

As mathematics development matured, people began to collect and categorize the different rules, formulas, and properties that had been discovered. This took place independently in many different parts of the world: Africa, Asia, Europe, North America, and South America. The mathematics that we use today is a combination of the work of literally thousands of people.

As you study our algebra book, be sure you understand the value and purpose of the concepts you're learning. Knowing **why** you are learning a concept helps you master it—and understand its relevance to your own life. That's why we begin each lesson explaining what you should learn and why you should learn it.

Remember, math is not a spectator sport—it's a valuable tool you can use in everyday life!

Roland E. Larson

Timothy D. Kanold

Lee Stiff

Real-Life Applications

Look through this list for things that interest you. Then find out how they are used with algebra.

Advertising 6, 286, 425, 586
Aeronautics 577
Agriculture 168, 266–267, 302, 351, 385, 391, 439, 500, 513, 517, 585
Air Traffic 40, 396, 707
Animal Studies 32, 141, 144, 146, 178, 309, 328, 411, 418, 437, 443–444, 476, 526, 545, 553, 557, 566, 570, 585–586, 624, 627, 630, 645, 661–662
Archaeology 564, 584
Architecture 209, 402, 487, 524, 566, 589, 657, 708
Astronomy 66, 227, 301, 309, 423–424, 426, 429–430, 448, 585, 700
Banking 7, 10–11, 17, 127, 145, 156–157, 171, 246, 281, 297, 410, 432, 435, 551–552
Biology 108, 113, 305, 423, 430, 434, 494, 525–526
Broadcasting 105, 286
Business 70, 72–73, 83, 85–86, 90, 110, 202, 215, 283, 286, 292, 297, 300, 325, 369, 375, 389, 403, 433, 436, 442, 483, 496, 531, 537, 570, 584, 592, 598, 645, 658
Chemistry 69, 72, 153, 169, 317, 362, 365, 367, 371, 408, 410, 414, 416, 422–423, 425, 497, 500, 532, 596, 697
Communication 210, 238, 246, 302
Construction 3, 25, 73, 105, 209, 355, 436, 457, 460
Consumer 31, 37, 73, 240, 247, 253, 268, 281, 287, 301, 332, 357, 371, 572–573, 580, 638, 648
Design 143, 145, 268, 402, 488, 510
Earth Science 16, 145, 162, 164–165, 171, 187, 318, 430, 456
Economics 13, 107–108, 139, 150, 152, 165, 173, 328, 357, 427, 429, 433, 469, 495, 520
Education 279–280, 484, 589, 625, 635, 654, 659
Engineering 428
Entertainment 31, 42, 51, 79, 85, 137, 165, 181, 194, 202, 246, 286, 301, 317, 331, 383, 385, 395, 440, 485, 491, 582
Environmental Science 34, 128, 169, 240, 328, 331, 338, 423, 456, 462, 501, 572, 580, 602
Finance 18, 22, 24, 76, 94, 106, 108, 111, 132, 137, 139, 152, 169, 171–172, 192, 247, 315, 337, 346–347, 350, 385, 404, 415, 432, 442, 554, 572, 608, 611, 630, 662
Fitness 49, 54, 246, 297
Geology/Mining 462, 469, 490, 579
Government 44, 50, 82, 107, 112, 161, 164, 481, 651, 657
Home Economics 105, 128, 168, 221, 231, 596, 662, 693
Law Enforcement 39, 43
Library Science 81, 110, 261
Medicine 25, 213, 348, 369, 436
Meteorology 53, 63, 92, 133, 145, 162, 182, 261, 269, 292, 297, 395, 431, 506, 592, 630, 662
Music 80, 103, 181, 532, 624, 637
Nutrition 278, 392
Oceanography 336, 566, 580, 585, 686
Paleontology 336, 410
Physics 10–11, 37, 40, 65, 67, 90–91, 93, 103, 110–113, 127, 132, 155, 158, 202, 219, 222, 240, 246, 273, 318, 364, 369, 396, 423, 428, 431, 460, 463, 474, 480, 482, 491, 496, 501, 557, 577–578, 590, 687, 699
Physiology 131, 188, 257, 625
Population 141–142, 145, 203, 216, 237, 240, 245, 254, 287, 302, 378, 409, 422, 429–430, 435, 442–444, 459–460, 469, 476, 496, 502, 513, 565, 585–586, 625
Psychology 441
Publishing 143, 185, 194, 207, 375, 386, 520, 584, 598
Retailing 22, 24, 28, 31, 43, 52, 73, 85, 90, 93–94, 98, 110–111, 150, 202, 251, 254, 265, 269, 274, 337, 368, 391, 395, 417, 421, 430, 436, 496, 501, 513–514, 540, 557
Social Studies 82, 112, 145, 161, 170, 179, 260, 287, 427, 650, 654, 656, 678, 680, 690, 705
Sociology 569, 583, 586–587
Space Exploration 423, 426
Sports 11, 24, 37, 71–72, 85, 90, 93, 96, 99, 110, 144, 152, 165, 168, 195, 200, 210, 215, 227, 232, 246, 256, 260, 274, 276, 282, 287, 298, 301, 317, 322, 324, 357–358, 370, 417, 422, 447, 454, 467–468, 483, 500, 540, 546, 553, 566, 576, 579, 582, 604, 609, 611, 622, 628, 631, 645, 652, 677, 702
Testing 41, 97, 317, 358, 442, 624
Travel 243–244, 275, 447, 476, 529, 546, 572, 604

CHAPTER
1

Connections to Algebra

	Chapter Overview	1
1.1	**Numbers and Number Operations**	2
1.2	**Variables in Algebra**	8
	Mixed Review	13
1.3	**Exponents and Powers**	14
	Programming a Calculator	19
1.4	**Order of Operations**	20
	Career Interview: Medical Technologist	25
	Mid-Chapter Self-Test	26
1.5	**Equations and Inequalities**	27
1.6	**Verbal Models and Algebraic Models**	33
	Mixed Review	38
1.7	**A Problem-Solving Plan**	39
	The Problem-Solving Process: Developing Strategies	46
1.8	**Exploring Data: Tables and Graphs**	49
	Chapter Summary	55
	Chapter Review	56
	Chapter Test	59

CHAPTER
2

Rules of Algebra

	Chapter Overview	61
2.1	**The Real Number Line**	62
2.2	**Addition of Real Numbers**	68
	Mixed Review	74
	Milestones: Origins of Algebra	74
2.3	**Subtraction of Real Numbers**	75
2.4	**Exploring Data: Matrices**	81
	Programming a Calculator	87
	Mid-Chapter Self-Test	88
2.5	**Multiplication of Real Numbers**	89
2.6	**The Distributive Property**	95
	Mixed Review	100
2.7	**Division of Real Numbers**	101
2.8	**Exploring Data: Rates and Ratios**	107
	Chapter Summary	114
	Chapter Review	115
	Chapter Test	119

CHAPTER 3 Solving Linear Equations

	Chapter Overview	121
3.1	**Solving Equations Using One Transformation**	122
3.2	**Solving Equations Using Two or More Transformations**	129
3.3	**Solving Equations with Variables on Both Sides**	135
	Mixed Review	140
3.4	**Linear Equations and Problem Solving**	141
	Career Interview: Picture Framer	146
	Mid-Chapter Self-Test	147
3.5	**Solving Equations That Involve Decimals**	148
3.6	**Literal Equations and Formulas**	154
	Mixed Review	159
3.7	**Exploring Data: Scatter Plots**	160
	Using a Graphing Calculator	166
	Chapter Summary	167
	Chapter Review	168
	Chapter Test	171
	Cumulative Review	172

CHAPTER 4 Graphing Linear Equations

	Chapter Overview	175
4.1	**Graphing Linear Equations in One Variable**	176
4.2	**Graphing Linear Equations in Two Variables**	183
	Using a Graphing Calculator	189
4.3	**Quick Graphs Using Intercepts**	190
	Mixed Review	196
	Milestones: Calculating through the Centuries	196
4.4	**The Slope of a Line**	197
	Mid-Chapter Self-Test	204
4.5	**Quick Graphs Using Slope-Intercept Form**	205
4.6	**Connections: Solutions and x-Intercepts**	211
	Mixed Review	216
4.7	**Graphs of Absolute Value Equations**	217
4.8	**Solving Absolute Value Equations**	223
	Chapter Summary	229
	Chapter Review	230
	Chapter Test	233

CHAPTER 5

Writing Linear Equations

Chapter Overview	235
5.1 Equations of Lines Using Slope-Intercept Form	236
5.2 Equations of Lines Given the Slope and a Point	242
Mixed Review	248
Career Interview: Counselor	248
5.3 Equations of Lines Given Two Points	249
5.4 Exploring Data: Fitting a Line to Data	255
Using a Graphing Calculator	262
Mid-Chapter Self-Test	263
5.5 Standard Form of a Linear Equation	264
5.6 Point-Slope Form of the Equation of a Line	270
Mixed Review	276
5.7 Problem Solving Using Linear Models	277
Chapter Summary	284
Chapter Review	285
Chapter Test	289

CHAPTER 6

Solving and Graphing Linear Inequalities

Chapter Overview	291
6.1 Solving Inequalities in One Variable	292
6.2 Problem Solving Using Inequalities	298
Mixed Review	304
Milestones: Ada	304
6.3 Compound Inequalities	305
Using a Graphing Calculator	311
Mid-Chapter Self-Test	312
6.4 Connections: Absolute Value and Inequalities	313
Mixed Review	319
6.5 Graphing Linear Inequalities in Two Variables	320
Using a Graphing Calculator	326
6.6 Exploring Data: Time Lines, Picture Graphs, and Circle Graphs	327
Chapter Summary	334
Chapter Review	335
Chapter Test	339
Cumulative Review	340

CHAPTER 7

Solving Systems of Linear Equations

	Chapter Overview	345
7.1	**Solving Linear Systems by Graphing**	346
	Using a Graphing Calculator	352
7.2	**Solving Linear Systems by Substitution**	353
	Mixed Review	359
	Career Interview: Pediatrician	359
7.3	**Solving Linear Systems by Linear Combinations**	360
7.4	**Problem Solving Using Linear Systems**	367
	Mid-Chapter Self-Test	373
7.5	**Special Types of Linear Systems**	374
	Mixed Review	380
7.6	**Solving Systems of Linear Inequalities**	381
7.7	**Exploring Data: Linear Programming**	387
	Chapter Summary	393
	Chapter Review	394
	Chapter Test	397

CHAPTER 8

Powers and Exponents

	Chapter Overview	399
8.1	**Multiplication Properties of Exponents**	400
8.2	**Negative and Zero Exponents**	406
	Mixed Review	412
	Milestones: Early Computers	412
8.3	**Division Properties of Exponents**	413
8.4	**Scientific Notation**	419
	Mixed Review	424
	Mid-Chapter Self-Test	425
8.5	**Problem Solving and Scientific Notation**	426
8.6	**Problem Solving: Compound Interest and Exponential Growth**	432
	Using a Graphing Calculator	438
8.7	**Exploring Data: Exponential Growth and Decay**	439
	Chapter Summary	445
	Chapter Review	446
	Chapter Test	449

CHAPTER 9

Quadratic Equations

	Chapter Overview	451
9.1	**Square Roots and the Pythagorean Theorem**	452
9.2	**Solving Quadratic Equations by Finding Square Roots**	458
	Mixed Review	464
	Career Interview: Printer	464
9.3	**Graphs of Quadratic Equations**	465
	Using a Graphing Calculator	471
9.4	**The Quadratic Formula**	472
	Mid-Chapter Self-Test	478
9.5	**Problem Solving Using the Discriminant**	479
	Mixed Review	485
9.6	**Graphing Quadratic Inequalities**	486
9.7	**Exploring Data: Comparing Models**	492
	Chapter Summary	498
	Chapter Review	499
	Chapter Test	503
	Cumulative Review	504

CHAPTER 10

Polynomials and Factoring

	Chapter Overview	507
10.1	**Adding and Subtracting Polynomials**	508
10.2	**Multiplying Polynomials**	515
	Mixed Review	521
	Milestones: Leonhard Euler (1707–1783)	521
10.3	**Multiplying Polynomials: Two Special Cases**	522
10.4	**Factoring: Special Products**	528
	Mid-Chapter Self-Test	534
10.5	**Factoring Quadratic Trinomials**	535
10.6	**Solving Quadratic Equations by Factoring**	541
	Mixed Review	547
	Using a Graphing Calculator	548
10.7	**Solving Quadratic Equations by Completing the Square**	549
	Chapter Summary	555
	Chapter Review	556
	Chapter Test	559

CHAPTER 11

Using Proportions and Rational Equations

	Chapter Overview	561
11.1	**Problem Solving Using Ratios and Proportions**	562
11.2	**Problem Solving Using Percents**	568
	Mixed Review	574
	Career Interview: Retailer	574
11.3	**Direct and Inverse Variation**	575
11.4	**Exploring Data: Probability**	581
	Mid-Chapter Self-Test	587
11.5	**Simplifying Rational Expressions**	588
	Mixed Review	593
11.6	**Multiplying and Dividing Rational Expressions**	594
11.7	**Dividing Polynomials**	600
	Using a Graphing Calculator	606
11.8	**Solving Rational Equations**	607
	Chapter Summary	613
	Chapter Review	614
	Chapter Test	617

CHAPTER 12

Functions

	Chapter Overview	619
12.1	**Functions and Relations**	620
12.2	**Linear Functions**	626
	Mixed Review	632
	Milestones: Unsolved Problems	632
12.3	**Exponential Functions**	633
12.4	**Quadratic Functions**	639
	Mid-Chapter Self-Test	645
12.5	**Rational Functions**	646
	Mixed Review	651
12.6	**Exploring Data: Stem-and-Leaf Plots, Box-and-Whisker Plots**	652
12.7	**Exploring Data: Measures of Central Tendency**	658
	Using a Graphing Calculator	664
	Chapter Summary	665
	Chapter Review	666
	Chapter Test	669
	Cumulative Review	670

CHAPTER 13	**Radicals and More Connections to Geometry**	
	Chapter Overview	674
13.1	**The Distance Formula**	676
13.2	**Simplying Radicals**	682
	Mixed Review	688
	Career Interview: Translation Services	688
13.3	**Operations with Radicals**	689
13.4	**Solving Radical Equations**	695
	Using a Graphing Calculator	701
	Mid-Chapter Self-Test	702
13.5	**The Tangent of an Angle**	703
	Mixed Review	709
13.6	**Formal Use of Properties of Algebra**	710
	Chapter Summary	716
	Chapter Review	717
	Chapter Test	720

Table of Squares and Square Roots	721
Properties, Models, Transformations	722
Glossary	725
Selected Answers	733
Index	781
Acknowledgments	791

Connections to Algebra

LESSONS

1.1 Numbers and Number Operations ▪ 2

1.2 Variables in Algebra ▪ 8

1.3 Exponents and Powers ▪ 14

1.4 Order of Operations ▪ 20

1.5 Equations and Inequalities ▪ 27

1.6 Verbal Models and Algebraic Models ▪ 33

1.7 A Problem-Solving Plan ▪ 39

1.8 Exploring Data: Tables and Graphs ▪ 49

Algebra is not just about x and y. It is also about toddlers. It models their world.

One of the goals of algebra is to recognize patterns and relationships that occur in real life. *Tables* can help you recognize patterns. For instance, the following table shows that between 1960 and 1990, the average family size in the United States decreased by about one tenth of a family member every five years.

(Source: U.S. Bureau of the Census)

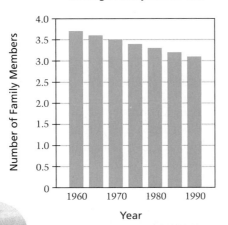

Average Family Size in U.S.

Number of Family Members

Year

Year	1960	1965	1970	1975	1980	1985	1990
Family Size	3.7	3.6	3.5	3.4	3.3	3.2	3.1

Once a pattern has been found, it can be used to answer questions about the real-life situation. For instance, from the pattern above you could estimate the 1995 average family size to be about 3.0. The *bar graph* gives a picture of the decreasing family size between 1960 and 1990.

1.1

Numbers and Number Operations

What you should learn:

Goal 1 How to represent numbers and number operations

Goal 2 How to use grouping symbols

Why you should learn it:

You can apply what you know about numbers and number operations to help solve problems in algebra.

Goal 1 Numbers and Number Operations

Much of what you will learn in algebra is based on numerical skills that you already have. For instance, you already know how to add, subtract, multiply, and divide numbers, and you will continue to use these skills in algebra.

Different kinds of numbers have different names. For example, the numbers 0, 1, 2, 3, and 4 are **whole numbers,** and the numbers $\frac{1}{2}$, $\frac{2}{3}$, and $\frac{5}{4}$ are **fractions.** What you call a number sometimes depends on the way you write the number. For example, the number $\frac{1}{2}$ can be written in three different forms.

Fraction form: $\frac{1}{2}$

Decimal form: 0.5

Percent form: 50%

Each of these forms represents the same number, which means that you could write $\frac{1}{2} = 0.5$ or $0.5 = 50\%$.

The decimal form of some numbers contains too many digits to write. For instance, no one could write *all* the digits of the decimal for $\frac{3}{7}$:

$$\frac{3}{7} = 0.4285714285\ldots$$

(The three dots mean that the number has more digits than are shown.) You can *approximate* this number to different degrees of accuracy. For instance, rounded to two decimal places, you could write

$$\frac{3}{7} \approx 0.43. \quad \textit{Rounded to two decimal places}$$

If you wanted an approximation that is more accurate, you could round to three decimal places and write

$$\frac{3}{7} \approx 0.429. \quad \textit{Rounded to three decimal places}$$

The symbol $\approx$ means *is approximately equal to.*

The number of decimal places that you should list when writing a decimal approximation depends on the context of the problem. For instance, with dollar amounts, you probably would not use more than two decimal places.

There are four basic operations that can be performed with numbers: **addition, subtraction, multiplication,** and **division.**

Example 1 — *Four Basic Number Operations*

a. *Addition:* The **sum** of 12 and 7 is 19.

$$12 + 7 = 19$$

b. *Subtraction:* The **difference** of 15 and 8 is 7.

$$15 - 8 = 7 \quad \textit{The difference of a and b is a} - \textit{b.}$$

c. *Multiplication:* The **product** of 3 and 6 is 18.

$$3 \cdot 6 = 18, \quad 3(6) = 18, \quad (3)6 = 18, \quad (3)(6) = 18$$

In algebra, we usually do not use the multiplication symbol $\times$ because it is easily confused with the letter x, which is used for another purpose.

d. *Division:* The **quotient** of 24 and 6 is 4.

$$24 \div 6 = 4, \quad \frac{24}{6} = 4 \quad \textit{The quotient of a and b is } \frac{a}{b}. \quad \blacksquare$$

You can perform each of the operations shown in Example 1 in your head. We call this **mental math.** For more complicated problems, you may want to use a calculator.

Real Life
Building Costs

Example 2 — *Building a Basketball Court*

A basketball court is 46 feet wide and 84 feet long. The court has a border that is 10 feet wide. The cost of a hardwood floor is $9 per square foot. How much will it cost to put a new floor on both the court and its border?

Solution To find the cost of the floor, multiply the cost per square foot times the area (in square feet). Recall that the area of a rectangle is found by multiplying its length times its width.

Verbal Model	Total cost	=	Cost per square foot	$\cdot$	Area (in square feet)

Labels
Cost per square foot = 9   ($ per square ft)
Area = Length $\cdot$ Width   (square ft)
Length = 10 + 84 + 10 = 104   (ft)
Width = 10 + 46 + 10 = 66   (ft)

Equation   Total cost = (9)(104)(66) = 61,776   ($)

Thus, it would cost $61,776 to put a new floor on the basketball court and its border. $\quad\blacksquare$

For problems that have more than one operation, it is important to know which operation to do first. **Grouping symbols** such as parentheses ( ) or brackets [ ] indicate the order in which the operations should be performed. Different orders can produce different results. For instance, the number $(3 \cdot 4) + 8 = 12 + 8 = 20$ is not the same as the number $3 \cdot (4 + 8) = 3 \cdot 12 = 36$.

A collection of numbers, operations, and grouping symbols is a **numerical expression.** When we *simplify* a numerical expression to find its value, we are *evaluating* the expression.

Example 3 *Evaluating Expressions Containing Grouping Symbols*

a.
$$16 - [(4 \cdot 5) - 6] = 16 - [20 - 6] \quad \textit{Simplify } 4 \cdot 5.$$
$$= 16 - 14 \quad \textit{Simplify } 20 - 6.$$
$$= 2 \quad \textit{Simplify } 16 - 14.$$

b.
$$\frac{210}{20 - (13 - 3)} = 210 \div (20 - 10) \quad \textit{Simplify } 13 - 3.$$
$$= 210 \div 10 \quad \textit{Simplify } 20 - 10.$$
$$= 21 \quad \textit{Simplify } 210 \div 10.$$

Connections
Technology

c. To evaluate the expression $[413.2 \div (12.5 \cdot 6.1)] - 2.6$, use a calculator and follow these steps.

$$\boxed{(} \ 413.2 \ \boxed{\div} \ \boxed{(} \ 12.5 \ \boxed{\times} \ 6.1 \ \boxed{)} \ \boxed{)} \ \boxed{-} \ 2.6 \ \boxed{=}$$

The calculator display of 2.819016393 can be rounded to 2.8. ■

Communicating about **ALGEBRA**

▶ **SHARING IDEAS about the Lesson**

Estimate for Reasonableness When you use a calculator to evaluate an expression, such as in Example 3, one way to check that the answer is reasonable is to estimate the value of the expression first. Using the methods of estimating you know, find three estimates of each answer and explain how you found them.

A. $[413.2 \div (12.5 - 6.1)] - 2.6$ **B.** $0.45 \cdot (1.92 - 0.84) \cdot 17.6$

EXERCISES

Guided Practice

▶ CRITICAL THINKING about the Lesson

Little League   In Exercises 1–6, use the bar graph showing the five states with the most Little League teams.
(Source: Little League Baseball, Inc.)

1. Which state has the most Little League teams?

2. Why do you think California has so many more teams than New Jersey?

3. Estimate the total number of teams from the five states listed.

4. Which of the following is a good estimate of the difference between the numbers of teams in New York and Florida?

    a. 14,000   b. 6,000   c. 7,000

    d. 10,000   e. 8,000

5. How did you arrive at the estimate in Exercise 3? In Exercise 4?

6. In Exercise 4, what would be a good estimate to the nearest hundred?

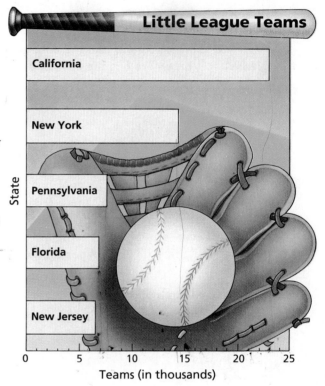

Little League Teams

States (top to bottom): California, New York, Pennsylvania, Florida, New Jersey

State

Teams (in thousands): 0   5   10   15   20   25

Independent Practice

In Exercises 7–14, use mental math.

7. What is the sum of 4 and 9? *13*

8. What is the sum of 12 and 6? *18*

9. What is the difference of 8 and 7? *1*

10. What is the difference of 9 and 2? *7*

11. What is the product of 4 and 6? *24*

12. What is the product of 7 and 3? *21*

13. What is the quotient of 16 and 4? *4*

14. What is the quotient of 5 and 1? *5*

In Exercises 15–28, evaluate the expression.

15. $[8 - 3(2)] \cdot 6$

16. $12 - [(4)(2) + 2]$

17. $[3(6) + 2] + 4$

18. $4 - [(2 \cdot 9) - 17]$

19. $24 \div [10 - (4 \div 2)]$

20. $12 + [16 \div (3 + 1)]$

21. $10 + [9 \div (1 + 2)]$

22. $[12 \div (1 + 5)] - 2$

23. $18 \div [(8)(2) - 7]$

24. $[(10 \cdot 3) - 10] \div 4$

25. $[12 \div (3 \cdot 2)] + 4$

26. $16 - [54 \div (3)(3)]$

27. $\dfrac{10}{(4 - 3) \cdot 2}$

28. $\dfrac{28}{(4)(2) - 4}$

In Exercises 29–34, use a calculator to evaluate the expression. Round your result to two decimal places. Use estimation to check your answer.

29. $[52.4 - (16.1 \div 3.6)] - 30.2$

30. $13.9 \div [(7.4 - 6.2) + 4.9]$

31. $42.1 \div [(3.2 \cdot 6.1) - 1.3]$

32. $[(16.0)(7.2 \div 3.9) + 6.2] - 29.8$

33. $[439.9 + (12.9 \div 4.1)] - (42.2)(6.1)$

34. $(9.4 \div 2.7) + [(4.3)(16.1) - 17.7]$

Geometry   In Exercises 35–37, find the area of the figure. (The area of a triangle is $A = \frac{1}{2}bh$, where b is the base and h is the height.)

35.

4 ft

←— 4 ft —→

36.

3 m

←——— 5 m ———→

37.

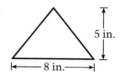

5 in.

←——— 8 in. ———→

38. *Cost of Fencing*   A swimming pool is 5 meters wide and 6 meters long. A concrete walk that is 2 meters wide surrounds the pool. Draw and label a diagram of the pool and walk. Then find how much it will cost for wooden fencing around the outside of the walk if the fencing sells for $13 per meter.

39. *Airplane Banner*   An airplane advertising banner has a height of $2\frac{1}{2}$ yards and a length of 15 yards. How many square yards of material are needed to make the banner?

ANNUAL PICNIC TOMORROW $2\frac{1}{2}$ yd

N59862

←——— 15 yd ———→

40. *Horse Show*   A circular arena for horses has a diameter of 200 feet. How far must a horse walk to go around the edge of the arena once? (The circumference of a circle is $C = \pi d$, where $\pi \approx 3.14$ and d is the diameter.)

Baseball Cards   In Exercises 41 and 42, use the chart showing the estimated value in 1991 of five rare baseball cards.

(Source: Sports Collectors Digest, Baseball Card Monthly Price Guide)

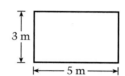

	Estimated Value	Number in Existence
Honus Wagner (T206 1909)	$110,000	50
Fred Lindstrom (U.S. Carmel 1932)	$ 25,000	1
Napoleon Lajoie (Goudey 1933)	$ 25,000	50
Joe Doyle (T206 1910)	$ 17,000	2
Eddie Plank (T206 1910)	$ 14,000	100

41. What is the total value of all the Honus Wagner cards in existence?

42. What is the total value of two Joe Doyle and three Eddie Plank cards?

43. Write $\frac{6}{5}$ as a decimal.

44. Write 50% as a fraction. .50

45. Write $\frac{3}{4}$ as a percent. .75

46. Write 60% as a decimal. 60

47. Write 0.32 as a fraction. $\frac{32}{100}$

48. Write 0.07 as a percent. 7%

49. Approximate $\frac{4}{9}$ to two decimal places. .44

50. Approximate $\frac{7}{6}$ to two decimal places.

Geometry   In Exercises 51 and 52, find the missing portion of the *circle graph.* (The portions total 100%.)

51.

52.

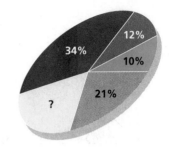

Geometry   In Exercises 53 and 54, find the area of the figure.

53.

54.

Exploration and Extension

Balance in a Savings Account   In Exercises 55–58, use the following data from a newly opened savings account.

Date	Deposit	Withdrawal	Interest Earned	Balance
June 1	$50.00			$50.00
June 15	$50.00			
June 30			$0.37	
July 15		$30.00		
July 30			$0.58	

55. What was the balance on June 15?

56. What was the balance on June 30?

57. What was the balance on July 15?

58. What was the balance on July 30?

1.2

Variables in Algebra

What you should learn:

Goal 1 How to evaluate variable expressions

Goal 2 How to represent real-life quantities using variable expressions

Why you should learn it:

You can use variables in algebra to represent numbers. These variables can be used to express number relationships, such as in the formula $d = rt$ for distance, rate, and time.

Goal 1 Evaluating Variable Expressions

A **variable** is a letter that is used to represent one or more numbers. The numbers are the **values of the variable.** An **algebraic expression** is a collection of numbers, variables, operations, and grouping symbols. Here are some examples.

Algebraic Expression	Meaning
$8y$	8 times y
$\dfrac{16a}{b}$	16 times a, divided by b
$4r + s$	4 times r, plus s

When each variable in an algebraic expression is replaced by a number, we say that we are *evaluating* the expression, and the resulting number is the **value of the expression.** For example, when $x = 2$, the value of the expression $4x$ is found by *substituting* 2 for x. In this case, the resulting value of the expression is $4(2) = 8$.

To evaluate an algebraic expression, use this *flowchart*:

Write the algebraic expression.	$\longrightarrow$	Substitute values for variables.	$\longrightarrow$	Simplify the numerical expression.

Example 1 *Evaluating an Algebraic Expression*

Evaluate $5x + 4y$ when $x = 3$ and $y = 2$.

Solution　To evaluate this expression, substitute 3 for x and 2 for y.

$$
\begin{aligned}
5x + 4y & \qquad \textit{Write the expression.} \\
= 5(3) + 4(2) & \qquad \textit{Substitute 3 for x and 2 for y.} \\
= 15 + 8 & \qquad \textit{Simplify 5(3) and 4(2).} \\
= 23 & \qquad \textit{Value of the expression}
\end{aligned}
$$

Thus, the expression $5x + 4y$ has a value of 23 when $x = 3$ and $y = 2$. ■

When substituting a number for a variable, you must replace each occurrence of the variable in the expression. For example, if $x = 3$, then:

$$x + (2x - 1) = 3 + [(2 \cdot 3) - 1] \quad \textit{Substitute 3 for x twice.}$$
$$= 3 + [6 - 1] \quad \textit{Simplify 2 · 3.}$$
$$= 3 + 5 \quad \textit{Simplify 6 - 1.}$$
$$= 8 \quad \textit{Value of the expression}$$

An algebraic expression can have different values when different numbers are substituted for the variable, as shown in Example 2.

Example 2 *Substituting Different Values for a Variable*

Evaluate the expression $(x + 7) \div 5$ when x has the following values.

a. $x = 3$ **b.** $x = 208$

Solution

Write the expression.		**Substitute values for x.**		**Simplify the expression.**
a. $\dfrac{x+7}{5}$	$=$	$\dfrac{3+7}{5}$	$=$	$\dfrac{10}{5} = 2$
b. $\dfrac{x+7}{5}$	$=$	$\dfrac{208+7}{5}$	$=$	$\dfrac{215}{5} = 43$

The parts of an expression formed as a sum, product, or quotient have special names.

Sum: $3x$ and 2 are **terms** of $3x + 2$.
Product: 4 and x are **factors** of $4x$.
Quotient: $5x$ is the **numerator** and 2 is the **denominator** of $\frac{5x}{2}$.

Example 3 *Using a Calculator to Evaluate an Expression*

Use a calculator to evaluate the following expression when $r = 8.6$ and $s = 4.3$. Round your result to one decimal place.

$$\frac{6.37(r + s)}{3.8}$$

Solution

$$\frac{6.37(r + s)}{3.8} = \frac{6.37(8.6 + 4.3)}{3.8} \quad \textit{Substitute 8.6 for r and 4.3 for s.}$$
$$\approx 21.6 \quad \textit{Round to one decimal place.}$$

One possible sequence of keystrokes is as follows.

$$6.37 \;\boxed{\times}\; \boxed{(}\; 8.6 \;\boxed{+}\; 4.3 \;\boxed{)}\; \boxed{\div}\; 3.8 \;\boxed{=}$$

Representing Real-Life Quantities

Algebraic expressions are often used in real-life situations. Here are some examples.

		Labels	Formula
Area of Rectangle	A = area		$A = lw$
	l = length		
	w = width		
Interest Earned	I = interest		$I = Prt$
	P = principal		
	r = interest rate (decimal)		
	t = time (years)		
Temperature	F = degrees Fahrenheit		$F = \frac{9}{5}C + 32$
	C = degrees Celsius		
Distance	d = distance		$d = rt$
	r = rate or speed		
	t = time		

Connections
Physics

Example 4 *Finding the Distance Traveled*

Suppose you are traveling in a car at a constant speed of 75 kilometers per hour for one and one-half hours. How far will you travel?

Solution Use the formula for distance.

$$d = rt \qquad \textit{Formula for distance}$$
$$= (75)(1.5) \qquad \textit{Substitute 75 for r and 1.5 for t.}$$
$$= 112.5 \qquad \textit{Simplify.}$$

Thus, you will travel a distance of 112.5 kilometers. ∎

Communicating about ALGEBRA

▶ **SHARING IDEAS about the Lesson**

Multiple Solutions Decide whether each statement is true or false when $a = 1$, $b = 2$, $c = 3$, and $x = 8$. If a statement is false, find values of the variables that make the statement true. (The values you find may differ from those found by other students.)

A. $2a = b$

B. $5a = b + 3$

C. $5c - x = 4b$

D. $7b - x = 2c$

E. $7 + b = x + a$

F. $8 + b = 7 + x$

EXERCISES

▶ **CRITICAL THINKING about the Lesson**

1. State the meaning of the variable expression $\frac{r}{3s}$ in words.
2. What is the variable expression for "6 times x, plus y"? $6 \cdot X + Y$
3. Evaluate the expression $8x$ when $x = 3$.
4. Evaluate the expression $9a - 2$ when $a = 1$.
5. Evaluate the expression $a - b$ when $a = 10$ and $b = 3$.
6. Evaluate the expression $2x + 4y$ when $x = 2$ and $y = 3$. Find other values for x and y that give the same result.

In Exercises 7–16, evaluate the expression.

7. $2x + 1$, when $x = 4$ 9
8. $x - 9$, when $x = 21$
9. $2r - s + 4$, when $r = 4$ and $s = 5$ 4
10. $3a + b$, when $a = 2$ and $b = 1$
11. $(a - 2) + 4a$, when $a = 4$ 18
12. $6a - (1 + a)$, when $a = 3$
13. $3x(4 + x)$, when $x = 2$ 36
14. $5y + 4(y - 3)$, when $y = 4$
15. $x \div (3y - 4)$, when $x = 6$ and $y = 2$
16. $[9 - (x \div 4)] + y$, when $x = 8$ and $y = 7$

In Exercises 17–20, evaluate $24 \div (x + 2)$ for the given value of x.

17. $x = 2$
18. $x = 0$
19. $x = 4$
20. $x = 10$

Technology   **In Exercises 21–24, use a calculator to evaluate the expression. Round your result to two decimal places. Use estimation to check your answer.**

21. $4.97a + 9.21$, when $a = 6.21$
22. $3.2(2.1a - 4.3)$, when $a = 4.8$
23. $6.9(x - 3.2y) - 56.2$, when $x = 19.1$ and $y = 1.1$
24. $15.9 \div (x + y)$, when $x = 3.2$ and $y = 3.4$

In Exercises 25–28, you may need to use the formulas on page 10.

25. *Artificial Turf*   A football field is 110 meters long and 49 meters wide. How many square meters of artificial turf are needed to cover the field?

26. *Interest Earned*   Suppose you deposit $80 in a savings account that pays an annual interest rate of 6%. How much interest would you earn in 9 months?

27. *Distance Traveled*   A car traveled for 2 hours at a constant speed of 72 kilometers per hour. How far did the car travel?

28. *Running*   If you jog 300 feet per minute, how many feet will you jog in an hour?

In Exercises 29–32, use mental math to evaluate the expression.

29. The sum of 6 and 11

30. The difference of 14 and 9

31. The product of 6 and 8

32. The quotient of 27 and 3

Technology　**In Exercises 33–36, use a calculator to evaluate the expression. Round your result to two decimal places, if appropriate. Use estimation to check your answers.**

33. $42.6 + 9.3$

34. $21.3 - 16.8$

35. $9.39 \div 6.12$

36. $3.9 \cdot 6.4$

In Exercises 37–40, evaluate the expression.

37. $10 - [8 \div (4 - 2)]$

38. $6 \cdot (12 \div 4) + 9$

39. $[(9 - 5) \cdot 4] \div 4$

40. $(16 + 4) \div (2 \cdot 5)$

41. Insert grouping symbols in the expression

$$30 - 36 \div 3 + 6$$

so that its value is 12.

42. Insert grouping symbols in the expression

$$12 \cdot 2 + 12 - 10$$

so that its value is 26.

43. *Geometry*　Write an algebraic expression that represents the perimeter of a triangle whose sides have lengths a, b, and c. (The perimeter of a triangle is the sum of the lengths of its sides.) Then use the expression to find the perimeter of each triangle.

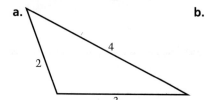

44. *Geometry*　Write an algebraic expression that represents the circumference of a circle whose radius is r. (The circumference of a circle is π times twice its radius, where $\pi \approx 3.14$.) Then use the expression to find the circumference of each circle.

a.

b.

c.

45. In Exercise 43, as the sides increase by one unit each, how does the perimeter change?

46. In Exercise 44, as each radius increases by one unit, how does the circumference change?

47. *Drink-Boxes*   Drink-box consumption in the United States increased in the years 1983 to 1990. An equation that approximates the millions of drink-boxes sold, D, in terms of the year, t, is

$$D = 270t - 200$$

where $t = 3$ corresponds to 1983. Use this equation to complete the table. *(Source: Nielsen ScanTrack, Tetra Pak, Inc.)*

Year	1983	1984	1985	1986	1987	1988	1989	1990
t	3	4	5	6	7	8	9	10
D	?	?	?	?	?	?	?	?

48. Use the information in Exercise 47 to construct a bar graph showing the number of drink-boxes sold in the United States from 1983 to 1990. Describe the pattern formed by the tops of the bars.

49. In 1990, the population of the United States was about 250 million. Find the average number of drink-boxes that Americans consumed *per person* in 1990.

50. Did the per person consumption of drink-boxes increase from 1983 to 1990? Why do you think this was so?

Mixed REVIEW

1. Evaluate $(17 - 9) + 28$. **(1.1)**

2. Write the sum as a fraction: $\frac{2}{3}$ and 3.

3. What is 10% of $245?

4. Which is greater, $\frac{1}{2}$ or 0.75?

5. What is the product of 9 and 4? **(1.1)**

6. What is the difference of 13 and 5? **(1.1)**

7. Evaluate $9 \div [3 + (11 - 5)]$. **(1.1)**

8. Evaluate $[(7 \cdot 3) - 2] + (8 \div 4)$. **(1.1)**

9. What is the quotient of 21 and 7? **(1.1)**

10. Evaluate $x - 2y$ when $x = 14$ and $y = 3$. **(1.2)**

11. Evaluate $3x + 1$ when $x = 2$. **(1.2)**

12. Evaluate $3x + 2$ when $x = 2$. **(1.2)**

13. Evaluate $\frac{1}{2}(x - 7)$ when $x = 11$. **(1.2)**

14. Evaluate $\frac{x}{2} + \frac{x}{4}$ when $x = 1$. **(1.2)**

15. Write an expression for the perimeter of a square with sides of length x. **(1.2)**

16. Find the perimeter of a rectangular field 103 feet long and 210 feet wide. **(1.2)**

17. Use a calculator to evaluate $1.4x + 7.4$ when $x = 3.2$. **(1.2)**

18. What is the average height: 72 in., 68 in., 60 in., 76 in., 64 in.?

19. What is the value of $\frac{1}{2}(2a - 3b)$ when $a = 9$ and $b = 4$? **(1.2)**

1.3

Exponents and Powers

What you should learn:

Goal 1 How to evaluate expressions containing exponents

Goal 2 How to use exponents in real-life problems

Why you should learn it:

You can use exponents to simplify writing in algebra as in the formula for the area of a square, $A = s^2$. You can also use exponents to simplify computation by using the ■ key on your calculator.

Goal 1 Expressions Containing Exponents

Exponents can be used to represent repeated multiplication. For instance, the expression 4^6 represents the number that you obtain when 4 is used as a factor 6 times.

$$4^6 = \underbrace{4 \cdot 4 \cdot 4 \cdot 4 \cdot 4 \cdot 4}_{6 \text{ factors of } 4}$$

The number 4 is the **base,** the number 6 is the **exponent,** and the number 4^6 is a **power.** The exponent represents the number of times the base is used as a factor. Exponential forms are read as follows.

7^2 is read as *seven to the second power* or as *seven squared.*
5^3 is read as *five to the third power* or as *five cubed.*
4^6 is read as *four to the sixth power.*

For a number raised to the *first power,* the exponent 1 is not usually written. For instance, simply write 5^1 as 5.

Example 1 Using an Exponent to Represent Repeated Multiplication

Use an exponent to represent the expression $2 \cdot 2 \cdot 2 \cdot 2 \cdot 2$.

Solution Because the number 2 is used as a factor 5 times, you know that the base is 2 and the exponent is 5. Thus, this expression can be written as

$$2 \cdot 2 \cdot 2 \cdot 2 \cdot 2 = 2^5.$$

Simplified, the value of this expression is 32. ■

Example 2 Evaluating an Algebraic Expression Involving an Exponent

Evaluate the expression x^3 when $x = 5$.

Solution

$$
\begin{aligned}
x^3 &= 5^3 && \textit{Substitute 5 for x.} \\
&= 5 \cdot 5 \cdot 5 \\
&= 125 && \textit{Value of the expression}
\end{aligned}
$$
■

Example 3 — Evaluating an Algebraic Expression Involving an Exponent

Evaluate the expression $(3a + 6b)^2$ when $a = 1$ and $b = 2$.

Solution

$$
\begin{aligned}
(3a + 6b)^2 &= [3(1) + 6(2)]^2 &&\textit{Substitute 1 for a and}\\
&&&\textit{2 for b.}\\
&= [3 + 12]^2 &&\textit{Simplify 3(1) and 6(2).}\\
&= 15^2 &&\textit{Simplify 3 + 12.}\\
&= 15 \cdot 15\\
&= 225 &&\textit{Value of the expression} \quad\blacksquare
\end{aligned}
$$

Connections

Technology

Example 4 — Calculators and Exponents

Evaluate the expression 6^7.

Solution   The expression

$$6^7 = \underbrace{6 \cdot 6 \cdot 6 \cdot 6 \cdot 6 \cdot 6 \cdot 6}_{\text{7 factors of 6}}$$

is difficult to evaluate with pencil and paper. The work is easier if you have a calculator with an exponent key. This key is often labeled as $\boxed{x^y}$, as $\boxed{y^x}$, or as $\boxed{\wedge}$. If your calculator has one of these keys, find out how the key works. The correct result is

$$6^7 = 279{,}936. \qquad\qquad\qquad\qquad\blacksquare$$

An exponent applies only to the number, variable, or expression that is immediately to its left. In the expression $2x^3$, the base is x, not $2x$. In the expression $(2x)^3$, the base is $2x$.

Example 5 — Exponents and Grouping Symbols

Evaluate $2x^3$ and $(2x)^3$ when $x = 4$.

Solution

a.
$$
\begin{aligned}
2x^3 &= 2(4^3) &&\textit{Substitute 4 for x.}\\
&= 2(64) &&\textit{Simplify } 4^3.\\
&= 128 &&\textit{Simplify 2(64).}
\end{aligned}
$$

b.
$$
\begin{aligned}
(2x)^3 &= (2 \cdot 4)^3 &&\textit{Substitute 4 for x.}\\
&= (8)^3 &&\textit{Simplify } 2 \cdot 4.\\
&= 512 &&\textit{Simplify } 8^3. \quad\blacksquare
\end{aligned}
$$

Many formulas for area and volume involve exponents. In fact, the words *squared* and *cubed* come from the formulas for the area of a square, $A = s^2$, and the volume of a cube, $V = s^3$. (In these formulas, s is the length of each side of the square or each edge of the cube.)

Connections
Geometry

Example 6 | *Surface Area*

Use exponents to write a formula for the surface area of a cube. Then use the formula to find the surface area of a cube whose edges are each 3 inches.

Solution Let s represent the length of each edge of the cube. Each of the six faces of the cube has an area of s^2, which means that the surface area, S, of the cube is $S = 6s^2$. Using this formula, you can find the surface area of a cube with 3-inch edges as follows.

$$S = 6s^2 \quad \textit{Formula for surface area of cube}$$
$$= 6(3^2) \quad \textit{Substitute 3 for s.}$$
$$= 6(9) \quad \textit{Simplify } 3^2.$$
$$= 54 \quad \textit{Simplify 6(9).}$$

Thus, the cube has a surface area of 54 square inches. (Note that this can be written as 54 in.^{2}) ∎

Communicating about **ALGEBRA**

▶ **SHARING IDEAS about the Lesson**

What Process to Use The surface area, S, of a sphere is

$$S = 4\pi r^2$$

where r is the radius of the sphere and $\pi \approx 3.14$.

A. A major feature of Epcot Center is called Spaceship Earth. The building is shaped like a sphere and has a diameter of 165 feet. Find the approximate surface area of the building. *(Source: Walt Disney World)*

B. Earth has a radius of approximately 6370 kilometers. Approximate the surface area of Earth.

C. Land forms 29.2% of the total surface area of Earth. Approximate the area of Earth's land.

D. Approximate the area of Earth's oceans.

Example 3 *Evaluating an Algebraic Expression Involving an Exponent*

Evaluate the expression $(3a + 6b)^2$ when $a = 1$ and $b = 2$.

Solution

$$(3a + 6b)^2 = [3(1) + 6(2)]^2 \qquad \textit{Substitute 1 for a and 2 for b.}$$
$$= [3 + 12]^2 \qquad \textit{Simplify 3(1) and 6(2).}$$
$$= 15^2 \qquad \textit{Simplify 3 + 12.}$$
$$= 15 \cdot 15$$
$$= 225 \qquad \textit{Value of the expression} \quad \blacksquare$$

Connections
Technology

Example 4 *Calculators and Exponents*

Evaluate the expression 6^7.

Solution   The expression

$$6^7 = \underbrace{6 \cdot 6 \cdot 6 \cdot 6 \cdot 6 \cdot 6 \cdot 6}_{\text{7 factors of 6}}$$

is difficult to evaluate with pencil and paper. The work is easier if you have a calculator with an exponent key. This key is often labeled as $\boxed{x^y}$, as $\boxed{y^x}$, or as $\boxed{\wedge}$. If your calculator has one of these keys, find out how the key works. The correct result is

$$6^7 = 279,936. \qquad \blacksquare$$

An exponent applies only to the number, variable, or expression that is immediately to its left. In the expression $2x^3$, the base is x, not $2x$. In the expression $(2x)^3$, the base is $2x$.

Example 5 *Exponents and Grouping Symbols*

Evaluate $2x^3$ and $(2x)^3$ when $x = 4$.

Solution

a. $2x^3 = 2(4^3) \qquad \textit{Substitute 4 for x.}$
$\qquad = 2(64) \qquad \textit{Simplify } 4^3.$
$\qquad = 128 \qquad \textit{Simplify 2(64).}$

b. $(2x)^3 = (2 \cdot 4)^3 \qquad \textit{Substitute 4 for x.}$
$\qquad = (8)^3 \qquad \textit{Simplify } 2 \cdot 4.$
$\qquad = 512 \qquad \textit{Simplify } 8^3. \qquad \blacksquare$

Many formulas for area and volume involve exponents. In fact, the words *squared* and *cubed* come from the formulas for the area of a square, $A = s^2$, and the volume of a cube, $V = s^3$. (In these formulas, s is the length of each side of the square or each edge of the cube.)

Connections

Geometry

Example 6   *Surface Area*

Use exponents to write a formula for the surface area of a cube. Then use the formula to find the surface area of a cube whose edges are each 3 inches.

Solution   Let s represent the length of each edge of the cube. Each of the six faces of the cube has an area of s^2, which means that the surface area, S, of the cube is $S = 6s^2$. Using this formula, you can find the surface area of a cube with 3-inch edges as follows.

$$S = 6s^2 \quad \textit{Formula for surface area of cube}$$
$$= 6(3^2) \quad \textit{Substitute 3 for s.}$$
$$= 6(9) \quad \textit{Simplify } 3^2.$$
$$= 54 \quad \textit{Simplify 6(9).}$$

Thus, the cube has a surface area of 54 square inches. (Note that this can be written as 54 in.^{2})

Communicating about ALGEBRA

▶ **SHARING IDEAS about the Lesson**

What Process to Use   The surface area, S, of a sphere is
$$S = 4\pi r^2$$
where r is the radius of the sphere and $\pi \approx 3.14$.

A. A major feature of Epcot Center is called Spaceship Earth. The building is shaped like a sphere and has a diameter of 165 feet. Find the approximate surface area of the building. *(Source: Walt Disney World)*

B. Earth has a radius of approximately 6370 kilometers. Approximate the surface area of Earth.

C. Land forms 29.2% of the total surface area of Earth. Approximate the area of Earth's land.

D. Approximate the area of Earth's oceans.

EXERCISES

Guided Practice

▶ **CRITICAL THINKING about the Lesson**

1. Express 18^3 in words (two different ways).
2. In the expression 18^3, what is 18 called?
3. In the expression 18^3, what is 3 called?
4. Use a calculator to evaluate 18^3.
5. Explain why x^2 is called x *squared.*
6. Explain why y^3 is called y *cubed.*

Independent Practice

In Exercises 7–15, write the expression in exponential form.

7. two cubed
8. x squared
9. nine to the y power
10. y to the ninth power
11. $3 \cdot 3 \cdot 3 \cdot 3$
12. $y \cdot y$
13. $a \cdot a \cdot a \cdot a \cdot a \cdot a$
14. $4 \cdot 4 \cdot 4$
15. $2x \cdot 2x \cdot 2x$

In Exercises 16–25, evaluate the expression.

16. y^2, when $y = 9$
17. a^4, when $a = 3$
18. $a^2 - 3$, when $a = 3$
19. $16 + x^3$, when $x = 2$
20. $(x + y)^2$, when $x = 3$ and $y = 4$
21. $x^2 + y^2$, when $x = 2$ and $y = 6$
22. $(2a)^2 - b$, when $a = 4$ and $b = 10$
23. $(6x + y)^2$, when $x = 1$ and $y = 4$
24. $3r^2 + 6s$, when $r = 2$ and $s = 3$
25. $4x - 3y^3$, when $x = 7$ and $y = 2$

Technology   **In Exercises 26–29, use a calculator to evaluate the expression. Use estimation to check your results.**

26. 9^5
27. 13^4
28. 5^9
29. 3^{11}

30. Find the area of a square with 8-inch sides.

31. Find the volume of a cube with 11-centimeter edges.

32. *Giraffe Exhibit*   The giraffe exhibit at a zoo is circular and bordered by a fence. The distance from the center of the exhibit to the fence is 60 feet. How much area do the giraffes have? (The area of a circle is $A = \pi r^2$, where $\pi \approx 3.14$ and r is the radius.)

33. *Tennis Ball*   A tennis ball has a diameter of 6.67 centimeters. What is the surface area of the ball?

34. *Compound Interest* $1000 is deposited in a savings account that is compounded annually at 6%. The balance, A, in the account after t years is $A = 1000(1 + 0.06)^t$. Find the balance after 1 year, 10 years, and 20 years.

The Louvre pyramid in Paris has a height of 20.6 meters and a square base with sides of 35 meters.

35. *Volume of a Pyramid*   The volume of a pyramid is one third the height times the area of the base. What is the volume of the Louvre pyramid?

36. *Volume of a Safe*   A fireproof safe has a cubical storage space inside. What is the volume of the storage space if each interior dimension is 12 inches?

Integrated Review

Technology   **In Exercises 37–40, use a calculator to evaluate the expression. Round your result to two decimal places. Use estimation to check your answer.**

37. 1.6^5 **38.** 3.9^3 **39.** 6.9^2 **40.** 4.3^4

41. What value of x would make the expression $x^2 + 1$ equal to 10?

42. What value of x would make the expression $x^3 - 3$ equal to 5?

Exploration and Extension

43. *Preparation Time*   In an English class, the suggested amount of time to spend on each paper triples for each new paper. If $1\frac{1}{2}$ hours was the suggested time for the first paper, how much time should be planned for the third paper?

44. *What an Allowance!*   If a child's one-penny allowance doubles every day for 30 days, how much is the allowance on the 30th day? (Day 1: 1¢, Day 2: 2¢, Day 3: 4¢, and so on)

45. Copy and complete the table on the right by evaluating the powers of 9. What pattern do you see for the last digit of each product?

9^1	9^2	9^3	9^4	9^5	9^6	9^7	9^8
?	?	?	?	?	?	?	?

46. Try the experiment described in Exercise 45 again, first with powers of 8 and then with powers of 7.

*Programmable calculators and computers can be instructed to evaluate an expression. The list of instructions is a **program**, and each separate instruction is a **program step**. When the calculator or computer performs the steps in a program, it is* executing *or* running *the program.*

Here are examples of two *flowcharts* for a program that will evaluate the algebraic expression $x^2 + 2x$ for different values of the variable x.

Programmable Calculator

Computer Program

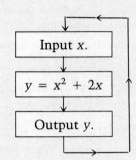

The following three versions of this program show steps that can be used with a Texas Instruments *TI-81*, a Casio *fx-7700G*, and a computer that has the BASIC computer language. When you run the program, enter the x-value when prompted, and the calculator or computer will display the value of the expression $x^2 + 2x$.

TI-81	**Casio fx-7700G**	**BASIC**
Prgm:EVALUATE	EVALUATE	10 REM EVALUATE
:Lbl 1	Lbl 1	20 PRINT "ENTER X"
:Disp "ENTER X"	"ENTER X"	30 INPUT X
:Input X	?→X	40 Y = X∧2 + 2*X
:X²+2X→Y	X²+2X→Y	50 PRINT Y
:Disp Y	Y	60 GOTO 10
:Goto 1	Goto 1	

Exercises

Use a programmable calculator or a computer to evaluate the following expressions when $x = 0$, $x = 1$, $x = 2$, and $x = 5.36$. (Round each result to two decimal places.)

1. $x^2 + 2x$ **2.** $60 - 9x$ **3.** $0.5x + 10$ **4.** $\frac{1}{3}x$

5. x^2 **6.** $x^2 + 1$ **7.** $3x^2 + 8x$ **8.** $5x^2$

1.4

Order of Operations

What you should learn:

Goal 1 How to use an established order of operations to evaluate algebraic expressions

Goal 2 How to evaluate expressions with a calculator

Why you should learn it:

You should use the order of operations that everyone agrees on so that you get the same results as everyone else. You should also know how to operate your calculator so that it performs operations in the desired order.

Goal 1 Using the Order of Operations

One of your goals as you study this book is to learn to communicate about algebra by reading and writing information about numbers.

One way to help avoid confusion when we are communicating algebraic ideas is to establish an **order of operations.** We do this by giving priorities to the different operations. First priority is given to exponents, second priority is given to multiplication and division, and third priority is given to addition and subtraction. Notice how we apply this order in Example 1.

Example 1 *Priority of Operations (without Grouping Symbols)*

Evaluate the expression $3x^2 + 1$ when $x = 4$.

Solution

$$\begin{aligned} 3x^2 + 1 &= 3 \cdot 4^2 + 1 && \textit{Substitute 4 for x.} \\ &= 3 \cdot 16 + 1 && \textit{Simplify } 4^2. \\ &= 48 + 1 && \textit{Simplify } 3 \cdot 16. \\ &= 49 && \textit{Simplify } 48 + 1. \end{aligned}$$

Notice the order of the three operations: Raise to a power first, multiply second, and add third. ∎

When you want to change the established order of operations for an expression, you *must* use parentheses or other grouping symbols. Notice in Example 2 how using grouping symbols in $3 \cdot 4^2 + 1$ gives expressions that have different values.

Example 2 *Priority of Operations (with Grouping Symbols)*

a. $(3 \cdot 4)^2 + 1 = 12^2 + 1 = 144 + 1 = 145$

b. $3(4^2 + 1) = 3(16 + 1) = 3(17) = 51$

c. $3 \cdot 4^{(2+1)} = 3 \cdot 4^3 = 3 \cdot 64 = 192$

d. $(3 \cdot 4)^{(2+1)} = 12^3 = 1728$ ∎

Operations that have the same priority, such as multiplication and division *or* addition and subtraction, are performed from left to right (the Left-to-Right Rule).

Example 3 *Using the Left-to-Right Rule*

a. $24 - 8 - 6 = (24 - 8) - 6$ *Work from left to right.*
$$= 16 - 6$$
$$= 10$$

b. $15 - 2 + 8 = (15 - 2) + 8$ *Work from left to right.*
$$= 13 + 8$$
$$= 21$$

c. $16 + 4 \div 2 - 3 = 16 + (4 \div 2) - 3$ *Divide before adding.*
$$= 16 + 2 - 3$$
$$= (16 + 2) - 3$$ *Work from left to right.*
$$= 18 - 3$$
$$= 15$$

Remember that the Left-to-Right Rule applies only to operations having the same priority. For Part **c,** we do not perform the operations from left to right because division has a higher priority than addition. On page 4, you saw how parentheses and brackets can be used to define the order in which operations should be performed. Working from left to right would have been correct in Part **c** only if "16 + 4" had been enclosed in parentheses. If you are writing an expression and want to make sure that you will not be misunderstood, you can use grouping symbols. For instance, to make sure that $24 \div 4 \div 2$ is correctly evaluated, it would be better to write $(24 \div 4) \div 2$.

We summarize the Order of Operations in the following list.

Order of Operations

To evaluate an expression involving more than one operation, use the following order.

1. First do operations that occur within symbols of grouping.

2. Then evaluate powers.

3. Then do multiplications and divisions from left to right.

4. Finally do additions and subtractions from left to right.

Evaluating Expressions with a Calculator

Many calculators use the Order of Operations used in this book, but some do not. Try using your calculator to see whether it gives a result that is listed in the next example.

Connections
Technology

Example 4 *Using a Calculator*

When you enter 4 $\boxed{+}$ 6 $\boxed{\div}$ 2 $\boxed{-}$ 1 $\boxed{=}$ on your calculator, does it display 6 or 4? Using the established order of operations, it should display 6.

$$4 + (6 \div 2) - 1 = 4 + 3 - 1 = 6$$

If it displays 4, it would have performed the operations as follows: $[(4 + 6) \div 2] - 1$. ■

Real Life
Retail Sales

Example 5 *Calculating Sales Tax*

Suppose you live in a state that charges 6% sales tax on clothes. You find two sweaters that you want to buy. One sweater costs $24.95 and the other costs $36.95. The salesclerk uses a calculator to compute your sales tax as follows.

24.95 $\boxed{+}$ 36.95 $\boxed{\times}$ .06 $\boxed{=}$

From the calculator display, the salesclerk tells you the sales tax is $27.17. You know this is too much. What went wrong?

Solution The calculator used the Order of Operations.

$$24.95 + (36.95)(0.06) \approx 24.95 + 2.22 = 27.17$$

The correct sales tax of $3.71 is obtained by using the following order of operations.

$$(24.95 + 36.95)(0.06) = (61.90)(0.06) \approx 3.71$$ ■

Communicating about ALGEBRA

▶ **SHARING IDEAS about the Lesson**

Systematic Guess and Check List the different values that can be obtained from each of the following expressions by performing the operations in different orders. Which value is correct using the established order of operations?

A. $100 - 50 - 10$

B. $4 + 3 \cdot 5 - 2$ 17

C. $18 - 6 + 5 - 4$

D. $24 \div 4 \div 2$

EXERCISES

▶ **CRITICAL THINKING about the Lesson**

1. If an expression without grouping symbols includes addition and an exponent, which operation is performed first?

2. If an expression without grouping symbols includes multiplication and division, which operation is performed first?

3. For the expression $4 + 16 \div 8 - 2$, where could you put grouping symbols to make sure the expression is correctly evaluated?

4. What are the values of $3 + (4 \cdot 9)$ and $(3 + 4) \cdot 9$? Using the Order of Operations, which of these is equal to $3 + 4 \cdot 9$?

Independent Practice

In Exercises 5–14, evaluate the expression.

5. $4 + 2 - 1$

6. $3 \cdot 1 + 4$

7. $8 \div 4 + 4 \cdot 2$

8. $5 + 8 \cdot 3 + 2$

9. $14 \div 7 + 3^2$

10. $2 \cdot 3^2 - 9$

11. $10 \cdot (3 + 1) - 16$

12. $13 + (3 \cdot 2)^2 - 8$

13. $10 - 3 \cdot 2$

14. $15 - 2 \cdot 2$

15. Which is correct?

    a. $\dfrac{8 \cdot 3}{4 + 3^2 - 1} = 8 \cdot 3 \div 4 + 3^2 - 1$

    b. $\dfrac{8 \cdot 3}{4 + 3^2 - 1} = 8 \cdot 3 \div (4 + 3^2 - 1)$

16. Which is correct?

    a. $\dfrac{(4 - 2)^2 + 5}{3} = (4 - 2)^2 + 5 \div 3$

    b. $\dfrac{(4 - 2)^2 + 5}{3} = [(4 - 2)^2 + 5] \div 3$

In Exercises 17–24, evaluate the expression.

17. $2 + 2x^3$, when $x = 2$

18. $16 - x^2 \div 12$, when $x = 6$

19. $x^2 + 2x + 1$, when $x = 5$

20. $x^3 - 4x + 9$, when $x = 4$

21. $2l + 2w$, when $l = 3$ and $w = 19$

22. $4r^2 - s$, when $r = 4$ and $s = 14$

23. $\dfrac{2x + y}{7}$, when $x = 12$ and $y = 11$

24. $6 + \dfrac{x}{y} \cdot 4$, when $x = 8$ and $y = 4$

Technology **In Exercises 25–30, two calculators were used to evaluate the expression. They gave different results. Which calculator used the established order of operations? Rewrite the calculator steps with grouping symbols so that both calculators will give the correct result.**

25. $16 \boxed{-} 4 \boxed{\div} 2 \boxed{\times} 5 \boxed{=}$
Calculator 1: 6, Calculator 2: 30

26. $15 \boxed{-} 6 \boxed{\div} 3 \boxed{-} 2 \boxed{=}$
Calculator 1: 1, Calculator 2: 11

27. $10 \boxed{+} 15 \boxed{\div} 5 \boxed{+} 16 \boxed{=}$
Calculator 1: 21, Calculator 2: 29

28. $4 \boxed{\times} 3 \boxed{+} 6 \boxed{\div} 2 \boxed{=}$
Calculator 1: 15, Calculator 2: 9

29. $12 \boxed{\div} 3 \boxed{+} 16 \boxed{\div} 4 \boxed{=}$
Calculator 1: 8, Calculator 2: 5

30. $8 \boxed{+} 22 \boxed{-} 15 \boxed{\div} 5 \boxed{=}$
Calculator 1: 3, Calculator 2: 27

31. *Brochure Error*   A sports arena is 314.5 feet long and 252.5 feet wide. The public relations department wrote a brochure on the history of the arena and used a calculator to compute the perimeter of the arena as follows:

$$2 \;\boxed{\times}\; 314.5 \;\boxed{+}\; 2 \;\boxed{\times}\; 252.5 \;\boxed{=}$$

The brochure states that the perimeter of the arena is 159,327.5 feet. Is this the correct perimeter? If not, what did the department do wrong?

32. *Sales Tax Error*   A family goes shopping for sneakers. One child's choice costs $35.99 and the other child's choice costs $42.99. If the sales tax is 7%, what would the sales tax be for both pairs of sneakers? If the cashier uses a calculator to obtain the sales tax and gets $39, what did the cashier do wrong?

33. *Pizza Project*   As a fund-raiser, a school band sold pizzas. The number of pizzas sold for each of three weeks was 1248, 741, and 402. Write an expression that represents the average number of pizzas sold per week. Evaluate the expression.

34. *Average Score*   Suppose your first three test scores in a math class are 87, 92, and 81. Write an expression that represents your average score. Evaluate the expression.

Integrated Review

35. *Geometry*   Write an expression for the perimeter of the triangle. Use the expression to find the perimeter when $x = 12.9$ centimeters.

36. *Geometry*   Write an expression for the perimeter of the figure. Use the expression to find the perimeter when $x = 4.2$ feet.

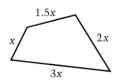

37. What is twice the area of a square with sides of length 2.9?

38. What is twice the volume of a cube with edges of length 2.9?

39. Write an expression that represents twice the area of a circle of radius r.

40. *Football Field*   Including the end zones, a football field is 360 feet by 160 feet. Use the picture at the right to approximate the total area of the floor (in green) of the Hubert Humphrey Metrodome (the home of the Minnesota Vikings).

In Exercises 41–44, insert grouping symbols in the expression so that any calculator would give the same value.

41. $4.3 + 6.9 \div 2.3$

42. $9.6 \cdot 1.3 - 3.6 \div 2.4$

43. $6.2 \div 3.1 + 4.7 \cdot 5.3$

44. $9.3 + 5.4 \cdot 1.1$

Exploration and Extension

45. *Geometry*   The area of a trapezoid with parallel bases of lengths b_1 and b_2 and height h is given by $A = \frac{1}{2}h(b_1 + b_2)$. (The variable b_1 is read "b sub 1," and the variable b_2 is read "b sub 2.") Find the area of a trapezoid whose height is 2 meters and whose bases are 6 meters and 10 meters.

Career Interview

Medical Technologist

Jyoti Mahajan is a medical technologist in a large hospital. She supervises the laboratory that performs the medical tests ordered by physicians.

Q: *Ms. Mahajan, did you learn everything you needed to know about this job in school?*

A: Not at all! We have so many new tests that we do now. I have learned at least as much on the job as I did in school.

Q: *Can you give us an example of something you have learned on the job?*

A: One of the most exciting new technologies we are using is monoclonal antibodies to detect diseases caused by viruses. The test is relatively simple to perform using our new machine with its built-in computer, but I had to learn to calibrate the machine, to judge when I have a good sample, and to interpret the results. All of these skills require mathematical reasoning since all of the data are numeric.

Q: *What impact has this new technology had on the practice of medicine?*

A: Because medical technologists can use these machines to obtain reliable results, doctors are now able to quickly and efficiently diagnose many diseases which they could not a few years ago.

Take this test as you would take a test in class. The answers to the exercises are given in the back of the book. (1.1)

1. Write $\frac{5}{8}$ in decimal form.

2. Write $\frac{1}{5}$ in percent form.

3. Find the sum of $\frac{1}{2}$ and $\frac{1}{4}$.

4. Find the difference of 6 and 2.

5. What is the product of 1 and 8?

6. What is the quotient of 7 and 21?

In Exercises 7–16, evaluate the expression. (1.2-1.4)

7. $2[3(4 \div 2) + 6] - 5$

8. $3 + [(4 - 1) \cdot 5]$

9. $3 \cdot 8 \div 2 - 9 \div 3$

10. $9 - 3 \cdot 2 + 1 \div 2$

11. $12 \div (5x - y)$, when $x = 2$ and $y = 1$

12. $(3x + 2) \cdot y$, when $x = 1$ and $y = 4$

13. $13 - 2x^2 \div 8$, when $x = 6$

14. $9x^2 - x \div 2$, when $x = 6$

15. $1.3x + 0.75$, when $x = 2.7$

16. $3.47 - 2.3y$, when $y = 1.25$

17. A rectangular region is two times longer than it is wide. The width of the region is 4 meters. What is the area? (1.2)

18. Write an expression for the volume of a cube whose sides are of length x. (1.3)

19. Several families who live in an apartment building plan to fence in a play area in the back of the building. The fence will extend out from each side of the building, x feet along both sides of the play area and 250 feet across the back. The apartment building is 150 feet wide. Write an expression for the number of feet of fencing needed. Evaluate the expression when $x = 75$ feet. (1.2)

250 ft
150 ft
x ft x ft
Apartment Building

20. Bowling pins are set up in an equilateral triangle that is approximately 35 inches deep with sides that are 40.5 inches long. How much area is needed for the placement of the pins? (1.2)

21. The surface area of a sphere is $s = 4\pi r^2$, where r is the radius of the sphere and π is approximately 3.14. A skateboard park is constructing a bowl for the skateboarders. If the radius of the bowl is 3 meters, how much surface area is available for the skateboarders? (1.3)

3 meters

1.5
Equations and Inequalities

What you should learn:

Goal 1 How to check and solve equations

Goal 2 How to check solutions of inequalities

Why you should learn it:

You can solve real-life problems by finding solutions of equations. You can check your solutions to help assure that you did not make a mistake.

Goal 1 Checking and Solving Equations

This lesson introduces you to three very important concepts: equations, solutions, and inequalities.

An **equation** is formed when an equal sign is placed between two expressions. The two expressions form the **left side** and the **right side** of the equation. Here are some examples.

$$4 - 1 = 3, \quad 3x + 1 = 7, \quad a + 3 = 3 + a$$

Equations that contain variables are **open sentences.**

When the variable in a single-variable equation is replaced by a number, the resulting statement may be true or false. If the resulting statement is true, then the number is a **solution** of the equation. For example, the number 2 is a solution of $3x + 1 = 7$ because $3(2) + 1 = 7$ is a true statement. We also say that the number 2 *satisfies* the equation.

Substituting a number into an equation to decide whether the number is a solution is called *checking* a possible solution.

Example 1 *Checking Possible Solutions*

Check whether the numbers 2, 3, and 4 are solutions of the equation $4x - 2 = 10$.

Solution To check each number, substitute the number into the equation. If the left and right sides of the equation have the same value, then the number is a solution. If the left and right sides have different values, then the number is not a solution.

x	Substitution	Conclusion
2	$4(2) - 2 = 6$	2 is not a solution.
3	$4(3) - 2 = 10$	3 is a solution.
4	$4(4) - 2 = 14$	4 is not a solution.

Thus, 3 is a solution, and 2 and 4 are *not* solutions, of the equation $4x - 2 = 10$.

Finding all the solutions of an equation is called *solving* the equation. Later in the book you will study several ways to systematically solve equations. Some equations, however, are simple enough to solve in your head. For example, to solve $x + 2 = 5$, ask yourself the question "What number plus 2 gives 5?" If you can see that the answer is 3, then you have solved the equation!

Example 2 Using Mental Math to Solve Equations

Equation	Mental Math
a. $x + 2 = 6$	What number plus 2 gives 6?
b. $x - 3 = 4$	What number minus 3 gives 4?
c. $2x = 10$	2 times what number gives 10?
d. $\frac{x}{3} = 1$	What number divided by 3 gives 1?
e. $x^3 = 8$	What number cubed gives 8?

Solution

a. The solution is 4 because $4 + 2 = 6$.
b. The solution is 7 because $7 - 3 = 4$.
c. The solution is 5 because $2 \cdot 5 = 10$.
d. The solution is 3 because $\frac{3}{3} = 1$.
e. The solution is 2 because $2^3 = 8$. ∎

Using mental math to solve equations is something that you already do in real life. You probably don't think of it as solving equations, but the process is the same.

Real Life
Retail Sales

Example 3 Buying Compact Disks

Suppose that you want to buy two compact disks that cost $14.95 each, tax included. You have only $25. How much more do you need?

Solution The mental math that you could use to solve this problem is

$$2(14.95) = 25 + \boxed{?}.$$

Since 2 times $14.95 is $29.90, you can conclude that you need $4.90 more to be able to buy both compact disks. ∎

Another type of open sentence is an **inequality.** An inequality is formed when an **inequality symbol** is placed between two expressions. Here are five kinds of inequality symbols.

Inequality Symbol	**Meaning**
$<$	is less than
$\leq$	is less than or equal to
$>$	is greater than
$\geq$	is greater than or equal to
$\neq$	is not equal to

A **solution** of an inequality is a number that produces a true statement when it is substituted for the variable in the inequality. For example, 3 is a solution of $x < 5$ because $3 < 5$ is a true statement.

Example 4   *Checking Solutions of Inequalities*

Decide whether 4 is a solution of each inequality.

a. $2x - 1 < 8$ **b.** $x + 4 > 9$ **c.** $x - 3 \leq 1$

Solution

Inequality	**Solution Check**
a. $2x - 1 < 8$	4 is a solution because $2(4) - 1 < 8$ is a true statement.
b. $x + 4 > 9$	4 is not a solution because $4 + 4 > 9$ is not a true statement.
c. $x - 3 \leq 1$	4 is a solution because $4 - 3 \leq 1$ is a true statement. ∎

Communicating about ALGEBRA

▶ **SHARING IDEAS about the Lesson**

A. Check whether 1, 2, 3, and 4 are solutions of $x^2 + 8 - 5x = 2$.

B. *Give an Argument.*   Match each equation with the correct description. Justify your answers.

1. $x + 2 = 6$ **a.** has no solution

2. $x + 2 = 2 + x$ **b.** has only one solution

3. $x + 2 = x + 3$ **c.** has many solutions

EXERCISES

▶ CRITICAL THINKING about the Lesson

In Exercises 1–6, decide whether what is shown is an expression, an equation, or an inequality. Explain your decision.

1. $6x + 1 = 12$ **2.** $2y - 3$ **3.** $5(y + 4) - 7$

4. $4 + 3x = 2 + x$ **5.** $2x + 1 \le 4$ **6.** $5x > 20$

7. Identify the left and right sides of the equation $13 + 4x = 2x + 1$.

8. Match the equation $5 - x = 1$ with one of the questions.
   a. What number can 5 be subtracted from to obtain 1?
   b. What number can be subtracted from 5 to obtain 1?
   c. What number can 1 be subtracted from to obtain 5?

Independent Practice

In Exercises 9–14, check whether the given number is a solution of the equation.

9. $3x + 1 = 13$,   4   **10.** $3 + 2x = 9$,   2   **11.** $4y + 2 = 2y + 8$,   3

12. $2y + y = 2y + 5$,   5   **13.** $5x - 2 = 11$,   2   **14.** $6x - 4 = 3$,   1

In Exercises 15–26, write a question that could be used to solve the equation. Then use mental math to solve the equation.

15. $x + 4 = 7$ **16.** $x + 6 = 11$ **17.** $x - 2 = 5$ **18.** $x - 5 = 1$

19. $3x = 12$ **20.** $2x = 6$ **21.** $\frac{x}{5} = 4$ **22.** $\frac{x}{4} = 5$

23. $2x + 1 = 7$ **24.** $2x - 1 = 9$ **25.** $x^3 = 27$ **26.** $x^3 = 1$

In Exercises 27–32, check whether the given number is a solution of the inequality.

27. $x - 2 < 6$,   7   **28.** $5 + x > 8$,   4   **29.** $6 + 2x \ge 10$,   2

30. $3x - 1 \ge 7$,   3   **31.** $4x - 3 < 0$,   1   **32.** $x - 7 \ge 11 - x$,   9

In Exercises 33–36, consider the problem, then answer the question about the equation that represents the problem.

Computer Center   Suppose that your school is building a new computer center. Four hundred square feet of the center will be available for computer stations. Each station requires 20 square feet. How many computer stations can be placed in the new center?

33. If this problem is represented by the equation $20x = 400$, what do the 20, the x, and the 400 represent?

Playing a Computer Game   Suppose you are playing a new computer game. You discover that for every eight screens you complete, you receive an energy bar. If you complete 96 screens, how many energy bars will you receive?

34. If this problem is represented by the equation $8x = 96$, what do the 8, the x, and the 96 represent?

Buying Gas   Suppose you are going on an automobile trip with a family of a friend and you have $65 to help pay for gas. It costs $18 to fill the tank. How many times can you completely fill the tank? How much money will you have left?

35. If this problem is represented by the equation $18x + y = 65$, what do the 18, the x, the y, and the 65 represent?

For most car-owners, gasoline expenses form a significant part of their monthly budget.

Buying a T-Shirt   Suppose you are at a shopping mall and see a T-shirt that you really like. The shirt costs $18.75, including tax. If you can save $5 a week, how many weeks must you save to buy the T-shirt? How much money will you have left?

36. If this problem is represented by the equation $5n - m = 18.75$, what do the 5, the n, the m, and the 18.75 represent?

Integrated Review

In Exercises 37–40, use mental math.

37. What is the sum of 6 and 5?

38. What is the difference of 15 and 9?

39. What is the product of 4 and 8?

40. What is the quotient of 12 and 3?

In Exercises 41–50, evaluate the expression.

41. $6 - [(3 \cdot 8) - 21]$

42. $[18 \div (3 + 3)] + 5$

43. $7 + [12 - (3)(4)]$

44. $16 - (12 \div 2)$

45. $x + 11$, when $x = 14$

46. $2n - 3$, when $n = 9$

47. $3y + 2x$, when $y = 7$ and $x = 2$

48. $7a - 4b$, when $a = 2$ and $b = 1$

49. $(x + y)^2$, when $x = 8$ and $y = 4$

50. $3s^2 + 6r^3$, when $s = 5$ and $r = 1$

In Exercises 51–57, write the indicated equation or inequality.

51. The sum of x and 15 is less than 29.

$x + 15 < 29$

52. The product of 9 and y is equal to 72.

$9y = 72$

53. The difference of x and 4 is equal to 18.

$x - 4 = 18$

54. The quotient of n and 3 is greater than or equal to 4.

$n \div 3 \geq 4$

55. The sum of three times x and 12 is equal to 32.

$3x + 12 = 32$

56. The winning score, x, was 20 points more than the losing score, y.

$x = 20 + y$

57. The surface temperature, V (in degrees Celsius), of the planet Venus is 380 degrees more than the temperature at which water boils (100 degrees).

$V = 380 + 100$

58. *Boeing 747* Let x represent the wingspan of a Boeing 747 jet aircraft and let y represent its length. What does the equation $1.2y = x$ say about the relationship between the length and width of a 747? Is a 747 longer than it is wide or wider than it is long?

length of Boeing 747 is 1.2 time longer than its wing span. longer than it is wide.

59. *College Entrance Exam Sample* Using the triangle provided, $x = \boxed{?}$

a. 59°

b. 60°

c. 61°

d. 62°

e. 63°

57°

61° $x°$

$57 + 61$

$\overline{118}$ $\dfrac{180}{118}$

$\overline{62°}$

In Exercises 60–63, solve the two equations. What do you notice to be true about the pair of equations?

All the variable in each pair are the same

60. $x + x = 12$ and $2x = 12$

61. $y - 8 = 10$ and $y = 18$

62. $2x + 4 = 8$ and $2x = 4$

63. $2a + 3a = 10$ and $5a = 10$

64. *The Tail of an Iguana* Let y represent the length of the tail of an iguana and x represent the length of the body of the iguana. What does the equation $y = 1.8x$ say about the relationship between the tail and body of an iguana?

Length of the body is 1.8 Times longer than the tail.

65. If an iguana has a body length of 30 centimeters, what is the length of the tail?

$30 \cdot 1.8 = 54$ cm

66. If an iguana has a tail length of 18 inches, what is the length of the body?

$18(1.8) = Body length. 10"$

If cornered by an enemy, an iguana uses its long tail as a lash.

1.6

Verbal Models and Algebraic Models

What you should learn:

Goal 1 How to translate verbal phrases into algebraic expressions

Goal 2 How to translate verbal sentences into algebraic equations and inequalities

Why you should learn it:

You can use mathematics to solve real-life problems if you first can translate verbal phrases and sentences into algebraic expressions, equations, and inequalities.

Goal 1 Translating Verbal Phrases

To help you translate a verbal phrase into an algebraic expression, you should look for words that indicate a number operation. The following list gives several examples.

	Verbal Phrase	Algebraic Expression
Addition:	The *sum* of 6 and a number	$6 + x$
	Eight *more than* a number	$y + 8$
	A number *plus* 5	$n + 5$
Subtraction:	The *difference* of 5 and a number	$5 - y$
	Four *less than* a number	$x - 4$
	Seven *minus* a number	$7 - n$
Multiplication:	The *product* of 9 and a number	$9x$
	Ten *times* a number	$10n$
	A number *multiplied by* 3	$3y$
Division:	The *quotient* of a number and 4	$\dfrac{n}{4}$
	Seven *divided by* a number	$\dfrac{7}{x}$

Notice that order is important for subtraction and division, but not for addition and multiplication. For example, "four less than a number" is written as $x - 4$, not $4 - x$. On the other hand, "the sum of 6 and a number" can be written as $6 + x$ or $x + 6$.

Example 1 *Translating Verbal Phrases*

a. Three more than five times a number can be written as

   $5n + 3.$ *Think: 3 more than what number?*

b. Two less than the sum of six and a number can be written as

   $(6 + m) - 2.$ *Think: 2 less than what number?*

c. One number decreased by the sum of 10 and the square of another number can be written as

   $x - (10 + y^2).$ *Think: x decreased by what number?* ■

1.6 ▪ *Verbal Models and Algebraic Models*   **33**

Writing algebraic expressions or equations that represent real-life situations is called *modeling* because the expression or equation is a **mathematical model** of the real-life situation. When you are writing a mathematical model, we suggest that you use three steps. First, write a verbal model; then, assign labels to the model; and finally, write the algebraic model.

| Write a verbal model. | → | Assign labels | → | Write the algebraic model. |

Real Life
Recycling

Example 2 — Writing an Expression as an Algebraic Model

A recycling center pays 3¢ apiece for aluminum cans and 5¢ apiece for certain glass bottles. Write an expression representing the total amount paid for a collection of cans and bottles.

Solution

Verbal Model

| Price per can | • | Number of cans | + | Price per bottle | • | Number of bottles |

Labels

Price per can = 0.03 (dollars per can)
Number of cans = n (cans)
Price per bottle = 0.05 (dollars per bottle)
Number of bottles = m (bottles)

Expression $0.03n + 0.05m$ **Algebraic model** ∎

Algebraic models can help you compute and organize data about real-life situations. For instance, you could use the model in Example 2 to compute the total amounts received for various numbers of aluminum cans and glass bottles. Your results could be organized in a table like the one below.

		Number of Cans, n						
		0	**5**	**10**	**15**	**20**	**25**	**30**
Number of Bottles, m	**0**	$0.00	$0.15	$0.30	$0.45	$0.60	$0.75	$0.90
	5	$0.25	$0.40	$0.55	$0.70	$0.85	$1.00	$1.15
	10	$0.50	$0.65	$0.80	$0.95	$1.10	$1.25	$1.40
	15	$0.75	$0.90	$1.05	$1.20	$1.35	$1.50	$1.65
	20	$1.00	$1.15	$1.30	$1.45	$1.60	$1.75	$1.90
	25	$1.25	$1.40	$1.55	$1.70	$1.85	$2.00	$2.15
	30	$1.50	$1.65	$1.80	$1.95	$2.10	$2.25	$2.40
	35	$1.75	$1.90	$2.05	$2.20	$2.35	$2.50	$2.65

Each dollar amount in the table was found by evaluating the expression $0.03n + 0.05m$ for appropriate values of n and m.

Translating Verbal Sentences

Verbal phrases about quantities in the English language translate to mathematical expressions. Verbal sentences translate to equations or inequalities.

Phrase	The sum of 6 and a number	$6 + x$
Sentence	The sum of 6 and a number is 14.	$6 + x = 14$
Sentence	7 times a number is less than 50.	$7x < 50$

Sentences that translate have words that tell how one quantity relates to another. For instance, in the first *sentence* above, "is" says that one quantity is equal to another.

Real Life

Nutrition

Example 3 Writing an Equation as an Algebraic Model

Cheddar cheese has 30 milligrams of cholesterol per ounce, and lean ground beef has 27 milligrams of cholesterol per ounce. A cheeseburger made with 4 ounces of lean ground beef has 123 milligrams of cholesterol. Write an equation that represents this information. (The other ingredients have no cholesterol.)

Solution

Verbal Model

Cheese cholesterol	+	Beef cholesterol	=	Total cholesterol

Labels

Cheese cholesterol per ounce $= 30$	(mg per oz)
Ounces of cheese $= x$	(oz)
Beef cholesterol per ounce $= 27$	(mg per oz)
Ounces of beef $= 4$	(oz)
Total cholesterol $= 123$	(mg)

Equation $30x + 27(4) = 123$ **Algebraic model** ■

Communicating about ALGEBRA

▶ **SHARING IDEAS about the Lesson**

Understand an Algebraic Model   Refer to the equation $30x + 27(4) = 123$ in Example 3.

A. Which term in the equation represents the number of milligrams of cholesterol in the cheese? Explain why this term is written as a product. *30x there is 30mg chol. per oz multiplied by how many ounces.*

B. If the cheeseburger contains one ounce of cheese, how many milligrams of cholesterol does it have? *30 mg.*

EXERCISES

▶ **CRITICAL THINKING about the Lesson**

In Exercises 1–3, consider the verbal phrase, *the difference of 8 and a number.*

1. The word *difference* indicates what operation? *subtraction.*
2. Translate the verbal expression into an algebraic expression. *8 − N*
3. Is order important in this expression? *yes*
4. List the three steps for writing a mathematical model. *1. write a verbal model) 2. assign labels 3. write the algebraic model.*

In Exercises 5–8, translate the sentence into an equation or an inequality.

5. The sum of a number *x* and 5 is 12. *$x + 5 = 12$*
6. The product of 4 and a number *n* is less than 36. *$4N < 36$*
7. The difference of a number *m* and 5 is less than 20. *$M - 5 < 20$*
8. The quotient of 10 and a number *y* is 5. *$\frac{10}{y} = 5$*

Independent Practice

In Exercises 9–14, translate the phrase into an algebraic expression.

9. 12 more than a number *$12N$*
10. 5 more than twice a number *$2N + 5$*
11. Half of a given number *$\frac{x}{2}$*
12. 3 less than 4 times a given number *$4x - 3$*
13. 11 plus the quotient of a number and 7 *$11 + \frac{7}{x}$*
14. A number divided by 6 *$\frac{x}{6}$*

In Exercises 15–20, match each verbal phrase on the left with its corresponding algebraic expression on the right.

15. Twelve decreased by three times a number *D*   **a.** $11 + \frac{1}{3}s$
16. Eleven more than $\frac{1}{3}$ of a number *a*   **b.** $3x - 12$
17. Eleven times a number plus $\frac{1}{3}$ *e*   **c.** $3(x - 12)$
18. Three increased by 12 times a number *F*   **d.** $12 - 3x$
19. The difference between three times a number and 12 *b*   **e.** $11s + \frac{1}{3}$
20. Three times the difference of a number and twelve *c*   **f.** $12x + 3$

In Exercises 21–24, translate the sentence into an equation or an inequality.

$16 + 5 = 36$ *3b*

21. Sixteen more than a number *s* is 36.
22. Ten is less than three times a number *b*.
23. Twenty-five decreased by a number *y* is 10.5. *$25 - y = 10.5$*
24. The product of 17 and a number *n* is one. *$17N = 1$*

25. *Geometry* Write an expression that represents the perimeter of the hexagon.

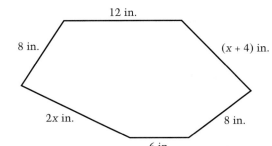

12 in.

8 in.

$(x + 4)$ in.

2x in.

8 in.

6 in.

$P = 8 + 12 + 6 + 8 + (x + 4) + 2x$

26. *Geometry* Write an expression that represents the area, A, of the shaded region. (The area of a circle is $A = \pi r^2$.)

12 cm

4 cm

$\pi\,12^2 = \text{Total area}$
$\pi\,4^2 = \text{Area of small circle}$

$\pi\,12^2 - \pi\,4^2 = \text{shaded area.}$

In Exercises 27–30, decide whether the equation is a correct translation of the verbal sentence.

Sentence	Equation
27. Half of the sum of six and a number is seven. *No*	$\frac{1}{2}(6 + n) = 7$
28. Seven less than three times a number is eight. *yes*	$7 - 3x = 8$
29. Three times the difference of two and a number is four. *no*	$(3 \cdot 2) - y = 4$
30. Four times the sum of a number and five is thirty-two. *yes*	$4(m + 5) = 32$

In Exercises 31–34, which equation correctly models the situation?

31. *Pizza Party* You and three friends bought a pizza. You paid $2.30 for your share ($\frac{1}{4}$ of the pizza). Let p be the cost of the pizza.

a. $4p = 2.30$ **b.** $\frac{1}{4}p = 2.30$

32. *Scale Model for a Car* A model for a new car is scaled $\frac{1}{10}$ of the actual size. The length of the model's body is 45. Let L be the actual length of the car's body.

a. $\frac{1}{10}L = 45$ **b.** $L = \frac{1}{10}(45)$

33. *Sports Cars* There are 24 sports cars in a car lot. Each car is either red or white. There are four fewer red cars than white cars. Let w be the number of white cars.

a. $w + (w - 4) = 24$ **b.** $w + 4 = 24$

34. *Coin Collection* Suppose you have a collection of rare coins. Your favorite coin will be fifty years old in only six years. Let c be the age of the coin now.

a. $c - 6 = 50$ **b.** $c + 6 = 50$

Integrated Review

In Exercises 35–38, write the expression in exponential form.

35. x raised to the seventh power x^7

36. Eight cubed 8^3

37. $y \cdot y \cdot y \cdot y \cdot y \cdot y$ y^6

38. $12 \cdot 12 \cdot 12 \cdot 12$ 12^4

$\frac{8}{6} \frac{8}{4}$

In Exercises 39–42, evaluate the expression.

39. $\frac{4x + 2y}{5}$, when $x = 1$ and $y = 8$ 4

40. $6 + \frac{x + 2}{y}$, when $x = 7$ and $y = 3$ 9

41. $3y^2 - w$, when $y = 8$ and $w = 27$ 165

42. $2x^3 - 3y$, when $x = 4$ and $y = 6$ $1,006$

$1024 - 18$

In Exercises 43–48, check whether the number is a solution of the equation or an inequality.

43. $7y + 2 = 4y + 8$, 2

44. $5x - 1 = 3x + 2$, 4

45. $32 - 5y > 11$, 3

46. $7m + 2 < 12$, 1

47. $9 - 7 \geq 12 - 9$, 9

48. $n + 2 \leq 2n - 2$, 4

Exploration and Extension

In Exercises 49–54, write a verbal phrase or sentence to represent the expression or equation.

49. $5 - 2x$

50. $3y - 4$

51. $6(3 + y)$

52. $r(y + 6)$

53. $5m - 2 = 14$

54. $15 - 2n = 7$

In Exercises 55 and 56, use the following information.

Super Bowl The San Francisco 49ers and the Cincinnati Bengals met in Super Bowl XVI and Super Bowl XXIII. The attendance at Super Bowl XXIII was 6141 less than the attendance at Super Bowl XVI. Let x represent the attendance at Super Bowl XVI.

55. Write an algebraic equation to represent the given information.

56. The attendance at Super Bowl XVI was 81,270. What was the attendance at Super Bowl XXIII?

Mixed REVIEW

1. What is the value of $17 - 5 + 3$? **(1.1)**

2. Evaluate $x^2 - 2$ when $x = 7$. **(1.3)**

3. Determine the value of $4 + 8 \cdot 4 - 1$. **(1.4)**

4. Determine the value of $22 - 4^2 \div 2$. **(1.4)**

5. What is the value of $2x^3 + x$ when $x = 3$? **(1.3, 1.4)**

6. Does $16 + x^2 \div 4 = 17$ when $x = 2$? **(1.3, 1.4)**

7. Is 3 a solution of $x^2 - 4 = 5$? **(1.5)**

8. Is 11 a solution of $2x - 9 = 13$? **(1.5)**

9. Solve $x - 1 = 5$. **(1.5)**

10. Solve $x^3 = 1$. **(1.5)**

11. Is 9 a solution of $2x - 3 < 15$? **(1.5)**

12. Is 2 a solution of $3 + 7x \geq 13$? **(1.5)**

13. Which are solutions of $3x + 4 \leq 16$: 2, 4, 6? **(1.5)**

14. Use a calculator to evaluate $3.8 + 18.2 \div 7 - 1.6$. **(1.4)**

15. If your state has a 7% sales tax, what is the total cost of a keyboard marked $149.95? **(1.4)**

16. A fund-raiser generates 25¢ for each drink-box sold and 40¢ for each submarine sandwich sold. Write an expression for the total amount of money raised by both. **(1.6)**

1.7

A Problem-Solving Plan

What you should learn:

Goal 1 How to use algebra to solve simple real-life problems

Goal 2 How to make an algebraic model for a real-life problem

Why you should learn it:

You can use algebra to solve a variety of real-life problems, such as costs, rates, averages, percent, etc.

Real Life
Law Enforcement

Goal 1 Using Algebra to Solve Problems

You may already know many ways to solve problems, such as guess and check, make a table, look for a pattern, and draw a diagram. In this course, you will continue to use problem-solving strategies you have already developed, and you will also learn how to use algebra to become an even better problem solver and decision maker.

In the problems in this (and every) lesson, don't be afraid to try to find the solution without using algebra. On the other hand, be sure that you also know *how* to use algebra routines to solve the problems. Then you will be able to apply these routines to more difficult problems.

Example 1 *Getting a Speeding Ticket*

Greg lives in a state in which speeders are fined $15 for each mile per hour over the speed limit. Greg was given a ticket for $180 for speeding on a road where the speed limit is 45 miles per hour. How fast was Greg driving?

Solution

Verbal Model

| $15 | • | Miles per hour over speed limit | = | Amount of speeding ticket |

Labels Miles per hour over speed limit $= x$
Amount of speeding ticket $= \$180$

Equation $15x = 180$ **Algebraic model**

Using mental math, you can solve this equation by finding the number that can be multiplied by 15 to obtain 180. After trying some numbers, you can see that $x = 12$. Therefore, Greg was driving 12 miles per hour over the speed limit (of 45). This means that he was driving 57 miles per hour. ■

Check your result with a table.

Speed	46	47	. . .	56	57
Fine	$15	$30	. . .	$165	$180

In Lesson 1.6, you studied the three steps for algebraic modeling. These steps can be used as part of your **general problem-solving plan.**

Real Life
Air Traffic Control

Example 2   *Piloting an Airplane*

A commercial jet aircraft is flying from Dallas to Nashville at a speed of 500 miles per hour. As the plane is passing over Little Rock, 360 miles from Nashville, an air-traffic controller at Nashville radios the pilot and says that the plane must wait two hours for clearance to land. At what speed should the aircraft fly from Little Rock to Nashville to arrive in two hours? Should the pilot reduce to this speed and fly directly to Nashville or must the pilot take some other action?

Nashville

Little Rock

Dallas

At high altitudes, a commercial jet aircraft must maintain speed of at least 350 miles per hour to avoid stalling.

A Problem-Solving Plan

Ask yourself what you need to know to solve the problem. Then **write a verbal model** that will give you what you need to know.

↓

Assign labels to each part of your verbal model.

↓

Use the labels to **write an algebraic model** based on your verbal model.

↓

Solve the algebraic model.

↓

Answer the original question. **Check** that your answer is reasonable.

Solution   To solve this problem, you need to know the speed it would take to fly 360 miles in two hours. A verbal model for this can be based on the formula (rate)(time) = (distance). You would also need to know something about reasonable speeds for commercial jet aircraft.

Verbal Model	Speed of airplane	$\cdot$	Flight time	$=$	Distance to travel

Labels   Speed of airplane = x (miles per hour)
Flight time = 2   (hours)
Distance to travel = 360   (miles)

Equation $2x = 360$ *Algebraic model*

$x = 180$ *Solution*

To arrive in two hours, the airplane should fly at 180 miles per hour. *Is the answer reasonable?* From the information given with the drawings, you can see that this speed is too slow. Therefore the pilot should take some other action, such as circling in a holding pattern, to use up some of the time. ■

Sometimes the solution of a real-life problem will involve an inequality, as shown in Example 3.

Real Life
Testing

Example 3 *Getting an A in Class*

Suppose you are taking a class that has five 100-point tests and one final test worth 200 points. You need an average of 90% to get an A in the class. Your scores for the first five tests are 88, 92, 87, 98, and 81. Is it possible to score high enough on the final test to get an A?

Solution

| **Verbal Model** | Sum of previous scores | + | Score on final test | ≥ | 90% of total test points |

Labels   Sum of previous scores $= 88 + 92 + 87 + 98 + 81$
$$= 446$$

Score on final test $= x$
90% of total test points $= 0.9[5(100) + 200] = 630$

Inequality $446 + x \geq 630$ **Algebraic model**

Since there are 200 points possible on the final test, it is possible for you to score high enough to get an A. In fact, any score of 184 or more would be enough. ∎

Communicating about ALGEBRA

Cooperative Learning

▶ **SHARING IDEAS about the Lesson**

Does the Answer Make Sense? When solving problems, always ask whether the answer makes sense. Work with a partner to explain why each of the answers below is suspicious, then write several similar problems.

A. A problem asked you to find the sales tax on a bottle of cologne, and your answer is $39.56. *No*

B. A problem asked you to find the area of a kitchen floor, and your answer is 736 square feet. *yes*

C. A problem asked you to find the interest on a $2000 deposit that is left in a savings account for one month, and your answer is $105.75. *No*

D. A problem asked you to find the time it takes for a passenger plane to travel from New York to Los Angeles, and your answer is $1\frac{1}{2}$ hours. *yes*

EXERCISES

Vietnam War Memorial, Washington, D.C. The Washington Monument is in the background.

Guided Practice

▶ **CRITICAL THINKING about the Lesson**

In Exercises 1–6, use the Problem-Solving Plan to answer the questions.

Send a Student to Washington   The science club at school is selling boxes of greeting cards at a profit of $1.50 each. The club needs $1800 more to have enough money for its trip to the Smithsonian Institution in Washington, D.C. How many boxes does it need to sell in order to earn $1800?

1. Write a verbal model that relates the number of boxes, the profit for each box, and the amount of money the club needs to raise.

2. Assign labels to the three parts of your model. What would you let *x* equal?

3. Use the labels to translate your verbal model into an equation.

4. Use mental math to solve the equation.

5. How many boxes of cards does the club need to sell?

6. How could you check your answer?

Independent Practice

In Exercises 7–12, consider the following question.

Walk or Take the Subway?   Suppose you are one mile from your home. You are in a hurry to get home and are trying to decide whether to walk or take the subway. You can walk at a speed of 4 miles per hour. The subway schedule states that the train comes by every 15 minutes, and you heard one come by 3 minutes ago. The subway ride takes 8 minutes. Which way would get you home faster?

7. How many minutes would it take to get home by subway if you took the next train?

8. Write a verbal model that relates the time it would take to walk home, your walking speed, and the distance to your home.

9. Assign labels to the three parts of your model. What should you let *t* equal?

10. Use the labels to translate your verbal model into an equation.

11. Use mental math to solve the equation.

12. Should you walk or take the subway? Explain.

In Exercises 13–18, consider the following question.

Disc Jockey or Live Band?   Suppose you are in charge of the music for a school dance. The school budget allows only $150 for music, which is enough to hire a disc jockey for 4 hours. You would rather hire a live band, but the band charges $75 an hour, and your school does not allow students who attend the dance to be charged an admission fee. If you ask each person who attends the dance to voluntarily contribute $0.75, how many must contribute to cover the extra cost for the band? *200*

2 has
.75 × 200 = $150⁰⁰

13. How much extra money do you need to raise? *150⁰⁰*

14. Write a verbal model that relates the extra cost, the number of contributors, and the suggested contribution amount. *150⁰⁰ 200 .75¢*

15. Assign labels to the three parts of your model.

16. Use the labels to translate your verbal model into an equation.

17. Use mental math to solve the equation.

18. How many students must contribute to cover the cost? *200*

In Exercises 19–24, consider the following question.

Keeping Peace in the Family   It's 9 o'clock on Saturday morning and your uncle calls. He wants you to go with him to your grandmother's home to help move furniture. He figures that it will take 1 hour to move the furniture. You already promised your mom that you would thoroughly clean your room (about 2 hours of work), *and* you have plans to go out with some friends at 6 o'clock in the evening. If your uncle can average 50 miles per hour driving to your grandmother's, what is the greatest distance she can live from you so that you can get everything done?

19. How many hours are available for driving to and from your grandmother's house?

20. Write a verbal model that relates the hours available, the speed of your uncle's car, and the greatest distance possible to your grandmother's home.

21. Assign labels to the three parts of your model.

22. Use the labels to translate your verbal model into an equation.

23. Use mental math to solve the equation.

24. Suppose that your grandmother lives 100 miles from you. Can you get everything done? Explain.

In Exercises 25–28, consider the following question.

Buying a Stereo   An appliance store sells two different stereo models. The model without a compact disk player is $350, and the model with a compact disk player is $432. Suppose you have a summer job that lasts for 12 weeks. You are fairly sure that you can save $30 a week, which would allow you to buy the model without the compact disk player. How much would you have to save each week to be able to buy the other model?

25. Write a verbal model that relates the number of weeks worked, the amount you save each week, and the price of the stereo with the compact disk player.

26. Assign labels to the three parts of your model.

27. Use the labels to translate your verbal model into an equation.

28. Use mental math to solve the equation. Tell what its solution means.

In Exercises 29–34, consider the following question.

Detective Work   Suppose you are a detective and have been assigned to a robbery case. The robbery occurred at 4:30 P.M., and you have a witness who spotted a suspect at a gas station 12 miles from the robbery site at 4:48 P.M. The suspect claims that it would have been impossible to get from the robbery site to the gas station in the given amount of time. Do you agree?

29. How much time would the suspect have had to go from the robbery site to the gas station?

30. Write a verbal model that relates the travel time, the rate of travel, and the distance from the robbery site to the gas station.

31. Assign labels to the three parts of your model.

32. Use the labels to translate your verbal model into an equation.

33. Use mental math to solve the equation.

34. Do you agree with the suspect? Explain.

35. *Playing Pinball*   Suppose you are playing a pinball machine that gives you five balls. In order to get an extra ball, you must have a score of at least 2500. On the first four balls, your points are 412, 613, 510, and 620. Let x represent the number of points you get on the fifth ball. Write an inequality that shows the values of x that will allow you to get an extra ball. What is the smallest value of x that is a solution of this inequality?

36. *Class Election*   Suppose you are running for class president. Your classmates have one week to vote for you or your opponent. Half-way through the week, you have 95 votes and your opponent has 120 votes. Forty-five more students will be voting. Let x represent the number of students (of the 45) who vote for you. Write an inequality that shows the values of x that will allow you to win the election. What is the smallest value of x that is a solution of this inequality?

Exploration and Extension

The highest averge lap speed attained on a closed-circuit motorcycle race is 160.3 miles per hour. The driver of the cycle was Yvon du Hamel, at Daytona International Speedway, Florida, March 1973. (Source: Guinness Book of World Records, 1991)

In Exercises 37–42, consider the following question.

Pit-Stop Problem   Suppose you enter a closed-circuit motorcycle race. Your goal is to cross the finish line at 10:20 A.M. At 6:20 A.M., you resume racing after making an unexpected pit stop that is 640 miles from the finish line. Do you think you can reach your goal?

37. How much time do you need to reach your goal?

38. Write a verbal model that relates the travel time you have, the distance, and the rate at which you must travel.

39. Assign labels to the three parts of your model.

40. Use the labels to translate your verbal model into an equation.

41. Use mental math to solve the equation.

42. Do you think you will meet your goal? Explain.

Problem Solving
Make an Algebraic Model

Write a verbal model.

Assign labels (values and variables).

Write an algebraic model (an equation or inequality) using the labels.

Solve the equation or inequality.
↓

Answer the original question. Check that your answer is reasonable.

Mobius Strip II, *1963, woodcut by*
M. C. Escher.

A Problem-Solving Plan

Problem solving is a process for discovering relationships; it is not simply a process for finding answers. In this text, problem solving is something you will do while you learn new skills. To help you solve problems successfully, you will have many problem-solving opportunities.

In Lesson 1.7, you were introduced to a systematic plan for solving problems algebraically, as shown in the flowchart at the left. First, write a *verbal model* for the problem. Then assign labels to the verbal model and write an *algebraic model* (an equation or inequality). Finally, solve the equation or inequality. You will be using this algebraic-model strategy throughout this algebra text.

Other problem-solving strategies can be used with and without algebraic modeling. In fact, in this chapter you have been informally introduced to the strategies *making a table, looking for a pattern, using a model,* and *drawing a diagram.* The uses of such strategies are

- to provide techniques for solving problems without using equations or inequalities.
- to provide insight and information when using the general algebraic-model plan. For example, it is often useful to draw a diagram to help you understand the algebraic model.
- to provide a second technique as a check to a problem solved algebraically. In Example 1 on page 39, *making a table* is used to check the solution provided by the algebraic model.

Some of the names for these nonalgebraic problem-solving strategies may be familiar already. On the following two pages, you will see how three such strategies can be used. Each strategy has a general "plan of attack" that may help you get started and then proceed through a problem. Each can be a powerful tool in your investigation of the problems and applications in this course.

There may be several ways to approach each of the following three problems. Since these are examples, a specific strategy is suggested at the left. However, an essential part of problem solving is making a decision about which strategy seems best to use.

Problem Solving
Guess, Check, Revise

Guess a reasonable solution based on data in the problem.

↓

Check the guess.

↓

Revise the guess and continue until a correct solution is found.

Example 1 A Puzzle with Parentheses

Insert parentheses so that the expression $54 - 6 \cdot 8 - 5$ has a value of 36.

Solution A strategy to try with this problem is *Guess, Check, and Revise*. Copy the expression, guess where to place the parentheses, and evaluate the expression. Always record each guess, because patterns in your results may help you with your next guess.

Original expression: $54 - 6 \cdot 8 - 5$

First guess: $(54 - 6)(8 - 5) = (48)(3)$. Too great.

Second guess: $(54 - 6)8 - 5 = (48)(8) - 5$. Too great.

Third guess: $54 - 6(8 - 5) = 54 - (6)(3) = 54 - 18 = 36.$ √

Problem Solving
Make a Table/ Look for a Pattern

Make a table using the data from the problem.

↓

Look for number patterns.

↓

Use a pattern to complete the table and/or find a solution.

Example 2 Mrs. Mellina's Strange Algebra Assignment

Mrs. Mellina tells her algebra students that they will have 1 problem for homework the first day, 1 the second day, 2 the third day, 3 the fourth day, 5 the fifth day, 8 the sixth day, and 13 on the seventh day. If she continues this pattern, how many problems will be assigned on the eleventh day?

Solution A strategy to try with this problem is *Make a Table/Look for a Pattern*. Use a table that shows the number of problems assigned each day.

Day	1	2	3	4	5	6	7	8	9	10	11
Number of problems	1	1	2	3	5	8	13	21	34	55	89

Do you see a pattern in the second row? It appears that the number of problems for each day is the sum of the numbers from the previous two days. Thus, day 8 will have 21 problems, day 9 will have 34 problems, day 10 will have 55 problems, and day 11 will have 89 problems!

Problem Solving
Draw a Diagram

Draw a diagram that shows the facts from the problem.

↓

Use the diagram to visualize the action of the problem.

↓

Use algebra to find a solution. Then check the solution against the facts.

Liberation, 1955, lithograph by M. C. Escher.

Example 3 | **Mr. Galloway's Quiz Bowl Budget**

Central High School is hosting an 8-team single-elimination Academic Quiz Bowl tournament. Mr. Galloway, the supervisor, must pay each moderator $25 per match. How much money should Mr. Galloway budget to pay the moderators?

Solution Mr. Galloway needs to know the total number of matches for the tournament. A strategy to try with this problem is *Draw a Diagram* of the matches for each round of the tournament.

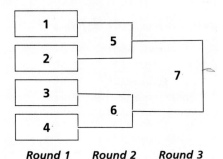

Round 1   Round 2   Round 3

From the diagram, Mr. Galloway can see that the first round has four matches, the second round has two, and the last round has one. Thus, he has a total of $4 + 2 + 1 = 7$ matches and must budget $(7)(\$25) = \$175$ for moderator fees.

Exercises

Decide which problem-solving strategy (or strategies) would be best to use and then solve the problems.

1. A rectangle has a perimeter of 24 centimeters. Its length and width are whole numbers. What are all the possibilities for the length and width? Which dimensions give the greatest area?

2. Insert parentheses so that the expression
   $$3 + 3 \div 3 \cdot 3 + 3 \cdot 3 - 3$$
   is equal to 18.

3. Example 3 above shows with a diagram that an 8-team elimination tournament requires 7 games. Now, instead of a diagram, use other strategies to find how many games would be needed in such a tournament for 128 teams.

4. Rafael is slicing a round pizza. He is challenged to use three straight cuts through the pizza to create as many pieces as possible. Draw a diagram that illustrates the most pieces possible.

1.8

Exploring Data: Tables and Graphs

What you should learn:

Goal 1 How to use tables to organize data

Goal 2 How to use graphs to model data visually

Why you should learn it:

You can use tables and graphs to help you see relationships among such data collections as survey results.

Real Life
Physical Fitness

Goal 1 Using Tables to Organize Data

The world you live in is becoming more and more complex. Almost every day of your life you will be given **data** that describe real-life situations. The word *data* is plural and it means facts or numbers that describe something.

A collection of data is easier to understand when it is organized in a table or in a graph. There is no "best way" to organize data, but there are many good techniques. Often it helps to put numbers in order (either increasing order or decreasing order). It also helps to group numbers so that patterns or trends are more apparent.

Example 1 *Burning Calories*

The average number of Calories that you burn per minute depends on your activity. Resting burns 1.1 Calories per minute, walking burns 5.5, swimming burns 10.9, and running burns 14.7. Suppose that you are the manager of a physical fitness center and want to create a poster that conveys this information to the members of the center. How would you organize the information?

Solution One way would be to find the number of Calories in several different common foods, as shown in the table at the left. Then calculate the number of minutes of each activity that is required to burn the Calories from each food. Finally make a table that compares the times required to burn the Calories from different foods.

Number of Calories in Foods	
Quarter-pound cheeseburger	520
Turkey deluxe sandwich	510
Beef burrito	466
Big roast beef sandwich	418
Two pieces pizza	380

Calories are averages taken from an analysis of eleven fast food restaurant chains.

Food	Time Required to Burn Calories			
	Resting	Walking	Swimming	Running
Cheeseburger	473 min	95 min	48 min	35 min
Turkey deluxe	464 min	93 min	47 min	35 min
Beef burrito	424 min	85 min	43 min	32 min
Beef sandwich	380 min	76 min	38 min	28 min
Pizza	345 min	69 min	35 min	26 min

Using Graphs as Visual Models

One of the most common ways to organize data is with a **bar graph.**

| **Example 2** | *Changes in Age Distribution in the United States* |

Real Life
Demography

The following bar graph gives the numbers of people in different age groups in the United States in 1970, 1980, and 1990. *(Source: U.S. Bureau of the Census)*

a. How many people who were between 10 and 19 years old lived in the United States in 1970?

b. Which age groups had the most people in 1970, in 1980, and in 1990? Can you see a pattern to your three answers?

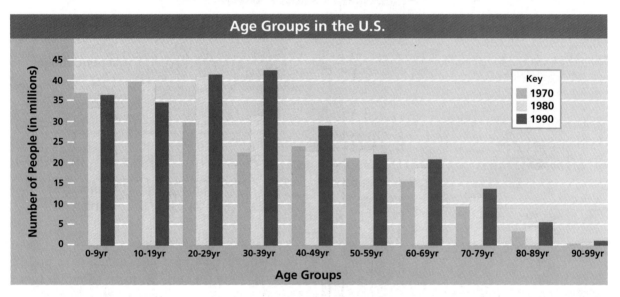

Solution

a. Look for the label *10–19* at the bottom of the graph. There are three bars above this label. The left bar represents 1970, the middle bar represents 1980, and the right bar represents 1990. From the scale given on the left side of the graph, you can read that there were about 40 million people between the ages of 10 and 19 in 1970.

b. In 1970, the age group 10–19 had the most people. In 1980, the age group 20–29 had the most people. In 1990, the group 30–39 had the most people. This makes sense because if there were more 10–19-year-olds than any other age group in 1970, then ten years later, in 1980, there should have been more 20–29-year-olds than any other age group. ∎

Real Life
Leisure Activities

Example 3 *Number of Movies Watched in a Week*

Thirty students in a class were asked to keep track of the number of movies each watched during a specific week. The results were as follows.

6, 3, 0, 10, 4, 1, 7, 2, 3, 4, 4, 4, 1, 3, 4
3, 5, 5, 7, 2, 5, 4, 3, 3, 0, 2, 4, 5, 1, 5

Organize these data to help show a pattern.

Solution Three common ways to organize a collection of numbers are shown below. The first is a **frequency distribution.** Note that the possible numbers are written *in order* and tally marks are used to count how many times each number occurs in the collection. The second is a **line plot.** Each × in the graph represents a number from the collection. A third is a bar graph, as shown below.

a.

Number	Tally	Frequency
10	I	1
9		0
8		0
7	II	2
6	I	1
5	IIIII	5
4	IIIIIII	7
3	IIIIII	6
2	III	3
1	III	3
0	II	2

Frequency distribution

b.

Line plot

c.

Bar graph

Communicating about **ALGEBRA**

▶ **SHARING IDEAS about the Lesson**

Interpreting Data   Use Examples 1–3 of this lesson.

A. Use the information given in Example 1 to find the number of minutes resting, walking, swimming, and running it would take to burn a sandwich that gives 350 calories.

B. Use the information given in Example 2 to approximate the number of 30–39-year-olds in the United States in 1970, 1980, and 1990.

C What is the average number of movies watched per student during the week discussed in Example 3?

1.8 ▪ *Exploring Data: Tables and Graphs*   **51**

EXERCISES

Guided Practice

▶ **CRITICAL THINKING about the Lesson**

1. What does the word *data* mean?

2. Can a table of numbers help organize data? Explain.

3. What is a frequency distribution?

4. When drawing a bar graph, does it help to make a frequency distribution first? Explain.

Independent Practice

5. *Track Records* Data for track records for an upcoming track meet must include the particular meet record, the school's record, the national high school record, and the world high school record for six running events: 100-meter dash, 200-meter dash, 400-meter dash, 800-meter run, 1500-meter run, and 3000-meter run. Describe two ways that these data could be organized in a table.

CD's, Record Albums, and Cassettes **In Exercises 7–10, use the bar graphs which show the numbers (in millions) of compact discs (CDs), record albums, and cassettes sold from 1986 to 1990.** (*Source: Recording Industry Association of America*)

6. In Exercise 5, do you think a table with four rows and six columns would be easier to read than a table with six rows and four columns? Explain.

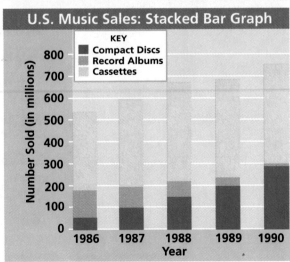

7. In which year did the compact disc sales approximately equal the record album sales? Which bar graph is easier to use to answer this question?

8. Which type(s) of recording had increasing sales from 1986 to 1990? Which had decreasing sales? Which bar graph is easier to use to answer these questions?

9. How does the lower **stacked bar graph** differ from the upper bar graph?

10. Was the total number of recordings (CDs, record albums, cassettes) sold each year increasing or decreasing? Which bar graph is easier to use to answer this question?

Number of Bagels	1	Bag of 6	Bag of 12
Total Price	$0.40	$1.89	$3.59

11. Which is the closest approximation of the cost per bagel when you
purchase a bag of six bagels?

   a. $0.20   **b.** $0.30   **c.** $0.40   **d.** $0.50   **e.** $0.60

12. What would be the *least* amount of money needed to purchase exactly 21 bagels?

   a. $5.88   **b.** $6.68   **c.** $7.19   **d.** $7.38   **e.** $8.40

Study Time   **In Exercises 13–16, use the following data which represent
the number of hours that 30 different students
in a class studied during a week.**

```
7,    4,   10,   8,   5,    2
7,   12,   3,    4,  12,    7
15,   3,   6,    9,  11,   10
7,    2,   8,    7,   5,    6
18,   6,   1,    0,  17,   13
```

13. Construct a frequency distribution for
these data.

14. What was the average number of hours
studied by a student in the class?

15. Find the error in the line plot above.

16. Sketch a bar graph for these data.

Weather Map   **In Exercises 17 and 18, refer to the weather map. Note
that this map uses different colors to represent different temperature
ranges. The temperatures shown on this map represent the average
minimum temperatures in each region.**
(Source: U.S. Department of Agriculture)

17. Approximate the average minimum temperature in Columbus, Ohio.

18. Approximate the average minimum temperature in Washington, D.C.

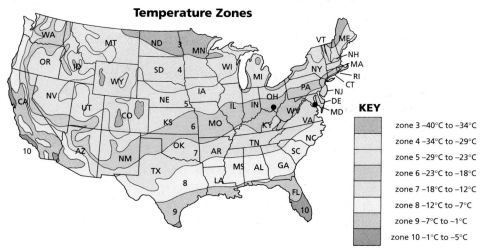

Temperature Zones

KEY
zone 3 –40°C to –34°C
zone 4 –34°C to –29°C
zone 5 –29°C to –23°C
zone 6 –23°C to –18°C
zone 7 –18°C to –12°C
zone 8 –12°C to –7°C
zone 9 –7°C to –1°C
zone 10 –1°C to –5°C

Perimeter and Area of a Rectangle   **In Exercises 19–22, suppose that you have 120 feet of fencing with which to enclose a rectangular region.**

19. Let W be the width of the rectangle and let L be the length. Write an equation involving W, L, and 120.

20. Copy and complete the following table which compares the areas of several rectangles whose perimeters are 120.

Width	10 ft	15 ft	20 ft	25 ft	30 ft	35 ft	40 ft	45 ft	50 ft
Length	?	?	?	?	?	?	?	?	?
Area	?	?	?	?	?	?	?	?	?

21. If the area is to be as large as possible, which of the following rectangles should you construct? Explain.
   a. A rectangle that is longer than it is wide
   b. A rectangle whose width is equal to its length (a square)

22. Construct a bar graph that compares the width of a rectangle, whose perimeter is 120 feet, with its area.

Exercise Activities   **In Exercises 23–24, use the bar graph which shows the percent of Americans in various age groups who participate in bike riding, exercise walking, or swimming at least six times a year.**
(Source: National Sporting Goods Association)

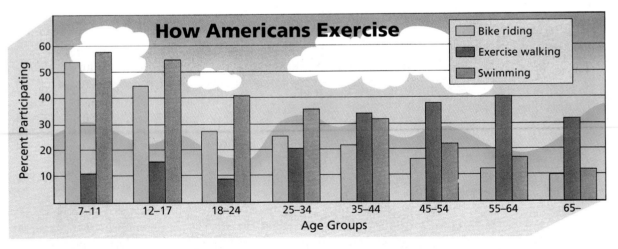

23. Which two of these three exercise activities do people tend to participate in less as they grow older?

24. What percent of people between the ages of 12 and 17 would you expect to ride a bike at least six times a year?

1 Chapter Summary

What did you learn?

Skills

1. Evaluate an expression
   - containing numbers, grouping symbols, and exponents. **(1.1, 1.3)**
   - containing variables. **(1.2)**
   - using the established order of operations. **(1.4)**
   - using a calculator. **(1.1–1.4)**

2. Check a solution of an equation or inequality. **(1.5)**

3. Solve an equation
   - by expressing the equation as a question, and then **(1.5)**
   - using mental math to answer the question. **(1.5, 1.6)**

4. Translate
   - a verbal phrase into an expression. **(1.6)**
   - a verbal sentence into an equation or inequality. **(1.6)**

Strategies

5. Create a problem-solving plan for a real-life situation
   - writing a *verbal model*, **(1.6)**
   - assigning *labels*, **(1.6)**
   - writing an *algebraic model*, **(1.6)**
   - using mental math to *solve* the model, **(1.7)**
   - answering questions about the real-life situation. **(1.7)**

6. Use algebra to enhance your problem-solving strategies. **(1.7)**

Exploring Data

7. Organize data with a table, frequency distribution, and graph. **(1.8)**

Why did you learn it?

The world you live in is becoming more and more technical. Many real-life situations involve data, numbers, and patterns that can be modeled by algebraic expressions, equations, and inequalities. By learning how to create and solve a mathematical model, you will be able to use the mathematical solution to answer questions in school, in business, and in your career.

How does it fit into the bigger picture of algebra?

In this chapter, you were introduced to many of the terms and goals of algebra. Communication is a very important part of algebra, so it is important that words such as *variable, expression, equation, solution,* and *inequality* become part of your vocabulary. Some people think of algebra as only a collection of rules. Algebra is much *more* than that. It is a language that can be used to answer questions about real-life situations.

1. Write $\frac{1}{8}$ in decimal form. **(1.1)**
2. Write $\frac{2}{5}$ in percent form. **(1.1)**
3. Write 0.75 in fraction form. **(1.1)**
4. Write 0.33 in percent form. **(1.1)**
5. Write 10% in decimal form. **(1.1)**
6. Write 25% in fraction form. **(1.1)**
7. Find the sum of 5 and $\frac{3}{2}$. **(1.1)**
8. Find the product of 9 and 9. **(1.1)**
9. What is the difference of 23 and 7? **(1.1)**
10. What is the quotient of 14 and 4? **(1.1)**

In Exercises 11–14, evaluate the given expression. (1.1)

11. $3 - [(4 \div 2) + 1]$
12. $3(7) + [9 - (18 \div 6)]$
13. $[(4 + 16) \div 5] - 2$
14. $\frac{(3)(5)}{(8 - 7) \cdot 3}$

15. Use a calculator to evaluate $[224.9 \div (4.3 + 16.5)] - 9.3$. **(1.1)**
16. Use a calculator to evaluate $14.4 + [(6.8 - 1.1) \cdot 4.7]$. **(1.1)**

In Exercises 17–20, evaluate the given expression. (1.2)

17. $2s - 3$, when $s = 14$
18. $(x + 4) \div 9$, when $x = 23$
19. $2x - 3y + 2$, when $x = 4$ and $y = 1$
20. $(3x - 5)(y + 2)$, when $x = 3$ and $y = 2$

21. Use a calculator to evaluate $2.6 + (3.9 \div x)$ when $x = 1.5$. **(1.2)**
22. Use a calculator to evaluate $3.7x - 6.2y$ when $x = 5.5$ and $y = 1.9$. **(1.2)**
23. Write "x raised to the fifth power" as an algebraic expression. **(1.3)**
24. Write the expression $9 \cdot 9 \cdot 9 \cdot 9 \cdot 9 \cdot 9 \cdot 9$ in exponential form. **(1.3)**

In Exercises 25–32, evaluate the given expression. (1.4)

25. $4 + 21 \div 3 - 3^2$
26. $(12 - 7)^2 + 5$
27. $\frac{6 + 2^2}{17 - 6 \cdot 2}$
28. $\frac{9 - 1 \cdot 7}{42}$
29. $12 - 2x^2$, when $x = 2$
30. $x^3 + x - 7$, when $x = 3$
31. $\frac{x - 3y}{6}$, when $x = 15$ and $y = 2$
32. $\frac{x^2}{y^2} + 4$, when $x = 4$ and $y = 2$

In Exercises 33–36, use mental math to solve the equation. (1.5)

33. $2x - 8 = 0$
34. $\frac{4}{x} = \frac{1}{2}$
35. $x^3 = 64$
36. $\frac{x}{8} = 0$

37. Is 7 a solution of the equation $x^2 - x + 2 = 44$? **(1.5)**
38. Is 4 a solution of $2x - 3 = 2$? **(1.5)**
39. Determine whether 3 is a solution of the inequality $9x - 3 > 24$. **(1.5)**
40. Determine whether 6 is a solution of the inequality $13 + 2x \le 25$. **(1.5)**

In Exercises 41 and 42, consider the problem, then answer the question about the equation that represents the problem. (1.6)

41. *Buying a Compact Disk*   Suppose you want to buy a compact disk that costs $15.90, including tax. If you can save $4.00 a week, how many weeks must you save to buy the compact disk?

   If this problem is represented by the equation $4x - y = 15.90$, what do the 4, the x, the y, and the 15.90 represent?

42. *Dance Supplies*   Suppose you are in charge of buying refreshments for a school dance. You are given $65 and each bottle of juice is 35¢. How many bottles of juice can you buy?

   If this problem is represented by the equation $0.35a + b = 65$, what do the 0.35, the a, the b, and the 65 represent?

In Exercises 43–48, write an algebraic expression, equation, or inequality for the phrase or sentence.

43. Six more than a number squared

44. Half of a number, decreased by nine

45. The quotient of a number and two is greater than seven

46. Nine plus the product of a number and six is less than or equal to twenty.

47. A number cubed minus another number is sixty.

48. The difference of a number and two times another number is ten.

49. *Calorie Counter*   A 12-ounce can of fruit punch has 180 Calories. A 12-ounce can of orange soda has 200 Calories. Write an expression that represents the number of Calories consumed if you drink x cans of fruit punch and y cans of orange soda.

50. *Buying Fishing Gear*   New line for your fishing reel will cost 2¢ a yard. Lures are on sale for $3.50 each. Write an expression that represents the total amount you will spend if you purchase x yards of line and y lures.

51. *A Riddle*   This rhyme is one of the world's oldest mathematical riddles:

   As I was going to St. Ives,
   I met a man with seven wives.
   Each wife had seven sacks.
   Each sack had seven cats.
   Each cat had seven kittens.
   Kittens, cats, sacks, and wives,
   How many were going to St. Ives?

   The number of kittens, cats, sacks, and wives is $7^4 + 7^3 + 7^2 + 7^1 = 2800$, but what is the answer to the riddle?

52. *Falcon in Flight*   A peregrine falcon sights a sparrow three miles away. If the falcon's average speed is 180 miles per hour during the attack, how long will it take for the falcon to reach the sparrow?

The peregrine falcon can attain speeds over 200 miles per hour when attacking its prey.

53. *Computer Screen*   A square computer screen has sides whose lengths are *s* inches each. Write an algebraic expression that represents the area of the computer screen. What is the area of the screen if *s* = 9 inches?

54. *Perimeter of a Picture*   A rectangular picture frame has sides of length 2*w* and 3*w*. Write an expression for the perimeter of the picture frame. What is the perimeter if *w* = 4 inches?

55. *Basketball Score*   Suppose that you are the second leading scorer in your high school's basketball league. The league's leading scorer has finished the season with a game average of 20 points (for 25 games). You have a 19.5-point game average and have yet to play your 25th game. How many points do you need to score to overtake the league's leading scorer?

Unemployment Rate   **In Exercises 56–58, use the following bar graph which shows the percentages of Americans (of working age) who were unemployed for each year from 1983 to 1988, according to the number of years of high school completed.**

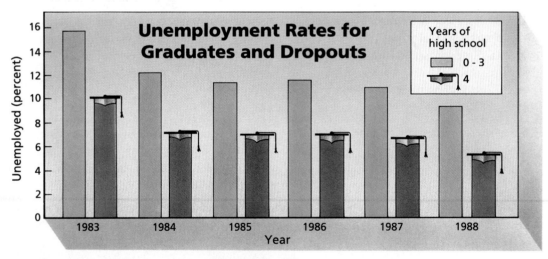

56. What percent of the people who went to three or fewer years of high school were unemployed in 1983?

57. Was the unemployment rate for Americans who had completed high school increasing or decreasing from 1983 to 1988?

58. Out of 100 working-age Americans who had completed high school in 1988, how many would you expect to have been unemployed?

For exercises 1 and 2, evaluate the expressions.

1. Evaluate $2(x - 3) + x^2 \div 4$ when $x = 6$.

2. Evaluate $9(x - y^2)$ when $x = 6$ and $y = 2$.

In Exercises 3–8, decide whether the statement is true or false.

3. $(3 \cdot 4)^2 = 3 \cdot 4^2$.

4. The quotient of 2 and 6 is 3.

5. $4 - 3 = 3 - 4$

6. $5 \div (3 - 1) + 1 > 5 - 3 \cdot 4 \div 6$

7. 10% of $27 is 27¢.

8. $14 - x^2 \leq 7$, when $x = 3$.

9. Use mental math to solve $7 - x = 4$.

10. Use mental math to solve $x^3 = 27$.

11. Insert grouping symbols in $13 + 7 \cdot 4 \div 2$ so that its value is 40.

12. Insert grouping symbols in $2x + 2 \cdot 4 - 3$ so that its value is 12 when $x = 5$.

13. If you can only travel 35 miles per hour, is $2\frac{1}{2}$ hours enough time to get to a concert that is 85 miles away?

14. Write an algebraic expression for the phrase "two times a number, decreased by the sum of another number squared and 2."

15. A zoo is building a glass cylindrical tank for the small sharks. The tank is 10 feet high and has a diameter of 16 feet. How much water is needed to fill the tank? (The volume of a right circular cylinder is $V = \pi r^2 h$, where r is the radius, h is the height, and $\pi \approx 3.14$.)

16. Members of the marching band are making their own color-guard flags. Each rectangular flag is 1.2 yards by 0.5 yards. How much fabric is needed to make 20 flags?

17. The distance between consecutive bases on a baseball diamond is 90 feet. What is the perimeter of the baseball diamond?

18. The senior class is planning a trip that will cost $35 per student. If $3920 has been collected from the seniors for the trip, how many have paid for their trip?

KEY

■ Dogs
■ Cats
■ Birds

19. The bar graph gives the numbers of homes in the U.S. that had household pets in 1983 and 1987.

(Source: American Veterinary Medical Association)

a. Approximately how many homes had a cat in 1983?

b. For which types of pets was the number of homes increasing?

Rules of Algebra

LESSONS

2.1 The Real Number Line ▪ 62

2.2 Addition of Real Numbers ▪ 68

2.3 Subtraction of Real Numbers ▪ 75

2.4 Exploring Data: Matrices ▪ 81

2.5 Multiplication of Real Numbers ▪ 89

2.6 The Distributive Property ▪ 95

2.7 Division of Real Numbers ▪ 101

2.8 Exploring Data: Rates and Ratios ▪ 107

Scientists are constantly trying to understand and predict patterns in Nature, using algebra as one of their most important tools.

Real Life
Earth Science

The Earth's Changing Sea Level

Changes in sea level occur primarily as the result of glacier activity. In an ice age, the sea level drops. In an age of ice melting, the sea level rises. At present, Earth is in an inter-glacial period. The graph at the left shows the variations in sea level for the eastern United States during the last 40,000 years.

On the graph, time is measured horizontally (in years), and sea level is measured vertically (in meters). On the horizontal scale, 0 corresponds to the present time, negative numbers correspond to past times, and positive numbers correspond to future times. On the vertical scale, 0 corresponds to the present sea level, negative numbers correspond to sea levels below the present level, and positive numbers correspond to sea levels above the present level.

During the last 5000 years, the sea level along the eastern United States has risen an average of one millimeter per year. (Since 1940, it has risen about three millimeters per year.)

2.1 The Real Number Line

What you should learn:

Goal 1 How to graph and compare real numbers using the real number line

Goal 2 How to find the opposite and the absolute value of a real number

Why you should learn it:

You can use the real number line as a model to help you visualize relationships among real numbers and to help you understand negative amounts such as "below zero" temperatures and negative velocities.

Goal 1 Graphing Real Numbers

The numbers used in algebra are **real numbers,** and they can be pictured as points on a horizontal line called a **real number line.** The point for 0 is the **origin.** Points to the left of 0 represent **negative numbers,** and points to the right of 0 **positive numbers.** Zero is neither positive nor negative.

The scale marks on the real number line are equally spaced and represent **integers.** An integer is either negative, zero, or positive.

$$\underbrace{\{\ldots, -3, -2, -1,}_{\text{Negative}}\ \underbrace{0,}_{\text{Zero}}\ \underbrace{1, 2, 3, \ldots\}}_{\text{Positive}}\ \textit{Integers}$$

By enclosing the numbers in braces { }, we are indicating that they form a **set.** The three dots on each side indicate that the list continues in both directions without end. For instance, the next integer to the left is -4, read as "negative four," and the next integer to the right is $+4$, or simply 4, read as "positive four," or simply "four."

The real number line contains points that represent fractions and decimals as well as integers. The point that corresponds to a number is the **graph** of the number, and drawing the point is called *graphing* the number or *plotting* the point.

Example 1 Graphing Numbers on the Real Number Line

Graph the numbers $\frac{1}{2}$ and -2.3 on the real number line.

Solution The point that corresponds to the positive number $\frac{1}{2}$ is one-half unit to the *right* of 0. The point that corresponds to the negative number -2.3 is 2.3 units to the *left* of 0.

Having the real number line as a *visual model* of the real numbers helps answer questions about real numbers. You already know that 5 is greater than 4, but what about -5 and -4? Which is greater? Graphing these numbers on the real number line gives you the answer. Numbers to the right get larger, numbers to the left get smaller. Because -4 is to the right of -5, you know that -4 is greater than -5.

-4 is greater than -5

The inequality symbols $<$ and $>$ can be used to show the **order** of two numbers.

Verbal Statement	Inequality	Number Line Interpretation
-4 is *greater* than -5.	$-4 > -5$	-4 is to the *right* of -5.
2 is *less* than 3.	$2 < 3$	2 is to the *left* of 3.

The statements $2 < 3$ and $3 > 2$ give the same information.

Example 2 *Ordering Real Numbers*

Write the numbers -2, 4, 0, 1.5, $\frac{1}{2}$, and $-\frac{3}{2}$ in increasing order.

Solution One way to order the numbers is to graph them on the real number line.

From the picture, the order is -2, $-\frac{3}{2}$, 0, $\frac{1}{2}$, 1.5, 4. ∎

Real Life
Meteorology

Example 3 *Comparing Temperatures*

A weather station in Alaska recorded the temperature (in degrees Celsius) each day at noon for one week.

a. Which noon temperature reading was the coldest?

b. Which days had noon temperatures below $-10°C$?

c. Which days had noon temperatures above $0°C$?

Solution

a. The coldest temperature was $-22°C$.

b. Days with noon temperatures below $-10°C$ were Sunday ($-17°C$), Monday ($-21°C$), Tuesday ($-22°C$), and Saturday ($-12°C$).

c. Only Thursday's noon temperature was above $0°C$. ∎

Day	Date	Temp.
Sun.	Mar. 3	$-17°C$
Mon.	Mar. 4	$-21°C$
Tue.	Mar. 5	$-22°C$
Wed.	Mar. 6	$-9°C$
Thu.	Mar. 7	$1°C$
Fri.	Mar. 8	$-3°C$
Sat.	Mar. 9	$-12°C$

Two points on the real number line that are the same distance from the origin but are on opposite sides of the origin are **opposites.** For instance, -3 and 3 are opposites of each other, but -2 and 4 are not opposites because -2 is closer to the origin than 4. As a special case, we will agree that 0 is its own opposite. In general, a and $-a$ are opposites. Thus, the opposite of $-a$ is $-(-a) = a$.

Example 4 *Finding the Opposite of a Number*

a. If $a = 5$, then $-a = -5$, the opposite of a.

b. If $a = -6$, then $-a = -(-6) = 6$, the opposite of a. ■

You should not assume that $-a$ is a negative number. For instance, in Example 4b, $-a = -(-6) = 6$, which is positive.

Properties of Opposites

1. If a is positive, then its opposite, $-a$, is negative.

2. The opposite of 0 is 0.

3. If a is negative, then its opposite, $-a$, is positive.

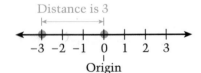

Distance is 3

Origin

The **absolute value** of a real number is the distance between the origin and the point representing the real number. For instance, the absolute value of -3 is 3, which we write as

$$|-3| = 3. \qquad \textit{The absolute value of } -3 \textit{ is } 3.$$

Example 5 *Finding the Absolute Value of a Number*

a. If a is a positive number, then $|a| = a$.

$$|4| = 4 \qquad \textit{The absolute value of 4 is 4.}$$

b. $|0| = 0 \qquad \textit{The absolute value of 0 is 0.}$

c. If a is a negative, then $|a|$ is the opposite of a. Another way of saying this is that if a is negative, then $|a| = -a$.

$$\left|-\tfrac{1}{2}\right| = -\left(-\tfrac{1}{2}\right) = \tfrac{1}{2} \qquad \textit{The absolute value of } -\tfrac{1}{2} \textit{ is } \tfrac{1}{2}. \quad ■$$

By the time the two solid rocket boosters disengage from the space shuttle Columbia, it has reached a speed of about 16,000 miles per hour. The liquid hydrogen fuel has a temperature of −258°C.

The **speed** of an object is the absolute value of its **velocity.** *Velocity* indicates both speed and direction. In Example 6, positive velocities are used for motion that is straight up. Negative velocities are used for motion that is straight down.

Connections
Physical Science

Example 6   *Finding Velocity and Speed*

A parachutist is falling at a rate of 20 feet per second.

a. What is the velocity, *v*, of the parachutist?

b. What is the speed, *s*, of the parachutist?

Solution

a. Because the motion is down, the velocity is negative. Thus, $v = -20$ feet per second.

b. The speed of an object is the absolute value of its velocity. Thus, $s = |-20| = 20$ feet per second. ■

Communicating about ALGEBRA

▶ **SHARING IDEAS about the Lesson**

Justify Your Response   True or false? Discuss your answers.

A. Each integer is either positive or negative.

B. The absolute value of a negative number is positive.

C. The expression $-a$ is always negative.

D. If *a* is negative and *b* is positive, then $a < b$.

E. If *a* and *b* are different real numbers, then either $a < b$ or $a > b$.

EXERCISES

Guided Practice

▶ **CRITICAL THINKING about the Lesson**

1. How is the inequality $5 < 6$ read? How can it be interpreted on a real number line?

2. Write an inequality for this sentence: Two is greater than negative three.

3. Decide whether the inequalities are true or false. Explain.

$$-4 < -5 \qquad -2 < 0 \qquad 6 > -7 \qquad -1 < -\tfrac{1}{2}$$

In Exercises 4–6, write an integer to represent the situation.

4. a loss of ten dollars

5. six feet above ground

6. two meters to the left

Independent Practice

In Exercises 7–14, graph the numbers on a number line. Which is greater?

7. 4 and -1

8. 3 and -3

9. $-\tfrac{1}{2}$ and 2

10. -1.5 and 2.5

11. 4.5 and -5.5

12. -1.3 and 2.1

13. -1.4 and $\tfrac{3}{4}$

14. -2 and $-\tfrac{2}{3}$

15. Write the numbers in increasing order.

$3.1, -1.9, 4, 0, \tfrac{1}{2}$, and $-\tfrac{1}{2}$

16. Write the numbers in increasing order.

$1.5, -\tfrac{1}{2}, 6, -4.6, -\tfrac{3}{4}$, and $\tfrac{1}{3}$

In Exercises 17–24, find the opposite of the number.

17. 6

18. -10

19. -2.4

20. 1.9

21. -9

22. 3.6

23. 0

24. -1

In Exercises 25–32, evaluate the expression.

25. $|5|$

26. $|-3|$

27. $\left|-\tfrac{4}{5}\right|$

28. $\left|\tfrac{1}{2}\right|$

29. $|3.2|$

30. $|-4.1|$

31. $|0|$

32. $|16.3|$

Brightness of a Star   **In Exercises 33 and 34, use the following information.**

A star's brightness to a person on Earth is measured by its apparent magnitude. The less the apparent magnitude, the brighter the star. The table lists several stars and their apparent magnitudes.

33. Which of the stars is the brightest?

34. Which are the dimmest?

Star	Apparent magnitude	Star	Apparent magnitude
Canopus	-0.73	Vega	0.04
Procyon	0.30	Sirius	-1.40
Pollux	1.16	Sun	-26.70
Deneb	1.25	Aldebaran	0.85
Beta Crucis	1.25	Alpha Centauri	-0.29

Greenwich, England, is on the 0° meridian. Standard time elsewhere is calculated from GMT. The table lists a few countries and the number of hours each differs from GMT.

Country	Standard Time (in hours)
Chile	−4
Libya	+1
Ireland	−1
Israel	+2
Kenya	+3
Japan	+9
Mexico	−7
Pakistan	+5

35. Which countries have standard times closest to GMT?

36. Which country has standard time farthest from GMT?

37. Which countries are west of Greenwich?

38. Which countries are east of Greenwich?

39. *Velocity of a Helicopter*   A helicopter is 240 feet above its landing pad. Twenty seconds later, it lands. What was its velocity? What was its speed?

40. *Bromley Alpine Slide*   The longest slide in the world is the 4600-foot Bromley Alpine Slide in Peru, Vermont. What speed must you have to complete the slide in 8 minutes?

Integrated Review

In Exercises 41–48, evaluate the expression.

41. $4x + 3y$, when $x = 2$ and $y = 1$

42. $2a - b$, when $a = 6$ and $b = 3$

43. $\frac{1}{4}x - y$, when $x = 9$ and $y = 5$

44. $\frac{1}{2}a + 4b$, when $a = 10$ and $b = 3$

45. $|-4| + |3|$

46. $|6| - |-1|$

47. $|x| + |y|$, when $x = -3$ and $y = -1$

48. $|y| - |x|$, when $y = -7$ and $x = 3$

In Exercises 49–52, use mental math to solve the equation.

49. $2a = 8$

50. $\frac{a}{3} = 3$

51. $\frac{x}{2} = 4$

52. $9 - y = 1$

Exploration and Extension

In Exercises 53–56, use mental math to solve the equation. Explain your answers.

53. $|x| = 2$

54. $|x| = 0$

55. $|x| = -1$

56. $|x| = |-x|$

2.2

Addition of Real Numbers

What you should learn:

Goal 1 How to add real numbers using a number line or Addition Rules

Goal 2 How to add real numbers using a calculator

Why you should learn it:

You can add positive and negative numbers to solve real-life problems, such as finding the cash balance on a business balance sheet.

Goal 1 Adding Real Numbers

Addition can be modeled with movements on the real number line. You add a positive number by moving to the right. You add a negative number by moving to the left. For instance, to find the sum of -2 and 3, you can start at -2 and move 3 units to the right, arriving at 1. This can be written as $-2 + 3 = 1$. Another way to find the sum is to start at 3 and move 2 units to the left, arriving at 1. This can be written as $3 + (-2) = 1$.

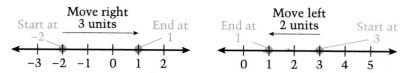

Note that adding in either order produces the same sum.

Example 1 Adding Real Numbers Using a Number Line

a. To add -5 and -2, start at -5 and move left 2 units to -7. The action can be written as $-5 + (-2) = -7$.

b. To add 5, -10, and 3, start at 5, move left 10 units to -5, and move right 3 units to -2. The action can be written as $5 + (-10) + 3 = -2$. ■

Problem Solving
Using a Model

Example 2 Finding the Number of Yards Gained

The Pittsburgh Steelers lose 4 yards on their first play and gain 12 yards on their second play. What is the net gain?

Solution The two plays can be represented on a real number line in which 0 represents the line of scrimmage.

The net gain can be written as $0 + (-4) + 12 = 8$. ■

The symbol $-$, used to represent a negative number, is a **negative sign.** A positive number is considered to have a **positive sign,** $+$. The following Addition Rules show how to find the sum of two real numbers without using a number line.

1. To add two numbers with the *same sign,* add their absolute values and write the common sign.

2. To add two numbers with *opposite signs,* find the difference of their absolute values and write the sign of the number with the greater absolute value.

Example 3   ***Adding Real Numbers Using Addition Rules***

a. Same sign

$$-4 + (-5) = -(4 + 5)$$
$$= -9$$

b. Opposite signs

$$3 + (-9) = -(9 - 3)$$
$$= -6 \quad \blacksquare$$

Properties of Addition

1. $a + b = b + a$	The order in which two numbers are added does not change their sum.
2. $a + 0 = a$	The sum of a number and 0 is the number.
3. $a + (-a) = 0$	The sum of a number and its opposite is 0.
4. $-(a + b) = -a + (-b)$	The opposite of a sum of two numbers is equal to the sum of the opposites of the numbers.

Connections

Physical Science

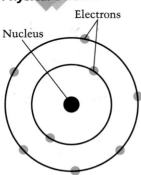

This Bohr model for an oxygen atom shows 8 electrons orbiting about a nucleus.

Example 4   ***Atoms and their Ions***

Atoms and ions are composed of electrons, neutrons, and protons. Each electron has a charge of -1, and each proton has a charge of $+1$. The total charge of an atom or ion is the sum of the charges of its electrons and protons. An atom has zero charge. An ion has a positive or negative charge. Which of the following arrangements represents an atom? An ion?

a. 8 electrons, 8 protons

b. 10 electrons, 8 protons

Solution

a. The total charge is $-8 + 8 = 0$. Thus it is an atom, not an ion.

b. The total charge is $-10 + 8 = -2$. Thus it is an ion. In chemistry, this oxygen ion is written as O^{-2}. $\quad \blacksquare$

Adding Real Numbers Using a Calculator

A calculator is useful for adding large numbers or numbers in decimal form. The key used to enter negative numbers depends on the type of calculator. Some calculators have a change-sign key $\boxed{+/-}$, others have a negation key $\boxed{(-)}$, and some have no key for entering negative numbers. On most calculators, the subtraction key $\boxed{-}$ cannot be used to enter a negative sign.

Example 5   *Evaluating a Sum Using a Calculator*

Use a calculator to evaluate $-2.6 + 3.1 + (-1.4)$.

Solution

Change-sign key   2.6 $\boxed{+/-}$ $\boxed{+}$ 3.1 $\boxed{+}$ 1.4 $\boxed{+/-}$ $\boxed{=}$

Negation key $\boxed{(-)}$ 2.6 $\boxed{+}$ 3.1 $\boxed{+}$ $\boxed{(-)}$ 1.4 $\boxed{=}$

With either keystroke sequence, the calculator display should read -0.9. ∎

A company has a profit when its income is greater than its expenses. It has a loss when income is less than expenses. Business losses are generally indicated by negative numbers.

Real Life
Business

Example 6   *Finding the Total Profit*

The balance sheet of a company shows a profit of $13,142.50 in January, a loss of $6,783.16 in February, and a profit of $2,589.82 in March. What was the overall profit during the first quarter? (January, February, and March form the first quarter of the year.)

Solution   The overall profit during the first quarter was

$$13,142.50 + (-6,783.16) + 2,589.82 = \$8,949.16.$$ ∎

Communicating about ALGEBRA

▶ **SHARING IDEAS about the Lesson**

Cooperative Learning

Work with a Partner and Use the Real Number Line

A. Show how to model the sum of -4 and 3 in two ways. Make a sketch to illustrate both ways.

B. Describe different ways the sum of -3, 2, and -1 can be modeled. Make a sketch to illustrate each way.

EXERCISES

Guided Practice

▶ CRITICAL THINKING about the Lesson

1. **True or False?** On a number line, adding a negative number can be shown by a move to the right. *False move to the left*

2. **True or False?** When adding numbers with opposite signs, subtract the smaller absolute value from the larger absolute value and attach the sign of the number with the larger absolute value. *True*

3. Is the order in which you add two numbers important? Illustrate your answer with an example that shows the sum of -3 and 2 in two ways on a number line. *No* $-3 + 2 = -1$ $2 + (-3) = -1$

4. The number zero is called the **additive identity**. Why do you think zero was given this name? *Any # added to zero is that identical #* $7 + 0 = 7$ $-7 + 0 = -7$

Independent Practice

In Exercises 5–12, use a number line to help you find the sum of the numbers.

5. -7 and 11

6. 3 and -4

7. -3 and $3\frac{1}{2}$

8. -2 and -8

9. -4 and 5

10. -5 and 4

11. -5, 8, and -2

12. 10, -17, and 1

In Exercises 13–20, use the Addition Rules to find the sum.

13. $-4 + 2 =$

14. $6 + 3 =$

15. $7 + 0 =$

16. $0 + (-6)$

17. $-11 + (-4)$

18. $12 + (-9)$

19. $5 + (-10) + (-3) =$

20. $-2 + 11 + (-7)$

In Exercises 21–24, evaluate the expression in two ways. (The results should agree.)

21. $-(8 + 5)$

22. $-[-(4+3)]$

23. $-[12 + (-6)]$

24. $-[1 - (-3)]$

In Exercises 25–28, use a calculator to evaluate the sum. Use an estimate to check.

25. $-11.4 + 6.2 + (-2.0)$

26. $5.8 + (-9.3) + 5.2$

27. $6.4 + 3.1 + (-6.4)$

28. $-2.9 + 5.7 + (-8.6)$

In Exercises 29–32, simplify the expression. (Sample: $2 + x + (-3) = -1 + x$)

29. $3 + x + (-8)$

30. $2x + 8 + (-8)$

31. $-6 + x + 2$

32. $3 + (-2) + p + 19$

33. *Los Angeles Raiders* The Los Angeles Raiders completed a pass for a gain of 37 yards. After the play was over, a flag was thrown and a 15-yard penalty was called against the Raiders. How many yards did the Raiders actually gain? Draw a diagram to help you.

$37 + (-15) = +22$

34. Championship Game   Suppose it is the game that decides the high school football championship. Your team is behind by five points and needs a touchdown to win. Starting on the opponent's 12-yard line, your team's final four plays result in an 8-yard completed pass, a loss of 4 yards on a quarterback sack, 2 yards gained by the fullback, and a 6-yard gain on a quarterback sneak as time runs out. Does your team win? Draw a diagram and explain.

35. Atom or Ion?   Find the total charge. Then decide whether you have an atom or an ion.

36. Chemical Symbol   For the elements in Exercise 35, which has a symbol of Na? Of Na^{+1}? Of F^{-1}?

	Electrons	Protons	Total charge	Atom or ion?
Sodium	10	11	?	?
Sodium	11	11	?	?
Fluorine	9	9	?	?
Fluorine	10	9	?	?

37. Second-Quarter Profit?   A company had a profit of \$3,412.53 in April, a profit of \$5,784.25 in May, and a loss of \$9,013.86 in June. Did the company enjoy a profit during this quarter? Explain.

38. Third-Quarter Profit or Loss?   A company had a loss of \$5,519.80 in July, a profit of \$2,337.06 in August, and a profit of \$3,615.11 in September. Did the company enjoy a profit during the third quarter of the year? Explain.

39. Televised Live   A soccer team from North Carolina has made it to the championship game in Oregon. The game is to be televised live and is scheduled to begin at 2:00 P.M. At what time will the game be seen in North Carolina?

40. What Time Is It?   Martha left California at 7:00 A.M. and flew to Disney World in Florida. The flight included $6\frac{3}{4}$ hours of airtime and two $1\frac{1}{2}$-hour stops. When she landed in Florida, what was the local time?

The continental United States has four time zones: Pacific, Mountain, Central, and Eastern.

Integrated Review

41. Find the opposite of -16.

42. Find the opposite of 0.

43. Find the absolute value of 7.

44. Find the absolute value of -11.

In Exercises 45–48, evaluate the expression.

45. $a^2 - 5$, when $a = 3$

46. $3x^3 - 9$, when $x = 2$

47. $(6s - t)^2$, when $s = 3$ and $t = 9$

48. $17 - (3m + 1)^2$, when $m = 1$

In Exercises 49 and 50, use mental math to solve the equation.

49. $5x = 15$

50. $\frac{21}{x} = 7$

51. *Grocery Scales*   Suppose you go to a grocery store to buy 5 kilograms of potatoes for a salad. You put several in a sack and find the weight is 3.8 kilograms. Let x represent the weight of the additional potatoes you need. Which of the following equations correctly model the situation?

   a. $x + 3.8 = 5$ **b.** $x + 5 = 3.8$ **c.** $5 - 3.8 = x$ **d.** $5 - x = 3.8$

   How many kilograms do you need? Check that this amount is a solution of each correct equation.

52. *Apartment Size*   An apartment is 26 feet by 30 feet. Which of the following equations correctly describes the relationship among the areas of the rooms as shown on the floor plan? Explain.

   a. $x + (192 + 140 + 100 + 120) = (26)(30)$

   b. $(26)(30) - (192 + 140 + 100 + 120) = x$

   How many square feet are in the area labeled with x square feet?

53. *Playing Putt-Putt*   Suppose that your sister challenges you to three rounds of Putt-Putt golf. In the first round, she wins by two strokes and finishes six over par. In the second round, you win by one stroke and finish three over par. In the final round, there is one hole left, and you are tied for the round. Your sister scores a two, giving her a round total of three over par. She says there is no way for you to win either that round or overall. Is she correct? Make a table to support your answer.

Exploration and Extension

In Exercises 54–56, use mental math to solve the equation.

54. $-6 = 3 + x$

55. $-29 + x = 16$

56. $-22 + (-14) = x + 5$

57. *Entrepreneur*   On Saturday, your brother decides to open a lemonade and cookie stand to earn money for a new video game that costs $29.95. It costs $2.00 to make a pitcher (16 glasses) of fresh lemonade and $5.00 to make a batch of cookies (60 cookies). He charges $0.30 for a glass of lemonade and $0.15 for a cookie. If he makes x batches of cookies and x pitchers of lemonade, which inequality models the outcome desired by your brother?

   a. $[16(0.30) - 2] x + [60(0.15) - 5] x \geq 29.95$

   b. $[16(0.30) - 2] x + [60(0.15) - 5] x \leq 29.95$

   What is the smallest integer value of x that will allow your brother to buy the game?

1. Evaluate $2y + 14$ when $y = 5$. **(1.2)**
2. Evaluate $(4 \div 2) + 3(8 - 7)$. **(1.1)**
3. Write $\frac{3}{8}$ in percent form. **(1.1)**
4. Which is greater, $-\frac{1}{2}$ or $-\frac{3}{4}$? **(2.1)**
5. Write $s \cdot s \cdot s \cdot s \cdot s$ in exponential form. **(1.3)**
6. Evaluate $2r^2 + 5y^3$ when $r = 4$ and $y = 2$. **(1.3)**
7. What value of t makes $t^3 - 4$ equal to 23? **(1.5)**
8. Find the absolute value of -4.3. **(2.1)**
9. Is 8 a solution of $x \div 4 + 3 \geq 5$? **(1.5)**
10. Is 5 a solution of $6y = 20 + 2y$? **(1.5)**
11. What is the product of 8 and 3? **(1.4)**
12. What is the quotient of 3 and 4? **(1.4)**
13. Evaluate $16.3 + 9.4 \cdot 2.9$. **(1.4)**
14. Evaluate $39.7 \div 16.2 + 5.5$. **(1.4)**
15. Write 4, -8, 3, 0, -5, -2, 1 in increasing order. **(2.1)**
16. What is the area of a circle with a radius of 6 centimeters? **(1.3)**
17. What is the volume of a cube with edges of 5 inches each? **(1.3)**
18. Write an inequality for "The difference of three times a number and 8 is less than 20." **(1.6)**

Milestones ORIGINS OF ALGEBRA

2000	1800	1600	1400	1200	1000	800	600	400	200	B.C. A.D.	200	400	600	800	1000	1200	1400

Rhind Papyrus, Egypt

Diophantus, Greece   al-Khowarizmi, Persia

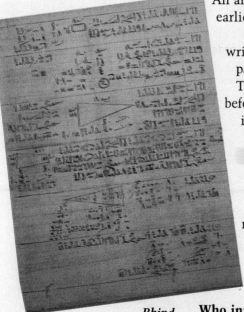

An ancient Egyptian papyrus, discovered in 1858, contains one of the earliest examples of mathematical writing in existence. The papyrus itself dates back to around 1650 B.C., but it is actually a copy of writings from two centuries earlier. The algebraic equations on the papyrus were written in words.

The Babylonians are believed to have explored algebraic concepts before the Egyptians. They also wrote their mathematical thoughts in words. Although this was cumbersome, the Babylonians were able to show some sophisticated algebraic solutions.

Diophantus, a Greek who lived around A.D. 250, is often called the Father of Algebra. He was the first to use abbreviated word forms in equations. In India, Hindu mathematicians, such as Brahmagupta (A.D. 628), worked with negative and irrational roots. In A.D. 825, Mohammed ibn-Musa al-Khowarizmi wrote a book with a practical discussion of equations and how to solve them. The book title, *Hisab al-jabr w'al-muqabalah*, contains the word *al-jabr*, which was later translated into the Latin word *algebra*.

Rhind Papyrus — **Who introduced the following: equal sign, multiplication sign (•), the use of letters as variables? In what century were they introduced?**

2.3 Subtraction of Real Numbers

What you should learn:

Goal 1 How to subtract real numbers using a Subtraction Rule or a calculator

Goal 2 How to simplify the difference of two algebraic expressions

Why you should learn it:

You can subtract positive and negative numbers by knowing how to rewrite a subtraction expression in terms of addition. This is useful in solving real-life problems such as finding differences in stock-market prices.

Goal 1 Subtracting Real Numbers

In Lesson 2.2, you learned that some addition expressions can be evaluated using subtraction. Here are two examples.

Addition		Corresponding Subtraction
$5 + (-3) = 2$	$\longleftrightarrow$	$5 - 3 = 2$
$9 + (-6) = 3$	$\longleftrightarrow$	$9 - 6 = 3$

In the first example, adding the opposite of 3 produces the same result as subtracting 3. In the second example, adding the opposite of 6 produces the same result as subtracting 6.

Subtraction Rule

To subtract b from a, add the opposite of b to a.

$$a - b = a + (-b)$$

The result is the difference of a and b.

In Lesson 2.2, you saw that the order in which two numbers are added doesn't affect their sum. For subtraction, however, different orders can produce different results.

$5 - 2 = 3$ *The difference of 5 and 2 is 3.*
$2 - 5 = -3$ *The difference of 2 and 5 is -3.*

Example 1 *Using the Subtraction Rule*

a. $-4 - 3 = -4 + (-3)$
$\qquad\quad = -7$

b. $10 - 11 = 10 + (-11)$
$\qquad\qquad = -1$

c. $5 - (-4) = 5 + 4$
$\qquad\qquad = 9$

d. $-\frac{3}{2} - (-\frac{1}{2}) = -\frac{3}{2} + \frac{1}{2}$
$\qquad\qquad\quad = -1$ ∎

When an expression is written as a *sum*, the parts that form the sum are the **terms** of the expression. For instance, the expression $-9 - x$ can be written as $-9 + (-x)$ and has two terms. The first term is -9, and the second term is $-x$.

Expressions containing more than one subtraction can also be evaluated by "adding opposites." Note how the Left-to-Right Rule for order of operations is used in Example 2.

Example 2 Repeated Subtraction and Addition

$$3 - (-4) - 2 + 8 = 3 + 4 + (-2) + 8 \qquad -(-4)$$
$$= 7 + (-2) + 8 \qquad 3 + 4$$
$$= 5 + 8 \qquad 7 + (-2)$$
$$= 13 \qquad 5 + 8 \qquad \blacksquare$$

On a typical day, over 200 million shares worth over $7.5 billion are bought and sold through the New York Stock Exchange. Stock prices often vary throughout a day. The closing price of each stock is the price of the last sale in the day. Changes in closing prices are usually given in multiples of eighths of dollars.

Real Life
Stock Market

Example 3 Finding the Value of a Stock

On Friday, May 10, 1991, the closing price of a share of Coca-Cola™ stock was $54\frac{3}{4}$. The daily changes in closing values during the following week were as follows.

Monday	Tuesday	Wednesday	Thursday	Friday
$-\frac{3}{8}$	$-\frac{1}{2}$	$-\frac{1}{8}$	$+1\frac{1}{4}$	$-\frac{1}{8}$

What was the closing price of a share on Friday, May 17, 1991?

Solution You could add and subtract fractions by hand to solve the problem, or you could use a calculator.

$$\text{Closing price} = 54\tfrac{3}{4} + \left(-\tfrac{3}{8}\right) + \left(-\tfrac{1}{2}\right) + \left(-\tfrac{1}{8}\right) + 1\tfrac{1}{4} + \left(-\tfrac{1}{8}\right)$$
$$= 54\tfrac{3}{4} - \tfrac{3}{8} - \tfrac{1}{2} - \tfrac{1}{8} + 1\tfrac{1}{4} - \tfrac{1}{8}$$
$$= 54\tfrac{7}{8}$$

Thus, the closing price on May 17 was $54\frac{7}{8}$ per share. $\blacksquare$

You can *simplify* the expression $8 + (-x + 1)$ by rewriting it as $9 - x$. The second form has fewer terms and fewer grouping symbols, but it is **equivalent** to the first because both expressions have the same value for each number represented by the variable. Whenever you are performing any algebraic operation, you can *substitute* an equivalent form of an expression without changing the result.

The next properties are useful for simplifying an expression.

Property	Statement	Example
Opposite of a Difference	$-(a - b) = -a + b$	$-(5 - 3) = -5 + 3$ $= -2$
Opposite of a Sum	$-(a + b) = -a - b$	$-(-8 + 5) = 8 - 5$ $= 3$

Example 4 *Simplifying before Evaluating*

Evaluate $7 - (2 - x)$ when $x = -3$.

Solution First, you can use the "opposite of a difference" property to write an equivalent expression. Then simplify before substituting.

$$
\begin{aligned}
7 - (2 - x) &= 7 - 2 + x & &\textit{Opposite of a Difference} \\
&= 5 + x & &\textit{Simplify } 7 - 2. \\
&= 5 + (-3) & &\textit{Substitute } -3 \textit{ for x.} \\
&= 2 & &\textit{Simplify } 5 + (-3).
\end{aligned}
$$

Communicating about ALGEBRA

▶ **SHARING IDEAS about the Lesson**

Demonstrate Understanding Which of the following pairs of expressions are equivalent? For all pairs that are not equivalent, find a value of x that produces different values for the two expressions. (For instance, the expressions $x - 4$ and $4 - x$ are not equivalent because when $x = 1$, they will have values of -3 and 3, respectively.)

Expression 1	Expression 2
A. $r - (-3)$	$r + 3$
B. $x - (2 + x)$	$x - 2 - x$
C. $5 - y - 2$	$(5 - y) + 2$

EXERCISES

▶ **CRITICAL THINKING about the Lesson**

1. **True or False?** Adding the opposite of a number is the same as subtracting the number. *True*

2. **True or False?** The difference of a and b is $a - b$. *True*

3. What is the first term of $-x + (-3)$? What is the second term? $-x$, -3

4. For two numbers, is the order in which subtraction is performed important? Give an example to support your answer. *yes* $5 - 2 = 3$ $2 - 5 = -3$

5. Evaluate $-3 - (-2) - (-1)$. $= 0$

6. Can $-(6 - 3)$ be simplified as $-6 + 3$? Explain. -3

Independent Practice

In Exercises 7–22, find the difference.

7. $3 - 8$ -5
8. $12 - 8$ 4
9. $7 - 4$ 3
10. $4 - 7$ -3
11. $\frac{6}{2} - \frac{3}{2}$ $1\frac{1}{2}$
12. $\frac{2}{3} - \frac{12}{3}$ -3.33
13. $-1 - 5$ -6
14. $-9 - 6$ -15
15. $8 - |-6|$ 2
16. $12 - |-7|$ 5
17. $-6 - |4|$ -10
18. $-3 - |5|$ -8
19. $|10| - 6.5$ 3.50
20. $|15| - 2.4$ 12.60
21. $\left|-\frac{3}{4}\right| - \frac{7}{4}$ -1
22. $\left|-\frac{7}{4}\right| - \frac{3}{4}$ 1

In Exercises 23–28, evaluate the expression.

23. $2 - (-6) - 7$ 1
24. $3 + (-4) - 2$ -3
25. $-6 + 5 - 4$ -5
26. $-11 - (-12) + 1$ 2
27. $5 - 3 + 12 - 9$ 5
28. $10 - 4 - 9 + 2$ -1

Technology **In Exercises 29–34, use a calculator to evaluate the expression. Use estimation to check your result.**

29. $4.8 - (-3.1) - 2.2$ 5.70
30. $7.1 - (-1.1) - 6.4$ 1.8
31. $-6.23 + 4.52 - (-2.75)$ 1.04
32. $-3.14 + 2.20 - (-3.21)$ 2.27
33. $-11.99 - (-11.99) + 6.8$ 6.8
34. $-17.3 + 0.0 + 4.2$ -13.10

In Exercises 35–42, evaluate the expression. Then simplify the expression and evaluate the simplified form. Check to see that the two values are equal. $4 - 3 = 1$

35. $4 - (1 + x)$, when $x = 2$ 1
36. $2 - (4 - t)$, when $t = 1$ -1 3
37. $15 - (-x + 7$, when $x = -6$ 16
38. $12 - (-2x) - 5$, when $x = -2$ 5
39. $-9 - (-13) - 7$, when $p = -7$ 11
40. $-8 - (-5) - 3$ when $r = -3$ 0
41. $-x - (3 - 8) + 4$, when $x = 10$

$-10 - (-5) + 4 = -1$

42. $-q - (7 + 6) + 2$, when $x = 9$ -20

$-9 - 13 + 2$

$500 = 40×8 + 115×4
320 + 460   780

43. *Monopoly*   Suppose you are playing Monopoly. So far you have collected $200 for passing **GO** and have received $300 from another player. But now you have drawn this card. If you own four hotels and eight houses, how much does this cost? Did you gain or lose money on this trip around the board? Explain.   *-280*

Community Chest

YOU ARE ASSESSED FOR STREET REPAIRS

$40 PER HOUSE
$115 PER HOTEL

© 1936 PARKER BROTHERS, INC.

MONOPOLY is a registered trademark of Parker Brothers, division of Tonka Corporation, and used with permission.

44. *Field Trip*   While on a field trip, you and a few classmates go exploring. You climb a hill and visit a cave before joining the rest of the class by the lake for lunch. You are curious to discover how high you actually climbed, so you find a map of the area. Here is a list of the various elevations.

A.	Parking lot	300 feet
B.	Start of trail	275 feet
C.	Foot of hill	325 feet
D.	Peak of hill	515 feet
E.	Cave on hill	440 feet
F.	Edge of lake	210 feet

How high is the hill? Determine the change in elevation between each two points. Find the total of these changes to discover your net change in elevation.

Escorted Tours   **In Exercises 45 and 46, use the bar graph.**

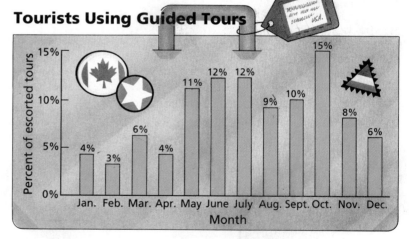

Tourists Using Guided Tours

This bar graph shows the percentages of tourists in the United States who went on escorted tours in 1990. (Source: The National Tour Association)

45. Complete the table by finding the monthly changes in the percentages given in the bar graph.

-2 +7 +10 -3 +1 +5 -7 +2 = 0

Month	J	F	M	A	M	J	J	A	S	O	N	D
Change in percentage	-2	-1	3	?	?	?	?	?	?	?	?	?

46. What is the overall change in percentage for the first six months? For the second six months? For the year?

In Exercises 47–50, use the numbers -3, $2\frac{1}{2}$, 4.3, -1.25, -5, $-2\frac{1}{2}$, and 1.

(handwritten: -5, -3, -2½, -1.25, 1, 2½, 4.3)

47. Write the numbers in increasing order.

48. Graph the numbers on the number line.

49. Which are less than 3 units from 0?

(handwritten: -1.25, -2½, 1, 2½)

50. Which are more than 3 units from 0?

(handwritten: 4.3)

In Exercises 51–54, evaluate the expression.

51. $6 + (1 - 3)$ *(handwritten: 6 + (-2)(4))*

52. $-5 + 11 = 6$

53. $-12 + 4 = -8$

54. $8 + (-2)$ *(handwritten: -6)*

In Exercises 55–58, use mental math to solve the equation.

55. $x - 8 = 10$ *(handwritten: x = 18)*

56. $x + 45 = 30$ *(handwritten: -15)*

57. $-[(-x) + 8] = 16$ *(handwritten: x = +24)*

58. $-(x - 5) = 8$ *(handwritten: 13)*

59. Consider the sums $-1 + (-1) = -2$ and $-1 + (-1) + (-1) = -3$.
Using these patterns, simplify $-x + (-x)$ and $-x + (-x) + (-x)$. *(handwritten: 2-x + 3-x)*

60. Consider the sums $-1 + (-2) = -3$ and $-2 + (-3) + (-4) = -9$.
Using these patterns, simplify $-x + (-2x)$ and $-2x + (-3x) + (-4x)$. *(handwritten: -3x + -9x, -5x)*

In Exercises 61–62, use Exercises 59 and 60 to simplify the expression.

61. $4 + (-x) + (-2x)$ *(handwritten: 4 + (-3x))*

62. $3 - [-x + (-x)]$ *(handwritten: 3 + 2x)*

Reading Music In Exercises 63–66, show that each measure has the correct number of beats.

In music, the time signature indicates the number of beats to a measure. Two common time signatures are $\frac{3}{4}$ (three beats to a measure) and $\frac{4}{4}$ (four beats to a measure).

Dotting a note means to hold it one and one-half times as long. The symbols 𝄽 and 𝄾 mean to rest, or not play anything, for one beat and one-half beat respectively.

Name	Symbol	Number of beats
Whole note	𝅝	4
Half note	𝅗𝅥	2
Quarter note	𝅘𝅥	1
Eighth note	𝅘𝅥𝅮	$\frac{1}{2}$
Sixteenth note	𝅘𝅥𝅯	$\frac{1}{4}$

63.

End of measure *(handwritten: 4)*

64.

(handwritten: 4)

65.

(handwritten: no)

66.

(handwritten: NO, 1½)

2.4

Exploring Data: Matrices

What you should learn:

Goal 1 How to organize data into a matrix

Goal 2 How to add and subtract two matrices

Why you should learn it:

You can use matrices for effective organization of many forms of real-life data, such as library statistics, political charts, and accounting spreadsheets.

Goal 1 Organizing Data in a Matrix

A **matrix** is a rectangular arrangement of numbers into rows and columns. For instance, the matrix

$$\begin{bmatrix} 3 & 1 & 0 \\ -1 & 2 & 4 \end{bmatrix}$$ *—— ROWS*
   —— ROWS
   columns

has two rows and three columns. The numbers in the matrix are called **entries.** In the above matrix, the entry in the second row and third column is 4. (The plural of *matrix* is *matrices.*)

Two matrices are **equal** if the entries in corresponding positions are equal.

$$\begin{bmatrix} 3 & -2 \\ \frac{1}{2} & 0 \end{bmatrix} = \begin{bmatrix} 3 & -2 \\ 0.5 & 0 \end{bmatrix} \qquad \begin{bmatrix} -4 & 7 \\ 0 & -1 \end{bmatrix} \neq \begin{bmatrix} 7 & -4 \\ 0 & -1 \end{bmatrix}$$

You can think of a matrix as a type of table that can be used to organize data.

Real Life
Library Science

	Circulation	Reference
Books	10,000	3,000
Magazines	500	6,000
Videos	2,000	500

Example 1 *Writing a Table as a Matrix*

Some of the books, magazines, and videos in a library can be checked out. Others are for reference only and must be used in the library. The table at the left shows how many of each are in the Springfield High School library.

Write this table as a matrix. How many reference books are in the library's collection?

Solution The matrix associated with this table has three rows and two columns.

$$\begin{array}{cc} & \text{Circulation} \quad \text{Reference} \end{array}$$

$$\begin{array}{c} \text{Books} \\ \text{Magazines} \\ \text{Videos} \end{array} \begin{bmatrix} 10,000 & 3,000 \\ 500 & 6,000 \\ 2,000 & 500 \end{bmatrix}$$

The number of reference books is 3,000 because that is the entry in the row labeled *Books* and the column labeled *Reference.*

To **add** or **subtract** matrices, you simply add or subtract corresponding entries, as shown in Example 2.

Example 2 *Adding and Subtracting Matrices*

a.
$$\begin{bmatrix} 4 & 2 \\ 0 & -3 \\ -5 & 1 \end{bmatrix} + \begin{bmatrix} 1 & 0 \\ 2 & -1 \\ 6 & -4 \end{bmatrix} = \begin{bmatrix} 4+1 & 2+0 \\ 0+2 & -3+(-1) \\ -5+6 & 1+(-4) \end{bmatrix}$$

$$= \begin{bmatrix} 5 & 2 \\ 2 & -4 \\ 1 & -3 \end{bmatrix}$$

b.
$$\begin{bmatrix} 10 & -4 \\ 5 & 0 \end{bmatrix} - \begin{bmatrix} 4 & 5 \\ -3 & 2 \end{bmatrix} = \begin{bmatrix} 10 & -4 & -4 & -5 \\ 5 & -(-3) & 0 & -2 \end{bmatrix}$$

$$= \begin{bmatrix} 10 & -4 & -4 & -5 \\ 5 & +3 & 0 & -2 \end{bmatrix}$$

$$= \begin{bmatrix} 6 & -9 \\ 8 & -2 \end{bmatrix}$$

You cannot add or subtract matrices that have different numbers of rows or columns. For instance, you cannot add a matrix that has three rows to a matrix that has only two rows.

Real Life
Political Science

Example 3 *Political Composition of Congress*

Find the number of Democrats, Republicans, and Independents in the Congress between 1977 and 1989.
(Source: United States Congress)

Senate	1977	1979	1981	1983	1985	1987	1989
Democrats	61	58	53	54	53	55	55
Republicans	38	41	46	46	47	45	45
Independents	1	1	1	0	0	0	0

House	1977	1979	1981	1983	1985	1987	1989
Democrats	292	276	243	269	252	258	259
Republicans	143	157	192	165	182	177	174
Independents	0	0	0	0	0	0	0

Solution The United States Congress is composed of the Senate and the House of Representatives. By adding the given matrices, you obtain a matrix that shows the political composition of the Congress.

Congress	1977	1979	1981	1983	1985	1987	1989
Democrats	353	334	296	323	305	313	314
Republicans	181	198	238	211	229	222	219
Independents	1	1	1	0	0	0	0

The profit that a company makes is the difference between its income (or revenue) and its expenses (or costs). For instance, if a company had income of $125,000 and expenses of $110,000, its profit would be $125,000 − $110,000 = $15,000.

Example 4 Finding the First-Quarter Profit

A retail company has two stores. The incomes and expenses (in dollars) for the two stores for three months are shown in the matrices.

January	Income	Expenses
Store 1	200,000	180,000
Store 2	110,000	120,000

February	Income	Expenses
Store 1	220,000	205,000
Store 2	135,000	130,000

March	Income	Expenses
Store 1	230,000	225,000
Store 2	140,000	125,000

a. Write a matrix that shows the first-quarter incomes and expenses for the two stores.

b. Find the first-quarter profit for each store.

Solution

a. To find the matrix for the first-quarter incomes and expenses, add the matrices for January, February, and March.

1st Quarter	Income ($)	Expenses ($)
Store 1	650,000	610,000
Store 2	385,000	375,000

b. Profit for Store 1 = 650,000 − 610,000 = $40,000
Profit for Store 2 = 385,000 − 375,000 = $10,000 ∎

Melencholia,
with detail below.
Albrecht Dürer (1471–1528)

Communicating about ALGEBRA

▶ **SHARING IDEAS about the Lesson**

A matrix that has the same number of rows and columns is a **square matrix**. A **magic square** is a square matrix whose rows, columns, and diagonals each add to the same sum. Find the missing entries in the following magic square with entries 1, 2, 3, . . . , 15, 16.

$$\begin{bmatrix} 16 & 3 & 2 & 13 \\ 5 & 10 & 11 & 8 \\ ? & ? & ? & ? \\ ? & ? & ? & ? \end{bmatrix}$$

EXERCISES

Guided Practice

▶ **CRITICAL THINKING about the Lesson**

In Exercises 1 and 2, use the matrix at the right.

$$\begin{bmatrix} 4 & -3 \\ 6 & 1 \\ -5 & -6 \end{bmatrix}$$

1. How many rows are in the matrix? How many columns? *3 rows 2 columns,*

2. What is the entry in the first row and second column? *-3*

3. If

$$\begin{bmatrix} 1 & 3 \\ -1 & 0 \end{bmatrix} = \begin{bmatrix} a & b \\ c & d \end{bmatrix},$$

   A = 1   C = -1
   B = 3   D = 0

   what are the values of a, b, c, and d?

4. Find the sum and difference of these matrices.

$$\begin{bmatrix} -1 & 0 & -4 \\ 2 & -3 & 0 \end{bmatrix}, \begin{bmatrix} 3 & -2 & 0 \\ -2 & 1 & -4 \end{bmatrix}$$

   sum
   $\begin{bmatrix} 2 & -2 & -4 \\ 0 & -2 & -4 \end{bmatrix}$

   Diff — $\begin{bmatrix} -4 & -2 & -4 \\ 0 & -4 & -4 \end{bmatrix}$

Independent Practice

In Exercises 5–8, decide whether the matrices can be added.

5. $\begin{bmatrix} 3 & -1 \\ 6 & 2 \end{bmatrix}, \begin{bmatrix} 3 & -3 \\ -2 & 1 \end{bmatrix}$ *yes*

6. $\begin{bmatrix} 2 & -1 & 6 \\ 3 & 0 & -9 \end{bmatrix}, \begin{bmatrix} -4 & 5 \\ 7 & 5 \end{bmatrix}$ *No*

7. $\begin{bmatrix} 4 & 2 & 6 \\ -6 & 3 & 9 \\ -1 & -2 & 1 \end{bmatrix}, \begin{bmatrix} 6 & 4 & -3 \\ 7 & -8 & 1 \end{bmatrix}$ *No*

8. $\begin{bmatrix} 9 & 4 & -6 \\ 6 & 1 & 3 \end{bmatrix}, \begin{bmatrix} -3 & -6 & 0 \\ 4 & -1 & 9 \end{bmatrix}$ *yes*

In Exercises 9–14, find the sum of the matrices.

9. $\begin{bmatrix} 4 & -1 \\ 6 & 0 \end{bmatrix} + \begin{bmatrix} 4 & -3 \\ -7 & 2 \end{bmatrix} = \begin{bmatrix} 8 & -4 \\ -1 & 2 \end{bmatrix}$

10. $\begin{bmatrix} 6 & -3 \\ -4 & -2 \end{bmatrix} + \begin{bmatrix} -5 & 3 \\ 4 & 3 \end{bmatrix} = \begin{bmatrix} 1 & 0 \\ 0 & 1 \end{bmatrix}$

11. $\begin{bmatrix} 2 & 1 & -2 \\ 3 & 0 & 3 \end{bmatrix} + \begin{bmatrix} 1 & -3 & 4 \\ 2 & 5 & -5 \end{bmatrix} = \begin{bmatrix} 3 & -2 & 2 \\ 5 & 5 & -2 \end{bmatrix}$

12. $\begin{bmatrix} 2 & 9 & -3 \\ 1 & 8 & -2 \\ -4 & 1 & 0 \end{bmatrix} + \begin{bmatrix} -1 & -6 & 4 \\ -1 & 2 & 6 \\ 2 & -4 & 2 \end{bmatrix} = \begin{bmatrix} 1 & 3 & 1 \\ 0 & 6 & 4 \\ -2 & -3 & 2 \end{bmatrix}$

13. $\begin{bmatrix} -1.3 & 2.4 & -6.9 \\ 15.8 & 0 & -3.4 \end{bmatrix} + \begin{bmatrix} 2.6 & 2.3 & -6.9 \\ 1.7 & 3.2 & -5.8 \end{bmatrix}$

    $\begin{bmatrix} 1.30 & 4.7 & 13.8 \\ 17.5 & 3.2 & 9.20 \end{bmatrix}$

14. $\begin{bmatrix} 6.1 & -1.7 \\ -1.3 & 4.4 \\ 3.2 & -5.9 \end{bmatrix} + \begin{bmatrix} 1.5 & 9.1 \\ -6.4 & 4.9 \\ 5.4 & -3.3 \end{bmatrix} = \begin{bmatrix} 7.6 & 7.4 \\ -7.7 & 9.3 \\ 8.6 & -9.2 \end{bmatrix}$

In Exercises 15–18, find the difference of the matrices.

15. $\begin{bmatrix} 9 & -4 \\ 2 & -4 \end{bmatrix} - \begin{bmatrix} 6 & 6 \\ -2 & -4 \end{bmatrix} = \begin{bmatrix} 3 & -10 \\ 4 & 0 \end{bmatrix}$

16. $\begin{bmatrix} 6 & 4 \\ 10 & -5 \end{bmatrix} - \begin{bmatrix} 7 & 1 \\ -1 & -6 \end{bmatrix} = \begin{bmatrix} -1 & 3 \\ 11 & 1 \end{bmatrix}$

17. $\begin{bmatrix} -3 & 1 \\ 0 & -9 \\ 1 & 7 \end{bmatrix} - \begin{bmatrix} 6 & 4 \\ -5 & 8 \\ -1 & 4 \end{bmatrix} = \begin{bmatrix} -9 & -3 \\ 5 & -17 \\ 2 & 3 \end{bmatrix}$

18. $\begin{bmatrix} -5 & 12 & -1 \\ -10 & 4 & 0 \end{bmatrix} - \begin{bmatrix} -3 & 0 & 1 \\ 9 & 2 & -2 \end{bmatrix} = \begin{bmatrix} -2 & 12 & -2 \\ -19 & 2 & 2 \end{bmatrix}$

In Exercises 19 and 20, use mental math to find a, b, c, and d.

19. $\begin{bmatrix} 2a & 3b \\ 2c - 4 & d \end{bmatrix} = \begin{bmatrix} 10 & 9 \\ 16 & -4 \end{bmatrix}$

20. $\begin{bmatrix} a & b + 1 \\ 4c & d - 1 \end{bmatrix} = \begin{bmatrix} 4 & 9 \\ 12 & 16 \end{bmatrix}$

21. *Video Rentals* A video store rents comedies, dramas, and horror movies. The table shows how many of each are new releases and how many of each are regular selections in the store.

	New releases	Regular selections
Comedy	25	215
Drama	30	350
Horror	25	180

$\begin{bmatrix} 25 & 215 \\ 30 & 350 \\ 25 & 180 \end{bmatrix}$

Write this table as a matrix. How many newly released comedy videos does the store have? 25

22. *On Sale* A music store is having a sale on some of its cassette tapes and compact disks. The table shows how many different titles are available at the sale price and how many are available at the regular price.

	Sale price titles	Regular price titles
Tapes	45	3000
Compact disks	20	2500

$\begin{bmatrix} 45 & 3000 \\ 20 & 2500 \end{bmatrix}$

Write this table as a matrix. How many compact disk titles are on sale? 20

23. *NFL Games* Find the number of games played by each of the four listed NFL Western Division teams in 1987 and 1989.

(Source: National Football League)

Wins	1986	1987	1988	1989		Losses/Ties	1986	1987	1988	1989
San Francisco	10	13	10	14		San Francisco	6	2	6	2
L.A. Rams	10	12	10	11		L.A. Rams	6	3	6	5
Atlanta	7	6	10	9		Atlanta	9	9	6	7
New Orleans	7	3	5	3		New Orleans	9	12	11	13

24. *Grade-Level Wage* The hourly wage rates for the clerk-typist positions at a company depend on the number of years of experience. The company decides to give $0.50 raises to all typists in grade level 4, $0.75 raises to all typists in grade level 5, and $1.00 raises to all typists in grade level 6. Find the entries for the *raise* matrix and determine the resulting wage-rate matrix.

Wage rates	0–1 yr	2–3 yr	4+ yr		Raises	0–1 yr	2–3 yr	4+ yr
Level 4	8.00	9.00	9.50		Level 4	8.50	9.75	10.5
Level 5	10.00	10.50	11.00	+	Level 5	10.50	11.25	12.0
Level 6	11.50	12.00	12.50		Level 6	12.00	12.75	13.5

Business   **In Exercises 25 and 26, use the following information.**

You decide to sell food at a fair to raise enough money to buy a bike for $200. You hold the sale on Saturday and Sunday. The income and expenses (in dollars) for the two days for each type of item are shown in these matrices.

	Saturday Income	Expenses
Burritos	33	15
Tacos	38	30
Cheeseburgers	65	18

18
8
47

	Sunday Income	Expenses
Burritos	39	18
Tacos	29	23
Cheeseburgers	78	21

21
6
57

25. Find the total profit you received from each item.

26. Did you raise enough money to pay for the bike?

$B = 39^{00}$
$T = 14^{00}$
$C = 104^{00}$
157^{00} short 43^{00}

Integrated Review

In Exercises 27–28, evaluate the expression.

27. $\begin{bmatrix} 2 & -1 \\ 3 & 6 \end{bmatrix} + \begin{bmatrix} 6 & 10 \\ -1 & -6 \end{bmatrix} =$ $\begin{bmatrix} 8 & 9 \\ 2 & 0 \end{bmatrix}$

28. $\begin{bmatrix} -4 & 5 \\ 6 & 2 \end{bmatrix} - \begin{bmatrix} 3 & -1 \\ -5 & 6 \end{bmatrix} =$ $\begin{bmatrix} -7 & 6 \\ 11 & -4 \end{bmatrix}$

29. Evaluate the expression $\frac{1}{2}x + 1$ when $x = \frac{1}{2}$. 1.25

30. Evaluate the expression $6x - 1$ when $x = \frac{1}{3}$. 1

31. Use mental math to solve the equation $\frac{x}{9} = 3$. $x = 27$

32. Use mental math to solve the equation $2x + 1 = 19$.
$x = 9$

Exploration and Extension

Business   **In Exercises 33–36, use the following information.**

A company has two stores. For Store 1, the May and June incomes were $98,000 and $81,500, and the May and June profits were $16,500 and $10,500. For Store 2, the May and June incomes were $61,800 and $72,900, and the May and June profits were $9,600 and $10,600.

33. Set up a matrix that shows the incomes of the two stores for May and June.

34. Set up a matrix for the profits of the two stores for May and June.

35. Use the two matrices you wrote in Exercises 33 and 34 to write a matrix that shows the expenses of the two stores in May and June.

36. What were the expenses of Store 2 in May? In June? In May and June?

Most programmable calculators and computers can store, add, and subtract matrices. Here we show how to use a Texas Instruments TI-81, a Casio fx-7700G, and the BASIC programming language to add the matrices at the right.

$$\begin{bmatrix} 2 & -1 & 0 \\ 3 & 2 & -1 \end{bmatrix} + \begin{bmatrix} 1 & 0 & -2 \\ 2 & -2 & -4 \end{bmatrix} = \begin{bmatrix} 3 & -1 & -2 \\ 5 & 0 & -5 \end{bmatrix}$$

TI-81

MATRIX
Cursor to EDIT, 1
2 ENTER (# of rows)
3 ENTER (# of cols)
Input 1st matrix in [A].
  [A] 2 × 3
  1,1 = 2
  1,2 = −1
  1,3 = 0
  2,1 = 3
  2,2 = 2
  2,3 = −1
MATRIX
Cursor to EDIT, 2
2 ENTER (# of rows)
3 ENTER (# of cols)
Input 2nd matrix in [B].
  [B] 2 × 3
  1,1 = 1
  1,2 = 0
  1,3 = −2
  2,1 = 2
  2,2 = −2
  2,3 = −4
2nd QUIT
2nd [A] + 2nd [B]
ENTER
Display will be
  [3 −1 −2]
  [5   0 −5]

Casio fx-7700G

MODE 0
F1 (A)
F6 F1 (DIM)
2 EXE (# of rows)
3 EXE (# of cols)
Input 1st matrix in [A].

A $\quad\underline{1}\quad\underline{2}\quad\underline{3}$
1 $\begin{bmatrix} 2 & -1 & 0 \\ 3 & 2 & -1 \end{bmatrix}$
2

PRE
F2 (B)
F6 F1 (DIM)
2 EXE (# of rows)
3 EXE (# of cols)
Input 2nd matrix in [B].

B $\quad\underline{1}\quad\underline{2}\quad\underline{3}$
1 $\begin{bmatrix} 1 & 0 & -2 \\ 2 & -2 & -4 \end{bmatrix}$
2

PRE
F3 (+)
Display will be

C $\quad\underline{1}\quad\underline{2}\quad\underline{3}$
1 $\begin{bmatrix} 3 & -1 & -2 \\ 5 & 0 & -5 \end{bmatrix}$
2

BASIC

```
10 DIM A(2,3)
20 DIM B(2,3)
30 FOR N = 1 TO 2
40   FOR J = 1 TO 3
50    READ A(N,J)
60   NEXT
70 NEXT
80 FOR N = 1 TO 2
90   FOR J = 1 TO 3
100   READ B(N,J)
110  NEXT
120 NEXT
130 FOR N = 1 TO 2
140  FOR J = 1 TO 3
150   PRINT A(N,J) + B(N,J);
160  NEXT
170 PRINT
180 NEXT
190 END
200 REM 1st Matrix A
210 DATA 2, − 1,0
220 DATA 3,2, − 1
230 REM 2nd Matrix B
240 DATA 1,0, − 2
250 DATA 2, − 2, − 4
```
Printout will be
  3 −1 −2
  5   0 −5

Exercises

Use a programmable calculator or a computer to find the sum and difference of the matrices.

1. $\begin{bmatrix} 1 & 2 & 5 \\ -2 & 0 & -3 \end{bmatrix}, \begin{bmatrix} 0 & -4 & -2 \\ 2 & 0 & 3 \end{bmatrix}$

2. $\begin{bmatrix} -3 & 4 & 2 \\ 6 & 1 & -4 \\ 0 & -2 & -5 \end{bmatrix}, \begin{bmatrix} 2 & 0 & -1 \\ -4 & 5 & 0 \\ 0 & -3 & 9 \end{bmatrix}$

Take this test as you would take a test in class. The answers to the exercises are given in the back of the book.

1. Which is greater, -5 or -4? **(2.1)**

2. Which is less, $-\frac{1}{2}$ or $-\frac{1}{3}$? **(2.1)**

3. Find the opposite of -6. **(2.1)**

4. Find the opposite of $\frac{3}{2}$. **(2.1)**

5. Evaluate $|-4|$. **(2.1)**

6. Evaluate $-|-3\frac{1}{3}|$. **(2.1)**

7. Evaluate $7 + (-5)$. **(2.2)**

8. Evaluate $-6 + 2$. **(2.2)**

9. Evaluate $-\frac{1}{2} + \frac{3}{2} + (-\frac{3}{4})$. **(2.2)**

10. Evaluate $9 + 7 + (-6.5) + 1.1$ **(2.2)**

11. Evaluate $6.7 + (-4.5) + 1.2$ **(2.2)**

12. Evaluate $-12.5 + 8.6 + (-3.8)$. **(2.2)**

13. Evaluate $0.4 + 7.2 + (-2.2)$. **(2.2)**

14. Evaluate $9.3 + (-10.5) + 1.2$. **(2.2)**

In Exercises 15–20, simplify the expression. Then evaluate the expression. (2.2, 2.3)

15. $2 - (x - 3)$, when $x = 4$

16. $3 - (-x) - (-\frac{1}{2})$, when $x = 1$

17. $-[y + (-6)] - (y + 4)$, when $y = -1$

18. $|r| - (r + 3)$, when $r = -5$

19. $s + (7 - s) - 4$, when $s = 0$

20. $s + |-\frac{3}{2}| - (8 - s)$, when $s = -2$

In Exercises 21 and 22, find the sum or difference. (2.2, 2.3, 2.4)

21. $\begin{bmatrix} 3 & 6 & 7 \\ 4 & 0 & 8 \\ -1 & 2 & -4 \end{bmatrix} + \begin{bmatrix} -3 & 6 & 0 \\ 1 & 8 & 4 \\ 1 & 6 & 5 \end{bmatrix}$

22. $\begin{bmatrix} -\frac{1}{2} & 3 & \frac{3}{4} \\ 10 & -7 & 4 \\ 6 & 9 & 0 \end{bmatrix} - \begin{bmatrix} \frac{1}{2} & 8 & \frac{3}{4} \\ 2 & 1 & 5 \\ 0 & -1 & -3 \end{bmatrix}$

23. A ball is falling from the third floor of an apartment building at a rate of 15 feet per second. What is its velocity? What is its speed? **(2.1)**

24. The water temperature in an outdoor pool is 60°F. The temperature rises 2°F each day for four days. Because of a rainstorm, the temperature drops 5°F on the fifth day. What is the temperature on the fifth day after the temperature drop? **(2.2)**

25. A scout troop needs to raise $500 for a week of camping. Income and expenses for three projects are shown in the table. Write this table as a matrix. Did the troop raise enough money for its trip? How much was it short or over? **(2.4)**

	Income (in dollars)	Expenses (in dollars)
Bowlathon	384	192
Car wash	150	10
Sub sale	400	200

26. The world's five tallest skyscrapers and their heights in feet and meters are as follows. Set up a matrix that contains this information. (Sears Tower, Amoco Building, and John Hancock Center are in Chicago. The other two buildings are in New York City.) **(2.4)**

Sears Tower: 1454 feet, 443 meters
World Trade Center: 1350 feet, 411 meters
Empire State Building: 1250 feet, 381 meters
Amoco Building: 1136 feet, 346 meters
John Hancock Center: 1127 feet, 344 meters

2.5

Multiplication of Real Numbers

What you should learn:

Goal 1 How to multiply real numbers using Properties of Multiplication

Goal 2 How to use calculators and units of measure in real number products

Why you should learn it:

You can multiply positive and negative numbers to solve real-life problems, such as multiplying velocity by time to find distance. You can also check units of measure to help assure that you did not make a mistake.

Goal 1 Multiplying Real Numbers

In this lesson, you will learn how to find products that have one or more negative factors. Here are two examples.

$$3(-2) = (-2) + (-2) + (-2) = -6$$
$$3(-1) = (-1) + (-1) + (-1) = -3$$

In both cases, multiplying a positive number and a negative number produces a negative number. One way to see what would happen if you multiplied two negative numbers is to look for patterns, such as:

One factor −3		**One Factor −2**		**One Factor −1**	
$(3)(-3) = -9$		$(3)(-2) = -6$		$(3)(-1) = -3$	
$(2)(-3) = -6$		$(2)(-2) = -4$		$(2)(-1) = -2$	
$(1)(-3) = -3$	Products increase by 3.	$(1)(-2) = -2$	Products increase by 2.	$(1)(-1) = -1$	Products increase by 1.
$(0)(-3) = 0$		$(0)(-2) = 0$		$(0)(-1) = 0$	
$(-1)(-3) = ?\ 3$		$(-1)(-2) = ?\ 2$		$(-1)(-1) = ?\ 1$	
$(-2)(-3) = ?\ 6$		$(-2)(-2) = ?\ 4$		$(-2)(-1) = ?\ 2$	

From these patterns, it makes sense that the missing numbers are positive. In other words, multiplying two negative numbers produces a positive number.

$(-1)(-3) = 3$	$(-1)(-2) = 2$	$(-1)(-1) = 1$
$(-2)(-3) = 6$	$(-2)(-2) = 4$	$(-2)(-1) = 2$

Properties of Multiplication

1. $a \cdot b = b \cdot a$ The order in which two numbers are multiplied does not change their product.

2. $1 \cdot a = a$ The product of one and a is a.

3. $0 \cdot a = 0$ The product of zero and a is 0.

4. $(-1) \cdot a = -a$ The product of −1 and a is the opposite of a.

5. $(a)(-b) = -ab$ The product of a and $-b$ is the opposite of ab.

6. $(-a)(-b) = ab$ The product of $-a$ and $-b$ is ab.

Example 1 **Products Involving Negative Factors**

a. $(-4)(5) = -(4)(5)$
    $= -20$

b. $(6)(-x) = (6)(-1)(x)$
    $= -6x$

c. $(-\frac{1}{4})(-4) = (\frac{1}{4})(4)$
    $= 1$

d. $(-\frac{2}{5})(-\frac{3}{4}) = \frac{6}{20}$ or $\frac{3}{10}$ ∎

The following rules can be helpful in simplifying products with three or more factors.

1. The product of an *even* number of negative factors is positive.

2. The product of an *odd* number of negative factors is negative.

Example 2 **Products with Three or More Factors**

a. $(-4)(-2)(-x) = -(4)(2)x$
    $= -8x$

b. $(-3)(5)(-y) = (3)(5)y$
    $= 15y$

c. $(-2)^4 = (-2)(-2)(-2)(-2)$
    $= 16$

d. $-2^4 = -(2 \cdot 2 \cdot 2 \cdot 2)$
    $= -16$

e. $(-x)^3 = (-x)(-x)(-x)$
    $= -x^3$ ∎

Be sure you understand why $(-2)^4$ is not the same as -2^4.

Example 3 **Real-Life Applications of Products of Negative Numbers**

a. A football team loses 3 yards on each of 4 downs. The net gain is

$$4(-3) = -12 \text{ yards.}$$

A gain of -12 means the same as a loss of 12.

b. A parachutist is falling with a velocity of -20 feet per second. The distance traveled in 3 seconds is

$$3(-20) = -60 \text{ feet.}$$

The negative distance indicates a downward motion.

Real Life
Retailing

c. To attract customers, a grocery store runs a sale on strawberries. The strawberries are *loss leaders*, which means the store loses money on the strawberries but hopes to make it up on other sales. Suppose 3000 baskets are sold at a loss of $0.15 each.

$$3000(-0.15) = -\$450.$$

The negative result indicates a loss of $450. ∎

Always be careful when using a calculator for evaluating a product involving negative numbers—especially with the change-sign key $\boxed{+/-}$.

Example 4   *Using a Calculator*

a. Expression   Change-Sign Key   Negation Key

$(-2)(-4)$ 2 $\boxed{+/-}$ $\boxed{\times}$ 4 $\boxed{+/-}$ $\boxed{=}$ $\boxed{(-)}$ 2 $\boxed{\times}$ $\boxed{(-)}$ 4 $\boxed{=}$

Your calculator should display 8 as an answer. The key-stroke sequence $\boxed{+/-}$ 2 $\boxed{\times}$ $\boxed{+/-}$ 4 $\boxed{=}$ is incorrect even though, in this instance, it may produce the correct answer.

b. Expression   Change-Sign Key   Negation Key

-3^4 3 $\boxed{y^x}$ 4 $\boxed{=}$ $\boxed{+/-}$ $\boxed{(-)}$ 3 $\boxed{\wedge}$ 4 $\boxed{=}$

Your calculator should display -81 as an answer. The key-stroke sequence $\boxed{+/-}$ 3 $\boxed{y^x}$ 4 $\boxed{=}$ will not produce the correct answer. ■

Most real-life applications of products involve rates such as miles *per* hour or dollars *per* year. Example 5 shows how to decide which unit of measure to assign to a product. Notice how the units for a rate can be written in fraction form.

Connections
Physical Science

Example 5   *Unit Analysis*

A car traveling 70 kilometers per hour for 2 hours will travel a distance of

$$\left(70 \ \frac{\text{kilometers}}{\text{hour}}\right)(2 \ \text{hours}) = 140 \ \text{kilometers}.$$

You can think of the "hours" as canceling each other. ■

Communicating about ALGEBRA

Connections
Unit Analysis

▶ **SHARING IDEAS about the Lesson**

Checking Your Work Apply the unit analysis technique of Example 5 to these products given in Example 3.

A. (4 downs) $\left(-3 \ \dfrac{\boxed{?}}{\boxed{?}}\right) = -12$ yds

B. (3000 $\boxed{?}$) $\left(-0.15 \ \dfrac{\boxed{?}}{\boxed{?}}\right) = -\$450$ (or -450 dollars)

EXERCISES

▶ **CRITICAL THINKING about the Lesson**

In Exercises 1–4, decide whether the statement is true or false and explain.

1. Multiplying a negative number by a positive number produces a positive number.

2. Multiplying a number by 0 produces the original number.

3. Multiplying a by b produces the same result as multiplying b by a.

4. The product of an odd number of negative factors is negative.

5. Does the order in which two numbers are multiplied affect their product?

6. If a is measured in feet per second and b in seconds, what is the unit for the product ab?

Independent Practice

In Exercises 7–30, find the product.

7. $(-6)(8)$	8. $(-3)(3)$	9. $(4)(-7)$	10. $(2)(-9)$
11. $(-1)(x)$	12. $(-4)(15p)$	13. $(16)(-3a)$	14. $(5)(-2c)$
15. $|(-5)|(6)$	16. $(6)|(-5)|$	17. $|(-2)(21)|$	18. $|(8)(-9)|$
19. $(-3)^2$	20. -4^2	21. $(-2x)^3$	22. $-3(x^2)$
23. $(-2)(-3)(-5)$	24. $(-10)(-4)(-2)$	25. $(-4)(x)(12)$	26. $(-2)(-x)(10)$
27. $(-8x)(7x)(-3)$	28. $(11)(-5y)(-6)$	29. $(\frac{1}{3}a)(-\frac{2}{5}a)(\frac{3}{4}a)$	30. $(-\frac{1}{4}b)(-\frac{1}{5}b)(\frac{1}{2}b)$

Technology In Exercises 31–34, use a calculator to find the product.
Round your result to two decimal places. Use estimation to check.

31. $(-2.68)(4.32)(-6.1)$

32. $(3.62)(-3.45)(3.68)$

33. $(4.97)(-2.13)^3(-7.35)$

34. $(-5.11)^2(-8.24)(-6.59)$

In Exercises 35–44, evaluate the expression.

35. $2x^2 - 4x$, when $x = -3$

36. $3x + x^2$, when $x = -7$

37. $-2x - 5x$, when $x = 4$

38. $-6x + x$, when $x = 9$

39. $-2(|x - 7|)$, when $x = -3$

40. $-5(|a - 4|)$, when $a = -4$

41. $(|9 + y|)(-1)$, when $y = -5$

42. $(|12 - m|)(-3)$, when $m = 6$

43. $-2x^2 + 3x + 1$, when $x = 5$

44. $-7x - (-4x^3)$, when $x = 4$

45. *Drop in Temperature* The daily high temperature is decreasing at a rate of 2°F per day. Let T represent the daily high temperature now. Write an expression for the high temperature in 5 days. The current high temperature is 82°F. Find the high temperature in 5 days. Check your answer by making a table and looking for a pattern.

46. *Smaller Fry*   Suppose you and your family go fishing every year in Canada. You find that the average length of the fish is decreasing by 1.8 cm per year. Let x represent the average length of the fish in 1988. Write an expression for the average length in 1992. If the average length was 76 cm in 1988, what was it in 1992? Check your answer by making a table and looking for a pattern.

83.2 cm

47. *Jumping Frogs*   People from around Calaveras County, California, have been training their frogs for the annual jumping competition. A measured jump consists of three consecutive leaps by the frog. A local favorite jumps six feet on the first leap, but then jumps six inches less than the previous leap on each of its last two leaps. Which of the following correctly represents the total length of the three leaps?

a. $6 + (6 - \frac{1}{2}) + (6 - \frac{1}{2})$

b. $6 + (6 - \frac{1}{2}) + 2(6 - \frac{1}{2})$

c. $6 + (6 - \frac{1}{2}) + [6 - 2(\frac{1}{2})]$

6   5/2   16-6'

Evaluate the correct expression. Did this jump beat the record set by Rosie the Ribeter? *No short (4'-4')*

The record at the annual Calaveras Jumping Jubilee is 21 feet $5\frac{3}{4}$ inches by a bullfrog named Rosie the Ribeter on May 18, 1986. Mark Twain's first popular story was "The Celebrated Jumping Frog of Calaveras County," published in 1865.

48. *Health Bar Promotion*   To promote sales, a grocery store lowered the price on its health bars from $0.55 to $0.45 per bar. During the first weekend of the sale, the store sold 1321 health bars. Describe in words what the expression $1321(0.55 - 0.45)$ represents.

49. *Train Crossing*   A train traveling at a speed of 80 kilometers per hour will reach a railroad crossing in 0.6 hour. Which of the following correctly represents the distance to the crossing?

a. $(80 \frac{\text{kilometers}}{\text{hour}})(0.6 \text{ hours})$ **b.** $(80 \frac{\text{kilometers}}{\text{hour}}) \div (0.6 \text{ hours})$

How far away is the crossing?

50. *Cycling*   How far behind the leaders will the trailers be after they have cycled for 90 minutes?

On a trip to Yellowstone Park, the lead riders of the Cheyenne cycling team average a speed of 20 miles per hour. The trailers average a speed of 17 miles per hour.

In Exercises 51–54, find the sum.

51. $6 + (-3.5)$ *2.5* **52.** $-7 + (-4)$ *−11* **53.** $-3^2 + 4$ *−5* **54.** $-5 + (-2)^3$ *−8 −13*

In Exercises 55–58, find the difference.

55. $12 - 9$ *3* **56.** $9 - 12$ *−3* **57.** $|-3| - 7$ *−4* **58.** $4 - |-8|$ *−4*

59. Solve for a, b, c, and d.

$$\begin{bmatrix} a & -4 \\ 0 & 1 \end{bmatrix} + \begin{bmatrix} 3 & b \\ c & 4 \end{bmatrix} = \begin{bmatrix} 10 & 6 \\ 8 & d \end{bmatrix}$$

60. Find the difference.

$$\begin{bmatrix} -6 & 2 & |4| \\ 0 & -9 & 18 \end{bmatrix} - \begin{bmatrix} -6 & (-1)^5 & 0 \\ 3 & 14 & |-5| \end{bmatrix}$$

In Exercises 61–64, multiply each matrix by the real number as shown in the sample.

Sample: $-2\begin{bmatrix} 2 & -1 \\ -3 & 0 \end{bmatrix} = \begin{bmatrix} -2(2) & -2(-1) \\ -2(-3) & -2(0) \end{bmatrix} = \begin{bmatrix} -4 & 2 \\ 6 & 0 \end{bmatrix}$

61. $-3\begin{bmatrix} 2 & 6 \\ -1 & -8 \end{bmatrix}$ **62.** $-7\begin{bmatrix} -2 & 0 & 3 \\ 2^2 & -11 & -8 \end{bmatrix}$

63. $-1\begin{bmatrix} 2x & -5y \\ -10m & 13n \end{bmatrix}$ **64.** $2\begin{bmatrix} x & 2y \\ -3m & 12n \end{bmatrix}$

65. *Sales Tax* The matrix at the right shows the prices of a sweatshirt, a pair of jeans, and a pair of sneakers at two stores. If the state sales tax on clothes is 5%, what does the following product represent?

Prices	Store 1	Store 2
Sweatshirt	$14.80	$13.95
Jeans	$32.95	$29.95
Sneakers	$85.50	$79.95

$$0.05\begin{bmatrix} 14.80 & 13.95 \\ 32.95 & 29.95 \\ 85.50 & 79.95 \end{bmatrix}$$

66. What is the sales tax on a pair of jeans in Store 1?

67. *T-Shirt Inventory* The matrix at the right shows the number of *Save the Whales* T-shirts in stock at three stores. If each T-shirt has a wholesale cost of $10.50, what does the following product represent?

Inventory	Store 1	Store 2	Store 3
Small	25	30	14
Medium	14	10	12
Large	16	12	10
X-Large	5	6	5

$$10.50\begin{bmatrix} 25 & 30 & 14 \\ 14 & 10 & 12 \\ 16 & 12 & 10 \\ 5 & 6 & 5 \end{bmatrix}$$

68. What is the inventory value of medium-size *Save the Whale* T-shirts in Store 2?

2.6

The Distributive Property

What you should learn:

Goal 1 How to use the Distributive Property

Goal 2 How to simplify expressions by combining like terms

Why you should learn it:

You can use the Distributive Property to simplify expressions and to make calculations easier.

Connections
Geometry

Goal 1 Using the Distributive Property

The Distributive Property is one of the most important properties in algebra. Before looking at the property, let's look at an example that shows why the property is true.

Suppose you want to find the area of a rectangle whose width is 3 and whose length is $x + 2$. There are two ways to do this: as the area of a single rectangle or as the sum of the areas of two rectangles.

Area of One Rectangle

$Area = 3(x + 2)$

Area of Two Rectangles

$Area = 3(x) + 3(2)$

Because both ways produce the same area, you can conclude that

$$3(x + 2) = 3(x) + 3(2).$$

This is an example of the **Distributive Property.** To distribute means to give something to each member of a group. In this equation, the factor 3 is "distributed" to *each* term of the sum $(x + 2)$.

The Distributive Property

The product of a and $(b + c)$ is given by

$$a(b + c) = ab + ac \quad \text{or} \quad (b + c)a = ba + ca.$$

The product of a and $(b - c)$ is given by

$$a(b - c) = ab - ac \quad \text{or} \quad (b - c)a = ba - ca.$$

Example 1 — Using the Distributive Property

a. $2(x + 5) = 2(x) + 2(5)$
$\qquad\qquad\quad = 2x + 10$

b. $(x - 4)x = x(x) - 4(x)$
$\qquad\qquad\quad = x^2 - 4x$

c. $(1 + 2x)8 = (1)8 + (2x)8$
$\qquad\qquad\quad\; = 8 + 16x$

d. $y(1 - y) = (y)(1) - y(y)$
$\qquad\qquad\quad = y - y^2$ ■

In Example 1, the middle steps are usually done as mental math, without writing the step. For instance, Part **a** would usually be written as $2(x + 5) = 2x + 10$.

The products in the next example are more difficult because the sum or difference is multiplied by a factor that has a negative sign. Study these examples carefully. Products like these are the cause of many "careless errors." For each product, remember the factor that has a negative sign must multiply *each* term.

Example 2 — Using the Distributive Property

a. $-3(x + 4) \quad = -3(x) + (-3)(4) \quad = -3x - 12$

b. $(y + 5)(-4) \quad = y(-4) + 5(-4) \quad = -4y - 20$

c. $(-1)(6 - 3x) = (-1)(6) - (-1)(3x) = -6 + 3x$

d. $(x - 1)(-9x) = x(-9x) - (1)(-9x) = -9x^2 + 9x$ ■

Example 3 — Bowling Handicap

Some bowling leagues are called *handicap leagues* because players are awarded extra points called a handicap. Players with low averages have larger handicaps than those with high averages. This tends to keep the competition close. Suppose your average is 145. The handicap in your league is 80% of the difference between 200 and your average. What is your handicap?

Solution

Verbal Model

$$\boxed{\text{Handicap}} = \boxed{80\%} \left(\boxed{200} - \boxed{\text{Your average}} \right)$$

Labels   Handicap $= H$
$\qquad\quad$ Your average $= 145$

Equation $H = 0.8(200 - 145)$ *Algebraic model*
$\qquad\quad\;\; = 0.8(55)$ *Simplify $200 - 145$.*
$\qquad\quad\;\; = 44$ *Simplify $0.8(55)$.*

Thus, your handicap is 44 points. Using the Distributive Property to evaluate $0.8(200 - 145)$, do you get the same result? ■

In a term that is the product of a number and a variable, the number is the **coefficient** of the variable. For instance, in the term $5x$, 5 is the coefficient of x. Remember that the terms of an expression are separated by *addition*.

$$5x - 3x = \underbrace{5x}_{\text{Term}} + \underbrace{(-3x)}_{\text{Term}} \quad \textit{Terms are separated by addition.}$$

Thus, the coefficient of x on the second term is -3.

The terms $5x$ and $-3x$ are called **like terms** because the variable part of each term is the same. The Distributive Property allows you to *combine like terms* in an expression by simply adding or subtracting coefficients.

$$5x - 3x = (5 - 3)x \quad \textit{Distributive Property}$$
$$= 2x \quad \textit{Simplify.}$$

[handwritten: 5 is the Coefficient of x]
[handwritten: Term 5x]

Example 4   *Simplifying by Combining Like Terms*

a. $8x + x = 8x + 1x$
$= (8 + 1)x$
$= 9x$

b. $4x^2 + 2 + 3x^2 = 4x^2 + 3x^2 + 2$
$= 7x^2 + 2$

c. $9 - x + 4 = 9 + 4 - x$
$= 13 - x$

d. $2(x - 4) + 5 = 2x - 8 + 5$
$= 2x - 3$ ∎

Remember that simplifying an expression is not the same as solving an equation. Simplifying means rewriting in simpler form. Solving means finding values of the variables.

Communicating *about* A L G E B R A

Real Life
Testing

▶ **SHARING IDEAS about the Lesson**

Understanding a Definition The following question appeared on a College Entrance Exam. Explain how this question is related to the Distributive Property.

If $y = 2x - 3$, then $-2y = \boxed{?}$.

a. $5x + 3$ **b.** $5x - 3$ **c.** $2x + 6$
d. $-4x - 6$ **e.** $-4x + 6$

EXERCISES

Guided Practice

▶ **CRITICAL THINKING about the Lesson**

In Exercises 1–4, decide whether the equation is true. Use the Distributive
Property to explain your answers.

1. $2(4 + 6) = 2(4) + 6$

2. $(4 + 6)2 = 4(2) + 6(2)$

3. $16(3 - 2) = 16(3) - 16(2)$

4. $(3 - 2)16 = 3 - 2(16)$

5. State the property that allows us to combine like terms.

6. Simplify $3x - 5 - 2x$.

7. Simplify $2(x - 3) + x$.

8. Simplify $-(x - 1) + 2x$.

Independent Practice

In Exercises 9–36, apply the Distributive Property.

9. $3(y + 6)$

10. $(x + 1)11$

11. $(4 - x)7$

12. $-4(y - 2)$

13. $(x + 5)(-2)$

14. $10(y - 6)$

15. $x(8 + x)$

16. $(x - 14)x$

17. $-y(y - 9)$

18. $-x(8 + x)$

19. $a(a - 2)$

20. $(3 + y)y$

21. $4(10 - 3x)$

22. $(16 + 3t)t$

23. $(4s + 3)(-5)$

24. $-13(1 - x)$

25. $(6x + 9)x$

26. $4x(x - 20)$

27. $(4 - 3x)(-6x)$

28. $-5s(s + 2)$

29. $2x(9 + x)$

30. $(12 + 9y)6$

31. $(12 - 5y)y$

32. $(5 - 2x)(-10x)$

33. $-8y(2y + 7)$

34. $x(18 + 2x)$

35. $-4a(3a - 4)$

36. $-a(5 - 2a)$

In Exercises 37–46, simplify the expression.

37. $4 + x - 1$

38. $x + 5 + x$

39. $2x^2 + 9x^2 + 4$

40. $10x - 4 - 5x$

41. $-3(x + 1) - 2$

42. $(2x - 1)(2) + x$

43. $11x + (8 - x)3$

44. $7x(2 - x) - 4x$

45. $-6x(x - 1) + x^2$

46. $x^2 - (4 + x^2)$

47. *How Much Are the Jeans?*   You want to buy a pair of jeans and a
$15 T-shirt. There is a 6% sales tax. If x represents the cost of the
jeans and you have $42, then the following inequality is a model
that shows what you can spend for the jeans.

$$\underbrace{15 + x}_{\substack{\text{cost of}\\\text{T-shirt and jeans}}} + \underbrace{0.06(15 + x)}_{\text{sales tax}} \leq 42$$

Simplify the left side of this inequality.

48. Suppose the jeans in Exercise 47 cost $25. Do you have enough
money to pay for both the T-shirt and jeans? What is the most that
you could pay for the jeans?

49. Bowling Handicap A handicap in a bowling league is 80% of the difference between 200 and a bowler's average score. (Players with averages of 200 or more have zero handicap.) Let H represent the handicap for a bowler with an average of A. Which of the following equations correctly model the relationship between H and A?

a. $H = 0.8(200 - A)$ **b.** $H = 160 - 0.8A$

c. $A = 0.8(200 - H)$ **d.** $A = 160 - 0.8H$

50. Changing the Handicap Formula Suppose your bowling league wonders if there might be a better way to compute handicaps than by the formula described in Exercise 49. It considers awarding a handicap of 90% of the difference between 180 and a bowler's average. Complete the following table, then compare the handicaps given by the two formulas.

Average (A)	120	130	140	150	160	170	180	190	200
H (old) $= 0.8(200 - A)$	64	56	48	40	32	24	16	8	0
H (new) $=$?	?	?	?	?	?	?	?	0	0

Give one advantage and one disadvantage of each handicap system.

51. Geometry Write an expression for the perimeter of the movie screen shown below and simplify.

52. Geometry Write an expression for the perimeter of the triangle shown below and simplify.

$X-2 + 2x+3 + X+11$

$X+9 + 2x+3, 2x^2+12$

53. Geometry Find the area of the rectangle in two different ways. Show how the results are related to the Distributive Property.

$A(b+c) = area$

$A \cdot b + A \cdot C = area$

54. Geometry Find the area of the blue rectangle in two different ways. Show how the results are related to the Distributive Property.

Integrated Review

Technology In Exercises 55–60, use a calculator to help you simplify the expression.

55. $3.6(x - 1.2)$ $3.6x - 4.32$

56. $9.1(4.3 + 1.1x)$ $39.13 + 10.01x$

57. $(6.1 - 32.3x)(-2)$ $-12.2 + 64.6x$

58. $-6.6(10.9 - 3.5x)$ $-71.94 + 23.1x$

59. $-4.1x(2.1x - 40.9)$ $-8.61x^2 + 167.69x$

60. $(3.3 - 0.9x)(-2x)$ $-6.6x + 1.8x^2$

In Exercises 61–66, simplify the left side of the equation by combining like terms. Then use mental math to solve the equation.

61. $6x - 3x = 12$

62. $8y - 4y = 48$

63. $6y + 3 - y = 8$

64. $4 + 2y - 4 = 16$

65. $-z + 4z = 27$

66. $4x - 8 - x = 1$

Exploration and Extension

In Exercises 67 and 68, evaluate the two matrix expressions. Does this suggest that multiplication of a matrix by a real number distributes over matrix addition and matrix subtraction?

67. $4\left(\begin{bmatrix} 2 & -1 \\ 4 & -6 \end{bmatrix} + \begin{bmatrix} -4 & 6 \\ 2 & 9 \end{bmatrix}\right), \quad 4\begin{bmatrix} 2 & -1 \\ 4 & -6 \end{bmatrix} + 4\begin{bmatrix} -4 & 6 \\ 2 & 9 \end{bmatrix}$

68. $2\left(\begin{bmatrix} -1 & 0 \\ 6 & 4 \end{bmatrix} - \begin{bmatrix} 3 & 6 \\ -7 & 1 \end{bmatrix}\right), \quad 2\begin{bmatrix} -1 & 0 \\ 6 & 4 \end{bmatrix} - 2\begin{bmatrix} 3 & 6 \\ -7 & 1 \end{bmatrix}$

69. *Common Error* Suppose that you are tutoring a friend in algebra. After learning the Distributive Property, your friend tries to apply the property to multiplication and obtains $2(xy) = 2x \cdot 2y$. Write a convincing argument to show your friend that this is not correct.

Mixed REVIEW

1. Insert grouping symbols in the expression $3 \div 4 - 1$ so that its value is 1. **(1.1)**

2. Insert grouping symbols in the expression $10 - 4 \cdot 2 \cdot 7$ so that its value is 14. **(1.1)**

3. Find the absolute value of -19. **(2.1)**

4. Write $\frac{2}{5}$ in percent form. **(1.1)**

5. Evaluate $\frac{1}{4}\left(-\frac{1}{2}\right) + 2$. **(2.5)**

6. Evaluate $11 - [54 \div (2)(9)]$. **(1.1)**

7. Evaluate $2x^3$ when $x = 5$. **(1.3)**

8. Evaluate $8x - 3y$ when $x = -1$ and $y = 3$. **(2.5)**

9. Evaluate $\frac{1}{5}(x + 4)$ when $x = -3$. **(2.2)**

10. Evaluate $|x| - 1 + (-x)$ when $x = -3$. **(2.2)**

11. Is $3 \cdot (6 - 2) + 17 = 3 \cdot 6 - 2 + 17$? **(1.5)**

12. Is -2 a solution of $4x + x^2 > 6x$? **(2.5)**

13. Is -1 a solution of $3x - (-8) \leq -9$? **(2.3)**

14. Simplify $-4x + 3 - 2(1 - x)$. **(2.6)**

15. Evaluate $(-11)(-3) + 12(-2)$. **(2.5)**

16. Evaluate $(-1.2)(3.8)(0.2)$. **(2.5)**

17. Graph $-\frac{4}{3}, -2\frac{1}{2}, 2, \frac{5}{8}, \frac{1}{3}$ on the number line. **(2.1)**

18. Use an exponent to write $3 \cdot 3 \cdot 3$. **(1.3)**

2.7

Division of Real Numbers

What you should learn:

Goal 1 How to express division as multiplication

Goal 2 How to divide real numbers using the Division Rule or a calculator

Why you should learn it:

You can divide positive and negative numbers by knowing how to express division as multiplication. This is useful in solving real-life problems, such as finding the frequency of a sound wave given its period.

Goal 1 Expressing Division as Multiplication

Just as subtraction can be expressed as addition, division can be expressed as multiplication.

Subtraction	**Corresponding Addition**
$8 - 3 = 5$	$8 + (-3) = 5$

Division	**Corresponding Multiplication**
$12 \div 4 = 3$	$(12)(\frac{1}{4}) = 3 \qquad \frac{12}{4} = 3$

Subtracting a number is the same as adding the *opposite* of the number, and dividing by a number is the same as multiplying by the *reciprocal* of the number. If $\frac{a}{b}$ is a number that is not zero, then its **reciprocal** is $\frac{b}{a}$. In particular, if a is not zero, then its reciprocal is $\frac{1}{a}$. The product of a number and its reciprocal is 1.

$$a \cdot \frac{1}{a} = 1 \quad \textit{Multiplying a by } \frac{1}{a} \textit{ produces 1.}$$

Division Rule

To divide a number a by a nonzero number b, multiply a by the reciprocal of b.

$$a \div b = a \cdot \frac{1}{b}$$

The result is the **quotient** of a and b.

Zero is the only real number that does not have a reciprocal. This means that you cannot divide a number by zero.

Example 1 *Expressing Division as Multiplication*

a. The reciprocal of 4 is $\frac{1}{4}$.
$$20 \div 4 = (20)(\frac{1}{4}) = 5$$

b. The reciprocal of $\frac{1}{3}$ is 3.
$$3x \div \frac{1}{3} = 3x \cdot 3 = 9x$$

c. The reciprocal of 2 is $\frac{1}{2}$.
$$\frac{3}{5} \div 2 = \frac{3}{5} \cdot \frac{1}{2} = \frac{3}{10}$$

d. The reciprocal of $\frac{2}{3}$ is $\frac{3}{2}$.
$$\frac{12}{\frac{2}{3}} = 12 \cdot \frac{3}{2} = 18$$

■

Dividing Real Numbers

Each division in Example 1 involves only positive numbers. Reciprocals can also be used in divisions that involve negative numbers.

Example 2 Division Involving Negative Numbers

a. $10 \div -2 = (10)\left(-\frac{1}{2}\right) = -5$ *Reciprocal of -2 is $-\frac{1}{2}$.*

b. $-1 \div 3 = -1 \cdot \frac{1}{3} = -\frac{1}{3}$ *Reciprocal of 3 is $\frac{1}{3}$.*

c. $\dfrac{-x}{-6} = -x \div -6 = -x\left(-\frac{1}{6}\right)$ *Reciprocal of -6 is $-\frac{1}{6}$.*

$\phantom{\dfrac{-x}{-6}} = \frac{1}{6}x$ or $\frac{x}{6}$

d. $\dfrac{-\frac{1}{3}}{4} = -\frac{1}{3} \div 4 = -\frac{1}{3} \cdot \frac{1}{4} = -\frac{1}{12}$ *Reciprocal of 4 is $\frac{1}{4}$.*

e. $\dfrac{1}{-\frac{3}{4}} = 1 \div -\frac{3}{4} = (1)\left(-\frac{4}{3}\right) = -\frac{4}{3}$ *Reciprocal of $-\frac{3}{4}$ is $-\frac{4}{3}$.*

■

Example 3 Simplifying a Quotient

$$\frac{32x - 8}{4} = (32x - 8)\left(\frac{1}{4}\right) \quad \text{\textit{Multiply by the reciprocal of 4.}}$$

$$= (32x)\left(\frac{1}{4}\right) - (8)\left(\frac{1}{4}\right) \quad \text{\textit{Distributive Property}}$$

$$= 8x - 2 \quad \text{\textit{Simplify.}}$$

■

Example 4 Evaluating an Expression

Evaluate the following expressions when $a = -2$ and $b = -3$.

a. $\dfrac{2a - b}{ab}$ **b.** $\dfrac{a + 2}{b}$ **c.** $\dfrac{a}{3 + b}$

Solution

a. $\dfrac{2a - b}{ab} = \dfrac{2(-2) - (-3)}{(-2)(-3)} = \dfrac{-4 + 3}{6} = \dfrac{-1}{6} = -\dfrac{1}{6}$

b. $\dfrac{a + 2}{b} = \dfrac{-2 + 2}{-3} = \dfrac{0}{-3} = 0$

c. $\dfrac{a}{3 + b} = \dfrac{-2}{3 + (-3)} = \dfrac{-2}{0}$ (Division by 0 is undefined.)   ■

In Example 4b, note that 0 can be divided by a nonzero number. The result will always be 0.

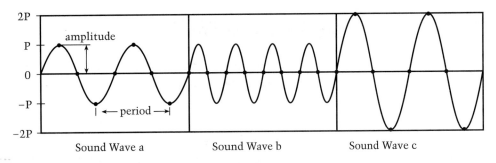

Sound Wave a   Sound Wave b   Sound Wave c

*Sound waves (vibrations) are measured by amplitude, period, and frequency. Amplitude measures the "height" of the wave, the period is the distance between adjacent wave "troughs," and the frequency is the number of waves passing a fixed point per second. Waves **a** and **b** have the same amplitude but different frequencies, whereas waves **a** and **c** have the same frequency but different amplitudes.*

Example 5 *Finding the Frequency of a Musical Note*

The musical note A above middle C has a period of $\frac{1}{440}$ second. What is the frequency of this note? How many sound waves does this note have per second?

Solution   The frequency is the reciprocal of the period.

$$\text{frequency} = \frac{1}{\text{period}} = \frac{1}{\frac{1}{440}} = 440$$

Thus, the note has 440 waves per second. (Higher notes have more waves per second, and lower notes have fewer.) ∎

Communicating about ALGEBRA

Connections
Technology

SHARING IDEAS about the Lesson

Using the Reciprocal Key   The following calculator keystrokes use the reciprocal key, labeled $\boxed{1/x}$ or $\boxed{x^{-1}}$, to find the reciprocal of -8. In either case, the display should be -0.125.

$-.13$

Using $\boxed{1/x}$ Key	Using $\boxed{x^{-1}}$ Key
8 $\boxed{+/-}$ $\boxed{1/x}$	$\boxed{(-)}$ 8 $\boxed{x^{-1}}$ $\boxed{=}$

A. Use a calculator to multiply -8 by $-0.125.$ Explain why the result is 1.

$-.875$ $-.88$

B. Use a calculator to divide 7 by -8 in two different ways: once using the division key and once using the reciprocal key. Which way do you prefer? Explain why.

EXERCISES

Guided Practice

▶ **CRITICAL THINKING about the Lesson**

1. **True or False?** Dividing a number is the same as multiplying by the opposite of the number. Explain your reasoning.

2. **True or False?** The product of a number and its reciprocal is 1. Explain your reasoning.

In Exercises 3–6, find the reciprocal of the number.

3. 22

4. -17

5. $\frac{4}{5}$

6. $-\frac{7}{2}$

7. What is the only number that does not have a reciprocal?

8. Is it possible to divide 0 by a nonzero number? If yes, what will be the result? If no, explain why.

Independent Practice

In Exercises 9–16, express the division as multiplication.

9. $16 \div 4$

10. $24 \div 8$

11. $2x \div \frac{1}{9}$

12. $\frac{1}{2}x \div 3$

13. $\frac{4}{9}$

14. $12x \div \frac{2}{3}$

15. $\frac{48}{\frac{1}{2}}$

16. $\frac{4}{\frac{3}{4}}$

In Exercises 17–36, perform the indicated division.

17. $6 \div 3$

18. $27 \div 9$

19. $9 \div \frac{1}{2}$

20. $8 \div \frac{1}{5}$

21. $\frac{92}{\frac{1}{2}}$

22. $\frac{16}{\frac{4}{9}}$

23. $-8 \div 4$

24. $36 \div -6$

25. $18 \div -9$

26. $-64 \div 16$

27. $-10 \div \frac{1}{9}$

28. $-33 \div -\frac{1}{2}$

29. $-\frac{1}{7} \div -3$

30. $-\frac{3}{4} \div 4$

31. $\frac{x}{4} \div 3$

32. $\frac{2x}{3} \div \frac{1}{2}$

33. $\frac{35x}{}$

34. $4x \div -\frac{1}{2}$

35. $\frac{84x}{}$

36. $-\frac{x}{4} \div 3$

In Exercises 37–40, use the Distributive Property to simplify the quotient.

37. $\frac{9x - 27}{3}$

38. $\frac{24x + 18}{-2}$

39. $\frac{-32 + x}{-8}$

40. $\frac{45 - 9x}{9}$

In Exercises 41–48, evaluate the expression.

41. $\frac{x - 0}{6}$, when $x = 12$ and $y = 0$

42. $\frac{r - 4}{s}$, when $r = 24$ and $s = \frac{1}{2}$

43. $\frac{3a - b}{a}$, when $a = \frac{1}{3}$ and $b = -2$

44. $\frac{16 - 4x}{y}$, when $x = 2$ and $y = \frac{1}{2}$

45. $\frac{15x - 10}{y}$, when $x = 3$ and $y = \frac{2}{3}$

46. $\frac{3a - 4b}{ab}$, when $a = -\frac{1}{3}$ and $b = \frac{1}{4}$

47. $\frac{ab}{2a - 8}$, when $a = 8$ and $b = 10$

48. $\frac{x}{4y + 6}$, when $x = \frac{3}{5}$ and $y = \frac{1}{2}$

49. *How Many Breadsticks?*   Suppose you made 60 ounces of dough for breadsticks. Each breadstick is made of $\frac{5}{4}$ ounces of dough. How many breadsticks can you make?

1200 bread sticks.

50. *For the Birds*   You have 126 feet of 1-inch by 8-inch wood. If you can make one birdhouse from $4\frac{1}{2}$ feet of wood, how many birdhouses can you make? *28*

51. *How Much Can I Make?*   Each birdhouse in Exercise 50 can be sold for $15. If the lumber and other supplies cost $32, how much profit can you make on *each* birdhouse? *$13.86*

52. *Is It Worth It?*   Each birdhouse in Exercise 50 takes you two hours to make. How much profit can you make per hour of work? *$6.93 per hr*

Broadcasting   **In Exercises 53–56, use the following information.**

The frequency of an AM station is obtained by multiplying the station number by 1000. For example, the station 1370 AM has a frequency of 1370 • 1000 = 1,370,000 vibrations per second. The frequency of an FM station is obtained by multiplying the station number by 1,000,000. For example, the station 101.7 FM has a frequency of 101.7 • 1,000,000 = 101,700,000 vibrations per second.

Amplitude modulation (AM)

Frequency modulation (FM)

53. Find the period of the radio waves transmitted by the radio station 1400 AM.

54. Find the period of the radio waves transmitted by the radio station 92.3 FM.

55. Find the radio station setting for a station transmitting waves that have a period of $\frac{1}{90,000,000}$ second. Is this an AM station or an FM station? Explain.

AM stations broadcast on frequencies between 535,000 and 1,705,000 vibrations per second. FM stations broadcast on frequencies between 88,000,000 and 108,000,000 vibrations per second.

56. Find the radio station setting for a station transmitting waves that have a period of $\frac{1}{905,000}$ second. Is this an AM station or an FM station? Explain.

In Exercises 57–68, simplify the expression.

57. $16 - 22$ *(−6)*

58. $9 - 7$

59. $24 \div 2$ *12 − .75*

60. $64 \div 4$

61. $4 \times \frac{2}{8} + (9 - 12)$ *(5)*

62. $6 + 9 \div \frac{1}{4} - 14$

63. $8 - 14 \div 2 \cdot 4$ *6*

64. $3 - 6^2 \div 2$

65. $(-4 \div \frac{3}{8})^2 - 9$ *−12 144−9 (135)*

66. $14 - (2 \div -\frac{1}{4})^2$

67. $|-2| - |-4|$ *8*

68. $2|-1| - |-3|$

−12

2 − 4 = −2

In Exercises 69–74, evaluate the expression.

69. $-x \div \frac{x}{2}$, when $x = 6$ *−12*

70. $14 \div y + 2$, when $y = \frac{2}{3}$

71. $\frac{x}{2} \times 8$, when $x = 4$ *¼*

72. $2 \div \frac{x}{9}$, when $x = 3$

73. $x \times 2$, when $x = \frac{1}{4}$ *$\frac{1}{8}$*

74. $8 \cdot x$, when $x = \frac{1}{8}$

75. *Make a Table, Find a Pattern* Complete the table by expressing each division as a product that has no decimal factor. Describe the pattern. Use the pattern to simplify the expression $\frac{x}{0.000001}$.

$\dfrac{x}{1}$	$\dfrac{x}{0.1}$	$\dfrac{x}{0.01}$	$\dfrac{x}{0.001}$	$\dfrac{x}{0.0001}$	$\dfrac{x}{0.00001}$
x	$10x$	$100x$	$1000x$	$10000x$	$100000x$

76. *Make a Table, Find a Pattern* Evaluate each expression and complete the table. Describe the pattern.

$\dfrac{(-1)^1}{(-1)^1}$	$\dfrac{(-1)^1}{(-1)^2}$	$\dfrac{(-1)^2}{(-1)^1}$	$\dfrac{(-1)^2}{(-1)^2}$	$\dfrac{(-1)^3}{(-1)^1}$	$\dfrac{(-1)^3}{(-1)^2}$	$\dfrac{(-1)^3}{(-1)^3}$
?	?	?	?	?	?	?

In Exercises 77–80, use the result of Exercise 76 to find the value of $\dfrac{(-1)^n}{(-1)^m}$. (Assume n and m are positive integers.)

77. n is even and m is odd.

78. n is even and m is even.

79. n is odd and m is even.

80. n is odd and m is odd.

81. *Antler Sale* In 1989, the antlers collected by the Boy Scouts in Jackson, Wyoming, were auctioned for $110,757. The total weight of the antlers was 7872 pounds. What was the average price per pound? The Boy Scouts donated 80% of the money to the National Elk Refuge to purchase food for wintering elk. What was the average amount per pound that the Boy Scouts kept?

Since 1965, the Boy Scouts of America in the Jackson District of Wyoming have been permitted to collect the freshly shed antlers of elk.

2.8

Exploring Data: Rates and Ratios

What you should learn:

Goal 1 How to use rates to relate quantities measured in different units

Goal 2 How to use ratios to relate quantities measured in the same units

Why you should learn it:

You can use rates to compare quantities with different units, such as the amount of money spent by a number of people. You can use ratios to compare quantities with like units, such as the areas of two rooms, both measured in square feet.

Real Life
Consumer Studies

Goal 1 Using Rates

If a and b are two quantities that are measured in *different* units, then the **average rate** (or **average number**) of a per b is $\frac{a}{b}$. Finding a rate is something that most people do instinctively. Here are two common examples.

- You drive a distance of 250 miles and use 11 gallons of gas. The average mileage for your car is

$$\frac{250 \text{ miles}}{11 \text{ gallons}} = \frac{250}{11} \frac{\text{miles}}{\text{gallon}} \approx 22.7 \text{ miles per gallon.}$$

- You get paid $20 for 4 hours of work. Your hourly rate is

$$\frac{20 \text{ dollars}}{4 \text{ hours}} = \frac{20}{4} \frac{\text{dollars}}{\text{hour}} = 5 \text{ dollars per hour.}$$

Example 1 *Spending in the United States*

The table shows some total amounts spent in the United States in 1990. How could you present this information to someone so that it is easier to understand?

1990 Spending *(Source: Census of Retail Trade.)*

Clothing & Shoes	Food (Restaurants)	Food (Grocery Stores)
$90,000,000,000	$180,000,000,000	$340,000,000,000

Solution   One way to personalize these large numbers is to find the average rate of spending *per person*. You can do this by dividing the spending amounts by the total population. (It was about 250 million in 1990.) For instance, the average amount spent per person for clothing and shoes in 1990 was

$$\frac{90,000,000,000 \text{ dollars}}{250,000,000 \text{ people}} = 360 \text{ dollars per person.}$$

By changing the amount to a *per person* rate, you allow people to compare themselves to the average. All three rates are summarized in the following table.

1990 Average Rate of Spending Per Person

Clothing & Shoes	Food (Restaurants)	Food (Grocery Stores)
$360 per person	$720 per person	$1360 per person

Example 2   Rate of Hair Growth

Elise has just returned from spending six months in Australia in a student exchange program. The second thing her mother said to Elise when she got off the plane was, "I can't believe how much your hair has grown." How much could Elise's hair have grown while she was gone? Why do you think Elise's mother noticed the difference in hair length?

Solution   The normal rate of growth for human hair is 3 to 5 inches per year. Even at the faster rate, Elise's hair would have only grown

$$\frac{5 \text{ inches}}{1 \text{ year}} \cdot \frac{1}{2} \text{ year} = 2.5 \text{ inches.}$$

As to why Elise's mother noticed the difference, this is one of the surprising things about people. We are very sensitive to relatively small changes in the appearance of people we know well. ■

Example 3   Currency Exchange

Suppose you visited Canada and took $175 to spend. The rate of currency exchange was $1.1515 Canadian dollars per U.S. dollar. If you exchanged the entire amount, how much did you receive in Canadian dollars? While in Canada, you spent everything but $32.50 (Canadian). How much could you exchange this for in U.S. dollars?

Solution   For the exchange from U.S. dollars to Canadian, you want to end up with Canadian dollars, so you need to write the exchange rate as a fraction with Canadian dollars in the numerator.

$$\frac{1.1515 \text{ Canadian dollars}}{1 \text{ U.S. dollar}} \cdot 175 \text{ U.S. dollars} = \$201.51 \text{ (Canadian)}$$

For the exchange from Canadian dollars to U.S. dollars, you want to end up with U.S. dollars, so you need to write the exchange rate as a fraction with U.S. dollars in the numerator.

$$\frac{1 \text{ U.S. dollar}}{1.1515 \text{ Canadian dollars}} \cdot 32.50 \text{ Canadian dollars} = \$28.22 \text{ (U.S.)}$$

■

Rates that are used to compare the prices per unit of consumer items are called **unit prices.** For instance, by comparing the unit prices of the following bottles of cologne, you can see that the larger bottle costs less per ounce.

4-ounce bottle: $\frac{20.95 \text{ dollars}}{4 \text{ ounces}} = \$5.24$ per ounce

6-ounce bottle: $\frac{29.95 \text{ dollars}}{6 \text{ ounces}} = \$4.99$ per ounce

Historic Quebec City, Canada

Using Ratios

If *a* and *b* are two quantities that are measured in the *same* units, then the ratio of *a* to *b* is $\frac{a}{b}$. The difference between a rate and a ratio is that a rate compares two quantities measured in different units, and a ratio compares two quantities measured in the same unit. (In itself, a ratio has no units.)

Often ratios are left in fractional form. For instance, in 1991 the Stevenson High School girls' volleyball team won 10 of its 16 games. Thus, the win-loss ratio was

$$\text{win-loss ratio} = \frac{\text{games won}}{\text{games lost}} = \frac{10 \text{ games}}{6 \text{ games}} = \frac{5}{3}.$$

Example 4 *Comparing Two Square Rooms*

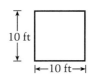

One bedroom in a house is 10 feet by 10 feet. The other bedroom is 15 feet by 15 feet. Which is a correct comparison of the sizes of the two rooms?

- The larger room has $1\frac{1}{2}$ times the area of the smaller room.
- The larger room has over twice the area of the smaller room.

Solution The ratio of the areas of the two rooms is

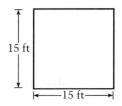

$$\frac{\text{area of larger}}{\text{area of smaller}} = \frac{225 \text{ square feet}}{100 \text{ square feet}} = \frac{225}{100} \text{ or } 2.25.$$

Thus, the second statement is correct. Drawing diagrams provides a visual check.

Communicating about **ALGEBRA**

Connections
Technology

▶ **SHARING IDEAS about the Lesson**

Finding Needed Information For many years, mathematicians wondered whether π was a **rational number.** That is, they wondered if π could be written as the ratio of two integers. Finally, in 1882, a mathematician named Ferdinand Lindemann published a proof that π is not rational. There are, however, rational numbers whose values are very close to *pi*.

A. Use a calculator to write the following in increasing order.

$$\pi, \ 3.1416, \ \frac{22}{7}, \ \frac{355}{113}$$

B. Which of the three rational numbers is closest in value to π?

EXERCISES

Guided Practice

▶ **CRITICAL THINKING about the Lesson**

1. Explain the difference between a rate and a ratio.

2. Would you use a rate or a ratio to compare unit prices?

3. Is the quotient of the circumference and the diameter of a circle a rate or a ratio? What is the symbol for this quotient?

4. Is a speed of 40 kilometers per hour a rate or a ratio? Is the quotient of 4 hours to 24 hours a rate or a ratio?

Independent Practice

5. *Motorcycle Mileage* A motorcycle uses 3 gallons of gasoline to travel 440 miles. Find the average number of miles per gallon.

6. *Car Mileage* A car uses 12 gallons to travel 460 miles. Find the average number of miles per gallon.

7. *Hourly Wage* You get paid $85 for working 20 hours. Find your hourly rate of pay.

8. *Hourly Wage* You get paid $127.50 for working 30 hours. Find your hourly rate of pay.

9. *Average Speed* A family drove 80 kilometers in $\frac{3}{4}$ hours. What was the average speed?

10. *Average Speed* A family drove m miles in $\frac{3}{4}$ hours. What was the average speed?

11. *Video Rental* The regular rental fee for a video is $1.79. The rental store runs a special on three movies for $4.99. What is the cost per video under the special? How much do you save per video?

12. *Frozen Yogurt Bars* A store sells a box of 5 frozen yogurt bars for $1.20. The same store sells a box containing 7 bars for $1.59. Find the unit price to determine which is the better buy.

13. *Average Golf Score* During a golf game, you score an 83 on an 18-hole course. What was your average score per hole? Is this average better or worse than a score of 44 for 9 holes of golf?

14. *Library Space* A library has 10,513 books and 255 shelves. All the shelves are full. What is the average number of books per shelf? If the library receives 659 new books from another library that is closing, approximately how many more shelves does it need?

15. *Compact Disk Collection* Suppose you have 127 compact disks. You want to buy storage cases that can hold 35 disks each. How many cases do you need? How many more compact disks can you buy before you need to buy another case?

An Average Day **In Exercises 16–25, yearly rates for the United States are given. Find the rate per day.**

(Source: On an Average Day, Fawcett Press, 1989)

16. 888,045 automobiles are stolen.

17. 352,225,000 colas are drunk at breakfast.

18. 1,572,481,430 credit card purchases are made.

19. 12,045 new consumer products are introduced.

20. 350,000,000,000 photocopies are made.

21. $450,000,000 is spent on sun-care products.

22. 88,695 patents are issued.

23. 20,440 house fires are started by arson.

24. 13,140,000,000 postage stamps are printed.

25. 24,820 animals are treated with acupuncture.

26. *Sales Tax*　You buy a new pair of high-top sneakers for $50. The tax on the shoes is $2.50. What is the ratio of the sales tax to the cost of the shoes?

27. *Height*　Your brother is 72 inches tall. The average height for males is 70 inches. What is the ratio of your brother's height to the average height for males?

28. *Who Is Faster?*　It takes you $3\frac{1}{2}$ hours to mow your lawn, and it takes your sister 3 hours. Find the ratio of your time to your sister's time. Find the ratio of your sister's time to yours. Are these two ratios reciprocals or opposites?

29. *Dog Shelter*　An animal shelter has housed 225 dogs during a 12-week summer. Now it is the last week of summer and there are 15 dogs in the shelter. What is the ratio of currently sheltered dogs to the total number of summer dogs? The average stay per dog is one week. Is the shelter busier than normal?

30. *Windbreaker Sale*　A windbreaker regularly sells for $32. You save $8 during a sale. What is the percent discount?

31. *Baseball Diamond*　What is the ratio of the baseball diamond's area to the baseball field's area?

32. *Field of Dreams*　The Cleveland Indians baseball team has a season record so far of 80 wins and 40 losses. What is the ratio of games won to total games played? What is the ratio of games lost to total games played?

The diamond portion is 90 feet by 90 feet. The entire field is 270 feet by 270 feet.

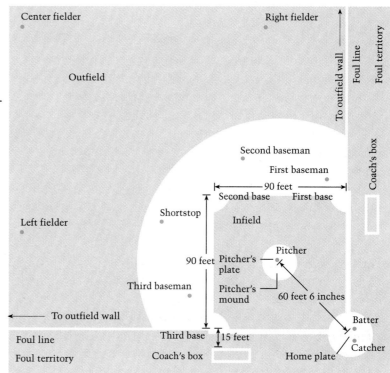

33. *Years of School* Maya completed eighth grade in 1992. What is the ratio of her completed number of years in school to the total number of years she will spend in school if her highest degree is the following? (Don't count kindergarten.)

- High school diploma, 1996
- Associate's Degree, 1998
- Bachelor's Degree, 2000
- Master's Degree, 2002
- Doctor's Degree, 2004

34. *Population* Using the matrix below, find the ratio of the U.S. population in 1980 to the world population in 1980. Compare this to the ratio of the U.S. population in 1989 to the world population in 1989. Is the ratio of the U.S. population to the world population increasing or decreasing? *(Source: U.S. Bureau of Census)*

Population   **1980**   **1989**

$$\begin{matrix} \text{World} \\ \text{U.S.} \end{matrix} \begin{bmatrix} 4{,}477{,}000{,}000 & 5{,}239{,}000{,}000 \\ 227{,}757{,}000 & 248{,}231{,}000 \end{bmatrix}$$

Gear Ratio **In Exercises 35 and 36, use the following information.**

The *gear ratio* of two connected gears, Gear A and Gear B, is the ratio of the number of teeth on Gear A to the number of teeth on Gear B. Gear ratios for vehicles are normally given in terms of the ratio of the "engine gear" to the "axle gear."

35. The diagram shows the gears for an experimental electric car called *Pohlmann E1*. What is the gear ratio for this car?

Axle gear

Engine gear

36. On a five-speed bicycle, the ratio of the pedal gear to the axle gear depends on which axle gear is engaged. Use the following table to find the gear ratios for the five different gears. (Ratios on five-speed bikes vary.) For which gear is it easiest to pedal? Why?

	1st Gear	2nd Gear	3rd Gear	4th Gear	5th Gear
Teeth on Pedal Gear	52	52	52	52	52
Teeth on Axle Gear	28	24	20	17	14

In Exercises 37–44, match the common name for a rate to one of the measures.

37. Speed *e*

38. Wage *h*

39. Pulse *a*

40. Density *F*

41. Time (in music) *g*

42. Unit Price *d*

43. Frequency *b.*

44. Air Pressure *c*

a. Heartbeats per minute

b. Vibrations per second

c. Pounds per square inch

d. Dollars per ounce

e. Miles per hour

f. Pounds per cubic inch

g. Beats per measure

h. Dollars per hour

Integrated Review

In Exercises 45–56, evaluate the expression.

45. $-3 + (-2)$ -1

46. $5 - (3 + 7)$

47. $2 + |-3| - 12$ -7

48. $11 - 4 + |-8|$

49. $6x - 4x$ $2x$

50. $-5y + 2y$

51. $4^3 - 8x$, when $x = 7$

52. $\frac{1}{12}(-11 - t^2)$, when $t = 2$

53. $\frac{1}{8}[m + (-5)]$, when $m = 21$ 2

54. $63x \div -3$, when $x = 7$

55. $49y \div \frac{7}{3}$, when $y = -1$ -21

56. $-3x - (-6)^2$, when $x = -9$

Exploration and Extension

57. *Photocopier*   The page on the left was put into a photocopier and reduced to produce the copy on the right. Estimate the ratio of the size of the original to the size of the copy.

58. *Map Scale*   Use the map of Arizona to approximate the distance between Tucson and Phoenix.

Original size

Size of Photocopy

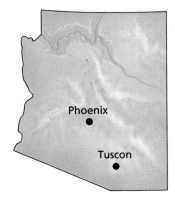

The scale of this map uses a ratio of 1 inch to 200 miles.

59. *That's a Lot of Cousins*   Let y be the number of cousins you have. Let x be the number of cousins your best friend has. The ratio of your cousins to your friend's cousins is 2 to 5. Write an equation that describes the relationship between the number of cousins you have and the number of cousins your friend has. If you have 12 cousins, how many does your friend have?

Chapter Summary

What did you learn?

Skills

1. Use a real number line
   - to graph real numbers. **(2.1)**
   - to order real numbers. **(2.1)**
   - to add real numbers. **(2.2)**
2. Find the absolute value of a real number. **(2.1)**
3. Find the opposite of a real number. **(2.1)**
4. Find the reciprocal of a real number. **(2.7)**
5. Add, subtract, multiply, and divide real numbers. **(2.2–2.7)**
6. Add and subtract matrices. **(2.4)**
7. Simplify expressions. **(2.2–2.7)**
   - Combine like terms. **(2.6)**
8. Use the Distributive Property. **(2.6)**

Strategies

9. Interpret real numbers in real-life settings. **(2.1–2.8)**
10. Find and use rates and ratios in real-life settings. **(2.8)**

Exploring Data

11. Use a matrix to organize data. **(2.4)**

Why did you learn it?

Many real-life situations can be modeled with algebraic expressions and with matrices. By learning to create, simplify, and evaluate algebraic expressions and matrices, you will be able to answer questions pertaining to the real world. Learning to create, simplify, and evaluate algebraic expressions will also help prepare you for the algebra that you will study later in this course.

How does it fit into the bigger picture of algebra?

All the numbers you worked with in Chapter 1 were either zero or positive. In this chapter, you studied rules for adding, subtracting, multiplying, and dividing with both positive and negative numbers. You should try to build an intuitive sense for the type of problems that are associated with negative numbers, such as losses, deficits, low temperatures, etc. This chapter introduces some of the rules of algebra. Your goal should be to practice using the rules so much that they become second nature as you become familiar with the bigger picture of algebra.

1. Graph 1 and -4 on the real number line. Which one is greater? **(2.1)**

1 is greater.

2. Graph $\frac{1}{2}$, $-\frac{2}{3}$, 0, -2, and $\frac{5}{3}$ on the real number line. Then list the numbers in increasing order. **(2.1)**

3. Graph -5 and its opposite on the number line. **(2.1)**

4. Graph $\frac{3}{4}$ and its opposite on the number line. **(2.1)**

5. What is the absolute value of -1.1? **(2.1)**

1.1

6. What is the absolute value of 4.5? **(2.1)**

In Exercises 7–24, evaluate the expression. (2.1, 2.2, 2.3, 2.5, 2.7)

7. $8 + (-4)$ *4*

8. $-5 + (-3) + 4$

9. $|-5| - 4$ *1*

10. $10 - (-2) - |5|$

11. $-[(-7) + 8]$ *-1*

12. $-[3 + (-4)]$

13. $-14.3 + (-5.5) + 6.2$ *-13.6*

14. $15.3 + (8.9) + (-7.4)$

15. $(-14)(-2)$ *28*

16. $(-9)(-2)(-\frac{1}{3})$

17. $\frac{3}{8} \div \frac{1}{2}$ *$\frac{6}{8}$ $\frac{3}{4}$*

18. $-16 \div -4$

19. $\frac{1}{3}m - m^2$, when $m = \frac{1}{2}$ *$\frac{1}{6} - \frac{1}{4}$ $-\frac{1}{12}$*

20. $-6x + 2|x - 3|$, when $x = -3$

21. $\frac{3r - 6s}{3}$, when $r = 1$ and $s = 2$ *-9 3*

22. $\frac{xy}{3x + 4y}$, when $x = 4$ and $y = \frac{1}{2}$

23. $4 + (-x) + 10$, when $x = 5$ *9*

24. $|m| - m + 3$, when $m = \frac{1}{2}$

In Exercises 25–28, simplify the expression. (2.3, 2.6, 2.7) *2x - 8*

25. $7(y - 1) + 10$

$7y - 7 + 10$ $7y + 3$

26. $3m^2 - (1 + 2m^2)$

27. $\frac{4x - 16}{2}$

28. $\frac{-45 + 15y}{-5}$

In Exercises 29 and 30, add or subtract the matrices. (2.4)

29. Add: $\begin{bmatrix} 3 & -\frac{1}{2} \\ 4 & 0 \\ 1 & -5 \end{bmatrix} + \begin{bmatrix} -4 & \frac{5}{2} \\ 6 & -3 \\ 7 & 2 \end{bmatrix}$ $= \begin{bmatrix} -1 & 2 \\ 10 & -3 \\ 8 & -3 \end{bmatrix}$

30. Subtract: $\begin{bmatrix} -\frac{3}{4} & \frac{1}{2} & \frac{3}{2} \\ \frac{5}{4} & \frac{1}{8} & \frac{3}{4} \end{bmatrix} - \begin{bmatrix} \frac{1}{4} & -\frac{3}{2} & 0 \\ -\frac{1}{4} & \frac{3}{8} & 1 \end{bmatrix}$.

In Exercises 31–34, use the table showing average monthly high and low temperatures and average days of rain or snow in San Francisco. (2.4)

	Jan	Feb	Mar	Apr	May	Jun	Jul	Aug	Sep	Oct	Nov	Dec
High Temperature (F)	56°	59°	61°	63°	65°	69°	69°	70°	72°	69°	64°	57°
Low Temperature (F)	40°	43°	44°	45°	48°	50°	52°	52°	52°	49°	45°	45°
Days of Rain or Snow	12	10	9	6	3	2	0	0	1	4	6	11

31. Write a matrix for the average high and low temperatures in San Francisco from November to April.

32. Which six-month period is San Francisco's rainy season, May through October or November through April?

33. During which months are the days getting warmer, on the average?

34. In which months are the average high and low temperatures farthest apart? Closest together?

35. *Opening a Parachute*   Carmen is skydiving and opens her parachute at a height of h feet. After the parachute opens, Carmen's velocity is -20 feet per second. What is her speed? Carmen lands on the ground one minute after her parachute opens. Which equation shows the height at which Carmen opened her parachute?

a. $h = \frac{60}{20}$ **b.** $60h = 20$ **c.** $h = 20 \cdot 60$

36. *Visiting Your Dad*   You live in New Mexico. It normally takes you three hours, traveling at 60 miles per hour, to get to your father's house in Texas. Because of construction, today's trip takes 4 hours. How far is it to your father's house? Which equation shows your average speed, r, on today's trip?

a. $r = \frac{180}{3}$ **b.** $3 = \frac{180}{r}$ **c.** $4r = 180$

37. *Flying to San Diego*   A pilot leaves Detroit at 7:00 A.M. and lands at San Diego six hours later. What time is it when the pilot lands at San Diego? (Use the map on page 72.)

38. *Annual Profit or Loss?*   A company had a loss of $1,002.91 in the first quarter, a loss of $565.77 in the second quarter, a profit of $14,232.01 in the third quarter, and a profit of $3,027.88 in the fourth quarter. What was its profit for the year?

In Exercises 39–41, decide whether the element is an atom or an ion.

39. Magnesium (Mg):
12 electrons, 12 protons

40. Magnesium (Mg):
10 electrons, 12 protons

41. Sodium (Na):
10 electrons, 11 protons

42. Which of Exercises 39–40 has an element with Mg^{+2} as its chemical symbol?

Where the Buffalo Roam   **In Exercises 43–45, use the table showing the average number of buffalo in four parks in the United States and Canada.**

Park	Number of Buffalo	Number of Acres
Elk Island National Park, Alberta	750	48,000
Wood Buffalo National Park, Alberta/Northwest Territories	3375	11,072,000
Wind Cave National Park, South Dakota	325	28,300
Yellowstone National Park, Idaho/Montana/Wyoming	2850	2,219,800

43. Find the average number of acres per buffalo in each park.

44. Which park has the greatest number of acres per buffalo?

45. Which park has the least number of acres per buffalo?

Earning Money   **In Exercises 46–49, use the information in the bar graph.**

The bar graph shows the percent of eighth graders in the United States who earn money after school. (Those who earned money in two or more jobs were asked to select their primary job.)

46. Out of 2000 eighth graders, how many would you expect to earn money primarily in a newspaper route?

47. Out of 3500 eighth graders, how many would you expect to earn money primarily by baby-sitting?

48. Out of 1500 eighth graders, how many *more* would you expect to do lawn work than farm work or manual labor?

49. Out of 1500 eighth graders, which of the following expressions tells you how many have earned money in some job? Explain your answer.

    a. $1500 - 0.325(1500)$
    b. $1500(1 - 0.325)$

Eighth Grade Survey
Jobs held after school

32.5%	Did not work for pay
19.6%	Lawn work
16.1%	Waiter/ odd jobs
14.7%	Newspaper route
8.5%	Babysitting
5.4%	Farm/ manual labor
3.2%	Clerk/ sales office

Chambered Nautilus   **In Exercises 50–53, use the following information.**

A chambered nautilus is a mollusk that builds its spiral shell by constructing new living chambers, each with the same shape. Each consecutive living chamber is 6.3% larger than the previous chamber.

50. Consider three consecutive living chambers. What percent larger is Chamber 3 than Chamber 1?

51. Consider two consecutive living chambers. What percent *smaller* is Chamber 1 than Chamber 2?

52. Consider four consecutive living chambers. If Chamber 1 has a volume of 3 cm³, what is the volume of Chamber 4?

53. After completing any given living chamber (call it Chamber 0), the nautilus must complete 18 more chambers to bring the spiral full circle. The 18th additional chamber will be about 2.85 times larger than Chamber 0. Does a. or b. describe the relative size of the 18th chamber to Chamber 0? Justify your answer.

    a. $(1.06)^{18}$ **b.** $(1.06)^{19}$

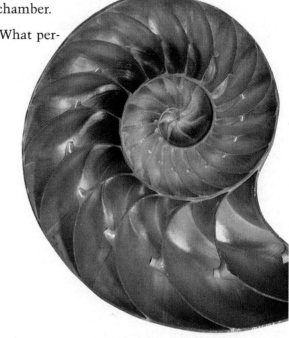

Human-Powered Submarines **In Exercises 54–57, use the information about human-powered submarines. Each of the submarines participated in the Second International Submarine Races held in June 1991, in Riviera Beach, Florida.** (*Source: Popular Science Magazine*)

54. Find the ratio of each submarine's width to its length. Which ratio is closest to the ideal ratio for minimum drag? (See page 121.)

55. Suppose a submarine had a speed of 3 knots. One knot is one nautical mile per hour. One nautical mile is 6080 feet. One mile is 5280 feet. What is the submarine's speed in miles per hour?

$$(3 \text{ knots})\left(\frac{1 \text{ n.mi/h}}{1 \text{ knot}}\right)\left(\frac{6080 \text{ ft}}{1 \text{ n.mi}}\right)\left(\frac{1 \text{ mi}}{5280 \text{ ft}}\right)$$

56. If each person can generate 0.3 horsepower, how much horsepower can a crew of two generate?

57. If the foot pedals have a 2 to 1 gear ratio to the submarine paddle axle, how many revolutions per minute must a crew member pump to make the paddles turn at 70 revolutions per minute?

West Virginia University
Length: 144 in.
Width: 36 in.

Texas A&M
University at Galveston
Length: 134 in.
Width: 48 in.

University of New Hampshire
Length: 184 in., Width 37 in.

University of California
at Santa Barbara
Length: 204 in., Width: 24 in.

Massachusetts Institute of Technology
Length: 126 in., Width: 24 in.

1. Write in increasing order. $-\frac{5}{4}, -\frac{5}{2}, \frac{3}{4}$

2. Which is correct?
   a. $-3 < -4$ b. $-3 > -4$

3. Evaluate $9 + (-10) + 2$.

4. Evaluate $-2.97 - 3.20 - (-0.02)$.

5. Evaluate $(-6)(4)(-1)$.

6. Evaluate $72 \div (-12)$.

7. Evaluate $\frac{4 - x}{-3}$, when $x = -1$.

8. Evaluate $1 - 2x^2$, when $x = -2$.

9. Simplify $-2x + 3 + 3x - 9$.

10. Simplify $3 - 4(x - 2)$.

11. Add the matrices.

$$\begin{bmatrix} 3 & -7 \\ \frac{1}{2} & 6 \\ 0 & 2 \end{bmatrix} + \begin{bmatrix} -4 & 2 \\ -\frac{1}{2} & 4 \\ 5 & \frac{1}{4} \end{bmatrix}$$

12. Subtract the matrices.

$$\begin{bmatrix} 2 & -\frac{2}{3} & 4 \\ 5 & 16 & -7 \end{bmatrix} - \begin{bmatrix} 5 & \frac{1}{3} & -1 \\ -2 & 8 & 4 \end{bmatrix}$$

In Exercises 13–18, decide whether the statement is true or false.

13. $4(x + 3) = 4(x) + 4(3)$

14. $(2 - y) - 7 = -7(2) + (-7)(y)$

15. Zero is its own opposite.

16. Zero is its own reciprocal.

17. One is its own opposite.

18. One is its own reciprocal.

19. A bus is moving at a rate of 100 kilometers per hour. How far will it travel in $3\frac{1}{2}$ hours?

20. A company had a first-quarter profit of $2,189.70, a second-quarter profit of $1,527.11, a third-quarter loss of $502.18, and a fourth-quarter loss of $266.54. What was its profit for the year?

21. Suppose you visit Taiwan, and the currency exchange rate is 27 Taiwanese dollars per U.S. dollar. How many Taiwanese dollars will you receive for $300 (U.S.)?

22. A first-grade class is going on a bus trip to an amusement park. The park requires groups to have one adult for every eight children. There are 3 teachers, 2 parents, and 36 children planning to go on the trip. Are there enough adults to meet the park's requirements?

23. A 1-liter bottle of seltzer water sells for $0.99. A 1.75-liter bottle sells for $1.79. Which size is the better buy?

24. The table shows the distribution of students at Lincoln High School by grade level and by sex. Write this table as a matrix. How many male students are in the tenth grade at Lincoln?

Lincoln	9th	10th	11th	12th
Males	307	323	290	289
Females	331	300	270	312

25. A parachutist is falling from a height of 1800 feet at a rate of 15 feet per second. Find the velocity and speed of the parachutist. When will the parachutist land on the ground?

CHAPTER
3

Solving Linear Equations

LESSONS

3.1 Solving Equations Using One Transformation ▪ 122

3.2 Solving Equations Using Two or More Transformations ▪ 129

3.3 Solving Equations with Variables on Both Sides ▪ 135

3.4 Linear Equations and Problem Solving ▪ 141

3.5 Solving Equations that Involve Decimals ▪ 148

3.6 Literal Equations and Formulas ▪ 154

3.7 Exploring Data: Scatter Plots ▪ 160

Dolphins are not only a beautiful example of graceful adaptation to ocean living, but they also seem to have a special fascination for humans.

Marine objects that encounter the least "drag" (or water resistance) are torpedo-shaped and are one fourth as wide as they are long. For instance, of the three torpedo shapes below, an object having the middle shape would encounter the least drag.

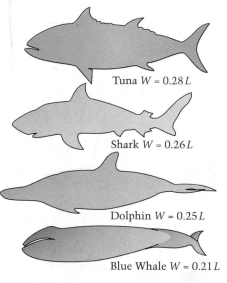

Tuna $W = 0.28L$

Shark $W = 0.26L$

Dolphin $W = 0.25L$

Blue Whale $W = 0.21L$

The bodies of some fish and marine mammals are shown fitted to streamlined shapes that have low water resistance.

The fastest-swimming fish and marine mammals have shapes that are close to ideal for minimizing drag. For instance, the width, W, and length, L, of a tuna are approximately related by $W = 0.28L$. The length of a tuna that is 20 inches wide can be approximated by solving the *linear equation* $20 = 0.28L$. Similarly, the length of a blue whale that is 30 feet wide can be approximated by solving the linear equation $30 = 0.21L$.

*(Source: **On Size and Life**, Scientific American Library)*

3.1

Solving Equations Using One Transformation

What you should learn:

Goal 1 How to solve equations systematically using addition, subtraction, and division

Goal 2 How to use reciprocals to solve equations

Why you should learn it:

You can use techniques shown in this lesson to solve equations that are too difficult to solve with mental math.

Goal 1 Solving Equations Systematically

You have been using mental math to solve equations. Now you will study techniques for solving equations systematically. Although many equations in this lesson can be solved using mental math, you should make sure you also know how to use systematic techniques to find a solution.

Two equations are **equivalent** if they have the same solution set. For instance, the equations $x - 3 = 0$ and $x = 3$ are equivalent because both have the number 3 as their only solution. To *transform* an equation into an equivalent equation, it is helpful to think of the equation as having two sides that are "in balance." Simplifying one side does not change the balance, so nothing has to be done to the other side. Adding a (nonzero) number to one side does change the balance, so the same number has to be added to the other side. The following transformations keep the sides of an equation in balance.

Transformations That Produce Equivalent Equations

	Original Equation	Equivalent Equation
1. Add the same number to *both* sides.	$x - 3 = 5$	$x = 8$
2. Subtract the same number from *both* sides.	$x + 6 = 10$	$x = 4$
3. Multiply *both* sides by the same nonzero number.	$\frac{x}{2} = 3$	$x = 6$
4. Divide *both* sides by the same nonzero number.	$4x = 12$	$x = 3$
5. Interchange the two sides.	$7 = x$	$x = 7$

In solving an equation, your goal is to isolate the variable on one side by using **inverse operations.** Addition and subtraction are inverse operations. Multiplication and division are also inverse operations.

Example 1 · Adding the Same Quantity to Both Sides

Solve $x - 5 = -13$.

Solution On the left side of the equation, 5 is subtracted from x. To isolate x, you need to apply the inverse operation by adding 5. Remember, however, to keep the balance you must add 5 to *both sides*.

$x - 5 = -13$	*Rewrite original equation.*
$x - 5 + 5 = -13 + 5$	*Add 5 to both sides.*
$x = -8$	*Simplify.*

The solution is -8. You should check this solution by substituting -8 for x in the original equation.

Check $(-8) - 5 = -13$ ∎

Each time you apply a transformation to an equation, you are writing a *solution step*. Notice that the solution steps are written "one below the other" with their equal signs aligned.

Example 2 · Subtracting the Same Quantity from Both Sides

Solve $-8 = n + 4$.

Solution On the right side of the equation, 4 is added to n. You can isolate n by subtracting 4 from both sides of the equation.

$-8 = n + 4$	*Rewrite original equation.*
$-8 - 4 = n + 4 - 4$	*Subtract 4 from both sides.*
$-12 = n$	*Simplify.*

The solution is -12. Check this in the original equation. ∎

Example 3 · Dividing Both Sides by the Same Quantity

Solve $4x = 128$.

Solution On the left side of the equation, x is multiplied by 4. You can isolate x by dividing both sides by 4.

$4x = 128$	*Rewrite original equation.*
$\dfrac{4x}{4} = \dfrac{128}{4}$	*Divide both sides by 4.*
$x = 32$	*Simplify.*

The solution is 32. Check this in the original equation. ∎

When you are solving an equation that involves a fractional coefficient, such as $\frac{1}{5}x = 30$, you can isolate the variable by multiplying by the reciprocal of the fraction.

Example 4   *Multiplying Both Sides by a Reciprocal*

Solve $\frac{1}{5}x = 30$.

Solution   On the left side of the equation, x is multiplied by the fraction $\frac{1}{5}$. You can isolate x by multiplying both sides of the equation by 5 (the reciprocal of $\frac{1}{5}$).

$$\frac{1}{5}x = 30 \qquad \textit{Rewrite original equation.}$$
$$5\left(\frac{1}{5}x\right) = 5(30) \qquad \textit{Multiply both sides by 5.}$$
$$x = 150 \qquad \textit{Simplify.}$$

The solution is 150. Check this in the original equation.   ■

Example 5   *Multiplying Both Sides by a Reciprocal*

Solve $-\frac{2}{3}m = 10$.

Solution

$$-\frac{2}{3}m = 10 \qquad \textit{Rewrite original equation.}$$
$$\left(-\frac{3}{2}\right)\left(-\frac{2}{3}m\right) = \left(-\frac{3}{2}\right)(10) \qquad \textit{Multiply both sides by } -\frac{3}{2}.$$
$$m = -15 \qquad \textit{Simplify.}$$

The solution is -15. Check this in the original equation.   ■

The equations in this lesson are called **linear equations** because each equation's variable occurs only to the first power and does not occur in a denominator. The equation $x^2 = 4$ is not linear because x occurs to the second power, and $6 = \frac{5}{x}$ is not linear because x is in the denominator. The transformations used to solve linear equations are based on rules of algebra called **properties of equality.**

Properties of Equality

1. If $a = b$, then $a + c = b + c$.   Addition Property

2. If $a = b$, then $a - c = b - c$.   Subtraction Property

3. If $a = b$, then $ca = cb$.   Multiplication Property

4. If $a = b$ and $c \neq 0$, then $\frac{a}{c} = \frac{b}{c}$.   Division Property

---

A common strategy for solving a real-life problem is to equate two ratios. Example 6 shows how this can be done using a property of similar triangles. Two triangles are **similar** if they have equal angles. The ratios of lengths of corresponding sides of similar triangles are equal.

Connections
Geometry

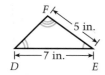

Example 6   *Similar Triangles*

The two triangles at the left are similar. What is the length of the side *AB*?

Solution   Use the fact that the ratio of the length of *AB* to the length of *DE* is equal to the ratio of the length of *BC* to the length of *EF*.

Verbal Model	$\dfrac{\text{Length of } AB}{\text{Length of } DE} = \dfrac{\text{Length of } BC}{\text{Length of } EF}$	

Labels   Length of $AB = x$ (inches)

            Length of $DE = 7$ (inches)

            Length of $BC = 10$ (inches)

            Length of $EF = 5$ (inches)

Equation $\dfrac{x}{7} = \dfrac{10}{6} \cdot 7 \cdot 2$ *Algebraic model*

               $x = 7 \cdot \dfrac{10}{5}$ *Multiply both sides by 7.*

               $x = 14$ *Simplify.*

The length of *AB* is 14 inches.   ■

Communicating about ALGEBRA

▷ **SHARING IDEAS about the Lesson**

Understand the Process   Think about the transformations used to solve equations.

A. To solve $\frac{2}{3}x = 7$, you should multiply both sides of the equation by what number?

B. Is 5 a solution of the equation $\frac{1}{7}x = \frac{5}{7}$? Explain why or why not. Does this equation have other solutions?

C. To solve $y - 5 = -13$, should you add 5 or 13 to both sides of the equation? Explain why.

D. Can you use mental math to solve $-\frac{3}{5}x = 81$? If not, multiply both sides of the equation by $-\frac{5}{3}$. Explain why this transformation gives the solution.

EXERCISES

▶ **CRITICAL THINKING about the Lesson**

1. **True or False?** Two equations are equivalent if they have the same solution set.

2. **True or False?** Adding the same number to both sides of an equation produces an equivalent equation.

3. **True or False?** Multiplying both sides of an equation by the same number produces an equivalent equation.

4. Which of the four basic operations (addition, subtraction, multiplication, and division) are inverses of each other?

5. Describe the transformation you would use to solve each of the following equations.

$$2x = 6 \quad x - 5 = 11 \quad 2 + n = 5 \quad \tfrac{1}{4}s = 3$$

6. State the four properties of equality.

In Exercises 7 and 8, decide whether the equations are equivalent.

7. $x + 10 = 3$ and $x = -7$

8. $8 - x = 4$ and $x = -4$

Independent Practice

In Exercises 9–12, state the inverse operation.

9. Add 31.

10. Subtract 27.

11. Multiply by -2.

12. Divide by 5.

In Exercises 13–24, solve the equation.

13. $4 + t = 13$

14. $m + 15 = -3$

15. $w - 5 = 11$

16. $x - (-3) = 4$

17. $y + 7 = -5$

18. $6 + n = 0$

19. $14 = b + 4$

20. $-3 = 7 + a$

21. $|-3| + n = 0$

22. $|-9| + z = -5$

23. $22 = s + 7$

24. $37 = r - (-8)$

In Exercises 25–48, solve the equation.

25. $10x = 100$

26. $-21m = 42$

27. $16 = -2a$

28. $15b = 5$

29. $256 = 16c$

30. $-4m = -16$

31. $400 = 25n$

32. $330 = -15p$

33. $\tfrac{1}{2}x = -40$

34. $\tfrac{1}{3}z = 78$

35. $0 = \tfrac{3}{5}t$

36. $-x = 4$

37. $-\tfrac{3}{4}L = 75$

38. $-\tfrac{4}{5}c = 20$

39. $\tfrac{1}{3}y = 3\tfrac{2}{3}$

40. $\tfrac{3}{4}z = -5\tfrac{1}{2}$

41. $-\tfrac{2}{5}x = -4$

42. $-\tfrac{2}{3}y = -4$

43. $\tfrac{x}{4} = 2$

44. $\tfrac{c}{7} = 15$

45. $\tfrac{x}{2} = -3$

46. $\tfrac{n}{-1} = -2$

47. $\tfrac{t}{2} = \tfrac{1}{2}$

48. $\tfrac{m}{-4} = -\tfrac{3}{4}$

49. *Checkbook Balance*   You thought the balance in your checkbook was $53, but when your bank statement arrived, you realized that you forgot to record a check. The bank says you have a balance of $47. Let x represent the value of the check that you forgot to record. Which of the following is a correct model for the situation? Solve the correct equation.

 a. $x + 47 = 53$ **b.** $x - 47 = 53$

50. *Bonus Points*   Suppose that a math test that you took had 100 regular points and 10 bonus points. You received a total score of 83, which included a 7-point bonus. Let x represent the score you would have had without the bonus. Which of the following is a correct model for this situation? Solve the correct equation.

 a. $x + 83 = 100$ **b.** $x + 7 = 83$

Similar Triangles   **In Exercises 51 and 52, the two triangles are similar. Find the length of the side marked x.**

51.

52.

Balanced Beam   **In Exercises 53 and 54, use the following information.**

For a uniform beam to balance on a fulcrum, as shown at the right, the ratio of the larger weight to the smaller weight must be equal to the ratio of the larger distance to the smaller distance.

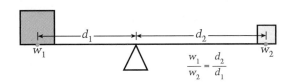

53. Two children, weighing 50 pounds and 70 pounds, are on a teeter-totter shown below. To balance, how far from the center should the 70-pound child sit?

54. You want to lift a 300-pound block shown below. You weigh 100 pounds. How far from the fulcrum should you be?

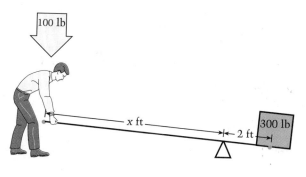

55. Baking A recipe for holiday bread calls for 6 cups of flour and 2 cups of sugar. You have only $4\frac{1}{2}$ cups of flour. You want to reduce the amount of sugar by the same proportion. Let x represent the amount of sugar you should use. Which of the following is a correct model for this situation? Solve the correct equation.

a. $\dfrac{x}{2} = \dfrac{4\frac{1}{2}}{6}$ **b.** $\dfrac{x}{2} = \dfrac{6}{4\frac{1}{2}}$

56. Recycling Newspaper You are asked to load a large pile of newspapers onto a truck. You decide to divide the pile into three smaller piles that each weigh 41 pounds. Let x represent the weight of the original pile. Which of the following is a correct model for this situation? Solve the correct equation.

a. $3x = 41$ **b.** $\dfrac{x}{3} = 41$

57. Day-Care Cost In 1990, the average weekly cost of day care in New York City was 190% of the average weekly cost of day care in Little Rock, Arkansas. The average weekly cost in New York was $95. Let x represent the Little Rock cost. Write an equation involving x and solve the equation. (**Source: Runzheimer International**)

58. Day-Care Cost In 1990, the average weekly cost of day care in Mobile, Alabama, was $\frac{14}{29}$ of the average weekly cost of day care in Minneapolis, Minnesota. The average weekly cost in Minneapolis was $87. Let x represent the Mobile cost. Write an equation involving x and solve the equation.

Integrated Review

In Exercises 59–78, evaluate the expression.

59. $-8 - 4 = -12$ **60.** $-3 + 7$

63. $3(6 - 2) = 12$ **64.** $(-4 + 1)(-2)$

67. $(-12)\left(\frac{3}{2}\right) = -18$ **68.** $(8)\left(-\frac{1}{2}\right)$

71. $\left(-\frac{3}{2}\right)\left(\frac{-2}{3}\right)$ **72.** $\left(\frac{4}{3}\right)\left(-\frac{3}{4}\right)$

75. $-8 \div 2 = -4$ **76.** $18 \div 6$

61. $-9 + 5 = -4$ **62.** $-5 + 9$

65. $(7 - 11)4 = -16$ **66.** $-5(8 + 2)$

69. $(-5)(-11) = 55$ **70.** $(6)(-13)$

73. $\left(\frac{1}{2}\right)\left(\frac{6}{4}\right) = \frac{3}{4}$ **74.** $\left(\frac{2}{7}\right)\left(\frac{7}{4}\right)$

77. $3.75 \div 0.25 = 15$ **78.** $10.6 \div 0.4$

Exploration and Extension

79. The perimeter of parallelogram $MATH$ below is 168. Find the lengths of its sides.

80. What is the greatest area of rectangle $QUAD$ below if x is chosen from $\{3, 5, 7\}$?

In Exercises 81–84, solve the equation.

81. $+(-x) = 15$ **82.** $-(-3x) = -21$

83. $-3 = x + (-7)$ **84.** $-|-8| = 15 - x$

3.2

Solving Equations Using Two or More Transformations

What you should learn:

Goal How to use two or more transformations to solve an equation

Why you should learn it:

You will need to use two or more transformations to solve most equations, such as formulas, that model real-life situations.

Goal **Using Two or More Transformations**

In Lesson 3.1, you solved equations using one transformation. Many equations, however, require two or more transformations. Here are some guidelines that can help you decide how to start. Once you have found a solution, check it in the original equation.

1. Simplify both sides of the equation (if needed).

2. Use inverse operations to isolate the variable.

Example 1 *Finding and Checking a Solution*

Solve $\frac{1}{3}x + 6 = -8$.

Solution Remember that your goal is to isolate the variable.

$\frac{1}{3}x + 6 = -8$	*Rewrite original equation.*
$\frac{1}{3}x + 6 - 6 = -8 - 6$	*Subtract 6 from both sides.*
$\frac{1}{3}x = -14$	*Simplify.*
$3\left(\frac{1}{3}x\right) = 3(-14)$	*Multiply both sides by 3.*
$x = -42$	*Simplify.*

Check Check that -42 satisfies the original equation.

$$\frac{1}{3}(-42) + 6 \stackrel{?}{=} -8 \qquad \textit{Substitute } -42 \textit{ for x.}$$

Because both sides equal -8, the solution is correct. ∎

Example 2 *Combining Like Terms First*

Solve $7x - 3x - 8 = 24$.

Solution

$7x - 3x - 8 = 24$	*Rewrite original equation.*
$4x - 8 = 24$	*Combine like terms 7x and $-3x$.*
$4x - 8 + 8 = 24 + 8$	*Add 8 to both sides.*
$4x = 32$	*Simplify.*
$\frac{4x}{4} = \frac{32}{4}$	*Divide both sides by 4.*
$x = 8$	*Simplify.*

The solution is 8. Check this in the original equation. ∎

Some solution steps can be performed mentally. In Example 3, the solution on the left shows all steps. The format on the right allows you to indicate your solution process but shows less work.

Example 3 *A Format for the "Expert" Equation Solver*

Solve $5x + 3(x + 4) = 28$.

Solution

All Steps Shown

$$5x + 3(x + 4) = 28$$
$$5x + 3x + 12 = 28$$
$$8x + 12 = 28$$
$$8x + 12 - 12 = 28 - 12$$
$$8x = 16$$
$$\frac{8x}{8} = \frac{16}{8}$$
$$x = 2$$

Steps Showing Process Only

$$5x + 3(x + 4) = 28$$
$$5x + 3x + 12 = 28$$
$$8x + 12 = 28$$
$$8x = 16 \quad \textit{Subtract 12.}$$
$$x = 2 \quad \textit{Divide by 8.}$$

The solution is 2. Check this in the original equation. ■

Example 4 *Showing the Process Only*

Solve $18 - (x + 2) = 21$.

Solution

$$18 - (x + 2) = 21 \quad \textit{Rewrite original equation.}$$
$$18 - x - 2 = 21 \quad \textit{Opposite of a sum}$$
$$16 - x = 21 \quad \textit{Simplify.}$$
$$-x = 5 \quad \textit{Subtract 16 from both sides.}$$
$$x = -5 \quad \textit{Divide both sides by } -1.$$

The solution is -5. Check this in the original equation. ■

Example 5 *Showing the Process Only*

Solve $-28 = 2(x + 3) - 5(x - 1)$.

Solution

$$-28 = 2(x + 3) - 5(x - 1) \quad \textit{Rewrite original equation.}$$
$$-28 = 2x + 6 - 5x + 5 \quad \textit{Distributive Property}$$
$$-28 = -3x + 11 \quad \textit{Combine like terms.}$$
$$-39 = -3x \quad \textit{Subtract 11 from both sides.}$$
$$13 = x \quad \textit{Divide both sides by } -3.$$

The solution is 13. Check this in the original equation. ■

Example 6 Multiplying by a Reciprocal First

Solve $66 = -\frac{6}{5}(x + 3)$.

Solution

$$66 = -\frac{6}{5}(x + 3) \qquad \text{\textit{Rewrite original equation.}}$$

$$\left(-\frac{5}{6}\right)(66) = \left(-\frac{5}{6}\right)\left(-\frac{6}{5}\right)(x + 3) \qquad \text{\textit{Multiply by reciprocal of} } -\frac{6}{5}.$$

$$-55 = x + 3 \qquad \text{\textit{Simplify.}}$$

$$-58 = x \qquad \text{\textit{Subtract 3 from both sides.}}$$

The solution is -58. Check this in the original equation. ∎

Real Life
Physiology

In the U.S., normal body temperature is given as 98.6°F. Most other countries state normal body temperature in degrees Celsius.

Example 7 Normal Body Temperature

The Fahrenheit and Celsius scales are related by the formula $F = \frac{9}{5}C + 32$. What is normal body temperature on the Celsius scale? Does a temperature of 38.5°C indicate a fever?

Solution Begin by substituting the normal body temperature of 98.6° for F in the equation $F = \frac{9}{5}C + 32$. Then, solve the resulting equation for C.

$$F = \frac{9}{5}C + 32 \qquad \text{\textit{Known formula}}$$

$$98.6 = \frac{9}{5}C + 32 \qquad \text{\textit{Substitute 98.6 for F.}}$$

$$66.6 = \frac{9}{5}C \qquad \text{\textit{Subtract 32 from both sides.}}$$

$$\frac{5}{9}(66.6) = \frac{5}{9}\left(\frac{9}{5}C\right) \qquad \text{\textit{Multiply by reciprocal of} } \frac{9}{5}.$$

$$37 = C \qquad \text{\textit{Simplify.}}$$

Thus, on the Celsius scale, normal body temperature is 37°C. A person with a temperature of 38.5°C would have a fever. ∎

Communicating about ALGEBRA

▶ **SHARING IDEAS about the Lesson**

Understanding Errors Your friend has written the following solution steps, but the answers don't agree with those given in the back of the book. Is the book wrong or did your friend make mistakes? Correct any mistakes you find and explain what your friend did wrong.

A. $2(x - 3) = 5$
$2x - 6 = 5$
$2x = 11$
$x = 4$

B. $5 - 3x = 10$
$-2x = 10$
$3x = 5$

C. $\frac{1}{4}x - 2 = 7$
$x - 2 = 28$
$x = 30$

EXERCISES

▶ **CRITICAL THINKING about the Lesson**

1. What is the first step you would use to solve $2x + 1 = 9$?

2. Check whether -3 is a solution of $2x + 4 = -2$.

3. Find the error(s) in the solution steps shown.

$$10x + 8 = -2$$
$$10x = 6$$
$$x = \frac{3}{5}$$

4. For the equation $\frac{4}{3}(x + 2) = 16$, which of the following steps would you use first? Explain.

  a. Apply the Distributive Property to the left side.

  b. Multiply both sides of the equation by the reciprocal of $\frac{4}{3}$.

Independent Practice

In Exercises 5–10, check whether the number is a solution of the equation.

5. $x - 10 = 16,\quad 6$

6. $\frac{1}{2}x - 9 = -2,\quad 14$

7. $\frac{2}{3}x + 1 = -5,\quad -9$

8. $4x - \frac{1}{2} = -\frac{3}{2},\quad -\frac{1}{2}$

9. $\frac{3x}{5} + 1 = 7,\quad -10$

10. $-4 - \frac{x}{9} = -8,\quad 36$

In Exercises 11–34, solve the equation.

11. $3x - 7 = 23$

12. $2x + 5 = 9$

13. $\frac{1}{4}x + 2 = 3$

14. $\frac{1}{2}x - 1 = -1$

15. $6 = 14 - 2x$

16. $9 - \frac{2}{3}x = -1$

17. $-4 + \frac{4}{5}x = -6$

18. $3x + \frac{1}{2} = -1$

19. $\frac{4x}{3} + 5 = -3$

20. $16 = 2 - \frac{2x}{5}$

21. $4x - 3x = 9$

22. $-6x + 4x = 2$

23. $x + 5x - 5 = 1$

24. $3x - 7 + x = 5$

25. $-2 = \frac{2x}{3} - x$

26. $-10 = \frac{1}{2}x + x$

27. $3(x - 2) = 18$

28. $12(2 - x) = 6$

29. $19 = 2(x + 1) - x$

30. $6 = \frac{3}{2}x + \frac{1}{2}(x - 4)$

31. $3x + \frac{3}{2}(2x - 1) = 2$

32. $55x - 3(9x + 12) = -64$

33. $\frac{9}{2}(x + 3) = 27$

34. $\frac{4}{9}(2x - 4) = 48$

35. *Hours of Labor* The bill (parts and labor) for the repair of an automobile was $357. The cost for parts was $285. The cost of labor was $32 per hour. Let x represent the number of hours of labor. Write an equation involving x and solve the equation to find the number of hours of labor.

36. *Band Fund-Raiser* Your school band sold stationery for $12 a box. The profit, P, in dollars is given by $P = 12x - 3640$, where x is the number of boxes sold. If the band made a profit of $2600, how many boxes of stationery were sold?

37. *Height of a Fountain* The upward velocity of the water in the stream of a particular fountain is given by the formula $v = -32t + 28$, where t is the number of seconds after the water leaves the fountain. While going upward, the water slows down until, at the top of the stream, the water has a velocity of zero. How long does it take each particle of water to reach the maximum height?

38. *Using the Problem-Solving Plan* An office is making 6 copies of a report that has 500 pages. One photocopier can copy 300 pages in an hour. The other photocopier is faster and can copy 500 pages in an hour. To find the time it would take the two copiers together to complete the project, you could construct the following verbal model.

Rate for 1st machine	·	Time to complete	+	Rate for 2nd machine	·	Time to complete	=	Total pages

Assign labels to this model to form an equation. Then solve the equation.

39. *Time to Complete a Project* Two people are working on a project. The first can complete $\frac{1}{6}$ of the project in an hour, and the second can complete $\frac{1}{8}$ of the project in an hour. How many hours would it take each person working *separately* to complete the project? Find the number of hours it would take them *together* to complete the project by solving the following equation for t.

$$\tfrac{1}{8}t + \tfrac{1}{6}t = 1$$

40. *Temperature in Quito* What is the average temperature in Quito, Ecuador, in degrees Celsius?

Quito, Ecuador, lies in the Andes highlands where the weather is springlike all year, and the average temperature is 57°F.

41. *Perimeter of a Rectangle* The length of a rectangle is 3 times its width, which means that the perimeter is given by

$$P = 2w + 2(3w),$$

where w is the width of the rectangle. The perimeter is 16 meters. What is the width?

42. *Distance on a Line* Solve for x in the figure at the right.

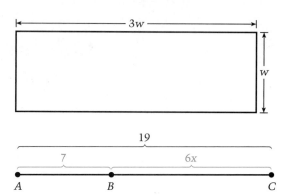

Integrated Review

In Exercises 43–50, evaluate the expression.

43. $2x + 4x$, when $x = 4$

44. $91y - 4 - 62y$, when $y = 2$

45. $s^2 - 2s + 1$, when $s = 3$

46. $42 - t^2$, when $t = 8$

47. $16 + 9x - 12y - x$, when $x = 1$ and $y = 2$

48. $3x - 4y + 9$, when $x = 4$ and $y = 4$

49. $4.9s - 12.1 + 9.7t$, when $s = 3.2$ and $t = 1.7$

50. $61.5 - 48.1x + 48.1y$, when $x = 2.2$ and $y = 0.3$

Exploration and Extension

51. *College Entrance Exam Sample* If $x(p + 1) = m$, then $p = \boxed{?}$

a. $m - 1$ **b.** m **c.** $\dfrac{m - 1}{x}$ **d.** $m - x - 1$ **e.** $\dfrac{m}{x} - 1$

52. Are the solution steps at the right correct? If not, explain the error(s) and write a correct set of solution steps.

$$6x + 12 = 18$$
$$6x + 12 - 12 = 18$$
$$6x = 18$$
$$x = 3$$

In Exercises 53–58, solve the equation two different ways. For each exercise, explain which method you prefer and why.

Sample: $\frac{1}{9}x + 1 = 4$

Method 1: Multiply first, subtract second.

$$\frac{1}{9}x + 1 = 4$$
$$x + 9 = 36$$
$$x = 27$$

Method 2: Subtract first, multiply second.

$$\frac{1}{9}x + 1 = 4$$
$$\frac{1}{9}x = 3$$
$$x = 27$$

53. $\frac{2}{3}x + 1 = \frac{1}{3}$

54. $\frac{1}{2}x - \frac{1}{4} = \frac{3}{4}$

55. $\frac{1}{2}(3x - 7) = 4$

56. $\frac{6}{11}(x - 4) = -36$

57. $-56 = \frac{8}{9}(4 - x)$

58. $-9 = \frac{3}{7}(-2x + 5)$

3.3

Solving Equations with Variables on Both Sides

What you should learn:

Goal 1 How to collect variables on one side of an equation

Goal 2 How to use algebraic models to answer questions about real-life situations

Why you should learn it:

You will need to write and solve equations with the variable on both sides for some real-life situations such as comparing costs.

Goal 1 Collecting Variables on One Side

Some equations have variables on both sides.

$$73 - 5x = 7x - 11, \quad 7(2 - m) = 3m + 4,$$
$$-7a = -12a - 65$$

The strategy for solving such equations is to *collect like variables* on the same side. Some people prefer to collect like variables on the left side, but we prefer the following guideline which avoids a negative coefficient.

- Collect variables on the side with the greater variable coefficient.

For instance, in the equation $x + 4 = 2x - 6$, the term $2x$ has a greater coefficient than x, so you can avoid a negative coefficient by collecting variables on the right.

Collect Variables on Right (Subtract x from both sides.)	**Collect Variables on Left** (Subtract $2x$ from both sides.)
$x + 4 = 2x - 6$	$x + 4 = 2x - 6$
$x + 4 - x = 2x - 6 - x$	$x + 4 - 2x = 2x - 6 - 2x$
$4 = x - 6$	$-x + 4 = -6$
$10 = x$	$-x = -10$
	$x = 10$

Example 1 Solving an Equation with Variables on Both Sides

Solve $7x + 19 = -2x + 55$.

Solution

$$
\begin{aligned}
7x + 19 &= -2x + 55 && \textit{Rewrite original equation.} \\
2x + 7x + 19 &= 2x - 2x + 55 && \textit{Add 2x to both sides.} \\
9x + 19 &= 55 && \textit{Simplify.} \\
9x + 19 - 19 &= 55 - 19 && \textit{Subtract 19 from both sides.} \\
9x &= 36 && \textit{Simplify.} \\
\frac{9x}{9} &= \frac{36}{9} && \textit{Divide both sides by 9.} \\
x &= 4 && \textit{Simplify.}
\end{aligned}
$$

The solution is 4. Check this in the original equation. ∎

In the next example, the steps that can be done with mental math are not shown.

Example 2 | *Showing the Process Only*

Solve $80 - 6y = 4y$.

Solution

$80 - 6y = 4y$	*Rewrite original equation.*
$80 = 10y$	*Add 6y to both sides.*
$8 = y$	*Divide both sides by 10.*

The solution is 8. Check this in the original equation, ■

The three equations in the next example are a little tricky. Be sure you can follow the steps that are shown.

Example 3 | *Solving More Complicated Equations*

a.

$4(1 - x) + 3x = -2(x + 1)$	*Original equation*
$4 - 4x + 3x = -2x - 2$	*Distributive Property*
$4 - x = -2x - 2$	*Combine like terms.*
$4 + x = -2$	*Add 2x to both sides.*
$x = -6$	*Subtract 4 from both sides.*

The solution is -6. Check this in the original equation.

b.

$\frac{1}{4}(12x + 16) = 10 - 3(x - 2)$	*Original equation*
$3x + 4 = 10 - 3x + 6$	*Distributive Property*
$3x + 4 = 16 - 3x$	*Combine like terms.*
$6x + 4 = 16$	*Add 3x to both sides.*
$6x = 12$	*Subtract 4 from both sides.*
$x = 2$	*Divide both sides by 6.*

The solution is 2. Check this in the original equation.

c.

$7(2 - x) = 5x$	*Original equation*
$14 - 7x = 5x$	*Distributive Property*
$14 = 12x$	*Add 7x to both sides.*
$\frac{14}{12} = x$	*Divide both sides by 12.*
$\frac{7}{6} = x$	*Reduce fraction.*

The solution is $\frac{7}{6}$. Check this in the original equation. ■

At most clubs, members get the club's services more cheaply than nonmembers, but before joining, you should decide how much you will use these services.

Example 4 *Using the Problem-Solving Plan*

A local store charges $8 to rent a video game for three days. You must be a member to rent from the store, but the membership is free. A video-game club in town charges only $3 to rent a game for three days, but membership in the club is $50 a year. Which membership is more economical?

Solution To decide which is more economical, find the number of rentals for which the two plans would cost the same.

Verbal Model

| Club rental | · | Number rented | + | Memb. fee | = | Store rental | · | Number rented |

⎴ Video Club ⎴ Video Store

Labels
Club rental fee = 3   (dollars per game)
Number rented = x (games)
Club membership fee = 50   (dollars)
Store rental fee = 8   (dollars per game)

Equation
$3x + 50 = 8x$ *Algebraic model*
$50 = 5x$ *Subtract 3x, both sides.*
$10 = x$ *Divide both sides by 5.*

Renting 10 video games in a year would cost the same at the club or the store. Renting more than 10, the club is more economical. Renting less than 10, the store is more economical. ■

By 1990, Nintendo, Sega Genesis, Gameboy, and Atari had produced over 2000 video games.

Communicating about ALGEBRA

▶ **SHARING IDEAS about the Lesson**

Understanding the Process

A. Write the steps you use to solve $-3x + 5 = 9x - 19$. Beside each step, write an explanation of the step. Then show how to check your answer.

[handwritten: 19 + 5 = 12x - 19; 24 = 12x + 19; x = 2]

B. Which step would you do first to solve the equation $6y - (3y - 6) = -14 + 5y$? Explain your answer.

[handwritten: The work in the brackets.]

EXERCISES

Guided Practice

▶ **CRITICAL THINKING about the Lesson**

1. True or False? When solving an equation with variables on both sides, it is convenient to collect the variables on the side with the *smaller* variable coefficient. Explain. _False. To keep them involving neg. #s._

2. True or False? The solution of $x = 2x$ is zero. Explain. _Subtract x from both side._
$$0 = x$$ _True._

Exercises 3–6 refer to solving the equation $(9 - x)9 = 4x - 10$.

3. After rewriting the equation, what would be your first step? Perform this step. $81 - 9x = 4x - 10$

4. Once you obtain $81 - 9x = 4x - 10$, should you subtract $4x$ from both sides or add $9x$ to both sides? Why? Perform this step. $81 = 13x - 10$

5. Once you obtain $81 = 13x - 10$, what should the next step be? Perform this step.

6. Solve for x. Check your result in the original equation.

Independent Practice

In Exercises 7–12, describe the first step you would use to solve the equation.

7. $x + 2 = 3x - 1$ 　　　 **8.** $-4x + 7 = 2x - 5$ 　　　 **9.** $6y - 18 = 12$ 　　　 **10.** $-16 + 4y = 11$

11. $7(1 - y) + 4y = -3(y + 2)$ 　　　 **12.** $10(2y - 4) = -1(6 - 9y) + 3y$

In Exercises 13–36, solve the equation. Check your result.

13. $4x + 27 = 3x$ 　　　　　　 **14.** $8y + 14 = 6y$ 　　　　　　 **15.** $-2m = 16m - 9$

16. $7n = -35n - 6$ 　　　　　 **17.** $12c - 4 = 4c$ 　　　　　　 **18.** $-25d + 10 = 15d$

19. $5r + 6 = -14r - 13$ 　　　 **20.** $7s - 8 = 10s + 1$ 　　　　 **21.** $12p - 7 = -3p + 8$

22. $-6q + 8 = 4q - 12$ 　　　 **23.** $-7 + 4m = 6m - 5$ 　　　 **24.** $-9 + 13g = 11 - g$

25. $8 - 9t = 21t - 17$ 　　　　 **26.** $20 + 8r = -4 + 5r$ 　　　 **27.** $6(3 - x) = 3x$

28. $-2(x - 5) = -x$ 　　　　　 **29.** $(-4 + y)10 = 2y$ 　　　　 **30.** $(-6a - 2)4 = 16a$

31. $9(b - 4) = 5(3b - 2)$ 　　 **32.** $-4(3 - n) = 11(4n - 3)$ 　 **33.** $\frac{1}{2}(8n - 2) = 16 - 30n$

34. $\frac{1}{3}(42 - 18z) = 2(8 - 4z)$ 　 **35.** $\frac{1}{4}(100 + 36s) = 15 - 4s$ 　 **36.** $\frac{2}{3}(24t - 9) = 8t + 23$

37. *Bike Safety* 　 Suppose you live near a park that has a bike trail you like to ride. The Park Department rents a bike with safety equipment for $5 a day. If you provide your own safety equipment, the bike rental is $3 a day. You could buy the equipment at a sports store for $28. How many times must you use the trail to justify buying your own safety equipment?

38. *Catching Up with Sis*   Kate is always reminding her younger brother Tony that she is taller than he is. Kate is 63 inches tall and is growing at a rate of $\frac{1}{3}$ inch per year. Tony is 60 inches tall and is growing at the rate of $2\frac{1}{3}$ inches per year. To find how long it will take for Tony to catch up with Kate, assign labels to the following verbal model, write the algebraic model, and solve it.

| Tony's height now | + | Tony's rate of growth | · | Number of years | = | Kate's height now | + | Kate's rate of growth | · | Number of years |

Summer Swimming   **In Exercises 39 and 40, use the following information.**

A new swimming pool is opening for 15 weeks during the summer. You can swim in the afternoon for $3 or buy a membership for $80 and pay only $1 for the afternoon session. Let *s* equal the number of times you go swimming. You are trying to decide whether to buy a membership or buy daily passes.

39. Which equation is a correct model for this problem?

    a. $1s + 80 = 3s$ **b.** $3s + 80 = s$ **c.** $3s = s - 80$

40. Solve the correct equation in Exercise 39 and interpret the solution.

Remote-Control Cars   **In Exercises 41 and 42, use the following information.**

The Fast Track company manufactures toy remote-control race cars, which it sells for $18 each. The production cost for the company is $2000 per day plus $13 per race car. Let *n* be the number of race cars sold in a day. The company needs to know how many cars it must sell in a day to break even.

41. Which equation is a correct model for this problem?

    a. $18n + 2000 = 13n$ **b.** $18n = 13n - 2000$ **c.** $18n = 13n + 2000$

42. Solve the correct equation in Exercise 41 and interpret its solution.

Integrated Review

In Exercises 43–48, simplify the expression.

43. $x - 2(x - 1)$ **44.** $4 - 3(2x - 2)$ **45.** $2(6 + 3x) - 8$

46. $-4(2 + 5y) + 10$ **47.** $7x[2 - (-5)] - 3x$ **48.** $-4m[-2 - (-6)] - 11(m + 1)$

In Exercises 49–54, decide whether the number is a solution of the equation.

49. $8(2 - x) = -4x$, 4   **50.** $-6(7 - a) = 4a$, 5   **51.** $\frac{1}{3}x + 10 = -12$, 7

52. $12 - \frac{1}{4}x = 32$, -80 **53.** $\frac{1}{2}x - 8 = \frac{1}{2}(x - 8)$, 18   **54.** $27 + 6x = 3x - 9$, -6

In Exercises 55–60, find any mistakes in the solution steps. If there are none, write *correct*. If there is a mistake, find the correct solution.

55.
$$20x - 4 = 6$$
$$20x - 4 + 4 = 6 + 4$$
$$20x = 10$$
$$x = 2$$

56.
$$-15 = 7x + 13$$
$$-15 - 13 = 7x + 13 - 13$$
$$\frac{-28}{7} = \frac{7x}{7}$$
$$x = -4$$

57.
$$-3(y + 12) = 51$$
$$-3y + 12 = 51$$
$$-3y = 39$$
$$y = -13$$

58.
$$(b - 4)8 = -12$$
$$b - 32 = -12$$
$$b = 20$$

59.
$$8y(4 - 1) = 2y - 6$$
$$24y = 6y - 6$$
$$30y = -6$$
$$y = -\frac{1}{5}$$

60.
$$(c + 6)7 = (4 - c)3$$
$$7c + 42 = 12 - 3c$$
$$10c = 30$$
$$c = 3$$

In Exercises 61 and 62, try to solve the equation for *x*. Does the equation have no solution, exactly one solution, or many solutions?

61. $3(4 - x) = -2x + 12 - x$

62. $8x - [4 - (-2)] = 8x$

63. Solve for *a*, *b*, *c*, and *d*.
$$\begin{bmatrix} 2a - 3 & -4b + 2 \\ -17c + 7 & 3d - 19 \end{bmatrix} = \begin{bmatrix} -4a + 7 & 6b - 23 \\ 93c - 153 & 14 - 3(d - 1) \end{bmatrix}$$

Mixed **REVIEW**

1. Write 5% in fraction form. **(1.1)**

2. Write 67% in decimal form. **(1.1)**

3. What is the quotient of 27 and 3? **(1.1)**

4. What is the product of $\frac{4}{3}$ and 9? **(1.1)**

5. Simplify $\frac{1}{3}(6 - 2x) - 4(1 + \frac{1}{3}x)$. **(2.3, 2.6)**

6. Simplify $(3x \div \frac{1}{2}) \div 6$. **(1.2)**

7. Use exponents to write $3 \cdot 3 \cdot x \cdot x \cdot x$. **(1.3)**

8. What is the absolute value of -32? **(2.1)**

9. What is the reciprocal of $-\frac{2}{7}$? **(2.7)**

10. What is the opposite of 15.3? **(2.1)**

11. Are 3 and 4 solutions of $3x - 4 \leq 6$? **(1.5)**

12. Evaluate $\frac{1}{2}(y + 6) \cdot 4y$ when $y = 1$. **(1.2)**

13. Write an expression for the perimeter of a rectangle whose length is $3\frac{1}{2}$ times its width. **(1.2)**

14. Insert grouping symbols so that $-9 + 4 \cdot x - 6$ has a value of -25 when $x = 11$. **(1.1, 1.2)**

In Exercises 15 and 16, translate into expressions, equations, or inequalities.

15. Two less than the sum of 3 times a number is less than 12. **(1.6)**

16. A number plus the product of 5 and another number. **(1.6)**

3.4

Linear Equations and Problem Solving

What you should learn:

Goal How to use a problem-solving plan for problems that fit linear models

Why you should learn it:

You can use linear models for many real-life situations such as comparing two quantities that are changing at different rates.

Real Life
Wildlife

Goal	**Using a Problem-Solving Plan**

In Lesson 1.7, you studied a general problem-solving plan.

Write a verbal model. → Assign labels. → Write an algebraic model. → Solve algebraic model. → Answer the question.

Remember that talking about a problem with another person is a good way to learn to form verbal models and to assign labels.

Example 1 *The Gazelle and the Cheetah*

A gazelle can run 73 feet per second for several minutes. A cheetah can run faster, but can only sustain its top speed for about 20 seconds. Gazelles seem to have an instinct for this difference because they will not run from a prowling cheetah until it enters their "safety zone." This is the distance the cheetah would need to run to overtake the gazelle in 20 seconds if both are running at top speed. How close should the gazelle let the cheetah come before it runs?

Solution During a 20-second run, the cheetah can travel $(88)(20)$ feet, and the gazelle can travel $(73)(20)$ feet. For the gazelle to outdistance the cheetah, it must start with a buffer distance.

Verbal Model

Gazelle's distance	+	Buffer distance	=	Cheetah's distance

Labels
Gazelle's distance = $(73)(20)$ (ft)
Cheetah's distance = $(88)(20)$ (ft)
Buffer distance = x (ft)

Equation
$(73)(20) + x = (88)(20)$ *Algebraic model*
$1460 + x = 1760$ *Simplify.*
$x = 300$ *Subtract 1460 from both sides.*

Thus, the gazelle should not let the cheetah get closer than 300 feet (the length of a football field). ∎

The long body and slender legs of the cheetah make it the fastest animal for running short distances. It can reach a speed of about 88 feet per second.

Example 2 *High School Enrollments*

Cleveland High is in a city, and West Lake High is in one of the city's suburbs. Cleveland High's enrollment has been decreasing at an average rate of 75 students per year, whereas West Lake High's enrollment has been increasing at an average rate of 60 students per year. Cleveland High has 3150 students, and West Lake High has 2475. If enrollments continue to change at the same rates, when will the two schools have the same number of students?

Solution   For each school, the change in enrollment is given by the rate per year times the number of years. Because Cleveland High's enrollment is decreasing, you subtract the change, and because West Lake High's enrollment is increasing, you add the change.

Verbal Model

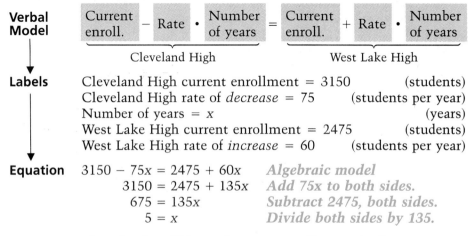

Cleveland High   West Lake High

Labels   Cleveland High current enrollment = 3150   (students)
Cleveland High rate of *decrease* = 75   (students per year)
Number of years = x (years)
West Lake High current enrollment = 2475   (students)
West Lake High rate of *increase* = 60   (students per year)

Equation
$$3150 - 75x = 2475 + 60x \qquad \textit{Algebraic model}$$
$$3150 = 2475 + 135x \qquad \textit{Add 75x to both sides.}$$
$$675 = 135x \qquad \textit{Subtract 2475, both sides.}$$
$$5 = x \qquad \textit{Divide both sides by 135.}$$

The schools will have the same enrollments in five years.   ■

The enrollment information in Example 2 is a good candidate for a bar graph. Notice how the bar graph shown below helps you "see" the changing enrollments at the two schools.

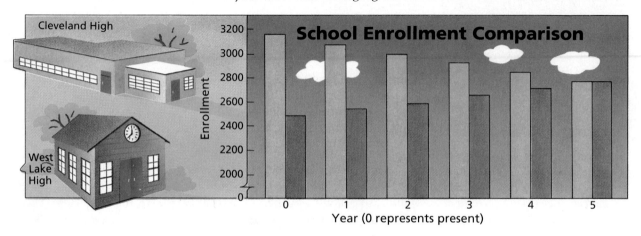

Cleveland High

West Lake High

School Enrollment Comparison

Enrollment

Year (0 represents present)

Real Life
Page Design

Example 3 **Designing a High School Yearbook**

The page of your school yearbook is $8\frac{1}{2}$ inches by 11 inches. The left and right margins are $\frac{3}{4}$ inch and $2\frac{7}{8}$ inches, respectively. The space between pictures is $\frac{3}{16}$ inch. How wide should you make each picture to fit three across the page?

Solution The total page width is made up of the widths of the left and right margins, 2 spaces, and 3 picture widths.

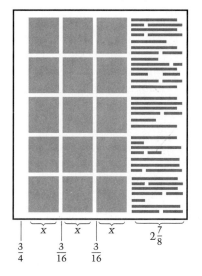

Verbal Model

| Margin widths | $+ 2 \cdot$ | Picture space | $+ 3 \cdot$ | Picture width | $=$ | Total width |

Labels

Margin width $= \frac{3}{4} + 2\frac{7}{8} = \frac{3}{4} + \frac{23}{8} = \frac{29}{8}$ (inches)

Picture-space width $= \frac{3}{16}$ (inches)

Picture width $= x$ (inches)

Total width $= 8\frac{1}{2}$ (inches)

Equation

$$\frac{29}{8} + 2\left(\frac{3}{16}\right) + 3x = 8\frac{1}{2} \qquad \textit{Algebraic model}$$

$$\frac{29}{8} + \frac{3}{8} + 3x = \frac{17}{2} \qquad \textit{Rewrite fractions.}$$

$$\frac{32}{8} + 3x = \frac{17}{2} \qquad \textit{Simplify } \frac{29}{8} + \frac{3}{8}.$$

$$3x = \frac{17}{2} - \frac{32}{8} \qquad \textit{Subtract } \frac{32}{8}, \textit{ both sides.}$$

$$3x = \frac{17}{2} - \frac{8}{2} \qquad \textit{Like denominators}$$

$$3x = \frac{9}{2} \qquad \textit{Simplify } \frac{17}{2} - \frac{8}{2}.$$

$$x = \frac{3}{2} \qquad \textit{Divide both sides by 3.}$$

Thus, each picture should be $1\frac{1}{2}$ inches wide. ◼

$\mathcal{C}ommunicating$ *about* **ALGEBRA**

▶ **SHARING IDEAS about the Lesson**

Extend the Problem Consider the page-design problem above.

A. The margins at the top and bottom of the page are $\frac{7}{8}$ inch each. The vertical space between pictures is $\frac{3}{16}$ inch. How high is each picture?

B. What is the width-to-height ratio of each photo?

C. Is this the same ratio as a photo that is 8 inches by 10 inches? If not, will you have to "crop" (trim) photos that are reduced from 8-by-10 originals?

EXERCISES

▶ **CRITICAL THINKING about the Lesson**

Running a Race   **In Exercises 1–4, use the following information.**

Two runners are running on a 21-kilometer course. The first runs at 10 kilometers per hour, and the second runs at 15 kilometers per hour. If the first runner is 7 kilometers past the starting line before the second runner starts, how far does each run before they are side by side? Use the following verbal model.

Rate of 1st runner	·	Time after 2nd runner starts	+	Distance advantage of 1st runner	=	Rate of 2nd runner	·	Time after 2nd runner starts

1. Assign labels to each part of the verbal model. Indicate the units of measure.
2. Write an algebraic equation.
3. Solve the equation. Interpret its solution.
4. How far does each run before they are side by side?

Independent Practice

Left Behind   **In Exercises 5–8, use the following information and the caption to the photograph.**

An elephant herd is migrating to greener plains. The herd is moving at about 10 miles an hour. One elephant strays from the herd, stops, and is left behind. Then it senses danger and begins running to catch up with the herd. It takes the stray elephant 5 minutes to reach the others. How far had the herd traveled when the stray elephant became frightened?

5. Write a verbal model for this problem.
6. Assign labels to each part of the model. Indicate the units of measure.
7. Write an equation that represents the model.
8. Solve the equation and answer the question.

An angry or a frightened elephant can run at a speed of about 25 miles per hour.

From 1987 to 1988 in the United States, the population of the western region increased by 982,000 and that of the midwest region increased by 222,000. In 1988, the population of the western region was 50,679,000 and that of the midwest region was 58,878,000. If the populations continue to change at the same rates, when will the populations of the western region and the midwest region be the same?

9. Write a verbal model for this problem.

10. Assign labels to each part of the model.

11. Write an equation that represents the model.

12. Solve the equation. What year will the populations be the same?

Cover Design   **In Exercises 13–17, use the following information.**

You want to include four photos on the cover of a program for the school play, two across the page. The cover is $6\frac{1}{2}$ inches wide, and the left and right margins are $\frac{3}{4}$ inch each. The space between the pictures is $\frac{1}{2}$ inch. How wide should you make the pictures?

13. Sketch a diagram of the cover.

14. Write a verbal model for this problem.

15. Assign labels to the model. Indicate the units of measure.

16. Write an equation that represents the model.

17. Solve the equation and answer the question.

Saving and Spending   **In Exercises 18–21, use the following information.**

Currently, you have $60 and your sister has $135. You decide to save $5 of your allowance each week, whereas your sister decides to spend her whole allowance plus $10 each week. How long will it be before you have as much money as your sister?

18. Write a verbal model for this problem.

19. Assign labels to the verbal model.

20. Write an equation that represents the model.

21. Solve the equation and answer the question.

Temperature Change   **In Exercises 22–25, use the following information.**

Suppose you live in Greenville, South Carolina, where the temperature is 69°F and going up at a rate of 2°F an hour. You are talking on the phone to your friend who lives in Waterloo, Iowa, where the temperature is 84°F and going down at a rate of 3°F an hour. If the temperatures continue to change at the same rates, how long would you and your friend have to talk before they would be equal?

22. Write a verbal model for this problem.

23. Assign labels to the model. Indicate the units of measure.

24. Write an equation that represents the model.

25. Solve the equation and answer the question.

In Exercises 26–33, find the resulting unit of measure.

26. (miles per hour) • (hours)

27. (feet per minute) • (minutes)

28. (meters) • (meters)

29. (liters) − (liters)

30. (hours per day) • (days)

31. (inches per foot) • (feet)

32. (centimeters) + (centimeters)

33. (hours) ÷ (days)

Exploration and Extension

The Rabbit and the Coyote **In Exercises 34–37, use the following information.**

As in the diagram, a rabbit is 30 feet from its burrow and can run 25 feet per second. A coyote that runs 50 feet per second spots the rabbit and starts running toward it.

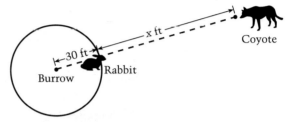

34. How long will it take the rabbit to get to its burrow?

35. Write an expression for the time it will take the coyote to get to the burrow.

36. Set the expressions from Exercises 34 and 35 equal to each other and solve for *x*.

37. Interpret your results.

Career Interview

Picture Framer

Henry Leventhal has been a picture framer for 22 years. "I specialize in frames and mats that need artistic or special decorative skills."

Q: *Does having a math background help you on the job?*

A: Yes. I use math every day. Adding, subtracting, dividing, and measuring in fractional amounts are all done before I cut the glass, mat board, paper, and frame. I also use math when I order materials. If I make a mistake, I have to pay for those materials!

Q: *How much math do you need on the job?*

A: My math skills came from school, but I had no idea I'd be applying them the way I do now in my work. When I interview job applicants, the first thing I do is ask them to find one eighth or one sixteenth of an inch on a ruler. Half the people fail the interview right there. They can't read a ruler!

Q: *What would you do if you were in high school again?*

A: I would learn more about how to use calculators and computers.

Take this test as you would take a test in class. The answers to the exercises are given in the back of the book.

In Exercises 1–12, solve the equation. (3.1, 3.2, 3.3)

1. $3m = 18$

2. $\frac{1}{4}p = 7$

3. $y - 6 = 7$

4. $x + \frac{1}{2} = 3$

5. $3s + 2 = 17$

6. $\frac{x}{4} + 10 = \frac{3}{4}$

7. $16(x - 2) - (x - 3) = 29$

8. $\frac{1}{4}(y + 8) + 6 = 10$

9. $12n + 2 - 3n = 5 - (n - 2)$

10. $y + 2 = 2y - 4$

11. $\frac{1}{2}(x - 2) = 3 - x$

12. $3p - 2 = \frac{1}{3}(6p + 5)$

In Exercises 13–15, correct any mistakes in the solution steps. (3.3)

13.
$$-2(x + 3) = 3x + 1$$
$$-2x - 6 = 3x + 1$$
$$-2x = 3x + 7$$
$$x = 7$$

(handwritten) $+2x \quad +2x$
$x = \frac{5x + 7}{}$
$-5x \quad -5x$
$-6x = +7$

14.
$$20x - (3 + 5x) = 8x + 4$$
$$15x - 3 = 8x + 4$$
$$15x = 8x + 7$$
$$7x = 7$$
$$x = 1$$

15.
$$3\left(\frac{1}{2}y - 4\right) = 4(y + 2)$$
$$\frac{3}{2}y - 12 = 4y + 8$$
$$-12 = \frac{5}{2}y + 8$$
$$-20 = \frac{5}{2}y$$
$$-8 = y$$
(handwritten) O.K.

16. You and three friends are eating a pizza with 12 pieces. Each person eats the same number of pieces. Let x represent the number of pieces each person eats. Which of the following equations is an algebraic model for the situation? **(3.4)**

a. $3x = 12$ **b.** $\frac{1}{3}x = 12$ **c.** $4x = 12$ **d.** $\frac{1}{4}x = 12$

17. You are mowing lawns for the summer. You charge \$5 per lawn and you have \$35 at the end of the day. Let x represent the number of lawns you mowed. Which *two* of the following equations are algebraic models for the situation? **(3.4)**

a. $5x = 35$ **b.** $\frac{1}{5}x = 35$ **c.** $x = \frac{1}{5}(35)$ **d.** $\frac{1}{35}x = 5$

18. On a sunny day, Julie, your 6-foot friend, casts a 4-foot shadow. What is the ratio of her height to her shadow length? A utility pole nearby casts a 20-foot shadow. The ratio of its height, H, to its shadow length is the same as the ratio of Julie's height to her shadow length. Draw and label a diagram of these relationships. Which equation will give you the height of the pole? **(3.4)**

a. $\frac{H}{20} = \frac{4}{6}$ **b.** $\frac{H}{20} = \frac{6}{4}$ **c.** $\frac{H}{20} = \frac{6}{3}$

19. What is the height of the pole in Exercise 18?

20. The city park is sponsoring a pet show. The number of cats, birds, and hamsters equals the number of dogs and turtles. There are 2 birds, 2 turtles, and 5 hamsters. There are twice as many dogs as cats. Let n be the number of cats. Which of the following is an algebraic model for the situation? **(3.4)**

a. $2n + 2 + 5 = n + 2$ **b.** $n + 2n = 2 + 2 + 5$ **c.** $n + 2 + 5 = 2n + 2$

3.5

Solving Equations That Involve Decimals

What you should learn:

Goal 1 How to find exact and approximate solutions of equations containing decimals

Goal 2 How to solve problems that use decimal measurements

Why you should learn it:

You will have to solve problems whose data are decimal amounts, such as with money, distances, and percents.

Goal 1 Solving Decimal Equations

All the equations in the first four lessons of this chapter involve integer or fraction coefficients and solutions. Techniques used to solve those equations can also be used to solve equations involving decimals. The difference, however, is that decimal solutions can involve *round-off error.*

Here is a simple example. Suppose three people want to share equally in the cost of a pizza. If the pizza costs $12.89 and x represents each person's share, then an algebraic model would be $3x = 12.89$. Thus, each person should pay

$$x = \underbrace{\frac{12.89}{3}}_{\text{Exact}} = 4.296666 \ldots \approx \underbrace{4.30.}_{\text{Rounded}}$$

The exact answer is not practical because our monetary system does not have coins worth $\frac{2}{3}$ of a cent. On the other hand, the rounded answer will yield a total of $12.90, which is one cent too much. The point is that you must round the answer and understand the error that is produced.

Example 1 Rounding for the Final Answer

Solve $-38x - 39 = 118$. (Round to two decimal places.)

Solution

$-38x - 39 = 118$	*Rewrite original equation.*
$-38x = 157$	*Add 39 to both sides.*
$x = \frac{157}{-38}$	*Divide both sides by -38.*
$x \approx -4.13$	*Use a calculator to divide; round to two decimal places.*

The solution is approximately -4.13.

Check When checking decimal answers that have been rounded, you must realize that the solution is not exact.

$-38x - 39 = 118$	*Rewrite original equation.*
$-38(-4.13) - 39 \overset{?}{=} 118$	*Substitute -4.13 for x.*
$-38(-4.13) \overset{?}{=} 157$	*Simplify.*
$156.94 \approx 157$	*Checks (approximately).* ∎

In Example 1, you did not have to use a decimal approximation until the last step. When the original equation involves decimals, you may have to round in intermediate steps, but you should keep as many decimal places as possible in those steps. For the final solution, you should normally write no more decimal places than appeared in the original equation.

Example 2 *Original Equation Involves Decimals*

Solve $3.57x - 37.40 = 0.23x + 8.32$.

Solution

$3.57x - 37.40 = 0.23x + 8.32$	*Rewrite original equation.*
$3.34x - 37.40 = 8.32$	*Subtract 0.23x from both sides.*
$3.34x = 45.72$	*Add 37.40 to both sides.*
$x = \frac{45.72}{3.34}$	*Divide both sides by 3.34.*
$x = 13.68862\ldots$	*Use calculator to divide.*
$x \approx 13.69$	*Round to two decimal places.*

The solution is approximately 13.69. Check this in the original equation. ∎

The next example shows a technique for avoiding decimals in intermediate steps.

Example 3 *Changing Decimal Coefficients to Integer Coefficients*

Solve $4.5 - 7.2x = 3.4x - 49.5$.

Solution Since the coefficients and constant terms each have only one decimal place, we can "clear the equation of decimals" by multiplying both sides by 10.

$4.5 - 7.2x = 3.4x - 49.5$	*Rewrite original equation.*
$45 - 72x = 34x - 495$	*Multiply both sides by 10.*
$45 = 106x - 495$	*Add 72x to both sides.*
$540 = 106x$	*Add 495 to both sides.*
$\frac{540}{106} = x$	*Divide both sides by 106.*
$5.094339\ldots = x$	*Use calculator to divide.*
$5.1 \approx x$	*Round to one decimal place.*

The solution is approximately 5.1. Check this in the original equation. ∎

Real-life measurements often contain decimals such as a salad for $2.45, a 1.3-mile jog, a body temperature of 98.6°F, a batting average of .315, and a sales tax of 7% = 0.07.

Real Life
Retail Purchase

Example 4   *How Much Can They Cost?*

You are shopping for earrings. The sales tax is 5%. You have a total of $18.37. What is your price limit for the earrings?

Solution

| Verbal Model | Earring price | + | Sales tax rate | · | Earring price | = | Total cost |

Labels   Earring price = x (dollars)
Sales tax rate = 0.05   (dollars per dollar)
Total cost = 18.37   (dollars)

Equation $x + 0.05x = 18.37$ *Algebraic model*
$1.05x = 18.37$ *Add like terms.*
$x = \dfrac{18.37}{1.05}$ *Divide both sides by 1.05.*
$x = 17.4952\ldots$ *Use a calculator.*
$x \approx 17.49$ *Round down.*

The answer was rounded *down* to $17.49 rather than *up* to $17.50. For a price of $17.50, the sales tax is $0.88 and you would be a penny short.   ■

Communicating about ALGEBRA

▶ **SHARING IDEAS about the Lesson**

Using the Problem-Solving Plan   You have $5.26 and want to call a town 105 miles away. How long can you talk?

A. Assign labels to the following verbal model.

| Verbal Model | 1st min | + | Addl. min rate | · | Num. of addl. min | = | Total cost |

Labels   Cost for 1st minute = ⬚ . 44   (dollars)
Rate for additional minutes = ⬚ . 28 (dollars per min)
Number of additional minutes = x (min)
Total cost = ⬚ 5.26   (dollars)

Distance (in miles)	Cost for 1st minute	Cost for addl. minute
1–10	$0.19	$0.10
11–16	$0.23	$0.12
17–22	$0.26	$0.15
23–30	$0.31	$0.19
31–40	$0.36	$0.21
41–55	$0.39	$0.25
56–70	$0.43	$0.27
71–124	$0.44	$0.28
125–196	$0.46	$0.31
197–292	$0.49	$0.34
293–354	$0.50	$0.36

B. Write and solve an equation for x, then answer the question.

EXERCISES

of means multiply

Guided Practice

▶ **CRITICAL THINKING about the Lesson**

1. Give an example of round-off error.

2. In 1990, the population of the United States was 249.6 million. During that year, Americans purchased 3.1 million basketballs. Which of the following is a better number to represent the number of Americans per new basketball in 1990? Explain.
   a. 80.516129   **b.** 80.5   *Non whole numbers are not meaningful.*

3. How can you clear the following equation of decimals? *multiply by 10*

   $$0.2x - 1.4 = 1.1x + 3.2$$

4. The solution of $7x = 3$, rounded to two decimal places, is 0.43. Which of the following is a better way to list the solution?
   a. $x = 0.43$ **b.** $x \approx 0.43$

Independent Practice

In Exercises 5–10, round the number to one decimal place. Use your calculator when appropriate.

5. -367.84159

6. 83.7461

7. $1.0847 + 62.5583$

8. $24.0321 - 21.8217$

9. $3.21(4.56)$

10. $4.57 \div 3.21$

In Exercises 11–16, round the number to two decimal places.

11. 5.364

12. -2.495

13. $-41.287 - 3.382$

14. $11.051(3.467)$

15. $-23.981(-4.598)$

16. $15.953 \div 3.476$

In Exercises 17–28, solve the equation. Round the result to two decimal places. Check your rounded solution.

17. $17x - 33 = 114$

18. $-3x + 51 = 104$

19. $-18 + 41a = 57$

20. $31 = 44 - 12m$

21. $25 = 14 - 10d$

22. $99 = 100t + 56$

23. $238 = 79z - 43$

24. $28 - 68c = 241$

25. $3(31 - 12x) = 82$

26. $5(-8x + 15) = 49$

27. $2(-5x + 4) = -x$

28. $-(x - 3) = 2(3x + 1)$

In Exercises 29–38, solve the equation. Round the result to two decimal places.

29. $15.74 - 2.36x = 18.66x - 12.23$

30. $5.423 - 6.411x = 8.213x + 3.081$

31. $2.7 - 3.6x = 8.4 + 23.7x$

32. $5.3 + 9.2x = 7.4x - 8.8$

33. $6(3.14 + 1.59x) = 12.29x - 4.37$

34. $18(1.01 - 2.30x) = 4.93x + 6.22$

35. $18.41x - 12.75 = (4.32x - 6.81)3$

36. $25.79x - 18.24 = (7.77 - 13.91x)(-6)$

37. $38.5x + 2.4 = -31.7 + 41.8x$

38. $26.4x - 3.2 = 5.9x - 32.1$

3.5 ▪ *Solving Equations That Involve Decimals*   **151**

39. *Buying a Sweatshirt* You have $32.14 to spend for a sweatshirt. The sales tax is 5%. What is the most the sweatshirt can cost?

40. *Buying a Dinner* You have $6.46 to spend for a dinner. There is no sales tax, but you want to leave a 15% tip. What is the most the dinner can cost?

In Exercises 41 and 42, use the following information.

The cross-country team ran 10.3 kilometers in 42.5 minutes during their workout. Let r be the speed in kilometers per minute.

41. Which equation models this problem?

    a. $42.5r = 10.3$ **b.** $10.3r = 42.5$

42. Solve for r and round the result to one decimal place.

In Exercises 43 and 44, refer to the information on page 121 on the "drag" of objects in the water.

43. Find the approximate length of a Greenland shark that is 23.5 inches wide.

44. Find the approximate length of a dolphin that is 31.5 inches wide.

Taking a Bath **In Exercises 45–48, use the following information.**

Suppose you are running water into a bathtub. You turn on the hot water first; it flows at a rate of 7.8 liters per minute. Two minutes later you turn on the cold water; it flows at a rate of 12.3 liters per minute. In how many minutes after the cold water is turned on will the hot and cold faucets have delivered the same amount of water?

45. Write a verbal model for this problem.

46. Assign labels to each part of the model. Indicate the units of measure.

47. Write an equation that represents your model.

48. Solve the equation and answer the question.

Fund-Raising **In Exercises 49 and 50, use the following information.**

To raise money, the Student Council of Daniels High School is selling magazine subscriptions. The Student Council will receive $150 from the magazine publisher plus 38% of the subscription money.

49. How much must the council sell in subscriptions to raise $300?

50. How much must the council sell in subscriptions to raise $500?

Integrated Review

In Exercises 51–59, solve the equation.

51. $|-3| + n = 15$

52. $2n + |-8| = 22$

53. $5x + (-4)^2 = 21$

54. $-(6)^2 + 19x = 15$

55. $3t - (-2t) + 14 = 6$

56. $7t + (-3t) - 8 = 16$

57. $3(10y - 12) + 15y = 54$

58. $x - 8 = 2 + 4x$

59. $12 + 2x = 8 - 5x$

60. Solve for a, b, c, and d. Round your results to two decimal places.

$$\begin{bmatrix} -2a & 3.1b \\ 0.57c & 3.2(d+48) \end{bmatrix} = \begin{bmatrix} 3.9 & -2.6b+5 \\ -8.6 & -d+1.7 \end{bmatrix}$$

61. *College Entrance Exam Sample*   A 15-gallon mixture of 20% alcohol has 5 gallons of water added to it. The strength of the mixture, as a percent, is near which of the following?

a. 12.5   **b.** 13.33   **c.** 15.0   **d.** 16.66   **e.** 20.0

Pet Ownership   **In Exercises 62–65, use the following information.**

Of all of the households in the United States, 30% have a dog, 22% have a cat, and 8% have some other pet. This map shows which counties in the Southwest have pet ownership rates above and below the average. Red counties have rates that are 20% or higher above the average. Yellow counties have rates that are up to 20% higher. Blue counties have rates that are lower than average. *(Source: CACI Marketing Systems)*

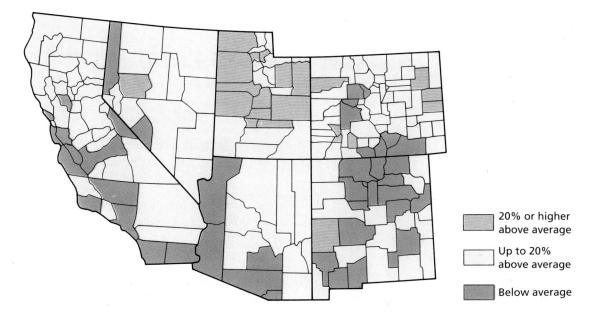

- 20% or higher above average
- Up to 20% above average
- Below average

62. Consider a county with 56,000 households that is shaded red on the map. What is the least number of households in this county that owns a dog?

63. Consider a county with 112,000 households that is shaded blue on the map. What is the greatest number of households in this county that own a cat?

64. If a county that is shaded yellow on the map has 74,000 households that own cats, what is the least number of households that could be in the county?

65. If a county that is shaded red on the map has 23,000 households that own dogs, what is the least number of households that could be in the county?

3.6

Literal Equations and Formulas

Goal How to solve literal equations, especially formulas, for a specified variable

Why you should learn it:

You can solve an equation such as $I = Prt$ for any of its variables, so you need to learn only one model, not many, for most real-life relationships.

Connections
Geometry

Goal **Solving Literal Equations**

A **literal equation** is an equation that uses more than one letter as a variable. For instance, $3x + y = 4$ is a literal equation because it uses two variables, x and y. The word *literal* comes from the Latin word for "letter." You can solve a literal equation for any one of its "letters."

Solve for x.	**Solve for y.**
$3x + y = 4$	$3x + y = 4$
$3x = 4 - y$	$y = 4 - 3x$
$x = \dfrac{4 - y}{3}$	

Example 1 *The Perimeter of a Rectangle*

The perimeter, P, of a rectangle is given by $P = 2W + 2L$, where W is the width and L is the length.

a. Solve this formula for W.

b. Use the result to find the width of a rectangle whose length is 24 cm and whose perimeter is 70 cm.

Solution

a.
$$P = 2W + 2L \qquad \textit{Formula for perimeter}$$
$$P - 2L = 2W \qquad \textit{Subtract 2L from both sides.}$$
$$\frac{P - 2L}{2} = W \qquad \textit{Divide both sides by 2.}$$

This gives the width in terms of perimeter and length.

b. Substitute $L = 24$ and $P = 70$ into the formula for width.

$$W = \frac{P - 2L}{2} \qquad \textit{Formula for width}$$
$$= \frac{70 - 2(24)}{2} \qquad \textit{Substitute 70 for P and 24 for L.}$$
$$= \frac{70 - 48}{2} \qquad \textit{Simplify 2(24).}$$
$$= \frac{22}{2} \qquad \textit{Simplify 70 - 48.}$$
$$= 11 \qquad \textit{Width}$$

Thus, the width is 11 cm. ∎

Sparking plug
Exhaust valve
Piston
Crankshaft
Camshaft
Inlet valve
Cooling water
Connecting rod

In a gasoline engine, power is produced by expanding gases that drive the pistons up and down. The pistons transfer the power to connecting rods, which turn the crankshaft.

The amount of horsepower produced by an engine whose pistons are turning a single crankshaft is

$$H = \left(\frac{1}{396,000}\right) PpArn,$$

where P is the average piston pressure, p is the piston stroke length, A is the piston area, r is the crankshaft revolutions per minute (RPM), and n is the number of pistons.

Real Life
Automotive Mechanics

Example 2   *Finding the Number of Pistons*

a. Solve the formula $H = \left(\frac{1}{396,000}\right) PpArn$ for n.

b. An automobile engine is producing 150 horsepower with an RPM of 2500. The average piston pressure is 120 pounds per square inch, the piston stroke length is 3.3 inches, and the piston area is 10 square inches. How many pistons does the engine have?

Solution

a. $H = \left(\frac{1}{396,000}\right) PpArn$ *Formula for horsepower*

$396,000H = PpArn$ *Multiply both sides by 396,000.*

$\dfrac{396,000H}{PpAr} = n$ *Divide both sides by factors PpAr.*

b. $H = 150$, $P = 120$, $p = 3.3$, $A = 10$, and $r = 2500$.

$$n = \frac{396,000H}{PpAr} = \frac{396,000(150)}{(120)(3.3)(10)(2500)} = \frac{5940}{990} = 6$$

Thus, the engine has 6 pistons.   ∎

The formula $I = Prt$ gives the interest earned after t years for a principal, P, at an annual interest rate, r. The balance after t years is the sum of the principal and the interest.

$$\underbrace{A}_{\text{Balance}} = \underbrace{P}_{\text{Principal}} + \underbrace{Prt}_{\text{Interest}}$$

Real Life
Finance

Example 3 *Finding the Principal*

a. Solve the formula $A = P + Prt$ for P.

b. How much should you deposit in a savings account at 6.5% interest annually to have a balance of $500 after one year?

Solution

a. The first step is to use the Distributive Property to write P as a factor.

$A = P + Prt$ *Formula for balance*
$A = P(1 + rt)$ *Distributive Property*
$\dfrac{A}{1 + rt} = P$ *Divide both sides by 1 + rt.*

This formula gives the principal in terms of the balance, interest rate, and time.

b. Substitute $A = 500$, $r = 0.065$, and $t = 1$ into the formula for principal.

$P = \dfrac{A}{1 + rt}$ *Formula for principal*

$= \dfrac{500}{1 + 0.065(1)}$ *Substitute values for A, r, and t.*

$= \dfrac{500}{1.065}$ *Simplify.*

≈ 469.48 *Principal*

Thus, you should deposit $469.48. ■

Communicating about ALGEBRA

▶ **SHARING IDEAS about the Lesson**

Cooperative Learning

A. **Work with a Partner**   The formula for the volume of a pyramid with a square base is $V = \frac{1}{3}hs^2$, where h is the height of the pyramid and s is the length of each side of the base. Solve this formula for h.

B. **Apply**   The Great Pyramid in Egypt has a volume of about 90 million cubic feet and a square base with sides of about 750 feet. Use the formula for h to approximate the height of the Great Pyramid.

EXERCISES

Guided Practice

▶ **CRITICAL THINKING about the Lesson**

1. **True or False?** A literal equation is an equation that has a variable on both sides of the equation. *False*

2. Which of the following are literal equations? Explain how you know.
   a. $2x + 4 = 5 - 3x$ **b.** $a - 6 = 3b + 9$ *2 variables*
   c. $4s + 9t = 16$ **d.** $3 = 27 - 24$

3. Solve the equation $3n + 4m = 9$ for m.

4. Solve the equation $I = Prt$ for r.

Independent Practice

In Exercises 5–16, solve for the indicated variable.

5. **Area of a Triangle**
   Solve for h: $A = \frac{1}{2}bh$

6. **Perimeter of a Rectangle**
   Solve for L: $P = 2L + 2W$

7. **Volume of a Rectangular Prism**
   Solve for L: $V = LWH$

8. **Volume of a Circular Cylinder**
   Solve for h: $V = \pi r^2 h$

9. **Markup**
   Solve for C: $S = C + rC$

10. **Discount**
    Solve for L: $S = L - rL$

11. **Investment at Simple Interest**
    Solve for r: $A = P + Prt$

12. **Investment at Compound Interest**
    Solve for P: $A = P(1 + r)^t$

13. **Area of a Trapezoid**
    Solve for b_1: $A = \frac{1}{2}h(b_1 + b_2)$

14. **Sum of a Geometric Sequence**
    Solve for r: $S = \frac{rL - a}{r - 1}$

15. **Last Term of an Arithmetic Sequence**
    Solve for n: $L = a + (n - 1)d$

16. **Sum of an Arithmetic Sequence**
    Solve for a: $S = \frac{n}{2}[2a + (n - 1)d]$

17. **Depth of a Water Trough** A water trough in the shape of a rectangular prism is 12 feet long and 3 feet wide. The trough has 9.4 cubic feet of water. How deep is the water in the trough?

12 ft |←3 ft→| 3 ft

18. **Height of a Circular Cylinder** The volume of a circular cylinder is 48π cubic centimeters. The radius of the cylinder is 2 centimeters. What is the height of the cylinder?

2 cm h cm

19. **Width of a Rectangle** A rectangle is 1.5 times as long as it is wide. The perimeter of the rectangle is 75 inches. Find the width of the rectangle.

20. *Length of Picture Frame*   A rectangular picture frame has a perimeter of 3 feet. The width of the frame is 0.62 times its height. Find the height of the frame.

21. The pressure, P, exerted on the floor by a person's shoe heel depends on the weight, w, of the person and the width of the heel, H. The formula is given by

$$P \approx \frac{1.2w}{H^2},$$

where the weight is in pounds and the heel width is in inches. The heels on Tim's shoes are 2 inches wide, and each exerts a pressure of 45 pounds per square inch. Estimate Tim's weight.

22. *Physics*   Newton's second law of motion states that force, F, is equal to the mass, m, times acceleration, a, or $F = ma$. A force of 20 newtons is acting on a mass of 10 kilograms. A newton is "one kilogram-meter per second per second." What is the acceleration?

23. *Compound Interest*   You earn 7.2% interest in one savings account and 5.3% interest in a second savings account. Your balance in *each* account at the end of two years is $324.75. How much money did you start with in each account? How much money did you earn from both accounts?

24. *Simple Interest*   You deposit $400 in a savings account. After one year, your balance is $428. What was your annual interest rate?

25. *Compound Interest*   You have a balance of $179.20 in your savings account two years after the account was opened. Your only transaction was the initial deposit. The annual interest rate is 6%. What was your initial deposit?

26. *Simple Interest*   You need $396.80 to buy a stereo. You deposit $320 into a savings account with 12% interest. How long will it be before you have enough money for the stereo?

Integrated Review

In Exercises 27–30, solve the equation.

27. $4t - 1 = 7$

28. $s - 35 + 9 = 10 - s$

29. $3(x - 1) = x + 9$

30. $\frac{1}{2}\left(\frac{1}{2}a + 4\right) = 8 - \frac{3}{4}a$

In Exercises 31–34, evaluate the expression.

31. $4V - 3H + 9$, when $V = \frac{1}{2}$ and $H = 4$

32. $9x + 36 - 4y$, when $x = 2$ and $y = 14$

33. $(1.2x - 1)^4 - 0.1$, when $x = 1.1$

34. $\frac{1}{2}(x - y)^2$, when $x = 2$ and $y = 4$

Growing Money **In Exercises 35–38, use the following information.**

With an interest rate of $r = 8\% = 0.08$, the formula for an investment with compound interest, $A = P(1 + r)^t$, can be written as $A = P(1.08)^t$.

35. Solve the equation $A = P(1.08)^t$ for P.

36. How much money must you deposit to have a balance of $10,000 in one year?

37. How much must you deposit if you are willing to wait 5 years?

38. Continue this process by completing the table. You may want to use the $\boxed{y^x}$ key on your calculator. From the table, how much would you have to deposit to earn a balance of $10,000 if you were willing to wait 100 years? 179.50 years?

Number of Years, *t*	10	15	20	30	50	100	180
Deposit, *P*	?	?	?	?	?	?	?

39. *Benjamin Franklin*   Benjamin Franklin died in 1790. In his will, he left $5000 each to the cities of Boston and Philadelphia to be used for public works. Part was to be used after 100 years and the rest was to be used after 200 years. Estimate the amount of money that each city could have had available in 1990, if the funds were invested at 5% compound interest.

Mixed REVIEW

1. Evaluate $(-37.2)(0.23) - 18.2 \div 4.9$. **(2.3, 2.5)**

2. Evaluate $\frac{3x}{4y} - \frac{1}{2}x$ when $x = \frac{1}{3}$ and $y = 2$. **(1.2)**

3. Find the sum of $\frac{1}{8}$ and $\frac{3}{4}$. **(1.1)**

4. Find the difference of 3 and -7. **(2.3)**

5. Simplify $3x(x - 4) + 2(1 - x)$. **(2.6)**

6. Evaluate x^4 when $x = 3$. **(1.3)**

7. Simplify $-4 + 2x + (-12)$. **(2.2)**

8. Evaluate $3 \div \left(\frac{4}{3} \cdot \frac{3}{8}\right) - 7$. **(1.1, 2.7)**

9. Solve $7x - 2x + 3 = 8$. **(2.6, 3.2)**

10. Solve $3x - 4 = 4$. **(3.2)**

11. Solve $\frac{4x}{3} - 5 = 7$. **(3.2)**

12. Solve $6x + 29 = -4x - 1$. **(3.3)**

In Exercises 13–16, write the phrase or sentence in algebraic form. **(1.6)**

13. 24 is equal to 3 more than the product of 7 and a number.

14. The product of 2 and a number, plus twice the product of 3 and another number is less than 20.

15. The sum of a number and 6, times the reciprocal of 4.

16. The difference of 4 and a number equals the same number.

3.7

Exploring Data: Scatter Plots

What you should learn:

Goal 1 How to use a coordinate plane to match points with ordered pairs of numbers

Goal 2 How to use a scatter plot

Why you should learn it:

You can plot pairs of measurements in the coordinate plane as a visual model in your search for relationships among the measurements.

Goal 1 Using a Coordinate Plane

In this lesson, you will learn how to use a coordinate plane to visualize relationships between two variables.

A **coordinate plane** is formed by two real number lines intersecting at a right angle. The horizontal line is the **horizontal axis,** or **x-axis,** and the vertical line is the **vertical axis,** or **y-axis.** The point at which the two lines meet is the **origin,** and the axes divide the plane into four parts called **quadrants.**

Each point in a coordinate plane corresponds to an **ordered pair** of real numbers. The first number of an ordered pair is called its **horizontal coordinate,** or **x-coordinate** and the second number is called its **vertical coordinate,** or **y-coordinate.** For instance, the ordered pair (2, 1) has a horizontal coordinate of 2 and a vertical coordinate of 1.

When we *plot* the points that correspond to ordered pairs in a collection, we make a **scatter plot** of the collection. When we speak of "point (a, b)," it will be clear from its use whether we mean an ordered pair or a geometric figure.

Example 1 *Fahrenheit and Celsius Scales*

The table shows some temperatures on the Celsius scale and the corresponding temperatures on the Fahrenheit scale.

C	0	5	10	15	20	25	30
F	32	41	50	59	68	77	86

To make a scatter plot for this table, write each pair of C-values and F-values as an ordered pair, and plot the corresponding points on a coordinate plane.

(0, 32), (5, 41), (10, 50), (15, 59), (20, 68), (25, 77), (30, 86)

Each ordered pair has the form (C, F). Thus, the ordered pair (0, 32) tells you that F has a value of 32 when C has a value of 0. In the scatter plot at the left, you can see that as the Celsius temperature increases, the Fahrenheit temperature also increases. ∎

Using a Scatter Plot

After the 1990 U.S. census, the 435 seats in the House of Representatives were redistributed among the 50 states (see table). State populations are given in thousands, and the rate is the number of people (in thousands) per representative.

	Pop.	Seats	Rate		Pop.	Seats	Rate		Pop.	Seats	Rate		Pop.	Seats	Rate
AK	552	1	552	IL	11,467	20	573	NC	6,658	12	555	SC	3,506	6	584
AL	4,063	7	580	IN	5,564	10	556	ND	641	1	641	SD	700	1	700
AR	3,678	6	613	KS	2,486	4	622	NE	1,585	3	528	TN	4,897	9	544
AZ	2,362	4	591	KY	3,699	6	617	NH	1,114	2	557	TX	17,060	30	569
CA	29,839	52	574	LA	4,238	7	605	NJ	7,749	13	596	UT	1,728	3	576
CO	3,308	6	551	MA	6,029	10	603	NM	1,522	3	507	VA	6,217	11	565
CT	3,296	6	549	MD	4,799	8	600	NV	1,206	2	603	VT	565	1	565
DE	669	1	669	ME	1,233	2	617	NY	18,045	31	582	WA	4,888	9	543
FL	13,003	23	565	MI	9,329	16	583	OH	10,887	19	573	WI	4,907	9	545
GA	6,508	11	592	MN	4,387	8	548	OK	3,158	6	526	WV	1,802	3	601
HI	1,115	2	558	MO	5,138	9	571	OR	2,854	5	571	WY	456	1	456
IA	2,787	5	557	MS	2,586	5	517	PA	11,925	21	568				
ID	1,012	2	506	MT	804	1	804	RI	1,006	2	503				

Real Life
**Congressional
Representation**

Example 2   *Number of Seats in the House*

In 1990, the population of the United States was 249,633,000. Ideally, how many people should each House seat represent? Make a scatter plot that depicts the number of seats, s, for a state and the number of people, p, represented by each seat.

Solution   Each seat should ideally represent

$$\frac{\text{U.S. Population}}{\text{Seats in House}} = \frac{249,633,000}{435} \approx 574,000 \text{ people.}$$

From the scatter plot, you can see that states with only one representative vary greatly as to the number of people per representative. As the number of representatives increases, the population per representative gets closer to 574,000.

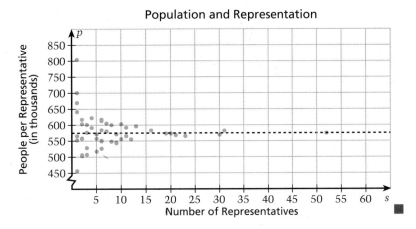

Population and Representation

Example 3 **Archery Sales in United States**

The total amount, A, spent on archery equipment each year in the United States from 1980 to 1990 is shown in the table. Amounts shown are in millions of dollars. The year is represented by t with $t = 0$ corresponding to 1980. Make a scatter plot to represent this data and describe the pattern.

Year, t	0	1	2	3	4	5	6	7	8	9	10
Amount, A	149	169	168	179	212	212	214	224	235	246	251

Solution   The scatter plot for this data is shown below. From the scatter plot, you can see that throughout the 1980's the amount spent tended to increase each year, and that the pattern of the points is approximately linear.

What is Spent on Archery Equipment

Communicating about **ALGEBRA**

▶ **SHARING IDEAS about the Lesson**

Finding a Relationship   The average June temperatures in several cities in the central part of the United States are shown in the table at the left. The table also shows the latitude degrees for the city.

A. Construct a scatter plot for these data.

B. Describe the relationship between the average June temperatures and the latitude positions.

C. St. Louis has an average June temperature of 74.6°F. Use the scatter plot to estimate the latitude of St. Louis.

City	Temp.	Lat.
Bismarck	64.3°	46.8°
Sioux Falls	68.4°	43.5°
Omaha	73.0°	41.2°
Kan. City	76.1°	39.1°
Wichita	73.6°	37.7°
Okla. City	77.0°	35.5°
Dallas	82.0°	33.2°
Houston	80.6°	29.8°

EXERCISES

▶ **CRITICAL THINKING about the Lesson**

1. Each point on a coordinate plane corresponds to which of the following?
   a. a real number
   b. an ordered pair of real numbers

2. In the ordered pair (3, 7), which number is the horizontal coordinate? Which is the vertical coordinate?

3. Write the ordered pairs that correspond to the points on the coordinate plane shown at the right.

4. Does the point $(2, -3)$ lie above or below the horizontal (x) axis? Does it lie to the left or right of the vertical (y) axis?

5. Plot the ordered pairs $(-3, 4)$, $(0, 3)$, $(2, -1)$, $(4, 0)$, $(-3, -1)$, and $(2, 2)$ on a coordinate plane.

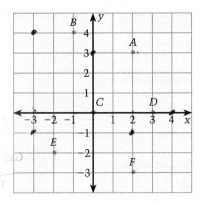

Independent Practice

In Exercises 6–8, write the ordered pairs that correspond to the points labeled A, B, C, D, E, and F in the coordinate plane.

6.

7.

8.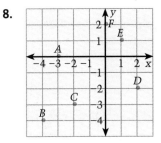

In Exercises 9–12, plot the ordered pairs on a coordinate plane.

9. $(-1, -4)$, $(0, 2)$, $(-3, 1)$, $(4, 0)$, $(-2, 1)$, $(3, 4)$

10. $(1, -4)$, $(-1, 0)$, $(2, 3)$, $(-4, -1)$, $(3, 2)$, $(1, 0)$

11. $(3, 1)$, $(0, -2)$, $(-1, -3)$, $(2, 2)$, $(-3, 0)$, $(4, 4)$

12. $(2, 0)$, $(0, 0)$, $(1, -1)$, $(-2, 0)$, $(-3, 3)$, $(-4, 4)$

In Exercises 13–18, use the scatter plots to answer the questions.

13. For the ordered pair (1990, 5), what is the value of *t*? What is the value of *C*?

14. What are the units of measure on the horizontal axis? What are the units of measure on the vertical axis?

15. Which of the following is true?
    a. *C* decreases as *t* increases.
    b. *C* is constant as *t* increases.
    c. *C* increases as *t* increases.

16. For the ordered pair (3, 6), what is the value of *x*? What is the value of *y*?

17. What are the units of measure on the horizontal axis? What are the units of measure on the vertical axis?

18. Which of the following is true?
    a. *y* decreases as *x* increases.
    b. *y* is constant as *x* increases.
    c. *y* increases as *x* increases.

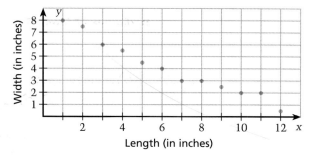

Temperature and Rainfall   **In Exercises 19–22, use the table below,** which shows the average January temperature and average January rainfall for several cities.

City	Temp.	Rainfall	City	Temp.	Rainfall
Baghdad, Iraq	50°F	0.9 in.	Mexico City, Mexico	54°F	0.2 in.
Beirut, Lebanon	57°F	7.5 in.	Montreal, Canada	14°F	3.8 in.
Berlin, Germany	31°F	1.9 in.	Moscow	15°F	1.5 in.
Buenos Aires, Argentina	74°F	3.1 in.	Nairobi, Kenya	66°F	1.5 in.
Calcutta, India	68°F	0.4 in.	Paris, France	37°F	1.5 in.
Colombo, Sri Lanka	79°F	3.5 in.	Reykjavik, Iceland	32°F	4.0 in.
Copenhagen, Denmark	33°F	1.6 in.	Rio de Janiero, Brazil	79°F	4.9 in.
Dublin, Ireland	41°F	2.7 in.	Rome, Italy	47°F	3.3 in.
Hong Kong	60°F	1.3 in.	Shanghai, China	40°F	1.9 in.
Jerusalem, Israel	48°F	5.1 in.	Taipei, Taiwan	60°F	3.8 in.
Los Angeles, United States	55°F	3.1 in.	Tokyo, Japan	38°F	1.9 in.
London, United Kingdom	40°F	2.0 in.	Wellington, New Zealand	63°F	3.2 in.

19. Construct a scatter plot that depicts the average January temperature and average January rainfall for the 24 cities. Use the horizontal axis to represent temperature.

20. Describe the relationship between average January temperatures and average rainfall around the world.

21. Do you notice any clusters of points on your scatter plot? If so, what do they represent?

22. What is the lowest average January temperature shown on your scatter plot? What is the highest?

Basketball Shoe Sales   **In Exercises 23 and 24, use the table showing the amount spent (in millions of dollars) each year on basketball shoes. In the table, t = 0 corresponds to 1980.** *(Source: National Sporting Goods Association)*

Year, t	0	1	2	3	4	5	6	7	8	9	10
Amount	86	80	81	119	159	185	187	169	226	254	264

23. Construct a scatter plot that shows the data.

24. Describe the sales pattern from 1980 to 1990.

Patterns in Our Solar System   **In Exercises 25 and 26, use the table showing the average surface temperature of each planet and the average distance of each planet (in millions of kilometers) from the sun.**

Planet	Mercury	Venus	Earth	Mars	Jupiter	Saturn	Uranus	Neptune	Pluto
Distance	58	108	150	228	778	1430	2875	4504	5900
Temperature	127°C	462°C	−16°C	−63°C	−148°C	−178°C	−216°C	−214°C	−228°C

25. Construct a scatter plot that shows the data.

26. Describe the relationship between the average distance from the sun and the average surface temperature. As the distance increases, does the temperature tend to increase or decrease? Explain.

Integrated Review

In Exercises 27–32, solve for the indicated variable.

27. $2y + x = 4$, x

28. $2y + x = 4$, y

29. $3b - (-2a) + 9 = -7$, a

30. $3b - (-2a) + 9 = -7$, b

31. $5m + 3n + 4 = -2n$, n

32. $12t - 2(3s) = 5t$, s

In Exercises 33–35, solve the equation.

33. $3a - (-21) = 7a - 7$

34. $-18 - 4c = 5 + 9c$

35. $5m - 3^2 = -4m - 18$

Exploration and Extension

36. *Favorite TV Shows*   Write a list of ten television shows. Put your favorite ones on the list and some you don't like. Arrange the shows in alphabetical order and make two copies. On one copy, rank the shows from 1 to 10 (1 for the most liked and 10 for the least liked). Then ask a friend to rank the shows (without looking at your rankings).

37. Make a scatter plot that relates your television likes and dislikes to your friend's likes and dislikes. What conclusions can you draw from the scatter plot?

A graphing calculator can be used to draw a scatter plot. Here we show how to use a Texas Instruments TI-81, a Casio fx-7700G, or BASIC to draw a scatter plot for the following collection of points. The scatter plot is shown at the right.

(1, 1.2), (1.5, 2.3), (2, 1.9), (2.5, 2.4), (3, 3.1)
(3.5, 3.5), (4, 3.8), (4.5, 4.7), (5, 4.9), (5.5, 5.7)

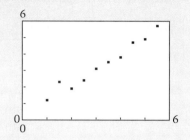

TI-81

RANGE (Set range.)
 Xmin = 0
 Xmax = 6
 Xscl = 1
 Ymin = 0
 Ymax = 6
 Yscl = 1
Y= CLEAR
2nd STAT
Cursor to DATA
2 (Clr Stat)
ENTER
2nd STAT
Cursor to DATA
1 (Edit)
Enter coordinates.
 x1 = 1   x6 = 3.5
 y1 = 1.2   y6 = 3.5
 x2 = 1.5   x7 = 4
 y2 = 2.3   y7 = 3.8
 x3 = 2   x8 = 4.5
 y3 = 1.9   y8 = 4.7
 x4 = 2.5   x9 = 5
 y4 = 2.4   y9 = 4.9
 x5 = 3   x10 = 5.5
 y5 = 3.1   y10 = 5.7
2nd STAT
Cursor to DRAW
2 (Scatter) ENTER

Casio fx-7700G

Range (Set range.)
 Xmin = 0
 max = 6
 scl = 1
 Ymin = 0
 max = 6
 scl = 1
EXE Range
SHIFT F5 (Cls) EXE
SHIFT CLR F2 EXE
MODE ÷
MODE 4
MODE SHIFT 1
F2 F3 F1
MODE SHIFT 3
MODE SHIFT +
Enter coordinates.
 1 SHIFT , 1.2 F1
 1.5 SHIFT , 2.3 F1
 2 SHIFT , 1.9 F1
 2.5 SHIFT , 2.4 F1
 3 SHIFT , 3.1 F1
 3.5 SHIFT , 3.5 F1
 4 SHIFT , 3.8 F1
 4.5 SHIFT , 4.7 F1
 5 SHIFT , 4.9 F1
 5.5 SHIFT , 5.7 F1

BASIC

```
10 XMIN = 0: XMAX = 6
20 YMIN = 0: YMAX = 6
30 XG = (40 − 1)/(XMAX − XMIN)
40 YG = (20 − 1)/(YMIN − YMAX)
50 CLS
60 FOR N = 1 TO 10
70    READ X,Y
80    XS = INT((X − XMIN)*XG) + 1
90    YS = INT((Y − YMAX)*YG) + 1
100    LOCATE YS,XS
110    PRINT "*";
120 NEXT N
130 FOR YS = 1 to 20
140    LOCATE YS,1
150    PRINT "|";
160 NEXT YS
170 PRINT STRING$(39," − ");
180 FOR N = 1 TO 40 STEP XG
190    LOCATE 20,INT(N)
200    PRINT " + ";
210 NEXT N
220 FOR N = 1 to 20 STEP − YG
230    LOCATE INT(N),1
240    PRINT " + ";
250 NEXT N: END
260 DATA 1,1.2, 1.5,2.3
270 DATA 2,1.9, 2.5,2.4
280 DATA 3,3.1, 3.5,3.5
290 DATA 4,3.8, 4.5,4.7
300 DATA 5,4.9, 5.5,5.7
```

Exercises

Use a graphing calculator or a computer to draw a scatter plot of the data.

1. (1, 5.1), (1, 4.8), (1, 4.7), (2, 4.3), (3, 3.8), (3, 3.2), (4, 2.8), (4, 2.4), (5, 1.8), (5, 1.2)

2. (1, 2.2), (1, 2.4), (1, 3.3), (2, 3.5), (3, 4.1), (3, 4.6), (4, 5.1), (4, 5.4), (5, 5.1), (5, 5.8)

3 Chapter Summary

What did you learn?

Skills
1. Solve a linear equation
   - using one transformation. **(3.1)**
   - using two or more transformations. **(3.2)**
   - with variables on both sides. **(3.3)**
   - involving decimals. **(3.5)**

2. Solve a literal equation
   - for one of its variables. **(3.6)**

Strategies
3. Create an algebraic model for a real-life situation
   - write a verbal model **(3.4)**
   - assign labels **(3.4)**
   - write a linear equation as an algebraic model **(3.4)**
   - use transformations to solve the equation **(3.4)**
   - answer questions about the real-life situation **(3.4)**

Exploring Data
4. Sketch a scatter plot of a data collection. **(3.7)**

5. Use a scatter plot to recognize patterns. **(3.7)**

Why did you learn it?

Linear models are the most commonly used algebraic models for real-life situations. By learning to write and solve linear models, you will be able to answer questions from a variety of fields: business, science, history, political science, engineering, and many more. Learning to create and solve linear models also prepares you for more complicated modeling that you will study later in this book.

How does it fit into the bigger picture of algebra?

In the first two chapters of this book, you used mental math to solve simple equations such as $x + 2 = 6$. But for solving complicated equations, such as $0.5(3x - 4) - 2(4x - 8) = 16$, you need other skills. But as messy as this equation might look, you saw that it really isn't that difficult, as long as you take it *one step at a time*. Remember that new mathematical skills are almost always built upon skills that you have already learned. The rules of algebra and the simplification techniques you learned in Chapter 2 form an essential part of the equation-solving techniques of Chapter 3.

In Exercises 1–12, solve the equation. (3.1, 3.2, 3.3)

1. $12 = x - 2$

2. $y + 4 = -6$

3. $\frac{m}{8} = \frac{1}{4}$

4. $7n = 28$

5. $3p - (-4) = 13$

6. $\frac{x}{6} + \frac{1}{3} = \frac{1}{2}$

7. $\frac{1}{4}(y + 8) = 0$

8. $16 = 5(1 - x)$

9. $9p + 7(p + 1) = 17 - 4p$

10. $\frac{1}{5}x - 3x + 2 = \frac{2}{5}x + 18$

11. $\frac{2}{3}(x - 4) = 3(x + 6)$

12. $\frac{1}{4}x + 16 = 3(\frac{1}{4}x + \frac{4}{3})$

In Exercises 13–18, solve the equation. Round your result to two decimal places. (3.5)

13. $5(x - 2) = -3(7 - 4x)$

14. $\frac{4}{9}y = 6(y + 6)$

15. $13.7t - 4.7 = 9.9 + 8.1t$

16. $4.6(2a + 3) = 3.7a - 4$

17. $-6(5.61x - 3.21) = 4.75$

18. $7(81.74x - 0.31) - 6.21 = 6(94.28x + 21.11)$

In Exercises 19–22, solve for the indicated variable. (3.6)

19. $4x - 3y = 2,\quad y$

20. $4x - 3y = 2,\quad x$

21. $A = \frac{1}{2}bh,\quad b$

22. $A = \frac{1}{2}h(b_1 + b_2),\quad b_2$

23. *Growing Tomatoes*   Suppose you are growing two different varieties of tomato plants on your balcony. The regular tomato plant is 12 inches tall and is growing at the rate of $\frac{3}{2}$ inches per week. The cherry tomato plant is 6 inches tall and is growing at the rate of 2 inches per week. In how many weeks will the two plants have the same height? **(3.4)**

Tomato   Cherry Tomato

24. *Odometer Reading*   You start a trip at 8:00 A.M. and the car's odometer reading is 65,660.1. At 4:00 P.M., when you reach your destination, the odometer reading is 66,035.8. What was your average speed? On the trip, you stopped for only an hour to have lunch and buy gas. What was your average *driving* speed? **(3.4)**

25. *Baking Bread*   You are baking raisin bread for a bake sale. For 2 loaves, the recipe calls for $2\frac{1}{2}$ cups of flour and $\frac{1}{3}$ cup of raisins. If you are making 5 loaves, how many cups of flour and raisins will you need? **(3.4)**

26. *Running a Race*   Two runners left the starting line at the same time. The first runner crossed the finish line in 30 minutes and averaged 12 kilometers per hour. The second crossed the finish line 5 minutes later. Use the following verbal model to find the speed of the second runner. **(3.4)**

Speed of 1st runner	•	Time for 1st runner	=	Speed of 2nd runner	•	Time for 2nd runner

27. Dwindling Rain Forest In 1990, the area covered by rain forest was decreasing at about 78,000 square miles per year. Suppose that the desert areas were increasing at about 50,000 square miles per year. At those rates, how many years would pass before Earth's deserts cover twice the land area that the rain forests cover? **(3.4)**

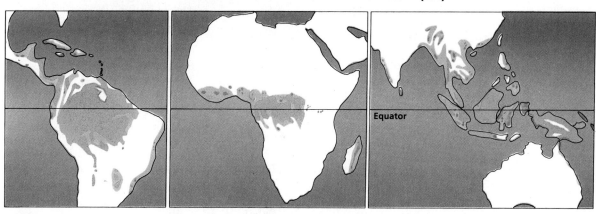

☐ Current areas of tropical rain forests   ☐ Areas where rain forests have disappeared

In 1990, there were about 35 million square miles of rain forest and 39.4 million square miles of desert. (Source: Smithsonian Institution)

28. Chemical Mixture Your science teacher instructs you to add 10 milliliters of Solution B, which is 70% water and 30% citric acid, to 20 milliliters of Solution A, which is 80% water and 20% citric acid. How many milliliters of acid are in the combined mixture? What percent acid is the combined mixture? **(3.5)**

29. Chemical Mixture You are still in the same science class (see Exercise 28), and your teacher says that she didn't want you to pour *all* of Solution B into Solution A—just enough to raise the acid percentage to 22%. How much of Solution B should you have poured into Solution A? Answer the question by assigning labels to the following verbal model and solving the resulting equation. **(3.5)**

$$\underbrace{\boxed{\text{Percent}} \cdot \boxed{\text{Total amount of mixture}}}_{\text{Acid in A}} + \underbrace{\boxed{\text{Percent}} \cdot \boxed{\text{Amount of mixture used}}}_{\text{Acid in B}} = \underbrace{\boxed{\text{Percent}} \cdot \boxed{\text{Total amount of mixture}}}_{\text{Acid in 22\% mixture}}$$

Percent acid in A = 0.2   (mL)   Volume of B added = x (mL)
Total volume of A = 20   (mL)   Percent acid in 22% solution = 0.22   (mL)
Percent acid in B = 0.3   (mL)   Total amount of 22% mixture = ☐?   (mL)

30. Buying a Book A book that you have been wanting to buy has just been reduced to 65% of its original price. The sales tax is 7%. You pay the cashier $25 and receive $3.13 in change. Use the following model to find the original price, p, of the book. **(3.5)**

$$\boxed{\$25} - \left(\boxed{\text{Discounted price}} + \boxed{\text{Sales tax \%}} \cdot \boxed{\text{Discounted price}} \right) = \boxed{\$3.13}$$

Imports and Exports   **In Exercises 31–36, use the scatter plot below and the stylized bar graph at the right.**   **(3.7)**

The bar graph at the right shows the 48 countries that traded the most in 1987. Each crate represents $10 billion of trade. The total amount traded is the sum of the total value of exports and imports. A country that exports more than it imports has a trade surplus. A country that imports more than it exports has a trade deficit.

☐ = $10bn

31. During which year(s) from 1975 to 1988 did the United States have a trade surplus? During which year(s) did it have a trade deficit?

32. During which year(s) from 1975 to 1988 did the United States have the greatest trade deficit?

33. Use the scatter plot to estimate the total U.S. imports in 1987 and the total exports in 1987. Add the two values. Does your estimate agree with the number given by the bar chart at the right? (It should.)

34. In 1987, Japan imported approximately $129 billion worth of merchandise. Approximate the amount that Japan exported in 1987. Did Japan have a trade surplus or a trade deficit?

35. In 1987, West Germany had a trade surplus of approximately $60 billion. How much did it import? How much did it export?

36. In 1987, France had a trade deficit of approximately $4.5 billion. How much did it import? How much did it export?

This scatter plot shows the total value of imports and exports (in billions of dollars) for the United States from 1975 to 1988.

U.S. Imports and Exports

U.S.A
W. Germany
Japan
France
U.K.
Italy
Canada
Netherlands
Belgium
Switzerland
Hong Kong
Taiwan
S. Korea
Sweden
Spain
China
Singapore
Austria
Australia
U.S.S.R.
Denmark
Brazil
Norway
Saudi Arabia
Finland
S. Africa
Mexico
Indonesia
India
Malaysia
Turkey
Ireland
Thailand
Yugoslavia
Portugal
Israel
Iran
E. Germany
Iraq
Venezuela
U.A.E.
Algeria
Greece
New Zealand
Kuwait
Nigeria
Philippines
Argentina

In Exercises 1–8, solve the equation.

1. $3c = 36$

2. $\frac{x}{4} = 20$

3. $4y - 3(y + 8) = 12$

4. $\frac{1}{4}m + 3 = 2$

5. $6 + 9x - 2 = 7x + (-2x) + 8$

6. $\frac{3x}{4} - 6 = x - 8$

7. $\frac{3}{8}(p - 8) + \frac{1}{8}p = -\frac{1}{2}(p - 7)$

8. $(3 \div 4) - r(r - \frac{1}{2}) = r(3 - r)$

In Exercises 9–12, solve the equation. Round your result to two decimal places.

9. $19x - 12 = 4(6 - 4x)$

10. $\frac{18y}{3} - 7 = 7y$

11. $27.3m - 45.1 = -13.2 + 6.8m$

12. $7(8.65x - 37.61) = (28.45 + 3.75x)(-4)$

In Exercises 13 and 14, solve for the indicated variable.

13. $C = 2\pi r, \quad r$

14. $S = 2\pi r^2 + 2\pi rh, \quad h$

15. A rectangular picture frame has a perimeter of 44.2 centimeters. The width of the frame is seven tenths of the length. What are the dimensions of the frame?

16. You and your cousin are earning money for your family's vacation trip. Your cousin averages $15 a week babysitting and receives one $5 bonus. You average $10 a week mowing lawns and $8 a week running errands for neighbors. After working the same number of weeks, you end up with $7 more than your cousin. How many weeks did you work? Use a verbal model, assign labels, and write an algebraic equation to answer the question.

17. You deposited $300 in a savings account. After one year, the balance was $314.70. Use the formula $A = P + Prt$ to find the interest rate for your account.

18. Construct a scatter plot for the data in the table. Assign the average daily temperature to the horizontal axis and assign latitude to the vertical axis. Describe any patterns you see in the scatter plot.

City	Average Temp.	Latitude	City	Average Temp.	Latitude
Albany, NY	47.3°F	42.39°N	Atlanta, GA	61.2°F	33.45°N
Atlantic City, NJ	53.1°F	39.27°N	Baltimore, MD	55.1°F	39.17°N
Boston, MA	51.5°F	42.21°N	Burlington, VT	44.1°F	44.28°N
Charlotte, NC	60.0°F	35.14°N	Columbia, SC	63.3°F	34.00°N
Concord, NH	45.3°F	43.12°N	Hartford, CT	45.3°F	41.46°N
Jacksonville, FL	68.0°F	30.20°N	Miami, FL	75.6°F	25.46°N
Mobile, AL	67.5°F	30.42°N	Norfolk, VA	59.5°F	38.40°N
New York, NY	54.5°F	40.43°N	Philadelphia, PA	54.3°F	39.47°N
Portland, ME	45.0°F	43.39°N	Providence, RI	50.3°F	41.50°N
Raleigh, NC	59.0°F	35.47°N	Richmond, VA	57.7°F	37.30°N

In Exercises 1–12, evaluate the expression.

1. $3 + 2(24 \div 6)$

2. $4.9 \div (4 + 3) + 0.6$

3. $[(13 - 8)^2 + 2] \div 3$

4. $32 \div (-4) - (2 - 8)$

5. $|3 - 10| - 3.7(4)$

6. $(6.8)^2 - |11.1 - 2.2|$

7. $(47 - 36.5)9 + 6.1$

8. $(29 + 1) \div (-5)$

9. $\dfrac{4(3 - 2)}{(6)(3)}$

10. $\dfrac{3^2 \cdot 4}{(42 - 21)}$

11. $\dfrac{3^2 - 8(6)}{7}$

12. $\dfrac{8 + 2(-4)}{6(-6)}$

In Exercises 13–18, solve the equation or inequality.

13. $4(x - 2) = 3^2 - x$

14. $\frac{1}{3}n + 3 = n - 2$

15. $9(2p + 1) - 3p > 4p - 6$

16. $(q - 12)3 \le 5q + 2$

17. $\dfrac{2y}{3} = \dfrac{8}{27}$

18. $\dfrac{m}{12} + \dfrac{5}{6} = \dfrac{5}{24}$

In Exercises 19–22, solve the equation or inequality. Round your result to two decimal places.

19. $3.2(x - 0.1) = 4.2$

20. $(19.8 - r)6.2 = 37.7r - 49.2$

21. $18t(4.2 - 36.1) < -86.13$

22. $41.2(2a - 0.6) > (0.25a + 3)99.9$

In Exercises 23 and 24, perform the matrix operation.

23. $\begin{bmatrix} 47 & -3 & 22 \\ 6 & -17 & 9 \end{bmatrix} + \begin{bmatrix} -33 & 18 & 10 \\ 44 & -24 & -44 \end{bmatrix}$

24. $\begin{bmatrix} 4 & 10 \\ -6 & 18 \\ 29 & -14 \end{bmatrix} - \begin{bmatrix} 56 & 2 \\ 4 & -11 \\ 29 & 7 \end{bmatrix}$

In Exercises 25–30, translate the phrase or sentence into an expression, an equation, or an inequality.

25. The difference of three times a number and 27

26. The quotient of 65 and a number is less than 14.

27. The sum of 27 and a number, multiplied by $\frac{1}{2}$, is 37.

28. The square of a number, plus 18, is greater than or equal to 87.

29. The absolute value of a number is less than the quotient of 36 and 5.

30. The square of forty less than two times a number

31. *Fund-Raiser*   The members of the school band are selling wrapping paper to raise money to attend a band competition. For each order of wrapping paper, the band makes $1. The fifty band members need a total of $550 to pay for registration fees, transportation, and food. Each band member will pay $3 toward the cost. How many orders of wrapping paper must the band members sell to meet their goal?

32. *Maple Syrup*   The table shows the retail price per gallon of maple syrup for 1976 through 1988. Construct a scatter plot of this information. Use the horizontal axis to represent the year and the vertical axis to represent the retail price. *(Source:* **The Vermont Almanac***)*

Year, t	1976	1977	1978	1979	1980	1981	1982
Price, p	$11.20	$12.00	$12.93	$14.26	$16.64	$18.60	$18.39

Year, t	1983	1984	1985	1986	1987	1988
Price, p	$17.95	$18.08	$19.05	$23.45	$28.10	$33.00

Cafeteria Tables   **In Exercises 33 and 34, use the following information.**

The school cafeteria got rid of some of the old tables and bought new ones. The old tables were 2 feet wide and 6 feet long. The new tables were the same width but were 8 feet long.

33. What is the ratio of the area of a new table to the area of an old table?

34. There are now 24 new tables in the cafeteria. If the cafeteria has the same table area as before, how many old tables were removed?

Seek-n-Find   **In Exercises 35 and 36, use the following information.**

Your sister received a Seek-n-Find puzzle book for her birthday. It took her 15 minutes to complete the first puzzle containing 30 words.

35. What was the average number of words she found per minute?

36. The daily puzzle in the newspaper contained 18 words which your sister found in 8 minutes. Did she find words faster in the newspaper or the puzzle book?

D	X	E	B	A	I	Z	W	K	M
O	E	L	O	N	E	C	H	B	O
G	B	E	A	R	K	A	A	A	U
C	G	P	R	O	K	M	L	T	S
M	E	H	O	R	S	E	E	F	E
O	H	A	S	E	A	L	T	O	X
M	O	N	K	E	Y	B	I	Y	X
L	G	T	I	G	E	R	B	O	W
Z	E	B	R	A	S	T	F	I	N
P	O	R	C	U	P	I	N	E	T

SEEK-N-FIND 20 Types of Mammals

37. *Shoe Sale*   The shoes you were saving for are now on sale for $17.56. The original price was $21.95. What percent is the discount?

38. *Geometry*   The volume of a right circular cylinder with a radius of 1.5 inches is 42.4 cubic inches. What is the height of the cylinder?

Graphing Linear Equations

LESSONS

4.1 Graphing Linear Equations in One Variable ▪ 176

4.2 Graphing Linear Equations in Two Variables ▪ 183

4.3 Quick Graphs Using Intercepts ▪ 190

4.4 The Slope of a Line ▪ 197

4.5 Quick Graphs Using Slope-Intercept Form ▪ 205

4.6 Connections: Solutions and x-Intercepts ▪ 211

4.7 Graphs of Absolute Value Equations ▪ 217

4.8 Solving Absolute Value Equations ▪ 223

San Francisco traffic is a colorful reminder of the millions of automobiles in the United States.

Real Life
Automobile Statistics

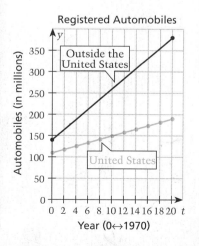

Registered Automobiles

Automobiles (in millions)

Outside the United States

United States

Year (0↔1970)

From 1970 to 1990, the number of registered automobiles in the United States increased by a rate of about 4 million automobiles per year. A model for this is $y = 4t + 110$, where y is the number of automobiles (in millions) and t is the year, with $t = 0$ corresponding to 1970. The graph of this model is shown in blue on the coordinate plane. It is a line whose y-intercept is 110 and whose slope is 4.

The black line in the coordinate plane is the graph of $y = 12t + 140$. It is a model for the number of registered automobiles in the world, excluding the United States.

(Source: Scientific American)

4.1 Graphing Linear Equations in One Variable

What you should learn:

Goal 1 How to graph horizontal and vertical lines in the coordinate plane

Goal 2 How to use equations of horizontal and vertical lines in real-life settings

Why you should learn it:

You can use horizontal and vertical lines as models of real-life situations, such as for approximating lines of latitude and longitude.

Goal 1 Horizontal and Vertical Lines

In this lesson, you will study relationships between two variables in which one of the variables always has the same value. For instance, in the following collection of ordered pairs, (x, y), the y-coordinates vary, but the x-coordinates are always 3.

y-coordinates vary.

$$(3, -3), \quad (3, -2), \quad (3, -1), \quad (3, 0), \quad (3, 1), \quad (3, 2), \quad (3, 3)$$

x-coordinates are the same.

The equation that represents this relationship between x and y is $x = 3$. In the coordinate plane, the *graph* of $x = 3$ is the vertical line that crosses the x-axis at 3 because *all* the points of this line, and *no other* points, have x-coordinate 3.

In a similar way, we could show that the graph of the equation $y = 2$ is a horizontal line. On this line, the x-coordinates vary and the y-coordinates are all 2.

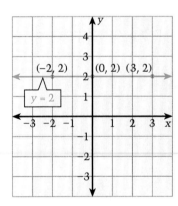

Equations of Horizontal and Vertical Lines

1. In the coordinate plane, the graph of $x = a$ is a vertical line.
2. In the coordinate plane, the graph of $y = b$ is a horizontal line.

Example 1   Sketching Horizontal and Vertical Lines

Sketch the graphs of $x = 8$ and $y = -2$. Find the point of intersection of the two graphs.

Solution   The graph of $x = 8$ is a vertical line because the y-coordinates can have any value, and the x-coordinates must have a value of 8. The graph of $y = -2$ is a horizontal line because the x-coordinates can have any value, and the y-coordinates must have a value of -2.

Vertical line	
x must be 8.	*y can have any value.*

$(8, y)$

Horizontal line	
x can have any value.	*y must be −2.*

$(x, -2)$

The point of intersection of these two lines must have an x-coordinate of 8 and a y-coordinate of -2. Thus, the point of intersection is $(8, -2)$. ■

Example 2   Writing Equations for Horizontal and Vertical Lines

Write equations for the horizontal line and the vertical line that pass through the point $(-1, 4)$.

Solution   Every point on the horizontal line through $(-1, 4)$ must have a y-coordinate of 4. Thus, the equation of the line is

  $y = 4$.   *Horizontal line*

Every point on the vertical line through $(-1, 4)$ must have an x-coordinate of -1. Thus, the equation of the line is

  $x = -1$.   *Vertical line* ■

Example 3   Describing an Activity to Match a Graph

The graph at the left shows three horizontal line segments. Describe a real-life situation that could be represented by this graph.

Solution   Here is one possible solution. Kareem is running a garage sale. Among the many items for sale is an old sweatshirt that Kareem marked at $6. After two hours, the sweatshirt has not been sold and Kareem marks the price down to $4. After two more hours, he puts the sweatshirt in a box marked *free*. After one more hour, someone finally takes the sweatshirt. ■

Using Horizontal and Vertical Lines

Example 4 *Alligator's Tail Length and Body Length*

The tail lengths and body lengths (in feet) of 24 alligators of different ages are shown in the table. (The ages range from 0 to 6 years.)

Tail	0.50	0.43	1.13	1.13	0.85	1.49	1.32	1.58
Body, *B*	0.44	0.40	1.05	1.04	0.80	1.37	1.23	1.47
Ratio, *r*	1.14	1.08	1.08	1.09	1.06	1.09	1.07	1.07
Tail	1.47	2.12	1.30	1.95	2.32	2.43	2.36	2.68
Body, *B*	1.36	1.95	1.22	1.80	2.14	2.25	2.17	2.47
Ratio, *r*	1.08	1.09	1.07	1.08	1.08	1.08	1.09	1.09
Tail	2.79	2.74	3.16	2.88	2.99	3.47	3.51	3.62
Body, *B*	2.57	2.54	2.91	2.66	2.76	3.19	3.22	3.35
Ratio, *r*	1.09	1.08	1.09	1.08	1.08	1.09	1.09	1.08

Sketch a graph that compares the body length, *B*, of each alligator with the ratio, *r*, of its tail length to its body length. What can you conclude from this graph?

Like many reptiles, the body proportions of alligators remain relatively constant during their lives. Unlike mammals, most baby reptiles are born as miniature versions of an adult.

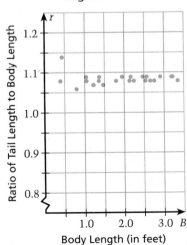

Alligator Dimensions

Solution Find an ordered pair for each alligator, with *B* as the first coordinate and *r* as the second coordinate.

Body Length, *B*   Ratio, *r*
$$\downarrow \qquad \downarrow$$
$$(0.44, 1.14), (0.40, 1.08), (1.05, 1.08), \ldots$$

The graph of the 24 points is shown at the left. Notice that the points lie approximately on the horizontal line $r = 1.1$. Thus, you can conclude that a model for the approximate ratio of the tail length of an alligator to its body length is

$$r = 1.1.$$

∎

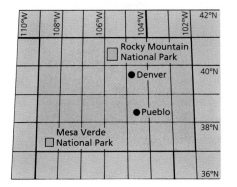

Example 5 *Borders of Colorado*

On a map, the borders of Colorado approximate a rectangle. The north and south borders of Colorado are latitudes 41° N and 37° N, respectively. The west and east borders are longitudes 109.1° W and 102.1° W, respectively. Which is farther to the west: 109.1° W or 102.1° W? Write equations for the lines containing the four borders of this state.

Solution   On maps, only nonnegative numbers name lines of latitude and longitude. Also, *N* and *S* mean "north" and "south" of the equator. *W* and *E* mean "west" and "east" of the prime meridian, which passes through Greenwich, England. Thus, the longitude line 109.1° W is farther west than the longitude line 102.1° W.

Latitude lines are also called *parallels* and longitude lines are also called *meridians*. Letting *P* represent the latitude and *M* represent the longitude, the four borders are as follows.

North Border	South Border	West Border	East Border
$P = 41$	$P = 37$	$M = 109.1$	$M = 102.1$
(Horizontal line)	(Horizontal line)	(Vertical line)	(Vertical line) ∎

Communicating *about* ALGEBRA

▶ **SHARING IDEAS about the Lesson**

Demonstrate Understanding   Use grid paper and draw a large picture of the coordinate plane.

A. Label five points on the *x*-axis.

B. What do you notice about the second coordinate of each point? What does this observation imply about the equation for the *x*-axis?

C. Use a similar procedure to determine the equation of the *y*-axis.

D. What are the coordinates of the origin (the point at which the *x*-axis and *y*-axis intersect)?

E. What is the equation of the line passing through $(-4, -2)$, $(-4, 0)$, and $(-4, 2)$, $x = -4$ or $y = -4$?

F. Explain why the equation $x = 1$ is a good way to describe the vertical line that intersects the *x*-axis at 1.

EXERCISES

Guided Practice

▶ **CRITICAL THINKING about the Lesson**

1. What is the x-coordinate in the ordered pair $(2, -1)$? *2*

2. What is the y-coordinate in the ordered pair $(-5, -3)$?

3. **True or false?** The graph of the equation $x = 4$ is a horizontal line. Explain. *True*

4. **True or false?** The graph of the equation $x = 4$ is a vertical line.

5. At what point do the graphs of $x = -4$ and $y = 6$ intersect? Sketch a visual model (graph) to verify your answer.

6. Sketch the horizontal line and the vertical line that pass through the point $(3, -2)$. Write an equation for each.

Independent Practice

In Exercises 7–10, match each equation with its graph.

7. $y = 2$ *c*

8. $x = -1$ *a*

9. $x = 2$ *d*

10. $y = -1$ *b*

a.

b.

c.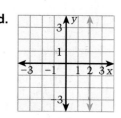

d.

In Exercises 11–14, sketch the lines on the coordinate plane. Then find the point at which the two lines intersect.

11. $x = 6$, $y = -1$

12. $x = 7$, $y = 3$

13. $x = -4$, $y = -5$

14. $x = -8$, $y = 2$

In Exercises 15–18, decide whether the point lies on the line.

15. $(-3, 4)$, $x = -3$

16. $(-7, -4)$, $x = -4$

17. $(8, 10)$, $y = 8$

18. $(9, -5)$, $y = -5$

In Exercises 19–22, write an equation for the graph.

19. A line, the x-coordinate of each point is 2.

20. A line, the y-coordinate of each point is 4.

21. A line, the y-coordinate of each point is -72.

22. A line, the x-coordinate of each point is -1.

In Exercises 23–30, write equations for the horizontal and vertical lines that pass through the point.

23. $(10, -6)$

24. $(8, -3)$

25. $(-21, -15)$

26. $(-4, -17)$

27. $(-5, 12)$

28. $(-9, 11)$

29. $(3, 0)$

30. $(0, -1)$

In Exercises 31–33, use the following information.

Your family participates in a television rating system in which a monitor keeps track of the channels you watch. The results are plotted on the graph at the right.

31. Describe what happened from noon to midnight.

32. How many hours was the television on during this 12-hour period?

33. Which channel was on the most? Explain your reasoning.

Violin Family Ratios **In Exercises 34–36, use the following information.**

The violin family includes the bass, the cello, the viola, and the violin. The size of each instrument determines its tone. The violin produces the highest tones, while the bass produces the deepest (lowest) tones. The matrix shows different measurements, in inches, for different parts of each instrument.

Violin Family	Bass	Cello	Viola	Violin
Total length	72	48	36	26
Body	48	32	24	17
Fingerboard	44	29	21	17
Neck	28	17	13	10

34. Find the ratios of the total lengths to the body lengths. Construct a graph that compares the ratios, y, with the total lengths, x. Describe the results.

35. Find the ratios of the neck lengths to the fingerboard lengths. Construct a graph that compares the ratios, y, with the fingerboard lengths, x. Describe the results.

36. Find and describe other similar ratios on the instruments.

Symphony Orchestras **In Exercises 37–39, use the following information.**

The number of symphony orchestras from 1980 to 1988 is shown in the table. *(Source: American Symphony Orchestra League)*

	1980	1981	1982	1983	1984	1985	1986	1987	1988
College/Community	1311	1311	1304	1306	1317	1317	1298	1301	1253
Urban/Major	261	261	268	266	255	255	274	271	319
Total in United States	?	?	?	?	?	?	?	?	?

1572 1572 1572 1572 1572 1572 1572 2751 2751

37. Complete the table.

38. Plot the data in the table on one coordinate plane.

39. Describe the results.

The temperature of Lake Michigan and the air temperature at O'Hare airport in Chicago are recorded at 2:00 P.M. during a week in October.

Date (x)	Oct. 17	Oct. 18	Oct. 19	Oct. 20	Oct. 21	Oct. 22	Oct. 23
Air Temperature (y)	62°F	58°F	52°F	51°F	59°F	61°F	60°F
Water Temperature (y)	53°F	53°F	53°F	53°F	53°F	53°F	53°F

40. Create two graphs, one for water temperature and one for air temperature.

41. For which graph do the points all have the same second coordinate?

42. What does this tell you about the variability of air and water temperatures?

Integrated Review

In Exercises 43–48, solve the equation for y.

43. $2x + 5y = 10$

44. $4y - 6x = 3$

45. $2y - 5x = 14$

46. $-6y - 8x = 22$

47. $3x - 7y = -2x + 19$

48. $9y + 10x = 21 + 18x$

In Exercises 49–52, decide whether the values of x and y satisfy the equation.

49. $3x - y = 17$, $x = 0$ and $y = 8$

50. $2y - x = 21$, $x = 5$ and $y = 13$

51. $4y - 7x = -20$, $x = 8$ and $y = 9$

52. $5x + 2y = 30$, $x = 4$ and $y = 0$

Exploration and Extension

Computer Graphics   **In Exercises 53 and 54, use the following information to find the coordinates of the vertices of the blue figure.**

Images on a computer screen can be represented by a collection of points in a coordinate plane. An object can be moved to the right or left by adding to or subtracting from the *x*-coordinate of each point. An object can be moved up or down by adding to or subtracting from the *y*-coordinate of each point.

53. 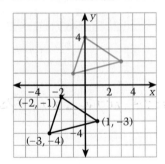 black triangle moves 2 units to the right and 5 units up to the blue triangle.

54. 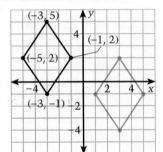 black diamond moves 6 units to the right and 3 units down to the blue diamond.

4.2

Graphing Linear Equations in Two Variables

What you should learn:

Goal 1 How to graph a linear equation from a table of values

Goal 2 How to interpret graphs of linear equations

Why you should learn it:

You can use linear equations and their graphs as models for many real-life relationships, such as for sales figures over time.

Goal 1 Graphing a Linear Equation

In Lesson 4.1, you saw that the graph of an equation containing only one variable was either a horizontal or a vertical line. In this lesson, you will see that the graph of a **linear equation** with *two* variables, $Ax + By = C$, is also a line.

The **graph** of an equation involving two variables, x and y, is the collection of *all* points (x, y) that are **solutions** of the equation. For instance, since $(1, 3)$ is a solution of $y = 2x + 1$, you know that $(1, 3)$ is a point on the graph of $y = 2x + 1$. But $(1, 3)$ is only *one* point on the graph. How many points does the graph have in all?

The answer is that most graphs have far too many points to list. So how, then, could you ever sketch a graph? One way is to make a table of values, graph enough solutions to recognize a pattern, and then connect the points.

Problem Solving
Look for a pattern

Example 1   *Constructing a Table of Values and Finding a Pattern*

Construct a table of values for $y = 2x + 1$ and graph the corresponding solutions. What is the pattern?

Solution   To construct a table of values, choose several x-values, substitute each x-value into the equation, and find the corresponding y-value.

Choose an x-value.	Substitute and find the y-value.	Find solution (x, y).
$x = -2$	$y = 2(-2) + 1 = -3$	$(-2, -3)$
$x = -1$	$y = 2(-1) + 1 = -1$	$(-1, -1)$
$x = 0$	$y = 2(0) + 1 = 1$	$(0, 1)$
$x = 1$	$y = 2(1) + 1 = 3$	$(1, 3)$
$x = 2$	$y = 2(2) + 1 = 5$	$(2, 5)$

The five solutions are shown in the graph at the left. The pattern formed by the points is that they all lie on a line. The *entire* line, including the parts that are not shown, is the *graph* of $y = 2x + 1$. *Each* point on the line is a solution of the equation $y = 2x + 1$.

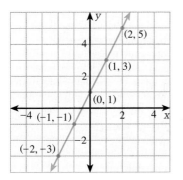

Before constructing a table of values, it is helpful to first solve for one variable in the equation, as shown in Example 2.

Example 2 — Rewriting before Constructing a Table

Sketch the graph of $4x + 2y = 1$.

Solution Begin by solving the given equation for y.

$$4x + 2y = 1 \qquad \textit{Original equation}$$
$$2y = -4x + 1 \qquad \textit{Subtract 4x from both sides.}$$
$$y = -2x + \tfrac{1}{2} \qquad \textit{Divide both sides by 2.}$$

Now choose several values of x and construct a table of values. For instance, when $x = 1$ the value of y is

$$y = -2(1) + \tfrac{1}{2} = -\tfrac{3}{2}.$$

Table of Values for $y = -2x + \tfrac{1}{2}$

Choose x.	-3	-2	-1	0	1	2	3
Evaluate y.	$\tfrac{13}{2}$	$\tfrac{9}{2}$	$\tfrac{5}{2}$	$\tfrac{1}{2}$	$-\tfrac{3}{2}$	$-\tfrac{7}{2}$	$-\tfrac{11}{2}$

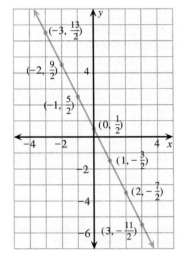

With this table of values, you have found seven solutions.

$$\left(-3, \tfrac{13}{2}\right), \left(-2, \tfrac{9}{2}\right), \left(-1, \tfrac{5}{2}\right), \left(0, \tfrac{1}{2}\right), \left(1, -\tfrac{3}{2}\right), \left(2, -\tfrac{7}{2}\right), \left(3, -\tfrac{11}{2}\right)$$

By plotting the points, you can see that they all lie on a line. The line through the points is the graph of the equation. ∎

Example 3 — Verifying Solutions of an Equation

Which of the points is on the graph of $x + 3y = 6$?

a. $(1, 2)$ **b.** $\left(-2, \tfrac{8}{3}\right)$

Solution

a. The point $(1, 2)$ is *not* on the graph of $x + 3y = 6$ because it is not a solution.

$$1 + 3(2) \overset{?}{=} 6 \qquad \textit{Substitute 1 for x and 2 for y.}$$
$$7 \neq 6 \qquad \textit{(1, 2) is not a solution.}$$

b. The point $\left(-2, \tfrac{8}{3}\right)$ is on the graph of $x + 3y = 6$ because it is a solution.

$$-2 + 3\left(\tfrac{8}{3}\right) \overset{?}{=} 6 \qquad \textit{Substitute} -2 \textit{ for x and } \tfrac{8}{3} \textit{ for y.}$$
$$-2 + 8 \overset{?}{=} 6 \qquad \textit{Simplify.}$$
$$6 = 6 \qquad \left(-2, \tfrac{8}{3}\right) \textit{ is a solution.}$$
∎

Interpreting Graphs of Linear Equations

The graph of a relationship between two variables can be used to give information about how the two variables are related.

Real Life
Publishing

Morning Newspapers Sold (in millions)

Year (0 ↔ 1980)

Evening Newspapers Sold (in millions)

Year (0 ↔ 1980)

Example 4 *Interpreting Graphs*

The top graph shows the number of morning newspapers sold each weekday in the United States from 1978 to 1990 with $x = 0$ corresponding to 1980. The bottom graph shows the number of evening papers sold during the same years. What do these two graphs tell you about newspaper sales? (*Source: Editor and Publisher Company*)

Solution   The top graph shows that morning newspaper sales were *increasing* over time, from about 27 million in 1978 to about 43 million in 1990. The bottom graph shows that evening newspaper sales were *decreasing*, from about 35 million in 1978 to about 20 million in 1990. During the 13-year period, many Americans were switching from evening newspapers to morning newspapers. ■

Communicating *about* **A L G E B R A**

▶ **SHARING IDEAS about the Lesson**

Drawing Graphs   Remember, the graph of an equation is a visual model of the equation.

A. Sketch the graphs of $y = x$ and $y = -x$ on the same coordinate plane. What do you notice about the two graphs?

B. Copy and complete the table for $y = -2x + 5$. Then sketch the graph of the equation.

x	−3	−2	−1	0	1	2	3
y	?	?	?	?	?	?	?

C. How many points are needed to determine a line? Justify your answer.

D. To construct a table of values for $y = \frac{3}{4}x - 8$, which values of x would you choose? Why?

EXERCISES

▶ **CRITICAL THINKING about the Lesson**

1. What is meant by a *solution* of $Ax + By = C$?

2. Define *graph* of an equation.

3. Which of the following are solutions of $3x - y = 2$?
   a. $(3, 1)$ **b.** $(1, 2)$ **c.** $(-1, -5)$ **d.** $(0, -2)$

4. Solve $4y - 6x = 10$ for y. Explain each step of the solution.

Independent Practice

In Exercises 5–8, decide which of the two points lies on the line. Justify your choice algebraically and graphically.

5. $2x + 3y = 10$ **6.** $2y - 4x = 6$ **7.** $6y - 3x = -9$ **8.** $-5x - 8y = 15$
 a. $(2, 2)$ **a.** $(1, 4)$ **a.** $(3, 0)$ **a.** $(-3, 0)$

 b. $(3, 1)$ **b.** $(-1, 1)$ **b.** $(2, -1)$ **b.** $(-2, -1)$

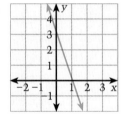

In Exercises 9–12, find several solutions of the equation.

9. $y = 2x - 4$ **10.** $y = 5 - 3x$ **11.** $y = 3(2x - 1)$ **12.** $y = \frac{1}{2}(6 - 4x)$

In Exercises 13–20, use a table of values to sketch the graph of the equation.

13. $y = -x + 2$ **14.** $y = -4x + 5$ **15.** $y = -(2 - x)$ **16.** $y = -2(x + 3)$
17. $y = \frac{1}{2}x + 4$ **18.** $y = -\frac{1}{2}x - 12$ **19.** $4x + 3y = 24$ **20.** $3x - 2y = -12$

In Exercises 21–24, match the equation with its graph.

21. $2x - y = 7$ **22.** $3x + y = 3$ **23.** $6x + 3y = 0$ **24.** $-2x + y = 5$

a.

b.

c.

d.

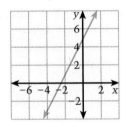

25. *What's the Temperature?* A surveyor on a trip to Antarctica sends back a report stating that the temperature has dropped to $-40°$. The surveyor's supervisor criticizes the report, saying that the surveyor should have said whether the temperature reading was in degrees Fahrenheit or Celsius. The surveyor replies that the scale wasn't necessary! Why?

26. *Misleading Graphs* Graphs can help us visualize relationships between two variables, but they can also be misused to imply results that are not correct. The two graphs below represent the *same* data points. Which graph is misleading and why?

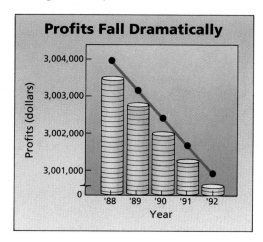

27. *Flood Waters* A river has risen 6 feet above flood stage. Beginning at a time of $t = 0$, the water level drops at the rate of two inches per hour. The number of feet above flood stage, y, after t hours is given by $y = 6 - \frac{1}{6}t$. Sketch a graph of the equation over the 12-hour period from $t = 0$ to $t = 12$.

28. How long does it take the river to recede to flood stage?

In Exercises 29 and 30, match the description with its visual model. Explain.

29. Your friend starts driving from home at 55 miles per hour for 3 hours, where d is the distance from home.

30. You start driving the 165 miles home at 55 miles per hour for 3 hours, where d is the distance from home.

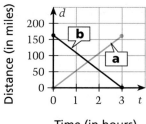

31. *High School Graduates* The table lists the number of graduates from Beecher High School. An algebraic model that approximates these data is $y = -6.5t + 1006$ with $t = 0$ corresponding to 1980. Graph the actual data and the model on the same coordinate plane. Use the model to estimate the number of graduates in 1992.

Year	1983	1984	1985	1986	1987	1988	1989	1990	1991	1992
t	3	4	5	6	7	8	9	10	11	12
Graduates, y	984	987	962	968	953	952	946	944	931	?

32. *Life Expectancy*   The table gives the life expectancy in the United States for a child (at birth). A mathematical model for the life expectancy in years during this period is $y = 0.3t + 65.6$ with $t = 0$ corresponding to 1950. Graph the actual data points and the model on the same coordinate plane. Use the model to estimate the life expectancy in the year 2000. *(Source: U.S. Bureau of Census)*

Year	1930	1940	1950	1960	1970	1980	1990	2000
t	−20	−10	0	10	20	30	40	50
Life Expectancy, y	59.7	62.9	68.2	69.7	70.8	73.7	75.6	?

Integrated Review

33. Sketch the graph of $x = 2$.

34. Sketch the graph of $y = -1$.

35. Sketch the graph of $y = 8$.

36. Sketch the graph of $x = -6$.

In Exercises 37–40, find the point of intersection of the two lines.

37. $x = -4$, $y = 7$

38. $x = 11$, $y = 5$

39. $x = -10$, $y = -12$

40. $x = 6$, $y = -18$

In Exercises 41–44, write equations for the horizontal and vertical lines that pass through the point.

41. $(6, -3)$ **42.** $(-12, -15)$ **43.** $(8, 21)$ **44.** $(-7, 9)$

Exploration and Extension

In Exercises 45 and 46, plot the points given in the table of values. Describe the relationship between *x* and *y*. Then write an equation that represents the relationship.

45.

x	−2	0	2	4	6	8	10
y	−6	−4	−2	0	2	4	6

46.

x	−3	−2	−1	0	1	2	3
y	5	4	3	2	1	0	1

47. Is the graph shown at the right more likely to represent a trip taken on a train, a bus, or an airplane? Explain your answer.

48. *Automobile Ownership*   In 1990, the United States had $33\frac{1}{3}\%$ of all registered automobiles in the world. What percent did the United States have in 1980? (Use the information on page 175.)

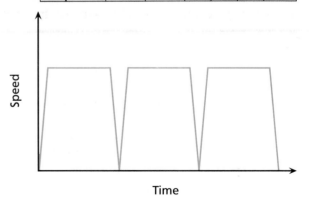

A graphing calculator or computer can be used to sketch the graph of an equation. Here we show how to use a Texas Instruments TI-81 and a Casio fx-7700G to sketch the graph of x − 2y = 2.

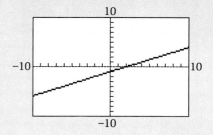

Using a graphing calculator is fairly easy, but there are four ideas you must remember.

- Solve the equation for *y* in terms of *x*.
- Set the range by entering the least and greatest *x* and *y* values and the scale (units per mark).
- Use parentheses if you are unsure of the calculator's order of operations.

TI-81

Solve given equation for y: $y = \frac{1}{2}x - 1$

$\boxed{RANGE}$ (Set range.)
  Xmin = −10
  Xmax = 10
  Xscl = 1
  Ymin = −10
  Ymax = 10
  Yscl = 1
$\boxed{Y=}$ $\boxed{(}$ 1 $\boxed{\div}$ 2 $\boxed{)}$ $\boxed{X|T}$ $\boxed{-}$ 1
  :Y₁ = (1/2)X − 1
  :Y₂ =
  :Y₃ =
  :Y₄ =
  $\boxed{GRAPH}$

  $\boxed{CLEAR}$ (Clear screen.)

Casio fx-7700G

Solve given equation for y: $y = \frac{1}{2}x - 1$

$\boxed{Range}$ (Set range.)
  Xmin = −10
  max = 10
  scl = 1
  Ymin = −10
  max = 10
  scl = 1
$\boxed{EXE}$ $\boxed{Range}$

$\boxed{SHIFT}$ $\boxed{F5}$ (Cls) $\boxed{EXE}$

$\boxed{Graph}$ $\boxed{(}$ 1 $\boxed{\div}$ 2 $\boxed{)}$ $\boxed{X,\theta,T}$ $\boxed{-}$ 1
  Graph Y = (1 ÷ 2)X − 1
$\boxed{EXE}$

$\boxed{SHIFT}$ $\boxed{F5}$ (Cls) $\boxed{EXE}$

Exercises

In Exercises 1–8, use a graphing calculator to sketch the graphs. (For 1–4, use the range shown above. For 5–8, use the indicated range.)

1. $y = -2x - 3$ **2.** $y = 2x + 2$ **3.** $x + 2y = -1$ **4.** $x - 3y = 3$

5. $y = x + 25$ **6.** $y = -x + 25$ **7.** $y = 0.1x$ **8.** $y = 100x + 2500$

5. RANGE	6. RANGE	7. RANGE	8. RANGE
Xmin = −10	Xmin = −10	Xmin = −10	Xmin = 0
Xmax = 10	Xmax = 10	Xmax = 10	Xmax = 100
Xscl = 1	Xscl = 1	Xscl = 1	Xscl = 10
Ymin = −5	Ymin = −5	Ymin = −1	Ymin = 0
Ymax = 35	Ymax = 35	Ymax = 1	Ymax = 15000
Yscl = 5	Yscl = 5	Yscl = .1	Yscl = 1000

4.3

Quick Graphs Using Intercepts

What you should learn:

Goal 1 How to find the intercepts of the graph of a linear equation

Goal 2 How to use intercepts to sketch a quick graph of a line

Why you should learn it:

You can quickly sketch the graph of a linear equation by plotting its intercepts. The graph allows you to see relationships between the variables.

Goal 1 Finding the Intercepts of a Line

In mathematics, we like to find efficient ways to solve problems. For instance, in Lesson 4.2 you sketched the graph of an equation by creating a table of values, plotting the corresponding points, and finally drawing the graph through the points. For *linear* equations, the following two observations suggest a more efficient way to sketch the graph.

- The graph of any linear equation, $Ax + By = C$, is a line.
- Two points are all that are needed to determine a line.

Two points that are usually convenient to use are the points at which the line intersects the x-axis and the y-axis.

Intercepts of a Line

Consider the line given by $Ax + By = C$.

1. The x-intercept of the line is the value of x when $y = 0$. To find the x-intercept, let $y = 0$ and solve for x in $Ax = C$.

2. The y-intercept of the line is the value of y when $x = 0$. To find the y-intercept, let $x = 0$ and solve for y in $By = C$.

Example 1 Finding Intercepts

a. To find the x-intercept of $x + 5y = 10$, let y be zero.

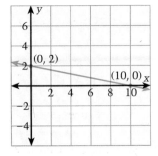

$$x + 5y = 10 \quad \textit{Original equation}$$
$$x + 5(0) = 10 \quad \textit{Substitute 0 for y.}$$
$$x = 10 \quad \textit{Solve for x.}$$

The x-intercept is 10. It occurs at the point $(10, 0)$.

b. To find the y-intercept of $x + 5y = 10$, let x be zero.

$$x + 5y = 10 \quad \textit{Original equation}$$
$$0 + 5y = 10 \quad \textit{Substitute 0 for x.}$$
$$y = 2 \quad \textit{Solve for y.}$$

The y-intercept is 2. It occurs at the point $(0, 2)$. ∎

Using Intercepts to Sketch a Quick Graph

The intercepts of a line provide a quick way to sketch the line.

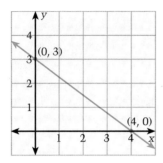

Quick Graph Using Intercepts

Example 2 *Sketching a Quick Graph*

Sketch the graph of $3x + 4y = 12$.

Solution First, find the intercepts.

x-Intercept (Let $y = 0$.)	**y-Intercept (Let $x = 0$.)**
$3x + 4y = 12$	$3x + 4y = 12$
$3x + 4(0) = 12$	$3(0) + 4y = 12$
$x = 4$	$y = 3$
x-intercept is 4.	y-intercept is 3.

To sketch the graph, draw a coordinate plane, plot points for the intercepts, and draw a line through them. In the graph shown at the left, the x-intercept occurs at $(4, 0)$, the point on the x-axis at which x is 4. The y-intercept occurs at $(0, 3)$, the point on the y-axis at which y is 3. ■

When using the quick-graph method to sketch a line, you should find the intercepts *before* you draw the coordinate plane. This will enable you to use an appropriate scale on each axis.

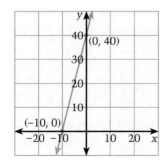

Quick Graph Using Intercepts

Example 3 *Using Intercepts to Determine Appropriate Scales*

Sketch the line given by $y = 4x + 40$.

Solution First, find the intercepts.

x-Intercept (Let $y = 0$.)	**y-Intercept (Let $x = 0$.)**
$y = 4x + 40$	$y = 4x + 40$
$0 = 4x + 40$	$y = 4(0) + 40$
$-40 = 4x$	$y = 40$
$-10 = x$	
x-intercept is -10.	y-intercept is 40.

From the values of the intercepts, you can see that the coordinate plane should have a y-axis that includes 40 and an x-axis that includes -10. Plotting points for the intercepts at $(-10, 0)$ and $(0, 40)$, and drawing the line through them produce the graph shown at the left. ■

Example 4 *Determining the Price of Tickets*

You are on the planning committee to organize a spaghetti dinner to raise funds for the zoo. Your goal is to sell $1500 worth of tickets. Based on last year's attendance (200 adults and 100 children), how much should you charge for an adult's ticket and a child's ticket?

Solution

Verbal Model	Adult ticket price	•	Number of adults	+	Child ticket price	•	Number of children	=	Total sales

Labels Adult ticket price = x (dollars per person)
Number of adults = 200   (people)
Child ticket price = y (dollars per person)
Number of children = 100   (people)
Total sales = 1500   (dollars)

Equation $200x + 100y = 1500$ **Algebraic model**

This equation has many solutions. For instance, you could charge $5 for everyone (5, 5), or you could charge $6 per adult and $3 per child (6, 3), or you could charge $4 per adult and $7 per child (4, 7). To get a better idea of the options, use a quick graph, as shown at the left. ∎

Communicating about **ALGEBRA**

▶ **SHARING IDEAS about the Lesson**

Understand Limitations The quick-graph method using intercepts cannot be used for every line.

A. What is the x-intercept of the line given by $x = -19$? Does this line have a y-intercept?

B. What is the y-intercept of the horizontal line passing through $(-34, 615)$? Does this line have an x-intercept?

C. What is the y-intercept of the line given by $y = 2x$? What is the x-intercept of the line given by $y = 2x$? Are the intercepts the same point or different points? How did you decide?

D. The quick-graph method using intercepts requires two intercepts that are different points. For which three types of lines is the quick-graph method using intercepts *not* applicable? Explain your reasoning.

EXERCISES

Guided Practice

▶ **CRITICAL THINKING about the Lesson**

1. True or False? The graph of a linear equation is a line.

2. How many points are needed to determine a line? Why?

3. How do you find the x-intercept of the line $2x - y = 4$?

4. How do you find the y-intercept of the line $2x - y = 4$?

5. Is -8 the x-intercept or the y-intercept of the line $y = \frac{1}{2}x + 4$?

6. Is the y-intercept of the line $y = 6x - 4$ equal to 6 or -4? Justify your answer.

Independent Practice

In Exercises 7–10, match the equation with its graph.

7. $y = 4x - 8$ **8.** $y = 4x - 4$ **9.** $y = 4x + 8$ **10.** $y = 4x + 4$

a.   **b.**   **c.**   **d.**

In Exercises 11–14, use the graph to find the x-intercept and y-intercept of the line.

11.   **12.**   **13.**   **14.**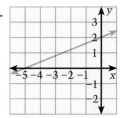

In Exercises 15–20, sketch the line with the given intercepts.

15. x-intercept: -3
    y-intercept: 7

16. x-intercept: 16
    y-intercept: 9

17. x-intercept: 9
    y-intercept: -8

18. x-intercept: -2
    y-intercept: -5

19. x-intercept: -11
    y-intercept: -7

20. x-intercept: -9
    y-intercept: 12

In Exercises 21–28, find the *x*-intercept of the line.

21. $x - 2y = 4$

22. $x + 4y = -2$

23. $2x - 3y = 6$

24. $5x + 6y = 95$

25. $-6x - 4y = 42$

26. $9x - 4y = 54$

27. $-x - 5y = 12$

28. $-13x - y = 39$

In Exercises 29–36, find the *y*-intercept of the line.

29. $y = 4x - 2$

30. $y = -3x + 7$

31. $y = 13x + 26$

32. $y = 6x - 24$

33. $3x - 4y = 16$

34. $2x - 17y = -51$

35. $-x + 8y = 40$

36. $6x + 9y = -81$

In Exercises 37–48, sketch the line. Label the *x*-intercept and *y*-intercept on the graph.

37. $y = 2 - x$

38. $y = x + 3$

39. $y = 3x + 9$

40. $y = -4 + 2x$

41. $3x + 5y = 15$

42. $4x + 3y = 24$

43. $-9x + 2y = 36$

44. $x - 6y = 36$

45. $5x - y = 35$

46. $10x + 7y = -140$

47. $y = -3x + 9$

48. $y = 10x + 50$

49. *Writing a Novel* Alicia Martínez has had her first novel accepted for publication. She signed contracts to receive a royalty rate of 5% of the retail price of each book. Alicia is now wondering how many paperback copies and how many hardback copies must be sold to earn her $100,000. Sketch a graph showing the possible sales combinations that could earn Alicia this amount.

50. Suppose Alicia's publisher sold 20,000 hardback copies. How many paperback copies must be sold for Alicia to realize her dream? Explain.

51. *Saturday Matinee* A theater charges $4 per person before 6:00 P.M. and $7 per person after 6:00 P.M. The total ticket sales for Saturday was $11,228. Sketch a graph showing the possible number of people who attended the theater before and after 6:00 P.M.

52. Suppose no one attended the theater before 6:00 P.M. How many people attended the theater after 6:00 P.M.? Explain.

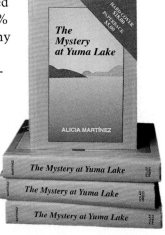

Integrated Review

53. Is $(1, -3)$ a solution of $4x - 3y = -5$?

54. Is $(-5, 4)$ a solution of $-5x - 4y = 9$?

In Exercises 55–58, solve for *y*.

55. $6x + 2y = 18$

56. $4x - y = 7$

57. $-9x - 3y = 2$

58. $5x + 20y = 10$

Technology—Graphing Calculator   **In Exercises 59 and 60, use the following information.**

The graph of $30x + 60y = 1800$ was sketched with a graphing calculator. The calculator screen is shown at the right.

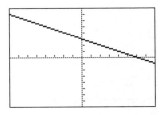

59. Find the *x*- and *y*-intercepts of the line.

60. Use the result from Exercise 59 to determine the distance between adjacent tick marks on the *x*-axis and the distance between adjacent tick marks on the *y*-axis.

Technology—Graphing Calculator   **In Exercises 61 and 62, use the following information.**

The graph of $64x - 16y = 256$ was sketched with a graphing calculator. The calculator screen is shown at the right.

61. Find the *x*- and *y*-intercepts of the line.

62. Use the result from Exercise 61 to determine the distance between adjacent tick marks on the *x*-axis and the distance between adjacent tick marks on the *y*-axis.

Women's 200-Meter Dash   **In Exercises 63 and 64, use the following information.**

The graph below shows the times for the women's 200-meter dash in the Summer Olympics from 1964 to 1988.

Year (0 ↔ 1960)

63. What are the coordinates of Florence Griffith Joyner's record time?

64. Do you think the line in the graph will continue to be a good model for the next 50 years? Explain.

Florence Griffith Joyner of the United States set a record of 21.34 seconds in the women's 200-meter dash in the 1988 Summer Olympics in Seoul, South Korea.

1. Evaluate $3x + 7$ when $x = 0$. **(1.2)**

2. Evaluate $\frac{1}{3}6a(4 - b)$ when $a = 1$ and $b = 3$. **(1.2)**

3. Solve $4(x - 1) = 2y$ for y. **(3.6)**

4. Solve $\frac{10}{9}x = 3x + y$ for x. **(3.6)**

5. What is the opposite of -3.2? **(2.1)**

6. What is the absolute value of $-3(-10)$? **(2.1)**

7. Evaluate $(3^2 - 1) \div 2^3$. **(1.3)**

8. Evaluate $4[(-5)^2 + (-10) - 7]$. **(2.5)**

9. Simplify $3(x^2 - 1) - 4(x - x^2)$. **(2.6)**

10. Simplify $x(x - 1) - (2 + x^2)$. **(2.6)**

11. Does $4 \cdot x + 3 \div 2 = 4 \cdot (x + 3) \div 2$? **(2.6)**

12. Does $\frac{1}{5}(16x + 2) = (16x + 2) \div 5$? **(2.7)**

13. Find $\begin{bmatrix} 0.4 & 9.2 \\ 6.3 & 7.8 \end{bmatrix} + \begin{bmatrix} -4.3 & 1.8 \\ -2.2 & 2.2 \end{bmatrix}$. **(2.4)**

14. Find $\begin{bmatrix} \frac{1}{4} & -\frac{3}{2} \\ \frac{3}{8} & \frac{7}{8} \end{bmatrix} - \begin{bmatrix} \frac{1}{8} & -\frac{3}{2} \\ -\frac{1}{8} & \frac{3}{4} \end{bmatrix}$. **(2.4)**

15. Is 0 a solution of $14x - 10 \geq 3x + 2$? **(1.5)**

16. Is 3 a solution of $\frac{1}{2}(1 - x) < -2$? **(1.5)**

17. Is -1 a solution of $4y^2 - 3 = 1$? **(1.5)**

18. Is 5.5 a solution of $-3(a - 9.5) = -12$? **(1.5)**

19. Is $(2, -1)$ a solution of $2x - y = 5$? **(4.2)**

20. Is $(0, 4)$ a solution of $y = 4$? **(4.1)**

Milestones   CALCULATING THROUGH THE CENTURIES

| 1550 | 1600 | 1650 | 1700 | 1750 | 1800 | 1850 | 1900 | 1950 | 2000 |

Pascal's Machine   Babbage's analytical engine   First electronic computer

Next to fingers, the abacus is the oldest calculating device known. Different forms of the abacus were used by Egyptians, Greeks, Romans, Hindus, and Chinese. From a tray containing sand or dust in which to write, the abacus gradually evolved into a wooden frame with beads that slid on thin bamboo rods.

A knotted cord was used by various cultures to count days and inventory livestock. In part of India, an elaborate knotted cord system was used to take the census in 1872.

In 1642, Blaise Pascal built an adding and subtracting machine that carried tens mechanically. In the 1830's, Charles Babbage began work on his analytical engine, hoping it would do complex calculations from a series of instructions, but lacking the technology to make it work. All of these devices and ideas have led to today's calculators and super computers.

Abacus (above). Pascal's "Machine Arithmetic" (below)

Find out when the Chinese began using bamboo rods to compute.

4.4

The Slope of a Line

epols

What you should learn:

Goal 1 How to find the slope of a line using two of its points

Goal 2 How to interpret slope as a constant rate of change or an average rate of change

Why you should learn it:

You can use slope to represent the rate of change of one quantity with respect to another, such as distance traveled compared to time used.

Goal 1 Finding the Slope of a Line

The *slope* of a nonvertical line is the number of units the line rises or falls for each unit of horizontal change from left to right.

The line shown below at the left rises 2 units for each unit of horizontal change from left to right. The slope of a line is represented by the letter m. Thus, this line has a slope of $m = 2$. Two points on a line are all that are needed to determine its slope.

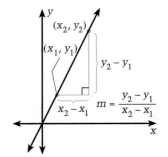

The Slope of a Line

The slope of the nonvertical line passing through the points (x_1, y_1) and (x_2, y_2) is

$$m = \frac{y_2 - y_1}{x_2 - x_1}. \quad \frac{rise}{run}$$

The numerator is read as "y sub 2 minus y sub 1" and is called the *rise*. The denominator is read as "x sub 2 minus x sub 1" and is called the *run*.

When the formula for slope is used, the order of subtraction is important. Given two points on a line, you can label either as (x_1, y_1) and the other as (x_2, y_2). After doing this, however, you must form the numerator and the denominator using the *same* order of subtraction.

Subtraction order is the same. → $\dfrac{y_2 - y_1}{x_2 - x_1}$ $\quad$ $\dfrac{y_2 - y_1}{x_1 - x_2}$ ← *Subtraction order is different.*

$\qquad\qquad\qquad\quad$ Correct $\qquad$ Incorrect

Example **1** **_A Line with a Positive Slope Rises_**

Find the slope of the line passing through $(-2, 0)$ and $(3, 1)$.

Solution   Let $(x_1, y_1) = (-2, 0)$ and $(x_2, y_2) = (3, 1)$.

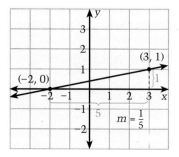

Positive slope, line rises.

$$m = \frac{y_2 - y_1}{x_2 - x_1} \quad \leftarrow \textit{Rise: Difference of y-values}$$
$$ \quad \leftarrow \textit{Run: Difference of x-values}$$

$$= \frac{1 - 0}{3 - (-2)} \quad \textit{Substitute values.}$$

$$= \frac{1}{3 + 2} \quad \textit{Simplify.}$$

$$= \frac{1}{5} \quad \textit{Slope is positive.}$$

Example **2**   **_A Line with Slope Zero Is Horizontal_**

Find the slope of the line passing through $(-1, 2)$ and $(2, 2)$.

Solution   Let $(x_1, y_1) = (-1, 2)$ and $(x_2, y_2) = (2, 2)$.

$$m = \frac{y_2 - y_1}{x_2 - x_1} \quad \leftarrow \textit{Rise: Difference of y-values}$$
$$ \quad \leftarrow \textit{Run: Difference of x-values}$$

$$= \frac{2 - 2}{2 - (-1)} \quad \textit{Substitute values.}$$

$$= \frac{0}{3} \quad \textit{Simplify.}$$

$$= 0 \quad \textit{Slope is zero.}$$

Slope zero, line is horizontal.

Example **3**   **_A Line with a Negative Slope Falls_**

Find the slope of the line passing through $(0, 0)$ and $(1, -1)$.

Solution   Let $(x_1, y_1) = (0, 0)$ and $(x_2, y_2) = (1, -1)$.

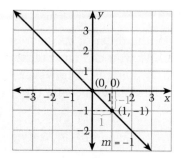

Negative slope, line falls.

$$m = \frac{y_2 - y_1}{x_2 - x_1} \quad \leftarrow \textit{Rise: Difference of y-values}$$
$$ \quad \leftarrow \textit{Run: Difference of x-values}$$

$$= \frac{-1 - 0}{1 - 0} \quad \textit{Substitute values.}$$

$$= \frac{-1}{1} \quad \textit{Simplify.}$$

$$= -1 \quad \textit{Slope is negative.}$$

Example 4 **The Slope of a Vertical Line Is Not Defined**

Apply the slope formula to the vertical line passing through (2, 4) and (2, 1).

Solution   Let $(x_1, y_1) = (2, 1)$ and $(x_2, y_2) = (2, 4)$

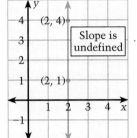

Slope is undefined

Vertical line

$$m = \frac{y_2 - y_1}{x_2 - x_1} \leftarrow \textit{Rise: Difference of y-values} \atop \leftarrow \textit{Run: Difference of x-values}$$

$$= \frac{4 - 1}{2 - 2} \qquad \textit{Substitute values.}$$

$$= \frac{3}{0} \qquad \textit{Division by 0 is undefined.}$$

Because division by 0 is undefined, the expression $\frac{3}{0}$ has no meaning. This is why the slope of a vertical line is undefined. (This will always happen with two points on a vertical line.) ■

Classification of Lines by Slope

1. A line with positive slope *rises* from left to right. $(m > 0)$
2. A line with negative slope *falls* from left to right. $(m < 0)$
3. A line with slope zero *is horizontal*. $(m = 0)$
4. A line with undefined slope *is vertical*. (m is undefined.)

Problem Solving
Make a Graph

The slope of a line not only tells you whether the line rises, falls, or is horizontal; it also tells you the steepness of the line. For two lines with positive slopes, the line with the greater slope is steeper. For two lines with negative slopes, the line with the slope of greater absolute value is steeper.

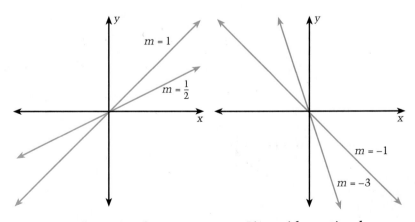

Lines with positive slopes   *Lines with negative slopes*

In real-life problems, slope is often used to describe a **constant rate of change** or an **average rate of change.** Units of measure such as miles per hour or dollars per year are usually used.

Real Life
Mountain Climbing

Using ropes, pitons (spikes), and snap links, a rock climber can scale a vertical cliff.

Example 5   *Slope as a Rate of Change*

Rebecca is climbing up a 500-foot cliff. By 1:00 P.M., she has climbed 125 feet up the cliff. By 4:00 P.M., she has reached an altitude of 290 feet. Find the average rate of change in Rebecca's altitude during the three hours. Give the rate in feet per hour.

Solution   Let t represent the time and y represent Rebecca's altitude. Her two positions are represented by (t_1, y_1) and (t_2, y_2).

1st time	1st altitude	2nd time	2nd altitude
↓	↓	↓	↓

$$(t_1, y_1) = (1, 125) \qquad (t_2, y_2) = (4, 290)$$

Use the formula for slope to find the average rate of change.

$$\begin{aligned}
\text{Rate of change} &= \frac{y_2 - y_1}{t_2 - t_1} && \begin{array}{l}\leftarrow \textit{Difference of altitudes} \\ \leftarrow \textit{Difference of times}\end{array} && \left(\frac{\text{feet}}{\text{hours}}\right) \\
&= \frac{290 - 125}{4 - 1} && \textit{Substitute values.} && \left(\frac{\text{feet}}{\text{hours}}\right) \\
&= 55 && \textit{Simplify.} && \left(\frac{\text{ft}}{\text{hour}}\right)
\end{aligned}$$

If Rebecca had been climbing at the rate of 55 feet per hour during the entire three hours, the rate of change in her altitude would be *constant*. It is more likely, however, that her rate varied, and 55 feet per hour represents the *average* rate of change during the three hours.   ■

Communicating *about* ALGEBRA

SHARING IDEAS about the Lesson

Using a Model   Use the formula for slope.

A. At 3:00 P.M., a car leaves a city. By 5:00 P.M., it has traveled 90 miles. Find its average speed.

B. At 7:00 P.M., the temperature is 63°F. At 10:00 P.M., it is 45°F. Find the average rate of change of the temperature.

EXERCISES

▶ **CRITICAL THINKING about the Lesson**

1. A student found the slope of the line through (3, 2) and (1, 4) to be $m = \frac{4-2}{3-1}$. What did the student do wrong? *TRANSPOSED.*

2. In the formula for slope, what is the numerator $y_2 - y_1$ called? *Rise.*

3. In the formula for slope, what is the denominator $x_2 - x_1$ called? *RUN.*

4. Explain what happens when the formula for slope is applied to a vertical line. $X = 0$

5. What is the slope of a horizontal line? *0*

6. Which of the following lines has the *least* slope? Why?

a.

b.

c.

d.
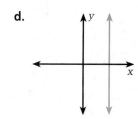

7. True or False? A line with positive slope rises from left to right. *True*

8. Give an example of the use of slope in a real-life problem.

Independent Practice

In Exercises 9–12, estimate the slope of each line.

9.

10.

11.

12.
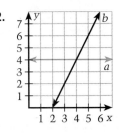

In Exercises 13–16, sketch the line with the given slope through the given point.

13. (2, 1), $m = 2$

14. $(0, -2)$, $m = -\frac{1}{2}$

15. $(-1, -1)$, $m = -\frac{2}{3}$

16. $(-3, 1)$, $m = -1$

In Exercises 17–28, plot the points and find the slope of the line passing through the points.

17. (0, 0), (4, 5)

18. $(0, 0)$, $(-1, -3)$

19. $(-3, -2)$, $(1, 6)$

20. $(0, -6)$, $(8, 0)$

21. (0, 6), (8, 0)

22. $(2, 4)$, $(4, -4)$

23. $(-6, -1)$, $(-6, 4)$

24. $(0, -10)$, $(-4, 0)$

25. $(1, -2)$, $(-2, -2)$

26. (3, 6), (3, 0)

27. (2, 2), $(-3, 5)$

28. (4, 1), (6, 1)

In Exercises 29–34, determine whether the line through the points rises from left to right, falls from left to right, is horizontal, or is vertical.

29. $(6, 9)$, $(4, 3)$

30. $(7, 4)$, $(-1, 8)$

31. $(5, 10)$, $(5, -4)$

32. $(-3, 1)$, $(9, 8)$

33. $(1, 1)$, $(4, -3)$

34. $(-6, 7)$, $(1, 7)$

In Exercises 35 and 36, find the rate of change between the two points. Give the unit of measure.

35. $(2, 2)$, $(9, 23)$
  x is measured in minutes.
  y is measured in inches.

36. $(3, 5)$, $(11, 69)$
  x is measured in years.
  y is measured in dollars.

In Exercises 37 and 38, use the following information to decide whether the points lie on the same line or form the vertices of a triangle.

Any two points on a line can be used to determine its slope. Any three points either lie on the same line or form the vertices of a triangle.

37. $(-2, 1)$, $(1, 2)$, $(3, 3)$

38. $(-2, -4)$, $(2, -2)$, $(6, 0)$

Price of Jeans   **In Exercises 39–42, use the graph at right, which shows average prices of jeans for the years 1950–1990.**

39. Estimate the average rate of change in price from 1950 to 1980.

40. Estimate the average rate of change in price from 1980 to 1990.

41. In which five-year periods is the rate of change positive? Does a positive rate of change mean a price increase or decrease?

42. Which five-year period had the largest price increase?

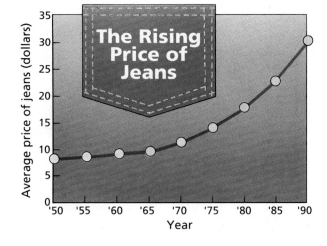

43. *Altitude of a Parachutist*   At 12:05, a parachutist is 8000 feet above the ground. At 12:08, the parachutist is 5400 feet above the ground. Find the average rate of change in feet per minute.

44. *Company Profits*   In 1990, a company had a profit of $1,300,000. In 1992, the company had a profit of $1,200,000. Find the average rate of change of its profit. (Give the result in dollars per year.)

45. *Symphony Orchestras*   In 1980, there were 1572 symphony orchestras in the United States. In 1988, there were 1572. Find the average rate of change in the number of symphony orchestras. (Give the result in symphony orchestras per year.)

(Source: American Symphony Orchestra League)

46. *Broadway Shows*   In 1980, there were 67 new productions on Broadway. In 1987, there were 31 new productions on Broadway. Find the average rate of change in the number of new productions. (Give the result in new productions per year.)

(Source: Variety Magazine)

Border Population Growth   **In Exercises 47–50, use the following information.**

Seven major population regions lie along our border with Mexico. The table shows the populations of four of them.

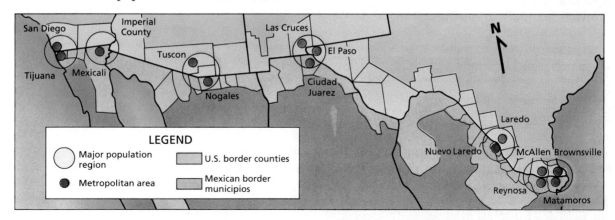

47. Find the average yearly rate of change in population for Juarez from 1980 to 1990.

48. Find the average yearly rate of change in population for Laredo from 1980 to 1990.

49. Which had a greater rate of change from 1980 to 1990: San Diego or Tijuana?

50. Which had a greater rate of change from 1980 to 1990: Tucson or Nogales?

U.S.	San Diego	Tucson	El Paso	Laredo
1980	1,876,900	534,500	580,600	100,300
1990	2,461,100	655,000	737,800	132,200
Mexico	Tijuana	Nogales	Juarez	N. Laredo
1980	480,000	71,000	591,000	203,300
1990	742,600	107,100	727,700	217,900

Integrated Review

In Exercises 51–54, solve for y.

51. $9x - 2y = 14$ 52. $5x + 9y = 18$ 53. $-6x + 3y = 18$ 54. $-2x - 2y = 7$

In Exercises 55–58, find the x-intercept and y-intercept of the line.

55. $3x - 12y = 16$ 56. $-2x + 4y = 16$ 57. $-14x + 3y = -42$ 58. $x - 21y = 7$

Exploration and Extension

59. Find x so that the line through $(3, 4)$ and $(x, 6)$ will have slope $-\frac{2}{5}$.

60. Find the slope of a line passing through $(0, 0)$ and $(5, -17)$.

61. Find the slope of the line $4x + 5y = 50$. Explain how you obtained the slope.

62. Find the slope of $y = -\frac{1}{2}x + 3$.

63. Find the y-intercept of each line graphed at the right. Describe an efficient way to find each y-intercept from the equation.

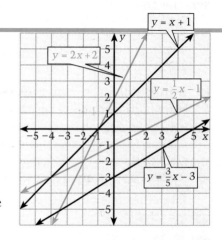

Take this test as you would take a test in class. The answers to the exercises are given at the back of the book.

1. Sketch the lines $x = -1$ and $y = 2$ on the same coordinate plane. What is the point at which the two lines intersect? **(4.1)**

2. Write equations for the horizontal line and the vertical line through $(4, -6)$. **(4. 1)**

3. Solve for y: $6x + \frac{1}{3}y = 9$. **(4.2)**

4. Solve for y: $x + \frac{3}{4}y = 4$. **(4.2)**

In Exercises 5 and 6, solve the equation for y, construct a table of values, and plot the points in the table. (4.2)

5. $\frac{12}{5}x - y = 4$

6. $3x + 4y = 3$

7. Is $\left(3, -\frac{4}{3}\right)$ a solution of $5x + 3y = 11$?

8. Is $(3, 5)$ a solution of $\frac{9}{2}x - y = 20$?

In Exercises 9 and 10, sketch the line and label the intercepts. (4.3)

9. $5x - 3y = 15$

10. $-7x + 4y = 28$

In Exercises 11–14, use the graph to determine your answer.

11. Which equation represents the line? **(4.2)**
   a. $3x - 3y = 0$ **b.** $x + y = 3$ **c.** $y - x = 3$

12. Which is not a solution? **(4.2)**
   a. $\left(-\frac{3}{2}, \frac{3}{2}\right)$ **b.** $\left(\frac{3}{2}, -\frac{3}{2}\right)$ **c.** $(1, 4)$

13. What is the x-intercept? **(4.3)**

14. What is the y-intercept? **(4.3)**

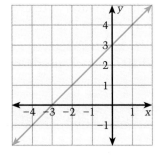

In Exercises 15 and 16, find the slope of the line through the two points. (4.4)

15. $(-1, 1), (20, 15)$

16. $\left(\frac{4}{3}, 2\right), \left(\frac{2}{3}, 6\right)$

In Exercises 17 and 18, find the rate of change between the two points. Give the unit of measure. (4.4)

17. $(2.5, 3.75), (4.0, 5.95)$
   x is in pounds.
   y is in dollars.

18. $\left(\frac{1}{2}, 200\right), (2, 1000)$
   x is in square miles.
   y is in people.

19. A fruit stand is selling baskets of apples for $4 and baskets of strawberries for $6. The total sales for the two fruits on Tuesday was $336. Sketch a graph showing the possible numbers of baskets of each fruit sold. **(4.2)**

20. In January, Luis had a balance of $1140 in a savings account. In April, Luis had a balance of $1450 in the account. Find the average rate of change of the balance. (Give your result in dollars per month.) **(4.4)**

4.5

Quick Graphs Using Slope-Intercept Form

What you should learn:

Goal 1 How to find slope and *y*-intercept from an equation

Goal 2 How to use the slope-intercept form to sketch a line and to solve real-life problems

Why you should learn it:

You can write an equation of a line in slope-intercept form to make it easier to sketch and use.

Goal 1 Finding the Slope and *y*-Intercept

In Lesson 4.4, you were given two points of a line and you learned how to find the slope of the line. Now suppose you are given an equation of a line. How could you find its slope?

One way would be to find two points on the line and use the formula for slope. Let's try this with the line $y = \frac{1}{2}x + 1$. Notice that no matter which pair of points we use to calculate the slope, the result is the same.

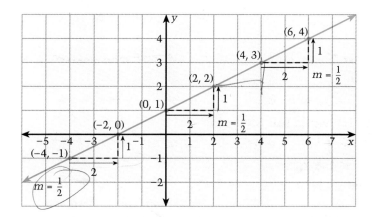

Another important observation is that the slope of the line is the coefficient of *x*. By substituting 0 for *x*, we can see that the *y*-intercept is the constant term in the equation.

$$\text{Slope } m \qquad y\text{-intercept } b$$

$$y = \frac{1}{2}x + 1$$

This result suggests a quick way to find the slope and the *y*-intercept. Just write the equation in the form $y = mx + b$.

Slope-Intercept Form of the Equation of a Line

The linear equation

$$y = mx + b$$

is in slope-intercept form. The slope of the line is *m*. The *y*-intercept is *b*.

Using Slope-Intercept Form

In Lesson 4.3, you learned to sketch a line quickly using the x-intercept and y-intercept. The *slope* and *y-intercept* can also be used to sketch a quick graph.

Example 1 · *Sketching a Quick Graph*

Sketch the graph of $-x + 3y = 6$.

Solution Begin by solving the equation for y.

$-x + 3y = 6$	*Original equation*
$3y = x + 6$	*Add x to both sides.*
$y = \frac{1}{3}x + 2$	*Divide both sides by 3.*

$\underbrace{\phantom{y = \frac{1}{3}x}}_{m} \underbrace{}_{b}$

You can sketch the line as follows. Plot the y-intercept, $(0, 2)$. Locate a second point by moving 3 units to the right and 1 unit up. Then draw the line through the two points.

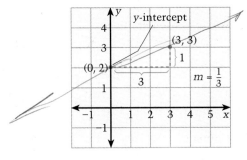

Plot the y-intercept. Then use slope to find a second point.

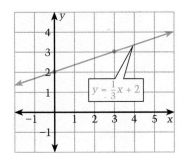

Draw the line that passes through the two points.

Two different lines that have the same slope are **parallel;** that is, they do not intersect.

Example 2 · *Sketching a Family of Parallel Lines*

Sketch the following lines on the same coordinate plane.

a. $y = -2x + 3$ **b.** $y = -2x$ **c.** $y = -2x - 1$

Solution Each of the lines has a slope of $m = -2$. The y-intercepts of each are the values of b, as follows.

a. $y = -2x + 3$ **b.** $y = -2x + 0$ **c.** $y = -2x + (-1)$

To sketch each line, plot its y-intercept. Then move 1 unit to the right and 2 units *down* (the slope is negative), and plot a second point. Finally, draw a line through the two points.

These students are planning a creative writing project that will give them some valuable insights into the realities of publishing a small book.

Problem Solving
Make a Graph

Example 3 Printing a Book

Your creative writing class wants to have selections of its poems and prose printed and bound into a book. The book will have 128 pages (8 *signatures* of 16 pages each). The inside pages will be printed with black ink, but the cover may have a full-color picture. A printer gives you the following prices:

With full-color cover: Cost is $750, plus $2.00 per book.
With single-color cover: Cost is $250, plus $1.75 per book.

Sketch the graphs of these two costs. Let x be the number of books printed and let C be the cost of printing x books.

Solution The two equations are as follows.

With full-color cover: $C = 750 + 2x$
With single-color cover: $C = 250 + 1.75x$

The graphs of both equations are lines. The first line has a C-intercept of 750 and a slope of 2. The second line has a C-intercept of 250 and a slope of 1.75. ■

Cost of Printing Books in the U.S.

Printing Costs (in 100s of dollars)

$C = 750 + 2x$

$C = 250 + 1.75x$

Number of Books (in hundreds)

Communicating about ALGEBRA

▶ **SHARING IDEAS about the Lesson**

Decision Making Refer to the problem in Example 3.

A. What do the C-intercepts represent? What do the slopes represent?

B. Your class plans to order and sell 500 copies. With full-color covers, how much should you charge for each book to cover the printing cost? With single-color covers, how much should you charge?

C. Suppose that your class could sell 750 copies. Could you afford to charge less per book? Explain your answer.

EXERCISES

$$m = \frac{y_2 - y_1}{x_2 - x_1}$$

Guided Practice

▶ CRITICAL THINKING about the Lesson

slope.   *y intercept.*

1. Can any pair of points on a line be used *yes.* to calculate the slope of the line? Explain.

2. In the form $y = mx + b$, what does m represent? What does b represent?

3. What word may be used to describe two different lines that have the same slope? *parallel*

4. What is the slope of the line given by $3x + 2y = 1$? What is the y-intercept?

$$\frac{2y = 1 - 3x}{2}$$
$$y = \frac{1}{2} - \frac{3}{2}x$$

Independent Practice

In Exercises 5–10, solve for y.

5. $5x + 7y = 0$

6. $2x - 4y = 0$

7. $3x + 4y = 12$

8. $-4x + 5y = 8$

9. $y + 10 = 0$

10. $y - 12 = 0$

In Exercises 11–16, find the slope and the y-intercept of the line.

11. $y = -2x + 1$

12. $y = 3x - 6$

13. $y = -4 + (-8x)$

14. $y = 4x - 20$

15. $x - y = 3x + 4$

16. $2y - x = 7x - 9$

In Exercises 17–28, write in slope-intercept form. Then sketch the line.

17. $2x - y - 3 = 0$

18. $x - y + 2 = 0$

19. $x + y = 0$

20. $x - y = 0$

21. $x + 2y - 2 = 0$

22. $3x - 2y - 2 = 0$

23. $3x - 4y + 2 = 0$

24. $10x + 6y - 3 = 0$

25. $y - 3 = 0$

26. $y + 5 = 0$

27. $2x + 3y - 4 = x + 5$

28. $-x + 4y + 3 = 2x - 7$

In Exercises 29–32, match the equation with its graph.

29. $y = \frac{1}{2}x + 1$

30. $y = \frac{1}{2}x - 1$

31. $y = x + 2$

32. $y = -x - 1$

a.

b.

c.

d.
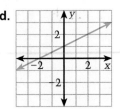

In Exercises 33–36, sketch the two lines on the same coordinate plane. Find the slope and x- and y-intercepts of the lines.

33. $y = -3x + 2$, $y = -3x - 2$

34. $y = -x + 6$, $y = -x + 10$

35. $y = 6x + 8$, $y = 6x - 2$

36. $y = \frac{4}{3}x - 1$, $y = \frac{4}{3}x + 3$

In Exercises 37–40, use the following information.

Two triangles are *similar* if their angles have the same measures. Corresponding sides of similar triangles have the same ratio. For instance, in the similar triangles at the right the ratio of *AB* to *BC* is equal to the ratio of *DE* to *EF*.

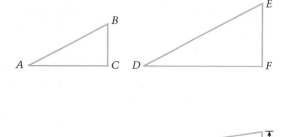

37. *Slope of a Subway Track* You are the supervisor for a construction project to build a subway track. Over one 200-foot (horizontal) portion, the track must rise 3 feet. You decide to check the elevation after your crew has covered 50 of the 200 feet. How much should the track have risen over 50 feet?

Not drawn to scale

38. *Architecture* You have designed plans for a house, and are now building a scale model. For the actual house, the center of the roof is 45 feet (horizontal) from the eaves and 18 feet higher than the eaves. For the model, the center is 10 inches (horizontal) from the eaves. How high should you build the center on the model?

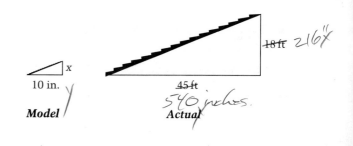

Model   *Actual*

39. *King Kong* You are visiting New York City with a friend and are standing by the World Trade Center—the building from which King Kong fell in the remake of the movie *King Kong*. In the original movie, King Kong fell from the Empire State Building. Your friend claims that the Empire State Building is taller than the World Trade Center. You disagree, so to find the height of the World Trade Center, you measure the building's shadow to be 170.25 feet. Then you measure the shadow cast by a 48-inch post to be 6 inches. A few calculations give you the height. Who was correct, you or your friend?

Post   *World Trade Center*   *Empire State Building*

40. *Connecting Slope and Similar Triangles* Find the slope of the line passing through the hypotenuse of each triangle in Exercises 37–39. Explain how these "similar triangle" problems are related to the fact that any two points on a line can be used to calculate the slope of the line.

41. Which line is parallel to $x + 3y = 2$?

 a. $y = \frac{1}{3}x + 5$ **b.** $y = -\frac{1}{3}x + 4$

42. Which line is parallel to $2x - 4y = 6$?

 a. $y = \frac{1}{2}x + 1$ **b.** $y = -\frac{1}{2}x - 1$

43. *Getting Ready for the Team*   Huan decides to lose weight before wrestling team practice begins. He weighs 148 pounds now and loses one pound per week for six weeks. Let w represent Huan's weight and let t represent the time in weeks. Plot points for his weights at one-week intervals, then draw a line through the points. Find the slope of the line. What does it represent? Find the w-intercept of the line. What does it represent?

44. *Making a Phone Call*   The cost of a telephone call between New York City and Philadelphia is $0.46 for the first minute and $0.31 for each additional minute. Let C represent the total cost of making a call that lasts for t minutes. Plot points for the costs of calls that last 1, 2, 3, 4, 5, and 6 minutes, then draw a line through the points. Find the slope of the line. What does it represent?

Integrated Review

In Exercises 45–48, evaluate the expression.

45. $\dfrac{-3 - (-4)}{5 - (-1)}$

46. $\dfrac{0 - 3}{9 - 3}$

47. $\dfrac{-2 - (-2)}{8 - 1}$

48. $\dfrac{6 - 10}{0 - (-4)}$

In Exercises 49–52, find five solutions of the equation.

49. $y = -2x + 4$

50. $y = 5x - 2$

51. $y = -\frac{5}{7}x$

52. $y = \frac{1}{2}x$

In Exercises 53–56, sketch the line that passes through (0, 2) with the given slope.

53. $m = 3$

54. $m = 0$

55. $m = -\frac{2}{3}$

56. $m = \frac{3}{4}$

Exploration and Extension

In Exercises 57 and 58, match the description with its visual model.

57. A person starts from home and rides a bike at a speed of 10 miles per hour.

58. A person starts 25 miles from home and drives toward home at a speed of 25 miles per hour.

A.

B.

59. Sketch the line that has a y-intercept of -4 and is parallel to $y = 2x + 3$.

60. Sketch the line that has a y-intercept of -8 and is parallel to $y = -\frac{1}{2}x + 5$.

61. Sketch the line that has a y-intercept of 2 and a slope of $-\frac{1}{8}$.

62. Sketch the line that has a y-intercept of 14 and a slope of 0.

4.6

Connections: Solutions and *x*-Intercepts

What you should learn:

Goal 1 How to use a graph as a quick check of a solution found algebraically

Goal 2 How to approximate solutions of real-life problems by using a graph

Why you should learn it:

You can use a graph to approximate related values by estimating coordinates of points on the graph.

René Descartes (1596–1650)

Goal 1 Using a Graphic Check for a Solution

You have already solved linear equations in one variable. For instance, you solved the equation $2x - 8 = 0$ as follows.

$2x - 8 = 0$ *Original equation*
$2x = 8$ *Add 8 to both sides.*
$x = 4$ *Divide both sides by 2.*

In Chapter 3, we emphasized the importance of checking this solution in the original equation. *You should continue to do that.* You may, however, also check a solution graphically.

To see how to do this, consider the line $y = 2x - 8$. Recall that the *x*-intercept of this line is the value of *x* when $y = 0$. In other words, the *x*-intercept of the line $y = 2x - 8$ is the solution of the equation $2x - 8 = 0$.

One-Variable Equation	**Two-Variable Equation**
The *solution* of	The *x-intercept* of
$2x - 8 = 0$	$y = 2x - 8$
is 4.	is 4.

Thus, to check the solution of $2x - 8 = 0$ graphically, sketch the graph of $y = 2x - 8$ and observe the *x*-intercept.

Using a Graphic Check of a Solution

The solution of a linear equation involving one variable *x* can be checked graphically with the following steps.

1. Write the equation in the form $ax + b = 0$.

2. Sketch the graph of $y = ax + b$.

3. The solution of $ax + b = 0$ is the *x*-intercept of $y = ax + b$.

The coordinate-plane connection between algebra and geometry is one of the greatest discoveries ever made in mathematics. Before René Descartes introduced the coordinate plane in 1637, mathematicians had no easy way of "seeing" a solution of an algebraic equation. Because of Descartes's contribution, the coordinate plane is often called the **Cartesian Plane.**

Example 1 · Using a Graphic Check of a Solution

Solve the equation $3x + 1 = -8$. Check your solution algebraically and graphically.

Solution

$$3x + 1 = -8 \qquad \text{\textit{Rewrite original equation.}}$$
$$3x = -9 \qquad \text{\textit{Subtract 1 from both sides.}}$$
$$x = -3 \qquad \text{\textit{Divide both sides by 3.}}$$

Algebraic Check   Substitute -3 for x in the original equation.

$$3(-3) + 1 \overset{?}{=} -8 \qquad \text{\textit{Substitute -3 for x.}}$$
$$-9 + 1 \overset{?}{=} -8 \qquad \text{\textit{Simplify.}}$$
$$-8 = -8 \qquad \text{\textit{The solution checks.}}$$

Graphic Check   Rewrite in the form $ax + b = 0$.

$$3x + 1 = -8 \qquad \text{\textit{Original equation}}$$
$$3x + 9 = 0 \qquad \text{\textit{Add 8 to both sides.}}$$

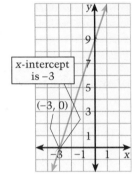

Now sketch the graph of $y = 3x + 9$, as shown at the left. Notice that the x-intercept is -3 (where $3x + 9 = 0$), which checks with the algebraic solution.   ∎

A graphic check can go wrong if you make a mistake when rewriting the original equation in the form $ax + b = 0$. Technology can be used to minimize this possibility, as shown in Example 2.

Connections
Technology

Example 2 · Using a Graphing Calculator or Computer

How could you use a graphing calculator to approximate the solution of $\frac{5}{6}(7x - 5) = 28 - \frac{3}{5}x$?

Solution   There are several ways to do this. One nice way that requires a minimum amount of algebra is to rewrite the original equation as

$$\frac{5}{6}(7x - 5) - \left(28 - \frac{3}{5}x\right) = 0.$$

Then, without simplifying, use a graphing calculator or computer to sketch the graph of

$$y = \frac{5}{6}(7x - 5) - \left(28 - \frac{3}{5}x\right).$$

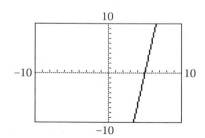

The result is shown at the left. Note that the x-intercept appears to be 5. (Each tick mark represents 1 unit.) You can verify this by substituting 5 for x in the original equation.   ∎

In Examples 1 and 2, we rewrote each equation so that the right side was zero. Then we set y equal to the left side, sketched the graph, and used the x-intercept (where $y = 0$) as a graphic check or graphic approximation.

A slightly different approach is sometimes helpful. For equations of the form $ax + b = c$, sketch, on the same coordinate plane, the graphs of $y = ax + b$ and $y = c$. The solution is the x-coordinate of the point at which they cross.

Real Life
Medical Careers

Example 3 *Projecting the Number of Registered Nurses*

From 1970 to 1990, the number of registered nurses in the United States could be approximated by the linear model $N = 53{,}600t + 732{,}000$. In this model, t represents the year with $t = 0$ corresponding to 1970. According to this model, when will the United States have 2,250,000 registered nurses?
(Source: U.S. Department of Health and Human Services)

Solution   Answer the question by solving the equation

$$53{,}600t + 732{,}000 = 2{,}250{,}000.$$

A way to approximate the answer is to sketch the graphs of

$$N = \underbrace{53{,}600t + 732{,}000}_{\text{Left side of equation}} \quad \text{and} \quad N = \underbrace{2{,}250{,}000}_{\text{Right side of equation}}$$

on the same coordinate plane. From the graph, you can see that there should be 2,250,000 nurses by 1998 or 1999. ■

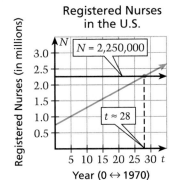

Registered Nurses in the U.S.

Registered Nurses (in millions)

$N = 2{,}250{,}000$

$t \approx 28$

Year (0 ↔ 1970)

Communicating about **A L G E B R A**

▷ **SHARING IDEAS about the Lesson**

Graphic Check   Match each solution with an x-intercept.

Solution	x-intercept
A. Solution of $2x = 10$	**a.** x-intercept of $y = 2x - 10$
B. Solution of $12x - 4 = 10x + 5$	**b.** x-intercept of $y = 3x - 2$
C. Solution of $2(x - 4) = 5(x - 2)$	**c.** x-intercept of $y = 2x - 9$

EXERCISES

▶ **CRITICAL THINKING about the Lesson**

In Exercises 1–3, use the equation $9x - 36 = 0$.

1. Solve the equation algebraically.

2. Write an equation whose graph you could use to check your solution. Sketch this graph.

3. What is the x-intercept of the graph?

4. True or False? The solution of $ax + b = 0$ is the x-intercept of $y = ax + b$. Explain your reasoning.

Independent Practice

In Exercises 5–8, match the equation with the line whose x-intercept is the solution of the equation.

5. $2x - 4 = 0$ **6.** $x + 6 = 0$ **7.** $x + 2 = 0$ **8.** $x - 6 = 0$

a.   b.   c.   d.

In Exercises 9–12, write an equation of a line whose x-intercept is the solution of the one-variable equation.

9. $9x + 4 = -4$ **10.** $10x - 3 = 19$ **11.** $5 - 3x = 16$ **12.** $14 + 4x = 15$

In Exercises 13–24, solve the equation. Check your solution algebraically and graphically.

13. $2x + 3 = 7$ **14.** $3x - 2 = -5$ **15.** $4x - 7 = -23$

16. $x - 9 = -6$ **17.** $5x + 17 = -13$ **18.** $5x - 17 = 8$

19. $4x + 3 = 5$ **20.** $5x + 7 = 9$ **21.** $9x - 6 = -10$

22. $8x - 5 = 1$ **23.** $4x - 6 = 10$ **24.** $-2x + 5 = 9$

Technology **In Exercises 25–30, use a graphing calculator to find the solution. Check your solution algebraically in the original equation.**

25. $6(x + 3) = 2(x + 5)$ **26.** $6(x + 2) = 5(x + 2)$ **27.** $\frac{6}{5}(x + 2) = 5x + \frac{1}{2}$

28. $x - \frac{1}{3} = \frac{5}{4}(x - 6)$ **29.** $\frac{3}{8}(x + 7) = \frac{1}{3}(x + 16)$ **30.** $\frac{3}{2}(x - 10) = \frac{2}{3}(x - 12)$

31. Attendance at Hockey Games The total yearly attendance at hockey games for the National Hockey League between 1980 and 1990 is approximately given by

$$A = 1,100,000t + 10,534,000$$

where A represents the number of people who attended the games and t represents the year, with $t = 0$ corresponding to 1980. According to this model, in what year did 16,034,000 people attend the games? Solve algebraically and graphically.

32. Cost The cost, y, of producing x units of a product is given by $y = 35x + 5000$. If the cost is $7625, how many units are produced? Solve algebraically and graphically.

Integrated Review

In Exercises 33–40, evaluate the expression.

33. $|-4|$

34. $-|6|$

35. $4 - |-3|$

36. $3|-5 + 2|$

37. $|1 - 2| + 3$

38. $16 - |-11 + 9|$

39. $-2|-8 + 2| + 7$

40. $-12 + |3 - 7|$

In Exercises 41 and 42, complete the table.

41. $y = 4x - 1$

x	−3	−2	−1	0	1	2	3
y	?	?	?	?	?	?	?

42. $y = -6x + 12$

x	−3	−2	−1	0	1	2	3
y	?	?	?	?	?	?	?

43. College Entrance Exam Sample The lines a and b are parallel. The length of the line segment d between the lines
  a. steadily increases as it is moved along lines a and b toward the right.
  b. steadily decreases as it is moved toward the left.
  c. fluctuates in both directions.
  d. remains constant.
  e. None of the above

44. Sketch the line with a slope $-\frac{1}{2}$ that passes through the point $(0, 9)$.

Dentists in the United States   **In Exercises 45 and 46, use the following information.**

From 1980 to 1987, the number of dentists could be approximated by $D = 2857t + 141,250$, where t represents the year with $t = 0$ corresponding to 1980. According to this model, when will the United States have 226,960 dentists?

Method 1. Sketch the lines $D = 2857t + 141,250$ and $D = 226,960$ on the same coordinate plane. Then estimate the t-coordinate of the point of intersection.

Method 2. Sketch the line $D = 2857t + 141,250$. Then, from 226,960 on the vertical axis, draw a dashed line to the graph and drop down to the t-axis to estimate the time.

45. Do both methods produce the same result? If so, what is the result?

46. Which method do you prefer? Why?

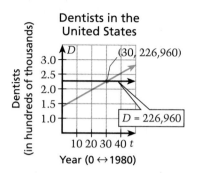

Dentists in the United States

Mixed **R E V I E W**

In Exercises 1–4, evaluate the expression.

1. $-6 - |-3|$ **(2.1)**   **2.** $6 - 2$ **(2.3)**   **3.** $|-7| - (-2)$ **(2.3)**   **4.** $4 - \left(-\frac{1}{3}\right)$ **(2.3)**

In Exercises 5 and 6, find the resulting unit of measure. **(2.5)**

5. (dollars per pound) • (pound)   **6.** (kilometers per second) • (second)

7. Simplify $|-3| + 2(x - 2)$. **(2.6)**   **8.** Simplify $2y - 3(y + 2)$. **(2.6)**
9. Evaluate $3x^2 + x$ when $x = -4$. **(2.5)**   **10.** Evaluate $3(n - 1) + 2n$ when $n = 5$. **(2.6)**
11. Solve for a: $4a - 2b = 0$. **(3.6)**   **12.** Solve for y: $-3(1 - y) + 4x = 1$. **(3.6)**
13. Is 5 a solution of $|x| + 2 = 7$? **(2.1)**   **14.** Is -5 a solution of $|x| + 2 = 7$? **(2.1)**
15. Evaluate $(22.66)(-41.20) \div 77.10$. **(2.7)**   **16.** Evaluate $\frac{1}{3}(x - 2)$ when $x = 3$. **(1.2)**

In Exercises 17–20, translate the phrase or sentence into an algebraic expression, equation, or inequality. **(1.6)**

17. A number decreased by 6 is less than or equal to 10.

18. Six more than the number y is equal to the quotient of a number x and 3.

19. The product of 3 and the opposite of 10, decreased by 1.

20. Twice the sum of x and y is equal to 20.

4.7 Graphs of Absolute Value Equations

What you should learn:

Goal 1 How to graph an absolute value equation

Goal 2 How to model a real-life situation using graphs of absolute value equations

Why you should learn it:

You can model some real-life situations with absolute value equations.

Goal 1 Graphing Absolute Value Equations

The absolute value of a number can be defined as follows.

$$|x| = \begin{cases} x, & \text{if } x > 0 \\ 0, & \text{if } x = 0 \\ -x, & \text{if } x < 0 \end{cases}$$

Example

$|5| = 5$
$|0| = 0$
$|-3| = -(-3) = 3$

In this lesson, you will learn to sketch the graph of absolute value equations. To begin, let's look at the graph of $y = |x|$. By constructing a table of values and plotting points, you can see that the graph is **V**-shaped and opens up. The **vertex** of this graph is $(0, 0)$.

x	y = |x|
−4	4
−3	3
−2	2
−1	1
0	0
1	1
2	2
3	3
4	4

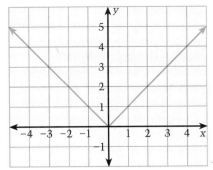

Other absolute value graphs are also **V**-shaped. Some open up and some open down. For those that open up, the vertex is the lowest point. For those that open down, the vertex is the highest point.

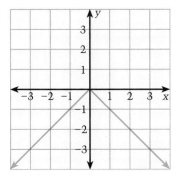

Graph of $y = -|x|$
Vertex at (0, 0), opens down.

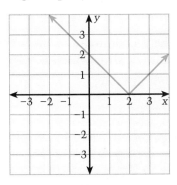

Graph of $y = |x - 2|$
Vertex at (2, 0), opens up.

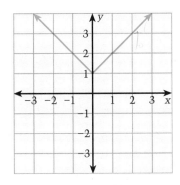

Graph of $y = |x| + 1$
Vertex at (0, 1), opens up.

Here are some guidelines that can help you sketch the graph of an absolute value equation.

> ### Sketching the Graph of an Absolute Value Equation
> To sketch the graph of $y = a|x + b| + c$, use the following steps.
>
> 1. Find the x-coordinate of the vertex by finding the value of x for which $x + b = 0$.
> 2. Make a table of values using the x-coordinate of the vertex, some x-values to its left, and some to its right.
> 3. Plot the points given in the table and draw a V-shaped graph (opening up or down) through the points.

Example 1 *Graphing an Absolute Value Equation*

Sketch the graph of $y = \frac{1}{2}|x + 2| - 3$.

Solution

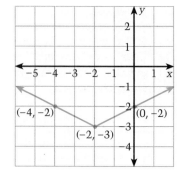

1. The x-coordinate of the vertex is -2 because that is the value of x for which $x + 2 = 0$.
2. Make a table, choosing x-values to the left and right of -2.

   Vertex
		-4	-2	0
x		-4	-2	0
$y = \frac{1}{2}|x + 2| - 3$		-2	-3	-2

3. Plot the points. Notice that the vertex is at $(-2, -3)$. Then draw a V-shaped graph through the points. ∎

Example 2 *Graphing an Absolute Value Equation*

Sketch the graph of $y = -2|x - 1| + 2$.

Solution

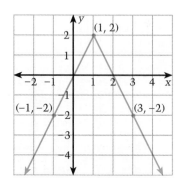

1. The x-coordinate of the vertex is 1 because that is the value of x for which $x - 1 = 0$.
2. Make a table, choosing x-values to the left and right of 1.

   Vertex
x	-1	1	3
$y = -2|x - 1| + 2$	-2	2	-2

3. Plot the points. Notice that the vertex is at $(1, 2)$. Then draw a V-shaped graph (opening down) through the points. ∎

Modeling a Real-Life Situation

When a ray of light, a sound wave, or an object moving in a straight line hits a smooth surface, it is reflected in a **V**-shaped path. The angle formed by the incoming path and the surface is equal to the angle formed by the surface and the outgoing path.

Connections
Physics

Example 3   *Finding the Path of a Billiard Ball*

Ana and Carlos are arguing about a pool shot. The cue ball cannot be moved, and each is trying to get the 10 ball into the corner pocket. Which one is right? (Assume that each is making a straight shot, with no spin on the ball.)

Ana says to imagine a line containing the corner pocket and the 10 ball. Then aim for the point at which the line intersects the opposite rail.

Carlos says to imagine equal angles between the path of the cue ball and the rail before and after the cue ball hits the rail. Then aim a hair past the point where the cue ball hits the rail to get a ricochet off the 10 ball.

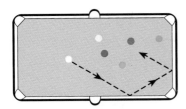

Solution   Carlos is right. The rail of a billiard table is a reflecting surface, which means that a ball will leave the rail at the same angle it hits the rail. Ana's shot would travel the path shown at the left.   ■

Communicating   *about*   A L G E B R A

Cooperative Learning

▶ **SHARING IDEAS about the Lesson**

Work with a Partner and Compare Models   Compare the graphs of the absolute value equations.

   A. $y = |x|$ and $y = |x| - 1$

   B. $y = |x|$ and $y = |x - 2|$

   C. $y = |x|$ and $y = -|x|$

   D. Which has a sharper corner: $y = |x|$ or $y = 2|x|$?

EXERCISES

▶ CRITICAL THINKING about the Lesson

1. True or False? The vertex of the graph of $y = |x + b|$ is $(-b, 0)$.

2. Is the vertex of the graph of $y = -|x|$ the lowest or highest point on the graph? Explain.

3. Find the coordinates of the vertex of the graph of $y = \frac{1}{4}|x + 4| - 2$.

4. Explain how to sketch the graph of $y = |x - 2| + 3$.

Independent Practice

In Exercises 5–8, match the equation with its graph. Describe the relationship between each graph and the graph of $y = |x|$.

5. $y = |x| - 1$ **6.** $y = |x| + 1$ **7.** $y = |x| - 2$ **8.** $y = |x| + 2$

a.

b.

c.

d.

In Exercises 9–12, match the equation with its graph. Describe the relationship between each graph and the graph of $y = |x|$.

9. $y = |x - 1|$ **10.** $y = |x + 1|$ **11.** $y = |x - 2|$ **12.** $y = |x + 2|$

a.

b.

c.

d.

In Exercises 13–24, find the coordinates of the vertex of the graph.

13. $y = |x| - 6$

14. $y = |x| + 5$

15. $y = -|x| - 3$

16. $y = |x + 6|$

17. $y = -2|x - 2|$

18. $y = \frac{1}{2}|x - 3|$

19. $y = |x + 3| - 2$

20. $y = |x - 3| + 1$

21. $y = -|x - 9| + 10$

22. $y = |x + 6| - 8$

23. $y = 2|x - 2| + 8$

24. $y = -\frac{1}{2}|x - 3| + 5$

In Exercises 25–28, match the equation with its graph.

25. $y = |x - 1| + 2$ **26.** $y = -|x - 2| - 1$ **27.** $y = -|x + 1| - 2$ **28.** $y = |x + 2| + 1$

a.   **b.**   **c.**   **d.**

In Exercises 29–32, complete the table of values.

29. $y = -2|x - 1| + 3$

x	-2	-1	0	1	2	3	4
y	?	?	?	?	?	?	?

30. $y = 3|x + 4| - 1$

x	-7	-6	-5	-4	-3	-2	-1
y	?	?	?	?	?	?	?

31. $y = \frac{3}{2}|x + 3| - 4$

x	-6	-5	-4	-3	-2	-1	0
y	?	?	?	?	?	?	?

32. $y = -\frac{3}{4}|x - 2| + 6$

x	-1	0	1	2	3	4	5
y	?	?	?	?	?	?	?

In Exercises 33–50, sketch the graph of the equation.

33. $y = |x| + 3$ **34.** $y = |x| - 4$ **35.** $y = |x| - 3$ **36.** $y = |x| + 4$

37. $y = |x + 3|$ **38.** $y = |x - 5|$ **39.** $y = |x - 3|$ **40.** $y = |x + 4|$

41. $y = 2|x|$ **42.** $y = 3|x|$ **43.** $y = -2|x|$ **44.** $y = -\frac{1}{2}|x|$

45. $y = |x + 3| - 2$ **46.** $y = -|x - 1| + 4$ **47.** $y = -2|x + 3| + 5$

48. $y = \frac{1}{2}|x + 4| - 2$ **49.** $y = 3|x - 2| - 1$ **50.** $y = -3|x - 1| + 1$

51. **True or False?** The graphs of $y = -2|x - 3| + 4$ and $y = 2|x - 3| + 4$ have the same vertex. Explain.

52. *Rug Weaving*   A coordinate plane has been drawn on the Navajo rug. Find absolute value equations for the four indicated graphs.

Wool used by the famous Navajo weavers is "homegrown," and dyed by hand.

53. *Laser Show*   You are setting up a laser show in the physical science lab. The laser is 40 feet from a corner of the lab and is aimed at a mirror on the adjoining wall. The mirror is the same height as the laser and is positioned as shown in the diagram. The laser beam travels along a path given by $y = \frac{4}{3}|x - 30|$. After the laser beam is reflected by the mirror, where will it hit the third wall?

Laser technology has come a long way since the first experiments with Light Amplification by Stimulated Emission of Radiation (L.A.S.E.R.).

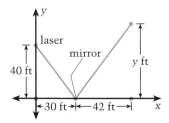

View from Above

Integrated Review

In Exercises 54–57, evaluate the expression.

54. $|-6 + 4| - 3$ **55.** $-2|9 - 12| + 1$ **56.** $-|-2 - (-1)| + 4$ **57.** $|-5 - (-5)| - 2$

In Exercises 58–61, evaluate the expression.

58. $|x - 2| - 5$, when $x = -2$ **59.** $-|x + 3| - 4$, when $x = -5$

60. $|-x + 1| + 3$, when $x = 3$ **61.** $-\frac{1}{2}|x + 2| + 4$, when $x = -1$

Exploration and Extension

Technology—Graphing Calculator   **In Exercises 62 and 63, use the equation to determine the horizontal and vertical scale units for the graphing calculator screen.**

62. $y = \frac{3}{5}|2x - 34| - 20$ **63.** $y = -\frac{1}{2}|x + 12| + 15$

4.8 Solving Absolute Value Equations

What you should learn:

Goal 1 How to solve and check absolute value equations using algebra

Goal 2 How to use a graph to check solutions of absolute value equations

Why you should learn it:

You can use absolute value equations to model many real-life situations, such as representing minimum and maximum amounts.

Goal 1 Solving and Checking Algebraically

You already know how to use mental math to solve some absolute value equations. For instance, you know that the equation $|x| = 8$ has *two* solutions: 8 and -8.

Expression inside absolute value sign can be positive.	**Expression inside absolute value sign can be negative.**
8 is a solution of $|x| = 8$ because $|8| = 8$.	-8 is a solution of $|x| = 8$ because $|-8| = 8$.

To solve a more general absolute value equation, use the fact that the expression inside the absolute value sign can be either positive or negative.

Example 1 *Solving an Absolute Value Equation*

Solve $|x - 2| = 5$.

Solution

$$|x - 2| = 5 \qquad \textit{Rewrite original equation.}$$
$$x - 2 = 5 \text{ or } x - 2 = -5 \qquad \textit{Expression can be 5 or } -5.$$
$$x = 7 \text{ or } \qquad x = -3 \qquad \textit{Add 2 to both sides.}$$

The equation has two solutions: 7 and -3. Check these solutions by substituting each into the original equation. ∎

Example 2 *Isolating the Absolute Value Expression*

Solve $|2x - 7| - 5 = 4$.

Solution First, isolate the absolute-value portion on one side of the equation.

$$|2x - 7| - 5 = 4 \qquad \textit{Rewrite original equation.}$$
$$|2x - 7| = 9 \qquad \textit{Add 5 to both sides.}$$
$$2x - 7 = 9 \text{ or } 2x - 7 = -9 \qquad \textit{Expression can be 9 or } -9.$$
$$2x = 16 \text{ or } \qquad 2x = -2 \qquad \textit{Add 7 to both sides.}$$
$$x = 8 \text{ or } \qquad x = -1 \qquad \textit{Divide both sides by 2.}$$

The equation has two solutions: 8 and -1. Check these solutions by substituting each into the original equation. ∎

Using a Graphic Check

In Lesson 4.6, you learned to use a graphic check for solutions of linear equations. You can use the same technique to check solutions of absolute value equations.

- Rewrite the one-variable equation so that the right side is zero.
- Set y equal to the left side and sketch the graph of the resulting two-variable equation.
- The x-intercepts of the graph of the two-variable equation should match the solutions of the one-variable equation.

Example 3   *Using a Graphic Check*

Check the solutions of $|x - 2| = 5$ graphically.

Solution   In Example 1, the solutions were found to be 7 and -3. You can check these solutions graphically as follows.

$$|x - 2| = 5 \quad \textit{Original one-variable equation}$$
$$|x - 2| - 5 = 0 \quad \textit{Rewrite with zero on right side.}$$

Set y equal to the left side of the rewritten equation.

$$y = |x - 2| - 5 \quad \textit{Form two-variable equation.}$$

Using the techniques in Lesson 4.7, you know that the graph of this equation is **V**-shaped and has a vertex at $(2, -5)$. From the graph, you can see that the x-intercepts occur at 7 and -3, which match the solutions. ■

Example 4   *Using a Graphic Check*

Check the solutions of $|2x - 7| - 5 = 4$ graphically.

Solution   In Example 2, the solutions were found to be 8 and -1. You can check these solutions graphically as follows.

$$|2x - 7| - 5 = 4 \quad \textit{Original one-variable equation}$$
$$|2x - 7| - 9 = 0 \quad \textit{Rewrite with zero on right side.}$$

Set y equal to the left side of the rewritten equation.

$$y = |2x - 7| - 9 \quad \textit{Form two-variable equation.}$$

The graph of this equation is **V**-shaped, opens up, and has a vertex at $(\frac{7}{2}, -9)$. From the graph, you can see that the x-intercepts occur at 8 and -1, which match the solutions. ■

Maximum

1155 (cubic inches)

Minimum

5 Gallons

Example 5 *Accuracy of Measurement*

To obtain certification by the Bureau of Weights and Measures, a gasoline pump must pump within 6 cubic inches of 5 gallons (1155 cubic inches) when its gauge reads 5 gallons. The inspector pumps gasoline into a container like that shown at the left. The reading on the gas pump is 5 gallons. To be certified, the gas level in the container must fall within the minimum and maximum amounts on the scale. What are these minimum and maximum amounts? Find an absolute value equation that models this situation and has the minimum and maximum amounts as its solutions.

Solution Using the information given with the photo, the amount pumped must be within 6 cubic inches of 1155 cubic inches. Thus, the minimum and maximum amounts are:

Minimum
$1155 - 6 = 1149$ cubic inches

Maximum
$1155 + 6 = 1161$ cubic inches

These two numbers can be expressed as solutions of the equation $|x - 1155| = 6$. Do you see why? ∎

Communicating about ALGEBRA

▶ **SHARING IDEAS about the Lesson**

Interpret a Model Solve each equation. Use the solutions to rephrase the statement.

A. $|x - 160| = 1$ To pass certification, the scale must weigh within one ounce of 160 ounces.

B. $|x - 189| = 86$ To be eligible for one of the 13 weight classes on the wrestling team, your weight must be within 86 pounds of 189 pounds.

C. $|x - 30| = 10$ To obtain a bonus, the pizza delivery driver must deliver the pizza in 30 minutes, plus or minus 10 minutes.

EXERCISES

Guided Practice

▶ **CRITICAL THINKING about the Lesson**

1. Solve $|x + 1| = 2$.

2. What equation could you graph to check the solutions of $|x + 1| = 2$?

3. Which two equations would you solve to find the solutions of $|x + 1| = 32$?

4. If a coordinate plane is drawn through the galley at the right, the mainstays would lie on the graph of $y = 82.5 - 0.92|x|$, where x and y are measured in feet. How far above the deck does the mast rise? Find the x-coordinates of the points at which the mainstays are attached to the deck.

Around 650 B.C., the Greeks invented a warship called the trireme. It had three rows of oars. The photo shows a modern replica of a trireme.

Independent Practice

In Exercises 5–10, solve the equation algebraically.

5. $|x + 4| = 3$

6. $|9 - x| = 4$

7. $|6 - x| = 9$

8. $|x + 12| = 8$

9. $|2x + 6| = 14$

10. $|3x - 4| = 7$

In Exercises 11–13, rewrite the equation so that the term involving absolute value is isolated on one side.

11. $6 + |x + 1| = 9$

12. $|x - 17| + 9 = 1$

13. $7 - |4 - x| = 12$

14. Use a graphic check that -2 is a solution of $|x - 5| = 7$.

15. Use a graphic check that -13 is a solution of $|x + 4| = 9$.

In Exercises 16–24, solve the equation.

16. $|x + 1| = 7$

17. $|x - 1| = 7$

18. $|3x - 2| - 2 = 5$

19. $|4x + 3| - 4 = 8$

20. $3 + |-2x + 9| = 10$

21. $6 + |-x - 5| = 9$

22. $|4 - 5x| - 8 = 15$

23. $|7 - 3x| - 10 = 4$

24. $2|3x - 7| + 2 = 4$

In Exercises 25–33, solve the equation. Use a graphic check.

25. $|x - 9| = 4$

26. $|x + 7| = 16$

27. $|2x - 4| + 6 = 9$

28. $4 + |x - 10| = 14$

29. $10 + |3x + 1| = 24$

30. $|2x + 9| - 15 = 36$

31. $2|x + \frac{1}{2}| - 1 = 9$

32. $3|x + \frac{1}{6}| + 5 = 17$

33. $3|4x + 9| - 2 = 6$

A Tent on Ice   **In Exercises 34–37, use the following information.**

If a coordinate plane were drawn through the tent at the right, the edges of the tent would lie on the graph of $y = -2|x - 5| + 10$, where x and y are measured in feet. The ropes that anchor the tent lie on the graph of $y = -\frac{1}{3}|x - 5| + 6$.

34. How tall is the tent?   *10'*

35. How wide is the tent at its base?   *10'*

36. Find the x-coordinates of the points at which the stakes are secured to the ice.   *23, -13*

37. How far are the stakes from the edge of the tent?   *13'*

38. *Earth's Orbit*   Because Earth travels in an elliptical orbit around the sun, the distance between Earth and the sun varies. The average distance is 92,950,000 miles, but the distance can vary 1,550,000 miles from the average. Find an absolute value equation that models this situation and has the minimum and maximum distances between Earth and the sun as solutions. What are the minimum and maximum distances?

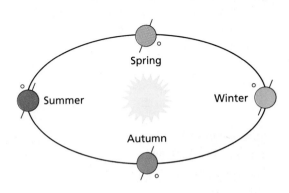

Spring

Summer

Winter

Autumn

39. *Boxing Weights*   A junior heavyweight boxer's weight must fall within 7 pounds of 183 pounds. Find an absolute value equation that models this situation and has the minimum and maximum weights for a junior heavyweight boxer as solutions. What are the minimum and maximum weights?

Integrated Review

In Exercises 40–45, evaluate the expression.

40. $2|4| + 6$

41. $3 - |8 - 4|$

42. $3^2 - |-4|$

43. $6^2 - 2|14 - 19|$

44. $|3 - 9| \cdot 2^2 + 1$

45. $-4|-5 + 1| - 12$

46. Write an equation of the horizontal line passing through $(-2, 4)$.

47. Write an equation of the vertical line passing through $(5, -3)$.

48. Find the slope and y-intercept of $x + 2y = 18$.

49. Find the slope and y-intercept of $6x - y = 3$.

50. Sketch the line whose slope is $\frac{3}{2}$ and whose y-intercept is -5.

51. Sketch the line whose slope is -4 and whose y-intercept is 12.

In Exercises 52 and 53, find the slope of the lines that contain each side of the graph.

52. $y = \frac{2}{3}|x - 4| - 2$

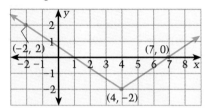

53. $y = -3|x + 10| + 4$

In Exercises 54–57, use the following information.

Sea level is considered to have an elevation of 0 feet. Elevation in North America ranges from below sea level in some valleys and canyons to far above sea level on mountain peaks.

The lowest elevation in North America is 282 feet below sea level near Badwater in Death Valley.

The highest elevation in North America is 20,320 feet above sea level at one of Mt. McKinley's peaks.

54. Plot the lowest and highest elevations in North America on a real number line. (Use a larger version of the number line shown at the right.) Find the point that lies midway between the highest and lowest points.

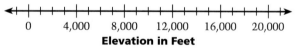

55. On your graph, shade the interval that represents all possible geographical elevations in North America.

56. Use the distance between the midpoint of the interval and each of the endpoints of the interval to write an *inequality* whose solutions represent all possible elevations in North America.

57. Plot and label the following locations on your graph.

Pikes Peak Colorado	Mount St. Helens Washington	Flag Knob Kentucky	Mount Sunflower Kansas	Mauna Loa Hawaii
14,100 feet	8365 feet	1658 feet	4039 feet	13,677 feet

4 Chapter Summary

What did you learn?

Skills

1. Sketch the graph of a linear equation in one variable. **(4.1)**
2. Write an equation of a horizontal or vertical line. **(4.1)**
3. Sketch the graph of a linear equation in two variables
   - using a table of values. **(4.2)**
   - using intercepts. **(4.3)**
   - using the slope-intercept form. **(4.5)**
4. Find the slope of a line
   - passing through two points. **(4.4)**
   - by writing its equation in slope-intercept form. **(4.5)**
5. Sketch the graph of an equation involving absolute value. **(4.7)**
6. Solve an equation involving absolute value. **(4.8)**

Strategies

7. Use a graph to check the solution(s) of
   - a linear equation. **(4.6)**
   - an equation involving absolute value. **(4.8)**
8. Interpret slope as a rate of change. **(4.4)**

Exploring Data

9. Create scatter plots and recognize linear patterns. **(4.1–4.6)**

Why did you learn it?

Linear models are the most commonly used algebraic models for real-life situations. By learning to sketch the graphs of linear models, you will be able to use them to help answer questions about the real world. Recognizing and using the algebra-geometry connection between equations and graphs is one of the most important skills you can acquire on your way to becoming a master problem solver.

How does it fit into the bigger picture of algebra?

If you were studying algebra 400 years ago, this chapter would not have been in your algebra text. At that time, algebra and geometry were separate branches of mathematics with few connections. Today, they are closely connected. You saw in this chapter that relationships between variables may be expressed in algebraic form as an equation, or in geometric form as a graph. For example, x and y could be related by a *linear equation* such as $y = x - 4$, whose graph is a line, or by an *absolute value equation* such as $y = |x - 4|$, whose graph is V-shaped. Drawing the graphs helps you understand the algebraic relationships.

In Exercises 1–4, sketch the two lines on the same coordinate plane. Then find the point at which the two lines intersect. (4.1)

1. $x = 0,\ y = -3$ **2.** $x = 7,\ y = -5$ **3.** $x = -6,\ y = 4$ **4.** $x = -2,\ y = 0$

In Exercises 5–8, decide whether the point lies on the line. (4.1)

5. $(-6, -9),\ y = -9$ **6.** $(3, 4),\ y = 3$ **7.** $(-3, 8),\ x = 8$ **8.** $(5, -5),\ y = 5$

In Exercises 9–12, use a table of values to sketch the graph of the equation. (4.2)

9. $y = -(2x + 2)$ **10.** $y = \frac{1}{3}x - 2$ **11.** $y = 7 - \frac{1}{2}x$ **12.** $y = -4(x + 1)$

In Exercises 13–16, match the equation with its graph. (4.3)

13. $2x + 3y = 10$ **14.** $-x + 4y = 8$ **15.** $3x - 5y = 15$ **16.** $4x - 5y = -20$

a.   **b.**   **c.**   **d.**

In Exercises 17–19, find the slope of the line passing through the points. (4.4)

17. $(2, -1),\ (3, 4)$ **18.** $(0, 8),\ (-1, 2)$ **19.** $(2, 4),\ (5, 0)$

In Exercises 20–22, find the slope and *y*-intercept of the line. (4.5)

20. $x + 11y = 2$ **21.** $x - 4y = 12$ **22.** $-x + 6y = -24$

In Exercises 23 and 24, sketch the line. Label the *x*-intercept and *y*-intercept. (4.3)

23. $x - 2y = 10$ **24.** $3x + 4y = -24$

In Exercises 25–28, solve the equation. Check your solution two ways. (4.6)

25. $3x - 6 = 0$ **26.** $5x - 3 = 0$

27. $-x + 8 = 0$ **28.** $-4x - 1 = 7$

In Exercises 29–32, construct a table of values, sketch the graph, and label the vertex. (4.7)

29. $y = |x| - 4$ **30.** $y = 2|x + 3| - 1$

31. $y = -3|x + 1| + 5$ **32.** $y = \frac{1}{2}|x - 6| + 2$

In Exercises 33–36, match the equation with its graph. (4.7)

33. $y = |x| - 4$ **34.** $y = |x - 1| + 1$ **35.** $y = |x + 1| + 1$ **36.** $y = |x + 1| - 1$

a.   **b.**   **c.**   **d.**

In Exercises 37–40, solve the equation. Check your solutions two ways. (4.8)

37. $4 + |x + 2| = 7$

38. $6 - 5|x - 1| = 1$

39. $7 - |2x + 6| = 4$

40. $|x + 8| - 6 = 2$

In Exercises 41–42, use the following information.

In 1990, a survey was taken to determine the ways in which American men and women measure success. Each respondent was allowed to list more than one measure. The results of the survey are shown below.
(Source: Roper Organization, New York)

41. The graph at the right shows the responses of the first one hundred women surveyed, concerning one of the measures of success. After each group of 10 responses was tallied, the total number who had responded yes to this particular measure of success was plotted. Which measure of success was being tallied?

42. What is the slope of the line that you think would best fit the points on the graph?

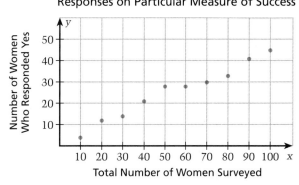

Responses on Particular Measure of Success

Recreational Boat Ownership   **In Exercises 43–46, use the following information.**

The graph at the right shows the number of recreational boats, y (in millions), that were in use in the United States from 1983 to 1988. The numbers on the t-axis represent the year. *(Source: National Marine Manufacturers Association)*

43. Between which two consecutive years did boat ownership change the most?

44. Between which two consecutive years did boat ownership change the least?

45. What was the average rate of change in boat ownership from 1983 to 1988? (List your result in millions of boats per year.)

46. What was the average rate of change in boat ownership from 1986 to 1988? (List your result in millions of boats per year.)

Sailboat Dimensions   **In Exercises 47–50, use the following information.**

An xy-coordinate plane has been drawn through the sailboat at the right. The edges of the two largest sails lie approximately on the graph of the equation $y = -2.2|x| + 30$, where x and y are measured in feet.

47. How tall are the sails?

48. Find the x-coordinates of the points that define the combined widths of the sails at their bases. What is the approximate combined base widths of the sails?

49. What is the ratio of the height of the sails to the combined base widths of the sails?

50. What are the slopes of the right and left edges of the two sails?

1. Sketch the graphs of $x = 7$ and $y = -1$. Then find the point at which the two graphs intersect.

2. Write the equation of the line passing through $(3, -1)$, $(3, 0)$, and $\left(3, -\frac{3}{4}\right)$.

3. Which point is on the graph of $\frac{5}{3}x + y = 1$?

   a. $\left(4, -\frac{17}{3}\right)$ **b.** $\left(2, \frac{10}{3}\right)$

4. Complete the table.

x	-9	-6	-3	0	3	6	9
$y = \frac{1}{3}x - 2$	?	?	?	?	?	?	?

In Exercises 5 and 6, find the intercepts and sketch the line.

5. $\frac{3}{8}x + y = 3$

6. $y = -x + 3$

In Exercises 7–10, find the slope of the line through the points.

7. $(5, 6)$, $(-9, 6)$

8. $(4, 0)$, $(1, -2)$

9. $\left(-3, -\frac{1}{2}\right)$, $\left(-6, -\frac{1}{4}\right)$

10. $(5, 70)$, $(5, 76)$

In Exercises 11–14, rewrite the equation in slope-intercept form.

11. $3y + 4x = 7$

12. $3(y - 1) = x - 3$

13. $\frac{1}{3}(y - 9) - (x - 1) = 6$

14. $\frac{1}{4}x + 4y = 4$

In Exercises 15 and 16, solve the equation. Check your solution(s) algebraically and graphically.

15. $2x - 3 = 7$

16. $2(x - 3) = -4$

In Exercises 17 and 18, find the vertex and sketch the graph.

17. $y = 2|x - 1| + 2$

18. $y = -3|x + 2| - 1$

In Exercises 19 and 20, solve the equation.

19. $|3x + 6| - 7 = 3$

20. $|x + 5| - 4 = 4$

21. A produce stand is selling two varieties of corn. Silver Queen sells for $1.50 a dozen, and Butter and Sugar sells for $1.25 a dozen. The total sales for one day was $375. Let x be the number of dozen ears of Silver Queen sold and let y be the number of dozen ears of Butter and Sugar sold. Sketch a graph that shows the possible values of x and y.

22. Water is in a liquid state if its temperature, t (in degrees Fahrenheit), satisfies the *inequality* $|t - 122| < 90$. Find the two solutions of the *equation* $|t - 122| = 90$. What do these solutions represent.

Writing Linear Equations

LESSONS

5.1 Equations of Lines
Using Slope-Intercept
Form ▪ 236

5.2 Equations of Lines
Given the Slope and a
Point ▪ 242

5.3 Equations of Lines
Given Two Points
▪ 249

5.4 Exploring Data:
Fitting a Line
to Data ▪ 255

5.5 Standard Form of a
Linear Equation
▪ 264

5.6 Point-Slope Form of
the Equation of a
Line ▪ 270

5.7 Problem Solving
Using Linear Models
▪ 277

*In Olympic competition, athletes
push the parameters of physical
achievement to higher and
higher levels.*

The points on this graph show the heights of the winning pole vault at the Olympic Games between 1956 and 1988. The winning heights can be approximated by the linear model $y = 0.14t + 7.32$. In this model, y is the height in feet and t represents the year, with $t = 56$ corresponding to 1956.

Pole Vault Winning Heights

Height (in feet) vs. Year

1956:	Bob Richards (U.S.)	14.96 ft
1960:	Don Bragg (U.S.)	15.43 ft
1964:	Fred Hansen (U.S.)	16.73 ft
1968:	Bob Seagren (U.S.)	17.71 ft
1972:	Wolfgang Nordwig (Germany)	18.04 ft
1976:	Tadeusz Slusarski (Poland)	18.04 ft
1980:	Wladyslaw Kozakiewicz (Poland)	18.96 ft
1984:	Pierre Quinon (France)	18.85 ft
1988:	Sergei Bubka (U.S.S.R.)	19.77 ft

5.1

Equations of Lines
Using Slope-Intercept Form

What you should learn:

Goal 1 How to use the slope-intercept form to write an equation of a line

Goal 2 How to model a real-life situation with a linear equation

Why you should learn it:

You can use equations of lines to model many types of real-life situations such as cost problems (e.g., long-distance phoning), in which total cost is a flat fee plus a use fee that is based on a rate.

Goal 1 Using the Slope-Intercept Form

In Chapter 4, you learned to find the slope and y-intercept of a line whose equation is given. In this lesson, you will study the reverse process. That is, you will learn to write an equation of a line using its slope and y-intercept. To do this, you need to use the slope-intercept form of the equation of a line.

$$y = mx + b \qquad \textit{Slope-intercept form}$$

Remember that the slope of the line is m and the y-intercept is b.

Example 1 *Writing an Equation of a Line*

Write an equation of the line whose slope is -2 and whose y-intercept is 5.

Solution From the given information about the line, you know that the slope, m, is -2 and the y-intercept, b, is 5. By substituting these values into the slope-intercept form, you obtain the following equation.

$$y = mx + b \qquad \textit{Slope-intercept form}$$
$$y = -2x + 5 \qquad \textit{Substitute} -2 \textit{ for m and 5 for b.} \quad \blacksquare$$

Example 2 *Using a Graph to Write the Equation of a Line*

Write an equation of the line shown at the left.

Solution Since the line "intercepts" the y-axis at the point $(0, -4)$, the y-intercept, b, is -4. The line also passes through the point $(2, 0)$, which is four units up from, and two units to the right of the point $(0, -4)$. Therefore, the slope of the line is

$$m = \frac{\text{rise}}{\text{run}} = \frac{4}{2} = 2.$$

Knowing the slope and y-intercept, you can write the equation of the line.

$$y = mx + b \qquad \textit{Slope-intercept form}$$
$$y = 2x - 4 \qquad \textit{Substitute 2 for m and 4 for b.} \quad \blacksquare$$

In 1980, the population of California was approximately 23,668,000. During the next 10 years, the population increased by approximately 617,100 people per year. (Source: U.S. Census Bureau)

Example 3   *A Linear Model for the Population of California*

Write a linear model for the population of California between 1980 and 1990. Sketch a graph of the linear model.

Solution

Problem Solving
Write an Equation

Verbal Model	Population of California	=	1980 population	+	Increase per year	•	Number of years from 1980

Labels   Population of California = P (people)
1980 population = 23,668,000   (people)
Increase per year = 617,100   (people per year)
Number of years from 1980 = t (years)

Equation $P = 23{,}668{,}000 + 617{,}100t$ **Linear model**

In slope-intercept form, this equation is

$$P = 617{,}100t + 23{,}668{,}000.$$

The graph of this model is shown below. Notice that the P-intercept represents the 1980 population, and the slope represents the rate of change in the population (in people per year).

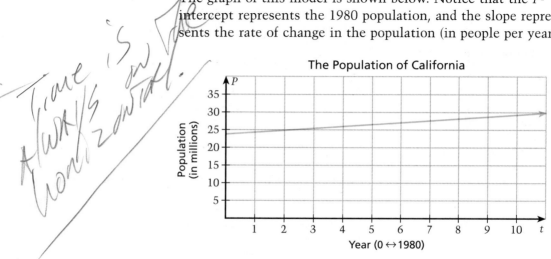

The Population of California

Population (in millions)

Year (0 ↔ 1980)

Example 4 — Writing a Linear Model for Phone Charges

Write a linear model for the cost of a long-distance call that costs $0.75 for the first minute and $0.50 for each additional minute.

Solution

	Total cost	=	Cost for first minute	+	Rate per additional minute	·	Number of additional minutes

Labels
Total cost = y (dollars)
Cost for first minute = 0.75 (dollars)
Rate per additional minute = 0.50 (dollars per min)
Number of additional minutes = x (minutes)

Equation $y = 0.75 + 0.5x$ **Linear model**

The slope of 0.5 is the cost per additional minute, and the y-intercept is the cost of the first minute. ■

Problem Solving
Verbal Model

This phone bill was generated by a computer, using the equation given in Example 4.

DATE	TIME	AREA-NUMBER	1st MIN	RATE	ADD'L MIN	AMOUNT
Jan 7	857PM	900 555 1829	$0.75	$0.50	4	$2.75
Jan 16	558PM	900 555 1829	$0.75	$0.50	1	$1.25
Jan 17	837PM	900 555 1829	$0.75	$0.50	17	
Jan 22	601PM	900 555 1829	$0.75	$0.50	9	
Feb 3	859PM	900 555 1829	$0.75			
Feb 15	916PM	900 555 1829				
Feb 21	955PM					

Communications Connection — Telephone Division

$$\boxed{0.75} + \boxed{0.50} \times \boxed{x} = \boxed{y}$$

Charge for first minute   Rate per additional minute   Number of additional minutes   Total charge (per call)

Communicating about ALGEBRA

▶ **SHARING IDEAS about the Lesson**

Compare with Linear Models The cost for calling a number in a city different from the one above is $1.25 for the first minute and $0.45 for each additional minute.

A. Write a linear model for the total cost of calling this second number.

B. Which would cost more: a seven-minute call to the first number (Example 4) or a seven-minute call to the second number?

C. Which would cost more: a 12-minute call to the first number or a 12-minute call to the second number?

EXERCISES

Guided Practice

▶ **CRITICAL THINKING about the Lesson**

1. What is the name of the $y = mx + b$ form of an equation of a line?

2. Is 5 the x-intercept or y-intercept of the line $y = 3x + 5$?

3. What is the slope and y-intercept of the line $y = -x$?

4. Write an equation of the line whose slope is -7 and whose y-intercept is $-\frac{2}{3}$.

5. Use the model given in Example 3 to estimate the population of California in 1994.

Renting a Bike   **In Exercises 6–8, Ed's Rentals charges a flat fee of $11 plus $1.50 per hour to rent a motorbike.**

6. Write an equation for the cost, y, of renting the motorbike for x hours.

7. Sketch the graph of the cost equation. Label the y-intercept on the graph.

8. Use the equation to find the cost of renting the motorbike for 12 hours.

Independent Practice

In Exercises 9–14, write an equation of the line.

9. The slope is 3; the y-intercept is -2.

10. The slope is 1; the y-intercept is 2.

11. The slope is -1; the y-intercept is 3.

12. The slope is -2; the y-intercept is 0.

13. The slope is $\frac{3}{2}$; the y-intercept is 3.

14. The slope is $-\frac{1}{4}$; the y-intercept is 1.

In Exercises 15–18, write an equation of the line shown in the graph.

15.

16.

17.

18.

Parallel Lines   **In Exercises 19 and 20, the lines are parallel. Write an equation for each.**

19.

20.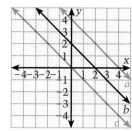

21. *Renting a Compact Car*   The Star Car Rental Company charges a flat fee of $30 plus 25¢ per mile to rent a compact car. Write a linear model that gives the total cost in terms of the number of miles driven.

22. *Renting a Full-Size Car*   The Maple Car Rental Company charges a flat fee of $45 plus 35¢ per mile to rent a full-size car. Write a linear model that gives the total cost in terms of the number of miles driven.

23. Use the equation you found in Exercise 21 to complete the table.

Miles (x)	25	50	75	100
Cost (y)	?	?	?	?

24. Use the equation you found in Exercise 22 to complete the table.

Miles (x)	25	50	75	100
Cost (y)	?	?	?	?

25. *Population of South Carolina*   In 1980, the population of South Carolina was approximately 3,122,000. During the next ten years, the population increased by approximately 38,400 people per year. Write a linear model that gives the population, P, of South Carolina in terms of the year, t. Let $t = 0$ correspond to 1980.

(Source: U.S. Census Bureau)

26. Use the equation you found in Exercise 25 to estimate the population of South Carolina in 1986.

27. *Traveling Home*   At noon, you are 200 miles from home. You are traveling home at 50 miles per hour. Write an equation that gives your distance from home, y, in terms of the time, t. Let $t = 0$ correspond to noon. Why does the line given by this equation have a negative slope?

28. Use the equation you found in Exercise 27 to complete the table.

Time (t)	1	2	3	4
Miles (y)	?	?	?	?

Water Conservation   **In Exercises 29 and 30, use the following information.**

A standard toilet uses approximately 5 gallons of water each time it is flushed. Installing a water dam (a device costing about $10) reduces water usage by approximately 50%. Consider a city that has 100,000 households, each with toilets that are flushed an average of 15 times per day.

29. Write a linear model for the city's water usage without water dams. How much water is used in one year?

30. Write a linear model for the city's water usage with water dams. How much water was saved in one year?

In Exercises 31–36, find the slope and the *y*-intercept of the line. Then sketch the line.

31. $y = -3x + 6$

32. $y = 2x - 5$

33. $y + 2x = 2$

34. $-y + 3x = -5$

35. $2y - 3x = 6$

36. $2y + 4x = 6$

In Exercises 37–42, determine whether the line is horizontal or vertical. Then sketch the line.

37. $y = -2$

38. $x = 3$

39. $x = 4$

40. $y = -5$

41. $2y = 6$

42. $3x = -6$

43. Can a horizontal line have an equation in slope-intercept form?

44. Can a vertical line have an equation in slope-intercept form?

45. Write an equation of the horizontal line whose *y*-intercept is 3.

46. Write an equation of the vertical line whose *x*-intercept is -4.

In Exercises 47 and 48, match the description with the linear model *y* = 10 or the linear model *y* = 10*x*.

47. A rental company charges $10 per hour to rent a sailboard. (There is no flat fee.)

48. A rental company charges a flat fee of $10 to rent an electric drill. (There is no hourly charge.)

In Exercises 49 and 50, write an equation of the line shown in the graph. Then describe a real-life problem that could be represented by the equation.

49.

50.

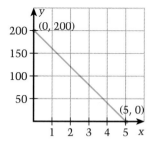

51. Write an equation of the line that has the same slope as $y = -\frac{2}{5}x + 1$ and the same *y*-intercept as $y = 2x - 3$. Then sketch all three lines.

52. Write an equation of the line that has the same slope as $y = \frac{3}{2}x - 4$ and the same *y*-intercept as $y = -\frac{2}{3}x + 3$. Then sketch all three lines.

5.2

Equations of Lines Given the Slope and a Point

What you should learn:

Goal 1 How to use slope and any point on a line to write an equation of the line

Goal 2 How to model a real-life situation with a linear equation

Why you should learn it:

You can model a real-life situation with a linear equation when you are given the rate of change taking place (the slope) and any pair of related values (one point on the line).

Goal 1 Using Slope and a Point on a Line

In Lesson 5.1, you learned how to write an equation of a line when you are given the slope of the line and the y-intercept of the line. You used the slope-intercept form of the equation of a line

$y = mx + b.$ *Slope-intercept form*

In this lesson, the use of this form is extended by showing how it can help find an equation of a line when you are given the slope of the line and *any* point on the line. Here is an example.

Example 1   *Writing an Equation of a Line*

Write an equation of the line that passes through the point $(6, -3)$ with a slope of -2.

Solution   The first step is to use the given information to find the y-intercept of the line. Since the line has a slope, m, of -2 and passes through the point $(x, y) = (6, -3)$, you can substitute the values $m = -2$, $x = 6$, and $y = -3$ into the slope-intercept form and solve for b.

$$y = mx + b \qquad \text{\textit{Slope-intercept form}}$$
$$-3 = (-2)(6) + b \qquad \text{\textit{Substitute } -2 \text{ for } m, 6 \text{ for } x, \text{ and}}$$
$$\text{\textit{-3 for } y.}$$
$$-3 = -12 + b \qquad \text{\textit{Simplify.}}$$
$$9 = b \qquad \text{\textit{Solve for b.}}$$

Thus, the y-intercept, b, is 9. Now you know both the slope and the y-intercept, and you can find an equation of the line using the slope-intercept form.

$$y = mx + b \qquad \text{\textit{Slope-intercept form}}$$
$$y = -2x + 9 \qquad \text{\textit{Substitute } -2 \text{ for } m \text{ and } 9 \text{ for } b.}$$

Graphic Check   The graph of the line is shown at the left. Note that the line crosses the y-axis at the point $(0, 9)$ and passes through the given point $(6, -3)$.

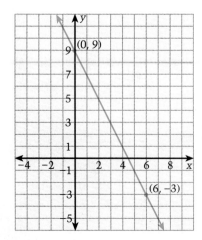

Goal 2 ## Modeling a Real-Life Situation

Between 1980 and 1990, the number of vacation trips taken by Americans increased by about 15 million per year. In 1985, Americans went on 340 million vacation trips.
(Source: U.S. Travel Data Center)

Real Life
Travel

Example 2   *A Linear Model for Vacation Travel*

Find an equation that gives the number of vacation trips, y (in millions), in terms of the year, t. Let $t = 0$ correspond to 1980.

Solution   Because the number of trips changed at a constant rate each year, you can model this problem using the linear equation $y = mt + b$. The constant rate is 15 million trips per year, so you know that the slope, m, is 15 (in millions). You also know an ordered pair, $(5, 340)$, that represents a point on the line. (Why?)

$$y = mt + b \qquad \textit{Slope-intercept form}$$
$$340 = (15)(5) + b \qquad \textit{Substitute 15 for m, 5 for t, and 340 for y.}$$
$$340 = 75 + b \qquad \textit{Simplify.}$$
$$265 = b \qquad \textit{Solve for b.}$$

The slope-intercept form of the equation is $y = 15t + 265$. ∎

You can use the equation in Example 2 to predict the number of vacation trips that Americans will take in a given year.

Example 3 *Using a Linear Model to Predict Vacation Travel*

About how many vacation trips will Americans take in 1998?

Solution   To answer this question, use the linear model from Example 2: $y = 15t + 265$. Since 1980 corresponds to $t = 0$, it follows that 1998 must correspond to $t = 18$.

$y = 15t + 265$ *Given model*
$y = 15(18) + 265$ *Substitute 18 for t.*
$y = 535$ *Trips in 1998*

Thus, you can estimate that Americans will take about 535 million vacation trips in 1998. The graph is shown below.

Communicating about ALGEBRA

▶ **SHARING IDEAS about the Lesson**

Estimate   Use the linear model in Example 3.

A. How many vacation trips were taken by Americans in 1990?

B. How many vacation trips will be taken by Americans in 1997?

C. During which year would there be about 400 million vacation trips?

D. In Example 3, the model $y = 15t + 265$ was developed, based on travel data between 1980 and 1990. Do you think this model is valid for earlier years such as 1950 or 1960? Explain your reasoning.

EXERCISES

Guided Practice

▶ **CRITICAL THINKING about the Lesson**

1. Describe the strategy used to find an equation of a line, given its slope and a point on the line. Sketch a flowchart for the steps.

2. When finding an equation of the line that passes through the point $(-2, 4)$ with a slope of $\frac{1}{3}$, begin by substituting values for m, x, and y into the slope-intercept form, $y = mx + b$. Which value should you substitute for m? Which value for x? Which value for y? What will these substitutions permit you to find?

In Exercises 3–6, write an equation of the line that passes through the point and has the given slope. Give the equation in slope-intercept form.

3. $(1, 3)$, $m = -2$ **4.** $(-6, 7)$, $m = 0$ **5.** $(8, -2)$, $m = \frac{1}{2}$ **6.** $\left(\frac{1}{2}, -\frac{3}{2}\right)$, $m = 9$

7. *Population of Naples*   Between 1980 and 1990, the population of Naples, Florida, increased by approximately 6000 people per year. In 1985, the population of Naples was 116,000. Find an equation that gives the population, y, of Naples in terms of the year, x. Let $x = 0$ correspond to 1980. *(Source: Naples Chamber of Commerce)*

8. Estimate the population of Naples in 1990.

Independent Practice

In Exercises 9–20, write an equation of the line that passes through the point and has the given slope. Write the equation in slope-intercept form.

9. $(-3, 6)$, $m = 2$ **10.** $(3, 2)$, $m = 1$ **11.** $(4, -2)$, $m = -1$ **12.** $(3, 1)$, $m = -3$

13. $(-2, -5)$, $m = -2$ **14.** $(1, 4)$, $m = 4$ **15.** $(4, -2)$, $m = \frac{1}{2}$ **16.** $(-6, 5)$, $m = \frac{1}{3}$

17. $(0, -1)$, $m = 3$ **18.** $(0, 4)$, $m = 2$ **19.** $(2, 5)$, $m = 0$ **20.** $(1, -3)$, $m = 0$

In Exercises 21–26, write the slope-intercept form of the equation of the line.

21. The line has a slope of $\frac{2}{3}$ and passes through the point $(-3, 4)$.

22. The line has a slope of $-\frac{1}{4}$ and passes through the point $(8, 3)$.

23.

24.

25.

26.
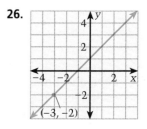

27. Find an equation of the line that crosses the x-axis at (3, 0) with a slope of $-\frac{1}{3}$.

28. Find an equation of the line that crosses the x-axis at $(-2, 0)$ with a slope of 2.

29. *Hockey Attendance* Between 1980 and 1990, the attendance at National Hockey League games increased by about 1,100,000 people per year. In 1989, 20,434,000 people attended National Hockey League games. Find an equation that gives the attendance, y, at National Hockey League games in terms of the year, x. Let x = 0 correspond to 1980. *(Source: National Hockey League)*

30. *Cable Television Subscribers* Between 1980 and 1990, the number of cable television subscribers increased by about 3600 per year. In 1987, there were 41,100 cable television subscribers. Find an equation that gives the number, y, of cable television subscribers, in terms of the year, x. Let x = 0 correspond to 1980. *(Source: Television and Cable Factbook)*

31. *Fitness Program* After 8 weeks on a fitness program, Greg can jog 30 miles a week. His average mileage gain has been 2 miles per week. Find an equation that gives Greg's mileage, m, in terms of the number, n, of weeks that he stays on the program.

32. *Savings Plan* Christina withdraws $7.50 per week from her savings account. After 12 weeks, the balance in her account is $452. Write an equation that gives the balance, y, of Christina's account in terms of the number of weeks, x. (Do not consider any interest earned by the account.)

Ancient Flour Mill **In Exercises 33 and 34, use the following information.**

The drawing at the right shows Roman flour mills on a hill near Barbégal in southern France. The mills are now in ruins, but during the fourth century A.D. this mill complex could grind enough flour to feed a population of 12,500 people. Water from the top of the hill flowed over 8 pairs of waterwheels, each powering grindstones. The angle of the hill is about 27°, which means that the slope of the hill is $\frac{1}{2}$. Each mill house was 15 feet by 8 feet. *(Source: Scientific American)*

33. Let the base of the left stairs represent the origin. Write a linear model for the line formed by the stairs.

34. Use the linear model to find the height of the stairs.

35. *Phone Call* Suppose the cost of a telephone call between New York and Philadelphia is $0.46 for the first minute and $0.31 for each additional minute. Write an equation that gives the total cost of the call, C, in terms of the length of the call, t.

36. *Taxi Ride* Use the information given with the photo to find an equation that gives the total cost of a taxi ride, y, in terms of the number of miles, x.

The cost of a taxi ride in Detroit is $2.50 for the first mile plus $1.30 for each additional mile.

Integrated Review

In Exercises 37–40, solve the equation for b.

37. $-2 = \frac{3}{2}(-4) + b$

38. $4 = \left(-\frac{2}{3}\right)(-6) + b$

39. $\frac{3}{2} = \left(-\frac{1}{6}\right)(3) + b$

40. $-\frac{2}{3} = \left(-\frac{1}{6}\right)(2) + b$

In Exercises 41–44, sketch the line that passes through the given point and has the given slope. Use the graph to estimate the y-intercept. Then find the actual y-intercept.

41. $(2, 4)$, $m = -\frac{1}{2}$

42. $(4, 8)$, $m = -2$

43. $(3, 6)$, $m = 2$

44. $(4, 0)$, $m = \frac{1}{2}$

45. Find an equation of the line that passes through the point $(-1, 4)$ and is parallel to the line $y = -2x + 5$.

46. Find an equation of the line that passes through the point $(2, 6)$ and is parallel to the line $y = x - 3$.

Exploration and Extension

Fund-Raising **In Exercises 47–51, use the following information.**

The school math club decides to have a fund-raising project. The club rents the movie *The Life and Times of René Descartes* for $19.75, and charges an admission fee of $0.25 per person.

47. Find an equation that gives the profit, P, in terms of the number of people, n, who attend the movie.

48. Sketch the graph of the equation you found in Exercise 47.

49. Which values of n are not relevant to this linear model? (Hint: For instance, $\frac{1}{2}$ of a person could not attend.)

50. Is it possible that the club will not make a profit? How many people must attend the movie so that the club will get its $19.75 back?

51. After counting the receipts, the club members found that they earned a profit of $40.75. How many people attended the movie?

1. Which is larger, $-\frac{1}{3}$ or $-\frac{1}{2}$? **(2.1)**

2. Find the sum of $\frac{2}{3}$ and $\frac{3}{2}$. **(1.1)**

3. Find the area of a 2-ft by 8-ft rectangle.

4. What is the average value of 3, 6, 8, and 13?

5. What number squared is 121?

6. What is 35% of 130?

7. Simplify $-(x - 4) + 2x$. **(2.6)**

8. Simplify $2(3x - 4) - 5(x - 4)$. **(2.6)**

9. Are the lines $2x = 3y$ and $3x = 2y$ parallel? **(4.5)**

10. Are the lines $y = 2x$ and $y = -2x$ parallel? **(4.5)**

11. Solve $2x - 4 = -x + 11$. **(3.3)**

12. Solve $3(x + 4) = -(x + 1) - 2$. **(3.3, 2.6)**

13. Evaluate $-3x + 15$ when $x = -1$. **(2.5)**

14. Evaluate $|2x + 3|$ when $x = -2$. **(2.1, 2.5)**

15. Graph $(-3, 5)$ and $(2, -6)$.

16. Graph $(2, 1)$ and $(-3, 4)$.

17. Sketch the graph of $y = -3x + 4$. **(4.5)**

18. Sketch the graph of $y = |x - 2|$. **(4.7)**

19. Write an equation of the line with a slope of 2 and a y-intercept of 3. **(5.1)**

20. Write an equation of the line that passes through $(1, -3)$ and has a slope of -1. **(5.2)**

Career Interview

Counselor

Anne Cavanaugh Sawan counsels outpatients in a community mental health center. She works with children, adolescents, and families experiencing difficulty. She acts as a resource to help them manage their problems.

Q: *Does having a math background help you on the job?*

A: Mathematics provides the confirmation of research studies. I rely on mathematical information to interpret, validate, and express results of my work.

Q: *How much of the math is done by computers? Does this mean that you do not need to understand math?*

A: Almost all research data are handled by computers; all formulas are input into programs to handle the data. However, I must still know how the formulas work, how to apply them, what type of a response will result, and how to judge the reasonableness of the results.

Q: *What would you like to tell kids about math?*

A: Math is really fun, especially when you see the connections and relevance it has to your everyday life. Math is a subject you will rely on all your life. Don't be afraid of making mistakes; you can learn a lot from your errors.

5.3

Equations of Lines Given Two Points

What you should learn:

Goal 1 How to write an equation of a line given two points on the line

Goal 2 How to model a real-life situation with a linear equation

Why you should learn it:

You can model a real-life situation with a linear equation when you are given two pairs of related values (two points on the line) such as quantities sold in two different time periods.

Goal 1 Equation of a Line Given Two Points

So far in this chapter, you have been finding equations of lines for which you were given the slope. In this lesson, you will encounter problems in which you must first find the slope. To do this, you must use the formula given in Chapter 4. The formula states that the slope of the line passing through the points (x_1, y_1) and (x_2, y_2) is

$$m = \frac{\text{rise}}{\text{run}} = \frac{y_2 - y_1}{x_2 - x_1}. \quad \textit{Formula for slope, m}$$

Note how this formula is used in Example 1.

Example 1 *Using the Slope Formula to Find the Equation of a Line*

Find an equation for the line that passes through the points $(1, 6)$ and $(3, -4)$.

Solution The first step is to find the slope of the line. You let $(x_1, y_1) = (1, 6)$ and $(x_2, y_2) = (3, -4)$. Then you have

$$m = \frac{y_2 - y_1}{x_2 - x_1} = \frac{-4 - 6}{3 - 1} = \frac{-10}{2} = -5.$$

Now you know the slope and a point, and you can use the steps from Lesson 5.2 to find an equation of the line. You let $m = -5$, $x = 1$, and $y = 6$ and solve for b as follows.

$y = mx + b$	*Slope-intercept form*
$6 = (-5)(1) + b$	*Substitute -5 for m, 1 for x, and 6 for y.*
$6 = -5 + b$	*Simplify.*
$11 = b$	*Solve for b.*

Thus, the y-intercept is $b = 11$, and the slope-intercept form of the equation of the line is $y = -5x + 11$.

Graphic Check Notice that the line has a y-intercept at 11. ■

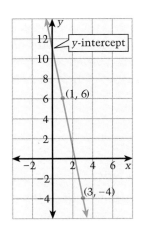

In Example 1, we used the point $(1, 6)$ to find the y-intercept. Try using the other point, $(3, -4)$, to see that you obtain the same value for b.

Example 1 suggests the following strategy for writing an equation of a line given two points on the line.

Writing an Equation of a Line Given Two Points

To write an equation of a nonvertical line given two points on the line, use the following steps.

1. *Find the slope:* Substitute the coordinates of the two given points into the formula for slope, $m = \frac{(y_2 - y_1)}{(x_2 - x_1)}$.

2. *Find the y-intercept:* Substitute the slope m and the coordinates of one of the points into the slope-intercept form, $y = mx + b$. Then solve for the y-intercept b.

3. *Write an equation of the line:* Substitute the slope m and the y-intercept b into the slope-intercept form, $y = mx + b$.

The next example shows how you can use these guidelines to find an equation of a line.

Example 2   *Writing an Equation of a Line Given Two Points*

A line passes through the points $(-3, 2)$ and $(5, -2)$. Write its equation in slope-intercept form.

Solution   The slope of the line is

$$m = \frac{y_2 - y_1}{x_2 - x_1} = \frac{-2 - 2}{5 - (-3)} = \frac{-4}{8} = -\frac{1}{2}.$$

To find the y-intercept, substitute $m = -\frac{1}{2}$, $x = -3$, and $y = 2$ into the slope-intercept form.

$y = mx + b$	*Slope-intercept form*
$2 = \left(-\frac{1}{2}\right)(-3) + b$	*Substitute $-\frac{1}{2}$ for m, -3 for x, and 2 for y.*
$2 = \frac{3}{2} + b$	*Simplify.*
$\frac{1}{2} = b$	*Solve for b.*

Using $b = \frac{1}{2}$ and $m = -\frac{1}{2}$, you can write the equation of the line as $y = -\frac{1}{2}x + \frac{1}{2}$. (Check to see that both of the given points lie on this line.)

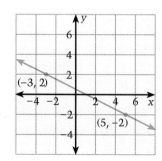

Graphic Check   Plot the points $(-3, 2)$ and $(5, -2)$ and then draw the line through the two points as shown at the left. This line appears to have slope $-\frac{1}{2}$ and y-intercept $\frac{1}{2}$. ■

Modeling a Real-Life Situation

In Example 3, you can see how the guidelines for finding the equation of a line, given two points, can be used to create a linear model for a real-life problem.

Real Life
Retailing

A store at a shopping mall sold 4180 pairs of designer jeans in 1986 and 5710 pairs in 1992.

Example 3 **A Linear Model for Sales of Jeans**

Write an equation that gives the number, y, of pairs of designer jeans sold in the store shown in terms of the year, x. (Let $x = 0$ correspond to 1980.)

Solution Assume that the number of jeans sold increased at a constant rate. This allows you to use a linear model. From the given information, you can find the following two points.

1986: $(6, 4180)$ and 1992: $(12, 5710)$

The slope of the line passing through these two points is

$$m = \frac{y_2 - y_1}{x_2 - x_1} = \frac{5710 - 4180}{12 - 6} = 255.$$

Now, using $m = 255$, $x = 6$, and $y = 4180$, you can find the y-intercept of the line.

$y = mx + b$ *Slope-intercept form*
$4180 = (255)(6) + b$ *Substitute 255 for m, 6 for x, and 4180 for y.*
$4180 = 1530 + b$ *Simplify.*
$2650 = b$ *Solve for b.*

Thus, the equation is $y = 255x + 2650$. ■

Communicating about ALGEBRA

▷ **SHARING IDEAS about the Lesson**

Estimate and Predict In Example 3, we developed the linear model $y = 255x + 2650$ to represent the number of pairs of designer jeans sold by a store.

A. What does the slope of 255 represent?

B. Estimate how many pairs of jeans were sold in 1991.

C. Solve the given linear model for x. Use the result to predict the year the store will sell 6475 pairs of jeans.

D. In 1990, the average price of jeans was $35.95. Estimate how much money the store received for jeans in 1990.

EXERCISES

▶ **CRITICAL THINKING about the Lesson**

1. Describe the strategy used to find an equation of the line that passes through two given points. Sketch a flowchart that shows the steps.

2. When finding an equation of a line passing through two points, you should begin by finding the slope m. Why?

3. What is the slope of the line that passes through $(1, -1)$ and $(2, 3)$?

4. Write an equation of the line that passes through $(1, -1)$ and $(2, 3)$.

In Exercises 5 and 6, consider a car dealer who sold 450 new cars in 1986 and 600 new cars in 1992.

5. Write an equation that gives the number of cars sold, y, in terms of the year, x. Assume that sales increased at a constant rate, and let $x = 0$ correspond to 1980.

6. Use the model that you found in Exercise 5 to estimate the number of new cars sold by the dealer in 1990.

Independent Practice

In Exercises 7–10, write the slope-intercept form of the equation of the line.

7.

8.

9.

10.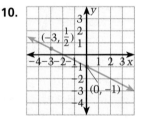

In Exercises 11–22, write the slope-intercept form of the equation of the line that passes through the two points.

11. $(-1, -1), (2, 8)$ 12. $(1, 2), (4, -1)$ 13. $(2, 0), (-4, -3)$ 14. $(3, 1), (-3, 5)$

15. $(1, -4), (-2, 8)$ 16. $(0, -4), (3, 2)$ 17. $(2, -5), (-1, 1)$ 18. $(-2, -1), (4, 2)$

19. $(1, 1), (4, 4)$ 20. $(1, 2), (2, 4)$ 21. $(1, 3), (3, 3)$ 22. $(-1, -2), (3, -2)$

23. Sketch the line that passes through $(2, 6)$ and $(-4, 3)$. Write its equation in slope-intercept form.

24. Sketch the line that passes through $(3, -3)$ and $(-3, 1)$. Write its equation in slope-intercept form.

25. Write an equation of the line whose x-intercept is -6 and whose y-intercept is -4.

26. Write an equation of the line whose x-intercept is -1 and whose y-intercept is 3.

27. *Carpet Purchase*   The Jacksons are planning to buy carpeting for several rooms in their house. They plan to use the same carpeting in each room. The family room requires 35 square yards of carpet and would cost $665. The living room requires 28 square yards of carpet and would cost $532. Write an equation that gives the cost, *y*, in terms of the total number of square yards of carpeting, *x*.

First Floor   *Second Floor*

28. Use the equation found in Exercise 27 to complete the table.

Square yards (*x*)	15	26	41	63	104
Cost (*y*)	?	?	?	?	?

Chunnel   **In Exercises 29 and 30, use the following information.**

The *Chunnel* is a tunnel built under the English Channel. It is one of the most ambitious engineering feats of the twentieth century.

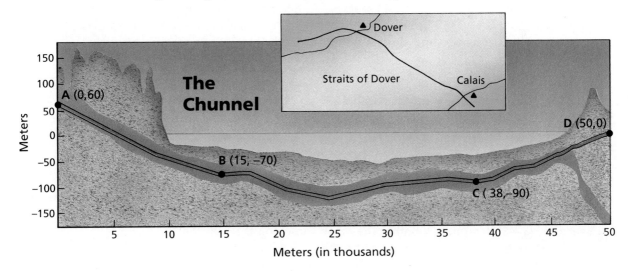

29. Use the diagram to write an equation of the line from point *A* to point *B*. What is the slope of this line?

30. Use the diagram to write an equation of the line from point *C* to point *D*. What is the slope of this line? Is the Chunnel steeper on the French side or the English side?

31. Profit from Shoe Sales A shoe store made a profit of $14,510 in 1988 and a profit of $21,260 in 1993. Write an equation that gives the profit, y, in terms of the year, x. Let $x = 0$ correspond to 1980 and assume that the profit followed a linear pattern.

32. Bookstore Sales A bookstore sold 576 copies of dictionaries in 1984 and 792 copies in 1992. Write an equation that gives the number, d, of dictionaries sold in terms of the year, t. Let $t = 0$ correspond to 1980 and assume that the sales followed a linear pattern.

33. Newspaper Circulation In 1975, Sunday newspapers in the United States had a circulation of 51,096,000. In 1985, the circulation had increased to 58,826,000. Write an equation that gives the Sunday circulation, y, in terms of the year, x. Let $x = 0$ correspond to 1970 and assume that circulation followed a linear pattern. *(Source: American Newspaper Publishers Association)*

34. Population of Western United States In 1950, the population of the western United States was 20,190,000. In 1980, the population was 43,200,000. Write an equation that gives the population, y, in terms of the year, x. Let $x = 0$ correspond to 1950 and assume that the population followed a linear pattern. *(Source: U.S. Bureau of Census)*

Integrated Review

In Exercises 35–38, sketch the line that passes through the given points. Use the graph to estimate the y-intercept of the line. Then find the actual y-intercept.

35. $(3, -3), (-6, 0)$ **36.** $(1, 1), (-3, -1)$ **37.** $(1, 1), (-5, -3)$ **38.** $(1, 2), (-4, 7)$

39. Find an equation of the line that passes through the point $(-4, 11)$ and has the same y-intercept as the line given by $y = -\frac{2}{3}x + 3$.

40. Find an equation of the line that passes through the point $(3, 7)$ and has the same y-intercept as the line given by $y = \frac{1}{2}x - 5$.

41. Find an equation of the line that passes through the point $(3, -4)$ and is parallel to the line passing through the points $(-4, -1)$ and $(2, 5)$.

42. Find an equation of the line that passes through the point $(4, -5)$ and is parallel to the line passing through the points $(2, 0)$ and $(-2, -2)$.

Exploration and Extension

In Exercises 43–46, determine whether the given three points lie on the same line. If they do, find an equation of the line.

43. $(-3, -1), (0, 1), (12, 9)$

44. $(4, -2), (-1, 2), (-8, 9)$

45. $(-2, -1), (3, 2), (7, 5)$

46. $(3, -3), (-1, 13), (1, 5)$

47. You are told that the points $(1.9, 7.11), (5, 13), (-3.3, -2.77)$, and $(-5, -6)$ lie on the same line. If you were asked to find the slope of the line, which two points would you choose and why?

5.4

Exploring Data: Fitting a Line to Data

What you should learn:

Goal 1 How to find a linear equation that approximates a set of data points.

Goal 2 How to use scatter plots to determine positive correlation, negative correlation, or no correlation

Why you should learn it:

You can use the equation of a best-fitting line to investigate trends in data, such as sports performances, and to make predictions.

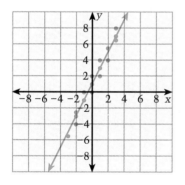

Goal 1 Fitting a Line to Data

In Lesson 5.3, you studied how to find an equation of the line that passes through *two* points. For this type of problem, there is always only one line—because two points determine exactly one line.

In this lesson, you will study problems that involve *several* data points. Usually, there is no single line that passes through all the data points, so you try to find the line that best fits the data. This is called the **best-fitting line.** For instance, in the graph shown below, the line given by $y = 2x + 1$ is the best-fitting line for the data points.

There are several different ways to find the best-fitting line for a given set of data points whose graph suggests a linear relationship. One way is to use a computer and formulas from a branch of mathematics called statistics. The statistical formula can *find* the best-fitting line. In this lesson, however, we use a graphical approach, which *approximates* the best-fitting line. The basic steps of this approach are given below.

Approximating the Best-Fitting Line: Visual Approach

To approximate the best-fitting line for a set of ordered pairs, use the following steps.

1. *Sketch a Scatter Plot:* Sketch a scatter plot for the data.

2. *Sketch the Line:* Sketch the line that appears to most closely follow the pattern given by the points. There should be about as many points above the line as below the line.

3. *Locate Two Points on the Line:* Locate two points on the line and approximate the x-coordinate and y-coordinate of each point. (These two points do not have to be two of the original data points.)

4. *Find an Equation of the Line:* Use the technique described in Lesson 5.3 to find an equation of the line that passes through the two points in Step 3.

Year	Winning Throw
1900	118.2 ft
1904	128.9 ft
1908	134.2 ft
1912	145.1 ft
1920	146.6 ft
1924	151.4 ft
1928	155.2 ft
1932	162.4 ft
1936	165.6 ft
1948	173.2 ft
1952	180.5 ft
1956	184.9 ft
1960	194.2 ft
1964	200.1 ft
1968	212.5 ft
1972	211.3 ft
1976	221.5 ft
1980	218.7 ft
1984	218.5 ft
1988	225.8 ft

Example 1 *The Olympic Games Discus Throw*

The winning Olympic Games discus throws from 1900 to 1988 are shown in the table. Approximate the best-fitting line for these throws. Let x represent the year, with $x = 0$ corresponding to 1900. Let y represent the winning throw.

Solution To begin, represent each of the winning throws by an ordered pair. For instance, the winning throw in 1900 is represented by (0, 118.2), and the winning throw in 1904 is represented by (4, 128.9). Next, plot the points given by the ordered pairs. Then sketch the line that best fits the points, as shown below.

Winning Olympic Discus Throws

The next step is to find two points that lie on the best-fitting line. From the graph, you might choose the points (8, 132) and (88, 230). The slope of the line passing through these two points is

$$m = \frac{y_2 - y_1}{x_2 - x_1} = \frac{230 - 132}{88 - 8} = \frac{98}{80} = 1.225.$$

To find the y-intercept of the line, substitute the values $m = 1.225$, $x = 8$, and $y = 132$ into the slope-intercept form.

$y = mx + b$	*Slope-intercept form*
$132 = (1.225)(8) + b$	*Substitute 1.225 for m, 8 for x, 132 for y.*
$132 = 9.8 + b$	*Simplify.*
$122.2 = b$	*Solve for b.*

Thus, the y-intercept, b, is 122.2, and the slope-intercept form of the equation of the best-fitting line is approximately

$$y = 1.225x + 122.2. \qquad \blacksquare$$

Forearm Length	Foot Length
22 cm	24 cm
20 cm	19 cm
24 cm	24 cm
21 cm	23 cm
25 cm	23 cm
18 cm	18 cm
20 cm	21 cm
23 cm	23 cm
24 cm	25 cm
20 cm	22 cm
19 cm	19 cm
25 cm	25 cm
23 cm	22 cm
22 cm	23 cm
24 cm	24 cm
20 cm	21 cm
18 cm	19 cm
24 cm	23 cm
24 cm	27 cm
21 cm	24 cm
22 cm	22 cm

Example 2 *Comparing Arm Length to Foot Length*

The data in the table contain the forearm lengths and foot lengths (without shoes) of 22 students in an algebra class.

Approximate the best-fitting line for these data. Let x represent the forearm length and let y represent the foot length.

Solution   To begin, plot points for the data, as shown in the graph. (Note that only 19 points are plotted because three of the points are repeated.)

Foot and Forearm Lengths

Next, sketch the line that appears to fit the points best and locate two points on the line: (19, 20) and (26, 26). The slope of the line passing through these two points is

$$m = \frac{y_2 - y_1}{x_2 - x_1} = \frac{26 - 20}{26 - 19} = \frac{6}{7} \approx 0.86.$$

To approximate the y-intercept of the line, substitute the values $m = 0.86$, $x = 19$, and $y = 20$ into the slope-intercept form.

$y = mx + b$	*Slope-intercept form*
$20 = (0.86)(19) + b$	*Substitute 0.86 for m, 19 for x, 20 for y.*
$20 \approx 16.3 + b$	*Simplify.*
$3.7 \approx b$	*Solve for b.*

Thus, the y-intercept, b, is approximately 3.7, and the slope-intercept form of the equation of the best-fitting line is approximately

$$y = 0.86x + 3.7.$$

Three scatter plots are shown below. In the first scatter plot, _x_ and _y_ have a **positive correlation,** which means that the points can be approximated by a line with a _positive slope._ In the second scatter plot, _x_ and _y_ have a **negative correlation,** which means that the points can be approximated by a line with a _negative slope._ In the third scatter plot, there is **no correlation** between _x_ and _y._

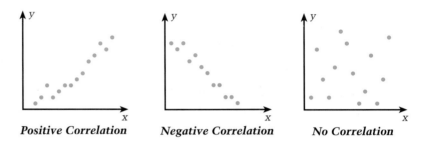

Positive Correlation   _Negative Correlation_   _No Correlation_

Communicating about **A L G E B R A**

▷ **SHARING IDEAS about the Lesson**

**Construct a Model** The total prize money for the Indianapolis 500 from 1980 to 1990 is shown in the table.
**(Source: Indianapolis Motor Speedway)**

A. Sketch a scatter plot. Let _x_ represent the year, with _x_ = 0 corresponding to 1980, and let _y_ represent the total prize money.

B. From your scatter plot, do _x_ and _y_ appear to have a positive correlation, a negative correlation, or no correlation?

C. Sketch the best-fitting line.

D. Locate two points on the line. (Your two points need not be the same as the points chosen by others in the class.)

E. Use your two points to approximate an equation of the line.

F. Use the equation you found to predict the total amount of prize money for the Indianapolis 500 in 1996.

Year	Prize Money
1980	$1,503,225
1981	$1,605,375
1982	$2,067,475
1983	$2,411,450
1984	$2,795,899
1985	$3,271,025
1986	$4,001,450
1987	$4,490,375
1988	$5,025,400
1989	$5,723,725
1990	$6,240,350

EXERCISES

Guided Practice

▶ CRITICAL THINKING about the Lesson

In Exercises 1–6, use the data shown on the graph.

On humid days, people tend to feel warmer than the actual temperature. To illustrate this, several people were asked how warm they felt. In each case, the actual temperature was 80° Fahrenheit, but the relative humidity varied from 25% to 98%.

1. The graph showing the data points for this experiment is called a ___?___ .

2. The line shown on the graph above is called the ___?___-___?___ line.

3. Use the two labeled points to find the slope of the line.

4. Find an equation of the line.

5. If the temperature is 80°F and the relative humidity is 0.80, how warm would it feel?

6. If the temperature is 80°F and it feels like 90°F, what is the relative humidity?

Independent Practice

In Exercises 7–10, decide whether _x_ and _y_ suggest a linear relationship.

7.

8.

9.

10.

In Exercises 11–13, approximate the best-fitting line for the scatter plot. State whether _x_ and _y_ have a positive or negative correlation.

11.

12.

13.

In Exercises 14 and 15, construct a scatter plot for the given data. Then find an equation of the line that you think best represents the data. State whether x and y have a positive correlation or a negative correlation.

14.

x	1.0	1.5	1.7	2.0	2.0	2.5	3.0	3.4	4.0	4.1	4.8	5.2
y	3.8	4.2	5.3	5.8	5.5	6.7	7.1	8.1	8.5	8.9	9.6	10.6

15.

x	3.0	3.5	3.7	4.0	4.0	4.5	5.0	5.4	6.0	6.1	6.8	7.2
y	10.1	9.7	8.6	8.1	8.4	7.4	6.8	5.8	5.6	5.2	4.3	3.5

16. *Baseball Salaries*   The average annual salary for major league baseball players from 1980 to 1990 is shown in the scatter plot at the right. In the graph, y represents the salary and x represents the year, with $x = 0$ corresponding to 1980. Find an equation of the line that you think best fits this data. Then use the equation to approximate the average annual salary in 1992. (*Source: Major League Baseball*)

Baseball Salaries

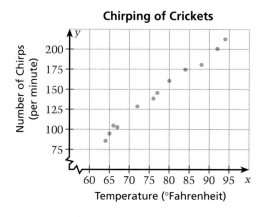

17. *Cricket Chirping*   Crickets make a chirping sound by rubbing their legs together. The number of chirps that a cricket makes per minute is related to the temperature, as shown in the scatter plot at the right. In the graph, y represents the number of chirps per minute and x represents the temperature in degrees Fahrenheit. Find an equation of the line that you think best fits this data. Then use the equation to approximate the number of chirps per minute made by a cricket when the temperature is 85°.

18. *American Workers*   The number of Americans who were employed in nonmilitary jobs between 1982 and 1988 is given in the table at the right. Sketch a scatter plot for this data and find an equation of the line that best fits the data. Use your equation to approximate the number of American workers in 1992. (*Source: U.S. Bureau of Labor Statistics*)

Year	Number of Workers
1982	99,526,000
1983	100,834,000
1984	105,005,000
1985	107,150,000
1986	109,597,000
1987	112,440,000
1988	114,968,000

19. *Average Temperatures*   The average June temperatures and latitudes of several cities in the central United States are shown in the table. Sketch a scatter plot for these data and find an equation of the line that best fits the data. Use your equation to approximate the average June temperature for a city in the central United States with a latitude of 40°. *(Source: P.C. U.S.A.)*

City	Lat.	Temp.
Bismarck	46.8°	64.3°F
Sioux Falls	43.5°	68.4°F
Omaha	41.2°	73.0°F
Kansas City	39.1°	76.1°F
Wichita	37.7°	73.6°F
Okla. City	35.5°	77.0°F
Dallas	33.2°	82.0°F
Houston	29.8°	80.6°F

Integrated Review

In Exercises 20–23, state whether the slope of the line passing through the two points is positive or negative.

20. (1, 4), (3, 5)   **21.** (2, 5), (4, 1)   **22.** (6, 1), (3, 8)   **23.** (5, 2), (4, 3)

In Exercises 24–27, find an equation of the line that passes through the two given points.

24. (2, 5), (6, 4)   **25.** (1, 4), (3, 7)   **26.** (3, 7), (7, 3)   **27.** (2, 6), (5, 4)

Exploration and Extension

Library Budgets   **In Exercises 28–31, use the following information.**

A school library is allocated money, B, each year to buy new books (scatter plot at left). The average price, P, of a new book is shown in the scatter plot at the right. In each, $t = 0$ corresponds to 1980.

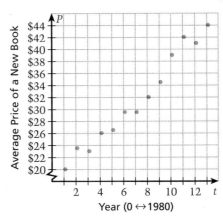

28. Find an equation of the line that you think best represents the amount of money given to the library for new books.

29. Find an equation of the line that you think best represents the average price of a new book.

30. What do the slopes of the two lines represent?

31. Suppose that you worked at the school library and wanted to ask the School Board to increase the library's annual allocation of money. How could you use the information to argue your case?

In Lesson 5.4, you studied the graphical approach for approximating a best-fitting line. Another approach is to use a calculator or computer programmed to find the best-fitting line.

In Chapter 3, we showed how to use a graphing calculator or computer to draw a scatter plot for the points listed below. To find the equation of the line that best fits these points, draw the scatter plot, then use the given program steps. Each program finds the coefficients a and b for the best-fitting line $y = a + bx$. The two graphing calculator programs also sketch the line and the scatter plot as shown at the right.

(1, 1.2), (1.5, 2.3), (2, 1.9), (2.5, 2.4), (3, 3.1)
(3.5, 3.5), (4, 3.8), (4.5, 4.7), (5, 4.9), (5.5, 5.7)

BASIC

```
10 FOR N = 1 TO 10
20    READ X,Y
30    SUMX = SUMX + X
40    SUMY = SUMY + Y
50    SUMXY = SUMXY + X*Y
60    SUMX2 = SUMX2 + X∧2
70 NEXT
80 BNUM = 10*SUMXY − SUMX*SUMY
90 BDENOM = 10*SUMX2 − SUMX∧2
100 B = BNUM/BDENOM
110 A = (SUMY − B*SUMX)/10
120 PRINT "A:";A
130 PRINT "B:";B
140 END
150 DATA 1,1.2, 1.5,2.3, 2,1.9, 2.5,2.4
160 DATA 3,3.1, 3.5,3.5, 4,3.8, 4.5,4.7
170 DATA 5,4.9, 5.5,5.7
```

TI-81

Enter data (See p. 166.)
[2nd] [STAT] [2] [ENTER]
   a = .3048484848
   b = .936969697
[Y=] Enter equation.
   : Y₁ = .305 + .937X
[2nd] [STAT]
Cursor to DRAW
[2] [ENTER]

Casio fx-7700G

Enter data (See p. 166.)
[EXE] [F6] [F1] [EXE]
   A
      0.3048484848
[F2] [EXE]
   B
      0.936969697
[GRAPH] Enter equation.
   Graph Y = .305 + .937X
[EXE]

Exercises

In Exercises 1 and 2, find the best-fitting line for the points.

1. (0, 1), (1, 2)
(1, 3), (2, 3)
(2, 3.5), (3, 4)
(3, 4.5), (4, 5.5)
(4, 6), (5, 5)
(5, 6), (5, 6.5)
(6, 7), (6, 8)
(7, 7.5)

2. (0, 8), (1, 7.5)
(1, 6), (2, 6.5)
(2, 6), (3, 5.5)
(3, 5), (4, 4)
(4, 3.5), (5, 3)
(5, 2.5), (6, 2)
(6, 1.5), (7, 1)
(7, 0)

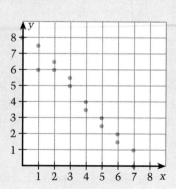

Take this test as you would take a test in class. The answers to the exercises are given in the back of the book.

1. Find an equation of the line whose slope is $-\frac{1}{3}$ and whose y-intercept is 4. **(5.1)**

2. Find an equation of the line whose graph is shown at the right. **(5.2)**

3. The Bargain Car Rental company charges a flat fee of $35 plus $0.40 per mile to rent a mid-size car. Write an equation that gives the total cost, C, in terms of the number of miles driven, x. **(5.1)**

4. Find an equation of the line that passes through $(-2, 4)$ with a slope of 3. **(5.2)**

5. Find an equation of the line that passes through $(3, -2)$ and is parallel to the line $y = -\frac{2}{3}x + 4$. **(5.2)**

6. Find an equation of the horizontal line that passes through $(-4, 3)$. **(5.2)**

7. Between 1980 and 1990, the amount spent on advertising in the United States increased by approximately $8.14 billion per year. In 1984, the total amount spent on advertising was $88.1 billion. Find an equation that gives the total amount spent on advertising, A, in terms of the year, t. Let $t = 0$ correspond to 1980. **(5.2)**

8. Find an equation of the line that passes through $(-3, 5)$ and $(4, 1)$. **(5.3)**

9. Find an equation of the line whose x-intercept is 5 and whose y-intercept is 4. **(5.3)**

10. The average weight of seven-year-old girls is 49 pounds. The average weight of eleven-year-old girls is 77 pounds. Use this information to find a linear model for the average weight, w, of girls who are x years old. Use the model to find the average weight of a ten-year-old girl. **(5.3)**

11. The table at the right shows the weight and wing area of several types of birds. Construct a scatter plot for these data and find an equation of the line that best fits the data. Let x represent the weight in grams. Let y represent the wing area in square centimeters. Use your equation to approximate the wing area of a bird whose weight is 400 grams. **(5.4)**

Bird	Weight	Wing Area
Sparrow	25 g	87 cm^2
Martin	47 g	186 cm^2
Blackbird	78 g	245 cm^2
Starling	93 g	190 cm^2
Dove	143 g	357 cm^2
Crow	607 g	1344 cm^2
Gull	840 g	2006 cm^2
Blue Heron	2090 g	4436 cm^2

5.5

Standard Form of a Linear Equation

What you should learn:

Goal 1 How to transform a linear equation into standard form

Goal 2 How to model a real-life situation using the standard form of a linear equation

Why you should learn it:

You can best model some real-life situations with a linear equation in standard form, such as when you must buy a combination of items with a fixed amount of money.

Goal 1 Transforming into Standard Form

Most of the linear equations in this chapter have been written in slope-intercept form.

$$y = mx + b \quad \textit{Slope-intercept form}$$

Another commonly used form is

$$Ax + By = C \quad \textit{Standard form}$$

which is called the **standard form** of the equation of a line. (This is also called the *general form* of the equation of a line.) Notice, in this form, that the variable terms are on the left side of the equation and the constant term is on the right side. One advantage of the standard form is that it can be used for *any* type of line, even a vertical line.

Example 1 *Transforming a Linear Equation into Standard Form*

Transform $y = \frac{2}{5}x - 3$ into standard form with integer coefficients.

Solution Note that this equation is given in slope-intercept form. To transform the equation into standard form, you need to isolate the variable terms on the left and the constant term on the right.

$$
\begin{aligned}
y &= \tfrac{2}{5}x - 3 & \textit{Slope-intercept form} \\
5y &= 2x - 15 & \textit{Multiply both sides by 5.} \\
-2x + 5y &= -15 & \textit{Subtract 2x from both sides.}
\end{aligned}
$$

A linear equation can have more than one standard form. For instance, if you multiplied both sides of the standard form listed above by -1, you would obtain $2x - 5y = 15$, which is also in standard form. ∎

There really is no *best form* of a linear equation. For some purposes, such as graphing using intercepts, the standard form is better. For other purposes, such as mentally visualizing the graph, the slope-intercept form is better. So you need to be able to transform equations from one form to another.

Example 2 *Writing an Equation in Standard Form*

Rewrite $y = 0.55x + 1.35$ in standard form with integer coefficients.

Solution Since $0.55 = \frac{55}{100}$ and $1.35 = \frac{135}{100}$, you can clear the equation of decimals by multiplying both sides by 100.

$$y = 0.55x + 1.35 \qquad \textit{Given equation}$$
$$100y = 55x + 135 \qquad \textit{Multiply both sides by 100.}$$
$$-55x + 100y = 135 \qquad \textit{Subtract 55x from both sides.}$$

This equation is in standard form with integer coefficients. However, you can simplify the equation further by dividing both sides of the equation by 5 to obtain $-11x + 20y = 27$. ■

Goal 2 Modeling a Real-Life Situation

The next example describes a real-life problem for which the standard form of a linear equation is a convenient model.

At the Kimchee Grocery Store, hamburger costs $2 per pound and boned chicken costs $3 per pound.

Problem Solving
Write an Equation

Example 3 *A Linear Model for Buying Party Food*

You are in charge of buying the hamburger and boned chicken for a party. You have $30 to spend, and are going to the Kimchee Grocery Store. Write an equation that represents the different amounts of hamburger and chicken that you can buy.

Solution

Verbal Model	Price per pound	•	Pounds of hamb.	+	Price per pound	•	Pounds of chicken	=	Total price

Labels Price of hamburger = 2   (dollars per pound)
Weight of hamburger = x (pounds)
Price of chicken = 3   (dollars per pound)
Weight of chicken = y (pounds)
Total price = 30   (dollars)

Equation $2x + 3y = 30$ **Linear model** ■

Example 4 *Interpreting a Linear Model*

Sketch the graph of the linear equation in Example 3. Then find several different amounts of hamburger and chicken that you can buy, and plot the corresponding points on the line.

Solution To sketch the graph, first write the equation in slope-intercept form.

$$2x + 3y = 30 \qquad \textbf{\textit{Standard form}}$$
$$3y = -2x + 30$$
$$y = -\tfrac{2}{3}x + 10 \qquad \textbf{\textit{Slope-intercept form}}$$

From this form, you see that the slope is $-\tfrac{2}{3}$ and the *y*-intercept is 10. Several different amounts of hamburger and chicken are shown in the table.

Party Shopping

Hamburger, *x*	0 lb	3 lb	6 lb	9 lb	12 lb	15 lb
Chicken, *y*	10 lb	8 lb	6 lb	4 lb	2 lb	0 lb

The points corresponding to these different amounts are shown on the graph. Note that as the number of pounds of hamburger increases, the number of pounds of chicken decreases, and vice versa. ■

Communicating about ALGEBRA

Cooperative Learning

▶ **SHARING IDEAS about the Lesson**

Work with a Partner and Use a Linear Model A garden supply store is making up 12-pound packages of potting soil. Each package contains topsoil that weighs 4 pounds per cubic foot and peat moss that weighs 3 pounds per cubic foot.

A. Write an equation in standard form that represents the different amounts of topsoil and peat moss that can be used in a 12-pound package. (Let *x* represent the number of cubic feet of topsoil and let *y* represent the number of cubic feet of peat moss.)

B. Write the equation in slope-intercept form.

C. Sketch the line represented by the equation.

D. Find several different amounts of topsoil and peat moss that can be used to make a 12-pound package. Then plot the corresponding points on the line.

E. What sizes, in cubic feet, are possible for the 12-pound packages of potting soil?

EXERCISES

▶ **CRITICAL THINKING about the Lesson**

1. What is the name of the $y = mx + b$ form of the equation of a line?

2. What is the name of the $Ax + By = C$ form of the equation of a line?

3. Write the equation $y = -\frac{1}{2}x + 5$ in standard form.

4. The equations $y = -\frac{2}{3}x + 3$ and $2x + 3y = 9$ are equivalent. Which form would you use for graphing the line represented by the equation? Which form would have been easier to write if you were creating a model for the different amounts of hamburger and chicken you could buy for $9 at the Kimchee Grocery Store?

5. You have $10 to buy tomatoes and avocados for a salad. Tomatoes cost $1.25 per pound and avocados cost $2 per pound. Write a linear equation that represents the different amounts of tomatoes, x, and avocados, y, that you could buy.

6. Use the linear model in Exercise 5 to complete the table.

Tomatoes, x	0 lb	1.6 lb	4 lb	6.4 lb	8 lb
Avocados, y	?	?	?	?	?

Independent Practice

In Exercises 7–18, write the equation in standard form with integer coefficients.

7. $3x - y - 6 = 0$

8. $x + 2y - 4 = 0$

9. $-4x + 3y + 18 = 0$

10. $2x - 3y - 12 = 0$

11. $x - 3 = 0$

12. $y + 4 = 0$

13. $y = -3x + 4$

14. $y = 2x - 7$

15. $y = -\frac{1}{3}x - 2$

16. $y = -\frac{3}{4}x + \frac{5}{4}$

17. $y = -\frac{1}{8}x + \frac{3}{8}$

18. $y = -0.4x + 1.2$

In Exercises 19 and 20, write equations (in standard form) of the horizontal line and the vertical line that pass through the point.

19. $(-1, 3)$

20. $(2, -4)$

In Exercises 21–24, write an equation (in standard form) of the line that passes through the point and has the given slope.

21. $(-4, 3)$, $m = -1$

22. $(0, 5)$, $m = 2$

23. $(3, -1)$, $m = 0$

24. $(-4, -2)$, $m = \frac{1}{2}$

In Exercises 25–28, write an equation (in standard form) of the line that passes through the two points.

25. $(2, 4)$, $(5, 6)$

26. $(-3, 3)$, $(6, 7)$

27. $(-2, -1)$, $(2, -3)$

28. $(-5, 4)$, $(2, -6)$

29. *Buying a Nut Mixture*   You are buying $24 worth of peanuts and cashews for a party. The peanuts cost $3 dollars per pound and the cashews cost $4 per pound. Write an equation for the different amounts of peanuts, *p*, and cashews, *c*, that you could buy.

30. Sketch the line representing the possible nut mixtures in Exercise 29. Then complete the table and label the points from the table on the graph.

Pounds of peanuts, *p*	0	2	4	6	8
Pounds of cashews, *c*	?	?	?	?	?

31. *Buying a Lawn Seed Mixture*   You are buying $48 worth of lawn seed that consists of two types of seed. One type is a quick-growing rye grass that costs $4 per pound, and the other type is a higher-quality seed that costs $6 per pound. Write an equation that represents the different amounts of $4 seed, *x*, and $6 seed, *y*, that you could buy.

32. Sketch the line representing the possible seed mixtures in Exercise 31. Then complete the table and label the points from the table on the graph.

Pounds of $4 seed, *x*	0	3	6	9	12
Pounds of $6 seed, *y*	?	?	?	?	?

In Exercises 33 and 34, use the following information.

Color Printing   In printing, different shades of color are often formed by "overprinting" two or more primary colors. In the color palette matrix at the right, the primary colors red and blue are overprinted to form different shades of purple. For instance, combining a 40% red screen with a 20% blue screen produces a more reddish purple than combining a 20% red screen with a 40% blue screen.

33. You are designing an advertising piece and want the background to be over-printed with red and blue screens. You want the *combined* percentage of red and blue screens to be 60%. Write a linear equation that represents the different percentages of red, *x*, and blue, *y*, you could use.

34. Trace the red-blue color palette matrix at the right and identify the possible shades you could use for a combined percentage of 60%. How does the pattern formed by the possible shades relate to the line whose equation you found in Exercise 33?

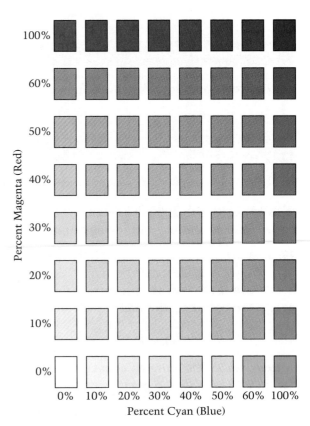

In Exercises 35–38, write the equation in slope-intercept form. Sketch the line.

35. $2x + y = 7$ **36.** $x + 2y = 6$ **37.** $-x + 3y = -6$ **38.** $6x - 2y = 1$

In Exercises 39–42, sketch the line. Label the *x*-intercept and *y*-intercept.

39. $2x + 3y = 6$ **40.** $3x - 7y = 21$ **41.** $-x + 4y = 8$ **42.** $-5x - 8y = 40$

43. *Temperature in Anchorage* The average monthly temperatures (in degrees Fahrenheit) in Anchorage, Alaska, for January through June are shown in the graph at the right. Approximate the best-fitting line for this data. Write your equation in standard form.

Temperatures in Anchorage

44. *Shoe Sales* The table shows sales (in billions of dollars) of athletic and sports footwear in the United States from 1980 to 1990. Sketch a scatter plot for the data. Let *y* represent the sales (in billions of dollars) and let *x* represent the year, with $x = 0$ corresponding to 1980. Then approximate the best-fitting line for the scatter plot. Write your equation in standard form. *(Source: National Sporting Goods Association)*

Year, x	1980	1981	1982	1983	1984	1985	1986	1987	1988	1989	1990
Sales, y	1.73	1.79	1.90	2.19	2.38	2.61	3.20	3.52	3.77	3.96	4.21

Exploration and Extension

In Exercises 45–47, refer to the equation 2*x* + 7*y* = 14.

45. What is the *x*-intercept of the graph? **46.** What is the *y*-intercept of the graph?

47. Multiply each term in the equation by $\frac{1}{14}$.

48. For the equation in Exercise 47, find a relationship between the denominators on the left side of the equation and the *x*- and *y*-intercepts.

In Exercise 49, use the intercept form of the equation of a line. You can see from the equation that the *x*-intercept is *a* and the *y*-intercept is *b*.

$$\frac{x}{a} + \frac{y}{b} = 1$$

49. Use the intercept form to find an equation for the line whose *x*-intercept is 2 and whose *y*-intercept is 3.

5.6

Point-Slope Form of the Equation of a Line

What you should learn

Goal 1 How to use the point-slope form to write an equation of a line

Goal 2 How to model a real-life situation using the point-slope form of a linear equation

Why you should learn it:

You can sometimes use the point-slope form as the most efficient way to find a linear model.

Goal 1 Using the Point-Slope Form

In Lesson 5.2, you studied one technique for using the slope of a line and a point on the line to write an equation of the line. In this lesson, you will study a different technique that involves a form called the **point-slope form** of an equation of a line.

To begin, consider the line containing the point $(x_1, y_1) = (2, 5)$ with a slope of $\frac{2}{3}$. Let (x, y) be any other point on the line. Because $(2, 5)$ and (x, y) are two points on the line, you know that the slope of the line is

$$m = \frac{\text{rise}}{\text{run}} = \frac{y - 5}{x - 2}.$$

Because the slope was given as $\frac{2}{3}$, you can write

$$\frac{y - 5}{x - 2} = \frac{2}{3}$$

$$y - 5 = \frac{2}{3}(x - 2).$$

This equation is said to be in point-slope form

$$y - y_1 = m(x - x_1),$$

where $y_1 = 5$, $m = \frac{2}{3}$, and $x_1 = 2$.

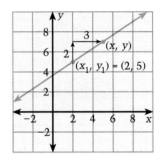

Point-Slope Form of the Equation of a Line

Consider a nonvertical line that passes through the point (x_1, y_1) with a slope of m. The **point-slope form** of the equation of the line is

$$y - y_1 = m(x - x_1).$$

When using the point-slope form, be sure you see the difference between (x_1, y_1) and (x, y). The coordinates x_1 and y_1 represent the *given* point on the line, and the coordinates x and y represent *any other* point on the line.

Example 1 | *Using the Point-Slope Form to Write an Equation*

Write an equation of the line shown at the left.

Solution Since the line passes through $(x_1, y_1) = (-3, 6)$ and $(x_2, y_2) = (1, -2)$, its slope is

$$m = \frac{y_2 - y_1}{x_2 - x_1} = \frac{-2 - 6}{1 - (-3)}$$

$$= \frac{-8}{4}$$

$$= -2.$$

To find an equation of the line, use the point-slope form and then simplify as follows:

$y - y_1 = m(x - x_1)$	*Point-slope form*
$y - 6 = -2(x - (-3))$	*Substitute -2 for m, -3 for x_1, 6 for y_1.*
$y - 6 = -2(x + 3)$	*Simplify.* ∎

Remember that the point-slope form, $y - y_1 = m(x - x_1)$, has *two* minus signs. Be sure to account for these signs when the point (x_1, y_1) involves negative numbers.

Example 2 | *Changing from Point-Slope Form to Slope-Intercept Form*

Write an equation of the line that passes through $(2, 3)$ with a slope of $-\frac{1}{2}$.

Solution Using the point-slope form with $(x_1, y_1) = (2, 3)$ and $m = -\frac{1}{2}$, you can write the following.

$y - y_1 = m(x - x_1)$	*Point-slope form*
$y - 3 = -\frac{1}{2}(x - 2)$	*Substitute $-\frac{1}{2}$ for m, 2 for x_1, 3 for y_1.*

Once you have used the point-slope form to find an equation, you can simplify your result to slope-intercept form, as follows.

$y - 3 = -\frac{1}{2}(x - 2)$	*Point-slope form*
$y - 3 = -\frac{1}{2}x + 1$	*Distributive Property*
$y = -\frac{1}{2}x + 4$	*Slope-intercept form*

Graphic Check Try sketching the graph of the line that passes through the point $(2, 3)$ with a slope of $-\frac{1}{2}$. From your graph, does it appear that the y-intercept is 4? ∎

You have now studied all of the commonly used forms of equations of lines. They are summarized in the following list.

Summary of Equations of Lines

Slope of a line through two points: $m = \dfrac{y_2 - y_1}{x_2 - x_1}$

Vertical line (undefined slope): $x = a$

Horizontal line (zero slope): $y = b$

Slope-intercept form: $y = mx + b$

Point-slope form: $y - y_1 = m(x - x_1)$

Standard form: $Ax + By = C$

Goal 2 ## Modeling a Real-Life Situation

The next example shows how to use a linear equation as a model for a parachute jump. A linear model is appropriate for that part of a parachute jump in which the parachute is open. This is why a parachute works. It creates such a large air resistance that the descent speed of the parachutist is constant (or nearly constant).

Descent speeds for parachutists vary. A speed of approximately 23 feet per second is common. That is the speed that would be attained by a person jumping (without a parachute) from a height of $8\frac{1}{2}$ feet. The parachutist must know proper landing techniques to avoid injury at such a landing speed.

Note that before the parachute opens, the parachutist's fall is an *acceleration*, which cannot be modeled with a linear equation.

Example 3   *A Linear Model for Parachute Jumping*

At 12:15, a parachutist jumps from a plane and opens the parachute. Eight seconds later the parachutist is 2000 feet above the ground. After five more seconds, the parachutist's height is 1900 feet. Write a linear equation that gives the height, y (in feet), of the parachutist in terms of the time, t. Let t be measured in seconds, with $t = 0$ corresponding to 12:15. Find the height of the parachutist at 12:16.

Solution   To find an equation for the model, use the two heights that are given in the problem.

> Height at 12:15:*08* is *2000* feet: Point (8, 2000)
> Height at 12:15:*13* is *1900* feet: Point (13, 1900)

The slope of the line that passes through these two points is

$$m = \frac{1900 - 2000}{13 - 8} = \frac{-100}{5} = -20.$$

Now, using the point-slope form with $m = -20$ and $(t_1, y_1) = (8, 2000)$, you can write the equation of the line as follows:

$$y - y_1 = m(t - t_1) \quad \text{\textit{Point-slope form}}$$
$$y - 2000 = -20(t - 8) \quad \text{\textit{Substitute} } -20 \text{ \textit{for} } m, 8 \text{ \textit{for} } t_1, 2000 \text{ \textit{for} } y_1.$$
$$y - 2000 = -20t + 160 \quad \text{\textit{Distributive Property}}$$
$$y = -20t + 2160 \quad \text{\textit{Slope-intercept form}}$$

To find the height at 12:16, let $t = 60$ (60 seconds after 12:15). At that time, the height of the parachutist is

$$y = -20(60) + 2160 = 960 \text{ feet.} \quad \blacksquare$$

Parachute Jump

Height (in feet) — (8, 2000), (13, 1900), (60, 960)
Time (in seconds)

Communicating about ALGEBRA

▶ **SHARING IDEAS about the Lesson**

Interpret a Model   Use Example 3 to answer the questions.

A. What does the slope of $m = -20$ represent in this problem? Why is this slope negative?

B. What does the y-intercept of $b = 2160$ represent?

C. What is the height of the parachutist at 12:15:30?

D. When will the parachutist land on the ground?

EXERCISES

▶ **CRITICAL THINKING about the Lesson**

1. Name the $y - y_1 = m(x - x_1)$ form of the equation of a line.

2. A line passes through $(2, -3)$ with a slope of 2. For the form $y - y_1 = m(x - x_1)$, what is the value of m? What is the value of x_1? What is the value of y_1?

3. Write an equation of the line that passes through $(2, -3)$ with a slope of 2.

4. Write the equation $y - 4 = -\frac{1}{2}(x + 2)$ in slope-intercept form.

5. Which of the points lie on the line $y + 2 = -2(x - 3)$?
   a. $(-1, 6)$ **b.** $(2, 2)$

Mountain Climbing   **In Exercises 6–8, use the following information.**

A mountain climber is scaling a 300-foot cliff. The climber starts at the bottom of the cliff at 12:00. At 12:30, the climber has moved 62 feet up the cliff. (Assume that the climber maintains a constant climbing rate.)

6. Write an equation that gives the height, y (in feet), of the climb in terms of the time, t (in hours).

7. At what time will the mountain climber reach the top of the cliff?

8. What is the slope of the line in Exercise 6? What does this slope represent?

Independent Practice

In Exercises 9–14, write an equation of the line that passes through the point and has the given slope. Then rewrite the equation in slope-intercept form.

9. $(1, 3)$, $m = \frac{1}{3}$

10. $(2, 4)$, $m = -2$

11. $(-1, 2)$, $m = -1$

12. $(-2, 3)$, $m = 2$

13. $(1, -1)$, $m = \frac{1}{2}$

14. $(3, -2)$, $m = -\frac{1}{2}$

In Exercises 15–18, write an equation of the line.

15.

16.

17.

18.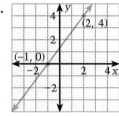

19. *Travel Time* You are flying from Montreal to Miami. You leave Montreal at 8:00 A.M. At 9:15 A.M., the pilot announces that you are flying over Washington, D.C. Use the map shown at the right to write a linear equation that gives the distance flown, *y*, in terms of the time, *x*. Let *x* = 0 correspond to 8:00 A.M. According to your equation, when will you reach Miami? (Assume that the plane is flying at a constant speed.)

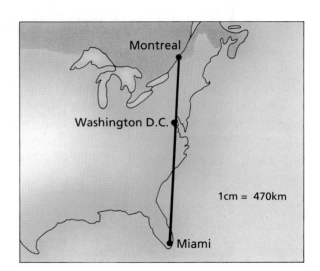

1cm = 470km

20. *Clue* The name of each of the six suspects is hidden on the graph. Write an equation of the line that contains each suspect's name. For example, the line that contains Mr. Green's name is $y = x + 11$.

```
18  Q T Y V D P N U M N V E W A Z U I T
17  R B F J K E Y R S K D C X F V T U I
16  O P L K E M H B C R R E D W S Q A Z
15  X S W R D P I O P L U N N Y T E F R
14  O K G U A R C S D W X R S U T E C F
13  D R I O J A H Y S S Q A X I O I L U
12  M R V G E D I K J S U W H R O U N T
11  F R E P H O X E U M C W N B Y T E D
10  W S S C T R E M C W S A I M N Y G T
 9  X R L A O E U V N R R F R S U W L F
 8  M X N E H L O R M M Z B D L E T S G
 7  Q W O Q P X M I W S X B H A E R W O
 6  P R J F N D S U L K A G N A E T K J
 5  K S O F G N I D S B K F Q F S D G G
 4  M R G B G N O K G T G N L N N F H A
 3  P G N B M F O G H M A P O G N E R P
 2  A P P N D F G F P I O R E F G V S A
 1  F G V Q A R N F K E F N D V A U F V
    1 2 3 4 5 6 7 8 9 10 11 12 13 14 15 16 17 18
```

Integrated Review

In Exercises 21–26, determine which form would be best to use to find an equation of the line. Explain your answer. Then use the form to find an equation of the line.

21. The line has a slope of $\frac{2}{3}$ and passes through the point (0, 4).

22. The line passes through the points (1, 3) and (−2, 4).

23. The line has a slope of 2 and a *y*-intercept of −3.

24. The line passes through the points (1, 6) and (1, −5).

25. The line has a slope of 1 and passes through the point (1, −4).

26. The line has a slope of 0 and passes through the point (2, 5).

In Exercises 27–30, match the equation with its graph.

27. $y - 2 = -2(x - 1)$ **28.** $y - 1 = \frac{1}{2}(x - 3)$ **29.** $y = 2(x - 1)$ **30.** $y = (-1)(x + 2)$

a.   b.   c.   d.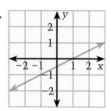

Exploration and Extension

31. Find an equation of the line passing through the point $(-6, 3)$ with a slope of $-\frac{5}{3}$. Sketch the line. Both coordinates of the point $(-6, 3)$ are integers. Describe the other points on the line that have integer coefficients. Of these, which two are closest to $(-6, 3)$?

32. *Basketball Attendance*   Find an equation of the line that gives the N.C.A.A. women's basketball attendance, y (in millions), in terms of the year, t. Let $t = 0$ correspond to 1980. Sketch a graph of the line. Use the equation to estimate the attendance in 1995.

N.C.A.A. women's basketball attendance in 1985 and 1990 was 2.9 million and 3.9 million, respectively. (Source: N.C.A.A.)

Mixed **REVIEW**

1. Evaluate $\frac{1}{2}(x - \frac{1}{2})$ when $x = \frac{1}{4}$.   **(2.6)**

2. Evaluate $\frac{3}{4}(3y - 2)$ when $y = \frac{1}{3}$.   **(2.6)**

3. Solve $3a + 2b = 4$ for b.   **(3.6)**

4. Solve $8m - 9n = 10$ for m.   **(3.6)**

5. Is 7 a solution of $x(x - 3) < 21$? **(1.5, 2.6)**

6. Is -6 a solution of $\frac{1}{4}(10 - x) \geq 4$? **(1.5, 2.6)**

7. Are $3 \div 4 + 2$ and $3 \div (4 + 2)$ equivalent?   **(1.4)**

8. Write an equation of the line that passes through $(-2, 1)$ and $(-1, 3)$.   **(5.3)**

9. Write an equation of the line that passes through $(2, 0)$ and $(-3, 4)$.   **(5.3)**

10. Write an equation of the line that passes through $(5, 4)$ with a slope of 4.   **(5.2)**

11. Write an equation of the line with a slope of 5 and a y-intercept of -3.   **(5.1)**

5.7

Problem Solving Using Linear Models

What you should learn:

Goal 1 How to create and use linear models to solve problems

Goal 2 How to make linear models that are accurate but simple to use

Why you should learn it:

You can use linear models efficiently and with good results only if they are simple and accurate.

As a salesclerk at a clothing store, Filipe receives a monthly base pay of $800 plus a 5% commission on the amount that he sells.

Real Life
Retail Sales

Goal 1 Creating and Using Linear Models

There are two basic types of real-life problems that can be solved with linear models. One type of problem involves a constant rate of change. (See Example 1.) The other type of problem involves two variables, x and y, such that the sum $Ax + By$ is a constant. (See Example 2.) You have already studied examples of both types of problems. In this lesson, you will study several more.

Example 1 *A Linear Model for Monthly Pay*

Write a linear model that gives Filipe's total monthly pay in terms of the amount of clothes he sells.

Solution

Verbal Model	Total pay	=	Commission rate	·	Amount sold	+	Base pay

Labels   Total pay = y (dollars)

Commission rate = 0.05 (percent in decimal form)

Amount sold = x (dollars)

Base pay = 800   (dollars)

Equation $y = 0.05x + 800$ **Linear model**

The commission rate represents a constant rate of change in Filipe's total pay of $0.05 per each dollar of clothes sold. For instance, if Filipe sold $4000 worth of clothes, his total monthly pay would be $y = 0.05(4000) + 800 = \$1000$. ■

Example 2 *Creating a Linear Model for Calorie Intake*

At Charles Drew High School, the main items on the lunch menu are often hamburgers and French fries. State law requires that school lunches contain at least 850 Calories. The hamburger bun has 80 Calories, a container of milk has 160 Calories, ground beef has 85 Calories per ounce, and French fries have 70 Calories per ounce. Write a linear equation that relates the number of ounces of ground beef, x, and the number of ounces of fries, y, that can be used to create a lunch consisting of 850 Calories.

Solution Since x ounces of ground beef have $85x$ Calories and y ounces of fries have $70y$ Calories, and 850-Calorie lunch consisting of a hamburger, fries, and milk must satisfy the following equation.

Ground beef	+	French fries	+	Hamburger bun	+	Milk	=	850 Calories

$$85x + 70y + 80 + 160 = 850$$
$$85x + 70y = 610$$ ∎

Mathematical modeling of real-life problems almost always has two phases. The first phase is to *create* the model, and the second phase is to *use* the model to answer questions about the real-life problem.

Example 3 *Using a Linear Model for Calorie Intake*

Use the linear model developed in Example 2 to find several ways that the school nutritionist could vary the amount of ground beef and French fries and still meet the state requirement of 850 Calories. Sketch a graph of your results.

Solution Before making up a table of values, it is helpful to rewrite the linear model in slope-intercept form.

School Lunch Menu

French Fries (ounces) / Ground Beef (ounces)

$$85x + 70y = 610 \qquad \textit{Standard form}$$
$$70y = -85x + 610 \qquad \textit{Subtract 85x from both sides.}$$
$$y = -\frac{85}{70}x + \frac{610}{70} \qquad \textit{Divide both sides by 70.}$$
$$y = -\frac{17}{14}x + \frac{61}{7} \qquad \textit{Slope-intercept form}$$

Using this form, you can calculate several different amounts of ground beef and fries that could be used to create an 850-Calorie lunch.

Beef, *x*	3.10 oz	3.45 oz	3.80 oz	4.15 oz	4.50 oz
Fries, *y*	4.95 oz	4.525 oz	4.10 oz	3.675 oz	3.25 oz

∎

Mathematical modeling has two basic goals: accuracy and simplicity. That is, you want the model to be accurate enough to be able to yield meaningful answers. On the other hand, you want the model to be simple enough to be usable.

Real Life
Education

Example 4 **A Mathematical Model for Classroom Computers**

The table shows the number of personal computers in use in American classrooms from kindergarten through high school between 1984 and 1988. *(Source: Future Computing Datapro, Inc.)*

Year	1984	1985	1986	1987	1988
Computers	590,000	870,000	1,170,000	1,480,000	1,760,000

Estimate the number of computers in use in American classrooms in 1992.

Computers in U.S. Schools

Computers (in 1000s): 2,000, 1,750, 1,500, 1,250, 1,000, 750, 500, 250

Year (0 ↔ 1980): 1 2 3 4 5 6 7 8 x

Solution To begin, it is helpful to plot the given points so that you can get a picture of how computer use was increasing between 1984 and 1988. In the scatter plot shown at the left, x represents the year, with $x = 0$ corresponding to 1980, and y represents the number of computers. From the scatter plot, it appears that the points can be approximated by a linear model. So as you did in Lesson 5.5, you can sketch the line that appears to best fit the points. Using the points (4, 590,000) and (8, 1,760,000), you can find the slope of the line to be

$$m = \frac{1,760,000 - 590,000}{8 - 4}$$
$$= \frac{1,170,000}{4}$$
$$= 292,500.$$

Then find the equation of the line using the point-slope form.

$y - y_1 = m(x - x_1)$ *Point-slope form*
$y - 590,000 = 292,500(x - 4)$ *Substitute 292,500 for m, 4 for x_1, and 590,000 for y_1.*

$y - 590,000 = 292,500x - 1,170,000$ *Distributive Property*
$y = 292,500x - 580,000$ *Slope-intercept form*

Now, using this model, you approximate the number of classroom computers in use in 1992 ($x = 12$) to be

$$y = 292,500(12) - 580,000 = 2,930,000.$$ ∎

Real Life
Education

Example 5 · *Comparing Model Results with Actual Results*

In Example 4, the model $y = 292{,}500x - 580{,}000$ was developed to represent the number of computers used in American classrooms between 1984 and 1988. How accurately does this model fit the given data?

Solution   Begin by using the model to find y-values for 1984 through 1988.

$$1984\ (x = 4)\!:\quad y = 292{,}500(4) - 580{,}000 = 590{,}000$$
$$1985\ (x = 5)\!:\quad y = 292{,}500(5) - 580{,}000 = 882{,}500$$
$$1986\ (x = 6)\!:\quad y = 292{,}500(6) - 580{,}000 = 1{,}175{,}000$$
$$1987\ (x = 7)\!:\quad y = 292{,}500(7) - 580{,}000 = 1{,}467{,}500$$
$$1988\ (x = 8)\!:\quad y = 292{,}500(8) - 580{,}000 = 1{,}760{,}000$$

The following table shows how the y-values given by the model compare to the actual y-values. The percent error is found by dividing the difference of each model y-value and actual y-value by the actual y-value.

Year	1984	1985	1986	1987	1988
Actual *y*-values	590,000	870,000	1,170,000	1,480,000	1,760,000
Model *y*-values	590,000	882,500	1,175,000	1,467,500	1,760,000
Percent error	0%	1.4%	0.4%	−0.8%	0%

Communicating about ALGEBRA

▶ **SHARING IDEAS about the Lesson**

Use a Model   Use the model developed in Example 4 to answer the questions.

A. Would you use this model to estimate the number of personal computers that were used in classrooms in 1980? Explain.

B. Based on the model, how many personal computers would you say were used in classrooms in 1990?

C. The model gives the total number of computers used in American classrooms. From the model, estimate how many computers were introduced to classrooms in each year.

280   *Chapter 5* ▪ *Writing Linear Equations*

EXERCISES

Guided Practice

▶ **CRITICAL THINKING about the Lesson**

Monthly Pay   **In Exercises 1–6, use the following information.**

Inés works at an electronics store in a shopping mall. Her base pay is $1000 a month. Inés also receives a commission of 2% of her sales total.

1. Write a linear model that gives Inés's total monthly pay, y, in terms of sales total, x.

2. Use the model to find Inés's monthly pay for sales totaling $25,000.

3. Sketch the graph of the linear model.

4. What is the slope of the line? What does the slope represent?

5. What is the y-intercept of the line? What does the y-intercept represent?

6. How much total sales must Inés have in order to earn $2000 in a month?

Independent Practice

Base Pay Plus Tips   **In Exercises 7–12, use the following information.**

Tim is a waiter in a restaurant. His base pay is $750 per month. Tim also earns tips amounting to 15% of the value of the meals he serves.

7. Write a linear model that gives Tim's total monthly pay, y, in terms of the value, x, of the meals he serves.

8. Use the model to find Tim's monthly pay for serving $5000 worth of meals.

9. Sketch the graph of the linear model.

10. What is the slope of the line? What does the slope represent?

11. What is the y-intercept of the line? What does the y-intercept represent?

12. How much must Tim serve in order to earn $2000 in a month?

Infant Weight   **In Exercises 13–16, use the following information.**

By the time an infant is one year old, she will weigh approximately three times the amount she weighed at birth.

13. Baby Carly weighed 7.5 pounds when she was born. Write a linear model that gives Carly's weight, y, in terms of her age, x, where x is measured in months.

14. Sketch the graph of the linear model. What does the slope represent?

15. What is the y-intercept of the line? What does the y-intercept represent?

16. How old will Carly be when she weighs 12.5 pounds?

17. *Ticket Purchase*   A school club visits a science museum. Student tickets cost $4.50 each. Nonstudent tickets cost $6.00 each. The club paid a total of $288 for the tickets. 48 student tickets were purchased. How many nonstudent tickets were purchased?

18. *Savings Accounts*   Jason has two savings accounts that pay 6% and 5.5% simple interest per year. Jason's interest for one year is $40.50. If Jason has $400 in the 6% account, how much does he have in the 5.5% account?

A basketball team scored 84 points: 2 points for each field goal and 1 point for each free throw.

Basketball Game   **In Exercises 19–22, use the given information.**

19. Write a linear equation that relates the number of field goals, x, with the number of free throws, y.

20. Write the equation in slope-intercept form.

21. Use the linear model to complete the table.

Field goals, x	20	25	30	35	40
Free throws, y	?	?	?	?	?

22. Sketch the line and plot the points from the table.

Integrated Review

College Students   **In Exercises 23–26, use the scatter plot, which shows the percent of male college students from 1970 to 1990.**

23. Write an equation of the best-fitting line for these data.

24. Complete the table, which compares the y-values from the best-fitting line with the actual y-values.

Year, t	0	5	10	15	20
Actual, y	59%	55%	48%	49%	45%
Model, y	?	?	?	?	?

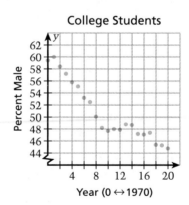

College Students

Percent Male — Year (0 ↔ 1970)

25. Construct a scatter plot that shows the percent of college students between 1970 and 1990 who were female.

26. Find an equation of the line that best fits the scatter plot found in Exercise 25. Describe a relationship between the equations for college males and college females.

282   *Chapter 5 ▪ Writing Linear Equations*

Restaurant Sales **In Exercises 27 and 28, use the scatter plot, which shows total sales for restaurants in the United States between 1980 and 1990.**

27. Write an equation of the best-fitting line.

28. Complete the table, which compares the *y*-values from the best-fitting line with the actual *y*-values.

Year, *t*	0	2	5	8	10
Actual, *y*	$90	$105	$134	$158	$176
Model, *y*	?	?	?	?	?

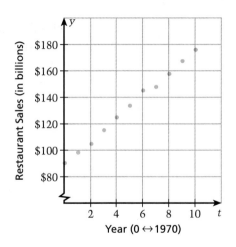

Year (0 ↔ 1970)

In Exercises 29–31, match the description with its graph. In each case, tell what the slope of the line represents (as a rate of change).

29. A person is paying $10 per week to a friend to repay a $100 loan.

30. An employee is paid $12.50 per hour plus $1.50 for each unit produced per hour.

31. A sales representative receives $20 per day for food, plus $0.25 for each mile driven.

a.

b.

c.

Exploration and Extension

Morning or Evening Paper? **In Exercises 32–35, use the following information.**

The total circulation of morning and evening newspapers in the United States in the 1980s can be approximated by the linear models

$y = 29.91 + 1.303t$ Morning newspaper circulation
$y = 32.27 - 1.216t$ Evening newspaper circulation

where *y* represents the circulation in millions and *t* represents the year, with *t* = 0 corresponding to 1980. *(Source: Editor and Publisher Company)*

32. Sketch the graphs of both equations on the same coordinate plane.

33. What does the slope of each line represent? Which type of newspaper had an increasing circulation? Which had a decreasing circulation?

34. In 1983, were there more morning or evening papers sold? In 1989?

35. During which year were the two circulations the same?

5 Chapter Summary

What did you learn?

1. Write an equation of a line using slope-intercept form
   - given its slope and its *y*-intercept. **(5.1)**
   - given its slope and one of its points. **(5.2)**
   - given two of its points. **(5.3)**
2. Write an equation of a line in standard form. **(5.5)**
3. Transform linear equations from one form to another. **(5.5)**
4. Write an equation of a line using point-slope form. **(5.6)**

Strategies
5. Create a linear model for a real-life situation
   - using the slope-intercept method. **(5.1–5.3)**
   - using the standard form model. **(5.5)**
   - using the point-slope method. **(5.6)**
6. Use a linear model to answer questions about real-life situations. **(5.5–5.7)**
7. Use graphing skills to provide graphic checks. **(5.1–5.7)**

Exploring Data
8. Find a best-fitting line for a collection of data points. **(5.4)**

Why did you learn it?

Many real-life situations have linear models. That is, the real-life situation can be represented by a linear equation. You can write the model in slope-intercept form if you know the constant rate of change (the slope) and an initial value (the *y*-intercept). Often, however, you are given the slope and a data point other than an initial value, or you are given two data points. In either case, you can still use the slope-intercept form by taking some additional steps. Sometimes the situation involves several scattered data points, so you try to find the linear model that best fits the data. A basic problem-solving strategy is to learn which form of a linear equation is best to use.

How does it fit into the bigger picture of algebra?

In this chapter, you studied techniques for writing equations of lines. Your basic strategy was to use the slope-intercept form that you had seen in Chapter 4. When an equation of a line is used to represent a real-life situation, it is called a **linear model.** In this chapter, you used the problem-solving strategies you studied in Chapter 1, the rules and simplification techniques you studied in Chapter 2, the systematic equation solving you studied in Chapter 3, and the graphing techniques you studied in Chapter 4.

In Exercises 1–4, write an equation of the line that has the given slope and *y*-intercept. (5.1)

1. Slope is 2; *y*-intercept is -6.

2. Slope is -1; *y*-intercept is 3.

3. Slope is $-\frac{1}{3}$; *y*-intercept is -1.

4. Slope is $\frac{2}{5}$; *y*-intercept is -5.

In Exercises 5–8, write an equation of the line. (5.1)

5.

6.

7.

8.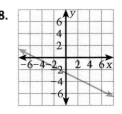

9. Find the slope and *y*-intercept of the line $y = -4x + 3$. Then sketch the line. **(5.1)**

10. Find the slope and *y*-intercept of the line $y = x - 7$. Then sketch the line. **(5.1)**

11. *Car Depreciation*   A car was bought in 1990 for $32,000. During the next five years, the value of the car depreciated by $3000 per year. Write an equation that gives the value, *y*, of the car in terms of the year, *x*. Let $x = 0$ correspond to 1990. **(5.1)**

12. Use the equation found in Exercise 11 to estimate the value of the car in 1996. **(5.1)**

In Exercises 13–20, write an equation of the line that passes through the point and has the given slope. Give the equation in slope-intercept form. (5.2)

13. $(6, -1)$, $m = 3$

14. $(-9, 4)$, $m = 2$

15. $(-3, 2)$, $m = -1$

16. $(-1, -6)$, $m = \frac{1}{3}$

17. $(2, 4)$, $m = 0$

18. $(2, -1)$, $m = -3$

19. $(5, -3)$, $m = \frac{1}{5}$

20. $(2, -4)$, $m = \frac{1}{2}$

In Exercises 21–23, write the slope-intercept form of the equation of the line. (5.2)

21.

22.

23.

In Exercises 24 and 25, find an equation of the line passing through the point and parallel to the line. (5.2)

24. $(2, -6)$, $y = -x - 7$

25. $(-1, 2)$, $y = 3x + 9$

26. *Company Profits*   Between 1980 and 1990, the annual profit for a company increased by about $50,000 per year. In 1988, the company had an annual profit of $1,300,000. Find an equation that gives the annual profit, P, in terms of the year, t. Let $t = 0$ correspond to 1980.   **(5.2)**

27. *Advertising Expense*   Advertising costs for the Save-More Store increase by about $32,000 per year. In 1992, $352,000 was spent on advertising. Find an equation that gives the amount spent on advertising, A, in terms of the year, t. Let $t = 0$ correspond to 1990.   **(5.2)**

In Exercises 28–35, write an equation of the line that passes through the given points. Give the equation in slope-intercept form.   (5.3)

28. $(1, -6), (-3, 2)$ **29.** $(1, 8), (-2, -1)$ **30.** $(2, 5), (-4, 1)$ **31.** $(3, -4), (-6, 2)$

32.   **33.**   **34.**   **35.**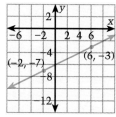

In Exercises 36–39, sketch the line that passes through the points. Use the graph to approximate the y-intercept of the line. Then find the actual y-intercept.   (5.3)

36. $(1, 1), (5, 2)$ **37.** $(-1, -2), (5, 8)$ **38.** $(-2, -3), (2, 4)$ **39.** $(-1, -1), (4, -1)$

In Exercises 40–43, find the equation of the horizontal line or the vertical line that passes through the point.   (5.1)

40. Vertical line: $(2, -4)$ **41.** Vertical line: $(-1, 8)$

42. Horizontal line: $(8, -3)$ **43.** Horizontal line: $(11, 6)$

44. *U.S. Households with Televisions*
Assume that the number of households with televisions increased at a constant rate from 1960 to 1985. Write an equation that gives the number, H, of households with televisions in terms of the year, t. Let $t = 0$ correspond to 1960.   **(5.7)**

45. *Turner Broadcasting Systems*   In 1985, the total revenue for Turner Broadcasting Systems was $350 million. By 1987, the total revenue was $650 million. Assume that the revenue increased at a constant rate. Write an equation that gives the revenue, R, in terms of the year, t. Let $t = 0$ correspond to 1980. *(Source: Turner Broadcasting System, Inc.)*   **(5.7)**

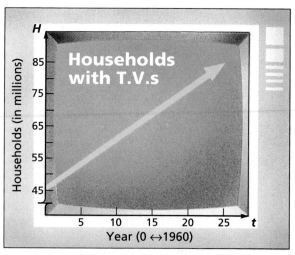

In 1960, 45,200,000 U.S. households had televisions. By 1985, the number had risen to 84,900,000. (Source: Television and Cable Factbook)

In Exercises 46 and 47, sketch the line that you think best approximates the data shown in the scatter plot. Then find an equation of the line. (5.4)

46.

47.

48. *World Population* The world population between 1980 and 1987 is given in the following table. Construct a scatter plot for this data and find an equation of the line that best fits the data. *(Source: U.S. Bureau of Labor Statistics)* **(5.7)**

Year	Population
1980	4,453,000,000
1981	4,528,000,000
1982	4,607,000,000
1983	4,684,000,000
1984	4,760,000,000
1985	4,854,000,000
1986	4,938,000,000
1987	5,024,000,000

49. *U.S. Voting* Construct a scatter plot showing the number of voters in presidential elections from 1960 to 1988. Then find an equation of the best-fitting line. *(Source: Committee for Study of American Electorate)* **(5.7)**

Year	U.S. Voters	President
1960	68,838,000	Kennedy
1964	70,645,000	Johnson
1968	73,212,000	Nixon
1972	77,625,000	Nixon
1976	81,603,000	Carter
1980	86,497,000	Reagan
1984	92,653,000	Reagan
1988	91,610,000	Bush

50. Write $x + 9y = 7$ in slope-intercept form. **(5.5)**

51. Write $3x + 5y = 5$ in slope-intercept form. **(5.5)**

52. Write $y = -\frac{1}{3}x + \frac{2}{3}$ in standard form. **(5.5)**

53. Write $y = \frac{3}{4}x + \frac{1}{2}$ in standard form. **(5.5)**

54. *Buying Party Dippers* Suppose that you buy $10 worth of broccoli and cauliflower for party dippers. The broccoli costs $2.00 per pound and the cauliflower costs $1.25 per pound. Write an equation in standard form that represents the different amounts (in pounds) of broccoli, B, and cauliflower, C, that you could buy. **(5.7)**

55. *Racquetball or Tennis?* Spike and Renée have $30 to spend at a health center. It costs $10 an hour for the use of the racquetball court and $5 an hour for the use of the tennis court. Write an equation in standard form that represents the time they can spend on each court, with x representing the number of hours on the racquetball court and y the hours on the tennis court. **(5.7)**

56. Use Exercise 54 to complete the table.

Broccoli, *B* (lb)	0	1	2	3	4	5
Cauliflower, *C* (lb)	?	?	?	?	?	?

57. Use Exercise 55 to complete the table.

Racquetball, *x* (hours)	0	1	2	3
Tennis, *y* (hours)	?	?	?	?

The number of office computers, both with and without networks, increased from 1984 to 1990. (Source: Gartner Group, Inc.)

58. *Office Computers with Networks* Find an equation of the best-fitting line for the scatter plot showing the number of office computers *with* networks from 1984 to 1990. Let N represent the number of computers and let t represent the year, with $t = 4$ corresponding to 1984. **(5.4)**

59. Use the equation found in Exercise 58 to complete the table, which compares the actual number of networked office computers with the number given by the model. **(5.4)**

Year, t	4	5	6	7	8	9	10
Actual, N	81,000	183,000	338,000	510,000	691,000	928,000	1,049,000
Model, N	?	?	?	?	?	?	?

60. *Office Computers without Networks* Find an equation of the best-fitting line for the scatter plot showing the number of office computers *without* networks from 1984 to 1990. **(5.4)**

61. Find the approximate rate of change in networked office computers from 1984 to 1990. **(5.4)**

62. Find the approximate rate of change in nonnetworked office computers from 1984 to 1990. **(5.4)**

63. Which type of office computer was increasing at a faster rate from 1984 to 1990: those with networks or those without networks? **(5.4)**

1. Find an equation of the line whose slope is $\frac{1}{4}$ and whose y-intercept is -3.

2. Find an equation of the line that passes through the point $(-2, 3)$ and has a slope of -2.

3. Sketch the line that passes through the points $(-4, 3)$ and $(2, -3)$. Then write the equation of the line in slope-intercept form.

4. Construct a scatter plot for the following data. Then find an equation of the line that you think best represents these data.

x	-6	-5	-3.5	-3	-2	-1	0	1	2	3
y	4	3	3	2	2	0	0.5	-1	-2.5	-3

5. Write an equation of the horizontal line that passes through the point $(2, 5)$.

6. Write an equation of the vertical line that passes through the point $(2, 5)$.

7. Rewrite the equation $-x + 5y = 20$ in slope-intercept form.

8. Sketch the line given by $-5x + 2y = 10$. Label the x- and y-intercepts.

9. Rewrite the equation $y = \frac{2}{17}x + 3$ in standard form.

10. Which of the following two lines are parallel to each other?
    a. $-5x - 2y = 18$ **b.** $2x + 5y = 12$ **c.** $5x + 2y = 6$

11. Elizabeth goes to a store to buy $24 worth of flour and cooking oil for her restaurant. The flour costs $1.20 per bag, and the cooking oil costs $2.40 per quart. Write an equation that represents the different amounts of flour and cooking oil that Elizabeth can buy.

12. Use the point-slope form to write an equation of the line that passes through the point $(-3, 1)$ with a slope of $\frac{1}{3}$.

13. Bob is traveling home at a constant speed. After one-half hour, he is 77.5 miles from home and after one hour, he is 55 miles from home. Write a linear equation that gives the distance from home, y (in miles), in terms of the time x (in hours). How long will it take Bob to get home?

14. A salesclerk for an appliance store receives monthly pay of $1250 plus a 4% commission on the appliances sold. Write a linear model that gives the total monthly pay, y, in terms of the amount of appliance sales, x.

15. Chris needs $150 to buy a new bike. She has already saved $30. Chris plans to earn the rest of the money by working at two part-time jobs. She earns $6 an hour at a grocery store and $4 an hour for baby-sitting. Write a linear equation that relates the number, x, of hours worked at the grocery store and the number, y, of hours baby-sitting that are necessary to earn enough money to buy the new bike.

Solving and Graphing Linear Inequalities

6.1 Solving Inequalities
in One Variable
▪ 292

6.2 Problem Solving
Using Inequalities
▪ 298

6.3 Compound
Inequalities ▪ 305

6.4 Connections:
Absolute Value and
Inequalities ▪ 313

6.5 Graphing Linear
Inequalities in Two
Variables ▪ 320

6.6 Exploring Data: Time
Lines, Picture Graphs,
and Circle Graphs
▪ 327

*The refraction of white light,
whether in the rainbow or
through a prism, creates many
beautiful effects.*

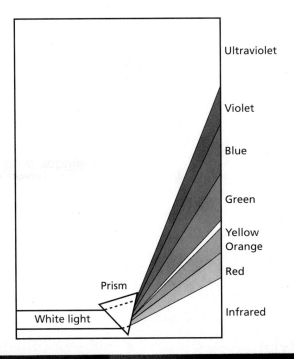

Ultraviolet

Violet

Blue

Green

Yellow
Orange

Red

Prism

Infrared

White light

White light from the sun is composed of light with different wavelengths. When white light passes through a prism, the prism separates the light into bands called the *spectrum*. Infrared light has the longest wavelengths and is bent the least. Ultraviolet light has the shortest wavelengths and is bent the most. You cannot see ultraviolet or infrared light. The *visible spectrum* consists of the bands of light from red to violet.

The wavelengths for different colors in the spectrum are as follows.

Color	Wavelength, w (nanometers)
Ultraviolet	$w < 400$
Violet	$400 \le w < 424$
Blue	$424 \le w < 491$
Green	$491 \le w < 575$
Yellow	$575 \le w < 585$
Orange	$585 \le w < 647$
Red	$647 \le w < 700$
Infrared	$700 \le w$

Goal 1 Graphing Linear Inequalities

The **graph** of a linear inequality in one variable is the graph on the real number line of all solutions of the inequality. There are four types of *simple inequalities*. (You will study compound inequalities in Lesson 6.3.)

Verbal Phrase	Inequality	Graph
All real numbers less than 3	$x < 3$	$-4\ -2\ \ 0\ \ 2\ \ 4$
All real numbers greater than -2	$x > -2$	$-3\ -2\ -1\ 0\ 1\ 2\ 3$
All real numbers less than or equal to 1	$x \le 1$	$-3\ -2\ -1\ 0\ 1\ 2\ 3$
All real numbers greater than or equal to 0	$x \ge 0$	$-3\ -2\ -1\ 0\ 1\ 2\ 3$

Notice on the graphs that we use an open dot for $<$ or $>$ and a solid dot for $\le$ or $\ge$.

Real Life

Meteorology

The July temperature in Mexico City is at least 12°C.

Example 1 *Sketching Graphs of Linear Inequalities*

a. The July temperature, T (in degrees Celsius), in Mexico City can be represented by the inequality $T \ge 12$. The graph is shown below.

$$-8 \quad -4 \quad 0 \quad 4 \quad 8 \quad 12 \quad 16 \quad 20 \qquad T$$

b. The highest elevation in Florida is 345 feet above sea level. If x is the elevation in feet at any location in Florida, then x must satisfy the inequality $x \le 345$. The graph is shown below.

$$\overset{\displaystyle 345}{0 \quad 50 \quad 150 \quad 150 \quad 200 \quad 250 \quad 300 \quad 350 \quad 400} \qquad x$$

c. During 1992, the monthly company profits, p, were in the red. *In the red* means "negative." The inequality for this statement is $p < 0$. The graph is shown below.

$$-3\ -2\ -1\ 0\ 1\ 2\ 3 \qquad p$$

Solving Linear Inequalities in One Variable

Solving a linear inequality in one variable is much like solving a linear equation in one variable. The goal is to isolate the variable on one side using transformations that produce equivalent inequalities. The transformations are similar to those given in Lesson 3.1, *but* there are two important differences. In the following list, notice that when you multiply or divide both sides of an inequality by a negative number, you must *reverse* the inequality to maintain a true statement. For instance, to reverse $<$, replace it with $>$.

Transformations That Produce Equivalent Inequalities	**Original Inequality**	**Equivalent Inequality**
1. Add the same number to *both* sides.	$x - 3 < 5$	$x < 8$
2. Subtract the same number from *both* sides.	$x + 6 \geq 10$	$x \geq 4$
3. Multiply *both* sides by the same *positive* number.	$\frac{1}{2}x > 3$	$x > 6$
4. Divide *both* sides by the same *positive* number.	$3x \leq 9$	$x \leq 3$
5. Multiply *both* sides by the same *negative* number and reverse the inequality.	$-x < 4$	$x > -4$
6. Divide *both* sides by the same *negative* number and reverse the inequality.	$-2x \leq 6$	$x \geq -3$

Example 2 *Solving a Linear Inequality (One Transformation)*

Solve $p + 5 \geq 3$.

Solution

$$
\begin{aligned}
p + 5 &\geq 3 && \textit{Rewrite original inequality.} \\
p + 5 - 5 &\geq 3 - 5 && \textit{Subtract 5 from both sides.} \\
p &\geq -2 && \textit{Simplify.}
\end{aligned}
$$

The solution is *all real numbers greater than or equal to* -2. The graph of this inequality is shown at the left. Check several numbers that are greater than or equal to -2 in the original inequality.

Graphic Check

The solution shown in Example 2 required only one transformation. Often, finding the solution of a linear inequality requires two or more transformations.

Example 3 *Using More than One Transformation*

Solve $2y - 5 < 7$.

Solution

$$
\begin{array}{ll}
2y - 5 < 7 & \textit{Rewrite original inequality.} \\
2y - 5 + 5 < 7 + 5 & \textit{Add 5 to both sides.} \\
2y < 12 & \textit{Simplify.} \\
\dfrac{2y}{2} < \dfrac{12}{2} & \textit{Divide both sides by 2.} \\
y < 6 & \textit{Simplify.}
\end{array}
$$

The solution is *all real numbers less than 6*. The graph of this inequality is shown below. Check several numbers that are less than 6 in the original inequality. (*Also* try checking some numbers that are greater than or equal to 6 to see that they are *not* solutions of the original inequality.)

Graphic Check

```
  ←——+——+——+——+——+——+——◁——+——→ y
      0   1   2   3   4   5   6   7
```

As you gain experience with solving linear inequalities, you may want to use the same "expert solver" format we discussed in Lesson 3.2. For instance, the solution in Example 3 could be streamlined as follows.

$$
\begin{array}{ll}
2y - 5 < 7 & \textit{Rewrite original inequality.} \\
2y < 12 & \textit{Add 5 to both sides.} \\
y < 6 & \textit{Divide both sides by 2.}
\end{array}
$$

Example 4 *Reversing an Inequality*

Solve $5 - x > 4$.

Solution

$$
\begin{array}{ll}
5 - x > 4 & \textit{Rewrite original inequality.} \\
5 - 5 - x > 4 - 5 & \textit{Subtract 5 from both sides.} \\
-x > -1 & \textit{Simplify.} \\
(-1)(-x) < (-1)(-1) & \textit{Multiply both sides by } -1 \\
 & \textit{and reverse inequality.} \\
x < 1 & \textit{Simplify.}
\end{array}
$$

The solution is *all real numbers less than 1*. The graph of this inequality is shown below. Check several numbers that are less than 1 in the original inequality.

Graphic Check

```
  ←——+——+——+——◁——+——+——→ x
    -3 -2 -1   0   1   2   3
```

Example 5 **Solving an Inequality with Variables on Both Sides**

Solve $2x - 4 \leq 4x - 1$.

Solution

$$2x - 4 \leq 4x - 1 \qquad \text{\textit{Rewrite original inequality.}}$$
$$2x - 4 + 4 \leq 4x - 1 + 4 \qquad \text{\textit{Add 4 to both sides.}}$$
$$2x \leq 4x + 3 \qquad \text{\textit{Simplify.}}$$
$$2x - 4x \leq 4x - 4x + 3 \qquad \text{\textit{Subtract 4x from both sides.}}$$
$$-2x \leq 3 \qquad \text{\textit{Simplify.}}$$
$$\frac{-2x}{-2} \geq \frac{3}{-2} \qquad \text{\textit{Divide both sides by} } -2 \text{ \textit{and reverse inequality.}}$$
$$x \geq -\frac{3}{2} \qquad \text{\textit{Simplify.}}$$

Graphic Check

The solution is *all real numbers greater than or equal to* $-\frac{3}{2}$. The graph of this inequality is shown at the left. Check several numbers that are greater than or equal to $-\frac{3}{2}$ in the original inequality.

In Examples 2, 3, 4, and 5, we have been writing the solution steps with the variable isolated on the left. Many people like to follow this convention, but it isn't required. Here's a streamlined format for Example 5.

$$2x - 4 \leq 4x - 1 \qquad \text{\textit{Rewrite original inequality.}}$$
$$-4 \leq 2x - 1 \qquad \text{\textit{Subtract 2x from both sides.}}$$
$$-3 \leq 2x \qquad \text{\textit{Add 1 to both sides.}}$$
$$-\frac{3}{2} \leq x \qquad \text{\textit{Divide both sides by 2.}}$$

Note that $-\frac{3}{2} \leq x$ and $x \geq -\frac{3}{2}$ are equivalent inequalities.

Communicating about **ALGEBRA**

▶ **SHARING IDEAS about the Lesson**

Explain Your Reasoning For each inequality, choose the inequality that is equivalent. Explain your reasoning.

Original Inequality	**Which is equivalent?**
A. $x - 3 < 10$	**a.** $x < 7$ **b.** $x < 13$
B. $2x \leq 8$	**a.** $x \leq 4$ **b.** $x \leq 6$
C. $-x \geq -2$	**a.** $x \geq 2$ **b.** $x \leq 2$
D. $2 > x$	**a.** $x < 2$ **b.** $x > 2$

EXERCISES

Guided Practice

▶ **CRITICAL THINKING about the Lesson**

1. Write the inequality for *all real numbers greater than or equal to 4.*

2. Write a verbal phrase that describes $x \leq -2$.

3. Sketch the graph of $x > 6$.

4. Solve the inequality $5 - 2x \geq 3$.

5. Is the number 4.78 a solution of $x < 5$? Is the number 6 a solution of $x < 6$? Explain.

6. Write an inequality that is equivalent to $2 < x$ but has x on the left side.

7. Explain why you must reverse the direction of the inequality symbol when multiplying by a negative number.

8. Sketch the graph of *all real numbers less than or equal to 4.* Then write an inequality that represents the graph.

Independent Practice

In Exercises 9–14, sketch a graph of the inequality.

9. $x > -4$

10. $x < 15$

11. $x \leq 9$

12. $x \geq -8$

13. $2 \leq x$

14. $3 \geq -x$

In Exercises 15–32, solve the inequality.

15. $x + 5 < 7$

16. $4 + x > -12$

17. $-x - 8 > -17$

18. $-3 + x < 19$

19. $6 + x \leq -8$

20. $x - 10 \geq -6$

21. $2x + 7 \geq 4$

22. $6 - 3x \leq 15$

23. $-4x - 2 \geq 10$

24. $2x + 5 \leq -13$

25. $-3 \leq 6x - 1$

26. $17 \geq 4x + 11$

27. $-x - 4 > 3x - 2$

28. $3x + 5 < -7x - 9$

29. $x + 3 \leq 2(x - 4)$

30. $2x + 10 \geq 7(x + 1)$

31. $-x + 4 < -2(x - 8)$

32. $-x + 6 > -(2x + 4)$

In Exercises 33–41, solve the inequality. Then match its solution with one of the graphs.

33. $3x - 1 \leq -7$

34. $10 \leq x + 6$

35. $5x - 7 < 3x + 9$

36. $12 - 2x > 10$

37. $3x + 2 \leq 14$

38. $-3 \geq 6x - 1$

39. $-9x + 2 < 14$

40. $2x - 6 < -x + 6$

41. $2x \geq -x + 6$

a.

b.

c.

d.

e.

f.

g.

h.

i.

42. *Temperatures in Buffalo*   In Buffalo, New York, January temperatures often do not exceed 0° Celsius. Write an inequality that describes the January temperatures, *T*, in Buffalo. Graph the inequality.

43. *Elevations in California*   The lowest elevation in California is 282 feet below sea level. Let *E* represent the elevation of any location in California. Write an inequality for *E*. Graph the inequality.

44. *Company Profits*   During 1993, each monthly company profit, *P*, was at least $1200. Write an inequality for this statement. Graph the inequality.

45. *Viking Ships*   The longest Viking ship that has been found is not quite 95 feet in length. Let *V* represent the lengths of known Viking ships. Write an inequality for *V*. Graph the inequality.

46. *Album Sales*   Let *d* represent the number of copies sold to date of Whitney Houston's debut album. Write an inequality describing *d*. Graph the inequality.

Whitney Houston's 1985 debut album sold 14 million copies in 2 years.

Integrated Review

In Exercises 47–50, solve the equation.

47. $|x + 2| = 8$ **48.** $|12 - x| = 6$

49. $|x - 3| = 9$ **50.** $|2x - 1| = 10$

51. *Fitness Program*   After 6 weeks, Marcia can continue an aerobics workout for 45 minutes. Her average weekly increase has been 5 minutes. Find an equation that gives Marcia's workout time, *t*, in terms of the number of weeks, *w*, that she is on the fitness program.

52. *Savings Account*   Nate deposits $6.25 per week in his savings account. After 15 weeks, the balance in his account is $598. Write an equation that gives the balance, *b*, of Nate's account in terms of the number of weeks, *w*. Disregard any interest earned.

53. Find an equation of the line that contains the point $(2, -4)$ and has a slope of $\frac{3}{2}$.

54. Find an equation of the line that contains the points $(-3, 6)$ and $(9, 1)$.

Exploration and Extension

55. Use the graph of $y = \frac{2}{3}x - 2$ to solve the inequality $\frac{2}{3}x - 2 < 0$. Explain your reasoning.

56. Use the graph of $y = -2x + 4$ to solve the inequality $-2x + 4 > 0$. Explain your reasoning.

6.2

Problem Solving Using Inequalities

What you should learn:

Goal 1 How to write and use a linear inequality as a model for a real-life situation

Why you should learn it:

You can model many real-life situations with linear inequalities, such as in finding quantities that exceed given amounts (records in sports, popular trends, profits over expenses).

Goal 1 Using Linear Inequalities as Models

Many of the real-life problems that you studied in Chapter 3 could have been worded so that the algebraic model was an inequality, rather than an equation. For instance, in Lesson 3.5, Example 4 described a situation in which you had $18.37 to buy a pair of earrings. The example asked you to find the price limit for the earrings so that the money you had could pay the 5% sales tax. Using an inequality as a model, where x is the price of the earrings, we could have written

$$x + 0.05x \leq 18.37. \quad \textit{Linear inequality as model}$$

The solution would then be $x \leq 17.49$, which says that the price of the earrings can be any amount less than or equal to $17.49.

Real Life
Athletics

Example 1 *Writing a Linear Model*

Suzanne and Jorah both ran in a 2-kilometer race. Suzanne finished ahead of Jorah, and Jorah's time for the race was 8 minutes. Write an inequality that describes Suzanne's average speed for the race.

Solution

Verbal Model	Suzanne's average speed	>	Jorah's average speed

$$\text{Suzanne's average speed} > \frac{\text{Distance}}{\text{Jorah's time}}$$

Labels   Suzanne's av. speed $= S$ (kilometers per min)
Jorah's distance $= 2$ (kilometers)
Jorah's time $= 8$ (minutes)

Inequality $S > \dfrac{2}{8}$ **Algebraic model**

Thus, Suzanne's average speed was greater than $\frac{1}{4}$ kilometer per minute. ∎

Real Life
Nutrition

Example 2 *Linear Models for Milk Consumption*

For which years did the consumption of low-fat milk by Americans exceed the consumption of whole milk? (Use a linear model.)

Solution Let W represent quarts of whole milk, L represent quarts of low-fat milk, and t represent the year, with $t = 0$ corresponding to 1970. Since whole milk consumption dropped from 103 quarts to 43 quarts in 20 years, the average rate of change was -3 quarts per year. The linear model is

$W = 103 - 3t$.   *Whole milk consumption*

Since low-fat milk consumption increased from 25 to 60 quarts per year, the average rate of change was 1.75 quarts per year. The linear model is

$L = 25 + 1.75t$.   *Low-fat milk consumption*

To find the years when low-fat milk consumption exceeded whole milk consumption, you can solve the following inequality.

Low-fat milk consumption	$>$	Whole milk consumption

$$25 + 1.75t > 103 - 3t \quad \textit{Algebraic model}$$
$$1.75t > 78 - 3t \quad \textit{Subtract 25 from both sides.}$$
$$4.75t > 78 \quad \textit{Add 3t to both sides.}$$
$$t > 16.4 \quad \textit{Divide both sides by 4.75.}$$

This suggests that Americans began drinking more low-fat milk than whole milk sometime during 1986. The graphs at the left show the linear models for both types of milk consumption. ■

Milk Consumption

Milk Consumption (in quarts)

Whole milk

Lowfat milk

16.4

125
100
75
50
25

5   10   15   20 t

Year (0↔1970)

Real Life
Business

Tying Flies

Learn to tie flies
at home for profit

R.T. Fisher & Company
P.O. Box 30
Riverside, Illinois 03905

Send $13.95 plus $1.05 for
shipping and handling

Example 3 **Starting a Small Business**

You see an advertisement for instructions on how to tie flies for fly-fishing. The cost of materials for each fly is $0.15. You plan to sell each fly for $0.58, and you want to make a profit of at least $200. How many flies will you need to tie and sell?

Solution Let x represent the number of flies. Then your sales in dollars will be $0.58x$, and your total expenses will be $0.15x + 15$. Why?

Verbal Model

| Total sales | Total expenses | Desired profit |

Labels
Total sales $= 0.58x$ (dollars)
Total expenses $= 0.15x + 15$ (dollars)
Desired profit $= 200$ (dollars)

Inequality

$$0.58x - (0.15x + 15) \geq 200 \qquad \textbf{Algebraic model}$$
$$0.58x - 0.15x - 15 \geq 200$$
$$0.43x - 15 \geq 200$$
$$0.43x \geq 215$$
$$x \geq 500$$

You need to tie and sell at least 500 flies. ∎

Communicating about ALGEBRA

Cooperative Learning

▶ **SHARING IDEAS about the Lesson**

Work with a Partner Use an inequality as a model for the following.

A. You want to run 2 miles in 12 minutes at the most. Write an inequality showing how fast you must run. Solve the inequality.

B. You want the area of a rectangle to be at least 100 square inches. The width of the rectangle is 10 inches. Write an inequality describing the length of the rectangle. Solve the inequality.

C. You want to start a business making wind chimes. Your equipment will cost $48. It costs you $3.50 to make each wind chime, and you sell each for $7.50. Write an inequality that shows the number you must make and sell to earn a profit of at least $300. Explain why you think this is the correct inequality. Then solve.

EXERCISES

Guided Practice

▶ **CRITICAL THINKING about the Lesson**

Mail-Order Purchase   **In Exercises 1–4, use the following information.**

You are placing an order for blank VCR tapes through the mail. Each tape costs $3, including tax. Shipping and handling costs are $2 for the entire order. If you cannot spend more than $20, how many tapes can you order?

1. Write a verbal model for this inequality.

2. Assign labels to each part of the model.

3. Write an inequality.

4. Solve the inequality.

Independent Practice

5. *Mercury*   Nearly 80% of the known elements are metals. The metallic element with the lowest melting point is Mercury. Write an inequality that describes the melting point, m (in degrees) Fahrenheit, of every other metallic element.

The New River Gorge Bridge is 1700 feet long.

The melting point of mercury is $-37.8°F$.

6. *Steel Arch Bridge*   The longest steel arch bridge is the New River Gorge Bridge near Fayetteville, West Virginia. Write an inequality that describes the length in feet, l, of every other steel arch bridge.

7. *Walking to School*   Walking at 250 feet per minute, it takes you 10 minutes to walk from your home to school. Your uncle's home is closer to school than yours. Write an inequality for the distance your uncle lives from school.

8. *Walk, Don't Run*   You enter a 3-mile-walk race and win. Your time is 30.2 minutes. Write an inequality about the average speed of the second-place walker.

9. *Amusement Park*   An amusement park charges $5 for admission and $0.80 for each ride. Suppose you go to the park with $13. Write an inequality that represents the possible number of rides you can go on. What is your maximum number of rides?

10. *Pizza*   You and your friends have a total of $12 to spend on a pizza. A large pizza with cheese costs $8 plus $0.40 for each additional topping, tax included. Use an inequality to find the number of toppings you can afford.

11. *Telephone Cost*   The cost of a long-distance telephone call is $0.48 for the first minute and $0.22 for each additional minute. Use an inequality to find the longest call that would not cost more than $4.

12. *Florida and New Jersey*   From 1960 to 1990, the population in Florida rose from about 4,900,000 to about 13,000,000, and the population in New Jersey rose from about 6,067,000 to about 7,747,000. For which years did the population of Florida exceed the population of New Jersey?
(Source: U.S. Census Bureau)

13. *Chicken or Pork?*   For which years did the United States consumption of chicken exceed the consumption of pork?

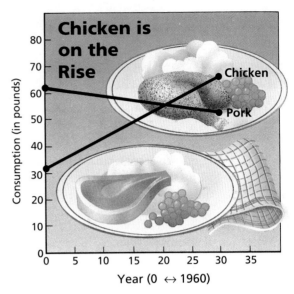

From 1960 to 1990, the average annual U.S. consumption of pork dropped from 62 pounds to 52 pounds. The average annual consumption of chicken rose from 31 pounds to 66 pounds. (Source: U.S. Department of Agriculture)

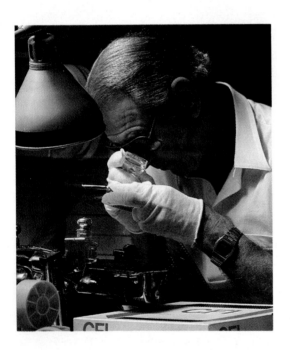

Editing film demands much concentration and expertise. When projected onto a screen, 35-millimeter film runs at 24 frames per second. A $2\frac{1}{2}$-hour movie has about 216,000 frames, after editing. The original film footage usually involves millions of frames.

14. *Animated Films*   Suppose each frame in an animated feature film takes at least one hour to draw. Write an inequality that describes the number of hours it would take to draw the frames needed for a 90-minute animated feature film.

15. *Work Force*   Suppose that you have 36 artists with each working 40 hours a week for 45 weeks a year. How many years would it take your artists to draw the film described in Exercise 14? (The first animated feature-length film was *Snow White and the Seven Dwarfs*, 1937. It took Walt Disney Studio artists over three years to draw the thousands of frames needed to make the film.)

16. For the area of the rectangle to be at least 36 square meters, what can x be?

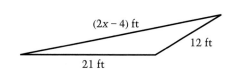

9 meters

x meters

17. For the perimeter of the triangle to be no more than 65 feet, what can x be?

$(2x - 4)$ ft

12 ft

21 ft

Integrated Review

In Exercises 18–25, solve the inequality.

18. $4x < -28$

19. $6 \geq x + 1$

20. $9y - 4 \geq 59$

21. $13 + 5x < 8$

22. $5 - 3x > 11$

23. $-2x + 3 > 3x - 7$

24. $4 + x \leq 16 - x$

25. $-9x - 2 \leq 16$

26. *College Entrance Exam Sample*   If $4 - x > 5$, then

    a. $x > 1$ **b.** $x > -1$ **c.** $x < 1$ **d.** $x < -1$ **e.** $x = -1$

27. *Powers of Ten*   Which is the closest estimate of the radius of Earth?

    a. 40 miles   **b.** 400 miles

    c. 4000 miles   **d.** 40,000 miles

28. *Powers of Ten*   Which is the closest estimate of the weight of a car?

    a. 200 pounds   **b.** 2000 pounds

    c. 20,000 pounds **d.** 200,000 pounds

Exploration and Extension

In Exercises 29–32, match the description with the correct inequality. Let negative numbers represent B.C. years and positive numbers represent A.D. years.

Hsia Dynasty
Potter's wheel is introduced

Chou Dynasty
Iron plows and swords come into wide use

Ch'in Dynasty
Great Wall of China is linked together

Six Kingdoms
China has no stable government

T'ang Dynasty
Grand Canal is built Gun powder is invented

221 B.C.   A.D. 220   A.D.618

2000 B.C.   1500 B.C.   1000 B.C.   500 B.C.   0   A.D.500   A.D.1000

Shang Dynasty
A logographic system of writing is developed

Han Dynasty
Paper is invented

29. Years in which paper could be used

30. Pre-Chou Dynasty years

31. Years before the Great Wall was completed

32. Years after gunpowder was invented

  a. $x < -221$ **b.** $x > 0$ **c.** $x < -1000$ **d.** $x > 618$

Mixed REVIEW

1. Find the quotient of $\frac{3}{8}$ and 2. **(1.1)**

2. Find the difference of $\frac{1}{3}$ and $\frac{1}{4}$. **(1.1)**

3. Evaluate $-|x - \frac{2}{3}| + 2x$ when $x = \frac{1}{6}$. **(2.1)**

4. Evaluate $y^2 + y(4 - y)$ when $y = 3$. **(2.6)**

5. Solve for b: $3(a - b) = 7$. **(3.6)**

6. Solve for y: $\frac{1}{2}(x - 2) + 3y = 6$. **(3.6)**

7. In Exercise 5, evaluate b when $a = \frac{1}{3}$. **(1.2)**

8. In Exercise 6, evaluate y when $x = 0$. **(1.2)**

9. Is 1 a solution for $5x - 3 < 2$? **(1.5)**

10. Is 3 a solution for $x^2 + 2 \geq 11$? **(1.5)**

11. Simplify $\frac{1}{4}(x - 2) + \frac{3}{4}(6 - 3x)$. **(2.6)**

12. Simplify $24 \div 6 + 3(x - 2)$. **(1.4, 2.6)**

13. Solve $|x - 2| + 3 = 5$. **(4.8)**

14. Solve $|16 - x| - 30 = -4$. **(4.8)**

15. Graph the points $(1, \frac{1}{2})$ and $(-1, -\frac{1}{2})$.

16. Graph the points $(-\frac{3}{4}, 6)$ and $(\frac{3}{4}, -6)$.

17. Sketch the graph of $|x + 2| - 3 = y$. **(4.7)**

18. Sketch the graph of $y = 3x - \frac{3}{2}$. **(4.7)**

19. Write an equation of the line that passes through $(-3, 0)$ and $(1, 2)$. **(5.3)**

20. Write an equation of the line that passes through $(-4, 3)$ with a slope of $-\frac{1}{3}$. **(5.6)**

Milestones ADA

1800	1850	1900	1950	2000
Augusta Ada Byron born	Translation and notes published		Programming language Ada developed	

```
WITH IO;
PACKAGE BODY COUNT IS
USE IO;

BEGIN
  PUT ("BEGIN");
  NEW:=LINE;
```

Example of an Ada Program; Augusta Ada Byron

When Charles Babbage strove to make his mechanical computer a reality in the 1830's and 1840's, his assistant was Augusta Ada Byron, Countess of Lovelace. Despite social customs that discouraged women from the pursuit of mathematical knowledge, Countess Lovelace studied mathematics through discussions, correspondences, and self-teaching. In 1842, a paper describing Babbage's ideas for his machine was published in French. Countess Lovelace translated the paper and added to it notes of her own, including a description of a rudimentary computer program. Some consider Countess Lovelace to be the world's first programmer.

In honor of her contribution to computer science, a programming language developed for the United States Department of Defense in the 1980's was named Ada. Based on Pascal, Ada addressed the need for a single programming language that could be used in every branch of the Defense Department. Today Ada is used by numerous organizations in many different applications.

What do you think were some of the social customs that discouraged women from studying mathematics? Do similar customs exist today?

6.3

Compound Inequalities

What you should learn:

Goal 1 How to solve and graph compound inequalities

Goal 2 How to model a real-life situation with a compound inequality

Why you should learn it:

Using compound inequalities, you can model many real-life situations, such as being above the timberline on a mountain *but* below the snow line.

Goal 1 Solving Compound Inequalities

In Lesson 6.1, you studied four types of simple inequalities. In this lesson, you will study **compound inequalities.** There are many types of compound inequalities. Here are two examples.

- All real numbers that are greater than or equal to zero *and* less than 4 can be represented by

  $0 \le x < 4.$

  This compound inequality is also written as $0 \le x$ *and* $x < 4$. The compound inequality $a < x < b$ is read as "x is **between** a and b." The compound inequality $a \le x \le b$ is read as "x is between a and b, *inclusive*."

- All real numbers that are less than -1 *or* greater than 2 can be represented by

  $x < -1 \quad or \quad x > 2.$

Real Life

Biology

Regions of Mt. Rainier

Example 1 *Compound Inequalities in Real Life*

On Mount Rainier, in Washington, the timberline occurs at about five thousand feet. Alpine meadows occur between about five thousand and six thousand feet. Above about six thousand feet, the mountain is covered by glaciers and permanent snowfields. Write inequalities that help describe these three regions of Mount Rainier.

Solution

a. The timber has elevations y (in feet) with

  $y \le 5000$ approximately.

b. The alpine meadows have elevations y (in feet) with

  $5000 \le y \le 6000$ approximately.

c. The glaciers and permanent snowfields have elevations y (in feet) with

  $6000 \le y \le 14{,}410$ approximately. ■

Example 2 Solving a Compound Inequality

Solve $-2 \le 3x - 8 \le 10$.

Solution For this type of inequality, your goal is to isolate the variable x between the two inequality signs.

$$-2 \le 3x - 8 \le 10 \quad \textit{Rewrite original inequality.}$$
$$6 \le \quad 3x \quad \le 18 \quad \textit{Add 8 to each expression.}$$
$$2 \le \quad x \quad \le 6 \quad \textit{Divide each expression by 3.}$$

Because x is between 2 and 6, inclusive, the solution is *all real numbers that are greater than or equal to 2 <u>and</u> less than or equal to 6*. The graph is shown at the left. Check several numbers between 2 and 6, inclusive, in the original inequality. ■

Graphic Check

Example 3 Solving a Compound Inequality

Solve $3x + 1 < 4 \text{ or } 2x - 5 > 7$.

Solution Any solution of this compound inequality is a solution of *either* of the simple parts, so you must solve each part separately.

$3x + 1 < 4$	*Left part*	$2x - 5 > 7$	*Right part*
$3x < 3$	*Subtract 1.*	$2x > 12$	*Add 5.*
$x < 1$	*Divide by 3.*	$x > 6$	*Divide by 2.*

The solution is *all real numbers that are less than 1 <u>or</u> greater than 6*. The graph is shown at the left. ■

Graphic Check

When you multiply or divide by a negative number to solve a compound inequality, remember that you have to reverse *both* inequality signs.

Example 4 Reversing Both Inequality Signs

Solve $-2 < -2 - x < 1$.

Solution

$$-2 < -2 - x < 1 \quad \textit{Rewrite original inequality.}$$
$$0 < -x < 3 \quad \textit{Add 2 to each expression.}$$
$$0 > x > -3 \quad \textit{Multiply each expression by } -1 \text{ and reverse both inequalities.}$$

To reflect the order of the number line, this compound inequality would usually be written as

$$-3 < x < 0.$$

Graphic Check

The solution is *all real numbers that are greater than -3 <u>and</u> less than 0*. The graph is shown at the left. ■

Modeling a Real-Life Situation

Problem Solving
Draw a Diagram

School is
somewhere on
this circle.

Friend's home
is somewhere
on this circle.

Example 5   *Describing Distances*

Suppose that you live three miles from school and your friend lives two miles from you. Write an inequality that describes the distances between the school and your friend's home.

Solution   A good way to begin this problem is to draw a diagram like the one shown at the left. Point *H* represents your home. Since you live three miles from school, the school must be located at a point on the circle with a radius of 3 and a center at *H*. By similar reasoning, your friend's home must be located at some point on the smaller circle. The closest your friend could live to the school would be 1 mile. The farthest would be 5 miles. Thus, the distance, *d*, between your friend's home and the school can be described by the inequality

$$1 \le d \le 5.$$

  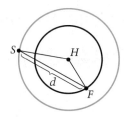

Smallest distance is 1 mile.   **Greatest distance is 5 miles.**   **Any distance between 1 and 5 is possible.** ■

Communicating about **ALGEBRA**

▷ **SHARING IDEAS about the Lesson**

Explain Your Reasoning   For each inequality, choose the inequality that is equivalent. Explain your reasoning.

Original Inequality   **Which is equivalent?**

A. $4 < x + 2 < 10$ **a.** $2 < x < 8$ **b.** $6 < x < 12$

B. $-4 \le 2x \le 6$ **a.** $-6 \le x \le 4$ **b.** $-2 \le x \le 3$

C. $-3 \le -x \le -2$ **a.** $3 \le x \le 2$ **b.** $2 \le x \le 3$

D. $3 < 2x + 1 < 7$ **a.** $1 < x < 3$ **b.** $2 < x < 4$

EXERCISES

Guided Practice

▶ **CRITICAL THINKING about the Lesson**

In Exercises 1–4, match the inequality with its graph.

1. $-2 \le x < 5$

2. $-1 < x \le 4$

3. $x < -1$ or $x \ge 4$

4. $x \le -2$ or $x > 5$

a. x
$-2 -1\ 0\ 1\ 2\ 3\ 4$

b. x
$-4 -2\ 0\ 2\ 4\ 6$

c. x
$-4 -2\ 0\ 2\ 4\ 6$

d. x
$-2 -1\ 0\ 1\ 2\ 3\ 4$

5. Solve the inequality $-2 \le 3x - 2 < 10$ and graph the solution.

6. Solve the inequality $2x - 3 < 5$ or $x - 4 \ge 0$ and graph the solution.

Independent Practice

In Exercises 7–14, solve the inequality.

7. $-6 < x - 4 \le 4$

8. $-5 < x - 6 < 4$

9. $-4 < 3 - x < 2$

10. $-10 \le 6 - 2x < 8$

11. $-10 \le -4x - 18 \le 30$

12. $7 \le -3x + 4 \le 19$

13. $6 - 2x > 20$ or $8 - x \le 0$

14. $-3x - 7 \ge 8$ or $-2x - 11 \le -31$

In Exercises 15–20, solve the inequality and graph the solution.

15. $2 \le x < 5$

16. $-3 < x \le -1$

17. $-12 < 2x - 6 < 4$

18. $-3 \le 6x - 1 < 3$

19. $-8 \le 1 - 3(x - 2) < 13$

20. $-19 < 3 - 4(x + 7) \le 5$

In Exercises 21–24, write an inequality for the statement and draw its graph.

21. x is between 7 and 4.

22. x is between -9 and 2.

23. x is less than 4 but is at least 0.

24. x is less than 2 but is at least -7.

In Exercises 25–28, solve the inequality and draw its graph. Then graphically check whether the given x-value is a solution by graphing the x-value on the same number line.

	Inequality	x-Value		Inequality	x-Value
25.	$-2 < 5x - 7 < 13$	1	**26.**	$-4 < 8x - 20 \le 12$	4
27.	$-3 < 3 - 4x < 3$	$\frac{1}{2}$	**28.**	$7 \le -2x + 21 < 31$	0

29. *Stamp Values*   Write a compound inequality that represents the different prices that a block of four "inverted" Curtiss Jenny stamps could have cost between 1918 and 1991.

This block of Curtiss Jenny stamps was printed in 1918. It sold for $550,000 in 1991.

30. *Size of Antelopes*   Antelopes come in all different sizes. The largest antelope, the derby eland, can weigh up to 2000 pounds. The springbok of South Africa, so-called from its ability to leap repeatedly 10 feet into the air when frightened, weighs a modest 75 pounds. The royal antelope, smallest of all, weighs as little as 7 pounds at adulthood. Write a compound inequality that represents the different weights of adult antelopes.

Dimensions of Our Galaxy   **In Exercises 31 and 32, use the diagram of distances in our galaxy.**

31. Which compound inequality best describes the distance, d (in miles), between Earth and one of the other eight planets?

   a. $10^7 < d < 10^{10}$ **b.** $10^8 < d < 10^{11}$
   c. $10^9 < d < 10^{12}$

32. Which compound inequality best describes the distance, d (in miles), between Earth and a star (other than the sun) in our galaxy?

   a. $10^{13} < d < 10^{18}$ **b.** $10^{13} < d < 10^{17}$
   c. $10^{17} < d < 10^{18}$

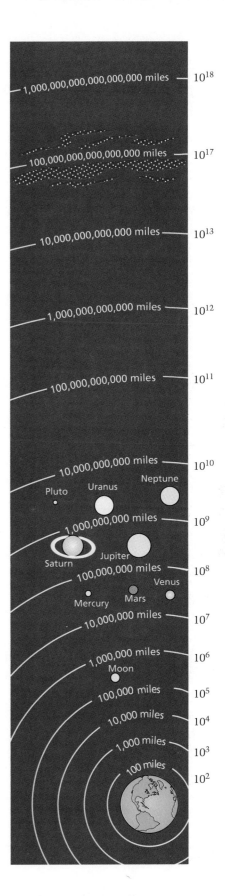

Meet Me at the Y   **In Exercises 33 and 34, use the following information.**

Jan lives in a mobile home 1 mile from the YWCA. Arlene lives
$\frac{1}{2}$ mile from Jan. Jan walks from her home to the Y, where she meets
Arlene, walks to Arlene's apartment, and then walks back home.

33. Write an inequality that describes the
various distances that Jan could have
walked. (Assume that each part of the
trip followed a straight path.)

34. Write an inequality that describes the
various distances that Arlene could live
from the YWCA.

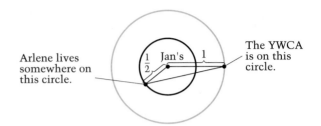

Arlene lives
somewhere on
this circle.

The YWCA
is on this
circle.

Integrated Review

35. *College Entrance Exam Sample*   Which of the following is the
graph of $x \geq -2$ *and* $x \leq 3$?

a.

b.

c.

d.

e.

In Exercises 36–38, write the inequality for the graph.

36.

37.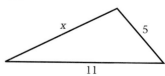

38.

In Exercises 39–44, solve the equation.

39. $|x - 1| = 7$

40. $|x - 3| = 9$

41. $|2x + 1| = 11$

42. $|3x - 2| = 5$

43. $17 = |5x - 2|$

44. $24 = |6x + 8|$

Exploration and Extension

Geometry   **In Exercises 45–48, write a compound inequality that
describes the possible lengths of the side of the triangle marked x. Use
the fact that the sum of the lengths of any two sides of a triangle is
greater than the length of the third side.**

45.

x

4

6

46.

x

8

9

47.

x

3

7

48.

x

5

11

Computers and some graphing calculators can be used to sketch the solution of an inequality in one variable. The following shows how to sketch a number line graph with a Texas Instruments TI-81 and with the BASIC programming language. In each program, the inequality is

$$-5 < 2x + 3.$$

The display screen for the graphing calculator is shown at the right. The graph of the solution appears one unit above the horizontal number line. Thus, from the display, it appears that the solution of the inequality is

$$x > -4.$$

You can check this result algebraically.

TI-81

MODE
Cursor to DOT, ENTER
RANGE (Set range.)
    Xmin = −10
    Xmax = 10
    Xscl = 1
    Ymin = −5
    Ymax = 5
    Yscl = 1
Y= CLEAR
(−) 5 2nd MATH 5 2 X|T + 3
    :Y₁ = −5<2X+3
    :Y₂ =
    :Y₃ =
    :Y₄ =
GRAPH
CLEAR (Clear screen.)

BASIC

```
 10 XMIN = − 10: XMAX = 10
 20 XG = (XMAX − XMIN)/(41 − 1)
 30 CLS
 40 FOR X = XMIN TO XMAX STEP XG
 50   XS = INT((X-XMIN)/XG + .5) + 1
 60   IF −5<2*X + 3 THEN Y = 1 ELSE Y = − 1
 70   YS = 9 − Y
 80   LOCATE YS,XS
 90   PRINT "*";
100 NEXT X
110 LOCATE 9,1
120 PRINT STRING$(41,"-");
130 FOR X = XMIN TO XMAX
140   LOCATE 9,INT((X-XMIN)/XG + .5) + 1
150   PRINT " +";
160 NEXT X
170 LOCATE 21,1
180 END
```

Exercises

Use a graphing calculator or a computer to sketch a graph of the inequality. State the solution shown by the graph. Then check the solution algebraically.

1. $-2x + 3 \geq 7$

2. $-3 < -x + 5$

3. $-3x + 2 \leq 4$

4. $5x + 1 < 4x + 5$

5. $-2x > -3x - 1$

6. $-x - 2 \leq 3x + 6$

Take this test as you would take a test in class. The answers to the exercises are given in the back of the book.

In Exercises 1–3, solve the inequality. Then match it with one of the graphs. (6.1)

1. $x + 2 > 4$

a. $\xleftarrow{\quad}\underset{10\ 11\ 12\ 13\ 14\ 15}{\longrightarrow} x$

2. $x - 7 \le 6$

b. $\xleftarrow{\quad}\underset{-5\ -4\ -3\ -2\ -1\ 0}{\longrightarrow} x$

3. $\frac{1}{4}x + 6 \ge 5$

c. $\xleftarrow{\quad}\underset{0\ 1\ 2\ 3\ 4}{\longrightarrow} x$

In Exercises 4–9, solve the inequality. (6.1)

4. $-3 \le x + 2 \le 5$

5. $-7 < 3x + 5 < 6$

6. $6 < 10 - 4x \le 34$

7. $-20 \le -5x < -5$

8. $-3x > 7$ or $3x \ge 7$

9. $\frac{3}{2}(x - 2) \le 6$ or $\frac{1}{5}(2x - 3) \ge 3$

In Exercises 10–13, write an inequality for the statement and draw its graph. (6.2)

10. x is more than 5 and less than 8.

11. x is between -3 and 2, inclusive.

12. x is greater than or equal to 0 or x is less than -1.

13. x is at least -4 but no more than 3.

In Exercises 14–16, sketch a graph of the inequality. (6.3)

14. $-3 < -3(x + 2) \le 5$

15. $0 \le -2(4 - x) < 8$

16. $\frac{1}{14}x > -1$ or $\frac{-1}{14}x + 1 > 7$

17. The Dodge'em Cars at Fun Park require children to be at least 52 inches tall to drive the cars. Write an inequality that describes the required heights. **(6.2)**

18. The length of a new pencil before sharpening is $7\frac{1}{2}$ inches, including the eraser. Suppose you discard the pencil when it is $2\frac{1}{2}$ inches long. Write a compound inequality that describes the size of a usable pencil. **(6.3)**

19. Granola in the bulk-food section of the grocery store is $1.96 per pound. You have $3 to spend on granola and strawberry yogurt. Write an inequality that describes how many pounds of granola you can purchase if you pay $0.69 for strawberry yogurt. Solve the inequality. **(6.2)**

20. Write a compound inequality that gives the possible lengths, x, of the side of the triangle. **(6.3)**

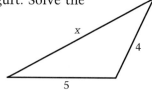

6.4

Connections: Absolute Value and Inequalities

What you should learn:

Goal 1 How to solve absolute value inequalities

Goal 2 How to model a real-life situation with an absolute value inequality

Why you should learn it:

You can use absolute value inequalities to model real-life situations about quantities within or outside of a number line interval, such as expenses being within 5% of budget.

Goal 1 Solving Absolute Value Inequalities

Which values of x would you say are solutions of the inequality

$$|x| < 2?$$

Since the absolute value of x is the distance between x and the origin, it follows that any number between -2 and 2 is a solution. In other words, the inequality $|x| < 2$ is equivalent to the compound inequality $-2 < x < 2$.

To translate more general absolute value inequalities to compound inequalities, use the following properties.

Translating Absolute Value Inequalities

1. The inequality $|ax + b| < c$ is equivalent to
$$-c < ax + b < c.$$

2. The inequality $|ax + b| > c$ is equivalent to
$$ax + b < -c \quad \text{or} \quad ax + b > c.$$

In the first statement, $<$ could be replaced by $\leq$. In the second statement, $>$ could be replaced by $\geq$.

Example 1   Solving an Absolute Value Inequality

Solve $|x - 4| < 3$.

Solution

$$|x - 4| < 3 \quad \textit{Rewrite original inequality.}$$
$$-3 < x - 4 < 3 \quad \textit{Write equivalent compound inequality.}$$
$$1 < \quad x \quad < 7 \quad \textit{Add 4 to each expression.}$$

The solution is *all real numbers that are greater than 1 <u>and</u> less than 7*. The graph is shown at the left. ∎

Graphic Check

Example 2 Solving an Absolute Value Inequality

Solve $|x + 1| \geq 2$.

Solution This absolute value inequality is equivalent to the following compound inequality.

$$x + 1 \leq -2 \quad or \quad x + 1 \geq 2$$

You can solve this inequality using the procedure described in Lesson 6.3.

$x + 1 \leq -2$	*First inequality*	$x + 1 \geq 2$	*Second inequality*
$x \leq -3$	*Subtract 1.*	$x \geq 1$	*Subtract 1.*

The solution is *all real numbers that are less than or equal to* -3 *or greater than or equal to 1*. The graph is shown below.

The next example shows how to write an absolute value inequality for a given graph.

Example 3 Writing an Absolute Value Inequality

Write an absolute value inequality to fit the graph shown below.

Solution To begin, write the compound inequality for the graph.

$$2 < x < 8$$

Then, to write the absolute value inequality, find the number that lies halfway between 2 and 8. This number is 5. (It lies 3 units from 2 and 3 units from 8.) Subtract 5 from each expression in the compound inequality.

$$2 - 5 < x - 5 < 8 - 5$$
$$-3 < x - 5 < 3$$

In this form, you can recognize the absolute value inequality to be

$$|x - 5| < 3.$$

For the inequality $|x - 5| < 3$, you can say that the range of solutions is from 3 less than 5 to 3 greater than 5.

```
10 PRINT "BUDGET EXP. ACTUAL EXP."
20    FOR N = 1 TO 2
30    READ B,A: PRINT USING "$###, ###.## ";B,A;
40    IF ABS(B−A)<.05*B THEN PRINT "APPROVED" ELSE PRINT
      "QUERIED"
50 NEXT
60 END
70 DATA 124500, 130290.18, 36500, 34383.29
```

This computer program compares actual expenses with budgeted expenses. It flags any expense that differs from its budget by 5% or more.

Real Life
Accounting

Example 4   *Budget Variance*

You are the manager of the accounting department of a large retail store and receive the following *budgeted* and *actual* expenses from the marketing department. How will the computer respond?

Item	Budgeted Expense, B	Actual Expense, A
a. Salaries	$124,500.00	$130,290.18
b. Travel	$36,500.00	$34,383.29

Solution

a. For salaries, $|B - A| = 5790.18$ and $0.05B = 6225.00$. The inequality $|B - A| < 0.05B$ is satisfied. The computer will print "APPROVED."

b. For travel, $|B - A| = 2116.71$ and $0.05B = 1825.00$. The inequality $|B - A| < 0.05B$ is *not* satisfied. The computer will print "QUERIED." ▪

Communicating about **A L G E B R A**

▶ **SHARING IDEAS about the Lesson**

Translate between Models Write an absolute value inequality for each graph.

A.

B.

EXERCISES

Guided Practice

▶ **CRITICAL THINKING about the Lesson**

1. True or False? $|x + 1| < 3$ means that $x + 1$ is between -3 and 3. Explain.

2. True or False? $|x| \geq 5$ means that x is less than -5 or greater than 5. Explain.

3. Solve $|x - 1| < 4$.

4. Solve $|x + 3| > 9$.

5. Match the inequality $|x| \geq 6$ with its graph.

6. Match the inequality $|x| < 8$ with its graph.

a.

a.

b.

b.

Independent Practice

In Exercises 7–12, match the absolute value inequality with its equivalent compound inequality.

7. $|x - 1| < 3$

8. $\left|x - \frac{1}{2}\right| \leq \frac{3}{2}$

9. $|x + 1| \leq 2$

10. $|x + 2| \geq 4$

11. $\left|x - \frac{5}{2}\right| > \frac{3}{2}$

12. $|x + 2| > 1$

a. $x < -3$ or $x > -1$

b. $-3 \leq x \leq 1$

c. $x \leq -6$ or $x \geq 2$

d. $-2 < x < 4$

e. $-1 \leq x \leq 2$

f. $x < 1$ or $x > 4$

In Exercises 13–18, solve the inequality.

13. $|x - 2| < 5$

14. $|1 + x| \geq 4$

15. $|2x - 1| > 3$

16. $|4 + x| \leq 9$

17. $|4 - x| \geq 2$

18. $|-x + 1| < 1$

In Exercises 19–30, solve the inequality. Then sketch its graph.

19. $|x + 8| < 9$

20. $|9 + x| \leq 7$

21. $|4 - x| < 5$

22. $|x + 12| < 36$

23. $|x - 12| \geq 6$

24. $|5 - x| > 18$

25. $|x + 1| > 17$

26. $|x - 9| \geq 4$

27. $|3x - 6| \geq 0$

28. $|10 - 4x| < 2$

29. $|1 + 2x| \leq 9$

30. $|2x + 3| > 4$

In Exercises 31–36, write an absolute value inequality to fit the graph.

31.

32.

33.

34.

35.

36.

316   *Chapter 6 ▪ Solving and Graphing Linear Inequalities*

37. Game Show A contestant on a television show must guess within $1000 of the actual price of a trip in order to win the trip. The actual price of the trip is $14,000. Write an absolute value inequality that shows the range of possible guesses that will win the trip.

38. Car Mileage Your car averages 25 miles per gallon. The actual mileage for city driving varies from the average by 4 miles per gallon, depending on the traffic conditions. Write an absolute value inequality that shows the range for the mileage that your car gets in the city.

39. Test Scores Suppose the test scores in your class range from 60 to 100. Write an absolute value inequality describing test-score range.

40. 400-Meter Run The members of your track team can run 400 meters between 58 seconds and 70 seconds. Write an absolute value inequality describing the times for the runners.

Fireworks In Exercises 41–44, match the color of the star burst with one of the color ranges in the spectrum. (Use the wavelengths for various colors of the spectrum given on page 291.)

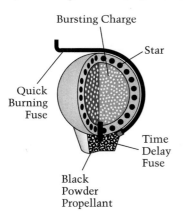

Bursting Charge

Star

Quick Burning Fuse

Time Delay Fuse

Black Powder Propellant

A star-burst fireworks shell contains a quick fuse that ignites the propellant powder, expelling the shell from a launch tube. A time-delay fuse sets off a bursting charge after the shell is far above the ground. The color of the "stars" is determined by the chemical compound used.

41. A fireworks star is made of strontium. When it is burned, strontium emits light at wavelengths given by $|w - 643| < 38$. What color is it?

42. A fireworks star is made of a copper compound. When it is burned, the compound emits light at wavelengths given by $|w - 455| < 23$. What color is it?

43. A fireworks star is made of barium chloride. When it is burned, barium chloride emits light at wavelengths given by $|w - 519.5| < 12.5$. What color is it?

44. A fireworks star is made of a sodium compound. When it is burned, the compound emits light at wavelengths given by $|w - 600| < 5$. What color is it?

45. *Grains of Sand* Sand is made up of loose pieces of rocks or minerals that are larger than silt but smaller than pebbles. Geologists define sand as grains that measure in diameter according to the graph below. Write an absolute value inequality describing the diameters of sand grains.

46. *It's Either Too Hot or Too Cold* Suppose you start the furnace whenever the temperature inside is 66°F or below and start the air conditioner whenever the temperature inside is 74°F or above. The graph below shows the temperatures at which you turn on the heat or air conditioner. Write an absolute value inequality that represents these temperatures.

$\longleftarrow$ | | | | | | | | | $\longrightarrow$ x
    62° 64° 66° 68° 70° 72° 74° 76°

Integrated Review

In Exercises 47–52, solve the inequality.

47. $-6 < x - 4 < 3$

48. $2 \le 9 + x \le 12$

49. $-4 \le -x + 9 \le 6$

50. $-11 < -2x + 3 < 11$

51. $-7 < 6x - 5 < 4$

52. $2 \le 8x - 14 \le 58$

In Exercises 53–58, graph the inequality.

53. $3x + 7 > 1$

54. $4x + 5 \ge 21$

55. $2x + 4 \le x + 3$

56. $4x + 7 < 3x + 3$

57. $-19 \le 2x - 9 \le -1$

58. $-4 < 5x - 9 < 26$

Exploration and Extension

Underwater Color **In Exercises 59 and 60, use the following information.**

As light passes through seawater, most of the light with a long wavelength is absorbed. Much of the light with a short wavelength is also absorbed.

59. Write an absolute value inequality approximating the wavelengths of light that reach a depth of 30 meters in seawater.

60. Write an absolute value inequality approximating the wavelengths of light that reach a depth of 60 meters in seawater.

Biology In Exercises 61–66, use the chart to write an absolute value inequality for the given sound frequency range.

Sound Frequency Ranges

☐ Emission
☐ Reception

Humans: 85 – 1,100 / 20 – 20,000
Dolphins: 7,000 – 120,000 / 150 – 150,000
Dogs: 452 – 1,080 / 15 – 50,000
Cats: 760 – 1520 / 60 – 65,000
Bats: 10,000 – 120,000 / 1,000 – 120,000
Grasshoppers: 7,000 – 100,000 / 100 – 15,000

Hertz (vibrations per second)
0   100   1,000   10,000   100,000

61. Frequencies people can emit

62. Frequencies people can receive that bats emit

63. Frequencies that dogs can receive that people cannot receive

64. Frequencies that a cat can receive but cannot emit

65. Frequencies that a grasshopper can emit that people can receive

66. Frequencies that people can emit that dolphins cannot receive

Mixed REVIEW

1. Write 35% in decimal form. **(1.1)**

2. Use exponents to write $x \cdot x \cdot y \cdot y \cdot y$. **(1.3)**

3. What is 7% of $3.40? **(2.7)**

4. What is two fifths of 375? **(2.7)**

5. What is the reciprocal of $-\frac{4}{3}$?

6. What is the opposite of $\frac{5}{6}$? **(2.1)**

7. Solve $3x + 4y = -20$ for y. **(3.6)**

8. Solve $\frac{1}{4}m - 2n = 3$ for n. **(3.6)**

9. Evaluate $x^2 + 2x - 3$ when $x = 4$. **(1.3)**

10. Evaluate $|3 - x| + |x|$ when $x = -1$. **(2.1)**

11. Simplify $3(x - 2) + \frac{1}{2}(4x - 3)$. **(2.6)**

12. Simplify $3(x - y) + \frac{3}{4}(4x + y)$. **(2.6)**

13. Solve $9x - 4 = \frac{1}{4}(3 - x)$. **(3.2)**

14. Solve $\frac{1}{4}(y - 4) = (2y + 6)\frac{3}{8}$. **(3.2)**

15. Sketch the graph of $y = -3|x + 2| - 2$. **(4.7)**

16. Sketch the graph of $6x + 7y = 42$. **(4.3)**

17. Are the lines $y = \frac{3}{4}x$ and $y = \frac{3}{4}x - 2$ parallel? **(4.5)**

18. Graph the inequality $\frac{1}{9}x - 1 \geq -x - \frac{1}{3}$. **(6.1)**

19. Find the slope and y-intercept of the line $y = -\frac{1}{2}x + 3$. **(4.5)**

20. Find the x-intercept and y-intercept of the line $-3y + 2x = 6$. **(4.3)**

6.5 Graphing Linear Inequalities in Two Variables

What you should learn:

Goal 1 How to graph a linear inequality in two variables

Goal 2 How to model a real-life situation using a linear inequality in two variables

Why you should learn it:

You can use linear inequalities to model real-life situations such as the possible gold content of ocean treasure.

Goal 1 Graphing Linear Inequalities

A **linear inequality** in x and y is an inequality that can be written in one of the following forms.

$$ax + by < c, \quad ax + by \le c, \quad ax + by > c, \quad ax + by \ge c$$

An ordered pair (a, b) is a **solution** of a linear inequality in x and y if the inequality is true when a and b are substituted for x and y, respectively. For instance, $(1, 3)$ is a solution of

$$4x - y < 2$$

because $4(1) - 3 < 2$ is a true statement.

Example 1 *Checking Solutions of Linear Inequalities*

Check whether the ordered pairs are solutions of $2x - 3y \ge -2$.

a. $(0, 0)$ **b.** $(0, 1)$ **c.** $(2, -1)$

Solution

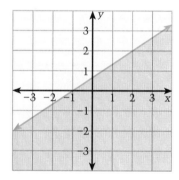

(x, y)	Substitute		Conclusion
a. $(0, 0)$	$2(0) - 3(0)$	$= 0 \ge -2$	$(0, 0)$ is a solution.
b. $(0, 1)$	$2(0) - 3(1)$	$= -3 < -2$	$(0, 1)$ is not a solution.
c. $(2, -1)$	$2(2) - 3(-1)$	$= 7 \ge -2$	$(2, -1)$ is a solution. ∎

The graph of $2x - 3y \ge -2$ is shown at the left. Every point in the shaded region is a solution of the inequality, and every other point in the plane is not a solution.

Sketching the Graph of a Linear Inequality

1. Sketch the graph of the corresponding linear equation. (Use a *dashed* line for inequalities with $<$ or $>$ and a *solid* line for inequalities with $\le$ or $\ge$.) This line separates the coordinate plane into two **half planes.**
2. Test a point in one of the half planes to find whether it is a solution of the inequality.
3. If the test point is a solution, shade its half plane. If not, shade the other half plane.

Example 2 — *Sketching the Graph of a Linear Inequality*

Sketch the graphs of the linear inequalities.

a. $x < -3$ **b.** $y \leq 4$

Solution

a. First, sketch the vertical line given by

$x = -3.$ *Use a dashed line.*

Next, test a point. The origin $(0, 0)$ is *not* a solution and it lies to the right of the line. Therefore, the graph of $x < -3$ is all points to the left of the line $x = -3$.

b. First, sketch the horizontal line given by

$y = 4.$ *Use a solid line.*

Next, test a point. The origin $(0, 0)$ *is* a solution and it lies below the line. Therefore, the graph of $y \leq 4$ is all points on or below the line $y = 4$.

When sketching the graph of a line, remember that it is helpful to first write the line in slope-intercept form.

Example 3 — *Writing in Slope-Intercept Form*

Sketch the graph of $x + y > 3$.

Solution   The corresponding equation is $x + y = 3$. To sketch this line, first write the equation in slope-intercept form.

$y = -x + 3$ *Slope-intercept form*

Then, sketch the line that has a slope of -1 and a y-intercept of 3. Use a dashed line. The origin $(0, 0)$ is *not* a solution and it lies below the line. Therefore, the graph of $x + y > 3$ is all points above the line. (Try checking a point above the line. Any one you choose will satisfy the inequality.)

Notice that for each inequality, we used the origin as a test point. You can use any point that is not on the line. The origin is often convenient to use because it is easy to evaluate expressions in which 0 is substituted for each variable.

Modeling a Real-Life Situation

In 1969, ocean divers found the remains of the Spanish ship **Girona** *that sank off the coast of Northern Ireland. Among other treasures, the divers found 405 gold coins and 756 silver coins.*

Real Life
Underwater Diving

Example 4 | *Finding Ocean Treasure*

You are diving for precious coins. Your recovery basket contains about 50 pounds of material! If gold coins weigh about $\frac{1}{2}$ ounce each and silver coins weigh about $\frac{1}{4}$ ounce each, what are the various proportions of coins you may have?

Solution The basket contains 800 ounces of material.

Verbal Model	Weight per coin	•	Num. gold coins	+	Weight per coin	•	Num. silver coins	≤	Weight in basket

Labels   Weight per gold coin $= \frac{1}{2}$ (oz. per coin)

Number of gold coins $= x$ (coins)

Weight per silver coin $= \frac{1}{4}$ (oz. per coin)

Number of silver coins $= y$ (coins)

Weight in basket $= 800$ (ounces)

Inequality $\frac{1}{2}x + \frac{1}{4}y \le 800$ **Linear model**

All possible solutions are shown in the graph.   ■

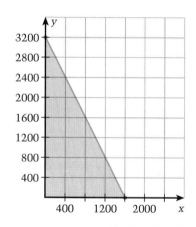

Communicating about ALGEBRA

▷ **SHARING IDEAS about the Lesson**

Make a Conjecture   A conjecture is a statement that you think is true but that has not been proved true.

A. Sketch the graph of $y < -2x + 8$. Does the graph lie above or below the line $y = -2x + 8$?

B. Sketch the graph of $y > x + 1$. Does the graph lie above or below the line $y = x + 1$?

C. Make a conjecture based upon **A** and **B**.

EXERCISES

▶ **CRITICAL THINKING about the Lesson**

1. What are the four forms of a linear inequality in x and y?

2. The graph of a linear inequality in x and y is a _____.

In Exercises 3–5, are (0, 2) and (2, 1) solutions of the inequality?

3. $2x - 3y \leq 4$

4. $-x + 4y > 0$

5. $y - \frac{2}{3}x \geq -2$

6. Sketch the graph of $y - 2x \leq 2$ and explain each step.

Independent Practice

In Exercises 7–10, is each ordered pair a solution of the inequality?

7. $3x - 2y < 2$; $(1, 3)$, $(2, 0)$

8. $y - 2x > 5$; $(4, 13)$, $(8, 1)$

9. $5x + 4y \geq 6$; $(-2, 4)$, $(5, 5)$

10. $5y + 8x \leq 14$; $(-3, 8)$, $(7, -6)$

In Exercises 11–14, sketch the graph of the inequality.

11. $x \geq 5$

12. $x \leq -3$

13. $y > -2$

14. $y < 8$

In Exercises 15–18, match the inequality with its graph.

15. $2x - y \leq 1$

16. $2x - y < 1$

17. $2x - y \geq 1$

18. $2x - y > 1$

a.

b.

c.

d.
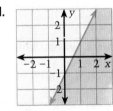

In Exercises 19–22, sketch the graph of the inequality.

19. $-x - y \leq 4$

20. $2x - y \geq 6$

21. $3x + y > 9$

22. $y - 4x < 0$

In Exercises 23–26, write an inequality for the half plane.

23.

24.

25.

26.

Camouflage experiment: Ask a person to stand 6 feet away. Before opening the book, tell the person that the picture you will show contains *at most* <u>six</u> horses. After letting the person look at the picture for 10 seconds, close the book and ask him or her to state the number of adult horses and the number of foals. Remind the person that the number of horses may be zero.

27. Let x represent the number of adult horses. Let y represent the number of foals. Write and graph an inequality that describes the numbers of adult horses and foals that the person could report seeing.

PINTOS by Bev Doolittle. © 1978 The Greenwich Workshop, Trumbull, Conn.

Billy Joe and Rosanne ride the same bus to school but have different homerooms. Thirty other students ride the same bus.

28. Let x represent the number of students other than Billy Joe on the bus from Billy Joe's homeroom. Let y represent the number other than Rosanne on the bus from Rosanne's homeroom. Write and graph an inequality that describes the different numbers of students on the bus who could be from Billy Joe's or Rosanne's homerooms.

Carver High School scored 42 points in its football victory over Central High School. In a football game, a field goal counts 3 points and a safety counts 2 points.

29. Let x represent the number of field goals scored. Let y represent the number of safeties scored. Write and graph an inequality that describes the different numbers of field goals and safeties that Carver could have scored.

A Full Lot of Cars   **In Exercise 30, use the following information.**

A car dealer sells several different car models. The dealer has $1,200,000 worth of cars on the lot. A sports model costs $20,000 and a sedan costs $12,000.

30. Let x represent the number of sports models on the lot. Let y represent the number of sedans. Write and graph an inequality in x and y that describes the different numbers of sports models and sedans on the lot. (Remember, none of the cars on the lot have to be sports models or sedans.)

Integrated Review

In Exercises 31–38, solve the inequality.

31. $3x - 1 > 7$

32. $6 - x \le 28$

33. $14x + 5 \le 4x - 15$

34. $-3x - 1 > -2x + 19$

35. $-5 < 3x + 4 \le 1$

36. $0 \le 9x - 63 < 18$

37. $-10 \le 3 - 2x \le 9$

38. $-1 < 4x + 5 < 0$

In Exercises 39–42, determine whether the ordered pair is a solution of the inequality.

39. $5x - 2y < 14;\ (2, -2)$

40. $x - 3y \le 17;\ (-5, -4)$

41. $-4x + y > 10;\ (-1, 14)$

42. $3x + 9y \ge -3;\ (-4, 1)$

In Exercises 43–50, sketch the graph of the line.

43. $x = -4$

44. $y = -9$

45. $y = 3$

46. $x = 7$

47. $x + y = 9$

48. $-2x + y = 11$

49. $3x - 2y = 12$

50. $x - 3y = 6$

Exploration and Extension

Geometry   **In Exercises 51 and 52, find four different inequalities so that each point in the shaded region is a solution of each inequality *and* each point that is not in the shaded region is not the solution of at least one inequality.**

51.

52.

A graphing calculator or computer can be used to sketch the graph of an inequality in x and y. Here we show how to use a Texas Instruments TI-81 *and a Casio* fx-7700G *to sketch the graph of*

$$x - 2y \leq 6.$$

The first step is to write the equivalent inequality that has y isolated on the left. For instance, $x - 2y \leq 6$ must first be written as

$$y \geq \tfrac{1}{2}x - 3.$$

TI-81

Isolate y on left: $y \geq \tfrac{1}{2}x - 3$.

$\boxed{RANGE}$ (Set range.)
  Xmin = −10
  Xmax = 10
  Xscl = 1
  Ymin = −10
  Ymax = 10
  Yscl = 1

$\boxed{Y=}$ $\boxed{CLEAR}$
$\boxed{2nd}$ $\boxed{DRAW}$ $\boxed{7}$ (Shade)
.5 $\boxed{X|T}$ $\boxed{-}$ 3 $\boxed{ALPHA}$ $\boxed{,}$ 10 $\boxed{)}$
  Shade(.5X − 3,10)
$\boxed{ENTER}$

Casio fx-7700G

Isolate y on left: $y \geq \tfrac{1}{2}x - 3$.

$\boxed{Range}$ (Set range.)
  Xmin = −10
  max = 10
  scl = 1
  Ymin = −10
  max = 10
  scl = 1

$\boxed{EXE}$ $\boxed{Range}$
$\boxed{SHIFT}$ $\boxed{F5}$ (Cls) $\boxed{EXE}$
$\boxed{MODE}$ $\boxed{SHIFT}$ $\boxed{\div}$ (Inequality mode)
$\boxed{Graph}$ $\boxed{F3}$ .5 $\boxed{X,\theta,T}$ $\boxed{-}$ 3
Graph Y≥.5X − 3
$\boxed{EXE}$

Exercises

In Exercises 1–8, use a graphing calculator to sketch the graph of the inequality. (For 1–4, use the range shown above. For 5–8, use the indicated range.)

1. $y < -2x - 3$ **2.** $y > 2x + 2$ **3.** $x + 2y \leq -1$ **4.** $x - 3y \geq 3$

5. $y < x + 25$ **6.** $y > -x + 25$ **7.** $y \leq 0.1x$ **8.** $y \geq 100x + 2500$

RANGE	RANGE	RANGE	RANGE
Xmin = −10	Xmin = −10	Xmin = −10	Xmin = 0
Xmax = 10	Xmax = 10	Xmax = 10	Xmax = 100
Xscl = 1	Xscl = 1	Xscl = 1	Xscl = 10
Ymin = −5	Ymin = −5	Ymin = −1	Ymin = 0
Ymax = 35	Ymax = 35	Ymax = 1	Ymax = 15000
Yscl = 5	Yscl = 5	Yscl = .1	Yscl = 1000

6.6

Exploring Data: Time Lines, Picture Graphs, and Circle Graphs

What you should learn:

Goal How to draw and interpret visual models, such as time lines, picture graphs, and circle graphs

Why you should learn it:

You can communicate effectively with visual models as well as with verbal models.

Goal **Using Visual Models**

The graphs used by many newspapers and magazines are meant to be eye-catching as well as informative. Each of the three types of graphs discussed in this lesson, *time-line graphs*, *picture graphs*, and *circle graphs*, is commonly used in presenting facts and figures in a somewhat informal way. Being able to interpret the information in such graphs is an important skill. Drawing these kinds of graphs gives you an opportunity to be creative and use your artistic ability.

A **time line** or **time-line graph** is often used to represent historical events. For instance, the time-line graph on page 303 shows the different dynasties that ruled China between 2000 B.C. and A.D. 1000.

Problem Solving
Make a Diagram

Example 1 *The History of Automobiles*

Create a time line that shows the history of automobiles in the United States.

Solution This project could (and probably should) be very detailed. Here, however, we show a time line with only a few important events in the history of automobiles.

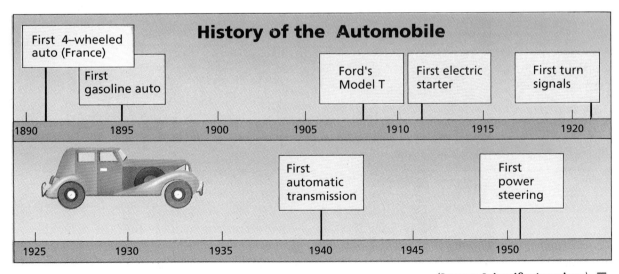

History of the Automobile

First 4–wheeled auto (France)

First gasoline auto

Ford's Model T

First electric starter

First turn signals

| 1890 | 1895 | 1900 | 1905 | 1910 | 1915 | 1920 |

First automatic transmission

First power steering

| 1925 | 1930 | 1935 | 1940 | 1945 | 1950 |

*(Source: **Scientific American**)* ◼

Saudi Arabia's Oil Production

Saudi Arabia

Total Opec

Barrels per Day (in millions)

Year

Picture graphs are usually stylized versions of bar graphs or graphs in the coordinate plane. The "pictures" in a picture graph provide a visual connection with the real-life quantities.

Example 2 **Oil Production by Saudi Arabia**

OPEC, the Organization of Petroleum Exporting Countries, was formed in 1960. In 1991, its members were Algeria, Ecuador, Indonesia, Iran, Iraq, Kuwait, Libya, Nigeria, Qatar, Saudi Arabia, United Arab Emirates, and Venezuela. Use the picture graph to estimate the ratio of Saudi Arabia's 1987 daily oil production to OPEC's 1987 daily oil production. *(Source: OPEC)*

Solution From the graph, estimate that Saudi Arabia's daily production in 1987 was 5 million barrels and OPEC's was 18 million barrels. Thus, the ratio of Saudi Arabia's production to OPEC's was approximately

$$\frac{5}{18} \approx 28\%.$$ ■

Connections
Biology

Example 3 **Raising a Litter of Kittens**

A mother cat was observed for six weeks after her kittens were born. In the graph on the left, each point of a line represents a time when the mother was *in* the box, while in the graph on the right, each point represents a time when all the kittens were *out of* the box. Notice that the first recorded information is at the top line of the graph, and that the vertical axis is then numbered from the top of the graph to the bottom, unlike most graphs you see. Describe the behavior of the mother and the kittens.

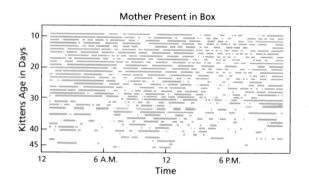

Mother Present in Box

Kittens Age in Days

Time

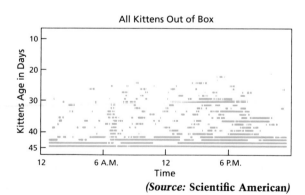

All Kittens Out of Box

Kittens Age in Days

Time

(Source: Scientific American)

Solution In the left graph, you can see that the older the kittens became, the more the mother left the box. In the right graph, you can see that the kittens stayed in their box until they were three weeks old. Then they began leaving for longer and longer times. ■

Circle graphs are used to show the relative sizes of different portions of a whole.

Example 4 *Rearranging Furniture*

Southwestern Bell Telephone Company surveyed 300 adults to find why they rearranged furniture in their homes. Of the 300, 108 said they were bored with the current arrangement, 57 said they moved to a new home, 48 said they redecorated, 45 said they purchased new furniture, and 42 had other reasons. Make a circle graph to show these results.

Solution To begin, you need to find the percentage that each type of response was of the total number of responses.

Bored	$\frac{108}{300} = 36\%$	Moved	$\frac{57}{300} = 19\%$
Redecorated	$\frac{48}{300} = 16\%$	New furniture	$\frac{45}{300} = 15\%$
Other	$\frac{42}{300} = 14\%$		

Next, you need to partition a circle into five sections corresponding to the five percentages. One way to do this is to divide the 360° "angle" at the center of the circle into 36% of 360° (360 • 0.36 ≈ 130°), 19% of 360° (360 • 0.19 ≈ 68°), etc. ■

Why People Rearrange Furniture

- Moving to new home — 36%
- Bored with arrangement
- 19%
- Other — 14%
- 15%
- 16%
- Redecorating
- Purchasing new furniture

Communicating about **ALGEBRA**

Services

Distribution

Manufacturing

Other

Agriculture and Fishing

Construction

Japanese Workers

Each figure represents 2% of the workforce

▶ **SHARING IDEAS about the Lesson**

Interpret a Graph In 1987, Japan had approximately 60 million people in its work force. The picture graph at the left shows the distribution of Japan's work force.

- ■ Manufacturing
- ■ Services
- ■ Agriculture & Fishing
- ■ Distribution
- ■ Construction
- ■ Other

A. What percent of Japan's work force was in construction?

B. Approximate the number of manufacturing workers.

C. Approximate the number of service workers.

D. How many more people worked in distribution than in agriculture and fishing?

EXERCISES

▶ CRITICAL THINKING about the Lesson

1. Use Example 1. You are considering buying a 1932 Chevrolet. The owner of the car tells you that all the parts are original. You notice that the car has an automatic transmission. Is the owner telling the truth?

2. Use Example 2. Estimate the ratio of Saudi Arabia's 1985 daily oil production to its 1988 daily oil production.

3. Use Example 3. Did the kittens leave the box primarily during times the mother was in the box or primarily during times the mother was out of the box?

4. Use Example 4. Suppose 500 people had been surveyed (instead of 300). Approximately how many people would you expect there to be in each category?

Independent Practice

Inventions   **In Exercises 5–8 below, match the inventor with the time he lived.**

5. Guglielmo Marconi (radio)

6. Alexander Graham Bell (telephone)

7. Percy Julian (synthetic cortisone)

8. Elias Howe (sewing machine)

    a. 1819–1867

    b. 1899–1975

    c. 1874–1937

    d. 1847–1922

Activity Pattern   **In Exercises 9 and 10, use the following time line.**

9. When did the woman have breakfast, lunch, and dinner?

10. How many hours did the woman sleep?

A psychologist recorded a woman's activities during a 24-hour day.

11. *Schedule*   Construct a time-line graph showing your schedule on an average day.

TV Rules   **In Exercises 12–15, use the picture graph below, which compares the percent of parents in 1976 and 1990 who had strict rules for TV watching.** *(Source: "Roper Report,"* USA Today)

12. In 1990, what percentage of parents had strict TV-watching rules for 13–17-year-old children?

13. In 1976, what percentage of parents had strict TV-watching rules for 7–12-year-old children?

14. Find the increase in percentage from 1976 to 1990 of parents who had strict TV-watching rules for 13–17-year-old children.

15. Find the increase in percentage from 1976 to 1990 of parents who had strict TV-watching rules for children 6 and under.

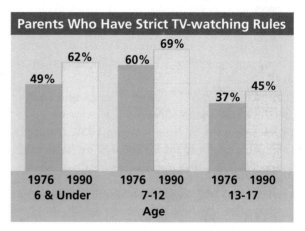

World Energy Sources   **In Exercises 16–19, use the time-line graph, which shows the world's sources of energy from 1860 to 1985.**
(Source: Scientific American)

16. In which decade did oil become the primary energy source?

17. In 1970, what was the second most common source of energy?

18. Approximate the amount of natural gas used in 1920.

19. How much more primary electricity was used in 1970 than in 1960?

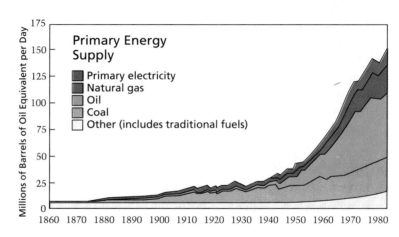

What Size Bed?   In Exercises 20 and 21, use the circle graph showing the sizes of beds that Americans bought in 1990.
(Source: International Sleep Products)

20. What percentage of people bought either queen or full-size beds?

21. What is the difference in the percentages of people who bought twin and full-size beds?

22. *Giving Flowers*   A survey of adults found that one third of American women gave flowers to a man during 1990. The reasons for giving the flowers were Romance (931), Cheer Him Up or Get Well (532), Sympathy (152), Birthday or Holiday (133), Congratulations (95), and Other (152). Construct a circle graph of this information.
(Source: American Floral Marketing Council)

23. *Electricity Consumption*   The average amounts of electricity (in kilowatt-hours) used by a United States household in 1990 were as follows: Refrigeration (1810), Lighting (1000), Water Heating (1540), Air-Conditioning (1180), Cooking (635), Other (1180). Make a circle graph to show this information. *(Source: Scientific American)*

What Color Bike?   In Exercises 24 and 25, use the circle graph showing the color of bicycles bought by Americans in 1989. During 1989, Americans spent $2,205,000 on bicycles.
(Source: Bicycle Market Research Institute)

24. How much money was spent on blue bicycles in 1989?

25. How much more money was spent on black bicycles than on blue bicycles in 1989?

Integrated Review

26. *Test Points*   You got 72% on a 150-point test. How many points did you get?

27. *Sales Tax*   You paid $26.74 for a sweater. The price of the sweater is $24.99. What was the percent of sales tax?

28. *Free Throws*   A basketball forward makes 80% of free throws taken. If there were 240 free throws in a season, how many free throws were made?

29. *Completed Passes*   A football team completes 56% of its passes. How many of 25 passes would you expect it to complete in a game?

30. *Baseball Card*   You bought a baseball card for $3.50 and later sold it for $5.00. What percent profit did you make?

In Exercises 31–36, graph the inequality.

31. $2x > 6$

32. $y \le 8$

33. $x + y \le 3$

34. $x - y > 5$

35. $x - 2y > 4$

36. $2x + y < 6$

37. *Estimation—Powers of Ten* Which best estimates the height of the Empire State Building?

  a. 125 feet   **b.** 1250 feet

  c. 12,500 feet   **d.** 125,000 feet

38. *Estimation—Powers of Ten* Which best estimates the annual salary of a manager of a fast-food restaurant?

  a. $3000   **b.** $30,000

  c. $300,000   **d.** $3,000,000

Exploration and Extension

United States History **In Exercises 39–42, use the time line showing the years in which the 26 amendments of the United States Constitution were passed.**

39. The Abolition of Slavery and the Civil Rights Amendments were passed three years apart, around the time of the Civil War. Which amendments are they?

40. Two amendments were passed soon after World War I. The second of these gave women the right to vote. Which amendment is it?

41. Franklin Delano Roosevelt was elected President of the United States for four consecutive terms. The first amendment passed after his presidency limited presidents to two terms. Which amendment is it?

42. The two amendments, Prohibition of Liquor and Repeal of Prohibition, were passed 14 years apart. Which amendments are they?

6

Chapter Summary

What did you learn?

Skills

1. Solve and graph an inequality in one variable.
   - Simple linear inequality **(6.1)**
   - Compound linear inequality **(6.3)**
   - Absolute value inequality **(6.4)**

2. Graph a linear inequality in two variables. **(6.5)**

3. Write an inequality to represent a graph.
   - Simple linear inequality in one variable **(6.1)**
   - Compound linear inequality in one variable **(6.3)**
   - Absolute value inequality in one variable **(6.4)**
   - Linear inequality in two variables **(6.5)**

Strategies

4. Use an inequality to model a real-life situation. **(6.1–6.5)**

5. Use an inequality to answer questions about real-life situations. **(6.1–6.5)**

Exploring Data

6. Create and interpret time lines, picture graphs, and circle graphs. **(6.6)**

Why did you learn it?

Many real-life situations have models that are inequalities. Think of how many verbal descriptions contain phrases such as "at most," "at least," "no more than," or "less than." For instance, suppose your goal for the school year is to earn a grade point average of *at least* 3.0, or suppose you are willing to spend *no more than* $15 on a pair of shorts. Inequalities generally have many solutions. There are many possible grade point averages that are at least 3.0, and there are many prices that are less than $15. When you are creating models of real-life situations, remember to look for phrases that indicate inequalities.

How does it fit into the bigger picture of algebra?

In this chapter, you studied techniques for solving and graphing linear inequalities. The first four lessons focused on linear inequalities in one variable and absolute value inequalities in one variable. In the fifth lesson, you learned that the graph of an inequality in two variables is a *half plane*. The sixth lesson described three types of visual models that can be used to represent data. When reviewing this chapter, look for connections between solving and graphing equations and solving and graphing inequalities.

In Exercises 1–4, graph the inequality on a number line. **(6.1)**

1. $x \geq -3$ **2.** $3 > x$ **3.** $-4 \geq x$ **4.** $x \leq 4$

In Exercises 5–20, solve the inequality. **(6.1, 6.3, 6.4)**

5. $3x + 5 \geq 4$

6. $\frac{2}{3}(x - 6) \geq 0$

7. $6 \geq \frac{1}{4}(3 + x)$

8. $75x - 50 < 55x - 30$

9. $-x + 5 < 2(x - 4)$

10. $(x - 6)4 > x + 30$

11. $3 < 1 - 6x < 6$

12. $-53 < 37 - 5x < 42$

13. $0 \leq \frac{1}{4}(x - 8) \leq 20$

14. $2(x + 3) < -4$ or $14x + (-3) > 4$

15. $-x + \frac{1}{2} \leq -\frac{3}{4}$ or $\frac{1}{4}(x + 2) < \frac{3}{4}$

16. $\frac{1}{3}(4 - x) > 6$ or $\frac{2}{5}(x + 7) \geq 4$

17. $|2x - 4| \geq 3$

18. $|x - \frac{1}{2}| \leq 3$

19. $|\frac{1}{3}x - \frac{2}{3}| > 6$

20. $|\frac{25}{3} - 5x| < \frac{5}{3}$

In Exercises 21–26, solve the inequality. Then graph the solution on a number line. **(6.1, 6.4)**

21. $5 - \frac{1}{2}x \leq -3$

22. $3(2x + 8) \geq 4(-2x - 4)$

23. $-4 < 3x + 1 < 4$

24. $\frac{1}{5}(x + 5) < \frac{2}{3}$ or $\frac{1}{5}(x + 5) > \frac{5}{4}$

25. $|4x - 5| < 20$

26. $|3 - \frac{1}{2}x| \geq 7$

In Exercises 27–30, match the absolute value inequality with the equivalent compound inequality. **(6.4)**

27. $|x - 2| \leq 3$ **28.** $|x + 1| \geq 2$ **29.** $|x - 1| < 4$ **30.** $|x + 2| > 1$

a. $-3 < x < 5$ **b.** $-1 \leq x \leq 5$ **c.** $x < -3$ or $x > -1$ **d.** $x \leq -3$ or $x \geq 1$

In Exercises 31–34, write an absolute value inequality to fit the graph. **(6.4)**

31.

32.

33.

34.

In Exercises 35–38, decide whether each ordered pair is a solution of the inequality. **(6.5)**

35. $\frac{1}{4}y - 2x + 3 \geq 4$; $(4, 0), (-4, -3)$

36. $2(y - x) < 0$; $(0, 0), (2, -1)$

37. $\frac{1}{2}x + \frac{1}{3}y > -3$; $(-2, 1), (-8, -9)$

38. $2x^2 + y \leq 14$; $(3, -2), (2, 7)$

In Exercises 39–42, sketch the graph of the inequality. **(6.5)**

39. $-2x + y > 4$ **40.** $-(\frac{1}{3}x + 3y) \leq 3$ **41.** $\frac{3}{8}(x + y + 8) \geq \frac{1}{4}$ **42.** $13x + y \geq 10x - 10$

43. *Dinosaur Height*   Let *h* represent the height of a dinosaur. Write an inequality that describes the range of heights of dinosaurs whose fossils have been found at Dinosaur National Park.

44. *Dinosaur Weight*   Let *w* represent the weight of a dinosaur. Write an inequality that describes the range of weights of dinosaurs whose fossils have been found at Dinosaur National Park.

Brachiosaurus

Dinosaur National Park, in northeastern Utah, has been one of the richest sources of dinosaur fossils in the world. Fossils of many different types of dinosaurs have been discovered at the park, ranging from Nanosaurus, about 12 inches tall and weighing about 5 pounds to Brachiosaurus, about 40 feet tall and weighing about 50 tons.

Nanosaurus

45. *Palindrome*   A palindrome is a word (having 3 or more letters) that is spelled the same backward or forward. For instance, *pop*, *noon*, and *madam* are palindromes. In the English language, the longest palindrome is *tattarrattat*. Write an inequality that describes the number of letters, *p*, in a palindrome in the English language. (What does *tattarrattat* mean?)

46. *Ocean Temperature*   Let *t* represent the surface temperature of an ocean in degrees Fahrenheit. Write an inequality that describes the different surface temperatures of Earth's oceans.

The highest surface temperature of an ocean is 86°F at different locations near the equator. The lowest temperature is 28°F at the North and South Poles.

Coin Collection   **In Exercises 47 and 48, use the following information.**

Your grandfather has given you a sack of old coins that he had stored in his attic for several years. The sack is tied and has an old tag that reads, "$24.50 cash." You collect dimes and nickels, so you are anxious to see how many of each are in the sack. Let *d* represent the number of dimes and let *n* represent the number of nickels.

47. Write an inequality of *d* and *n* that describes the different numbers of dimes and nickels that could be in the sack.

48. Sketch a graph of the inequality. Is (0, 35) a solution? If so, what does it represent?

Frozen Yogurt   **In Exercises 49 and 50, use the following information.**

The softball team coach offers to buy frozen yogurt cones for each member of the team. Counting the coach, the team has 15 members. The coach has only $18 to spend on the cones. A large cone costs $1.35, and a small cone costs $0.90. Let *x* represent the number of large cones and let *y* represent the number of small cones.

49. Write an inequality that describes the different numbers of large and small cones the coach could buy.

50. Sketch the graph of the inequality. Is (15, 0) a solution of the graph? Can the coach afford large cones for all the players?

Fuel Use   **In Exercises 51–54, use the graph, which shows the average amount of fuel used per person in 1988 in several countries. (Traditional fuels are wood and other fuels that can be gathered or harnessed by an individual.)**

51. Which country in the list uses more traditional fuels than commercial fuels?

52. Estimate how much more energy the United States uses per person than Mexico uses per person.

53. Estimate the annual delivered energy per capita of commercial fuels used by the United States.

54. Estimate the annual delivered energy per capita of traditional fuels used by Brazil.

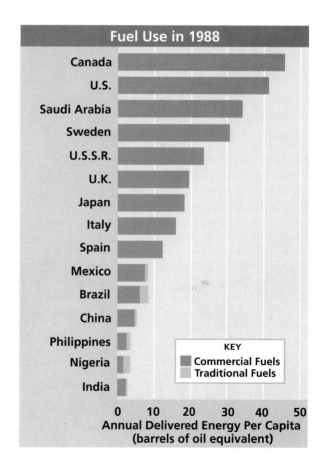

Fuel Use in 1988

Canada
U.S.
Saudi Arabia
Sweden
U.S.S.R.
U.K.
Japan
Italy
Spain
Mexico
Brazil
China
Philippines
Nigeria
India

0   10   20   30   40   50
Annual Delivered Energy Per Capita (barrels of oil equivalent)

KEY
Commercial Fuels
Traditional Fuels

Forest Fire   In Exercises 55–58, use the information in the diagram showing ecological stages of a forest fire in Yellowstone National Park.

Old-growth forest is struck by lightning. Forest burns. Most vegetation is destroyed. Lodgepole pines protect their seeds during the fire.

Stage 1. *Lodgepole pine saplings grow to 15 or 20 feet. Many species of animals return to the forest.*

55. Solve the inequalities to find the years for each of the four stages of regrowth.
Stage 1 $|x - 25| \leq 25$
Stage 2 $|x - 100| \leq 50$
Stage 3 $|x - 225| \leq 75$
Stage 4 $x - 300 \geq 0$

56. Use the solutions from Exercise 55 to create a time line showing the four stages of regrowth.

Stage 2. *Pines reach heights up to 50 feet and form dense stands that block the sun from the forest floor.*

57. How many forest fires occurred in Yellowstone during 1988? Of these, what percent were started by lightning?

58. How many acres of Yellowstone forest burned in 1988? How does this number compare with the number of acres that burned between 1972 and 1987?

Stage 3. *Lodgepole pines thin out. Second-generation trees appear. Increased sunlight aids vegetation growth on forest floor.*

Stage 4. *Original trees die. Dead branches and trees accumulate. The forest is again highly flammable.*

In Exercises 1–10, solve the inequality. Then sketch its graph.

1. $\frac{3}{4}x + 6 \leq 3$

2. $7 - x > 12$

3. $4x + 3 \leq 3x - 1$

4. $-(4 - x) \geq 2(3 - x)$

5. $-3x - 7 > 7x + 11$

6. $-6 \leq \frac{1}{4}(3 - x) \leq 12$

7. $8 < 3x - 4 < 17$

8. $2x + 1 \geq 7$ or $-3x - 4 \geq 2$

9. $\left|\frac{3}{5}x - 2\right| < 7$

10. $|8 - 3x| \geq 12$

In Exercises 11 and 12, write an absolute value inequality to fit the graph.

11.

12.

13. Which of the ordered pairs are solutions of $2x + 2y \geq 3$?

    a. $(0, 4)$ **b.** $\left(\frac{3}{4}, \frac{3}{4}\right)$ **c.** $\left(-1, -\frac{1}{2}\right)$

In Exercises 14–16, sketch the graph of the inequality.

14. $-3y + 2x \geq 6$

15. $6y - 2x + 2 < 8$

16. $2x + 4y \leq 6$

17. In 1984, the United States produced 68.7 million tons of paper and paperboard. Other countries' production of paper that year was Japan, 21.3 million tons; Canada, 15.7 million tons; the Soviet Union, 10.5 million tons; and West Germany, 10.1 million tons. Make a circle graph to compare the amounts of paper produced by these five leading paper producers.

18. The first step in producing paper is cutting the wood into chips $\frac{1}{2}$ inch to 1 inch long. Write an inequality to describe the size of the wood chips.

19. Paper is made in a continuous roll that can be up to 33 feet wide with a paper-making machine called the Fourdrinier machine. Write an inequality describing the possible widths a paper-making machine can produce. (Assume that the smallest width is 12 feet.)

20. Several friends go rafting on the Deschutes River in Oregon. The group rents six rafts and launches all the rafts at the same time. Write an inequality that describes the average rates (in miles per hour) for the six rafts.

The first raft to finish the 3-mile trip takes 45 minutes. The last raft to finish takes 60 minutes.

In Exercises 1–4, write equations of the horizontal line and the vertical line that pass through the point.

1. $(-3, 4)$ $\left(-2, -\frac{1}{2}\right)$ **3.** $(7, 6.2)$ **4.** $\left(0, -\frac{4}{3}\right)$

In Exercises 5–8, find the slope and *y*-intercept of the line. Sketch the graph of the line.

5. $y = -3x + 2$ **6.** $y = 2\left(\frac{2}{3}x - 4\right)$ **7.** $3x + 2y = 14$ **8.** $\frac{1}{3}y - 6x = 4$

In Exercises 9–12, find the slope of the line containing the points.

9. $(6, -2), (0, 5)$ **10.** $(3, 7), (-6, 7)$ **11.** $\left(\frac{1}{2}, \frac{3}{4}\right), (-3, 6)$ **12.** $(5, 5), (20, 25)$

In Exercises 13–16, match the equation with its graph.

13. $y = 3x - 1$ **14.** $y = -\frac{1}{4}x + 2$ **15.** $y = \frac{1}{2}x + 3$ **16.** $y = -x - 2$

a.   **b.**   **c.**   **d.**

In Exercises 17–20, write an equation of the line that has the given slope and passes through the given point.

17. $m = 3, (4, 9)$ **18.** $m = -\frac{1}{2}, (5, 0)$ **19.** $m = -5, (-3, 6)$ **20.** $m = \frac{7}{3}, (0, 3)$

In Exercises 21–24, write an equation of the line that passes through the two points.

21. $(0, 6), (4, 9)$ **22.** $\left(\frac{2}{3}, -1\right), \left(\frac{4}{9}, 7\right)$

23. $(4.2, -3.6), (7.0, 3.4)$ **24.** $(56, 19), (37, -19)$

In Exercises 25–28, complete the table. Then sketch the graph of the equation.

25. $y = -|x + 2| - 3$

x	−4	−3	−2	−1	0	1
y	?	?	?	?	?	?

26. $y = \frac{1}{3}|x - 4| + 6$

x	1	2	3	4	5	6	7
y	?	?	?	?	?	?	?

27. $y = -2|x + 2| - 2$

x	−4	−3	−2	−1	0	1
y	?	?	?	?	?	?

28. $y = |4x - 4| + 6$

x	−2	−1	0	1	2	3	4
y	?	?	?	?	?	?	?

In Exercises 29–32, find the vertex of the graph.

29. $y = |x + 3| - 6$ **30.** $y = |2x - 4| - 9$ **31.** $y = \frac{1}{2}|x + 4| + 4$ **32.** $y = -3|x + 6| + 1$

In Exercises 33–36, match the inequality with its graph.

33. $x \leq 3$ **34.** $-1 < x \leq 2$ **35.** $x \geq -3$ **36.** $x < 1$ or $x > 2$

a.

b.

c.

d.

In Exercises 37–40, solve the inequality. Then match the inequality with its graph.

37. $|x - 2| < 4$ **38.** $|4x - 6| \leq 4$ **39.** $\left|\frac{1}{4}x + 2\right| > 1$ **40.** $\left|x + \frac{3}{2}\right| \geq \frac{3}{2}$

a.

b.

c.

d.

In Exercises 41–44, sketch the graph of the inequality.

41. $-2x + 3y \geq x + 9$ **42.** $\frac{1}{2}x + 2y > 4$ **43.** $-\frac{1}{2}(2x + y) < 1$ **44.** $-y \geq 3x - 1$

Popcorn and Peanuts **In Exercises 45 and 46, use the following information.**

At a baseball game you are selling popcorn for $1.00 per box and peanuts for $1.50 per bag. Total sales for the day are $150. Let x be the number of boxes of popcorn sold and y the number of bags of peanuts sold.

45. Sketch a graph that shows the possible values of x and y.

46. If you sold 36 bags of peanuts, how many boxes of popcorn were sold?

Savings Plan **In Exercises 47–50, use the following information.**

At the beginning of the school year, you put $20 in a savings account. During the school year, you plan to deposit $3 a week in the account.

47. Write an equation that gives the account balance, y, in terms of the number of weeks, x. (Do not count interest.)

48. Sketch the graph of the equation.

49. What does the slope represent?

50. What does the y-intercept represent?

You want to save enough money to buy a season ticket for the local hockey team. Since ticket prices haven't been announced, you are not sure how much to save. Prices for a season ticket for the past six years are shown in the table.

Season	1986–87	1987–88	1988–89	1989–90	1990–91	1991–92
Price	$200	$210	$225	$225	$240	$250

51. Sketch a scatter plot for the data in the table. Let $x = 0$ represent the 1986–87 season. Let y represent the ticket price.

52. Sketch the best-fitting line. Find an equation for the line.

53. What does the slope represent?

54. How much should you save to buy a season ticket?

History of Computers   **In Exercises 55–60, use the following information.**

In 5000 B.C., the abacus was invented by the Chinese. The following time line shows several other important dates in the history of calculating devices. Use the time line to match the inventor with the invention.

55. Blaise Pascal (1623–1662)

56. Charles Babbage (1791–1871)

57. William Oughtred (1574–1660)

58. Herman Hollerith (1860–1929)

    a. First adding machine

    b. Analytic machine

    c. Census machine

    d. Slide rule

59. *Slide Rule*   The slide rule was used by engineers and scientists to make calculations before the widespread availability of hand-held calculators. How many years was the slide rule used in making calculations?

60. *UNIVAC I*   In 1951, *UNIVAC I* became the first computer to be designed for business use. CBS News used it the following year to predict the winner of the presidential election. Who was elected President that year?

Jury Duty   **In Exercises 61 and 62, use the following information.**

The circle graph at the right shows the results of a survey in which members of juries were asked why they had been willing to serve. *(Source: The Defense Research Institute)*

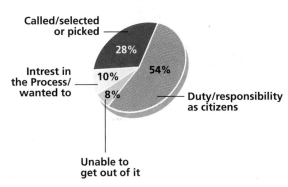

**Why Citizens
Serve on Juries**

Called/selected
or picked

28%

Intrest in
the Process/
wanted to   10%   54%

8%   Duty/responsibility
as citizens

Unable to
get out of it

61. A trial jury usually consists of 12 members. How many of the 12 jurors would you expect to be serving on the jury because they felt it was their responsibility?

62. Out of 75 people who have served on a jury, how many would you expect to have served because they were unable to get out of jury duty?

Wild Geese   **In Exercises 63–65, use the following information.**

There are more than 40 species of wild geese in the world. The adult birds typically weigh between $3\frac{1}{4}$ and $8\frac{3}{4}$ pounds. Geese are migratory birds, flying south for the winter and north for the summer. When migrating, the snow goose can fly 1700 miles in $2\frac{1}{2}$ days.

63. What is the average speed of a migrating snow goose?

64. A duck's migration journey is usually shorter than a goose's. If a duck travels 975 miles in 24 hours, is it traveling faster or slower than a snow goose?

65. Write a compound inequality for the weight of adult geese.

Flying Formation   **In Exercises 66 and 67, use the following information.**

The graph at the right shows the flying pattern used by migrating geese. Some naturalists believe the flock follows a single lead bird during the entire migratory flight. Others believe that the lead bird changes and that the V-formation creates air currents that make flying easier for the rest of the birds.

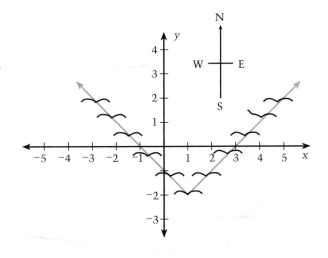

66. Write an absolute value equation that models the flying formation shown in the coordinate plane.

67. The flying formation at the right is heading south. Write an absolute value equation of a flying formation heading north.

Solving Systems of
Linear Equations

7.1 Solving Linear
Systems by Graphing
▪ 346

7.2 Solving Linear
Systems by
Substitution ▪ 353

7.3 Solving Linear
Systems by Linear
Combinations ▪ 360

7.4 Problem Solving
Using Linear Systems
▪ 367

7.5 Special Types of
Linear Systems ▪ 374

7.6 Solving Systems of
Linear Inequalities
▪ 381

7.7 Exploring Data:
Linear Programming
▪ 387

According to the data analyzed on the opposite page, the slogan "Made in the U.S.A." may have special significance for this woman working in the garment industry.

Real Life
The Garment Industry

Made in the U.S.A.

Value (in billions of dollars)

24
20
16 — Domestic
12
8
4
0

Import

80 81 82 83 84 85 86 87

Year

Between 1980 and 1987, the value of clothing manufactured in the United States increased from $17.1 billion to $22.5 billion. During the same years, the value of imported clothing increased from $6.4 billion to $20.5 billion. This tendency to import more and more clothing, together with automation in the garment industry, has contributed to the loss of over 100,000 jobs in the United States.

7.1

Solving Linear Systems by Graphing

What you should learn:

Goal 1 How to solve a system of linear equations by graphing

Goal 2 How to model a real-life situation using a system of linear equations

Why you should learn it:

You can model many real-life situations, such as multiple investments, with systems of linear equations. Graphing provides a visual model of situations and their solutions.

Goal 1 Graphing a Linear System

Until now, most of the problems in this text have involved just one equation in either one or two variables. Many real-life problems, however, involve two or more equations in two or more variables. For example, consider the following problem.

A total of $9000 is invested in two funds paying 5% and 6% annual interest. The combined annual interest is $510. How much of the $9000 is invested in each fund?

Letting x be the amount in the 5% fund and y be the amount in the 6% fund, you can model the problem with *two* linear equations.

$$\begin{cases} x + y = 9000 & \textit{Sum of two funds is \$9000.} \\ 0.05x + 0.06y = 510 & \textit{Total interest is \$510.} \end{cases}$$

These two equations form a **system of linear equations** or simply a **linear system.** (We will solve this linear system in Example 3.)

A **solution** of a system of linear equations in two variables is an ordered pair (a, b) that satisfies each equation.

Example 1   *Checking a Solution Algebraically*

Check that $(2, -1)$ is a solution of the system.

$$\begin{cases} 3x + 2y = 4 & \textit{Equation 1} \\ -x + 3y = -5 & \textit{Equation 2} \end{cases}$$

Solution   To check $(2, -1)$ as a solution, substitute 2 for x and -1 for y in each equation.

Equation 1: $3(2) + 2(-1) = 6 - 2 = 4$
Equation 2: $-(2) + 3(-1) = -2 - 3 = -5$ ■

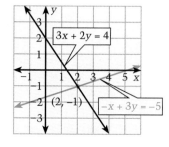

Graphic Check

Sketch a quick graph of each equation and find the point at which the two lines intersect. For instance, quick graphs at the left of the two linear equations of Example 1 suggest that they do indeed share $(2, -1)$ as a solution.

Example **2** *The Graph-and-Check Method*

Solve the system.

$$\begin{cases} x + y = -2 & \textit{Equation 1} \\ 2x - 3y = -9 & \textit{Equation 2} \end{cases}$$

Solution To sketch the two lines, first write the equations in slope-intercept form.

$$\begin{cases} y = -x - 2 & \textit{Slope: } -1, \textit{ y-intercept: } -2 \\ y = \frac{2}{3}x + 3 & \textit{Slope: } \frac{2}{3}, \textit{ y-intercept: } 3 \end{cases}$$

The two lines appear to intersect at $(-3, 1)$. To check this, substitute -3 for x and 1 for y in *each* equation in the original system.

Equation 1: $(-3) + (1) = -3 + 1 = -2$
Equation 2: $2(-3) - 3(1) = -6 - 3 = -9$ ∎

Real Life

Finance

Example **3** *Finding the Amounts Invested*

A total of $9000 is invested in two funds paying 5% and 6% annual interest. The combined annual interest is $510. How much of the $9000 is invested in each fund?

Solution

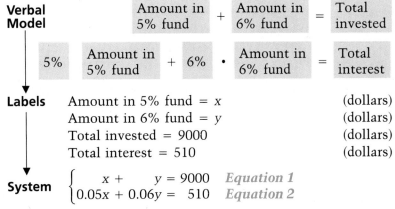

Verbal Model	Amount in 5% fund	+	Amount in 6% fund	=	Total invested

| | 5% | Amount in 5% fund | + 6% • | Amount in 6% fund | = | Total interest |

Labels   Amount in 5% fund = x (dollars)
Amount in 6% fund = y (dollars)
Total invested = 9000 (dollars)
Total interest = 510 (dollars)

System $\begin{cases} x + y = 9000 & \textit{Equation 1} \\ 0.05x + 0.06y = 510 & \textit{Equation 2} \end{cases}$

The first line has intercepts at $(9000, 0)$ and $(0, 9000)$. The second line has intercepts at $(10{,}200, 0)$ and $(0, 8500)$. The graphs of the two lines appear to intersect at $(3000, 6000)$. This solution *checks* with the original statement of the problem.

Graphic Check

$3000 + 6000 = 9000$ *Sum of funds is $9000.*
$0.05(3000) + 0.06(6000) = 510$ *Total interest is $510.* ∎

Example **4** Health-Care Careers

Use the matrix below to approximate the year in which the number of health-care workers in nonhospital jobs would equal the number in hospital jobs. (Assume that numbers in both types of employment fit linear models.)

Connections
Discrete Mathematics

Employees (in millions)

	1985	1990
Hospital	4.3	4.8
Nonhospital	3.6	4.6

Solution Let t represent the year, with $t = 0$ corresponding to 1985. Let y represent the number of employees in millions. From 1985 to 1990, the number of workers in hospitals increased at a rate of 0.1 million workers per year. During that same time, the number of nonhospital health-care workers increased at a rate of 0.2 million workers per year. Using the slope-intercept form, you can write the following models.

$$\begin{cases} y = 0.1t + 4.3 & \textit{Health-care workers (hospital)} \\ y = 0.2t + 3.6 & \textit{Health-care workers (nonhospital)} \end{cases}$$

From the graph, you can see that the number of nonhospital workers would equal the number of hospital workers in 1991 or 1992. *(Source: U.S. Bureau of Labor Statistics)*

In the graph: $y = .1t + 4.3$ and $y = .2t + 3.6$, with axes "Millions of Employees" and "Year (0 ↔ 1985)".

Communicating about **ALGEBRA**

▷ **SHARING IDEAS about the Lesson**

Use Models   You should be able to use both the algebraic and the graphical models of a linear system.

A. Explain what it means to *solve* a system of linear equations.

B. Check whether $(-3, 1)$ is a solution of the system.

$$\begin{cases} -4x + 5y = 17 & \textit{Equation 1} \\ 9x + y = -17 & \textit{Equation 2} \end{cases}$$

C. Use the graph-and-check method to solve the system.

$$\begin{cases} 2x - y = 8 & \textit{Equation 1} \\ -x + 2y = -1 & \textit{Equation 2} \end{cases}$$

EXERCISES

Guided Practice

▶ **CRITICAL THINKING about the Lesson**

In Exercises 1–3, use the system of linear equations at the right.

$$\begin{cases} 4x - 2y = 8 \\ -3x + 6y = 3 \end{cases}$$

1. Graph the system.

2. From the graph, which of the following appears to be a solution of the system: $(3, 2), (3, -2), (-3, 2), (-3, -2)$?

3. Confirm your answer for Exercise 2 algebraically. Show, algebraically, why one of the pairs in Exercise 2 is not a solution of the system.

In Exercises 4–6, graph and check to solve the system.

4. $\begin{cases} y = x + 1 \\ y = -x + 5 \end{cases}$

5. $\begin{cases} y = -\frac{1}{2}x + 4 \\ y = 2x - 6 \end{cases}$

6. $\begin{cases} 3x - y = 5 \\ -x + 2y = 0 \end{cases}$

Independent Practice

In Exercises 7–12, decide whether the ordered pairs are solutions of the system.

7. $\begin{cases} 3x + 2y = 4 \\ -x + 3y = -5 \end{cases}$ $(2, -1), (-3, 2)$

8. $\begin{cases} x + y = 6 \\ 2x - 5y = 10 \end{cases}$ $(3, 3), (4, 2)$

9. $\begin{cases} x + y = -2 \\ 2x - 3y = -9 \end{cases}$ $(-2, 3), (-3, 1)$

10. $\begin{cases} 4x - 5y = 0 \\ 6x - 5y = 10 \end{cases}$ $(5, 4), (10, 8)$

11. $\begin{cases} 2x + y = 4 \\ 4x + 3y = 9 \end{cases}$ $(\frac{5}{2}, 2), (\frac{3}{2}, 1)$

12. $\begin{cases} 3x - 2y = -4 \\ -4x + 3y = 5 \end{cases}$ $(0, 2), (-2, -1)$

In Exercises 13–16, solve the linear system.

13. $\begin{cases} 2x + y = 4 \\ x - y = 2 \end{cases}$

14. $\begin{cases} x + 3y = 2 \\ -x + 2y = 3 \end{cases}$

15. $\begin{cases} x - y = 0 \\ 3x - 2y = -1 \end{cases}$

16. $\begin{cases} 2x - y = 2 \\ 4x + 3y = 24 \end{cases}$

In Exercises 17–36, graph and check to solve the system.

17. $\begin{cases} y = -x + 3 \\ y = x + 1 \end{cases}$

18. $\begin{cases} y = -x \\ y = x \end{cases}$

19. $\begin{cases} y = 2x - 4 \\ y = -\frac{1}{2}x + 1 \end{cases}$

20. $\begin{cases} y = -2x + 6 \\ y = 2x + 2 \end{cases}$

21. $\begin{cases} 3x - 4y = 5 \\ x = 3 \end{cases}$

22. $\begin{cases} 5x + 4y = 18 \\ y = 2 \end{cases}$

23. $\begin{cases} 4x - 3y = -6 \\ 4x - 2y = 0 \end{cases}$

24. $\begin{cases} 3x + 6y = 15 \\ -2x + 3y = -3 \end{cases}$

25. $\begin{cases} 2x - 3y = 8 \\ 4x + 3y = -2 \end{cases}$ **26.** $\begin{cases} -4x + 3y = 10 \\ 7x + y = 20 \end{cases}$ **27.** $\begin{cases} x - 8y = -40 \\ -5x + 8y = 8 \end{cases}$ **28.** $\begin{cases} -x + 5y = 6 \\ 2x - 6y = -4 \end{cases}$

29. $\begin{cases} 4x + 5y = 20 \\ \frac{5}{4}x + y = 4 \end{cases}$ **30.** $\begin{cases} -3x + 4y = -5 \\ 4x + 2y = -8 \end{cases}$ **31.** $\begin{cases} x + y = -1 \\ 2x - y = -8 \end{cases}$ **32.** $\begin{cases} -3x + y = 10 \\ -x + 2y = 0 \end{cases}$

33. $\begin{cases} x + 3y = 11 \\ -x + 3y = 7 \end{cases}$ **34.** $\begin{cases} 3x - y = -2 \\ x - 3y = 2 \end{cases}$ **35.** $\begin{cases} 2x + y = 5 \\ 3x - 5y = 1 \end{cases}$ **36.** $\begin{cases} x + 7y = -5 \\ 3x - 2y = 8 \end{cases}$

37. *Investment Problem*   A total of $12,000 is invested in two funds paying 5% and $7\frac{1}{2}$% annual interest. The combined annual interest is $850. Copy the following verbal model. Assign labels. Then solve the resulting linear system to find how much of the $12,000 is invested in each fund.

$$\boxed{\text{Amount in 5\% fund}} + \boxed{\text{Amount in } 7\frac{1}{2}\text{\% fund}} = \boxed{\text{Total invested}}$$

$$\boxed{5\%} \cdot \boxed{\text{Amount in 5\% fund}} + \boxed{7\frac{1}{2}\%} \cdot \boxed{\text{Amount in } 7\frac{1}{2}\text{\% fund}} = \boxed{\text{Total interest}}$$

38. *Investment Problem*   A total of $25,000 is invested in two funds paying 5% and 6% annual interest. The combined annual interest is $1400. How much of the $25,000 is invested in each fund?

39. *Living by the Coast*   The matrix gives the percents of Americans who live in a county that is within 50 miles of a coastal shoreline (including the Great Lakes shoreline, but excluding Hawaii or Alaska) and who live further inland. For each location, use a linear model to represent the percent living there at time t, with $t = 0$ corresponding to 1940. Sketch the graphs of the resulting linear equations. From the graphs, estimate when the percent who lived near the coast equaled the percent who lived inland.
(Source: U.S. Bureau of Census)

Population	1940	1990
Near Coast	46%	53%
Interior	54%	47%

The coastal region of the 48 contiguous U.S. states contains 467,000 square miles, or 16% of the total land area. The population density in the coastal region is six times the population density in the interior.

KEY
.... Coastal Shoreline
☐ Coastal States
▨ Interior States

40. *Color or Monochrome?*   The matrix gives the number of monochrome and color computer monitors sold in the United States in 1984 and in 1990. For each type of monitor, use a linear model to represent the sales. (Let t represent the year with $t = 0$ corresponding to 1984.) Sketch the graphs of the resulting linear equations. From the graphs, estimate when the number of color monitors sold will equal the number of monochrome monitors sold.
(Source: DataPro, Inc.)

Monitors (in millions)

$$\begin{array}{c} \\ \text{Monochrome} \\ \text{Color} \end{array} \begin{array}{cc} 1984 & 1990 \\ \left[\begin{array}{cc} 6.9 & 24.3 \\ 3.1 & 21.7 \end{array} \right. & \left] \begin{array}{c} \\ \\ \end{array} \right. \end{array}$$

Integrated Review

In Exercises 41–44, decide whether the ordered pair is a solution of the equation.

41. $y = 3x + 11$, $(3, 2)$

42. $y = 5x - 7$, $(3, 8)$

43. $y = 8x - 4$, $(-1, 12)$

44. $y = 6x + 2$, $(2, -10)$

In Exercises 45–48, graph the equation.

45. $2x + y = 4$

46. $5x - 2y = 3$

47. $x + 4y = 8$

48. $-x - 3y = 12$

In Exercises 49–52, find an equation of the line passing through the two points.

49. $(-1, 3)$, $(4, 8)$

50. $(2, 6)$, $(5, 1)$

51. $(-2, -7)$, $(5, 1)$

52. $(3, -1)$, $(2, 8)$

In Exercises 53–56, find the slope of the line.

53. $3x + 6y = 4$

54. $7x - 4y = 10$

55. $2x - 8y = 12$

56. $-5x + 2y = 7$

In Exercises 57–60, solve for y. Then evaluate y for the given value of x.

57. $3x + y = 5$; $x = 2$

58. $-x + 4y = 7$; $x = 9$

59. $-2x + 5y = 4$; $x = -3$

60. $6x - 8y = 22$; $x = -1$

Exploration and Extension

Red Meat or Poultry   **In Exercises 61 and 62, use the following information.**

The table shows the average amounts of red meat and poultry eaten by Americans each year.

Year	1970	1975	1980	1985	1990
Red Meat	152 lb	139 lb	146 lb	141 lb	131 lb
Poultry	48 lb	50 lb	60 lb	68 lb	91 lb

61. Create scatter plots for the amounts of red meat and poultry eaten. Then approximate the best-fitting lines for the data. (Let t represent the year with $t = 0$ corresponding to 1970.)

62. Do you think that the average number of pounds of poultry eaten by Americans will ever equal the average number of pounds of red meat eaten? Explain.

A graphing calculator or computer can be used to graph a system of linear equations. Here we show how to use a Texas Instruments TI-81 and a Casio fx-7700G to graph the following system.

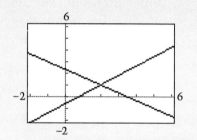

$$\begin{cases} 2x + 3y = 7 & \text{\textit{Equation 1}} \\ 4x - 5y = 3 & \text{\textit{Equation 2}} \end{cases}$$

The display at the right shows the graph of the system. Note that the two lines appear to intersect at the point (2, 1). To check this, substitute 2 for x and 1 for y in each equation.

Graph of Linear System

TI-81

Solve Equation 1 for y: $y = -\frac{2}{3}x + \frac{7}{3}$

Solve Equation 2 for y: $y = \frac{4}{5}x - \frac{3}{5}$

$\boxed{RANGE}$ (Set range.)

  Xmin $= -2$
  Xmax $= 6$
  Xscl $= 1$
  Ymin $= -2$
  Ymax $= 6$
  Yscl $= 1$

$\boxed{Y=}$ $\boxed{(}$ $\boxed{(-)}$ 2 $\boxed{\div}$ 3 $\boxed{)}$ $\boxed{X\,T}$
$\boxed{+}$ $\boxed{(}$ 7 $\boxed{\div}$ 3 $\boxed{)}$ $\boxed{ENTER}$
$\boxed{(}$ 4 $\boxed{\div}$ 5 $\boxed{)}$ $\boxed{X\,T}$
$\boxed{-}$ $\boxed{(}$ 3 $\boxed{\div}$ 5 $\boxed{)}$

  :Y$_1$ = (−2/3)X + (7/3)
  :Y$_2$ = (4/5)X − (3/5)
  :Y$_3$ =
  :Y$_4$ =

$\boxed{GRAPH}$

$\boxed{CLEAR}$ (Clear screen.)

Casio fx-7700G

Solve Equation 1 for y: $y = -\frac{2}{3}x + \frac{7}{3}$

Solve Equation 2 for y: $y = \frac{4}{5}x - \frac{3}{5}$

$\boxed{Range}$ (Set range.)

  Xmin $= -2$
  max $= 6$
  scl $= 1$
  Ymin $= -2$
  max $= 6$
  scl $= 1$

$\boxed{EXE}$ $\boxed{Range}$
$\boxed{SHIFT}$ $\boxed{F5}$ (Cls) $\boxed{EXE}$
$\boxed{MODE}$ $\boxed{SHIFT}$ $\boxed{+}$
$\boxed{Graph}$ $\boxed{(}$ $\boxed{(-)}$ 2 $\boxed{\div}$ 3 $\boxed{)}$ $\boxed{X,\theta,T}$
    $\boxed{+}$ $\boxed{(}$ 7 $\boxed{\div}$ 3 $\boxed{)}$
  Graph Y = (−2 ÷ 3)X + (7 ÷ 3) $\boxed{EXE}$
$\boxed{Graph}$ $\boxed{(}$ 4 $\boxed{\div}$ 5 $\boxed{)}$ $\boxed{X,\theta,T}$
    $\boxed{-}$ $\boxed{(}$ 3 $\boxed{\div}$ 5 $\boxed{)}$
  Graph Y = (4 ÷ 5)X − (3 ÷ 5) $\boxed{EXE}$
$\boxed{SHIFT}$ $\boxed{F5}$ (Cls) $\boxed{EXE}$

Exercises

In Exercises 1–4, use a graphing calculator to solve the linear system. (Use an appropriate range setting and check your result in each of the original equations.)

1. $\begin{cases} 2x - 5y = -6 \\ 3x - 2y = 2 \end{cases}$

2. $\begin{cases} 3x + y = -2 \\ 4x + y = -4 \end{cases}$

3. $\begin{cases} -0.25x - y = 2.25 \\ -1.25x + 1.25y = -1.25 \end{cases}$

4. $\begin{cases} 0.8x + 0.6y = -1.2 \\ 1.25x - 1.5y = 12.75 \end{cases}$

7.2

Solving Linear Systems by Substitution

What you should learn:

Goal 1 How to use substitution to solve a linear system

Goal 2 How to model a real-life situation using a system of linear equations

Why you should learn it:

You can model many real-life situations, such as cost comparisons, with linear systems. Some systems can be solved easily using substitution.

Goal 1 Substituting to Solve a Linear System

In this lesson, you will study an algebraic method—substitution—for solving a linear system. The basic steps in the method are as follows.

1. *Solve* one of the equations for one of its variables.

2. *Substitute* this expression into the other equation and solve for the other variable.

3. *Substitute* this value into the revised first equation and solve.

4. *Check* the solution pair in each of the original equations.

Example 1 *The Substitution Method*

Solve the linear system.

$$\begin{cases} -x + y = 1 & \textit{Equation 1} \\ 2x + y = -2 & \textit{Equation 2} \end{cases}$$

Solution Begin by solving Equation 1 for y.

$$y = x + 1 \qquad \textit{Revised Equation 1}$$

Substitute this expression for y in Equation 2 and solve for x.

$$\begin{array}{ll} 2x + y = -2 & \textit{Equation 2} \\ 2x + (x + 1) = -2 & \textit{Substitute } x + 1 \textit{ for } y. \\ 3x + 1 = -2 & \textit{Simplify.} \\ 3x = -3 & \textit{Subtract 1 from both sides.} \\ x = -1 & \textit{Solve for } x. \end{array}$$

You now know that the value of x in the solution is -1. To find the value of y, substitute the value of x into the revised Equation 1.

$$\begin{array}{ll} y = x + 1 & \textit{Revised Equation 1} \\ y = -1 + 1 & \textit{Substitute } -1 \textit{ for } x. \\ y = 0 & \textit{Solve for } y. \end{array}$$

The solution is $(-1, 0)$. Check to see that it satisfies each of the original equations. ∎

When using the substitution method, you will obtain the same solution (x, y) whether you solve for y first or x first. Thus, you should begin by solving for the variable that is more efficient to isolate. For instance, in the system

$$\begin{cases} 3x - 2y = 1 & \textit{Equation 1} \\ x + 4y = 3 & \textit{Equation 2} \end{cases}$$

it is easier to first solve the second equation for x. On the other hand, in the system

$$\begin{cases} 2x + y = 5 & \textit{Equation 1} \\ 3x - 2y = 11 & \textit{Equation 2} \end{cases}$$

it is easier to first solve the first equation for y.

If neither variable has a coefficient of 1 or -1, you can still use the substitution method. In such cases, however, the method discussed in Lesson 7.3 is usually more efficient.

Example 2   *The Substitution Method*

Solve the linear system.

$$\begin{cases} 2x + 2y = 3 & \textit{Equation 1} \\ x - 4y = -1 & \textit{Equation 2} \end{cases}$$

Solution   Begin by solving Equation 2 for x.

$$x = 4y - 1 \qquad \textit{Revised Equation 2}$$

Substitute this expression for x in Equation 1 and solve for y.

$$
\begin{aligned}
2x + 2y &= 3 && \textit{Equation 1} \\
2(4y - 1) + 2y &= 3 && \textit{Substitute } 4y - 1 \textit{ for } x. \\
10y - 2 &= 3 && \textit{Simplify.} \\
10y &= 5 && \textit{Add 2 to both sides.} \\
y &= \tfrac{1}{2} && \textit{Solve for } y.
\end{aligned}
$$

The value of y in the solution is $\frac{1}{2}$. To find the value of x, substitute this value into the revised Equation 2.

$$
\begin{aligned}
x &= 4y - 1 && \textit{Revised Equation 2} \\
x &= 4\left(\tfrac{1}{2}\right) - 1 && \textit{Substitute } \tfrac{1}{2} \textit{ for } y. \\
x &= 1 && \textit{Solve for } x.
\end{aligned}
$$

The solution is $\left(1, \frac{1}{2}\right)$. Check to see that it satisfies each of the original equations. ■

When you use the substitution method, you can still use a graphic check. For instance, the graph at the left shows a graphic check for the linear system in Example 2.

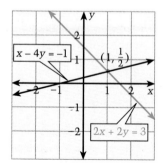

Graphic Check

Modeling a Real-Life Situation

A 4-bulb conventional fixture costs $50, plus $1 for each bulb. The fixture uses 175 watts.

A 2-bulb retrofit fixture costs $120, plus $1 for each bulb. The fixture uses 70 watts.

Cost of Lighting

(Graph: Total Cost (in dollars) on vertical axis from 50 to 200; Time (in hours) on horizontal axis labeled 2000 4000 6000 8000 t. Two lines labeled "Retrofit Fixture" and "Conventional Fixture".)

Example 3 *Comparing Costs*

You are building a convenience store and are considering two different types of fluorescent light fixtures: conventional and retrofit. A retrofit fixture is more expensive but uses less electricity. Electricity in your region costs $0.08 per kilowatt-hour. Show why a retrofit fixture can be considered more economical.

Solution The total cost of buying and operating each type of fixture is given by the following verbal model.

Total cost	=	Fixture & bulb cost	+	Cost per kilowatt-hour	•	Number of kilowatts	•	Number of hours

Let y represent the total cost (in dollars) of buying and operating a fixture for t hours. The verbal model gives two linear equations, one for a conventional fixture and one for a retrofit fixture.

$$\begin{cases} y = \ \ 54 + (0.08)(0.175)t \quad \textit{Cost for conventional fixture} \\ y = 122 + (0.08)(0.070)t \quad \textit{Cost for retrofit fixture} \end{cases}$$

The graphs suggest that at a certain time the retrofit fixture becomes more economical. Using substitution, the solution of the system is $t \approx 8100$ hours and $y \approx \$167$. This means it becomes more economical after working for about 8100 hours (about 1 year at 24 hours a day). ∎

Communicating about ALGEBRA

Cooperative Learning

▶ **SHARING IDEAS about the Lesson**

Work with a Partner and Extend Information Extend the ideas of Example 3 to the following.

A. The convenience store has 8 light fixtures. How much would the two types of fixtures cost to purchase and operate for 2 years?

B. In 1990, there were 1.5 billion light fixtures in U.S. buildings. What are the potential energy savings per year for the U.S. by using more efficient light fixtures?

EXERCISES

▶ **CRITICAL THINKING about the Lesson**

In Exercises 1–4, use the following linear system.

$$\begin{cases} x + y = 9 & \text{\textit{Equation 1}} \\ 2x + 5y = 30 & \text{\textit{Equation 2}} \end{cases}$$

1. Solve Equation 1 for y.

2. Substitute the expression for y into Equation 2 and solve for x.

3. Substitute the value of x into Equation 1 and solve for y. What is the solution of the linear system?

4. Explain how you can check the solution algebraically and graphically.

Independent Practice

In Exercises 5–8, use substitution to solve the system. Use the graphs to check your solution.

5. $\begin{cases} x - y = 0 \\ x + y = 2 \end{cases}$

6. $\begin{cases} x + y = 1 \\ 2x - y = 2 \end{cases}$

7. $\begin{cases} 2x + y = 4 \\ -x + y = 1 \end{cases}$

8. $\begin{cases} x - y = -5 \\ x + 2y = 4 \end{cases}$

In Exercises 9–28, use substitution to solve the system.

9. $\begin{cases} y = x - 3 \\ 4x + y = 32 \end{cases}$

10. $\begin{cases} y = x + 4 \\ 3x + y = 16 \end{cases}$

11. $\begin{cases} 4x + 3y = 31 \\ y = 2x + 7 \end{cases}$

12. $\begin{cases} 4x + 5y = 48 \\ y = 3x + 2 \end{cases}$

13. $\begin{cases} 2x \quad\;\; = 5 \\ x + y = 1 \end{cases}$

14. $\begin{cases} 3x - y = 0 \\ \qquad y = 6 \end{cases}$

15. $\begin{cases} x - y = 2 \\ 2x + y = 1 \end{cases}$

16. $\begin{cases} x - 2y = -10 \\ 3x - y = 0 \end{cases}$

17. $\begin{cases} x - y = 0 \\ 2x + y = 0 \end{cases}$

18. $\begin{cases} x - 2y = 0 \\ 3x - y = 0 \end{cases}$

19. $\begin{cases} x - y = 0 \\ 5x - 3y = 10 \end{cases}$

20. $\begin{cases} x + 2y = 1 \\ 5x - 4y = -23 \end{cases}$

21. $\begin{cases} 2x - y = -2 \\ 4x + y = 5 \end{cases}$

22. $\begin{cases} -3x + 6y = 4 \\ 2x + y = 4 \end{cases}$

23. $\begin{cases} \frac{1}{5}x + \frac{1}{2}y = 8 \\ x + y = 20 \end{cases}$

24. $\begin{cases} \frac{1}{2}x + \frac{3}{4}y = 10 \\ \frac{3}{2}x - y = 4 \end{cases}$

25. $\begin{cases} -3x + y = 4 \\ -9x + 5y = 10 \end{cases}$

26. $\begin{cases} 5x + 3y = 11 \\ x - 5y = 5 \end{cases}$

27. $\begin{cases} x + 4y = 300 \\ x - 2y = 0 \end{cases}$

28. $\begin{cases} 3x + y = 13 \\ 2x - 4y = 18 \end{cases}$

29. *Buffet Dinner*   The cost of a buffet dinner for a family of six was $61.70 ($11.95 adults, $6.95 children). Assign labels to the verbal model below. Then solve the resulting linear system to find how many family members paid each price.

Number of people over 12	+	Number of people 12 & under	=	Total number

Price per person over 12	·	Number of people over 12	+	Price per person 12 & under	·	Number of people 12 & under	=	Total price

30. *Football Tickets*   You are selling tickets at a high school football game. Student tickets cost $2 and general admission tickets cost $3. You sell 1957 tickets and collect $5035. How many of each type of ticket did you sell?

31. *Comparing Costs*   One car model costs $12,000 and costs an average of $0.10 per mile to maintain. Another car model costs $14,000 and costs an average of $0.08 per mile to maintain. If one of each model is driven the same number of miles, after how many miles would the total cost of one model be the same as the other?

32. *Comparing Costs*   A discount grocery store offers two types of memberships with annual membership fees of $25 and $100. With the $25 membership, you get the "regular discount." With the $100 membership, you get an additional 10% discount. For how many dollars worth of undiscounted groceries would the two memberships cost the same?

Caught in the Doldrums   **In Exercises 33 and 34, use the following information.**

On May 3, 1976, a team of adventurers, piloted by a Caroline Islands navigator, sailed from Hawaii on a traditional twin-hulled canoe called the *Hokule'a*. Sailing into northeast trade winds, the canoe maintained a course represented on the chart by $y = -\frac{3}{2}x - 215$. Sailing into southeast trade winds, the canoe maintained a course corresponding to $y = 7x + 1026$. At the point of intersection of these two paths, the canoe was caught in the "doldrums" and made little headway for 5 or 6 days.

33. Find the coordinates of the doldrums.

34. The equation of the line passing through Hawaii and Tahiti on the chart is $36x + 7y = -5483$. Find the coordinates of Hawaii and Tahiti.

35. *Uphill and Downhill*   Suppose you can run 250 meters per minute downhill and 180 meters per minute uphill. One day you run 1557 meters in 7.6 minutes always either uphill or downhill. Assign labels to the verbal model. Then solve the resulting linear system to find the number of meters you ran uphill and downhill.

$$\boxed{\text{Meters uphill}} + \boxed{\text{Meters downhill}} = \boxed{\text{Total meters}}$$

$$\frac{\boxed{\text{Meters uphill}}}{\boxed{\text{Rate uphill}}} + \frac{\boxed{\text{Meters downhill}}}{\boxed{\text{Rate downhill}}} = \boxed{\text{Total time}}$$

36. *How Many of Each?*   Your math teacher tells you that next week's test is worth 100 points and contains 29 problems. Each problem is worth either 5 points or 2 points. Because you are studying systems of linear equations, your teacher says that for extra credit you should be able to figure out how many problems of each value are on the test. How many of each value are there?

Integrated Review

In Exercises 37–42, solve for *y*.

37. $2x + 3y = 8$

38. $x - 5y = 9$

39. $9x - 2y = 24$

40. $2x - 2y = 19$

41. $3x - 4y = 14$

42. $-6x + 8y = 36$

In Exercises 43–48, simplify the expression.

43. $(2x + 3y) + (-2x + 5y)$

44. $26 - (16y + 4) + (9y - x)$

45. $(x - 4y) - 14(3 - x) + y$

46. $(5y + 6x) - (4x - 3y)$

47. $2x(4 + x) - (y - 5)$

48. $9(y + 6) + (7x + y)(-3)$

In Exercises 49–52, solve the linear system by graphing.

49. $\begin{cases} x - y = 1 \\ 2x + y = 8 \end{cases}$

50. $\begin{cases} x - 2y = -10 \\ 4x + y = -4 \end{cases}$

51. $\begin{cases} x - 4y = 2 \\ 5x + y = -32 \end{cases}$

52. $\begin{cases} -x - y = 3 \\ 2x - y = 6 \end{cases}$

Exploration and Extension

53. *Dimensions of a Rectangle*   The area of the rectangle is *y* and the perimeter is $2y + 2$. What are the dimensions of the rectangle?

54. *Dimensions of a Triangle*   The area of the triangle is $3x$ and the perimeter is $5x - 4$. Find the length of each side of the triangle.

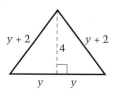

1. Simplify $3(x - 2) + (-4)^2$. **(2.6)**
2. Simplify $3(x - y) + 4x - y$. **(2.6)**
3. Evaluate $\frac{1}{3}(4 - x) + 2x$ when $x = \frac{1}{2}$. **(2.6)**
4. Evaluate $(|x| + 3)x + 2$ when $x = -3$. **(2.6)**
5. Solve $m(n + 1) + 2n = \frac{1}{2}$ for n. **(3.6)**
6. Solve $\frac{2}{3}r + 3s = 4$ for r. **(3.6)**
7. Solve $3y + \frac{1}{2}(4 - y) = 3$. **(3.2)**
8. Solve $|x + \frac{3}{4}| \leq 3$. **(6.1)**
9. Solve $|x - 2| - \frac{1}{4} > 0$. **(6.1)**
10. Solve $3(x - \frac{2}{3}) = \frac{1}{4}(2x + 3)$. **(3.2)**
11. What is the product of $\frac{3}{4}$ and $\frac{8}{9}$?
12. What is the quotient of $\frac{27}{5}$ and $\frac{9}{10}$?

13. Is 18 a solution for $\frac{7}{8}(x - 2) = 14$? **(1.2)**
14. Is -3 a solution for $\frac{1}{4}|x| - x \geq 0$? **(2.1)**

In Exercises 15–20, write an equation of the line that passes through the two points or that passes through the point and has the given slope. (5.2, 5.3)

15. $(-3, 2), (-4, 6)$
16. $(-4, 2), (-1, -3)$
17. $(-1, -1), (-3, -4)$
18. $(0, -2), m = -\frac{3}{2}$
19. $(4, -8), m = \frac{1}{4}$
20. $(2, 5), m = 0$

Career Interview

Pediatrician

Bettye Kearse is a pediatrician. In her practice, Dr. Kearse oversees the proper growth and development of children, as well as provides acute care during emergencies.

Q: *Did you always want to be a doctor?*
A: Well, I really thought I wanted to be a genetics researcher. While I found the results of research fascinating, I felt I needed a more people-oriented career. My father, grand-father, uncles, and husband are doctors, and found the practice of medicine personally fulfilling.

Q: *What math classes did you take in high school?*
A: I took algebra, geometry, and trigonometry. I liked math, especially algebra. I hate to admit it, but I had no math courses in college.

Q: *Does having a math background help you in your career?*
A: The main math application in pediatrics is in recommending medicinal dosages. Medicines for children are prescribed according to their weight. We use this rate: x mg per y kg of body mass.

7.3

Solving Linear Systems by Linear Combinations

What you should learn:

Goal 1 How to use linear combinations to solve a linear system

Goal 2 How to model a real-life situation using a system of linear equations

Why you should learn it:

You can model many real-life situations, such as compositions of chemical mixtures and compounds, with linear systems. Some systems are solved most easily using linear combinations.

Goal 1 Using Linear Combinations

In this lesson, you will learn a third way to solve a linear system—the *linear combination method.* The basic steps in this method are as follows.

1. *Arrange* the equations with like terms in columns.
2. *Study* the coefficients of x (or y). *Multiply* one or both equations by an appropriate number to obtain new coefficients for x (or y) that are opposites.
3. *Add* the equations and solve for the remaining variable.
4. *Substitute* the value obtained in Step 3 into either of the original equations and solve for the other variable.
5. *Check* the solution in each of the original equations.

Example 1 The Linear Combination Method

Solve the linear system.

$$\begin{cases} 4x + 3y = 1 & \text{\textit{Equation 1}} \\ 2x - 3y = 1 & \text{\textit{Equation 2}} \end{cases}$$

Solution In this linear system, the coefficients for y are opposites. By adding the two equations, you obtain an equation that has only one variable, x.

$$
\begin{array}{ll}
4x + 3y = 1 & \text{\textit{Equation 1}} \\
\underline{2x - 3y = 1} & \text{\textit{Equation 2}} \\
6x \qquad\;\; = 2 & \text{\textit{Sum of equations}}
\end{array}
$$

Therefore, $x = \frac{1}{3}$. By substituting this value into Equation 1, you can solve for y.

$$
\begin{array}{ll}
4x + 3y = 1 & \text{\textit{Equation 1}} \\
4\left(\frac{1}{3}\right) + 3y = 1 & \text{\textit{Substitute } \frac{1}{3} \text{ for x.}} \\
3y = -\frac{1}{3} & \text{\textit{Subtract } \frac{4}{3} \text{ from both sides.}} \\
y = -\frac{1}{9} & \text{\textit{Solve for y.}}
\end{array}
$$

The solution is $\left(\frac{1}{3}, -\frac{1}{9}\right)$. Check this solution in each of the original equations. ∎

To obtain coefficients (for one of the variables) that are opposites, you often need to multiply one or both of the equations by an appropriate number.

Example 2   *The Linear Combination Method*

Solve the linear system.

$$\begin{cases} 3x + 5y = 6 & \textit{Equation 1} \\ -4x + 2y = 5 & \textit{Equation 2} \end{cases}$$

Solution   You can obtain coefficients of x that are opposite by multiplying the first equation by 4 and multiplying the second equation by 3. By adding the resulting equations, you obtain an equation that has only one variable, y.

$$\begin{array}{lll} 3x + 5y = 6 & \rightarrow & 12x + 20y = 24 \quad \textit{Multiply by 4.} \\ -4x + 2y = 5 & \rightarrow & \underline{-12x + 6y = 15} \quad \textit{Multiply by 3.} \\ & & 26y = 39 \quad \textit{Sum of equations} \end{array}$$

Therefore, $y = \frac{3}{2}$. By substituting this value into Equation 2, you can solve for x.

$$\begin{array}{ll} -4x + 2y = 5 & \textit{Equation 2} \\ -4x + 2(\frac{3}{2}) = 5 & \textit{Substitute } \frac{3}{2} \textit{ for } y. \\ -4x + 3 = 5 & \textit{Simplify.} \\ -4x = 2 & \textit{Subtract 3 from both sides.} \\ x = -\frac{1}{2} & \textit{Solve for x.} \end{array}$$

The solution is $\left(-\frac{1}{2}, \frac{3}{2}\right)$. Check this solution in each of the original equations. ∎

Guidelines for Solving a System of Linear Equations

To decide which method (graphing, substitution, or linear combinations) to use to solve a system of linear equations, consider the following.

1. The *graphing* method is useful for approximating a solution, checking a solution, and for providing a visual model of the problem.

2. To find an exact solution, use either *substitution* or *linear combinations*.

3. For linear systems in which one variable has a coefficient of 1 or -1, *substitution* may be more efficient.

4. In other cases, the *linear combinations* method is usually more efficient.

Ever since Archimedes jumped out of his tub, yelling "Eureka!", science students have known how to use Archimedes' fluid-displacement principle to relate the *weight* of an object to its *volume*. This relationship enabled Archimedes to prove that his king's "gold" crown was a forgery.

Example **3**   *Exposing a Forgery*

A "gold" crown, suspected of containing some silver, was found to have a weight of 45 ounces, and a volume of 5 cubic inches. Gold weighs 11 ounces per cubic inch. Silver weighs 6 ounces per cubic inch. Is there silver mixed with the gold, and if so, how much?

Solution   Using a system of equations, you can model the effect that silver would have on the volume and weight of the crown.

Archimedes' Solution

1. Gold block balances crown.

2. Silver block balances crown.

3. Gold: low-water level.

4. Crown: mid-water level.

5. Silver: high-water level.

Verbal Model

| Gold volume | + | Silver volume | = | Total volume |

| Gold weight | + | Silver weight | = | Total weight |

Labels

Volume of gold $= G$ (cubic inches)
Volume of silver $= S$ (cubic inches)
Total volume $= 5$ (cubic inches)
Weight of gold $= 11G$ (ounces)
Weight of silver $= 6S$ (ounces)
Total weight $= 45$ (ounces)

System

$$\begin{cases} G + S = 5 & \text{\textit{Total volume is 5 cubic inches.}} \\ 11G + 6S = 45 & \text{\textit{Total weight is 45 ounces.}} \end{cases}$$

You can solve the system by multiplying the first equation by -6 and adding the result to the second equation to give $5G = 15$. The solution is $G = 3$ in.^{3} and $S = 2$ in.^{3}. ■

Communicating *about* **A L G E B R A**

▶ **SHARING IDEAS about the Lesson**

> ***Relate Ideas***   How is the five-step diagram of Archimedes' solution related to the "system solution" shown in Example 3?

EXERCISES

Guided Practice

▶ **CRITICAL THINKING about the Lesson**

In Exercises 1–3, use linear combinations to solve the system.

1. $\begin{cases} 2x + 3y = 7 \\ -2x + 2y = -2 \end{cases}$

2. $\begin{cases} 3x - 4y = 7 \\ 2x - y = 3 \end{cases}$

3. $\begin{cases} 2x + 3y = 1 \\ 5x - 4y = 14 \end{cases}$

In Exercises 4–6, solve the linear system by the method that you think is best. Explain why you chose that method.

4. $\begin{cases} 4x + 2y = 6 \\ -4x + 5y = 1 \end{cases}$

5. $\begin{cases} y = -2x + 4 \\ y = \frac{1}{2}x - 1 \end{cases}$

6. $\begin{cases} 4x + y = 9 \\ 7x - 8y = 6 \end{cases}$

Independent Practice

In Exercises 7–10, use linear combinations to solve the system. Use the graphs to check your solution.

7. $\begin{cases} 2x + y = 4 \\ x - y = 2 \end{cases}$

8. $\begin{cases} x + 3y = 2 \\ -x + 2y = 3 \end{cases}$

9. $\begin{cases} x - y = 0 \\ 3x - 2y = -1 \end{cases}$

10. $\begin{cases} 2x - y = 2 \\ 4x + 3y = 24 \end{cases}$

In Exercises 11–28, use linear combinations to solve the system.

11. $\begin{cases} x - y = 4 \\ x + y = 12 \end{cases}$

12. $\begin{cases} -x + 2y = 12 \\ x + 6y = 20 \end{cases}$

13. $\begin{cases} 3x - 5y = 1 \\ 2x + 5y = 9 \end{cases}$

14. $\begin{cases} x + 2y = 14 \\ x - 2y = 10 \end{cases}$

15. $\begin{cases} x + 7y = 12 \\ 3x - 5y = 10 \end{cases}$

16. $\begin{cases} 2x + 3y = 18 \\ 5x - y = 11 \end{cases}$

17. $\begin{cases} 5x + 2y = 7 \\ 3x - y = 13 \end{cases}$

18. $\begin{cases} 4x + 3y = 8 \\ x - 2y = 13 \end{cases}$

19. $\begin{cases} 3x + 2y = 10 \\ 2x + 5y = 3 \end{cases}$

20. $\begin{cases} 4x + 5y = 7 \\ 6x - 2y = -18 \end{cases}$

21. $\begin{cases} 6x - 5y = 3 \\ -12x + 8y = 5 \end{cases}$

22. $\begin{cases} \frac{2}{3}x + \frac{1}{6}y = \frac{2}{3} \\ 3x - y = 12 \end{cases}$

23. $\begin{cases} 2u + v = 120 \\ u + 2v = 120 \end{cases}$

24. $\begin{cases} 5u + 6v = 14 \\ 3u + 5v = 7 \end{cases}$

25. $\begin{cases} 3a + 3b = 7 \\ 3a + 5b = 3 \end{cases}$

26. $\begin{cases} 5a + 4b = 4 \\ 4a + 5b = \frac{31}{8} \end{cases}$

27. $\begin{cases} 10m + 16n = 140 \\ 5m - 8n = 60 \end{cases}$

28. $\begin{cases} 7m - 13n = 14 \\ 28m - 39n = 35 \end{cases}$

29. *Focal Length of a Camera* When parallel rays of light pass through a convex lens, they are bent inward and meet at a *focus*. The distance from the center of the lens to the focus is called the *focal length*. The equations of the lines containing the two bent light rays in the camera are

$$\begin{cases} x + 3y = 1 \\ -x + 3y = -1 \end{cases}$$

where x and y are measured in inches. Which of these equations is the upper ray? What is the focal length?

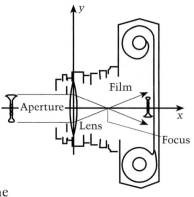

30. *Waggle Dance* Two bees have each found a food source. The first bee's path back to the hive follows the line $y = \frac{4}{5}x$. The second bee's path follows the line $y = -2x + 3$. Their paths cross at the hive. Find the coordinates of the hive.

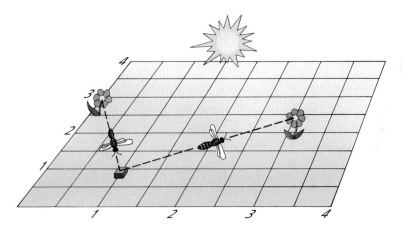

The waggle dance of a scout bee communicates the direction and distance of a food source. When the direction of the food source is the same as that of the sun, the waggle dance points straight up on the vertical honeycomb. When the source is 60° to the left of the sun, the waggle dance is oriented 60° to the left of vertical.

31. *Airplane Speed* It took 3 hours for an airplane, flying against a head wind, to travel the 900 miles from Birmingham, Alabama, to Duluth, Minnesota. On this portion of the trip, the "ground speed" of the plane was 300 miles per hour. On the return trip, the flight took only 2 hours, with a ground speed of 450 miles per hour. During both flights, the speed and direction of the wind and the airspeed of the plane were constant. Assign labels to the verbal model. Then solve the resulting equation to find the speed of the wind and the airspeed of the plane.

| Airspeed | − | Wind speed | = | Ground speed against wind |

| Airspeed | + | Wind speed | = | Ground speed with wind |

32. *Boat Speed* A motorboat went 10 miles upstream in 1 hour. The return trip took only 30 minutes. Assume that the "water speed" and the current speed were constant during both parts of the trip. Find the water speed of the boat and the current speed.

33. *Gold Bracelet*   A bracelet that is supposed to be 18-karat gold weighs 238 grams. The volume of the bracelet is 15 cubic centimeters. The bracelet is made of gold and copper. Gold weighs 19.3 grams per cubic centimeter, and copper weighs 9 grams per cubic centimeter. Is the bracelet really 18-karat gold?

34. *Acid Mixture*   You are making an acid solution in science class. Five liters of the 40% acid solution are obtained by mixing a 20% solution with a 60% solution. How much of each must you use?

Jewelry is rarely made of 24-karat gold (which means 100% gold) because gold is a soft metal. Other metals such as copper are mixed with the gold to obtain greater strength. An 18-karat gold piece contains three-fourths gold (by weight) and one-fourth of some other metal.

Integrated Review

In Exercises 35–38, match the linear system with its correct graph. Then use linear combinations to solve the system.

35. $\begin{cases} 9x - 3y = -1 \\ 3x + 6y = -5 \end{cases}$
36. $\begin{cases} 5x + 3y = 18 \\ 2x - 7y = -1 \end{cases}$
37. $\begin{cases} x - 2y = 5 \\ 6x + 2y = 7 \end{cases}$
38. $\begin{cases} -6x + 4y = -12 \\ 3x - 4y = 8 \end{cases}$

a.   **b.**   **c.**   **d.**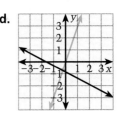

39. *College Entrance Exam Sample*   Given the system of equations $3x + 2y = 4$ and $6x - 3y = 6$, what does y equal?

   a. 14   **b.** $\frac{14}{6}$ **c.** 2   **d.** $\frac{11}{7}$ **e.** $\frac{2}{7}$

40. Check the solution found for the linear system in Exercise 39 by graphing.

In Exercises 41–48, solve the linear system by the method you think is best. Explain why you chose that method.

41. $\begin{cases} 2x - 4y = 8 \\ x + 2y = 5 \end{cases}$
42. $\begin{cases} 2x - 3y = 6 \\ 4x + 9y = 8 \end{cases}$
43. $\begin{cases} 3x - 3y = 9 \\ 2x + 3y = 12 \end{cases}$
44. $\begin{cases} 5x + 2y = 10 \\ 3x - 6y = 12 \end{cases}$

45. $\begin{cases} 5x - y = 7 \\ x + 4y = 16 \end{cases}$
46. $\begin{cases} 6x + y = 8 \\ -4x + 2y = 9 \end{cases}$
47. $\begin{cases} -4x + 5y = 20 \\ 2x + 3y = 8 \end{cases}$
48. $\begin{cases} 7x - 5y = 18 \\ 8x + y = 24 \end{cases}$

Winter and Summer Solstice   **In Exercises 49 and 50, use the following information.**

Solstice is the time each year that the sun is at its northernmost or southernmost position. In the Northern Hemisphere, the northernmost position occurs on the summer solstice (the day with the most sunlight). The southernmost position occurs on the winter solstice (the day with the least sunlight).

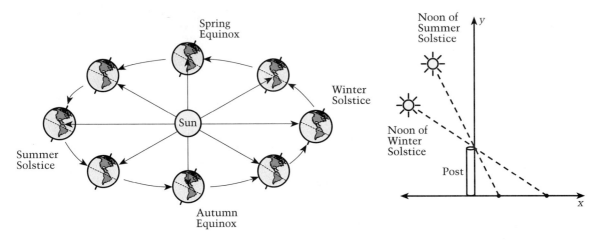

49. Match each solstice in the diagram on the right above with one of the equations in the system.

$$\begin{cases} 2x + 3y = 30 \\ 2x + y = 10 \end{cases}$$

Solve this system and interpret your solution in the diagram. The units on the axes are measured in feet.

50. In the diagram, find the distance between the two points on the x-axis. Use the diagram to explain how ancient people could create calendars.

Exploration and Extension

In Exercises 51 and 52, complete the system with the constants that will ensure the given solution.

System	Solution	System	Solution

51. $\begin{cases} \frac{1}{2}x + 6y = \boxed{?} \\ 4x - \frac{1}{3}y = \boxed{?} \end{cases}$ $(8, 12)$ **52.** $\begin{cases} -5x + \frac{6}{5}y = \boxed{?} \\ 3x - \frac{2}{3}y = \boxed{?} \end{cases}$ $\left(\frac{3}{5}, \frac{1}{2}\right)$

In Exercises 53 and 54, find the equations of the lines that pass through the given points. Then solve the resulting linear system.

53. Equation 1: $(-2, -4)$, $(6, 2)$
Equation 2: $(4, -2)$, $(-1, 5)$

54. Equation 1: $(-2, 3)$, $(5, 2)$
Equation 2: $(-1, 3)$, $(2, 4)$

7.4

Problem Solving Using Linear Systems

What you should learn:

Goal 1 How to write and use a linear system as a real-life model

Why you should learn it:

Many real-life situations, such as octane mixtures for gasoline, can be modeled with linear systems.

Goal 1 **Using Linear Systems as Models**

You have already modeled several situations with linear systems. In this lesson, you will practice using the linear-systems model to solve additional problems.

Remember that the key steps are writing a *verbal model*, assigning *labels*, writing an *algebraic model*, *solving* the algebraic model, and *answering* the question of the original problem. Remember that you have *three* methods for solving the system: graphing, substitution, and linear combinations.

Real Life
Petroleum Industry

Example 1 *Octane Ratings*

You work in a gasoline refinery. One refining system produces 90-octane gasoline and another produces 96-octane gasoline. How much of each of these gasolines should you mix to produce 600 gallons of 92-octane gasoline?

Solution To begin, assume that 600 gallons of 92-octane gasoline contains $(0.92)(600) = 552$ gallons of isooctane.

8% Heptane

92% Isooctane

Octane rating is a measure of a gasoline's resistance to engine knock. Isooctane is 100-octane (knock resistant) and heptane is 0-octane (knock prone). A 92-octane gasoline has the same resistance to knocking as a mixture that is 92% isooctane and 8% heptane.

Verbal Model	Volume of 90-octane	+	Volume of 96-octane	=	Volume of 92-octane
	Isooctane in 90-octane	+	Isooctane in 96-octane	=	Isooctane in 92-octane

Labels
Volume of 90-octane gasoline $= x$ (gallons)
Volume of 96-octane gasoline $= y$ (gallons)
Volume of 92-octane gasoline $= 600$ (gallons)
Isooctane in 90-octane gasoline $= 0.90x$ (gallons)
Isooctane in 96-octane gasoline $= 0.96y$ (gallons)
Isooctane in 92-octane gasoline $= 552$ (gallons)

System
$$\begin{cases} x + y = 600 & \textit{Volume is 600 gallons.} \\ 0.9x + 0.96y = 552 & \textit{Isooctane is 552 gallons.} \end{cases}$$

Using the linear combinations method, you can multiply the first equation by -0.9 and add the result to the second equation. The solution is 400 gallons of 90-octane and 200 gallons of 96-octane. ■

In 1990, approximately $4.2 billion worth of athletic shoes were sold in the United States. Of this amount, 22.4% came from the sale of walking shoes, 21% from gym shoes and sneakers, 11.1% from jogging and running shoes, and 9.3% from tennis shoes.

Real Life
Inventory Control

Example 2   *The Cash Register Wasn't Working*

You are the manager of a shoe store. On Sunday morning, you are going over the sales receipts for the past week. They show that 240 pairs of walking shoes were sold. Style A sells for $66.95, and Style B sells for $84.95. The total receipts for the two types were $17,652. The cash register was supposed to keep track of the number of each type sold. It malfunctioned. Can you find out how many of each type were sold?

Solution

Verbal Model

$$\boxed{\text{Number of Style A}} + \boxed{\text{Number of Style B}} = \boxed{\text{Total number}}$$

$$\boxed{\text{Receipts for Style A}} + \boxed{\text{Receipts for Style B}} = \boxed{\text{Total receipts}}$$

Labels

Number of Style A $= x$	(pairs of shoes)
Number of Style B $= y$	(pairs of shoes)
Total number sold $= 240$	(pairs of shoes)
Receipts for Style A $= 66.95x$	(dollars)
Receipts for Style B $= 84.95y$	(dollars)
Total receipts $= 17{,}652$	(dollars)

System
$$\begin{cases} x + y = 240 & \textit{Number sold is 240.} \\ 66.95x + 84.95y = 17{,}652 & \textit{Receipts are \$17,652.} \end{cases}$$

Using the substitution method, you can solve the first equation for $x = 240 - y$ and substitute $240 - y$ into the second equation. After simplifying, you will obtain $18y = 1584$. The solution is 152 pairs of Style A and 88 pairs of Style B. ■

Example 3 | Choice of Two Jobs

You are offered two different jobs selling dental supplies. One has an annual salary of $20,000 plus a year-end bonus of 1% of your total sales. The other has a salary of $15,000 plus a year-end bonus of 2% of your total sales. How much would you have to sell to earn the same amount in each job?

Solution

Total Earnings for Two Jobs

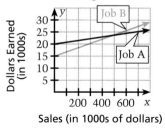

Dollars Earned (in 1000s)
Sales (in 1000s of dollars)

Problem Solving
Draw a Graph

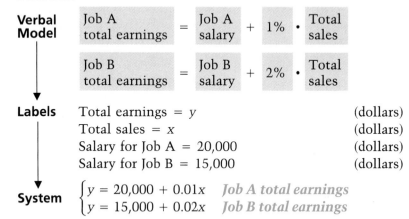

Verbal Model

$$\boxed{\text{Job A total earnings}} = \boxed{\text{Job A salary}} + \boxed{1\%} \cdot \boxed{\text{Total sales}}$$

$$\boxed{\text{Job B total earnings}} = \boxed{\text{Job B salary}} + \boxed{2\%} \cdot \boxed{\text{Total sales}}$$

Labels

Total earnings $= y$	(dollars)
Total sales $= x$	(dollars)
Salary for Job A $= 20{,}000$	(dollars)
Salary for Job B $= 15{,}000$	(dollars)

System

$$\begin{cases} y = 20{,}000 + 0.01x & \textit{Job A total earnings} \\ y = 15{,}000 + 0.02x & \textit{Job B total earnings} \end{cases}$$

This system is a good candidate for solution by graphing or by substitution. You must sell about $500,000 in dental supplies to earn the same amount in each job. If you think you can sell $800,000 in supplies, which job would you take? ■

Communicating about ALGEBRA

▶ ### SHARING IDEAS about the Lesson

Apply the Problem-Solving Plan Two airplanes fly in opposite directions from the same airport. The second plane flies 50 miles an hour faster than the first, but it starts one-half hour later. Two hours after the first plane started, the planes are 1825 miles apart. How fast is each flying?

A. Write verbal models, one relating speeds, the other relating distances. Assign labels and write a linear system that models the problem. (Did each fly the same number of hours?)

B. Solve the linear system using *all three* methods studied in this chapter. Which method seems best for this system? Explain

EXERCISES

▶ **CRITICAL THINKING about the Lesson**

Price Per Gallon   **In Exercises 1–4, use the following information.**

The total cost of 15 gallons of regular unleaded gasoline and 10 gallons of premium unleaded gasoline is $35.50. Premium unleaded costs $0.20 more per gallon than regular unleaded. What is the cost per gallon of each type of gasoline?

1. Write a verbal model for this problem.

2. Assign labels to the verbal model.

3. Use the labels to write a linear system.

4. Solve the system and answer the question.

Independent Practice

5. *Fuel Mixture*   Five hundred gallons of 82-octane gasoline is obtained by mixing 80-octane gasoline with 86-octane gasoline. How much of each must be used?

6. *How Many Karats?*   A necklace that weighs 156.5 grams is made of gold and copper. The necklace has a volume of 12 cubic centimeters. What percent of the weight of the necklace is gold? Describe the percentage of gold in terms of karats. (Gold weighs 19.3 grams per cubic centimeter, and copper weighs 9 grams per cubic centimeter.)

7. *Relay Race*   The total time for a two-member team in a 5160-meter relay race is 16 minutes. The first runner on the team averages 300 meters per minute and the second runner averages 360 meters per minute. How many minutes did the first runner keep the baton before passing it to the second runner? Use the following verbal model to help answer the question.

$$\boxed{\begin{array}{c}\text{Time for}\\\text{1st runner}\end{array}} + \boxed{\begin{array}{c}\text{Time for}\\\text{2nd runner}\end{array}} = \boxed{\begin{array}{c}\text{Total}\\\text{time}\end{array}}$$

$$\boxed{\begin{array}{c}\text{Distance for}\\\text{1st runner}\end{array}} + \boxed{\begin{array}{c}\text{Distance for}\\\text{2nd runner}\end{array}} = \boxed{\begin{array}{c}\text{Total}\\\text{distance}\end{array}}$$

8. *Average Speed*   A van travels for two hours at an average speed of 40 miles per hour. For how long must the van then travel at an average speed of 55 miles per hour to raise the overall average speed to 45 miles per hour? What is the total time traveled?

9. *I Can't Believe I Ate All That*   You and your friend go to a Mexican restaurant. You order 2 tacos and 3 enchiladas, and your friend orders 3 tacos and 5 enchiladas! One bill was $7.80 plus tax, and the other bill was $12.70 plus tax. How much was each taco and each enchilada?

10. *Birthday Party*   You are buying decorations for a birthday party. The before-tax total for 3 rolls of crepe paper and 20 balloons is $11.40. After you start decorating, you need more supplies. You buy 2 more rolls of crepe paper and 10 more balloons for $7.20. How much did each roll of crepe paper and each balloon cost?

11. *Dimensions of a Rectangle*   The perimeter of the rectangle is 22 meters, and the perimeter of the triangle is 12 meters. Find the dimensions of the rectangle.

12. *Dimensions of a Room*   A dorm room at a college your sister is considering seems small. The room is rectangular and has a perimeter of 42 feet. The room is 4 feet longer than it is wide. What are the dimensions of the room?

13. *Finding Absolute Zero*   To calculate *absolute zero* (the complete absence of heat) a chemist uses the following procedure. First, the chemist takes several readings for the volume and temperature of three gases: CH_4 (methane), H_2O (water steam), and N_2O (nitrous oxide), as shown in the graph. Then the chemist finds a linear equation that relates the volume (in liters) and temperature (in degrees Celsius) of each gas.

$$\begin{cases} -2T + 302V = 546.4 & \textit{Methane} \\ -T + 228V = 273.2 & \textit{Water} \\ -3T + 1872V = 819.6 & \textit{Nitrous Oxide} \end{cases}$$

The measurements are taken only at temperatures for which the compounds are gases, as shown by the solid part of each line in the graph. However, if each line is extended, as shown by the dashed part, all three lines intersect at a common point, which is called *absolute zero*. What is absolute zero on the Celsius scale?

14. *Tree Growth*   You planted a 16-inch hemlock tree that grows at a rate of 4 inches per year. Then 5 years later you planted a 10-inch blue spruce tree that grows at a rate of 6 inches per year. In how many years after you planted the hemlock tree will the two trees be the same height? How tall will the trees be?

In Exercises 15–18, decide whether the ordered pair is a solution of the system.

15. $\begin{cases} 2x - 5y = 16 \\ -x + 4y = -11 \end{cases}$ $(3, -2)$

16. $\begin{cases} x + 5y = 26 \\ 3x - 6y = 33 \end{cases}$ $(1, 5)$

17. $\begin{cases} 2x + 5y = -7 \\ -3x - 6y = 24 \end{cases}$ $(-6, 1)$

18. $\begin{cases} 6x + 4y = 36 \\ 3x - 6y = -54 \end{cases}$ $(0, 9)$

In Exercises 19–30, solve the linear system by the method you think is best. Explain why you chose that method.

19. $\begin{cases} -3x + 2y = 6 \\ y = 1 \end{cases}$

20. $\begin{cases} x + 3y = -3 \\ x = -3 \end{cases}$

21. $\begin{cases} 3x + y = 14 \\ -x + y = 2 \end{cases}$

22. $\begin{cases} x + 5y = 45 \\ 2x - y = 2 \end{cases}$

23. $\begin{cases} 9x - 2y = 4 \\ -5x + y = 1 \end{cases}$

24. $\begin{cases} 3x + 5y = 17 \\ \frac{1}{2}x + y = 3 \end{cases}$

25. $\begin{cases} 2x - 7y = -27 \\ 6x + 5y = -3 \end{cases}$

26. $\begin{cases} 10x - 3y = 17 \\ -7x + y = 9 \end{cases}$

27. $\begin{cases} x + 4y = 9 \\ 3x + 8y = 32 \end{cases}$

28. $\begin{cases} 3x - 2y = 17 \\ -2x - 5y = 14 \end{cases}$

29. $\begin{cases} 9x - 5y = 45 \\ -2x + 21y = -10 \end{cases}$

30. $\begin{cases} 6x - y = -32 \\ 2x + 13y = 16 \end{cases}$

31. *Estimate within Reason* Which is the best estimate for the racing speed of a thoroughbred racehorse?

  a. 3.5 miles per hour **b.** 35 miles per hour
  c. 350 miles per hour **d.** 3500 miles per hour

32. *Estimate within Reason* Which is the best estimate for the population of the United States?

  a. 250,000 **b.** 2,500,000 **c.** 25,000,000 **d.** 250,000,000

33. *Surveying* Two surveyors are trying to determine distances to a waterfall. They visualize a triangle formed by their positions, A and B, and the top of the waterfall, C. They also visualize a coordinate plane that contains the triangle. In this coordinate plane, point A has coordinates $(1, 0)$ and point B has coordinates $(1.5, 0)$, where x and y are measured in miles. The line containing AC is given by $24x - y = 24$, and the line containing BC is given by $6x + y = 9$. Find the distance between the line segment AB and the top of the waterfall.

Take this test as you would take a test in class. The answers to the exercises are given in the back of the book.

In Exercises 1–6, determine which of the ordered pairs is a solution of the system. **(7.1)**

1. $\begin{cases} 4x - 4y = 4 \\ -2x + y = 2 \end{cases}$ $(-3, -4), (2, 6)$

2. $\begin{cases} \frac{1}{2}x + 2y = \frac{27}{2} \\ 12x + y = -5 \end{cases}$ $(-1, 7), (4, -5)$

3. $\begin{cases} 3x + 5y = 9 \\ -x + 2y = 8 \end{cases}$ $(-2, 3), (4, 6)$

4. $\begin{cases} 3x + 2y = 11 \\ 11x + 8y = 35 \end{cases}$ $(1, 3), (9, -8)$

5. $\begin{cases} -12x + y = 15 \\ 6x - 2y = -15 \end{cases}$ $\left(-\frac{3}{2}, -3\right), \left(-\frac{5}{6}, 5\right)$

6. $\begin{cases} x + 7y = 4 \\ x + y = 1 \end{cases}$ $\left(\frac{1}{2}, \frac{1}{2}\right), \left(\frac{1}{4}, \frac{3}{4}\right)$

In Exercises 7 and 8, solve the linear system by graphing. **(7.1)**

7. $\begin{cases} -2x + 3y = 6 \\ 2x + y = 10 \end{cases}$

8. $\begin{cases} -2x + y = 2 \\ x - y = 1 \end{cases}$

In Exercises 9–14, use substitution to solve the system. **(7.2)**

9. $\begin{cases} x + 3y = 7 \\ 4x - 7y = -10 \end{cases}$

10. $\begin{cases} -6x - 5y = 28 \\ x - 2y = 1 \end{cases}$

11. $\begin{cases} \frac{1}{2}x + \frac{3}{4}y = 9 \\ -2x + y = -4 \end{cases}$

12. $\begin{cases} 4x + y = -1 \\ -5x - y = 0 \end{cases}$

13. $\begin{cases} x - 6y = -19 \\ 3x - 2y = -9 \end{cases}$

14. $\begin{cases} 4x + y = 14 \\ 3x + 2y = 8 \end{cases}$

In Exercises 15–20, use linear combinations to solve the system. **(7.3)**

15. $\begin{cases} -2x - 3y = 4 \\ 2x - 4y = 3 \end{cases}$

16. $\begin{cases} 5x + 7y = 35 \\ 4x - 7y = 1 \end{cases}$

17. $\begin{cases} 4x + 3y = 1 \\ -2x + 9y = -4 \end{cases}$

18. $\begin{cases} 10x + 3y = 2 \\ 8x + 6y = 16 \end{cases}$

19. $\begin{cases} 3x - 5y = -4 \\ -9x + 7y = 8 \end{cases}$

20. $\begin{cases} 3x + 7y = -4 \\ -15x - 14y = 6 \end{cases}$

21. A total of $8000 is invested in 2 funds paying 4% and 5% annual interest. The combined annual interest is $350. How much of the $8000 is invested in each fund? **(7.4)**

22. You go to the video store to rent 5 movies for the weekend. Movies rent for $2 and $3. You spend $13. How many $2 movies did you rent? How many $3 movies did you rent? **(7.4)**

23. Your teacher is giving a test worth 150 points. There are 46 three- and five-point questions. How many of each are on the test? **(7.4)**

24. You are in charge of ordering softballs for three different leagues. The Pony League uses an 11-inch softball priced at $2.25. The Junior and Senior Leagues use a 12-inch softball priced at $2.75. The invoice smeared in the rain. You can still read the totals, 80 softballs for $210. How many of each size are there? **(7.4)**

Special Types of Linear Systems

What you should learn:

Goal 1 How to visualize the solution possibilities for linear systems

Goal 2 How to identify a linear system as having many solutions

Why you should learn it:

You can interpret linear-system models for real-life situations as having no solution, one solution, and many solutions.

Goal 1 Visualizing the Solution Possibilities

In the first four lessons of this chapter, each linear system had exactly one solution. The graphical model of the system consisted of two lines intersecting in one point.

Two other types of linear systems are possible. Their graphical models and descriptions are shown below.

A linear system whose equations graph as parallel lines has no solution.

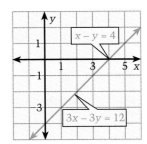

A linear system whose equations graph as the same line has every point on the line as a solution.

Example 1 *A Linear System with No Solution*

Show that the linear system has no solution.

$$\begin{cases} 2x + y = 3 & \text{\textit{Equation 1}} \\ 4x + 2y = 8 & \text{\textit{Equation 2}} \end{cases}$$

Solution You can use any of the three methods to show that the system has no solution. Using the graphing method, you could rewrite each equation in slope-intercept form.

$$\begin{cases} y = -2x + 3 & \text{\textit{Revised Equation 1}} \\ y = -2x + 4 & \text{\textit{Revised Equation 2}} \end{cases}$$

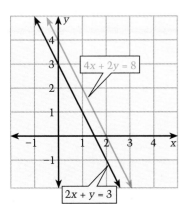

You can see that the lines have the same slope but different y-intercepts. Thus, the lines are parallel and nonintersecting, which means that the system has no solution. If you try using substitution or linear combinations to solve the system, you will obtain a meaningless "equation." For instance, multiplying Equation 1 by -2 and adding the result to Equation 2 produces $0 = 2$, which makes no sense. ∎

Example 2   *A Linear System with Many Solutions*

Show that the linear system has many solutions.

$$\begin{cases} 2x + y = 3 & \text{\textit{Equation 1}} \\ 4x + 2y = 6 & \text{\textit{Equation 2}} \end{cases}$$

Solution   You can use any of the three methods to show that the system has many solutions. Using the graphing method, rewrite each equation in slope-intercept form.

$$\begin{cases} y = -2x + 3 & \text{\textit{Revised Equation 1}} \\ y = -2x + 3 & \text{\textit{Revised Equation 2}} \end{cases}$$

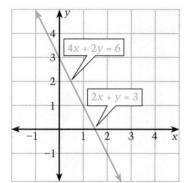

From these equations, you can see that each equation represents the same line. Thus, any point on the line is a solution. If you apply the substitution or linear combination method to the original equations, you will obtain an equation like $6 = 6$ or $0 = 0$, which is a signal that the system has many solutions. For instance, multiplying Equation 1 by -2 and adding the result to Equation 2 produces $0 = 0$. ■

Real Life
Paper Production

Example 3   *U.S. Paper Production*

The amounts of newsprint paper and tissue paper (in millions of tons) that were produced between 1985 and 1988 are shown in the matrix. Find a linear model for the number of tons of each type of paper. Then use the models to predict the year that tissue production will be equal to newsprint production.
(Source: American Paper Institute)

Connections
Discrete Mathematics

Paper production

(millions of tons)	1985	1986	1987	1988
Newsprint	5.4	5.6	5.8	6.0
Tissue	4.9	5.1	5.3	5.5

Solution   Let y represent the number (in millions) of tons of paper produced. Let t represent the year, with $t = 0$ corresponding to 1985. The production of both types of paper increased by 0.2 million tons per year.

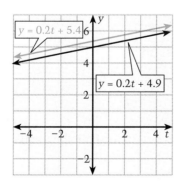

$$\begin{cases} y = 0.2t + 5.4 & \text{\textit{Newsprint production}} \\ y = 0.2t + 4.9 & \text{\textit{Tissue production}} \end{cases}$$

By graphing the system, you obtain a pair of parallel lines, as shown at the left. From the graph, you can see that if newsprint production and tissue production *continue to change at the same rates as they did between 1985 and 1988*, then tissue production will never be equal to newsprint production. ■

Example 4 *Didn't We Already Know That?*

Paco and Diego, from Santiago, are visiting Chile's Easter Island 2300 miles to the west in the South Pacific. To measure the heights of two statues, Paco and Diego tried a technique they had learned in algebra. At 2:00 P.M., they measured the shadow lengths of the statues to be 18 feet and 27 feet. At 3:00 P.M., they measured the shadow lengths again and found them to be 20 feet and 30 feet. Later, however, they were unable to use their measurements to determine the heights of the statues. Why?

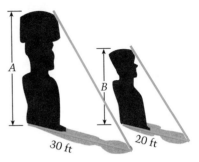

Shadow lengths at 2:00 P.M.   *Shadow lengths at 3:00 P.M.*

Solution Let A represent the height of the first statue and B represent the height of the second. Using the fact that the ratios of corresponding sides of similar triangles are equal, Paco and Diego wrote the following two equations.

$$\begin{cases} \dfrac{A}{B} = \dfrac{27}{18} & \textit{2:00 P.M. measurements} \\ \dfrac{A}{B} = \dfrac{30}{20} & \textit{3:00 P.M. measurements} \end{cases}$$

At this point, they got stuck—because both equations graph as the same line. All that Paco and Diego found from these measurements was that $A = \frac{3}{2}B$. In other words, they found that the height of the first statue is one and one-half times the height of the second. ∎

Easter Island, in the South Pacific, has more than 600 massive stone statues called moai. The statues were carved hundreds of years ago, and some are over 40 feet high.

Communicating *about* **ALGEBRA**

▶ **SHARING IDEAS about the Lesson**

Plan Another Approach Help Paco and Diego find the heights of the statues.

What could Paco and Diego have done to find the heights of the two statues? (You may want to look at the exercises in Lesson 4.5.)

EXERCISES

Guided Practice

▶ **CRITICAL THINKING about the Lesson**

1. Describe the graphical model for a linear system that has no solution.

2. Describe the graphical model for a linear system that has many solutions.

3. Describe the graphical model for a linear system that has exactly one solution.

In Exercises 4–6, give a graphical description of the system.

4. $\begin{cases} -4x + 2y = 12 \\ -6x + 3y = 8 \end{cases}$

5. $\begin{cases} 3x - 5y = -14 \\ 2x + 6y = 8 \end{cases}$

6. $\begin{cases} -9x + 12y = 18 \\ 6x - 8y = 12 \end{cases}$

Independent Practice

In Exercises 7–12, match the graphical model with one of the linear systems.

7.

8.

9.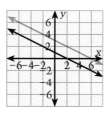

a. $\begin{cases} -2x + 4y = 1 \\ x - 2y = 3 \end{cases}$

b. $\begin{cases} 3x - 2y = 6 \\ -6x + 4y = -12 \end{cases}$

c. $\begin{cases} 2x + y = 4 \\ -4x - 2y = -8 \end{cases}$

10.

11.

12.

d. $\begin{cases} -x + y = 1 \\ x - y = 1 \end{cases}$

e. $\begin{cases} x - y = 2 \\ -3x + 3y = -6 \end{cases}$

f. $\begin{cases} x + 2y = 6 \\ x + 2y = 2 \end{cases}$

In Exercises 13–24, graph the system and describe its solution(s).

13. $\begin{cases} x + y = 8 \\ x + y = -1 \end{cases}$

14. $\begin{cases} 3x - 2y = 0 \\ 3x - 2y = -4 \end{cases}$

15. $\begin{cases} 3x - 2y = 3 \\ -6x + 4y = -6 \end{cases}$

16. $\begin{cases} x - 3y = 2 \\ -2x + 6y = 2 \end{cases}$

17. $\begin{cases} 3x + 2y = 2 \\ 6x + 4y = 14 \end{cases}$

18. $\begin{cases} -3x + 10y = 15 \\ 3x - 10y = -15 \end{cases}$

19. $\begin{cases} -x + 4y = -21 \\ 3x - 12y = -21 \end{cases}$

20. $\begin{cases} 2x - 6y = 5 \\ 3x - 9y = 2 \end{cases}$

21. $\begin{cases} 6x - 3y = 4 \\ -4x + 2y = -\frac{8}{3} \end{cases}$

22. $\begin{cases} 6x - 5y = 3 \\ -12x + 10y = 5 \end{cases}$

23. $\begin{cases} \frac{3}{4}x + \frac{1}{2}y = 10 \\ -\frac{3}{2}x - y = 4 \end{cases}$

24. $\begin{cases} \frac{2}{3}x + \frac{1}{6}y = \frac{2}{3} \\ 4x + y = 4 \end{cases}$

In Exercises 25–28, find a linear system for the graphical model. If only one line is shown, find two different equations for the line.

25.

26.

27.

28.

In Exercises 29–32, find one value of _n_ so that the linear system has many solutions. Then find a second value of _n_ so that the linear system has no solution. Graph both results.

29. $\begin{cases} x - y = 4 \\ 2x - 2y = n \end{cases}$

30. $\begin{cases} x - y = 2 \\ -3x + 3y = n \end{cases}$

31. $\begin{cases} 4x - 12y = n \\ -2x + 6y = 3 \end{cases}$

32. $\begin{cases} 9x + 6y = n \\ 1.8x + 1.2y = 4 \end{cases}$

33. *Perspective in Art*   The drawing of a room at the right uses *perspective* to create the illusion of depth. Which of the lines that are supposed to be parallel (in three dimensions) are actually drawn parallel (in two dimensions)?

34. *Optical Illusion*   If the lines that contain the line segments marked *AB* and *CD* were used to form a system of linear equations, would the system have exactly one solution, no solution, or many solutions? Explain.

Which is longer? The line segment forming the front of the rug or the line segment forming the back of the room.

U.S. Population   **In Exercises 35 and 36, use the following information.**

The male and female populations of the United States from 1960 to 1990 are shown in the matrix. *(Source: U.S. Bureau of Census)*

Population (in millions)	Male	Female
1960	89	91
1970	100	105
1980	111	117
1990	122	128

35. Construct two scatter plots, one for the male population and one for the female population. Then find the line that best fits each scatter plot.

36. Discuss the system of linear equations you found in Exercise 35. Are the two lines parallel? Do you think that the number of men in the United States will equal the number of women before the year 2000? Explain.

In Exercises 37 and 38, use the following information.

The graphs show the percentage changes in types of households in the United States and the percentage changes in racial or ethnic background of the U.S. population. (Source: U.S. Bureau of Census)

Types of Households

Population by Race

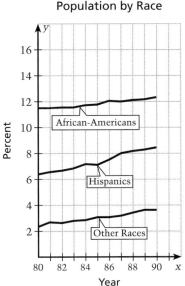

37. Which of the five graphs showing the percentages of different types of households do you think will intersect during the 1990s? Explain.

38. To make the second chart, the U.S. population was categorized into four groups: white, African-American, Hispanic, and other. Use the three given graphs to sketch the graph for the white population.

39. *A Number Trick* Write a linear equation for the description at the right. Let x represent the number that is chosen and let y represent the final result. To find which number a person would have to choose to obtain a final result of 1, solve the system consisting of the equation you wrote and the equation $y = 1$. Explain your result.

> *Choose any number.*
> *Add 10 to the number.*
> *Multiply the result by 2.*
> *Subtract 18 from the result.*
> *Multiply the result by one half.*
> *Subtract the original number.*

Integrated Review

In Exercises 40–51, solve the linear system by the method you think is best.

40. $\begin{cases} 2x - y = -4 \\ x + 2y = 3 \end{cases}$

41. $\begin{cases} x + y = 22 \\ x - y = 8 \end{cases}$

42. $\begin{cases} y - 2x = 1 \\ y - 2x = -3 \end{cases}$

43. $\begin{cases} 3x + 2y = 18 \\ 5x - 2y = 14 \end{cases}$

44. $\begin{cases} 2x + y = 4 \\ -2x + 3y = -12 \end{cases}$

45. $\begin{cases} 2x - 5y = 3 \\ 4y - x = -3 \end{cases}$

46. $\begin{cases} \frac{1}{2}y = x + 3 \\ y = 2x + 6 \end{cases}$

47. $\begin{cases} x + y = 5 \\ x - y = 3 \end{cases}$

48. $\begin{cases} 3x - y = 9 \\ 6x - 2y = 10 \end{cases}$

49. $\begin{cases} 3x + 2y = 10 \\ 4x - y = -1 \end{cases}$

50. $\begin{cases} 7 = 2x - y \\ 5 = x + y \end{cases}$

51. $\begin{cases} x + y = 2 \\ x - 3y = 5 \end{cases}$

In Exercises 52 and 53, correct the graphical model so that it matches
the linear system.

52. $\begin{cases} 7x + 3y = 15 \\ \frac{7}{3}x + y = 5 \end{cases}$

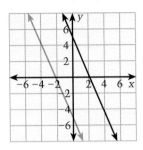

53. $\begin{cases} -x + 3y = 3 \\ 2x - 6y = 6 \end{cases}$

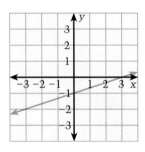

In Exercises 54 and 55, decide whether the lines are parallel. If they
aren't, solve the system.

54. $\begin{cases} 200y - x = 200 \\ 199y - x = -198 \end{cases}$

55. $\begin{cases} 25x - 24y = 0 \\ 13x - 12y = 120 \end{cases}$

Mixed REVIEW

1. Evaluate $3 + 6 \div 3 - 2$. **(1.4)**

2. Which number is larger, $-\frac{5}{4}$ or $-\frac{4}{3}$? **(2.1)**

3. Add. $\begin{bmatrix} -2 & 4 \\ 3 & 6 \end{bmatrix} + \begin{bmatrix} 6 & -2 \\ 3 & 8 \end{bmatrix}$ **(2.4)**

4. Add. $\begin{bmatrix} -3 & 7 \\ 4 & -5 \end{bmatrix} + \begin{bmatrix} 8 & 6 \\ -3 & -1 \end{bmatrix}$ **(2.4)**

5. Solve $3a + 4b - 6 = 0$ for b. **(3.6)**

6. Solve $3m - 2n = 2n + 6$ for n. **(3.6)**

7. Is $(-3, 2)$ a solution for $3x + 2y < -4$? **(6.5)**

8. Is $(4, 3)$ a solution for $\frac{1}{2}x - \frac{1}{6}y \geq 1$? **(6.5)**

9. Write $3x + \frac{1}{4}y = 6$ in slope-intercept form. **(5.1)**

10. Write $y = \frac{1}{4}(x + 4)$ in general form. **(5.5)**

11. Is 6 a solution for $4a \div 3 = 8$? **(1.5)**

12. Is $\frac{7}{2}$ a solution for $3 \div b \cdot 7 < 6$? **(1.5)**

13. Find the difference of -3 and -6. **(2.3)**

14. Find the sum of $\frac{1}{3} + \frac{1}{6}$. **(2.2)**

15. Evaluate $3x^2 + x - 7$ when $x = -1$. **(1.3)**

16. Evaluate $\frac{1}{4}(8 + |y|) + 6$ when $y = 4$. **(2.6)**

17. Solve $6x + \frac{1}{2}(x + 2) = 5$. **(3.2)**

18. Solve $\frac{1}{3}(3 - y) - \frac{2}{3}y = 8$. **(3.2)**

19. Write an equation of the line passing through $(0, -3)$ with a slope of $\frac{1}{4}$. **(5.2)**

20. Write an equation of the line passing through $\left(-\frac{1}{2}, \frac{3}{2}\right)$ and $(4, 2)$. **(5.3)**

7.6

Solving Systems of Linear Inequalities

What you should learn:

Goal 1 How to solve a system of linear inequalities by graphing

Goal 2 How to model a real-life situation using a system of linear inequalities

Why you should learn it:

You can model many real-life situations, such as finding boundaries of regions, with systems of linear inequalities.

Goal 1 **Solving Inequalities by Graphing**

In Lesson 6.5, you studied linear inequalities in two variables. Remember from that lesson that the graph of a linear inequality in two variables is a half plane. The boundary line of the half plane is dashed if the inequality is $<$ or $>$ and solid if the inequality is $\leq$ or $\geq$. Here are some examples.

Graph of $y < 2$ *Graph of $x \geq -1$*   *Graph of $y > x - 2$*

Two or more linear inequalities form a system of linear inequalities. A solution is an ordered pair that is a solution of each inequality in the system. The graph of a system is the graph of *all* solutions of the system.

Example 1 *Graphing a System of Linear Inequalities*

Sketch the graph of the system of linear inequalities.

$$\begin{cases} y < 2 & \textit{Inequality 1} \\ x \geq -1 & \textit{Inequality 2} \\ y > x - 2 & \textit{Inequality 3} \end{cases}$$

Solution   The half plane corresponding to each inequality is shown above. The graph of the system is the *intersection* of the three half planes. For instance, the point (0, 0) is in the graph of the system because it is a solution of each inequality. The point (0, 3) is not in the graph of the system because it is not a solution of the first inequality. (It is a solution of the other two inequalities, but that isn't good enough to be a solution of the system.)

When sketching the graph of a system of linear inequalities, it is helpful to find each corner point (or *vertex*). For instance, the graph at the left has three corner points: $(-1, 2)$, $(-1, -3)$, and $(4, 2)$.

Example **2** **Graphing a System of Linear Inequalities**

Sketch the graph of the system of linear inequalities.

$$\begin{cases} y < 4 & \text{\textit{Inequality 1}} \\ y > 1 & \text{\textit{Inequality 2}} \end{cases}$$

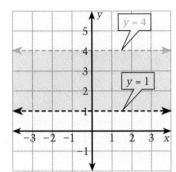

Solution The graph of the first inequality is the half plane *below* the horizontal line

$$y = 4. \qquad \text{\textit{Upper boundary}}$$

The graph of the second inequality is the half plane *above* the horizontal line

$$y = 1. \qquad \text{\textit{Lower boundary}}$$

The graph of the system is the horizontal band that lies *between* the two horizontal lines (where $y < 4$ and $y > 1$). ■

Example **3** **Graphing a System of Linear Inequalities**

Sketch the graph of the system of linear inequalities. Find a vertex of the graph.

$$\begin{cases} y \le x + 2 & \text{\textit{Inequality 1}} \\ y \ge -\frac{1}{2}x + 5 & \text{\textit{Inequality 2}} \end{cases}$$

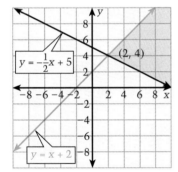

Solution The graph of the first inequality is the half plane *on and below* the line $y = x + 2$. The graph of the second is the half plane *on and above* the line $y = -\frac{1}{2}x + 5$. The graph of the system is the shaded region shown at the left. The vertex of the graph is the point of intersection of the two lines $y = x + 2$ and $y = -\frac{1}{2}x + 5$, which is $(2, 4)$. ■

Here are some guidelines that may help you sketch the graph of a system of linear inequalities.

Graphing a System of Linear Inequalities

1. Sketch the line that corresponds to each inequality. (Use a dashed line for inequalities with $<$ or $>$ and a solid line for inequalities with $\le$ or $\ge$.)

2. Lightly shade the half plane that is the graph of each linear inequality. (Colored pencils may help you distinguish the different half planes.)

3. The graph of the system is the intersection of the shaded half planes. (If you used colored pencils, it is the region that has been shaded with *every* color.)

Example 4 | *Finding the Boundaries of a Region*

You are redecorating your bedroom with a scenic mural. One corner of the mural has to be cut away around the edges of a built-in bookcase. Use the bookcase dimensions shown (in feet) to find a system of inequalities that defines the region to be cut out.

Solution First, define a coordinate plane that covers the entire mural, using the bottom and left edges as axes. Next, find the boundary for the diagonal line by writing an equation of the line passing through the points (4, 4) and (6, 0). The equation is $y = -2x + 12$. The system of linear inequalities that describes the region follows.

$$\begin{cases} y \leq 4 & \textit{On and below } y = 4 \\ y \geq 0 & \textit{On and above x-axis} \\ x \geq 0 & \textit{On and to right of y-axis} \\ y \leq -2x + 12 & \textit{On and below } y = -2x + 12 \end{cases}$$

■

Communicating *about* **ALGEBRA**

▶ **SHARING IDEAS about the Lesson**

Use a Graph Describe or sketch the graph of the system.

A. Which quadrant forms the graph of $\begin{cases} x < 0 \\ y > 0 \end{cases}$?

B. Sketch the graph of the system.

$$\begin{cases} y \geq 0 & \textit{Inequality 1} \\ x \geq 0 & \textit{Inequality 2} \\ y < -x + 4 & \textit{Inequality 3} \end{cases}$$

C. Sketch the graph of the system.

$$\begin{cases} y \geq 0 & \textit{Inequality 1} \\ x \geq 0 & \textit{Inequality 2} \\ y < -x + 4 & \textit{Inequality 3} \\ y > -x + 2 & \textit{Inequality 4} \end{cases}$$

EXERCISES

▶ **CRITICAL THINKING about the Lesson**

1. **True or False?** A solution of a system of linear inequalities is an ordered pair that is a solution of any one of the inequalities in the system. Explain.

2. What is a *vertex* of the graph of a system of linear inequalities?

In Exercises 3–6, decide whether the ordered pair is a solution of the system of linear inequalities. Justify your answer algebraically and graphically.

$$\begin{cases} x + y \le 2 \\ x - y > 0 \\ y \ge -2 \end{cases}$$

3. $(1, 0)$ 4. $(4, 3)$ 5. $(1, -1)$ 6. $(-1, 2)$

Independent Practice

In Exercises 7–12, match the graph with one of the systems of linear inequalities.

7.

8.

9.

10.

11.

12.

a. $\begin{cases} 2x + y \le 4 \\ x + 2y > -4 \end{cases}$

b. $\begin{cases} x + 2y \le 4 \\ -x + 2y < 4 \end{cases}$

c. $\begin{cases} 2x + y \le 4 \\ 2x + y \ge -4 \end{cases}$

d. $\begin{cases} 2x + y \ge -4 \\ x - 2y < 4 \end{cases}$

e. $\begin{cases} x - 2y \ge -4 \\ x - 2y \le 4 \end{cases}$

f. $\begin{cases} 2x + y < 4 \\ -2x + y \le 4 \end{cases}$

In Exercises 13–24, sketch the graph of the system of linear inequalities.

13. $\begin{cases} x \ge 0 \\ y \ge 0 \\ x \le 2 \\ y \le 4 \end{cases}$

14. $\begin{cases} x \ge -1 \\ y \ge -1 \\ x \le 1 \\ y \le 2 \end{cases}$

15. $\begin{cases} x + y \le 1 \\ -x + y \le 1 \\ y \ge 0 \end{cases}$

16. $\begin{cases} \frac{3}{2}x + y < 3 \\ x > 0 \\ y > 0 \end{cases}$

17. $\begin{cases} x + y \le 5 \\ x \ge 2 \\ y \ge 0 \end{cases}$

18. $\begin{cases} 2x + y \ge 2 \\ x \le 2 \\ y \le 1 \end{cases}$

19. $\begin{cases} -\frac{3}{2}x + y < 3 \\ \frac{1}{4}x + y > -\frac{1}{2} \\ 2x + y < 3 \end{cases}$

20. $\begin{cases} -\frac{1}{7}x + y < \frac{36}{7} \\ \frac{5}{2}x + y < \frac{5}{2} \\ \frac{6}{5}x + y > \frac{6}{5} \end{cases}$

21. $\begin{cases} x & \geq 1 \\ x - 2y \leq 3 \\ 3x + 2y \geq 9 \\ x + y \leq 6 \end{cases}$ **22.** $\begin{cases} x + y < 10 \\ 2x + y > 10 \\ x - y < 2 \end{cases}$ **23.** $\begin{cases} x - 3y \geq 3 \\ x - 3y \leq 12 \end{cases}$ **24.** $\begin{cases} x + y < 3 \\ x + y > -1 \end{cases}$

In Exercises 25–28, find the vertices of the graph of the system.

25. $\begin{cases} x + y \leq 12 \\ 3x - 4y \leq 15 \\ x \geq 0 \\ y \geq 0 \end{cases}$ **26.** $\begin{cases} \frac{1}{2}x + y \leq 2 \\ x - y \leq 1 \\ x \geq 0 \\ y \geq 0 \end{cases}$ **27.** $\begin{cases} 5x - 3y \geq -7 \\ 3x + y \leq 7 \\ x + 5y \leq -7 \end{cases}$ **28.** $\begin{cases} x + 2y \geq 0 \\ 5x - 2y \leq 0 \\ -x + y \leq 3 \end{cases}$

In Exercises 29–32, write a system of linear inequalities that defines the polygon.

Polygon	Vertices		Polygon	Vertices
29. Rectangle	(2, 1), (5, 1), (5, 7), (2, 7)		**30.** Parallelogram	(0, 0), (4, 0), (1, 4), (5, 4)
31. Triangle	(0, 0), (5, 0), (2, 3)		**32.** Triangle	(−1, 0), (1, 0), (0, 1)

33. *Planning a Party*   You are planning a party and want to have two types of hot snacks: stuffed mushrooms and cheese sticks. Each stuffed mushroom costs $0.25 to make, and each cheese stick costs $0.15 to make. You want to have enough so that each person can have at least two stuffed mushrooms and at least three cheese sticks. There are going to be at most 40 people at the party, and you do not want to spend more than $45. Write a system of linear inequalities that shows the various numbers of stuffed mushrooms and cheese sticks that you could make. Graph your result.

34. *Work Schedule*   Suppose you can work a total of no more than 20 hours a week at your two jobs. Your baby-sitting job pays $3 an hour, and your cashier job pays $5 an hour. You need to earn at least $80 a week. Write a system of linear inequalities that shows the various numbers of hours you could work at each job. Graph your result.

An Herb Garden   **In Exercises 35–38, use the picture of the herb garden.**

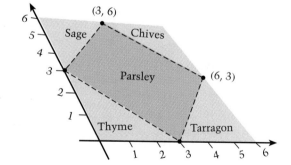

35. Find a system of inequalities that defines the region containing thyme.

36. Find a system of inequalities that defines the region containing sage.

37. Find a system of inequalities that defines the region containing parsley.

38. Find the area of each of the herb regions.

39. Desktop Publishing   Suppose you are creating a "family-tree" book. You scan this photo into your computer. Then you use the "cut-and-paste" feature to electronically *crop* and insert the photo into a page. Use the coordinates below to write a system of linear inequalities defining the crop lines and the part of the photo containing the people.

(19, 8) •

(0, 6) •

(0, 0) •   (19, 0) •

School Kids with Teacher, 1924 *The entire student body and faculty of a country school in Sanish (now New Town), North Dakota. (Note from one of the authors, Ron Larson: The fourth and fifth from the right are my mom and dad.)*

Integrated Review

In Exercises 40–43, sketch the line.

40. $2x - 6y = 18$ **41.** $x + 3y = -9$ **42.** $-3x + y = 21$ **43.** $7x + 2y = 28$

In Exercises 44–47, sketch the graph of the inequality.

44. $x \geq 2$ **45.** $y < 2 - x$ **46.** $2y - x \geq 4$ **47.** $4x - 2y \leq 12$

Exploration and Extension

Complements of "Old Glory"   **In Exercises 48 and 49, use the following drawing.**

If you stare at the white dot in the center of the flag for 30 seconds, then look at a blank sheet of white paper, the image of the United States flag should appear *in its correct colors!* This optical sensation stems from a property of human vision that no one quite understands. If the human eye stares at a color long enough, it begins to produce sensations of the complementary color. (Red is the complement of green, white is the complement of black, and blue is the complement of orange.)

48. Write a system of linear inequalities that defines the region containing the flag.

49. Would it be possible to write a system of linear inequalities whose graph is one of the stars in the flag? Explain.

7.7

Exploring Data: Linear Programming

What you should learn:

Goal 1 How to solve a linear programming problem

Goal 2 How to model a real-life situation using linear programming

Why you should learn it:

With linear programming, you can model many real-life situations, such as finding ways to maximize profit and minimize cost.

Goal 1 Linear Programming Problems

Many real-life problems involve a process called *optimization*, which means finding the minimum or maximum value of some quantity. In this lesson, you will study one type of optimization process called **linear programming.**

A linear programming problem consists of a system of linear inequalities called **constraints** and an **objective quantity,** such as cost or profit, that can be minimized or maximized. To find the minimum or maximum value of the objective quantity, first find all the vertices of the graph of the constraint inequalities. Then evaluate the objective quantity *at each vertex.* The smallest value is the minimum, and the largest value is the maximum.

Example 1 *Solving a Linear Programming Problem*

Find the minimum value and maximum value of

$$C = 3x + 2y \quad \textit{Objective quantity}$$

subject to the following constraints.

$$\begin{cases} x \geq 0 \\ y \geq 0 \\ x + y \leq 4 \end{cases} \quad \textit{Constraints}$$

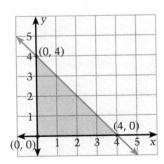

Solution The graph of the constraint inequalities is shown at the left. The three vertices are (0, 0), (4, 0) and (0, 4). To find the minimum and maximum values of *C*, evaluate $C = 3x + 2y$ at each of the three vertices.

At (0, 0): $C = 3(0) + 2(0) = 0$ *Minimum value of C*
At (4, 0): $C = 3(4) + 2(0) = 12$ *Maximum value of C*
At (0, 4): $C = 3(0) + 2(4) = 8$

The minimum value of *C* is 0. It occurs when $x = 0$ and $y = 0$. The maximum value is 12, when $x = 4$ and $y = 0$. ■

It is important to try evaluating *C* at other points in the graph of the constraints. The value of *C* will be always greater than or equal to 0 and less than or equal to 12. For instance, at the point (2, 1) the value of *C* is 8.

Example 2 Solving a Linear Programming Problem

Find the minimum value and maximum value of

$$C = 4x + y \qquad \textit{Objective quantity}$$

subject to the following constraints.

$$\begin{cases} x \geq 1 \\ x \leq 4 \\ y \geq 2 \\ y \leq 5 \end{cases} \qquad \textit{Constraints}$$

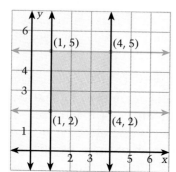

Solution The graph of the constraint inequalities is shown at the left. The four vertices are (1, 2), (1, 5), (4, 5) and (4, 2). To find the minimum and maximum values of C, evaluate $C = 4x + y$ at each of the four vertices.

At (1, 2): $C = 4(1) + (2) = 6$ *Minimum value of C*
At (1, 5): $C = 4(1) + (5) = 9$
At (4, 5): $C = 4(4) + (5) = 21$ *Maximum value of C*
At (4, 2): $C = 4(4) + (2) = 18$

The minimum value of C is 6. It occurs when $x = 1$ and $y = 2$. The maximum value of C is 21. It occurs when $x = 4$ and $y = 5$. ∎

Example 3 Solving a Linear Programming Problem

Find the minimum value and maximum value of

$$C = 5x + 4y \qquad \textit{Objective quantity}$$

subject to the following constraints.

$$\begin{cases} x \qquad \geq 0 \\ \qquad y \geq 0 \\ x + 2y \leq 4 \\ x - \ y \leq 1 \end{cases} \qquad \textit{Constraints}$$

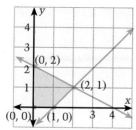

Solution The graph of the constraint inequalities is shown at the left. The four vertices are (0, 0), (1, 0), (2, 1) and (0, 2). To find the minimum and maximum value of C, evaluate $C = 5x + 4y$ at each of the four vertices.

At (0, 0): $C = 5(0) + 4(0) = 0$ *Minimum value of C*
At (1, 0): $C = 5(1) + 4(0) = 5$
At (2, 1): $C = 5(2) + 4(1) = 14$ *Maximum value of C*
At (0, 2): $C = 5(0) + 4(2) = 8$

The minimum value of C is 0. It occurs when $x = 0$ and $y = 0$. The maximum value of C is 14. It occurs when $x = 2$ and $y = 1$. ∎

Connections
Discrete Mathematics

Example 4   *Finding the Maximum Profit*

You own a bicycle manufacturing plant and can assemble bicycles using two processes. The hours of unskilled labor, machine time, and skilled labor *per bicycle* are given in the matrix. You can use up to 4200 hours of unskilled labor and up to 2400 hours each of machine time and skilled labor. How many bicycles should you assemble by each process to obtain a maximum profit?

Assembly Hours	Process A	Process B	
Unskilled labor	3	3	*Process A earns a profit*
Machine time	1	2	*of $45 per bike, and*
Skilled labor	2	1	*Process B earns a profit*

Process B earns a profit of $50 per bike.

Solution   Let *a* and *b* represent the number assembled with each process. Because you want a maximum profit, *P*, the objective quantity is

$P = 45a + 50b$.   *Profit factors for each process*

The constraints are as follows.

$$\begin{cases} 3a + 3b \le 4200 & \textit{Unskilled labor: Up to 4200 hours} \\ a + 2b \le 2400 & \textit{Machine time: Up to 2400 hours} \\ 2a + b \le 2400 & \textit{Skilled labor: Up to 2400 hours} \\ a \ge 0, b \ge 0 & \textit{Cannot produce negative amounts.} \end{cases}$$

The profits at vertices of the region are as follows.

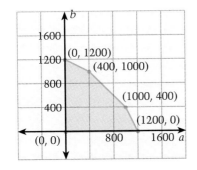

At (0, 1200): $P = \$60,000$
At (400, 1000): $P = \$68,000$ *Maximum profit*
At (1000, 400): $P = \$65,000$
At (1200, 0): $P = \$54,000$
At (0, 0): $P = \$0$

The maximum profit is obtained by making 400 bicycles with Process A and 1000 bicycles with Process B.   ∎

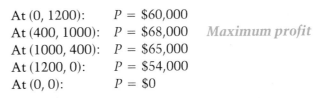

Communicating about **ALGEBRA**

▶ **SHARING IDEAS about the Lesson**

Vary the Conditions   How many bicycles should you produce by each process of Example 4 if the profit per bicycle is $30 for Process A, $65 for Process B?

EXERCISES

▶ **CRITICAL THINKING about the Lesson**

1. How are constraints used to solve a linear programming problem?

2. How is the objective quantity used to solve a linear programming problem?

3. What does the word *optimize* mean?

In Exercises 4–6, use the objective quantity $C = 5x + 7y$ and the vertices (0, 2), (0, 4), (1, 5), (6, 3), (5, 0), and (3, 0).

4. Graph the region determined by the given vertices.

5. Find the minimum value of the objective quantity.

6. Find the maximum value of the objective quantity.

Independent Practice

In Exercises 7–10, sketch the graph of the constraints. Label the vertices of the graph.

7.
$$\begin{cases} x + 3y \le 15 \\ 4x + y \le 16 \\ x \ge 0 \\ y \ge 0 \end{cases}$$

8.
$$\begin{cases} x + y \le 3 \\ x + 2y \le 4 \\ x \ge 0 \\ y \ge 0 \end{cases}$$

9.
$$\begin{cases} 2x + 2y \le 10 \\ x + 2y \le 6 \\ x \ge 0 \\ y \ge 0 \end{cases}$$

10.
$$\begin{cases} x + 2y \le 6 \\ 2x + y \le 6 \\ x \ge 0 \\ y \ge 0 \end{cases}$$

In Exercises 11–14, find the minimum and maximum values of the objective quantity C.

11. $C = 3x + 2y$
Constraints:
$$\begin{cases} x + y \le 7 \\ x \le 5 \\ y \le 5 \\ x \ge 0 \\ y \ge 0 \end{cases}$$

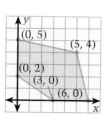

12. $C = 3x + 4y$
Constraints:
$$\begin{cases} 3x + y \le 18 \\ x + y \le 8 \\ x + 4y \le 20 \\ x \ge 0 \\ y \ge 0 \end{cases}$$

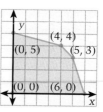

13. $C = 5x + 6y$
Constraints:
$$\begin{cases} 2x + 3y \ge 6 \\ 4x + y \le 24 \\ x + 5y \le 25 \\ x \ge 0 \\ y \ge 0 \end{cases}$$

14. $C = 6x + 7y$
Constraints:
$$\begin{cases} 6x + 5y \le 30 \\ 3x + 2y \ge 6 \\ x \ge 0 \\ y \ge 0 \end{cases}$$

In Exercises 15–22, find the minimum and maximum values of the objective quantity C.

15. $C = x + 2y$ Constraints:
$$\begin{cases} x + y \leq 6 \\ x \quad\quad \geq 0 \\ \quad\quad y \geq 0 \end{cases}$$

16. $C = 3x + y$ Constraints:
$$\begin{cases} 2x + y \leq 4 \\ x \quad\quad \geq 0 \\ \quad\quad y \geq 0 \end{cases}$$

17. $C = 6x + 5y$ Constraints:
$$\begin{cases} x \quad \leq 5 \\ x \quad \geq 2 \\ \quad y \leq 4 \\ \quad y \geq 3 \end{cases}$$

18. $C = 7x + 2y$ Constraints:
$$\begin{cases} x \leq 7 \\ x \geq 3 \\ y \leq 5 \\ y \geq 2 \end{cases}$$

19. $C = 4x + y$ Constraints:
$$\begin{cases} x + 2y \leq 8 \\ x + \quad y \leq 6 \\ x \quad\quad \geq 0 \\ \quad\quad y \geq 0 \end{cases}$$

20. $C = 2x + 3y$ Constraints:
$$\begin{cases} x + 3y \leq 9 \\ 2x + \quad y \leq 8 \\ x \quad\quad \geq 0 \\ \quad\quad y \geq 0 \end{cases}$$

21. $C = 4x + 3y$ Constraints:
$$\begin{cases} 2x + 3y \geq 6 \\ 3x - 2y \leq 9 \\ x + 5y \leq 20 \\ x \quad\quad \geq 0 \\ \quad\quad y \geq 0 \end{cases}$$

22. $C = x + 6y$ Constraints:
$$\begin{cases} 2x + 3y \geq 6 \\ 3x - 2y \leq 9 \\ x + 5y \leq 20 \\ x \quad\quad \geq 0 \\ \quad\quad y \geq 0 \end{cases}$$

23. *Mixing Juices*   You work at a store that sells bottled fruit juice. You are trying to decide how much of two different blends of apple and pineapple juice to prepare.
- Blend A: 30% apple juice, 70% pineapple juice, profit of $0.60 per liter.
- Blend B: 60% apple juice, 40% pineapple juice, profit of $0.50 per liter.
- Fruit juice in stock: 1200 liters of apple juice, 1400 liters of pineapple juice.

Use linear programming to find how much of each blend you should prepare to obtain a maximum profit. (Hint: How much apple juice is in a liter of Blend A?)

24. *Truck Farming*   You have 100 acres of land to grow lettuce and peas. You want to decide how many acres of each crop to plant to make a maximum profit.
- Lettuce: Investment per acre is $120, and income per acre is $150.
- Peas: Investment per acre is $200, and income per acre is $260.
- Maximum amount you can invest: $15,000

Use linear programming to find how many acres of each crop you should plant. (Hint: How much is the investment for x acres of lettuce?)

25. *Computer Monitors*   You are the manager of a store that sells home computers. You are getting ready to order next month's stock and are trying to decide how many of each of two models of monitors to order to obtain a maximum profit.
- Model A: Your cost is $250; your profit over cost is $45.
- Model B: Your cost is $400; your profit over cost is $50.
- Your combined sales of Models A and B will not exceed 250 units.
- You do not want to order more than $70,000 worth of the two models.

Use linear programming to find how many of each model to order.

26. *Health Drink* You are hunting for a special health drink that you read about, but you can't find one with the recommended amounts of protein and carbohydrates. You find two drinks that have the right ingredients but the wrong proportions. You wonder how much of each to drink and still keep your cost down.

- Recommended Minimum Daily Amount: 3 cups for protein, 5 cups for carbohydrates
- Blend A: 25% protein; 75% carbohydrate; cost is $0.25 per cup
- Blend B: 50% protein; 50% carbohydrate; cost is $0.20 per cup

Use linear programming to find how many cups of each blend you could drink to meet your minimum daily requirement with a minimum cost.

Integrated Review

In Exercises 27–34, sketch the graph of the inequality.

27. $x \leq 4$ **28.** $y \leq 3$ **29.** $3x > y$ **30.** $y \leq 3 + x$

31. $5x + 3y \geq -15$ **32.** $6 - 2y < x$ **33.** $y + 3x > 6$ **34.** $y > 2x - 4$

In Exercises 35–38, sketch the graph of the system of linear inequalities.

35. $\begin{cases} 2x + y \leq 4 \\ 2x + 3y \leq 6 \\ x \geq 0 \\ y \geq 0 \end{cases}$ **36.** $\begin{cases} x + y \leq 27 \\ 2x + 5y \leq 90 \\ x \geq 0 \\ y \geq 0 \end{cases}$ **37.** $\begin{cases} y \geq -2 \\ y \leq 4 \\ x \geq 0 \end{cases}$ **38.** $\begin{cases} 2x - 3y \geq 0 \\ 2x - y \leq 8 \\ y \geq 0 \end{cases}$

In Exercises 39–42, solve the system of linear equations.

39. $\begin{cases} 3x - 2y = 18 \\ 4x + y = 13 \end{cases}$ **40.** $\begin{cases} 2x + 5y = 26 \\ -x + 3y = 20 \end{cases}$ **41.** $\begin{cases} -5x + y = 9 \\ 5x + 6y = 19 \end{cases}$ **42.** $\begin{cases} 4x - 2y = 2 \\ 3x + 3y = 24 \end{cases}$

Exploration and Extension

In Exercise 43, find the minimum value of the objective quantity C. Explain why the objective quantity does not have a maximum value.

43. $C = 2x + 2y$
Constraints:
$\begin{cases} x + 2y \geq 3 \\ 3x + 2y \geq 5 \\ x \geq 0 \\ y \geq 0 \end{cases}$

44. Find a system of constraints whose graph is the region shown at the right. Then find an objective quantity that has a maximum at the vertex (2, 1).

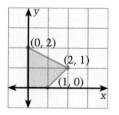

Chapter Summary

What did you learn?

Skills

1. Solve a system of linear equations
   - by graphing.   **(7.1)**
   - by substitution.   **(7.2)**
   - by linear combinations.   **(7.3)**
2. Identify the number of solutions of a linear system.   **(7.5)**
3. Solve a system of linear inequalities.   **(7.6)**
4. Solve a linear programming problem.   **(7.7)**

Strategies

5. Use a system of linear equations to model a real-life situation. **(7.1–7.5)**
6. Use a system of linear inequalities to model a real-life situation. **(7.6)**

Exploring Data

7. Use linear programming to solve a real-life problem. **(7.7)**

Why did you learn it?

Systems of linear equations and systems of linear inequalities occur often as models of real-life situations. One common application is to use a system of linear equations to compare two changing quantities and the rates at which they are changing. For instance, you might want to compare the number of a certain item manufactured in the United States in each of the past ten years with the number that were imported, and how those numbers changed over the ten years. Another common type of application is finding the parts of a mixture. For instance, you might want to find the number of adult tickets and the number of children's tickets sold for a performance. The information you gain from studying systems that model real situations will help you make decisions about those situations.

How does it fit into the bigger picture of algebra?

In this chapter, you studied *systems* of linear equations and linear inequalities. There are three basic methods for *solving* a system made up of two linear equations. You can graph both equations and find the point of intersection of the graphs. You can solve for a variable in one equation and substitute the resulting expression in the other equation. Or you can add a multiple of one equation to the other equation. One of your goals should be to become skilled at all three methods. Another goal—just as important, is to learn the advantages and disadvantages of each method. Using an appropriate method to solve a system of linear equations is part of becoming an efficient problem solver.

In Exercises 1–6, solve the linear system by graphing. (7.1, 7.5)

1. $\begin{cases} 3x + 8y = 4 \\ \frac{3}{2}x + 4y = 2 \end{cases}$

2. $\begin{cases} -x + y = 3 \\ x + y = 7 \end{cases}$

3. $\begin{cases} 2x - 3y = -3 \\ \frac{1}{3}x + 2y = -3 \end{cases}$

4. $\begin{cases} 3x + 5y = 7 \\ 6x + 10y = 8 \end{cases}$

5. $\begin{cases} -2x - 3y = -8 \\ 6x + 2y = 24 \end{cases}$

6. $\begin{cases} 5x - 2y = -17 \\ 3x + 6y = -3 \end{cases}$

In Exercises 7–18, use substitution to solve the linear system. (7.2, 7.5)

7. $\begin{cases} x + 3y = 0 \\ 4x - 2y = -14 \end{cases}$

8. $\begin{cases} 3x - 4y = 6 \\ -x + y = -1 \end{cases}$

9. $\begin{cases} \frac{1}{3}x + y = 2 \\ 2x + 6y = 12 \end{cases}$

10. $\begin{cases} 4x - 3y = -2 \\ 4x + y = 4 \end{cases}$

11. $\begin{cases} x + \frac{3}{8}y = 1 \\ 8x + 3y = 4 \end{cases}$

12. $\begin{cases} -2x + y = 4 \\ 4x - 3y = -7 \end{cases}$

13. $\begin{cases} x - y = 14 \\ 7x - 15y = 50 \end{cases}$

14. $\begin{cases} 3x + y = 11 \\ x + 2y = -3 \end{cases}$

15. $\begin{cases} 5x - 2y = 4 \\ x - 0.4y = 0.8 \end{cases}$

16. $\begin{cases} -2x - 5y = 7 \\ 7x + y = -8 \end{cases}$

17. $\begin{cases} 0.25x - 1.25y = 10.25 \\ x - 5y = 20 \end{cases}$

18. $\begin{cases} x + \frac{1}{2}y = 2 \\ 6x + 4y = 15 \end{cases}$

In Exercises 19–30, use linear combinations to solve the linear system. (7.3, 7.5)

19. $\begin{cases} 8x + 3y = 15 \\ 5x - 2y = -10 \end{cases}$

20. $\begin{cases} 3x + 5y = -16 \\ -2x + 6y = -36 \end{cases}$

21. $\begin{cases} 7x - 3y = -1 \\ 4x + 6y = -16 \end{cases}$

22. $\begin{cases} 2x - 3y = 1 \\ -2x + 3y = 1 \end{cases}$

23. $\begin{cases} -4x - 5y = 7 \\ 3x + 10y = -24 \end{cases}$

24. $\begin{cases} 4x - 5y = 2 \\ 600x - 750y = 300 \end{cases}$

25. $\begin{cases} -6x + 5y = 18 \\ 7x + 2y = 26 \end{cases}$

26. $\begin{cases} 2x - 15y = -20 \\ -4x + 5y = 5 \end{cases}$

27. $\begin{cases} 2x + y = 0 \\ x - 4y = 24 \end{cases}$

28. $\begin{cases} \frac{1}{2}x + \frac{1}{3}y = 8 \\ \frac{1}{4}x + \frac{1}{6}y = 12 \end{cases}$

29. $\begin{cases} \frac{1}{9}x + \frac{1}{3}y = 4 \\ -\frac{1}{3}x - 3y = -18 \end{cases}$

30. $\begin{cases} \frac{5}{12}x - \frac{2}{3}y = \frac{1}{3} \\ \frac{1}{3}x - \frac{8}{15}y = \frac{4}{15} \end{cases}$

In Exercises 31–36, sketch the graph of the system of linear inequalities. (7.6)

31. $\begin{cases} x \geq -3 \\ y \geq 0 \\ y \leq 4 \end{cases}$

32. $\begin{cases} x < 5 \\ y > -2 \\ \frac{1}{2}x + y > -2 \end{cases}$

33. $\begin{cases} x \geq 0 \\ 3x - y \leq 7 \\ 2x + y \leq 2 \end{cases}$

34. $\begin{cases} x + y \leq 5 \\ x + y \geq -5 \\ x - y \leq 5 \\ x - y \geq -5 \end{cases}$

35. $\begin{cases} 3x + 2y \leq 12 \\ x + 2y \leq 8 \\ x \geq 0 \\ y \geq 0 \end{cases}$

36. $\begin{cases} \frac{2}{5}x + y \geq 4 \\ 3x + y \geq 6 \\ y \geq 0 \end{cases}$

In Exercises 37–39, find the maximum and minimum value of the objective quantity C.   (7.7)

37. $C = 3x - 2y$
Constraints:
$$\begin{cases} x \geq & 1 \\ x \leq & 4 \\ y \geq & -3 \\ y \leq & 2 \end{cases}$$

38. $C = 4x + y$
Constraints:
$$\begin{cases} x \geq & 0 \\ y \geq & 0 \\ y \leq & -2x + 6 \end{cases}$$

39. $C = x + 3y$
Constraints:
$$\begin{cases} x & \geq 0 \\ & y \geq 0 \\ -3x + 4y \leq 12 \\ 6x + y \leq 30 \end{cases}$$

In Exercises 40 and 41, use the following information.

A triangle is formed by the lines $y = 0$, $x - y = 1$, and $3x + 2y = 18$.

40. Find the vertices of the triangle.

41. Find the area of the triangle.

42. *Common Nails*   The manager of a hardware store orders the same number of 2-penny nails and 60-penny nails. The total weight of the order is 390 pounds. How many pounds of each did the manager order?

Type of nail	2-Penny	60-Penny
Nails per pound	847	11

Southern and Northern Hemispheres   **In Exercises 43 and 44, use the following information.**

The average daily high temperature in Auckland, New Zealand, decreases from January to May. The average daily high temperature in Mexico City, Mexico, increases during the same time of year.

43. Write equations for the average daily high temperatures in Auckland and Mexico City.

44. In which month is it most likely that the daily high temperatures for the two cities are closest together?

Temperature Comparison

45. *Concert Contract*   You are a concert promoter and sign a contract with a rock group. In the contract, you guarantee an attendance of at least 12,500 and total ticket receipts of at least $225,000. The tickets to the concert will cost $15 and $25, and you agree to give the rock group $5 out of each $15 ticket and $7.50 out of each $25 ticket. Use linear programming to find the minimum amount of money you have guaranteed the rock group. (The graph of the constraints is shown at the right.)

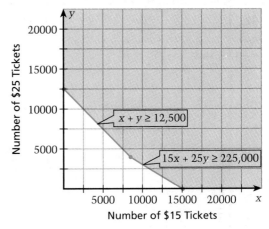

46. *Radio Frequency*   One airplane is flying away from the VOR station. Its course is the line $3x - 2y = -2$. Another airplane is flying toward the VOR station on the line $x + y = 6$. Find the coordinates of the VOR station.

47. *On or Off Course?*   The pilot of the first plane is alerted by the VOR equipment. The plane's coordinates are (10, 17). Is the plane off course or did the VOR equipment malfunction?

A VOR (very high frequency omnidirectional radio) station emits radio signals that enable a pilot to stay on course. If a plane veers off course, the VOR equipment alerts the pilot.

Beech P.35

Piper PA 31P

McDonnell Douglas DC-7C

Tupolev TU-114

McDonnell Douglas DC-9

Boeing 747 B

Tupolev TU-144

48. *Was That a Bird or a Plane?*   A Beech P.35 leaves Dulles International Airport near Washington, D.C., and flies at 176 mph to Chicago's Midway Airport. The Beech flies at an altitude of 10,000 feet during the 600-mile trip. At the same time, a Douglas DC-9 leaves Midway Airport for Dulles International and flies at 561 mph at an altitude of 33,000 feet. Approximate the time that the DC-9 is over the Beech.

49. *Pie-in-the-Sky?*   Your friend Julie tells you that she flew from Reno, Nevada, to Salt Lake City, Utah, to watch the Utah Jazz play the Golden State Warriors. She flew in a Piper PA-31P Navajo at 266 mph. She claims to have made the 850-mile round–trip and watched the game in five hours. Is that possible?

In Exercises 1–3, solve the linear system by graphing.

1. $\begin{cases} x + 2y = 0 \\ 3x + 4y = 2 \end{cases}$

2. $\begin{cases} 5x - y = 12 \\ 3x - 2y = 3 \end{cases}$

3. $\begin{cases} -4x + 7y = -2 \\ -x - y = 5 \end{cases}$

In Exercises 4–9, use substitution to solve the linear system.

4. $\begin{cases} 2x - 5y = -12 \\ -4x + y = 6 \end{cases}$

5. $\begin{cases} -3x + 5y = 11 \\ x - 2y = -5 \end{cases}$

6. $\begin{cases} -x + 3y = 4 \\ 2x - 6y = -8 \end{cases}$

7. $\begin{cases} 5x + y = 3 \\ 10x + 2y = 0 \end{cases}$

8. $\begin{cases} 6x + y = 12 \\ -4x - 2y = 0 \end{cases}$

9. $\begin{cases} 7x + 4y = 5 \\ x - 6y = -19 \end{cases}$

In Exercises 10–15, use linear combinations to solve the linear system.

10. $\begin{cases} 8x - 4y = -11 \\ 6x + 2y = -2 \end{cases}$

11. $\begin{cases} -7x + 2y = -5 \\ 10x - 2y = 6 \end{cases}$

12. $\begin{cases} \frac{1}{4}x - \frac{3}{4}y = -2 \\ 2x - 6y = -16 \end{cases}$

13. $\begin{cases} 6x + 7y = 5 \\ 4x - 2y = -10 \end{cases}$

14. $\begin{cases} 4x + 7y = -11 \\ 14x - 12y = -2 \end{cases}$

15. $\begin{cases} -x + \frac{1}{3}y = -6 \\ 3x - y = -16 \end{cases}$

In Exercises 16–18, graph the system of linear inequalities.

16. $\begin{cases} y > \frac{3}{2}x + \frac{3}{2} \\ y < -\frac{1}{4}x - \frac{1}{2} \end{cases}$

17. $\begin{cases} x \geq 2 \\ y \leq 5 \\ y \geq x - 3 \end{cases}$

18. $\begin{cases} x > 1 \\ y \geq -1 \\ y > -2x + 5 \end{cases}$

In Exercises 19 and 20, find the minimum and maximum value of the objective quantity C.

19. $C = 3x + 2y$

Constraints:
$$\begin{cases} x \leq 3 \\ x \geq 1 \\ y \leq 6 \\ y \geq 2 \end{cases}$$

20. $C = 4x + 5y$

Constraints:
$$\begin{cases} 3x + y \leq 10 \\ x + y \leq 6 \\ x \geq 0 \\ y \geq 0 \end{cases}$$

21. A local herb shop is producing two natural perfumes: *Gentle Rose* and *Rich Gardenia*. The owner of the shop asks you to help decide how much of each to produce. The owner, who has equipment that can make up to 3000 ounces of perfume, cannot afford to spend more than $9000. Use the table and linear programming to find how many bottles of each scent to produce to make a maximum profit.

Scent	Gentle Rose	Rich Gardenia
Bottle size	2-ounce	1.5-ounce
Cost per bottle	$3	$6
Profit over cost (per bottle)	$4	$5

CHAPTER 8

Powers and Exponents

LESSONS

8.1 Multiplication Properties of Exponents ▪ 400

8.2 Negative and Zero Exponents ▪ 406

8.3 Division Properties of Exponents ▪ 413

8.4 Scientific Notation ▪ 419

8.5 Problem Solving and Scientific Notation ▪ 426

8.6 Problem Solving: Compound Interest and Exponential Growth ▪ 432

8.7 Exploring Data: Exponential Growth and Decay ▪ 439

The cockpit displays shown here are actually part of a flight simulator that has been programmed, in this particular case, to represent for the pilot-in-training an approach to Hong Kong International Airport.

**Cockpit Displays
(1920-1970)**

Number of Cockpit Displays

125
100
75
50
25

10 20 30 40 50 *t*

Year (0↔1920)

Between 1920 and 1970, the number, *n*, of cockpit displays in commercial aircraft increased about 4.5% per year. The French *Concorde*, built in 1970, had over 130 cockpit displays. A model that approximates this is $n = 15(1.045)^t$, where *t* is the year, with $t = 0$ corresponding to 1920. Concern for the amount of information that pilots can handle has reversed this trend. The *Airbus*, introduced in the late 1980's, has fewer than 100 cockpit displays.

(Source: Lockheed Corporation)

8.1

Multiplication Properties of Exponents

What you should learn:

Goal 1 How to use the multiplication properties of exponents to evaluate powers and simplify expressions

Goal 2 How to use powers and the exponential change equation as models in real-life settings

Why you should learn it:

You can use exponents in models of real-life situations that involve exponential change, and for repeated factors, such as in formulas for area and volume.

Goal 1 Multiplying with Exponents

Recall from Lesson 1.3 that exponents can be used to represent repeated multiplication. For instance, a^n represents the number that you obtain when a is used as a factor n times.

$$a^n = \underbrace{a \cdot a \cdot a \cdot \cdots \cdot a \cdot a}_{n \text{ factors of } a}$$

The number a is the **base,** and the number n is the **exponent.** The expression a^n is called a **power** and is read as "a to the nth power."

To multiply two powers that have the *same* base, you add exponents. To see why this is true, notice what happens when you multiply a^2 and a^3.

$$a^2 \cdot a^3 = \overbrace{\underbrace{a \cdot a}_{2 \text{ factors}} \cdot \underbrace{a \cdot a \cdot a}_{3 \text{ factors}}}^{5 \text{ factors}} = a^5 = a^{2+3}$$

Multiplication Properties of Exponents

Let a and b be numbers and let m and n be positive integers.

1. To multiply powers having the same base, add the exponents.

$a^m \cdot a^n = a^{m+n}$ *Product of Powers Property*

2. To find a power of a power, multiply the exponents.

$(a^m)^n = a^{m \cdot n}$ *Power of a Power Property*

3. To find a power of a product, find the power of each factor and multiply.

$(a \cdot b)^m = a^m \cdot b^m$ *Power of a Product Property*

Example 1   *Using the Product of Powers Property*

a. $5^3 \cdot 5^6 = 5^{3+6} = 5^9$ **b.** $x^2 \cdot x^3 \cdot x^4 = x^{2+3+4} = x^9$ ■

Example 2 — Using the Power of a Power Property

a. $(2^4)^3 = 2^{4 \cdot 3} = 2^{12}$ **b.** $(y^2)^4 = y^{2 \cdot 4} = y^8$

c. $[(a + 1)^2]^5 = (a + 1)^{2 \cdot 5}$ **d.** $[(-3)^3]^2 = (-3)^{3 \cdot 2}$
$\quad\quad\quad\quad = (a + 1)^{10}$ $\quad\quad\quad\quad = (-3)^6$ ∎

Example 3 — Using the Power of a Product Property

a. $(6 \cdot 5)^2 = 6^2 \cdot 5^2$ **b.** $(2xy)^3 = (2 \cdot x \cdot y)^3$
$\quad\quad\quad = 36 \cdot 25$ $\quad\quad\quad = 2^3 \cdot x^3 \cdot y^3$
$\quad\quad\quad = 900$ $\quad\quad\quad = 8x^3y^3$

c. $(-3a)^2 = (-3 \cdot a)^2$ **d.** $-(3a)^2 = -(3 \cdot a)^2$
$\quad\quad\quad = (-3)^2 \cdot a^2$ $\quad\quad\quad = -(3^2) \cdot a^2$
$\quad\quad\quad = 9a^2$ $\quad\quad\quad = -9a^2$ ∎

Goal 2 — Using Powers as Models in Real Life

The Great Pyramid at Giza was built about 2600 B.C. to house the burial chamber of King Khufu (called Cheops by the Greeks). About two million stone blocks, averaging 2.5 tons each, were used in the building. Deep within the pyramid is the Grand Gallery, a corridor measuring 153 feet long and 28 feet high, which is regarded as one of the marvels of ancient architecture.

Real Life
Architecture

Example 4 — The Great Pyramid

Some of the upper stones of the Great Pyramid of Cheops have long ago disappeared, but the original height was 481 feet. Each side of the square base measures 752 feet. How many cubic feet of space did the original pyramid occupy?

Solution   The volume of a pyramid is one third the height times the area of the base. Thus, this pyramid has a volume of

$$\tfrac{1}{3}hB = \tfrac{1}{3}(481)(752)^2 \approx 91{,}000{,}000 \text{ cubic feet.}$$ ∎

Example 5 _Stacking Paper_

A piece of notebook paper is about 0.0032 of an inch thick. Start with one piece of paper and double the stack 25 times. How tall will the stack be in inches? In feet? In miles?

Solution   After doubling the stack once, you will have 2 pages. After doubling twice, you will have 2^2. After doubling three times, you will have $2^2 \cdot 2$, or 2^3 pages. From this pattern, you can see that after doubling 25 times, you will have 2^{25} pages. To find the height, h, of this stack, multiply 0.0032 of an inch per page by 2^{25} pages.

$$
\begin{aligned}
h = 0.0032 \cdot 2^{25} &\approx 107{,}374.2 \text{ inches} & \textit{Use a calculator.}\\
&\approx 8{,}947.8 \text{ feet} & \textit{Divide by 12.}\\
&\approx 1.7 \text{ miles} & \textit{Divide by 5280.} \quad\blacksquare
\end{aligned}
$$

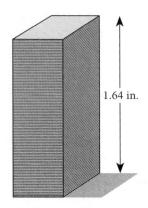

1.64 in.

After doubling 9 times, the stack is about 1.64 inches tall.

The equation $h = 0.0032 \cdot 2^{25}$ in Example 5 is an **exponential equation.** In the general form of an exponential equation $y = C(a)^x$, C is an initial amount, a is a "change" factor, and x is the number of times the change occurs. (Note that the variable x is an exponent.) If $a > 1$, the equation is a model for **exponential growth.** If $a < 1$, the equation is a model for **exponential decay.**

Communicating about ALGEBRA

▶ **SHARING IDEAS about the Lesson**

Visualize Exponential Change   Think about the expression 2^x.

A. Fill in the table of values. Then, for these values, sketch the graphs of $y = 2x$ and $y = 2^x$ on the same coordinate plane.

x	1	2	3
2x	2	4	6
2^x	2	4	8

B. If you were offered a job that paid $2x$ dollars or 2^x dollars for x hours of work, which pay scale would you choose? Explain.

C. After working 8 hours, how much more could you make for working 2 additional hours if your hourly rate is 2^x dollars?

EXERCISES

Guided Practice

▶ **CRITICAL THINKING about the Lesson**

1. Can x^8y^4 be simplified? Explain. *No*

2. Simplify $(a^{10})^3$. What property did you use? *Power of a power.* a^{30}

3. Is $a^5 \cdot a^3 = a^{15}$? Why or why not? *No, add powers, having same base* a^2

4. Is $(-3b)^4 = -12b^4$? Why or why not? *No*

5. Simplify $a^3 \cdot a^4$. Confirm your result by letting $a = 2$ and evaluating the expression in both its original form and its simplified form.

6. Use a calculator to evaluate $(1.06)^{11}$. Round your result to two decimal places.

7. In the general exponential equation $y = C(a)^x$, suppose that $a = 2$, and $x = 3$. Describe how y changes when x is increased by 1.

$y = c(2)^3$

8. Identify each of these equations as a model of exponential growth or of exponential decay.
   a. $y = 3^x$ **b.** $y = 0.5(3)^x$
   c. $y = (0.5)^x$ **d.** $y = 2(0.5)^x$

Independent Practice

In Exercises 9–41, simplify, if possible.

9. $4^2 \cdot 4^3 = 4^5$
10. $6^5 \cdot 6^4 - 6 \cdot 6$
11. $[(-9)^2]^4$
12. $10^2 \cdot 10^9$ 10^{11}
13. $x \cdot x^5 = x^6$
14. $(5^5)^4$
15. $[(2x + 3)^3]^2$
16. $(2x)^3$
17. $(3 \cdot 7)^4$
18. $[(5 + x)^3]^6$
19. $(-5a)^2$
20. $(16 \cdot 2)^2$
21. $(4a)^2 \cdot a$
22. $6^2 \cdot (6x^3)^2$
23. $[(-3xy)^2]^3$
24. $(x \cdot x^2)^3 \cdot 3x$
25. $(3a)^2 \cdot (-4a)^4$
26. $(9a^3)^2 \cdot (2a)^3$
27. $2x^3 \cdot (3x)^2$
28. $3y^2 \cdot (2y)^3$
29. $(-ab)(a^2b)^2$
30. $(-rs)(rs^3)^2$
31. $(-2xy)^3(-x^2)$
32. $(-3cd)^3(-d^2)$
33. $(4a^2)^3(\frac{1}{2}a^3)^2$
34. $(8b^3)^2(\frac{1}{4}b^2)^2$
35. $(-x)^5(-x)^2(-x)^3$
36. $(-y)^4(-y)^3(-y)^2$
37. $(2t)^3(-t^2)$
38. $(-w^3)(3w^2)^2$
39. $(abc^2)^3(a^2b)^2$
40. $(r^2st^3)^2(s^4t)^3$
41. $(-3xy^2)^3(-2x^2y)^2$

In Exercises 42–47, evaluate the expression when $a = 1$ and $b = 2$.

42. $(a^4)^3$
43. $b^3 \cdot b^4$
44. $(a^2 \cdot b)^3$
45. $(a^2b)^5$
46. $(b^2 \cdot b^3) \cdot (b^2)^4$
47. $[(a + 4)^2]^3 \cdot (a + 4)$

In Exercises 48–50, say which number is larger.

48. $(5 \cdot 7)^3$ or $5 \cdot 7^3$
49. $5^4 \cdot 2^5$ or $(5 \cdot 2)^5$
50. $(4^5 \cdot 4^{10})$ or 4^{50}

In Exercises 51 and 52, solve the equation for x.

51. $4^2 \cdot 4^4 = 4^x$

52. $(3^2)^9 = 3^x$

In Exercises 53 and 54, give a convincing argument to explain why the property is true.

53. the Power of a Power

54. the Power of a Product

Technology **In Exercises 55–60, use a calculator to evaluate the expression. Round the results to two decimal places when appropriate.**

55. $(1.1 + 3.3)^3$

56. $5.5^3 \cdot 5.5^4$

57. $2.4^4 \cdot 2.4^2$

58. $(4.0 + 3.9)^2$

59. $(2.9^3)^5$

60. $(9.1^2)^4$

Native Americans in Cahokia **In Exercises 61 and 62, use the following information.**

Over 900 years ago, Native Americans lived in a city called Cahokia, in what is now Illinois. The city had over 30,000 inhabitants and contained several temple mounds. Some of the mounds were over 10 stories tall. The base of the Great Temple Mound covered 15 acres, 2 acres more than the base of the largest pyramid in Egypt.

Native American mounds were built as burial places and as platforms to hold temples and the houses of chiefs. Thousands of these mounds still stand in the U.S. and Canada.

61. The volume of the Great Temple Mound was $\frac{1}{3}\left(\frac{1}{2}\right)(800^3 - 600^3)$ cubic feet. Evaluate this volume.

62. A cubic foot of soil weighs about 90 pounds. How many pounds of soil had to be moved to construct the Great Temple Mound?

In Exercises 63–66, solve the equation $y = C(a)^x$ for the given values.

63. $C = 2$;
$a = 1$;
$x = 50$

64. $C = 1$;
$a = 2$;
$x = 2$

65. $C = 2$;
$a = \frac{1}{2}$;
$x = 3$

66. $C = 4$;
$a = \frac{3}{4}$;
$x = 2$

In Exercises 67–70, identify each of the equations as a model of exponential growth or of exponential decay.

67. $y = 500(1.03)^8$

68. $y = 10(0.99)^{10}$

69. $y = 1000(0.03)^{25}$

70. $y = 0.75(1.01)^{50}$

In Exercises 71–74, evaluate the expression.

71. $a^2 + 2$ when $a = 3$

72. $3x^2 - 5$ when $x = 5$

73. $x^2 + y^3$ when $x = 1$ and $y = 4$

74. $2a^4 - b^3$ when $a = 2$ and $b = 3$

Geometry   **In Exercises 75–77, use the following information.**

The opposite angles of a parallelogram have equal measures.

75. The figure shown is a parallelogram. Solve for x and y.

76. Find the measures of the angles of the parallelogram.

77. Show that the sum of the four angle measures is 360°.

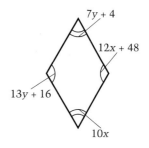

$7y + 4$

$12x + 48$

$13y + 16$

$10x$

Exploration and Extension

78. *Voice Messages*   Between 1985 and 1990, the number, n, of businesses using voice messages increased about 70% per year. The number in year t can be modeled by

$$n = 3960 \cdot 1.7^t$$

where $t = 1$ corresponds to 1986. (3960 is how many thousands of businesses used voice messages in 1985.) If this pattern continued, estimate the number of businesses that used voice messages in 1992. *(Source: Dataquest)*

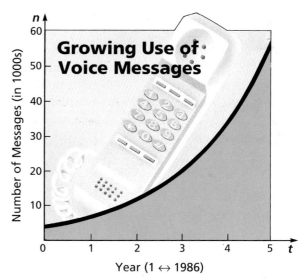

Growing Use of Voice Messages

Number of Messages (in 1000s)

Year (1 ↔ 1986)

Profit   **In Exercises 79 and 80, use the circle graph and the following information.**

Between 1981 and 1990, the annual profit, P, for the H. J. Heinz Company increased about 13% per year. The profit (in millions of dollars) in year t can be modeled by $P = 167.25 \cdot (1.13)^t$, where $t = 1$ corresponds to 1981. *(Source: H. J. Heinz)*

79. Complete the table. If the pattern continues, what would you predict the profit to be in 1994?

Year, t	1981	1983	1985	1987	1990
Profit ($), P	?	?	?	?	?

The H.J. Heinz Company Division

Heinz U.S.A.

Ore-Ida & Weight Watchers food

19.1%

15.4%

3.2% Weight Watchers classes

9.0%

8.0%

Star-Kist tuna

International 40.5%

Pet food

4.8% Hubinger

80. How much of the profit for 1990 was due to the Star-Kist Tuna division of H. J. Heinz?

8.2

Negative and Zero Exponents

What you should learn:

Goal 1 How to use negative and zero exponents in algebraic expressions

Goal 2 Using powers as models in real-life settings

Why you should learn it:

The study of negative and zero exponents helps you to interpret exponential models of real-life settings.

Goal 1 Using Negative and Zero Exponents

In this lesson, you will learn how to evaluate negative and zero exponents. To see how to define negative and zero exponents, consider the following pattern.

$$2^5 = 32, \ 2^4 = 16, \ 2^3 = 8, \ 2^2 = 4, \ 2^1 = 2$$

Each time the exponent decreases by one, the value of the power is halved. If this pattern was to continue, the value of 2^0 would be half of 2, or 1. The value of 2^{-1} would be half of 1, or $\frac{1}{2}$.

$$2^0 = 1, \ 2^{-1} = \frac{1}{2}, \ 2^{-2} = \frac{1}{2^2}, \ 2^{-3} = \frac{1}{2^3}, \ 2^{-4} = \frac{1}{2^4}$$

This pattern suggests how to define negative and zero exponents.

Definition of Negative and Zero Exponents

Let a be a *nonzero* number and let n be a positive integer.

1. The expression a^{-n} is the reciprocal of a^n.

$$a^{-n} = \frac{1}{a^n}, \quad a \neq 0$$

2. A nonzero number to the zero power is 1.

$$a^0 = 1, \quad a \neq 0$$

Note in this definition that a^0 is defined as 1 only if $a \neq 0$. The expression 0^0 is undefined.

Example 1 *Evaluating Powers That Have Negative and Zero Exponents*

a. $2^{-2} = \frac{1}{2^2} = \frac{1}{4}$

b. $(-2)^0 = 1$

c. $(2x)^{-3} = \frac{1}{(2x)^3} = \frac{1}{2^3 \cdot x^3}$
$$= \frac{1}{8x^3}$$

d. $3 \cdot 3^{-1} = 3 \cdot \frac{1}{3}$
$$= 1$$

Expressions with positive exponents are usually considered to be simpler than expressions with negative exponents.

Example 2 *Simplifying Expressions That Have Negative Exponents*

Simplify $2x^{-2}y^{-3}$ by rewriting with positive exponents.

Solution

$$2x^{-2}y^{-3} = 2 \cdot \frac{1}{x^2} \cdot \frac{1}{y^3} \quad \textit{Definition of negative exponent}$$

$$= \frac{2}{x^2 y^3} \quad \textit{Multiply fractions.} \quad \blacksquare$$

Informally you can think of rewriting expressions in positive exponent form as "moving factors" from a denominator to a numerator or vice versa.

$$\frac{3x^{-2}}{4} = \frac{3}{4x^2} \quad \textit{Move from numerator to denominator.}$$

$$\frac{1}{3x^{-4}} = \frac{x^4}{3} \quad \textit{Move from denominator to numerator.}$$

The next example shows how the multiplication properties of exponents can be used with negative or zero exponents.

Example 3 *Using Multiplication Properties of Exponents*

a. $3^{-2} \cdot 3^2 = 3^{-2+2}$
$= 3^0 = 1$

b. $(4^{-2})^2 = 4^{-2 \cdot 2}$
$= 4^{-4} = \frac{1}{4^4}$

c. $(5a)^{-2} = 5^{-2} \cdot a^{-2}$
$= \frac{1}{5^2} \cdot \frac{1}{a^2} = \frac{1}{5^2 a^2}$

d. $\frac{1}{a^{-n}} = (a^{-n})^{-1}$
$= a^{-n \cdot (-1)} = a^n \quad \blacksquare$

Since you can now find a meaning for zero exponents and negative exponents, you can get a better idea of the shape of the graph of $y = 2^x$ in the next Example.

Example 4 *Extending the Graph of* $y = 2^x$

Sketch the graph of $y = 2^x$.

Solution First make a table of values that includes $x \leq 0$.

x	3	2	1	0	-1	-2	-3
2^x	8	4	2	$2^0 = 1$	$2^{-1} = \frac{1}{2}$	$2^{-2} = \frac{1}{4}$	$2^{-3} = \frac{1}{8}$

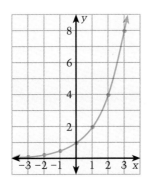

Now sketch the graph. Notice how the graph has a y-intercept of 1, and that it gets closer to the negative side of the x-axis as x values get less. $\quad \blacksquare$

The worst (known) nuclear accident occurred in 1986 at the Chernobyl nuclear power plant. The amount of radioactive material released into the atmosphere was never revealed.

Goal 2 **Using Powers as Models in Real Life**

In Lesson 8.1, you studied some models of exponential growth. Example 5 models exponential decay. Note that the **half-life** of a radioactive substance is that period of time during which the initial mass of the substance is reduced by one-half. After two half-life periods have elapsed, the initial mass will have been reduced by one-quarter, and so on.

Example 5 *Modeling Exponential Decay*

Suppose that 10 grams of the plutonium isotope Pu-239 were released in the Chernobyl nuclear accident. (The half-life of Pu-239 is about 25,000 years.) The number of grams remaining after h half-life periods have elapsed is

$$W = 10\left(\tfrac{1}{2}\right)^h.$$

Sketch a graph that shows how much of the 10 grams will remain after 5 half-life periods.

Solution To begin, make a table of values showing the number of grams left after h half-life periods.

Half-life periods, h	0	1	2	3	4	5
Grams, W	10	5.00	2.50	1.25	0.625	0.3125

By plotting the points given in the table and connecting them with a smooth curve, you can obtain the graph shown at the left. The shape of the graph on the left is typical of an exponential decay model. ■

Half-Life of Plutonium-239

Half-life Periods

Communicating *about* **ALGEBRA**

▷ **SHARING IDEAS about the Lesson**

Extend Your Thinking Graph $y = \left(\tfrac{1}{2}\right)^x$ for $-3 \le x \le 3$.

EXERCISES

Guided Practice

▶ **CRITICAL THINKING about the Lesson**

1. True or False? If a is positive, a^{-n} is positive. Explain your reasoning. _True._

2. Simplify $a^5 \cdot a^{-5}$. The result implies that a^5 and a^{-5} are ⬚ of each other.

3. Rewrite $5a^{-3}b^{-2}$ with positive exponents. Why does the 5 stay in the numerator?

4. Simplify $3c^{-5} \cdot 4c^4$. Can a simplified form have a negative exponent?

5. If $a^0 = 1$ $(a \neq 0)$, what point do all graphs of the form $y = (a)^x$ have in common? Is this true for $y = 2(a)^x$?

Independent Practice

In Exercises 6–17, rewrite the expression using positive exponents.

6. x^{-7}

7. x^{-9}

8. $5x^{-4}$

9. $3x^{-2}$

10. $\dfrac{1}{2x^{-3}}$

11. $\dfrac{1}{4x^{-5}}$

12. $x^{-2}y^3$

13. x^6y^{-7}

14. $3x^{-3}y^{-8}$

15. $6x^{-2}y^{-4}$

16. $\dfrac{1}{7x^{-4}y^{-1}}$

17. $\dfrac{1}{2x^{-10}y^{12}}$

In Exercises 18–29, evaluate the expression.

18. 3^{-2}

19. 2^{-4}

20. $-4^0 \cdot \dfrac{1}{2^{-2}}$

21. $4^{-3} \cdot 4^2$

22. $6^3 \cdot 6^{-1}$

23. $8^4 \cdot 8^{-4}$

24. $7^{-9} \cdot 7^9$

25. $(5^{-3})^2$

26. $(-4^{-2})^{-1}$

27. $-6 \cdot (-6)^{-1}$

28. $5 \cdot 5^{-1}$

29. $2^0 \cdot 3^{-3}$

In Exercises 30–41, rewrite the expression using positive exponents.

30. $(-3)^0 x$

31. $(5y)^{-2}$

32. $(-2x)^{-3}$

33. $(-4a)^0$

34. $(-3x)^{-1} \cdot 2y$

35. $(4xy)^{-2}$

36. $(3x)^{-1}$

37. $(2a^{-3})^3$

38. $\dfrac{4}{b^{-2}}$

39. $\dfrac{5}{a^{-4}}$

40. $\dfrac{1}{(4x)^{-3}}$

41. $\dfrac{1}{(2y)^{-5}}$

In Exercises 42–45, say if the graph of the function contains the point (0, 1).

42. $y = -3^x$

43. $y = 4^x$

44. $y = 3 \cdot 1^x$

45. $y = 50^x$

46. *Population of Missouri*   Between 1970 and 1990, Missouri's population increased at the rate of 0.47% per year. The population, P, in year t is given by

$$P = 4{,}903{,}000 \cdot 1.0047^t.$$

where $t = 0$ corresponds to 1980. Find the population in 1970, 1980, and 1990.

47. *Population of Buffalo*   Between 1970 and 1990, the population of Buffalo, New York, decreased at the rate of 0.82% per year. The population, P, in year t is given by

$$P = 1{,}025{,}000 \cdot 0.9918^t$$

where $t = 0$ corresponds to 1980. Find the population in 1970, 1980, and 1990.

Sunlight produces radioactive carbon (carbon-14), which is absorbed by living plants and animals. Once the plant or animal dies, it stops absorbing carbon-14. Using carbon-14's half-life of 5700 years, scientists are able to approximate the age of plant or animal fossils by determining the percent of carbon-14 in the fossil.

48. Suppose the animal skull in the photograph contained 40 nanograms of carbon-14 when the animal was living. The amount (in nanograms) of carbon-14 in the skull h half-life periods after the animal died was

$$W = 40\left(\frac{1}{2}\right)^h.$$

Complete the table.

A paleontologist uses a brush to clean soil deposits from an animal skull found in the Badlands, South Dakota.

Half-life periods, h	0	1	2
Nanograms, W	?	?	?

49. Upon testing the animal skull, the paleontologist finds that it contains 15 nanograms of carbon-14. Use the table you completed in Exercise 48 to estimate the age of the skull in years.

Swiss Bank Account   **In Exercises 50 and 51, use the following information.**

Swiss banks have the reputation of being safe and confidential. Because of the secrecy given to depositors, some accounts charge a "negative interest."

50. Suppose you deposited $500,000 in a Swiss bank account that charged an interest of 2% per year. The balance in your account after t years is given as

$$A = 500,000 \cdot (0.98)^t.$$

Complete the table.

Year, t	0	2	4	6	8	10
Dollars, A	?	?	?	?	?	?

51. In 1980, money was put into a Swiss bank account that charges 1% interest per year. The balance in the account is

$$A = 633,067.45 \cdot (0.99)^t$$

where $t = 0$ corresponds to 1990. How much was deposited in 1980? What is the 1990 balance? What will the balance be in 2000?

52. *College Entrance Exam Sample* $p^8 \times q^4 \times p^4 \times q^8 = \boxed{?}$

a. $p^{12}q^{12}$ **b.** p^4q^4 **c.** $p^{32}q^{32}$ **d.** $p^{64}q^{64}$ **e.** $p^{16}q^{16}$

In Exercises 53–58, evaluate the expression.

53. 4^3

54. $(-2)^5$

55. $\left(-\frac{2}{3}\right)^2$

56. -8^2

57. $25 - 3^2 \cdot 2$

58. $(12 - 9)^3 \cdot 4 + 36$

In Exercises 59–64, simplify the expression.

59. $a^4 \cdot a^6$

60. $x^2 \cdot y^4 \cdot x^3$

61. $(-t^2)^3$

62. $(4z)^2$

63. $(m \cdot n)^5$

64. $(3a \cdot 2b)^3$

Exploration and Extension

In Exercises 65–68, match the equation with the graph.

65. $y = 2x$ **66.** $y = 2^x$ **67.** $y = \frac{1}{2}x$ **68.** $y = \left(\frac{1}{2}\right)^x$

a.   **b.**   **c.**   **d.**

Elk Antlers   **In Exercises 69–71, use the following information.**

The antler length, *a*, and the shoulder height, *s*, of an adult male elk are related (approximately) by the model

$$a = -40 + (32.5)(1.02)^s$$

where *a* and *s* are measured in inches.

69. Complete the table.

Shoulder height (in.), *s*	50	60	70	80
Antler length (in.), *a*	?	?	?	?

70. Estimate the antler length of the Irish elk shown in the photo at the right.

71. Which is greater? An elk's shoulder height or its antler spread? (The spread is twice the length.)

This is a skeleton of an Irish elk, now extinct. It had a shoulder height of about 58 inches.

1. Find the difference of $\frac{3}{7}$ and $\frac{2}{5}$. **(1.1)**
2. Find the sum of $2x$ and $3x$. **(2.6)**
3. What is 37% of 150?
4. What is $\frac{3}{4}$ of 64?
5. Solve $6a + 5b = 10$ for a. **(3.6)**
6. Solve $45r - 9s = -27$ for r. **(3.6)**
7. Solve $x^2 - 3x + 12 = x(3 + x)$. **(3.3)**
8. Solve $\frac{1}{4}(8x + 2) = -\frac{1}{3}(4 - x)$. **(3.3)**
9. Write $3x + 2y = 6$ in slope-intercept form. **(5.1)**
10. Write $y = -\frac{1}{2}x + 2$ in standard form. **(5.5)**
11. Simplify $3x + 4(3 - x) + 2$. **(2.6)**
12. Simplify $\frac{1}{2} - \frac{3}{4}(y - 12) + \frac{3}{2}$. **(2.6)**
13. Evaluate $3x^2 + 4x^3$ when $x = -1$. **(2.1)**
14. Evaluate $5p + 3p(4 - p)$ when $p = 3$. **(1.2)**
15. Is 3 a solution of $3x + 2 > 9$? **(1.5)**
16. Is $\frac{1}{4}$ a solution of $4(x - 3) \le -10$? **(1.5)**
17. Is $(-2, 3)$ a solution of $3x + 6y \ge 12$? **(6.5)**
18. Is $(4, -2)$ a solution of $\frac{1}{2}x - y \ge 3$? **(6.5)**
19. Solve the system: $\begin{cases} 3x - 2y = -4 \\ -5x + y = 3 \end{cases}$ **(7.3)**
20. Solve the system: $\begin{cases} 6x - 2y = 3 \\ 4x + 2y = 6 \end{cases}$ **(7.3)**

Milestones   EARLY COMPUTERS

1800   1850   1900   1950   2000

Babbage draws plans for computer   Mark I ENIAC

*ENIAC (Electronic
Numerical Integrator
and Calculator)*

The idea of a computer was conceived by Charles Babbage in the 1830's. It took more than one hundred years to turn Babbage's idea into a working machine. In 1944, Howard Aiken completed the Mark I, an electromechanical machine programmed by punched cards. The first all-electronic computer, ENIAC, was completed in 1946. It was 100 feet long, 10 feet high, and 3 feet wide. The ENIAC was programmed by the setting of switches and wiring panels. It greatly increased calculation speed.

The first computers had to be programmed each time they were used. This was extremely time-consuming, and because of the number of steps involved, there were often mistakes made. In the 1940's, John von Neumann suggested that instructions could be stored electronically in the machines. This dramatically reduced the time required to operate the machines. Through technological advances such as the invention of the integrated circuit and its miniaturization onto a silicon chip, computers are now extraordinarily faster, smaller, and less expensive than the original machines.

Find out what each of the following people contributed to computer science: William Shockley, Grace Hopper, and John Mauchley.

Goal 1 Dividing with Exponents

In Lesson 8.1, you learned that you can multiply powers that have the same base by adding exponents. To divide powers that have the same base, you subtract exponents. To see why this is true, let's look at the quotient of 2^5 and 2^3.

$$\frac{2^5}{2^3} = \frac{\overbrace{2 \cdot 2 \cdot 2 \cdot 2 \cdot 2}^{5 \text{ factors}}}{\underbrace{2 \cdot 2 \cdot 2}_{3 \text{ factors}}} = \underbrace{2 \cdot 2}_{2 \text{ factors}} = 2^2 = 2^{5-3}$$

This suggests one of the division properties of exponents.

Division Properties of Exponents

Let a and b be numbers and let m and n be integers.

1. To divide powers having the same base, subtract exponents.

   $$\frac{a^m}{a^n} = a^{m-n}, \qquad a \neq 0 \qquad \textit{Quotient of Powers Property}$$

2. To find a power of a quotient, find the power of the numerator and the power of the denominator and divide.

   $$\left(\frac{a}{b}\right)^m = \frac{a^m}{b^m}, \qquad b \neq 0 \qquad \textit{Power of a Quotient Property}$$

Example 1   *Using the Quotient of Powers Property*

a. $\dfrac{5^4}{5^3} = 5^{4-3}$
$= 5^1$
$= 5$

b. $\dfrac{(-6)^3}{(-6)^3} = (-6)^{3-3}$
$= (-6)^0$
$= 1$

c. $x^2 \cdot \dfrac{1}{x^3} = \dfrac{x^2}{x^3}$
$= x^{2-3}$
$= x^{-1}$
$= \dfrac{1}{x}$

d. $\dfrac{8^2 \cdot 8}{8^5} = \dfrac{8^3}{8^5}$
$= 8^{3-5}$
$= 8^{-2}$
$= \dfrac{1}{8^2}$

Notice that the final steps of **c** and **d** above were to write the results as bases with positive exponents.

Example **2** Using the Power of a Quotient Property

a. $\left(\frac{2}{3}\right)^2 = \frac{2^2}{3^2} = \frac{4}{9}$　　　　**b.** $\left(\frac{1}{x}\right)^3 = \frac{1^3}{x^3} = \frac{1}{x^3}$

c. $\left(-\frac{3}{2}\right)^3 = \left(\frac{-3}{2}\right)^3$　　**d.** $\left(\frac{4}{5}\right)^{-2} = \frac{4^{-2}}{5^{-2}}$

$\qquad\qquad = \frac{(-3)^3}{2^3}$　　　　　　　　$= \frac{5^2}{4^2}$

$\qquad\qquad = \frac{-27}{8}$　　　　　　　　　$= \frac{25}{16}$　■

Example 3 Simplifying Expressions

Simplify $\frac{2x^2y}{3x} \cdot \frac{9xy^2}{y^4}$.

Solution

$$\frac{2x^2y}{3x} \cdot \frac{9xy^2}{y^4} = \frac{(2x^2y)(9xy^2)}{(3x)(y^4)} \quad \textit{Multiply fractions.}$$

$$= \frac{18x^3y^3}{3xy^4} \quad \textit{Product of Powers Property}$$

$$= 6x^2y^{-1} \quad \textit{Quotient of Powers Property}$$

$$= \frac{6x^2}{y} \quad \textit{Write with positive exponents.} \quad ■$$

Goal **2**　**Using Powers as Models in Real Life**

Real Life

Environment

Example 4 Tolerable Amounts of Mercury

Methylmercury is a constituent of industrial waste that, even in very small amounts, is harmful to humans and other animals. The U.S. Food and Drug Administration forbids the sale of fish having more than 1 part methylmercury per one million (10^6) parts of body weight. Suppose you are an FDA inspector and test a 2-kilogram fish that has 3 milligrams of methylmercury. Would this fish meet the FDA requirements? (One milligram is 10^{-3} grams, and one kilogram is 10^3 grams).

Solution　The ratio of methylmercury to body weight is

$$\frac{3 \cdot 10^{-3} \text{ grams}}{2 \cdot 10^3 \text{ grams}} = \frac{1.5}{10^6}$$

$$= 1.5 \text{ parts per million.}$$

This fish has 50% more methylmercury than FDA standards allow.　■

Although the next Example is not primarily concerned with exponential change, you may want to compare the graph of the stock listings with the graph on page 407.

Toxic levels of methylmercury threaten bald eagle populations.

Stocks Listed with the "NYSE"

Number of Shares Listed (in millions) — N axis values: 70,000; 60,000; 50,000; 40,000; 30,000; 20,000; 10,000

Year (0 ↔ 1960), t axis values: −10, 0, 10, 20

Real Life
Finance

Example 5   *Shares Listed on the New York Stock Exchange*

The number of shares (in millions) listed on the New York Stock Exchange from 1940 to 1990 can be modeled by

$$N = 6000 \cdot 1.09^t$$

where t is the year, with $t = 0$ corresponding to 1960. Find the ratio of shares listed in 1990 to the shares listed in 1940.

Solution   For 1990, use $t = 30$ and for 1940, use $t = -20$.

$$\frac{\text{Number listed in 1990}}{\text{Number listed in 1940}} = \frac{6000 \cdot 1.09^{30}}{6000 \cdot 1.09^{-20}}$$

$$= 1.09^{30-(-20)}$$

$$= 1.09^{50} \qquad \textit{Use a calculator.}$$

$$\approx 74.4$$

There were 74.4 times as many listed in 1990 as in 1940.   ■

Communicating about ALGEBRA

▶ **SHARING IDEAS about the Lesson**

Evaluate a Process   Which process for simplifying do you prefer, John's or Valerie's? Why? Simplify the expression, using steps different from these.

John's Solution

$$\left(\frac{a^{-2}}{b^5}\right)^{-3} = \frac{(a^{-2})^{-3}}{(b^5)^{-3}}$$

$$= \frac{a^6}{b^{-15}}$$

$$= a^6 b^{15}$$

Valerie's Solution

$$\left(\frac{a^{-2}}{b^5}\right)^{-3} = \left(\frac{1}{a^2 b^5}\right)^{-3}$$

$$= (a^2 b^5)^3$$

$$= a^6 b^{15}$$

EXERCISES

Guided Practice

▶ **CRITICAL THINKING about the Lesson**

1. Can $\frac{x^{10}}{y^4}$ be simplified? Why or why not?

2. Does $\frac{x^{-4}}{x^{-5}}$ simplify as x or $\frac{1}{x}$?

3. When you divide powers with the same base, do you add or subtract exponents?

4. What is the relationship between $\frac{x^4}{x^2}$ and $\frac{x^{-4}}{x^{-2}}$? Are they equivalent or are they reciprocals of each other? Explain.

Independent Practice

In Exercises 5–16, evaluate the expression.

5. $\frac{6^6}{6^4}$

6. $\frac{8^3}{8^1}$

7. $\frac{(-4)^6}{(4)^8}$

8. $\frac{(-3)^9}{(-3)^9}$

9. $\frac{2^2}{2^{-3}}$

10. $\frac{8^3 \cdot 8^2}{8^5}$

11. $\frac{7^4 \cdot 7^1}{7^7}$

12. $\left(\frac{3}{4}\right)^2$

13. $\left(\frac{5}{3}\right)^3$

14. $\left(-\frac{2}{3}\right)^3$

15. $\left(-\frac{4}{5}\right)^2$

16. $\left(\frac{9}{6}\right)^{-1}$

In Exercises 17–28, simplify the expression.

17. $\left(\frac{2}{x}\right)^4$

18. $\frac{x^4}{x^5}$

19. $\left(\frac{1}{x}\right)^6$

20. $x^3 \cdot \frac{1}{x^2}$

21. $x^7 \cdot \frac{1}{x^9}$

22. $\frac{3x^2y^2}{3xy} \cdot \frac{6xy^3}{3y}$

23. $\frac{4xy^3}{2y} \cdot \frac{5xy^{-3}}{x^2}$

24. $\frac{16x^3y}{-4xy^3} \cdot \frac{-2xy}{-x}$

25. $\frac{-9x^5y^7}{x^2y^3} \cdot \frac{(2xy)^2}{-6x^2y^2}$

26. $\frac{6x^{-2}y^2}{xy^{-3}} \cdot \frac{(4x^2y)^{-2}}{xy^2}$

27. $\frac{7x^{-1}y^3}{x^2y^{-2}} \cdot \frac{(3xy^2)^{-1}}{xy}$

28. $\left(\frac{2xy^{-2}y^4}{3yx^{-1}}\right)^{-2} \cdot \left(\frac{4xy}{2x^{-1}y^3}\right)^2$

Mercury Levels **In Exercises 29 and 30, use the information from Example 4.**

29. As the FDA inspector, you test a $4\frac{1}{2}$-kilogram fish and find that it has 4 milligrams of methylmercury. Does this fish meet FDA requirements?

30. A fish weighing 9 kilograms is found to contain 11 milligrams of methylmercury. As an FDA inspector, do you allow this fish to be sold? If not, how much would the fish have to weigh for 11 milligrams of methylmercury to be acceptable?

31. Toys "Я" Us   From 1980 to 1990, the sales for Toys "Я" Us increased by about the same percent each year. The sales, S (in millions of dollars), in year t can be modeled by

$$S = 640\left(\tfrac{5}{4}\right)^t$$

where $t = 0$ corresponds to 1980. Find the ratio of the 1989 sales to the 1984 sales.

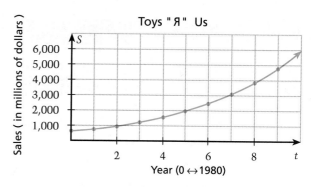

Toys "Я" Us

Sales (in millions of dollars)

Year (0 ↔ 1980)

32. Human Memory   Suppose that you memorized a list of 200 Spanish vocabulary words. Unfortunately, each week you forgot one fifth of the words that you knew the previous week. The number of words, S, you still remember after n weeks can be modeled by

$$S = 200\left(\tfrac{4}{5}\right)^n.$$

Complete the table showing the number of words you remembered after n weeks. How many weeks does it take to forget all but three words? Explain your answer.

Weeks, n	0	1	2	3	4	5	6	7	8
Words, S	?	?	?	?	?	?	?	?	?

33. Olympic Rowing   Shells (boats) used in rowing competition usually have 1, 2, 4, or 8 rowers. Top speeds for racing shells in the Olympic 2000-meter races can be modeled by

$$s = 16.3(1.0285)^n$$

where s is the speed in kilometers per hour and n is the number of rowers. Use the model to estimate the ratio of the speed of an 8-rower shell to the speed of a 2-rower shell.

34. Olympic Participation   From 1932 to 1988, the number of countries that participated in the summer Olympic Games increased by about 2.6% per calendar year. The number of participating countries, n, in year t can be modeled by

$$n = 83(1.026)^t$$

where $t = 0$ corresponds to 1960. (The model does not account for the 1976 or 1980 Olympics because of the boycotts in those years.) Use the model to estimate the ratio of 1988 participants to 1932 participants.

In Exercises 35–40, simplify the expression.

35. $(x^3)^5$　　　**36.** $(a^5)^3$　　　**37.** $x^5 \cdot x^3$　　　**38.** $n^3 \cdot n^{-5}$　　　**39.** $\dfrac{x^{-5}}{x^3}$　　　**40.** $\dfrac{b^3}{b^5}$

In Exercises 41–48, simplify the expression. Then evaluate it for the given values of the variables.

41. $x^3 \cdot x^2 y$; $x = 2$, $y = 3$

42. $a^6 b \cdot a^{-4} b^2$; $a = 10$, $b = -5$

43. $(2x)^2 \cdot (3y^2)^2$; $x = -1$, $y = 2$

44. $(5n^3 m)^4 \cdot (2nm)^2$; $n = 0$, $m = 2$

45. $(xy^4)^{-1} \cdot \left(\dfrac{1}{x^2 y^3}\right)^{-2}$; $x = 2$, $y = 5$

46. $\left(\dfrac{1}{3a^3 b^2}\right)^{-4} \cdot (-3a^{10} b^9)^{-1}$; $a = 4$, $b = 6$

47. $(10r^7 s^{11})^0 \cdot \left(\dfrac{s^2}{rs^3}\right)^{-2}$; $r = 12$, $s = -1$

48. $-\left(\dfrac{x^2 y^3}{x^4 y^2}\right) \cdot \left(\dfrac{2x^7 y^4}{x^5 y^6}\right)^{-2}$; $x = 2$, $y = 3$

Exploration and Extension

In Exercises 49–52, simplify the expression.

49. $x^a \cdot x^a$　　　　**50.** $2^{7x+1} \cdot 2^{3x+4}$　　　　**51.** $\dfrac{x^{a+2}}{x^{a-2}}$　　　　**52.** $\dfrac{x^b}{x^{b+1}}$

Flapping Wings　　**In Exercises 53–56, use the following information.**

When in flight, small birds flap their wings more often than large birds. The number of times per second, n, that a bird flaps its wings during normal flight can be modeled by $nw = 6^3$, where w is the wing length in centimeters. *(Source: On Size and Life)*

The bee hummingbird has a wing length of about 3.5 centimeters.

The California gull has a wing length of about 55 centimeters.

53. How many times per second does the hummingbird above flap its wings?

54. How many times per second does the California gull above flap its wings?

55. What is the ratio of the number of times a bee hummingbird flaps its wings in a second to the number of times a California gull flaps its wings in a second?

56. How would you explain the fact that large birds do not need to flap their wings as often in flight as small birds?

8.4

Scientific Notation

What you should learn:

Goal 1 How to use scientific notation to express large and small numbers

Goal 2 How to perform operations with numbers in scientific notation, with and without a calculator

Why you should learn it:

You can use scientific notation as a convenient way to write very small numbers, like those used in scientific measurements, or very large numbers, like those that give statistical information about the United States.

Goal 1 Using Scientific Notation

In this lesson, you will learn to write decimal numbers in scientific notation. Scientific notation is based on powers of ten.

Decimal form	Power of 10	Name
1,000,000,000	10^9	One billion
1,000,000	10^6	One million
1,000	10^3	One thousand
10	10^1	Ten
1	10^0	One
0.1	10^{-1}	One tenth
0.001	10^{-3}	One thousandth
0.000001	10^{-6}	One millionth

Scientific notation uses powers of ten to express decimal numbers. Here are two examples.

$$1.2 \times 10^3 = 1.2(1000) = 1200$$
$$3.5 \times 10^{-1} = 3.5(0.1) = 0.35$$

Numbers in scientific notation are written $c \times 10^n$, where c is a decimal number greater than or equal to 1 and less than 10.

Example 1 Rewriting Scientific Notation in Decimal Form

a. $1.345 \times 10^2 = 134.5$ Move decimal point 2 places.

b. $3.67 \times 10^4 = 36,700$ Move decimal point 4 places.

c. $7.8 \times 10^{-1} = 0.78$ Move decimal point 1 place.

d. $4.103 \times 10^{-5} = 0.00004103$ Move decimal point 5 places. ■

Example 2 Rewriting Decimals Using Scientific Notation

a. $2450 = 2.45 \times 10^3$ Move decimal point 3 places.

b. $1.78 = 1.78 \times 10^0$ Move decimal point 0 places.

c. $0.000722 = 7.22 \times 10^{-4}$ Move decimal point 4 places. ■

To multiply, divide, or find powers of numbers in scientific notation, use the properties of exponents.

Example 3   *Computing with Scientific Notation*

a. $(1.4 \times 10^4)(7.6 \times 10^3)$

$\quad = (1.4 \cdot 7.6) \times (10^4 \cdot 10^3)$ *Regroup.*

$\quad = 10.64 \times (10^7)$ *Simplify.*

$\quad = 1.064 \times 10^8$ *Scientific notation*

b. $\dfrac{1.2 \times 10^{-1}}{4.8 \times 10^{-4}}$

$\quad = \dfrac{1.2}{4.8} \times \dfrac{10^{-1}}{10^{-4}}$ *Rewrite as a product of fractions.*

$\quad = 0.25 \times 10^3$ *Simplify.*

$\quad = 2.5 \times 10^2$ *Scientific notation* ∎

Most scientific calculators automatically switch to scientific notation to display large (or small) numbers that exceed the display range. Try multiplying 98,900,000 times 500. If your calculator follows standard conventions, its display should be similar to $\boxed{4.945\ E\ 10}$. This means that the result is 4.945×10^{10}.

To *enter* numbers in scientific notation, your calculator should have an exponential entry key labeled $\boxed{EE}$, $\boxed{EXP}$, or $\boxed{SCI}$.

Connections
Technology

Example 4   *Using a Calculator with Scientific Notation*

Use a calculator to evaluate the following.

a. $78{,}000 \times 2{,}400{,}000{,}000$ **b.** $0.000000748 \div 500$

Solution

a. Since $78{,}000 = 7.8 \times 10^4$ and $2{,}400{,}000{,}000 = 2.4 \times 10^9$, you can use the following keystrokes.

                                Display

7.8 $\boxed{EE}$ 4 $\boxed{\times}$ 2.4 $\boxed{EE}$ 9 $\boxed{=}$ $\boxed{1.872\ E\ 14}$

Therefore, the product is 1.872×10^{14}.

b. Since $0.000000748 = 7.48 \times 10^{-7}$ and $500 = 5.0 \times 10^2$, you can use the following keystrokes.

                                Display

7.48 $\boxed{EE}$ 7 $\boxed{+/-}$ $\boxed{\div}$ 5.0 $\boxed{EE}$ 2 $\boxed{=}$ $\boxed{1.496\ E\ -9}$

Therefore, the quotient is 1.496×10^{-9}. ∎

Real Life
Retail Sales

Dollars Spent on Sports Clothes–1990

1.8 Swimming
1.5 Golf
1.3 Alpine Skiing
1.3 Camping
1.0 Hunting

Dollars (in billions)

In 1989, the USA produced 2.8 billion barrels of crude oil. (Source: Energy Information Administration, 1989)

Example 5 *Average Amount Spent on Swimwear*

Find the average amount that an American spent on swimwear in 1990. (The U.S. population in 1990 was 250 million.)

Solution From the chart, you know that the total amount spent on swimwear in 1990 was $1.8 billion.

$$\text{Average amount per person} = \frac{\text{Total amount}}{\text{Number of people}}$$

$$= \frac{1.8 \text{ billion}}{250 \text{ million}}$$

$$= \frac{1.8 \times 10^9}{2.5 \times 10^8}$$

$$= 0.72 \times 10^1$$

$$= 7.2$$

The average amount spent per person was $7.20. ∎

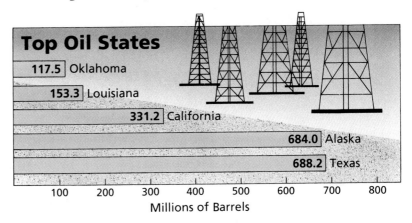

Top Oil States

117.5 Oklahoma
153.3 Louisiana
331.2 California
684.0 Alaska
688.2 Texas

100   200   300   400   500   600   700   800
Millions of Barrels

Communicating about ALGEBRA

Cooperative Learning

▶ **SHARING IDEAS about the Lesson**

Work with a Partner and Use Notation Show how to use scientific notation to help solve the problem.

A. What percent of the crude oil produced in the United States in 1989 was produced in Louisiana?

B. Evaluate successive powers of 5 with your calculator.

$$5^6, 5^7, 5^8, 5^9, \ldots, 5^{17}$$

List your results. For what powers of 5 does your calculator display scientific notation?

C. The mass of one proton is 1.67×10^{-24} gram. One atom of copper has 29 protons. Find the mass of the protons in 2.37×10^{17} atoms of copper.

EXERCISES

▶ CRITICAL THINKING about the Lesson

1. The following numbers are equal. Which one is in scientific notation?
   a. 912   **b.** 9.12×10^2

2. To write 0.000032 in scientific notation, how many places must you move the decimal point?

3. Which is equal to 62,000, 6.2×10^4 or 6.2×10^{-4}?

4. What is one thousand times one millionth? Write your answer in scientific notation.

Independent Practice

In Exercises 5–12, rewrite the scientific notation in decimal form.

5. 1.09×10^6 **6.** 2.345×10^8 **7.** 6.21×10^0 **8.** 9.4675×10^4

9. 8.52×10^{-3} **10.** 7.021×10^{-5} **11.** 8.67×10^{-2} **12.** 4.73×10^0

In Exercises 13–20, rewrite the decimal in scientific notation.

13. 93,000,000   **14.** 900,000,000   **15.** 1,637,000,000   **16.** 67.8

17. 0.000435   **18.** 0.008367   **19.** 0.004392   **20.** 0.0875

In Exercises 21–26, evaluate the expression without a calculator. Write the result in decimal form.

21. $6 \times 10^{-2} \cdot 3 \times 10^4$ **22.** $5 \times 10^5 \cdot 5 \times 10^{-5}$ **23.** $4 \times 10^4 \cdot 2 \times 10^{-1}$

24. $6 \times 10^{-3} \cdot 7 \times 10^{-4}$ **25.** $9 \times 10^{-3} \cdot 4 \times 10^8$ **26.** $8 \times 10^4 \cdot 10 \times 10^{-1}$

Technology   **In Exercises 27–32, use a calculator to evaluate the expression. Write the result in both decimal form and in scientific notation.**

27. $8,000,000 \cdot 623,000$ **28.** $3,000,000 \cdot 43,000$ **29.** $0.000345 \cdot 8,980,000,000$

30. $345,000 \cdot 0.000086$ **31.** $(3.28 \times 10^{-6})^4$ **32.** 0.000045^3

In Exercises 33–36, write the number in scientific notation.

33. *Carbon Atom*   An atom of carbon has a mass of 0.00000000000000000000004 gram.

34. *Population of the United States*   In 1990, the United States population was about 250,000,000.

35. *Quarterback Salary*   Jim Kelly, the quarterback for the Buffalo Bills football team, was paid $4,800,000 in 1990.

36. *Metric Conversion*   One meter is equal to one thousandth of a kilometer.

37. *A Flea and a Whale*   A whale has a mass of 1.0×10^5 kilograms. A flea has a mass of 3.0×10^{-4} kilogram. What is the ratio of the mass of a whale to that of a flea?

38. *Population Increase*   In 1990, Earth's population was increasing by about 8.5×10^7 people per year. Suppose you live in a city whose population increase includes 2000 newborn per year. What percent of Earth's population increase is your city contributing?

39. *Size of the Universe*   The universe is 2.1×10^{23} miles wide. Find the reciprocal of this distance.

40. *Size of a Cell*   Most cells are about 2.5×10^{-3} centimeter in diameter. Find the reciprocal of this distance.

41. *Atoms in the Sun*   The volume of the sun is about 8.5×10^{31} cubic inches. There are about 1×10^{57} atoms in the sun. What is the average number of atoms per cubic inch in the sun?

42. *Sunlight*   Light travels from the sun to Earth in approximately

$$\frac{9.3 \times 10^7}{1.1 \times 10^7} \text{ minutes.}$$

Write this time in decimal form.

43. *Distance to a Star*   A light-year is approximately 5.88×10^{12} miles. Estimate the distance between Earth and Beta Andromedae in miles.

44. *Mass of a Gold Atom*   A proton and a neutron each weigh 1.67×10^{-24} gram. An electron weighs 9.11×10^{-28} gram. Find the mass of one atom of gold.

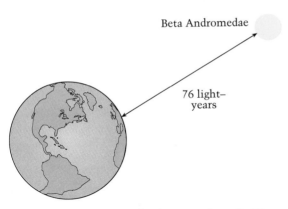

Beta Andromedae

76 light–years

The star Beta Andromedae is approximately 76 light-years from Earth.

An atom of gold has 79 protons, 79 neutrons, and 79 electrons.

Daily Life in the United States   **In Exercises 45–48, consider the population of the United States to be 250 million and consider a year to have 365 days.**

45. Approximately 1.6×10^{10} disposable diapers are thrown into the trash each year. How many are thrown each day?

46. Approximately 1.095×10^{12} gallons of sewage is dumped off the coasts of the United States yearly. How much is dumped each day?

47. Approximately 7.7×10^{10} dollars is given by individuals to charitable groups in a year. What is the average amount given per person?

48. Approximately 7.1×10^9 greeting cards are given yearly. What is the average number of greeting cards received per person?

49. Arrange the numbers in increasing order.

$(9.1 \times 10^4)^4$ $(9.1 \times 10^2)^{10}$ $(9.1 \times 10^5)^4$ $(9.1 \times 10^{10})^2$

50. Which is greater, $\dfrac{1}{4 \times 10^5}$ or $\dfrac{1}{4 \times 10^6}$?

In Exercises 51 and 52, find the slope of the line passing through the two points.

51. $(3.4 \times 10^4, 6.2 \times 10^5), (1.4 \times 10^4, 9.0 \times 10^5)$

52. $(1.9 \times 10^9, 4.6 \times 10^2), (9.9 \times 10^9, 3.4 \times 10^2)$

In Exercises 53 and 54, use the chart.

53. How much did people in the United States spend on mechanical pencils in 1989? Write your answer in scientific notation.

54. How much did people in the United States spend on fountain pens in 1989? Write your answer in scientific notation.

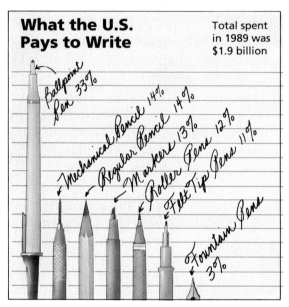

What the U.S. Pays to Write

Total spent in 1989 was $1.9 billion

Ballpoint Pen 33%
Mechanical Pencil 14%
Regular Pencil 14%
Markers 13%
Roller Pens 12%
Felt Tip Pens 11%
Fountain Pens 3%

55. *Speed of Light* The speed of light is approximately 2.9979×10^{10} centimeters per second. Convert this speed to miles per second by evaluating the expression.

$$\frac{2.9979 \times 10^{10} \text{ cm}}{\text{sec}} \cdot \frac{1 \text{ in.}}{2.54 \text{ cm}} \cdot \frac{1 \text{ ft}}{12 \text{ in.}} \cdot \frac{1 \text{ mi}}{5280 \text{ ft}}$$

56. *Speed of a Jet* The fastest speed attained by a jet aircraft is 1.93×10^5 feet per minute. What is this speed in feet per second? In miles per hour?

Mixed REVIEW

1. Evaluate $(3 + 2) \div (27 - 2)$. **(1.1)**

2. Evaluate $12 \div 3 \cdot (4 - 1)$. **(1.1)**

3. Solve $|x + 2| = 3$. **(4.8)**

4. Solve $-3|x + 2| = -9$. **(4.8)**

5. Simplify $3x \cdot (3x)^2 \cdot x^4$. **(1.3)**

6. Simplify $p^2 \cdot q^3 \cdot p^2 q^2$. **(1.3)**

7. Sketch the graph of $3|x - 2| = y$. **(4.7)**

8. Sketch the graph of $8x + 9y = 72$. **(4.3)**

9. What is the reciprocal of x^3? **(2.7)**

10. What is the opposite of $3y$? **(2.1)**

11. Solve $3y + 2(3 - 6y) = 12$. **(3.2)**

12. Solve $(t - 2)\frac{1}{3} - 5t \geq 6$. **(6.1)**

13. Evaluate $3y + 2y^2$ when $y = -3$. **(2.5)**

14. Evaluate $\frac{1}{4}x \div (3 - x)$ when $x = \frac{1}{2}$. **(1.2)**

Take this test as you would take a test in class. The answers to the exercises are given in the back of the book.

In Exercises 1–12, simplify the expression. (8.1, 8.2, 8.3)

1. $q^3 \cdot q^2$

2. $x^2 \cdot x^2 \cdot x^3$

3. $(n^5)^2$

4. $-(t^3)^2$

5. $-3s^2 \cdot 8s^3$

6. $5x^{-5}$

7. $(-2b)^{-2}$

8. $4c^0$

9. $\dfrac{4x^2y}{2xy^2}$

10. $\dfrac{p^{-3}}{p^2}$

11. $\dfrac{4q^4}{3q^{-3}}$

12. $\dfrac{4w^2z^4}{5y^3z^2} \cdot \dfrac{10z^2}{2wy}$

In Exercises 13–18, evaluate the expression. (8.1, 8.2)

13. $6^2 \cdot 6^0$

14. $4^3 \cdot 4^{-4}$

15. $\left(\dfrac{3}{4}\right)^2$

16. $\left(\dfrac{5}{2}\right)^{-2}$

17. $(0.3 + 2.5)^4$

18. $(3^2)^3$

In Exercises 19 and 20, write the number in decimal form. (8.4)

19. 1.0079×10^7

20. 5.006×10^{-4}

In Exercises 21 and 22, write the number in scientific notation. (8.4)

21. 3,789,650

22. 0.00000179

In Exercises 23 and 24, evaluate the expression. (8.4)

23. $(6.2 \times 10^5) \cdot (1.1 \times 10^{-7})$

24. $(5.9 \times 10^{-2}) \div (4.7 \times 10^{-4})$

25. The volume of a sphere can be found by the formula $V = \frac{4}{3}\pi r^3$, where $\pi \approx 3.14$ and r is the radius of the sphere. A spherical 9-inch balloon has a radius of $\frac{9}{2}$. How many cubic inches of air does it hold? **(8.1)**

26. If a water balloon has a diameter of 4 inches, how much water does it hold?

27. Some radioisotopes have a short half-life. The half-life of C-11 is 20 minutes. If you start with 16 grams of C-11, the number of grams remaining after h half-life periods would be $W = 16\left(\frac{1}{2}\right)^h$. Complete the table and use the results to sketch the graph. **(8.2)**

Half-life periods, h	0	1	2	3	4
Grams, W	?	?	?	?	?

28. In one year, 153,900,000,000 pieces of mail are sent via the U.S. Postal Service. Of these, 59,730,000,000 are direct-mail advertising. What percent of the total volume of mail is direct-mail advertising? Use scientific notation to determine your answer. **(8.4)**

8.5

Problem Solving and Scientific Notation

What you should learn:

Goal How to use scientific notation to solve real-life problems requiring very large or very small numbers

Why you should learn it:

You can use scientific notation to help manage the manipulation of large and small numbers, such as in problems about space travel.

Goal | **Using Scientific Notation in Real Life**

Remember the steps of the general problem-solving plan:

Write a verbal model. → Assign labels. → Write an algebraic model. → Solve the algebraic model. → Answer the question.

Example 1 *Landing on the Moon*

On July 20, 1969, the first humans set foot on the moon. The technology required was extremely complicated. The moon is a moving target. *Apollo 11* had to aim at a point far ahead in the moon's orbit. When *Apollo 11* left its temporary "parking orbit" around Earth, its speed was 24,300 miles per hour. After that, its speed decreased continuously until it reached a point at which Earth and the moon exerted equal gravitational pull. The balance of forces at this "equal-gravity" point can be modeled by

$$\frac{\text{Mass of Moon}}{\text{Square of distance to moon's center}} = \frac{\text{Mass of Earth}}{\text{Square of distance to Earth's center}}.$$

The mass of Earth is 1.318×10^{25} pounds. The distance from the equal-gravity point to Earth's center is 2.205×10^5 miles. The distance to the moon's center is 2.446×10^4 miles. Find the mass of the moon.

Solution Let m be the mass of the moon. Substitute the mass of Earth and the two distances into the model and solve for m.

$$\frac{m}{(2.446 \times 10^4)^2} = \frac{1.318 \times 10^{25}}{(2.205 \times 10^5)^2}$$

$$m = \frac{(1.318 \times 10^{25})(2.446 \times 10^4)^2}{(2.205 \times 10^5)^2}$$

$$= \frac{1.318 \times 2.446^2 \times 10^{33}}{2.205^2 \times 10^{10}}$$

$$m \approx 1.622 \times 10^{23} \text{ pounds}$$

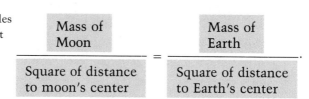

Moon

69 miles
Parking Orbit

2.446×10^4 mi

Equal Gravity Point

2.205×10^5 mi

Earth

118 miles

Parking Orbit

426 *Chapter 8 ▪ Powers and Exponents*

In 1969, Alaska auctioned gas and oil leases on 4.5×10^5 acres for about $900 million, an average cost of about $2000 per acre.

Connections
U.S. History

Example 2 The Purchase of Alaska

In 1867, the United States purchased Alaska from Russia for $7.2 million. The total area of Alaska is about 3.78×10^8 acres. What was the price per acre?

Solution

$$\frac{\text{Price}}{\text{per acre}} = \frac{\text{Total price}}{\text{Number of acres}} = \frac{7.2 \text{ million}}{3.78 \times 10^8}$$

$$= \frac{7.2 \times 10^6}{3.78 \times 10^8}$$

$$\approx 1.9 \times 10^{-2}$$

$$= 0.019 \text{ dollars per acre}$$

The price was about 2¢ per acre. ■

Real Life
Economics

Example 3 Comparing Prices

What is the ratio of the cost per acre of Alaskan land leased for gas and oil in 1969 to its purchase price in 1867?

Solution

$$\frac{1969 \text{ cost per acre}}{1867 \text{ cost per acre}} = \frac{2000}{0.02} = \frac{2.0 \times 10^3}{2.0 \times 10^{-2}} = 1.0 \times 10^5$$

Thus the land leased for about one hundred thousand times its purchase price. (The average cost of living in the United States increased by only three or four times from 1867 to 1969.) ■

Engineers at the University of Wisconsin-Madison have created nickel microgears that have a diameter of only 1.0×10^{-4} meter. The holes in the gears are too small for a human hair to fit through.

Real Life
Engineering

$\leftarrow 2.4 \times 10^{-2} \text{ m} \rightarrow$

Example 4   *Gear Ratio*

Suppose that a microgear is connected to a gear the size of a quarter. What is the gear ratio of the quarter to the microgear?

Solution   The way to get an exact answer would be to know the number of teeth on each gear. Without that, you can approximate the gear ratio by finding the ratio of the two circumferences. (The circumference of a circle is π times its diameter.)

$$\text{Gear ratio} \approx \frac{\text{Circumference of quarter}}{\text{Circumference of microgear}} = \frac{\pi(2.4 \times 10^{-2})}{\pi(1.0 \times 10^{-4})}$$

$$= 2.4 \times 10^2$$
$$= 240$$

The gear ratio is 240, which means that the microgear would turn 240 times each time the quarter turns once! ■

Communicating about ALGEBRA

▶ **SHARING IDEAS about the Lesson**

Find Needed Information   Information needed to solve this problem may be found elsewhere in this lesson.

The ratio of gravity on the surface of the moon to gravity on Earth's surface is given by

$$\frac{\text{Mass of moon}}{\text{Square of moon's radius}} \div \frac{\text{Mass of Earth}}{\text{Square of Earth's radius}}.$$

What is this ratio? (The radius of Earth is about 3960 miles. The radius of the moon is about 1080 miles.)

EXERCISES

Guided Practice

▶ **CRITICAL THINKING about the Lesson**

1. List the five steps of the general problem-solving plan.

Busy as a Bee   **In Exercises 2–6, use the following information.**

How many flowers must the 80,000 workers in a bee colony visit to provide the amount of honey the colony will consume in one year?

2. Write a verbal model for this problem.

3. Assign labels to the model.

4. Write an algebraic model for the problem.

5. Solve the algebraic model.

6. Answer the question. Give your answer in scientific notation.

Hard-working Bees

To make 2.2 pounds of honey, workers must visit 45–64 million flowers.

A large bee colony consumes 500 pounds of honey a year.

Independent Practice

7. *Sunlight on Jupiter*   The distance between Jupiter and the sun is 7.8×10^8 kilometers. Light travels at a speed of about 3.0×10^5 kilometers per second. How long does it take light to travel from the sun to Jupiter?

8. *Earth and Jupiter*   The distance between Earth and the sun is 1.5×10^8 kilometers. Write an inequality that describes possible distances, d, between Earth and Jupiter.

Louisiana and Gadsden Purchases   **In Exercises 9 and 10, use the following information.**

The Louisiana Purchase, in 1803, added 8.28×10^5 square miles to the United States. The cost of this land was $15 million. The Gadsden Purchase, 1853, added 2.94×10^4 square miles and cost $10 million.

9. Find the average cost of a square mile for each of these two purchases.

10. There are 640 acres in a square mile. Find the average cost of an acre for each of these two purchases.

Thirteen Colonies 1776
Addition of 1783
Louisiana Purchase 1803
Red River Cession 1818
Florida Cession 1819
Texas Annexation 1845
Oregon Country Purchase 1846
Mexican Cession 1848
Gadsden Purchase 1853

The table shows the number of manufacturers' coupons distributed in the United States between 1985 and 1989. (*Source: A. C. Nielson Company*)

Year	1985	1986	1987	1988	1989
Coupons distributed	1.999×10^{11}	2.252×10^{11}	2.383×10^{11}	2.474×10^{11}	2.676×10^{11}
Percent redeemed	3.25%	3.15%	3.02%	2.87%	2.65%
Number redeemed	?	?	?	?	?

11. Find the number of coupons *redeemed* in each year.

12. Suppose that the average coupon value was $0.25. What was the total value of unredeemed coupons over the five-year period? Write your answer in scientific notation.

13. *Cells of Mammals*   Ribosomes are composed of different types of proteins and RNA (ribonucleic acid). A typical cell of a mammal contains about 10×10^{7} ribosomes. The volume of a ribosome is about 2.5×10^{-17} cubic centimeter. What is the minimum volume of a typical mammal cell?

14. *Heartbeats in a Lifetime*   Consider a person whose heart beats 80 times per minute and who lives to be 75 years old. Estimate the number of times the person's heart beats in all.

15. *Batter Up!*   A baseball pitcher can throw the ball to home plate in about 0.5 second. The distance between the pitcher's mound and home plate is 60.5 feet. This means that the ball is traveling at a rate of

$$\frac{121 \text{ feet}}{\text{second}} \cdot \frac{\text{meter}}{3.28 \text{ feet}} \cdot \frac{1000 \text{ millimeters}}{\text{meter}}$$

$$\approx 36.9 \times 10^{3} \text{ millimeters per second.}$$

In this photo of a bacterium, the red areas are ribosomes attached to chains of RNA called polysomes.

To hit a home run, a batter has a leeway of only about 20 millimeters in the point of contact between bat and ball. What is the most that the batter's timing could be off and still result in a home run? (Hint: Find the time that it takes the ball to travel 20 millimeters.)

16. *Travel to a Star*   The star Sirius A is 8.265×10^{13} kilometers from Earth. The space probe *Voyager 2* was 4.494×10^{9} kilometers from Earth in September 1989. Suppose that *Voyager 2* was headed for Sirius A. What percent of its journey was complete by September 1989?

17. *Population Density of the United States*   The United States has a land area of 3.54×10^{6} square miles. In 1990, the population of the United States was 2.5×10^{8}. What was the population density (people per square mile) of the United States in 1990?

In Exercises 18–26, simplify the expression.

18. $(5x^4)(2x^0)$

19. $(3y^2)(8y^3)$

20. $\dfrac{2a^2}{a^3}$

21. $\dfrac{4b^3}{b^7}$

22. $(-3xy^4)(4xy^{-3})$

23. $(6x^3y)(7x^{-1}y^8)$

24. $\dfrac{12(x^2y^4)^0}{-6x^{-2}y^2}$

25. $\left(\dfrac{5x^3}{y}\right)^{-2}$

26. $\left(\dfrac{3}{4}\right)^2 \cdot \left(\dfrac{2}{3}\right)^4$

In Exercises 27 and 28, write the number in scientific notation.

27. 0.00000065

28. 24,000,000,000

In Exercises 29 and 30, write the number in decimal form.

29. 2.65×10^{15}

30. 4.316×10^{-11}

In Exercises 31 and 32, evaluate the expression.

31. $4.2 \times 10^{-5} \cdot 6.1 \times 10^8$

32. $5.04 \times 10^{12} \cdot 8.97 \times 10^{-7}$

Lightning   **In Exercises 33–36, use the following information.**

Approximately 44,000 thunderstorms and 8 million lightning flashes take place daily around the world. In the United States, lightning annually causes about 150 deaths and $20 million in property damage. It sets 10,000 forest fires a year, which destroy $30 million worth of timber.
(Source: Scientific American)

33. Approximate the number of lightning flashes that occur each year on Earth.

34. What is the average number of lightning flashes in a thunderstorm?

35. Sound travels at a speed of 1100 feet per second. Suppose you see a lightning flash and then count, "One-one-thousand, two-one-thousand, three-one-thousand, four-one-thousand, five-one-thousand" before you hear the thunder. About how far away was the lightning?

36. The length of a normal lightning flash varies between 300 feet and 4 miles. Write an inequality that describes the possible lengths (in feet) of a normal lightning flash.

8.6

Problem Solving: Compound Interest and Exponential Growth

What you should learn:

Goal 1 How to use the compound interest formula

Goal 2 How to use models for exponential growth to solve real-life problems

Why you should learn it:

You can use an exponential growth model for situations that increase regularly by a fixed percent, such as the growth of an embryo.

Goal 1 Computing Compound Interest

Money can work for you if you place it in a savings or investment account. At an annual interest rate of r, a principal, P, earns *simple interest* of Pr in one year. Think of r as a decimal, and thus, 6% of P is $P(0.06)$. The balance, A_1, at the end of the first year is the sum of the principal and the interest.

$$A_1 = P + Pr$$
$$A_1 = P(1 + r) \qquad \textit{Balance after one year}$$

If the balance is left in the account for another year, the new balance, A_2, at the end of the second year would be

$$A_2 = A_1(1 + r) = P(1 + r)^2. \qquad \textit{Balance after two years}$$

This formula represents **compound interest.** Compound interest is paid on the original principal *and* on interest that becomes part of the account.

Compound Interest Formula

If a principal, P, earns an annual interest rate of r, then the balance after t years will be

$$A = P(1 + r)^t.$$

Real Life

Finance

Example 1 *Finding the Balance in an Account*

a. $500 is deposited in an account that pays 6% annual interest compounded yearly. What is the balance after 10 years?

$$A = P(1 + r)^t \qquad \textit{Compound interest formula}$$
$$= 500(1 + 0.06)^{10} \qquad \textit{P = 500, r = 0.06, t = 10}$$
$$= 500(1.06)^{10} \qquad \textit{Use a calculator.}$$
$$= \$895.42$$

b. $250 is deposited in an account that pays 5.5% interest compounded yearly. What is the balance after 8 years?

$$A = P(1 + r)^t \qquad \textit{Compound interest formula}$$
$$= 250(1 + 0.055)^8 \qquad \textit{P = 250, r = 0.055, t = 8}$$
$$= 250(1.055)^8 \qquad \textit{Use a calculator.}$$
$$= \$383.67$$

Using Models for Exponential Growth

In Lesson 8.1, you learned that in the exponential model $y = C(a)^x$, if $a > 1$, the change is exponential **growth.** The compound interest formula is an example of an exponential growth model. An initial amount, C, is multiplied by a **growth factor** $(1 + r)$ each time period. At each stage, the amount increases by r percent. (The percentage increase, r, is positive and is written in decimal form.)

$C(1 + r)^1$ *Amount at time 1*
$C(1 + r)^2$ *Amount at time 2*

Real Life
Economics

Example **2**   *Cafeteria Workers*

In 1975, the average hourly wage of school cafeteria workers in the United States was $2.53. Between 1975 and 1990, this increased by $0.285 per year. During the same years, the cost of living in the United States increased by an average of 6.2% per year. Did the average hourly wage of school cafeteria workers keep up with inflation? *(Source: National Survey of Salaries and Wages in Public Schools)*

Solution   Let W be the hourly wage in year t, with $t = 0$ corresponding to 1975. Because the average wage increased by the *same amount* each year, you can use a *linear* model.

$W = 0.285t + 2.53$ *Linear model for hourly wage*

Because the cost of living increased by the *same percent* each year, you can use an *exponential growth* model.

$C = 2.53(1.062)^t$ *Exponential growth model*

The table compares values of W and C for four different years.

Wages and Cost of Living

Average Hourly Wage

Year (0 ↔ 1975)

Year, t	0 (1975)	5 (1980)	10 (1985)	15 (1990)
Hourly wage, **W**	$2.53	$3.96	$5.38	$6.81
Cost of living, **C**	$2.53	$3.42	$4.62	$6.24

You can use either the table or the graph to see that the hourly wage did keep up with inflation during the 15-year period. ■

In Example 2, the linear model grew more quickly than the exponential model over 15 years. Over long time periods, however, an exponential growth model will eventually overtake a linear model. For instance, in Example 2, suppose that the cost of living continues to increase at 6.2% per year. By the year 2000, cafeteria workers would need an hourly wage of $11.38 to keep up. They couldn't do that by continuing to get annual raises of $0.285 per hour. Why?

Through mitosis, a fertilized egg repeatedly doubles its number of cells. Cells soon begin to show new structural and biochemical characteristics, and within five weeks, the embryo shows recognizable features.

Weight Gain
by Human Embryos

Connections
Biology

Example 3   Growth of a Human Embryo

Growth of a human embryo is approximately exponential, increasing at about 28.5% each day. A model for the weight of a human embryo is

$$W = 0.0125 \cdot 1.285^t$$

where W is the weight in milligrams and t is the age of the embryo in days. Sketch the graph of this model.

Solution   Begin by making a table of values.

Age, t	0	7	14	21	28	35	42	45
Weight, W	0.0125	0.07	0.42	2.42	14.0	81.0	469	994

The graph of the model is shown at the left.   ■

Communicating about ALGEBRA

▶ **SHARING IDEAS about the Lesson**

Make a Decision   Use tables and graphs to compare the two salary offers. Which is linear growth? Which is exponential growth? Which salary plan would you prefer? Explain.

A. You are offered job A with a starting salary of $24,000. Each year for 10 years you will be given a 4% raise.

B. You are offered job B with a starting salary of $24,000. Each year for 10 years you will be given a $1000 raise.

EXERCISES

▶ **CRITICAL THINKING about the Lesson**

1. **True or False?** Any quantity that increases by the *same percent* each year can be represented by an exponential growth model.

2. One thousand dollars is deposited in an account that pays interest at the rate of 5% compounded yearly. What is the balance after 10 years?

3. In the exponential growth model $y = C(1 + r)^t$, what is the growth factor?

4. In the exponential growth model of Exercise 3, what does *r* represent?

Independent Practice

5. *What Is the Balance?* A principal of $100 is deposited in an account that pays 7% interest compounded yearly. Find the balance after 5 years.

6. *What Is the Balance?* A principal of $1200 is deposited in an account that pays 5% interest compounded yearly. Find the balance after 10 years.

7. *How Much Should I Deposit?* How much must you deposit in an account that pays 6.5% interest compounded yearly to have a balance of $600 after 8 years?

8. *How Much Should I Deposit?* How much must you deposit in an account that pays 7% interest compounded yearly to have a balance of $200 after 5 years?

In Exercises 9–12, match the graph with the description.

9. Deposit: $200, Annual rate: 6%

10. Deposit: $200, Annual rate: 9.5%

11. Deposit: $550, Annual rate: 8%

12. Deposit: $550, Annual rate: 4.5%

a.

b.

c.

d.
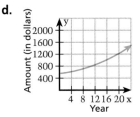

13. *Population of Texas* From 1960 to 1990, the population of Texas increased by about 1.94% per year. Write an exponential growth model that gives the population, *P*, in terms of the year, *t*. Let *t* = 0 represent 1960.

14. Estimate the population of Texas in 1970, in 1980, and in 1990.

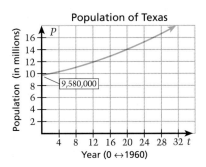

Managing a Business   In Exercises 15 and 16, match the graph with the description. Which business would you rather own? Explain.

15. A business has a $10,000 profit in 1980. The profit increases by $2500 per year for 10 years.

a.
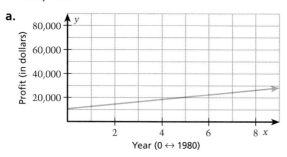

16. A business has a $10,000 profit in 1980. The profit increases by 25% per year for 10 years.

b.
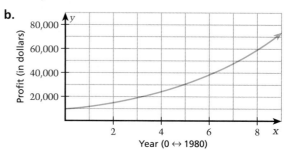

In Exercises 17 and 18, write an exponential growth equation.

17. *M.D.'s in the United States*   From 1970 to 1990, the number of doctors of medicine in the United States increased by about 3.4% per year.

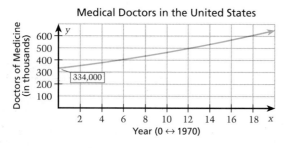

18. *Furniture Sales*   From 1970 to 1990, the total wholesale furniture sales in the United States increased by about 10% per year.

In Exercises 19 and 20, follow the instructions below.

Write a linear growth equation for the earnings. Then write an exponential growth equation showing what the earnings would have been in order to keep up with the inflation rate. (From 1975 to 1990, the inflation rate averaged 6.2% per year.) Did the workers' earnings keep up with inflation?

19. *Construction*   From 1975 to 1990, the average weekly earnings of construction workers in the United States increased by $17.46 per year.

20. *School Bus Drivers*   From 1975 to 1990, the average hourly wage of school bus drivers in the United States increased by $0.36 per year.

In Exercises 21–26, evaluate the expression.

21. $-3x^3$, when $x = \frac{1}{2}$

22. 2^x, when $x = 5$

23. $(1 + y)^y$, when $y = 3$

24. $5x^4 - 9$, when $x = 1.1$

25. $a^2 - 4$, when $a = 4.9$

26. $3^{2b} - 4(9^b)$, when $b = 2$

In Exercises 27–30, write the number in scientific notation.

27. 0.00462

28. 54,000

29. 67,500,000

30. 0.000000751

31. *College Entrance Exam Sample*   A man runs 5 miles per hour for $1\frac{1}{2}$ hours. If a woman runs the same distance in 1 hour, what is the woman's average speed in miles per hour?

 a. 10   **b.** $9\frac{1}{2}$ **c.** $7\frac{1}{2}$ **d.** 5   **e.** $4\frac{1}{2}$

32. *College Entrance Exam Sample* $(x^a)^b = \boxed{?}$.

 a. x^{a+b} **b.** x^{ab} **c.** y^{ax} **d.** b^{xa}

A bird egg has two diameters, the average of which can be related to the length of the adult bird. The average egg diameter for a robin is 23.8 mm; for a house wren, 14.0 mm; and for a chickadee, 13.0 mm.

Bird Eggs   **In Exercises 33–36, use the graph, which relates the average, *A* (in millimeters), of the two diameters of a bird egg with the length, *L* (in centimeters), of an adult bird.**

33. Which model best represents the growth curve shown?
 a. $L = (0.09)(1.237)^A$
 b. $L = 12 + (0.09)(1.237)^A$
 c. $L = 12 + [(0.09)(1.237)]^A$

34. Estimate the length of an adult house wren from the graph.

35. Estimate the length of an adult house wren using the exponential growth model.

36. Use the exponential growth model to find the ratio of the length of a chickadee to the length of a robin.

Egg Size and Adult Size

Length (in cm) / Egg Diameter (in mm)

The graphing calculator feature in Chapter 5 described how to use a graphing calculator to find a best-fitting line. Here we show how to use a graphing calculator to find a best-fitting exponential growth or decay model. The calculator will find two numbers, a and b, for the exponential growth model $y = a(b^x)$. The best-fitting exponential growth model for the following points is $y = 0.931(1.54)^x$. The graph of the model and the scatter plot of the points are shown at the right.

(1, 1.2), (1.5, 2.1), (2, 2.2), (2.5, 2.6), (3, 3.7)
(3.5, 4.3), (4, 5.9), (4.5, 6.4), (5, 7.8), (5.5, 9.5)

TI-81

Enter data. (See p. 166.)
| 2nd | | STAT | | 4 | | ENTER |

   a = .9311818813
   b = 1.542462151

| Y= | Enter equation.

   :Y₁ = .931*1.54/\X

| 2nd | | STAT |

Cursor to DRAW
| 2 | | ENTER |

Casio fx-7700G

Exercises

In Exercises 1 and 2, find the best-fitting exponential growth model for the points.

1. (0, 1), (1, 1.4), (2, 3), (3, 5), (4, 8)
   (5, 12), (6, 20), (7, 30), (8, 50), (9, 80)

2. (0, 0.5), (1, 0.6), (2, 0.8), (3, 1.0), (4, 1.4)
   (5, 1.8), (6, 2.7), (7, 3.6), (8, 4.9), (9, 7.0)

Exploring Data: Exponential Growth and Decay

Goal 1 How to use models for exponential growth and decay to solve real-life problems

Why you should learn it:

You can use an exponential decay model for situations that decrease regularly by a fixed percent, such as the dwindling number of farms in the United States.

Goal 1 Using Exponential Models

In Lesson 8.6 you learned that compound interest is an example of *exponential growth*, which can be modeled with the general equation

$$y = C(1 + r)^t \quad \textit{Exponential growth}$$

where C is an initial amount, r is the percentage *increase* (expressed as a decimal), and t is the time period (in years).

Exponential decay occurs when the amount *decreases* by the same percent r for each time period. A model for exponential decay is

$$y = C(1 - r)^t \quad \textit{Exponential decay.}$$

Because the percentage r is greater than zero, the base $(1 - r)$ is less than 1.

Real Life
Agriculture

Example 1 *Number of Farms in the United States*

Between 1960 and 1990, the number of farms in the United States decreased by about 2.1% each year. In 1960, there were 4 million farms. How many farms were there in 1990?
(Source: U.S. Department of Agriculture)

Solution Let F be the number of farms in year t, with $t = 0$ corresponding to 1960. Use the above model for exponential decay with $C = 4,000,000$ and $r = 0.021$.

$$\begin{aligned} F &= C(1 - r)^t &&\textit{Exponential decay} \\ &= 4,000,000(1 - 0.021)^t &&\textit{C = 4,000,000, r = 0.021} \\ &= 4,000,000(0.979)^t &&\textit{Exponential decay model} \end{aligned}$$

To find the number of farms in 1990, substitute $t = 30$ into the model.

$$\begin{aligned} F &= 4,000,000(0.979)^{30} &&\textit{Evaluate F when t = 30.} \\ &\approx 2,116,000 &&\textit{Number of farms in 1990} \end{aligned}$$

There were about 2,116,000 farms in the United States in 1990.

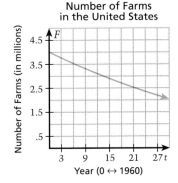

Number of Farms in the United States

Number of Farms (in millions)

Year (0 ↔ 1960)

*World Champion chess player Gary Kasparov is shown playing chess in 1989 with a computer using a program called **Deep Thought**. Kasparov won the match, despite the computer's ability to analyze ten moves ahead.*

Real Life
Chess

Example 2 *Computers and Chess*

A computer program for playing chess is rated on the number of future moves it can analyze. On a typical chess play, there are 38 possible positions. For subsequent moves, the number of possible positions, P, is given by $P = (38)^t$, where t is the number of moves. A computer program called *Deep Thought,* which was designed at Carnegie-Mellon University in Pittsburgh, can analyze 10 future moves. The computer can analyze 750,000 positions per second. Is it possible that *Deep Thought* analyzed all possible future positions for 10 moves into the future when it played Kasparov?

Solution To find the time required to analyze all possible positions, divide the number of positions by the number of positions that can be analyzed in a second.

$$\frac{\text{Number of positions}}{\text{Positions per second}} = \frac{38^{10}}{750,000}$$

$$= \frac{6.278 \times 10^{15}}{7.5 \times 10^5}$$

$$\approx 8.37 \times 10^9 \text{ seconds}$$

$$= 2,325,000 \text{ hours}$$

Thus, *Deep Thought* could not have analyzed all possible positions. In fact, the Carnegie-Mellon team found it was necessary to analyze only about 6 positions for each move. This meant that *Deep Thought* had to analyze only 6^{10} positions, which it could do in about 80 seconds.

(Source: Scientific American)

Example 3 — *Human Memory Model*

Two faculty members at Ohio Wesleyan University conducted an experiment to determine how much high school algebra and geometry a person remembers after graduating from college. The experiment, which was conducted with 1743 volunteers, found that those who had studied math through calculus in college forgot only about 0.45% per year. Those who took no college math courses tended to forget about 2.38% per year. Show an algebraic model and a graphical model for the amount of high school algebra and geometry each group remembered over 50 years. *(Source: Science News)*

Solution   Let p be the percent (in decimal form) of high school algebra and geometry that a person remembers. Using exponential decay, you can write the following models.

$$p = 1(1 - 0.0045)^t \qquad \textit{Took college calculus.}$$
$$= 0.9955^t$$

$$p = 1(1 - 0.0238)^t \qquad \textit{Took no college math.}$$
$$= 0.9762^t$$

The table compares the percents remembered.

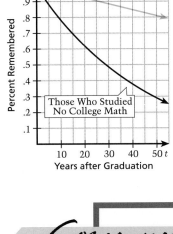

How Much Algebra and Geometry are Remembered

Percent Remembered / Years after Graduation

Those Who Studied College Calculus

Those Who Studied No College Math

Years, *t*	0	10	20	30	40	50
Percent (calc), *p*	100%	95.6%	91.4%	87.3%	83.5%	79.8%
Percent (none), *p*	100%	78.6%	61.8%	48.5%	38.2%	30.0%

Using the table to sketch the graphs, you can see that forgetting only about 2% more per year results in a big difference after 50 years. ■

Communicating about ALGEBRA

► SHARING IDEAS about the Lesson

Interpret a Model   Use the algebraic or graphical form of a model for exponential growth and decay.

A. Sketch the graphs of $y = 0.8^x$ and $y = 0.9^x$ on the same coordinate plane. What can you conclude from the two graphs?

B. An ocean sunfish, the mola mola, weighs about 1.5×10^{-5} pound when it hatches from an egg. By the time it reaches adulthood, it has doubled its weight 26 times! How much does an adult mola mola weigh?

EXERCISES

▶ **CRITICAL THINKING about the Lesson**

1. Which of the following represent exponential decay? Explain.

   a. $y = 0.97^t$ **b.** $y = 1.02^t$ **c.** $y = \left(\frac{4}{3}\right)^t$ **d.** $y = \left(\frac{2}{3}\right)^t$

2. For the exponential decay model $y = 0.96^t$, by what percent does the amount decrease for each time period?

3. *Business Decline*   A business earned $75,000 in 1980. Then its earnings decreased by 2% each year for 10 years. Write an exponential decay model for the earnings, E, in year t. Let $t = 0$ represent 1980.

4. *Trying to Be Perfect*   In 1980, the company you own lost 10,000 hours of work time due to employee illness. Beginning that year, you introduced a health awareness program for company employees. Each year for 10 years the number of lost hours decreased by 12%. How many hours were lost to illness in 1990? If the number of lost hours continued to drop by 12% each year, would you live long enough to see it drop to zero?

Independent Practice

5. *I Thought the Test Was on Friday*   You spend 3 hours Thursday night studying vocabulary words for your French class. There are going to be 50 words on the test, and on Friday morning you know them all. When you get to school, however, you find out that the test is on Monday. Suppose that without further study, you forget 10% of the vocabulary words each day. How many will you remember for Monday's test?

6. *Memory Course*   You enroll in a weekend course that teaches you memorization techniques. The techniques improve your ability to remember vocabulary words. How many of 50 vocabulary words would you forget if, after completing the memory course, you forget 5% each day for three days?

7. *Declining Enrollments*   The Mesa School District had a declining student population from 1985 to 1992. The enrollment in 1985 was 1240. Each year for seven years, the enrollment decreased by 2%. Complete the table showing the enrollment for each year and sketch a graph of the results.

Year	1985	1986	1987	1988	1989	1990	1991	1992
Enrollment	?	?	?	?	?	?	?	?

8. *Endangered Species*   From 1980 to 1990, the number of elephants living in Africa decreased by about 6.8% per year. There were about 1,200,000 elephants living in Africa in 1980. Write an exponential decay model showing the number of elephants, *E*, in Africa in year *t*. Let *t* = 0 represent 1980. Use the model to estimate the number of elephants in Africa in 1990.
(Source: African Wildlife Foundation, Kenya)

9. *Men and Women in the Work Force*
From 1975 to 1990, the *difference* between the numbers of working men and working women in the United States was decreasing by about 3% per year. Write an exponential decay model for the difference, *D*, between the number of working men and working women in year *t*. Let *t* = 0 represent 1980. How many more men than women were in the work force in 1990? *(Source: U.S. Bureau of Labor Statistics)*

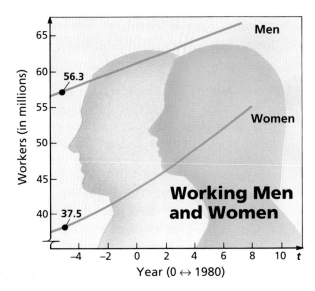

Integrated Review

In Exercises 10–13, match the equation with its graph.

10. $y = 5 - 3x$ **11.** $y = 5(1.6)^x$ **12.** $y = 5 + 3x$ **13.** $y = 5(0.6)^x$

a.   **b.**   **c.**   **d.**

14. *Space Probes*   On September 15, 1989, NASA calculated estimates for the distances (in miles) that different space probes had traveled from Earth. Place the probes in order, from the closest to Earth to the farthest from Earth.

a. *Pioneer 11:* 2.705×10^9 **b.** *Voyager 1:* 3.641×10^9 **c.** *Pioneer 6:* 6.2×10^7

d. *Pioneer 12:* 1.0×10^8 **e.** *Magellan:* 4.0×10^7 **f.** *Voyager 2:* 2.793×10^9

g. *Pioneer 10:* 4.382×10^9 **h.** *Voyager 7:* 7.8×10^7 **i.** *Pioneer 8:* 1.42×10^8

15. *Space Probes*   *Voyager 1* was launched on September 5, 1977. *Pioneer 10* was launched on March 2, 1972. Which has had a greater average speed?

16. *Photocopy Reduction*   You are using the photocopier to put a picture of a dollar bill on a graph you are making for your algebra class. The copier can only reduce to 72% of the original size. A dollar bill is 6.1 inches by 2.6 inches. How many times must you reduce the picture to obtain the size shown at the right? (It is legal to copy U.S. currency if the copy is black-and-white and smaller than $\frac{3}{4}$ actual size or greater than $\frac{3}{2}$ actual size.)

17. *Baby Mammals*   The gestation time for a mammal is, in general, related to the birth weight of the mammal's baby. (The gestation time is the time between fertilization and birth.) Mammals that have small babies have short gestation times. Mammals that have large babies have long gestation times. A model that relates the gestation time, t (in days), to average birth weight, w (in kilograms), is $t = 142(1.016)^w$. Use the model to approximate the gestation time for the mammals listed in the table. Does the gestation time for humans (average birth weight ≈ 3 kilograms) fit this model?

Mammal	Bear	Lion	Sheep	Deer	Seal	Cow	Giraffe	Elephant
Weight, w	0.5 kg	1.2 kg	4.1 kg	18 kg	33.5 kg	40 kg	68 kg	100 kg
Days, t	?	?	?	?	?	?	?	?

Population of the United States   **In Exercises 18 and 19, use the following information.**

The population of the United States is shown in the graph at the right. The population can be modeled by

$$P = 6,893,000 + 672,240t^2$$

where $t = 0, 1, 2, 3, \ldots$ represent the years 1800, 1810, 1820, 1830, ... This model is *not* an exponential growth model. It is a second-degree model of the type you will study in the next chapter.

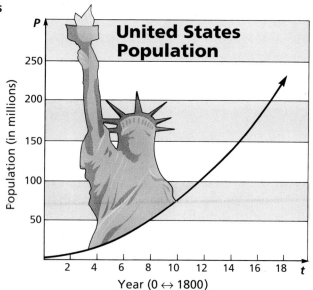

18. Use the model to estimate the United States population in 1990.

19. By what percent did the United States population increase from 1900 to 1930? By what percent did the population increase from 1960 to 1990? From these results, explain why the United States population has not increased according to exponential growth.

8 Chapter Summary

What did you learn?

Skills

1. Evaluate powers
   - using multiplication properties of exponents. **(8.1)**
   - involving negative and zero exponents. **(8.2)**
   - using division properties of exponents. **(8.3)**
2. Convert numbers from decimal form to scientific notation. **(8.4)**
3. Convert numbers from scientific notation to decimal form. **(8.4)**
4. Perform operations with numbers in scientific notation. **(8.4)**
5. Use the formula for compound interest. **(8.6)**

Strategies

6. Use scientific notation in problem solving. **(8.5)**
7. Use exponential growth and decay to model real-life problems. **(8.6, 8.7)**

Exploring Data

8. Sketch the graphs of exponential growth and decay models. **(8.6, 8.7)**

Why did you learn it?

The linear models you studied in Chapters 3–7 are used very often in real-life situations. There are, however, many real-life problems that do not fit linear models. One of the most common types of nonlinear models is exponential growth and exponential decay. In this chapter, you studied many examples of both types of exponential models. For instance, the balance in a savings account can be modeled with exponential growth, and human memory can be modeled with exponential decay.

How does it fit into the bigger picture of algebra?

In this chapter, you studied properties of exponents, scientific notation, and situations such as growth and decay that can be modeled with exponents.

Using properties of exponents, you can multiply and divide powers, and find powers of products and quotients. Using scientific notation, you can perform operations with very large and very small numbers. And, using exponential growth and decay, you can model two more types of real-life situations.

The models you studied in Chapters 3–7 are *linear*—their graphs are lines. The exponential growth and decay models in this chapter are *nonlinear*—their graphs are curves.

In Exercises 1–24, simplify the expression. (8.1, 8.2, 8.3)

1. $b^2 \cdot b^7$

2. $(p^3)^4$

3. $(a^2)^3 \cdot a^3$

4. $x^2 \cdot (xy)^2$

5. $(4m)^2 \cdot m^3$

6. $(3a)^3 \cdot (2p)^2$

7. $8^2 \cdot (xy)^2 \cdot 2x$

8. $w^3 \cdot (3w)^4$

9. q^0

10. p^{-2}

11. $(a^2b)^0$

12. $(x^{-2}y^3)^{-2}$

13. $\frac{p^4}{p^2}$

14. $\frac{3b^2}{9b^5}$

15. $\frac{(4x^2)^2}{4x^4}$

16. $\frac{x^2 \cdot y^0 \cdot 3^2}{x^3 \cdot y^{-4}}$

17. $\frac{(2p)^{-2} \cdot pq}{(p^2q)^4 \cdot p^0}$

18. $\left(\frac{m}{n}\right)^3 \cdot m^2n^{-4}$

19. $\left(\frac{3a^2}{b}\right)^3 \cdot \frac{2b^{-1}}{3^2 \cdot a}$

20. $\left(\frac{w^{-2}}{z^4}\right)^{-3}$

21. $\frac{(3pq)^2}{2p^{-2}} \cdot \frac{4p^{-1}q^4}{p^2}$

22. $\frac{5m^2n}{m^4} \cdot \left(\frac{m^{-3}}{n}\right)^{-2}$

23. $\frac{(3w)^4}{z^{-2}} \cdot (w^{-2}z)^{-2}$

24. $\frac{(3x)^{-3}}{3y^3} \cdot \frac{x^{-2}y^2}{x^{-4}}$

In Exercises 25–30, write the number in decimal form. (8.4)

25. 6.667×10^{-3}

26. 3.75×10^{-1}

27. 9.81×10^{-7}

28. 1.29×10^2

29. 7.68×10^5

30. 5.44×10^9

In Exercises 31–36, write the number in scientific notation. (8.4)

31. 0.0588

32. 0.000769

33. 0.0000000233

34. 523,000,000

35. 7950

36. 1,234,000,000

In Exercises 37–48, evaluate the expression. (8.2, 8.3, 8.4)

37. $\frac{3^2}{3^5}$

38. $2^{-1} \cdot 2^5$

39. $\left(\frac{2^{-1}}{3^2}\right)^{-2} \cdot \frac{1}{2 \cdot 3^3}$

40. $(3^5 \cdot 5^2) \cdot 3^{-4}$

41. $2^{-3} \cdot 4^2 \cdot 5^{-1} \cdot (3^2)^0$

42. $\frac{(37 \cdot (24)^2)^2}{37 \cdot (24)^4}$

43. $\frac{2.4 \times 10^{-6}}{1.2 \times 10^{-12}}$

44. $(7.6 \times 10^2) \cdot (2.0 \times 10^4)$

45. $\frac{3.33 \times 10^4}{6.66 \times 10^{12}}$

46. $\frac{9.6 \times 10^{-4} \cdot 4.8 \times 10^6}{2.4 \times 10^8 \cdot 2.4 \times 10^{-2}}$

47. $\frac{3.6 \times 10^{-4}}{7.2 \times 10^6} \cdot 1.8 \times 10^{-2}$

48. $\frac{9.9 \times 10^6}{1.1 \times 10^{-4}}$

49. *Retail Sales*   In 1990, about 1.615×10^{12} dollars were spent in retail purchases in the United States. What was the average amount spent per day? What was the average amount spent per American in 1990? (Use a population of 250 million.) (8.5)

50. Use the information given in Exercise 49 to find the average amount spent on retail purchases each day by an American in 1990.

Geometry   **In Exercises 51 and 52, use the following information.   (8.2)**

The edge of cube A is 5 meters. The edge of cube B is $\frac{5}{2}$ meters.

51. What is the volume of cube A? What is the volume of cube B?

52. What is the ratio of the edge of cube A to the edge of cube B? What is the ratio of the volume of cube A to the volume of cube B? What do you notice about this number?

Modes of Travel   **In Exercises 53–56, use the following information.   (8.5)**

In 1990, Americans traveled 417,800,000,000 miles by aircraft and 1,900,000,000,000 miles by motor vehicle.

53. How many more miles were traveled by motor vehicle than by aircraft?

54. What was the total traveled by motor vehicle and by aircraft?

55. What is the ratio of the miles traveled by aircraft to the miles traveled by motor vehicle?

56. Approximate the average number of miles traveled by motor vehicle per American in 1990.

National Basketball Association (NBA)   **In Exercises 57–60, use the following information and graph.   (8.6, 8.7)**

The NBA ticket sales and television fees, T (in millions of dollars), from 1980 through 1990 can be modeled by $T = 60 + (50)(1.29)^t$, where $t = 0$ represents 1980. NBA sales, S (in millions of dollars), of items such as logo T-shirts and backboards can be modeled approximately by the equation $S = 20(1.48)^t$.

57. What was the annual percentage increase for sales of related items?

58. Which model is represented by graph A? by graph B?

59. For which years did sales of related items exceed ticket sales and television fees?

60. Use the graphs to estimate the NBA's total revenue from both sources in 1980; in 1990. Then use the models to estimate the total revenues.

In Exercises 61–64, match the equation with its graph.

61. $y = 3x$

62. $y = 3^x$

63. $y = \frac{1}{3}x$

64. $y = \left(\frac{1}{3}\right)^x$

a.

b.

c.

d.

Total Eclipse of the Sun   **In Exercises 65–68, use the following information.**

During a total solar eclipse, the moon completely covers Earth's view of the sun. The sun has a diameter of 8.64×10^5 miles, and the moon has a diameter of 2.16×10^3 miles. The distance between the sun and Earth varies between 9.15×10^7 miles and 9.45×10^7 miles. The distance between the moon's center and Earth's surface varies between 2.2×10^5 miles and 2.5×10^5 miles.

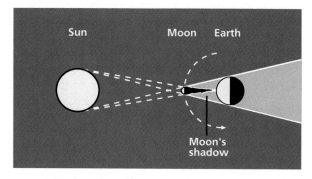

65. Find the ratio of the diameter of the sun to the diameter of the moon.

66. Complete the table by finding the ratios of the sun-to-Earth distances and moon-to-Earth distances.

Moon-to-Earth Distance (in miles)	Sun-to-Earth Distance (in miles)	
	Minimum 9.15×10^7	*Maximum* 9.45×10^7
Minimum 2.2×10^5	Ratio = ?	Ratio = ?
Maximum 2.5×10^5	Ratio = ?	Ratio = ?

67. The diagram at the right shows two spheres of diameters 15 inches and 3 inches. The ratio of these two diameters is the same as the ratio of the distance between C and the center of A and the distance between C and the center of B. If a person was farther than 4 inches away from B, could B totally block the person's view of A? Explain.

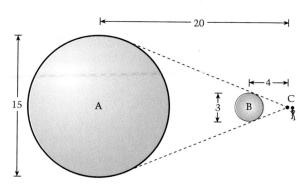

68. Use the results of Exercises 65–67 to explain why it is possible to have a total eclipse of the sun. Can this happen during the moon's *aphelion* (when the moon is farthest from Earth)?

In Exercises 1–12, simplify the expression.

1. $a^2 \cdot a^5$

2. $x^0 \cdot x^3$

3. $x^{-4} \cdot x^2$

4. y^{-3}

5. $(b^2)^8$

6. $(a^{-1})^2$

7. $\dfrac{q^3}{q^6}$

8. $(3a)^2(a^{-3})$

9. $(mn)^2 \cdot m^3$

10. $3x^4 \cdot 4x^{-2} \cdot x^3$

11. $\left(\dfrac{m^3}{mn^2}\right)\left(\dfrac{n}{m}\right)^4$

12. $\dfrac{x^{-1}y^2}{xy} \cdot \dfrac{x^2y^3}{y^{-2}}$

In Exercises 13–18, evaluate the expression.

13. 3^4

14. 5^{-2}

15. $(375^2)^0$

16. $\dfrac{5 \cdot 2^5}{2^4}$

17. $\left(\dfrac{3}{4}\right)^3 \cdot 4^2 \cdot 3^0$

18. $(6 \cdot 2)^3 \cdot 6^{-2}$

In Exercises 19 and 20, write the number in decimal form.

19. 3.65×10^6

20. 5.779×10^{-9}

In Exercises 21 and 22, write the number in scientific notation.

21. 2,440,000,000

22. 0.000000129

23. In 1989, 1.2×10^5 United States companies spent 6.3×10^{10} dollars on research and development. What was the average amount per company spent on research and development?

24. The world's largest pyramid was built by the Aztec Indians in Cholula, Mexico. It was 177 feet tall, and each side of its square base measured 1400 feet. What was the volume of this pyramid? (The volume of a pyramid is $\frac{1}{3}hb$, where h is the height and b is the area of the base.)

25. Suppose that you inherited $1000 when you were eight years old. You put $500 in a savings account that earned 5% annually. You used the remainder of the money to buy stock in a new company. For the next 6 years, the value of the stock decreased 5% a year. Now that 6 years have passed, what is the balance of the savings account? How much is your stock worth? How does the sum of these two values compare to the value of your original inheritance?

The Cholula Pyramid, in Mexico, is still largely buried underground. The base is estimated to cover nearly 45 acres.

CHAPTER

9

Quadratic Equations

LESSONS

9.1 Square Roots and the Pythagorean Theorem ▪ 452

9.2 Solving Quadratic Equations by Finding Square Roots ▪ 458

9.3 Graphs of Quadratic Equations ▪ 465

9.4 The Quadratic Formula ▪ 472

9.5 Problem Solving Using the Discriminant ▪ 479

9.6 Graphing Quadratic Inequalities ▪ 486

9.7 Exploring Data: Comparing Models ▪ 492

In a nuclear reactor like this one, the controlled fission of a nuclear fuel such as uranium converts mass into energy.

Numbers whose square roots are integers or quotients of integers are **perfect squares.** For example, 16 and 0.25, or $\frac{1}{4}$, are perfect squares. The square roots of numbers that are not perfect squares are **irrational numbers.** For example, the numbers $\sqrt{2}, \sqrt{3}, \sqrt{5}$, and $\sqrt{6}$ are all irrational. To approximate an irrational square root, you can use a calculator that has a *square root key* $\boxed{\sqrt{x}}$.

Example 2 *Evaluating Square Roots*

Evaluate the square root *exactly* if possible. Otherwise, approximate the square root and round the result to two decimal places.

a. $-\sqrt{121}$ **b.** $\sqrt{\frac{36}{25}}$ **c.** $\sqrt{0.09}$ **d.** $\sqrt{7}$

Solution

a. $-\sqrt{121} = -11$ $(-11)^2 = 121$

b. $\sqrt{\frac{36}{25}} = \frac{6}{5}$ $\left(\frac{6}{5}\right)^2 = \frac{36}{25}$

c. $\sqrt{0.09} = 0.3$ $(0.3)^2 = 0.09$

d. $\sqrt{7} = 2.645751311\ldots$ *Use a calculator that has*
≈ 2.65 $\boxed{\sqrt{x}}$.
                           Round to 2 decimal places. ■

Connections
Technology

Example 3 *Evaluating an Expression That Has a Square Root*

Evaluate $\sqrt{b^2 - 4ac}$ when $a = 1$, $b = -2$, and $c = -3$.

Solution   Substitute the values of a, b, and c as follows.

$$\sqrt{b^2 - 4ac} = \sqrt{(-2)^2 - 4(1)(-3)}$$
$$= \sqrt{4 + 12} \qquad \textit{Simplify.}$$
$$= \sqrt{16} \qquad \textit{Simplify.}$$
$$= 4 \qquad \textit{The positive square root of 16 is 4.} ■$$

Connections
Technology

Example 4 *Evaluating an Expression with a Plus or Minus Symbol*

Evaluate $\dfrac{1 \pm 2\sqrt{3}}{4}$.

Solution   This expression represents *two* numbers. Use a calculator as follows.

Keystrokes	Display	Rounded
$\boxed{(}$ 1 $\boxed{+}$ 2 $\boxed{\times}$ 3 $\boxed{\sqrt{x}}$ $\boxed{)}$ $\boxed{\div}$ 4 $\boxed{=}$	1.116025404	1.12
$\boxed{(}$ 1 $\boxed{-}$ 2 $\boxed{\times}$ 3 $\boxed{\sqrt{x}}$ $\boxed{)}$ $\boxed{\div}$ 4 $\boxed{=}$	-0.616025404	-0.62 ■

Using the Pythagorean Theorem

Connections
Geometry

The word *theorem* means "a statement that can be proven to be true." The **Pythagorean theorem** states a relationship for the three sides of a right triangle. In a right triangle, the **hypotenuse** is the side opposite the right angle. The other two sides are the **legs** of the triangle. The theorem is named after the Greek mathematician Pythagoras (about 585–500 B.C.). Records of its use in northern Africa, however, predate Pythagoras.

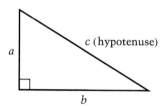

The Pythagorean Theorem

For any right triangle, the sum of the squares of the lengths of the legs, a and b, equals the square of the length of the hypotenuse, c.

$$a^2 + b^2 = c^2 \qquad \textit{Pythagorean form}$$

Example 5   *Distance to Second Base*

The length of each side of a square baseball diamond is 90 feet. What is the distance from home plate to second base?

Problem Solving
Draw a Diagram

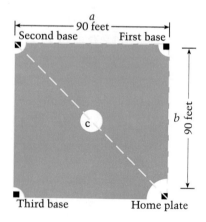

Solution   The diagonal from home plate to second base is the hypotenuse of a right triangle. Each leg is 90 feet long.

$$
\begin{aligned}
c^2 &= a^2 + b^2 & &\textit{Pythagorean theorem}\\
&= 90^2 + 90^2 & &\textit{Substitute 90 for a and b.}\\
&= 8100 + 8100 & &\textit{Simplify.}\\
&= 16{,}200 & &\textit{Simplify.}
\end{aligned}
$$

From the definition of a square root, c must be the positive square root of 16,200. (It wouldn't make sense to use the negative square root.) Thus, you can write

$$
\begin{aligned}
c &= \sqrt{16{,}200} & &\textit{Use a calculator.}\\
&\approx 127.3 \text{ feet.} & &\textit{Round to one decimal place.}
\end{aligned}
$$

The distance is 127.3 feet.   ■

Communicating about **A L G E B R A**

▶ **SHARING IDEAS about the Lesson**

Use Technology   Use a calculator to evaluate each expression. (Round to two decimal places.)

A. $2\sqrt{13}$ **B.** $5 - 3\sqrt{2}$ **C.** $\dfrac{-3 \pm \sqrt{(3)^2 - 4(1)(-2)}}{2}$

EXERCISES

Guided Practice

▶ **CRITICAL THINKING about the Lesson**

1. **True or False?** If $b^2 = a$, then b is a square root of a.

2. Which statements are true? Give an example of each true statement.
   a. A number can have no square root.
   b. A number can have only one square root.
   c. A number can have two different square roots.
   d. A number can have more than two square roots.

3. Evaluate $\sqrt{25}$, $-\sqrt{25}$, and $\pm\sqrt{25}$.

4. Find the numbers represented by
   $$3 \pm \sqrt{(-3)^2 - 4\left(\tfrac{1}{2}\right)(-8)}.$$

5. Give three examples of perfect squares, one an integer, one a fraction, and one a decimal number.

6. Is $\sqrt{2}$ irrational? Is $\frac{144}{99}$ a square root of 2? Is $\frac{7064}{4995}$ a square root of 2? Explain.

Independent Practice

In Exercises 7–14, find all square roots of the number. Check your results.

7. 64	**8.** 144	**9.** -9	**10.** 0
11. $\frac{4}{9}$	**12.** $\frac{25}{16}$	**13.** 0.16	**14.** 0.25

In Exercises 15–30, evaluate the expression. Give the exact value if possible. Otherwise, give an approximation to two decimal places.

15. $-\sqrt{256}$	**16.** $\sqrt{49}$	**17.** $\sqrt{11}$	**18.** $\sqrt{121}$
19. $\sqrt{100}$	**20.** $-\sqrt{169}$	**21.** $\sqrt{36}$	**22.** $\sqrt{23}$
23. $\sqrt{42}$	**24.** $\sqrt{0.75}$	**25.** $\sqrt{0.04}$	**26.** $-\sqrt{\frac{25}{100}}$
27. $\sqrt{\frac{81}{324}}$	**28.** $\sqrt{6.25}$	**29.** $-\sqrt{\frac{1}{64}}$	**30.** $\sqrt{26}$

In Exercises 31–34, evaluate $\sqrt{b^2 - 4ac}$ for the given values of a, b, and c.

31. $a = 4$, $b = 5$, $c = 1$

32. $a = -2$, $b = 8$, $c = -8$

33. $a = 3$, $b = -7$, $c = 6$

34. $a = 12$, $b = 13$, $c = 3$

Technology **In Exercises 35–38, use a calculator to evaluate the expression. Round results to two decimal places. Use estimation to check results.**

35. $\dfrac{2 \pm 5\sqrt{6}}{2}$

36. $\dfrac{3 \pm 4\sqrt{5}}{4}$

37. $\dfrac{7 \pm 3\sqrt{2}}{-1}$

38. $\dfrac{5 \pm 6\sqrt{3}}{3}$

Geometry   In Exercises 39–42, use the area, *A*, to find the length of the indicated side or radius. (Use $\pi \approx 3.14$.)

39. Square: $s = \sqrt{A}$ **40.** Square: $s = \sqrt{A}$ **41.** Circle: $r = \sqrt{\dfrac{A}{\pi}}$ **42.** Circle: $r = \sqrt{\dfrac{A}{\pi}}$

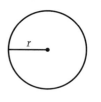

$A = 27.04$ $A = 12.96$ $A = 50.24$ $A = 153.86$

Biosphere 2   In Exercises 43 and 44, use the following information.

Biosphere 2, in Arizona, is a large terrarium that covers 3 acres and reaches a height of 10 stories. The structure contains 7 biomes (miniature versions of ecological communities). These include a savanna, freshwater and salt-water marshes, a farm, a desert, and an ocean. To test the possibility of creating miniature "Earth environments" on other planets, 8 people were sealed in Biosphere 2 for 2 years.

43. Biosphere 2 covers over 130,000 square feet. If its layout was in the shape of a single square, what would be its dimensions?

44. The "ocean" in Biosphere 2 has 110,000 cubic feet of sea water and is 25 feet deep. If a square swimming pool was 25 feet deep and held 110,000 cubic feet of water, how long would each side be?

Geometry   In Exercises 45 and 46, use the formula $h = \frac{1}{2}\sqrt{3}s$ for the height, *h*, of an equilateral triangle whose sides are of length *s*.

45. Find the height of an equilateral triangle with 2-inch sides.

46. Find the area of an equilateral triangle with 2-inch sides.

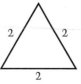

47. *Length of a Ladder*   A ladder is placed against the trunk of a cherry tree. It reaches a height of 10 feet on the tree. The bottom of the ladder extends 5 feet from the base of the tree. How long is the ladder?

48. *Fallingwater* How long is the hanging staircase at Fallingwater from the bottom step to the top step?

Fallingwater, near Pittsburgh, Pennsylvania, was designed by the American architect Frank Lloyd Wright. One of its many unique features is a hanging staircase that descends from the second floor to the stone steps of the "plunge pool." The staircase is 7 feet high and is cut from a 12-foot-long hole in the stone.

49. *Diagonal of a Football Field* A football field is 360 feet by 45 feet. How long is the walk from one corner diagonally to the opposite corner?

50. *Repairing a Gate* The diagonal crossbar of an old wooden gate has rotted. The gate is rectangular, 3 feet by 4 feet. How long is the crossbar?

Integrated Review

Geometry **What is the unit of measure for *s*?**

51. $s^2 = 64$ square miles

52. $s^2 = 200$ square inches

In Exercises 53–56, square the expression.

53. $-3a$

54. $7b$

55. $2x^2y$

56. $3xy^3$

In Exercises 57–60, use mental math to solve the equation.

57. $x^2 = 9$

58. $y^2 = 16$

59. $y^3 = 8$

60. $-(x^2) = -36$

Exploration and Extension

In Exercises 61–64, simplify the positive square root.

The positive square root of an integer that is the product of a *perfect square* and another integer can be simplified using the property $\sqrt{ab} = \sqrt{a} \cdot \sqrt{b}$. For example, 12 is the product of 4 and 3, which means that $\sqrt{12}$ can be written as $\sqrt{12} = \sqrt{4 \cdot 3} = \sqrt{4} \cdot \sqrt{3} = 2\sqrt{3}$.

61. $\sqrt{8}$

62. $\sqrt{18}$

63. $\sqrt{27}$

64. $\sqrt{75}$

9.2

Solving Quadratic Equations by Finding Square Roots

What you should learn:

Goal 1 How to solve a quadratic equation by finding square roots

Goal 2 How to use quadratic models in real-life settings

Why you should learn it:

You can model many situations, such as population growth in the United States, with quadratic models.

Goal 1 Solving a Quadratic Equation

A **quadratic equation** in x is an equation that can be written in the **standard form**

$$ax^2 + bx + c = 0, \qquad a \neq 0.$$

In this form, a is the **leading coefficient.**

In this lesson, you will learn how to find the real-number solutions of quadratic equations of the form $ax^2 + c = 0$.

Solving $x^2 = d$ by Finding Square Roots

1. If d is positive, then $x^2 = d$ has two solutions: $x = \pm\sqrt{d}$.
2. The equation $x^2 = 0$ has one solution: $x = 0$.
3. If d is negative, then $x^2 = d$ has no solution.

Example 1 *Solving Quadratic Equations*

a. The equation $x^2 = 4$ has two solutions: $x = \pm 2$.

b. The equation $x^2 = 5$ has two solutions: $x = \pm\sqrt{5}$.

c. The equation $x^2 = 0$ has one solution: $x = 0$.

d. The equation $x^2 = -1$ has no solution. ∎

Example 2 *Transforming before Finding Square Roots*

Solve $3x^2 - 48 = 0$.

Solution

$3x^2 - 48 = 0$	*Rewrite original equation.*
$3x^2 = 48$	*Add 48 to both sides.*
$x^2 = 16$	*Divide both sides by 3.*
$x = \pm\sqrt{16}$	*Find square roots.*
$x = \pm 4$	*16 is a perfect square.*

The solutions are 4 and -4. Check these results in the original equation. ∎

Using Quadratic Models in Real Life

In Exercise 22 of Lesson 8.7, you were asked to use a quadratic model to predict when the population of the United States would reach 300 million. In that lesson, you may have used a "guess and check" approach to solving the problem. Now, however, you can solve the problem by finding square roots.

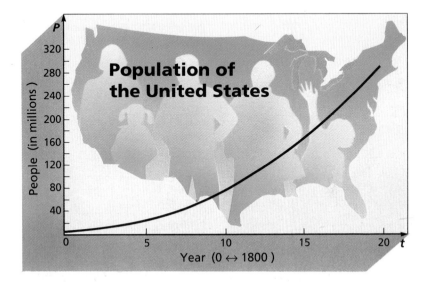

The U.S. population can be modeled by
$P = 6,893,000 + 672,240t^2$,
*where t = 0, 1, 2, ... ,
represents 1800, 1810, 1820, ...*

Real Life
Population Studies

Example 3   *Population of the United States*

Use the quadratic model given with the graph to estimate the year that the United States population will reach 300 million.

Solution

$6,893,000 + 672,240t^2 = P$	*Quadratic model*
$6,893,000 + 672,240t^2 = 300,000,000$	*Substitute 300 million for P.*
$672,240t^2 = 293,107,000$	*Subtract 6,893,000.*
$t^2 \approx 436$	*Divide by 672,240.*
$t \approx \sqrt{436}$	*Find positive square root.*
$t \approx 20.9$	*Use a calculator.*

The model predicts the United States population will reach 300 million in the year 2009.* (Note that we used the positive square root because a negative solution wouldn't make sense in this problem.)   ■

*In 1990, the U.S. Census Bureau's predictions for 2009 varied between 263 million and 303 million. The differences come from different assumptions about birth, death, and immigration rates.

The distance formula $d = rt$ is used for problems in which the rate or speed is *constant*. When an object (with little air resistance) is dropped, its speed continually *increases*. The height, h (in feet), of such an object is given by the model

$$h = -16t^2 + s \qquad \textit{Falling object model}$$

where s is the height in feet from which the object was dropped, and t is the number of seconds during which it has fallen. This model works for Earth's gravitational force.

Real Life
Construction Safety

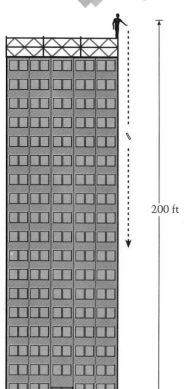

200 ft

Example 4 — Watch Out Below!

A construction worker on the top floor of a building accidentally drops a heavy wrench. How many seconds will it take to hit the ground? (Assume it drops from a height of 200 feet.)

Solution Because the wrench drops from a height of 200 feet, the model for the height of the wrench at time t is $h = -16t^2 + 200$. The table gives heights at different times.

Time, t in seconds	0.0	0.5	1.0	1.5	2.0	2.5	3.0	3.5
Height, h in feet	200	196	184	164	136	100	56	4

From the table, you can say that the wrench will take a little more than $3\frac{1}{2}$ seconds to hit the ground. Another way to solve the problem is to solve the quadratic equation for the time that gives a height of $h = 0$ feet.

$$-16t^2 + 200 = h \qquad \textit{Falling object model}$$
$$-16t^2 + 200 = 0 \qquad \textit{Substitute 0 for h.}$$
$$200 = 16t^2 \qquad \textit{Add } 16t^2 \textit{ to both sides.}$$
$$12.5 = t^2 \qquad \textit{Divide both sides by 16.}$$
$$\sqrt{12.5} = t \qquad \textit{Find the positive square root.}$$
$$3.54 \approx t \qquad \textit{Use a calculator.}$$

The wrench will take about 3.54 seconds to hit the ground. ∎

Communicating about ALGEBRA

▶ **SHARING IDEAS about the Lesson**

Extend the Idea A free falling body accelerates at the rate of 32 feet per second every second.

In Example 4, find, or approximate, the speed of the wrench when it hit the ground.

EXERCISES

▶ **CRITICAL THINKING about the Lesson**

1. Which of the following are quadratic equations?

   a. $-3x + 5 = 0$ **b.** $x^2 - 1 = 0$ **c.** $x^2 - 3x^3 = 0$ **d.** $-3 + 4x + x^2 = 0$

In Exercises 2–4, write in standard form and find the leading coefficient.

   2. $-3x^2 + 5 = 0$ **3.** $\frac{1}{2}x^2 + 9x - 3 = 0$ **4.** $-8x - x^2 + 4 = 0$

In Exercises 5–8, solve the equation. If there are no solutions, state the reason.

   5. $x^2 = 17$ **6.** $x^2 = 0$ **7.** $x^2 = -4$ **8.** $x^2 = 6$

Independent Practice

In Exercises 9–20, solve the equation.

   9. $x^2 = 9$ **10.** $h^2 = 25$ **11.** $6x^2 = 600$ **12.** $\frac{1}{5}x^2 = 5$

   13. $3x^2 = 363$ **14.** $2b^2 = 98$ **15.** $t^2 + 2 = 11$ **16.** $t^2 - 57 = 87$

   17. $\frac{1}{2}x^2 - 1 = 7$ **18.** $4y^2 + 7 = 8$ **19.** $2s^2 - 5 = 27$ **20.** $81x^2 - 5 = 20$

Technology   **In Exercises 21–28, use a calculator to solve the equation. Round the results to two decimal places.**

   21. $3x^2 + 2 = 56$ **22.** $7y^2 - 12 = 23$ **23.** $2x^2 - 5 = 7$ **24.** $\frac{2}{3}n^2 - 6 = 2$

   25. $\frac{1}{2}x^2 + 3 = 8$ **26.** $4x^2 + 9 = 41$ **27.** $6s^2 - 2 = 0$ **28.** $5a^2 + 10 = 20$

In Exercises 29–32, an object is dropped from a height h. How long does it take to reach the ground? (Assume there is no air resistance.)

   29. $h = 64$ feet   **30.** $h = 144$ feet   **31.** $h = 500$ feet   **32.** $h = 600$ feet

33. *Geometry*   The surface area of a cube is 150 square feet. Find the length of each edge.

34. *Geometry*   The surface area of a sphere is 80 square meters. Find the radius. (Use $\pi \approx 3.14$.)

$S = 4\pi r^2$

35. *Free Lunches*   The number, L (in millions), of free lunches served in public schools in the United States from 1970 to 1990 can be modeled by $L = -7.75t^2 + 1860$, where t is the year, with $t = 0$ corresponding to 1982. During which years were 1736 million free lunches served? During which years were 1364 million free lunches served?

(Source: U.S. Dept. of Agriculture)

Free Public School Lunches

36. *Motion Picture Theaters*   The number, M (in thousands), of motion picture theaters in the United States from 1970 to 1990 can be modeled by $M = 0.037t^2 + 10$, where t is the year, with $t = 0$ corresponding to 1980. Use this model to estimate the year in which there will be 19.5 thousand motion picture theaters in the United States.

Number of Movie Theaters in United States

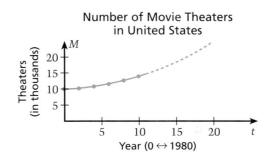

Hardness of Minerals   **In Exercises 37 and 38, use the following information.**

Geologists use the Vickers scale to measure the hardness of minerals. The hardness, V, of a mineral can be determined by hitting the mineral with a wedge-shaped diamond and measuring the depth, d, of the indentation. A model that relates mineral hardness with the indentation depth in millimeters is $Vd^2 = 1.89$.

Fluorite: V = 180

Sulfur: V = 40

Wulfenite: V = 85

37. Find the depth of the indentation of each of the minerals shown above.

38. Which mineral shown above is the hardest? Which is the softest? Why do you think the Vickers scale test uses a diamond to test the hardness of other minerals?

In 1971, astronaut David Scott demonstrated that a feather and a hammer fall at the same rate on the moon because the moon has no atmosphere (and hence no air resistance). The height, h (in feet), of a falling object on the moon is given by

$$h = -\frac{27}{10}t^2 + s.$$

39. If a hammer and feather are dropped 5 feet from the surface of the moon, how long will it take for each to hit the surface?

40. On Earth, how long would it take the hammer to hit the ground? Would the feather hit the ground after the same amount of time? Explain.

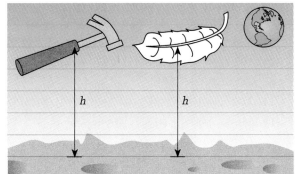

Integrated Review

In Exercises 41–44, evaluate the expression.

41. $4x^2 + 9x - 14$ when $x = 3$

42. $x^2 - 4x + 9$ when $x = 4$

43. $-4ac$ when $a = 5$ and $c = 2$

44. $-16t^2 + s$ when $s = 4$ and $t = 4$

In Exercises 45–50, solve for x.

45. $2x - 9 = 7$

46. $5x - 9 = 11$

47. $\frac{1}{4}x + 6 = 8$

48. $\frac{1}{3}x - 4 = -1$

49. $\sqrt{x} - 1 = 5$

50. $\sqrt{x} + 3 = 4$

Exploration and Extension

51. Complete the table. Use the points (x, y) from the table to sketch the graph of $y = x^2 + 2$.

x	−3	−2	−1	0	1	2	3
y	?	?	?	?	?	?	?

52. The points $(x_1, 7)$ and $(x_2, 10)$ are on the graph of the equation given in Exercise 51. What are the x-coordinates?

In Exercises 53 and 54, there are two different ordered pairs (x, y) that are solutions of the system. Find the two ordered pairs.

53. $\begin{cases} -5 + 2x^2 = 27 \\ x + y = 4 \end{cases}$

54. $\begin{cases} \frac{1}{3}x^2 + 2 = 5 \\ 2x + y = 4 \end{cases}$

1. Write the reciprocal of a^4. **(2.7)**

2. Write the reciprocal of 3. **(2.7)**

3. Solve $p(1 + q) = 2 + q$ for p. **(3.6)**

4. Solve $3x - 4y = -20$ for y. **(3.6)**

5. Evaluate $3x^3 + 2x - 2$ when $x = -2$. **(1.3)**

6. Evaluate $3z^0 + 4z^{-1}$ when $z = \frac{1}{4}$. **(8.2)**

7. What is the slope of $y = 5x + 6$? **(4.4)**

8. What is the slope of $3y + 2 = 0$? **(4.4)**

9. Write 1,299,000,000 in scientific notation. **(8.4)**

10. Write 0.000000496 in scientific notation. **(8.4)**

11. Is 2 a solution of $1 + 2x < 4x$? **(1.5)**

12. Is 6 a solution of $3x - 6 = 10$? **(1.5)**

13. Write $10x - 4y = -16$ in slope-intercept form. **(4.5)**

14. Write $y = \frac{1}{3}x - 2$ in standard form. **(5.5)**

15. Simplify $3x(1 + x) - x^2 + x$. **(2.6)**

16. Simplify $(x^2y^{-3})^{-2} \cdot x^2y^{-4}$. **(8.1)**

17. Solve $|x - 3| = 6$. **(4.8)**

18. Solve $|2x + 4| \leq 12$. **(4.8)**

19. Evaluate $2.2 \times 10^{-6} \cdot 3.6 \times 10^4$ **(8.4)**

20. Evaluate $7.6 \times 10^{-6} \div (2.5 \times 10^8)$. **(8.4)**

Career Interview

Printer

Jeffrey Wong is the printer at and manager of a printing company. He is involved in all aspects of running the business—from purchasing, to sales, to managing employees. He quotes estimates, sets up business agreements with customers, and processes orders.

Q: What led you into this career?

A: I was trained as an engineer. After working in that field for a number of years, I decided to take over the family printing business.

Q: Has new technology changed your job experiences?

A: Many new printing machines and equipment have come on the market. Most have built-in functions that can take care of some computations we used to do by hand.

Q: Does this mean you don't need to understand math?

A: No. All the functions on a new printer don't mean a thing if I don't know how they can be used, or how they impact on what's happening during a particular process.

Q: What would you like to tell kids about math?

A: Often kids think that if they are good in English, then they don't need to worry about math, and vice versa. But we really need to do well in both. English is the vehicle to express your thoughts and feelings; math is the key to meeting everyday needs.

9.3

Graphs of Quadratic Equations

What you should learn:

Goal 1 How to sketch the graph of a quadratic equation

Goal 2 How to use quadratic models in real-life settings

Why you should learn it:

You can use visual models to help you see relationships between two variables, such as the height reached and the distance traveled by a projectile.

Goal 1 Sketching a Quadratic Equation

A **quadratic equation** in x and y is an equation that can be written in the **standard form**

$$y = ax^2 + bx + c, \quad a \neq 0.$$

Every quadratic equation has a U-shaped graph called a **parabola.** If the leading coefficient a is positive, the parabola *opens up*. If the leading coefficient is negative, the parabola *opens down*.

Graph of $y = x^2$

x	y
-3	9
-2	4
-1	1
0	0
1	1
2	4
3	9

Graph of $y = -x^2 + 4$

x	y
-3	-5
-2	0
-1	3
0	4
1	3
2	0
3	-5

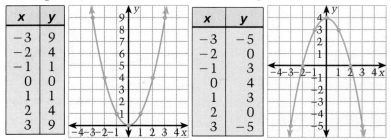

On a parabola that opens up, the lowest point is the **vertex.** On a parabola that opens down, the highest point is the vertex. The vertical line passing through the vertex is called the **axis of symmetry.** This line divides a parabola into two parts that are mirror images of each other.

> **Graph of a Quadratic Equation**
> The graph of $y = ax^2 + bx + c$ is a parabola.
>
> **1.** If a is positive, the parabola opens up.
> **2.** If a is negative, the parabola opens down.
> **3.** The vertex has an x-coordinate of $-\dfrac{b}{2a}$.
> **4.** The axis of symmetry is the vertical line $x = -\dfrac{b}{2a}$.

To sketch the graph of a quadratic equation, first find the x-coordinate of the vertex. Then construct a table of values, using x-values to the left and right of the vertex. Finally, plot the points and connect them with a U-shaped graph.

Example **1** **Sketching a Quadratic Equation**

Sketch the graph of $y = x^2 - 2x - 3$.

Solution In standard form $ax^2 + bx + c$, the coefficients are $a = 1$, $b = -2$, and $c = -3$. The x-coordinate of the vertex is

$$-\frac{b}{2a} = -\frac{-2}{2(1)} = 1. \quad \textit{x-coordinate of vertex}$$

Using x-values to the left and right of this x-value, construct a table of values.

Vertex

x	-2	-1	0	1	2	3	4
$y = x^2 - 2x - 3$	5	0	-3	-4	-3	0	5

The vertex is $(1, -4)$ and the axis of symmetry is $x = 1$. Plot the points given in the table and connect them with a U-shaped curve that opens up. ■

In Example 1, notice that the graph has two x-intercepts, at $(-1, 0)$ and $(3, 0)$, and one y-intercept, at $(0, -3)$.

Example **2** **Sketching a Quadratic Equation**

Sketch the graph of $y = -\frac{1}{2}x^2 - x + 4$.

Solution For this quadratic equation, $a = -\frac{1}{2}$, $b = -1$, and $c = 4$. The x-coordinate of the vertex is

$$-\frac{b}{2a} = -\frac{-1}{2\left(-\frac{1}{2}\right)} = -1. \quad \textit{x-coordinate of vertex}$$

Using x-values to the left and right of this x-value, construct a table of values.

Vertex

x	-5	-4	-3	-2	-1	0	1	2	3
$y = -\frac{1}{2}x^2 - x + 4$	$-3\frac{1}{2}$	0	$2\frac{1}{2}$	4	$4\frac{1}{2}$	4	$2\frac{1}{2}$	0	$-3\frac{1}{2}$

The vertex is $\left(-1, 4\frac{1}{2}\right)$, and the axis of symmetry is $x = -1$. Plot the points given in the table and connect them with a U-shaped curve that opens down. ■

The graph in Example 2 has x-intercepts at $(-4, 0)$ and $(2, 0)$. The y-intercept occurs at $(0, 4)$.

Using Quadratic Models in Real Life

Lisovskaya's Olympic Shot Put

Natalya Lisovskaya of the Soviet Union won the shot put competition in the 1988 Olympics. The path of the winning throw is given by
$y = -0.01464x^2 + x + 5.$

Real Life
Sports

Example 3 *Length and Height of a Shot Put Throw*

What was the maximum height of the shot thrown by Lisovskaya? How long was her winning throw?

Solution   The maximum height occurred at the vertex of the parabolic path. The x-coordinate of the vertex is

$$-\frac{b}{2a} = -\frac{1}{2(-0.01464)} \approx 34.15. \quad \textit{x-coordinate of vertex}$$

To find the height of the shot put at the vertex, substitute this x-value into the equation $y = -0.01464x^2 + x + 5$.

$$y = -0.01464(34.15)^2 + (34.15) + 5 \approx 22.1$$

The maximum height was about 22.1 feet. To find the length of the winning throw, you need to find the x-value that yields a y-value of 0. From the table, you can see that the shot hit the ground when x was a little less than 73 feet.

Distance, x	40 ft	50 ft	60 ft	70 ft	71 ft	72 ft	73 ft
Height, y	21.6 ft	18.4 ft	12.3 ft	3.3 ft	2.2 ft	1.1 ft	−0.02 ft

Communicating about ALGEBRA

▶ **SHARING IDEAS about the Lesson**

Use a Diagram   Sketch the graphs of the quadratic equations on the same coordinate plane and describe the relationship among the graphs.

A. $y = x^2 - 1$ $\quad y = x^2$ $\quad y = x^2 + 1$

B. $y = -x^2 - 4$ $\quad y = -x^2$ $\quad y = -x^2 + 4$

EXERCISES

▶ **CRITICAL THINKING about the Lesson**

1. Write the equation $y = -3 + 4x - x^2$ in standard form.

2. The graph of a quadratic equation is called a $\boxed{?}$.

3. How can you use a to decide whether the graph of $y = ax^2 + bx + c$ opens up or down?

4. **True or False?** The axis of symmetry of the graph of $y = ax^2 + bx + c$ is parallel to the y-axis (or *is* the y-axis). Explain.

5. Find the vertex of the graph of $y = 2x^2 + 4x - 2$.

6. Find the axis of symmetry of the graph of $y = -3x^2 + 3x + 1$.

Independent Practice

In Exercises 7–12, decide whether the graph of the equation opens up or down. Then find the coordinates of the vertex.

7. $y = 2x^2 + 4$ **8.** $y = -5x^2$ **9.** $y + 4x^2 = 0$

10. $y - 3x^2 = -2x$ **11.** $y + 5x^2 = -x + 10$ **12.** $y - 6x^2 = 3x + 12$

In Exercises 13–18, find the coordinates of the vertex and the equation of the axis of symmetry.

13. $y = 3x^2 + 2x + 4$ **14.** $y = 2x^2 + 3x + 6$ **15.** $y = -4x^2 - 4x + 8$

16. $y = 3x^2 - 9x - 12$ **17.** $y = 2x^2 + 7x - 21$ **18.** $y = -x^2 + 4x + 16$

In Exercises 19–36, sketch the graph of the equation. Label the vertex.

19. $y = x^2 + x + 2$ **20.** $y = -x^2 + 2x - 1$ **21.** $y = -2x^2 + 6x - 9$

22. $y = 2x^2 - 3x + 4$ **23.** $y = 6x^2 - 3x + 4$ **24.** $y = 5x^2 + 4x - 5$

25. $y = 4x^2 - x + 6$ **26.** $y = -3x^2 - x + 7$ **27.** $y = -5x^2 + 2x - 2$

28. $y = 6x^2 - 4x - 1$ **29.** $y = -3x^2 - 5x + 3$ **30.** $y = -2x^2 - 3x + 2$

31. $y = x^2 + 6x + 5$ **32.** $y = -4x^2 - 3x + 6$ **33.** $y = -\frac{1}{2}x^2 - 3x + 4$

34. $y = \frac{1}{3}x^2 + 3x - 2$ **35.** $y = -2x^2 + \frac{1}{3}x - 1$ **36.** $y = 3x^2 - \frac{1}{2}x + 4$

You've Got to Have the Right Angle   **In Exercise 37, use the information given in Example 3.**

37. Natalya Lisovskaya's winning throw in the shot put was at a 45° angle. If the shot had been thrown at a 40° angle or 50° angle, would it have gone farther? Explain.

    Throw at 40° angle: $y = -0.0125x^2 + 0.84x + 5$
    Throw at 50° angle: $y = -0.0177x^2 + 1.19x + 5$

Water Sprinkler   **In Exercises 38 and 39, use the following information.**

The paths of the water from a water sprinkler are shown for three different settings.

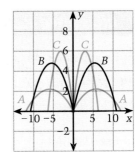

35°: $y = -0.06x^2 + 0.70x + 0.5$
60°: $y = -0.16x^2 + 1.73x + 0.5$
75°: $y = -0.60x^2 + 3.73x + 0.5$

x and *y* are measured in feet.

38. Find the height of each vertex and the radius of the region covered by each setting.

39. Do you think there is an angle setting for the sprinkler that will cover a greater area? Use the equation given by $y = -0.08x^2 + x + 0.5$ to help answer the question. What angle do you think this equation represents?

World Production of Gold   **In Exercises 40 and 41, use the following information.**

From 1970 to 1990, the annual world production, *G*, of gold in thousands of ounces, can be modeled by

$G = 47{,}974 - 2446t + 167t^2$

where *t* is the year, with $t = 0$ corresponding to 1970. The graph of this model is shown at the right. **(Source: U.S. Bureau of Mines)**

40. During which years between 1970 and 1990 was the world production of gold decreasing? During which years was the production increasing? How are these questions related to the vertex of the graph?

41. The United States used to be on the *gold standard*, which had the effect of keeping the price of gold artificially low. In 1971, the United States went off the gold standard. How did this affect the world production of gold?

In Exercise 42, use the following information.

From 1950 to 1990, the average annual consumption, *C*, of cigarettes per American (18 or older) can be modeled by

$C = 4024.5 + 51.4t - 3.1t^2$

where *t* is the year, with $t = 0$ corresponding to 1960. The graph of the model is shown at the right. **(Source: U.S. Centers for Disease Control)**

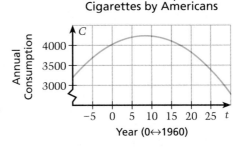

42. From 1966 on, all cigarette packages were required by law to carry a health warning. Did the warnings have any effect? Explain.

In Exercises 43–48, solve the equation.

43. $16 + t^2 = 32$

44. $s^2 - 40 = -4$

45. $2m^2 - 30 = 20$

46. $24 = 4n^2 - 12$

47. $12 + 3a^2 = 2a^2 + 16$

48. $6a^2 = 3a^2 + 108$

In Exercises 49–54, match each equation with its graph.

49. $y = x^2 - 2x + 3$

50. $y = 2x + 3$

51. $y = 3 - 2x$

52. $y = 2^x + 2$

53. $y = -x^2 - 2x + 3$

54. $y = 2^{-x} + 2$

a.

b.

c.

d.

e.

f.
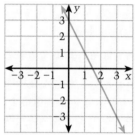

In Exercises 55–60, evaluate the expression. If necessary, use a calculator and round the result to two decimal places.

55. $-4ac$, $a = \frac{1}{2}$, $c = 12$

56. $-4ac$, $a = -2$, $c = 7$

57. $b^2 - 4ac$, $a = 6$, $b = 6$, $c = 1$

58. $b^2 - 4ac$, $a = -5$, $b = 3$, $c = 1$

59. $\sqrt{b^2 - 4ac}$, $a = 8$, $b = -10$, $c = 2$

60. $\sqrt{b^2 - 4ac}$, $a = 6.2$, $b = 12.1$, $c = -4.3$

Exploration and Extension

In Exercises 61–63, sketch the graphs of all three equations on the same coordinate plane. Describe how the three graphs are related.

61. $\begin{cases} y = x^2 - x + 1 \\ y = x^2 - x + 3 \\ y = x^2 - x - 2 \end{cases}$

62. $\begin{cases} y = x^2 + x + 1 \\ y = \frac{1}{2}x^2 + x + 1 \\ y = 2x^2 + x + 1 \end{cases}$

63. $\begin{cases} y = x^2 - 2x + 1 \\ y = x^2 - 4x + 4 \\ y = x^2 - 6x + 9 \end{cases}$

64. Use the result of Exercise 61 to describe how a change in the value of c changes the graph of $y = ax^2 + bx + c$.

65. Use the result of Exercise 62 to describe how a change in the value of a changes the graph of $y = ax^2 + bx + c$.

You can use the zoom *feature of a graphing calculator to approximate the solutions of an equation to any desired accuracy. The four graphs below show four steps in approximating the positive solution of $x^2 - 3 = 0$ to be $x \approx 1.73$. (The solution is $x = \sqrt{3} \approx 1.732$.) By repeated zooming, you can obtain whatever accuracy you need.*

1.

Sketch the graph of $y = x^2 - 3$.

RANGE Xmin $= -10$ Ymin $= -10$
           Xmax $= 10$ Ymax $= 10$
           Xscl $= 1$ Yscl $= 1$

2.

Zoom once to get a better view of the positive x-intercept. (Each range will change automatically.)

3.

Zoom a second time to get an even better view. Use the cursor keys to determine that the x-intercept is about 1.74.

4.

Set x-values to range from 1.7 to 1.8, with an x-scale of 0.01. From the graph, you can approximate the x-intercept to be 1.73.

RANGE Xmin $= 1.7$ Ymin $= -.1$
           Xmax $= 1.8$ Ymax $= .1$
           Xscl $= .01$ Yscl $= .1$

Exercises

In Exercises 1–6, use a graphing calculator to solve the equation. Give each solution to two decimal places.

1. $3x^2 - 20x + 5 = 0$ **2.** $-4x^2 + 6x + 7 = 0$ **3.** $-x^2 + 5x - 1 = 0$

4. $0.1x^2 + 4.3x - 5.1 = 0$ **5.** $-1.4x^2 + 5.2x - 4.8 = 0$ **6.** $2.87x^2 - 9.43x - 4.53 = 0$

9.4

The Quadratic Formula

What you should learn:

Goal 1 How to use the quadratic formula to solve a quadratic equation

Goal 2 How to use quadratic models in real-life settings

Why you should learn it:

You can model many situations, such as the motion of falling objects, with quadratic models.

Goal 1 Using the Quadratic Formula

In Lesson 9.2, you learned how to solve quadratic equations of the form $ax^2 + c = 0$ by finding square roots. In this lesson, you will learn how to solve *any* quadratic equation.

The formula for the solutions is called the **quadratic formula.** This is one of the oldest and most famous formulas in mathematics. No one knows who first discovered it, but versions of it were used as long ago as 2000 B.C. in Babylonia (now Iraq).

The Quadratic Formula

The solutions of the quadratic equation $ax^2 + bx + c = 0$ are

$$x = \frac{-b \pm \sqrt{b^2 - 4ac}}{2a}.$$

You may find it helpful to memorize this formula: *"The opposite of b, plus or minus the square root of b-squared minus 4ac, all divided by 2a."*

Example 1 *Using the Quadratic Formula*

Solve $x^2 + 5x - 14 = 0$.

Solution

$x^2 + 5x - 14 = 0$

$$x = \frac{-5 \pm \sqrt{5^2 - 4(1)(-14)}}{2(1)} \qquad x = \frac{-b \pm \sqrt{b^2 - 4ac}}{2a}$$

$$a = 1, b = 5, c = -14$$

$$x = \frac{-5 \pm \sqrt{25 + 56}}{2} \qquad \textit{Simplify.}$$

$$x = \frac{-5 \pm \sqrt{81}}{2} \qquad \textit{Simplify.}$$

$$x = \frac{-5 \pm 9}{2} \qquad \textit{Solutions}$$

The equation has two solutions.

$$x = \frac{-5 + 9}{2} = 2 \quad \text{and} \quad x = \frac{-5 - 9}{2} = -7$$

Check these solutions in the original equation. ∎

Remember that *before* you can apply the quadratic formula, you must first write the equation in standard form, $ax^2 + bx + c = 0$.

Example 2 **Writing in Standard Form**

Solve $2x^2 - 3x = 8$.

Solution

$$2x^2 - 3x = 8 \qquad \textit{Rewrite original equation.}$$
$$2x^2 - 3x - 8 = 0 \qquad \textit{a = 2, b = -3, c = -8}$$
$$x = \frac{-(-3) \pm \sqrt{(-3)^2 - 4(2)(-8)}}{2(2)}$$
$$x = \frac{3 \pm \sqrt{9 + 64}}{4} \qquad \textit{Simplify.}$$
$$x = \frac{3 \pm \sqrt{73}}{4} \qquad \textit{Solutions}$$

The equation has two solutions.

$$x = \frac{3 + \sqrt{73}}{4} \approx 2.89 \quad \text{and} \quad x = \frac{3 - \sqrt{73}}{4} \approx -1.39 \qquad \blacksquare$$

An algebraic check of solutions that have been rounded can be messy. Often, a graphic check is easier. To check the solutions in Example 2, sketch the graph of $y = 2x^2 - 3x - 8$. The two x-intercepts correspond to the two solutions.

Example 3 **Finding the x-Intercepts of a Graph**

Find the x-intercepts of $y = -x^2 - 2x + 5$.

Solution   The x-intercepts occur when $y = 0$.

$$0 = -x^2 - 2x + 5 \qquad \textit{Substitute 0 for y.}$$
$$x^2 + 2x - 5 = 0$$
$$x = \frac{-2 \pm \sqrt{2^2 - 4(1)(-5)}}{2(1)} \qquad x = \frac{-b \pm \sqrt{b^2 - 4ac}}{2a}$$
$$\textit{a = 1, b = 2, c = -5}$$
$$x = \frac{-2 \pm \sqrt{4 + 20}}{2} \qquad \textit{Simplify.}$$
$$x = \frac{-2 \pm \sqrt{24}}{2} \qquad \textit{Solutions}$$

The x-intercepts of the graph of $y = -x^2 - 2x + 5$ are

$$x = \frac{-2 + \sqrt{24}}{2} \approx 1.45 \quad \text{and} \quad x = \frac{-2 - \sqrt{24}}{2} \approx -3.45.$$

Note that the x-intercepts are equidistant from the vertex of the parabola. $\qquad \blacksquare$

Using Quadratic Models in Real Life

In Lesson 9.2, you studied the model for the height of a falling object that is *dropped*. For an object that is *thrown* down or up, the model changes to have an extra term. Problems involving these two models are *vertical motion* problems.

Models $h = -16t^2 + s$ *Object is dropped.*

$h = -16t^2 + vt + s$ *Object is thrown.*

Labels h = height   (feet)

t = time in motion   (seconds)

s = initial height   (feet)

v = initial velocity   (feet per second)

Remember that v is the velocity, not the speed.

Real Life

Hot Air Balloon

Example 4   *When Does It Hit the Water?*

Your brother is riding in a hot-air balloon over a lake. From an altitude of 4000 feet, he throws a rock straight down toward the water. When the rock leaves his hand, its speed is 30 feet per second. How long will it take the rock to hit the water?

Solution   Because the rock is thrown down, its initial velocity is $v = -30$ feet per second. The initial height is $s = 4000$ feet. The rock will hit the water when height h is 0.

$h = -16t^2 - 30t + 4000$ *Vertical motion model*

$0 = -16t^2 - 30t + 4000$ *Substitute 0 for h.*

$16t^2 + 30t - 4000 = 0$ *a = 16, b = 30, c = -4000*

$$t = \frac{-30 \pm \sqrt{30^2 - 4(16)(-4000)}}{2(16)}$$

$$t = \frac{-30 \pm \sqrt{256{,}900}}{32}$$

$$t \approx 14.9 \quad \text{or} \quad -16.8$$

As a solution, -16.8 doesn't make sense in this case, so the rock will hit the water about 14.9 seconds after it is thrown. ∎

Communicating about **A L G E B R A**

▶ **SHARING IDEAS about the Lesson**

Extend the Idea   In Example 4, the rock is thrown.

If the rock were *dropped*, when would it hit the water?

EXERCISES

Guided Practice

▶ **CRITICAL THINKING about the Lesson**

1. **True or False?** The quadratic formula states that the solutions of the equation $ax^2 + bx + c = 0$ are "the opposite of b, plus or minus the square root of b minus $4ac$, all divided by $2a$."

2. Describe the two models for vertical motion.

3. State the values of a, b, and c from the standard form of the equation $5 = 6 + 9x - x^2$.

4. Solve $x^2 + x - 2 = 0$.

5. Sketch the graph of $y = x^2 + x - 2$ and label the x-intercepts.

6. Describe the relationship between the x-intercepts found in Exercise 5 and the solutions found in Exercise 4.

Independent Practice

In Exercises 7–10, write the quadratic equation in standard form.

7. $-3x^2 + 5x = 9$

8. $5 - 2x + x^2 = 0$

9. $-4 + 3x + x^2 = 5$

10. $9x - 7x^2 = 16$

In Exercises 11–14, find the value of $b^2 - 4ac$ for the equation.

11. $2x^2 - 3x - 1 = 0$

12. $4x^2 + 4x + 1 = 0$

13. $3x^2 - 2x - 5 = 0$

14. $x^2 - 11x + 30 = 0$

In Exercises 15–20, use the quadratic formula to solve the equation.

15. $4x^2 - 13x + 3 = 0$

16. $3y^2 + 11y + 10 = 0$

17. $2x^2 + 7x + 3 = 0$

18. $x^2 - 6x + 7 = 0$

19. $5y^2 + 2y - 2 = 0$

20. $2x^2 + 4x - 3 = 0$

In Exercises 21–26, solve the quadratic equation by the most convenient method (finding square roots or the quadratic formula). Explain why you chose your method.

21. $6x^2 + 20x + 5 = 0$

22. $t^2 = 27$

23. $x^2 - 625 = 0$

24. $4u^2 - 49 = 0$

25. $-2x^2 + 6x + 1 = 0$

26. $x^2 + 14x + 49 = 0$

In Exercises 27–32, find the x-intercepts of the graph of the equation.

27. $y = x^2 + 2x + 15$

28. $y = x^2 - 6x - 7$

29. $y = x^2 + x - 20$

30. $y = x^2 + 8x + 12$

31. $y = x^2 + x - \frac{3}{4}$

32. $y = x^2 + \frac{7}{3}x - 2$

33. *Royal Gorge Bridge*   If a rock was dropped from the Royal Gorge Bridge into the Arkansas River, how long would it take for the rock to hit the water? (Assume there is no air resistance.) Do you think there is a regulation *against* dropping objects off this bridge? Explain your answer.

34. *Royal Gorge Bridge*   How much sooner would the rock reach the Arkansas River if it was thrown straight down with an initial speed of 30 feet per second?

35. *The Owl and the Mouse*   An owl is circling a field at a height of 100 feet and sees a mouse. The owl folds its wings and begins to dive with an initial speed of 10 feet per second. Estimate the time the mouse has to escape.

The Royal Gorge Bridge near Canon City, Colorado, is the highest suspension bridge in the world. The bridge is 1053 feet above the Arkansas River.

36. *Play It Again in Metric*   An owl is circling a field at a height of 30.5 meters and sees a mouse. The owl folds its wings and begins to dive with an initial speed of 3 meters per second. Estimate the time the mouse has to escape. (Use the vertical motion model $h = -4.9t^2 + vt + s$, where h is height in meters, v is initial velocity in meters per second, and s is initial height in meters.)

37. *Flying Time*   The cities of Chicago, Atlanta, and Toronto approximate the vertices of a right triangle. How long would it take a plane flying at 500 miles per hour to fly from Atlanta to Toronto?

38. *Depth of a Submarine*   The sonar of a Navy cruiser detects a submarine that is 3000 feet from the cruiser. The angle between the water surface and the submarine is 45°. How deep is the submarine?

39. *Population of Mexico*   The population, P (in thousands), of Mexico between 1930 and 1990 can be modeled by

$P = 19.2t^2 + 31.6t + 16964.5$

where t is the year, with $t = 0$ corresponding to 1930. Find the year in which the population of Mexico will reach 100,000,000. Demonstrate your result graphically.

40. *Practicing Lawyers*   The number, L, of practicing lawyers in the United States between 1960 and 1985 can be modeled by

$$L = 273,063 + 2.225t + 471t^2$$

where t is the year, with $t = 0$ corresponding to 1960. During which year were approximately 321,000 lawyers practicing in the United States? Does your algebraic solution agree with the graph?

(Source: American Bar Foundation)

Integrated Review

In Exercises 41 and 42, evaluate the expression.

41. $\sqrt{16 - 4(3)(1)}$

42. $\sqrt{36 - 4(2)(-4)}$

In Exercises 43–45, check whether the number is a solution of the equation.

43. $2x^2 - 4x + 9 = 9, 2$

44. $3x^2 + 3x + 4 = 12, -2$

45. $x^2 - 9x + 7 = 11, 6$

In Exercises 46–48, sketch the graph of the equation. Label the x-intercepts on the graph.

46. $y = x^2 + 4x - 45$

47. $y = x^2 - x - 6$

48. $y = 2x^2 - 7x + 3$

Exploration and Extension

In Exercises 49 and 50, find the axis of symmetry of each graph and show that it lies midway between the two x-intercepts of the graph. Show how you could use this "two-part" form of the quadratic formula,

$$x = \frac{-b}{2a} \pm \frac{\sqrt{b^2 - 4ac}}{2a},$$

to find the distance between the axis of symmetry of a parabola and either of its x-intercepts.

49. $y = x^2 - 6x + 5$

50. $y = x^2 + 3x - 18$

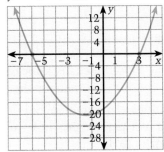

Take this test as you would take a test in class. The answers to the exercises are given in the back of the book.

In Exercises 1–6, find all square roots of the number. (9.1)

1. 64

2. 121

3. 0.0064

4. $\frac{49}{100}$

5. $\frac{1}{81}$

6. 0.01

In Exercises 7–12, evaluate the square root. Give the exact value, if possible. Otherwise, give an approximation to two decimal places. (9.1)

7. $\sqrt{4}$

8. $\sqrt{1}$

9. $\sqrt{8}$

10. $\sqrt{2.25}$

11. $\sqrt{0.1}$

12. $\sqrt{50}$

In Exercises 13–18, solve the equation. (9.2)

13. $\frac{1}{3}x^2 - 27 = 0$

14. $25x^2 - 37 = 588$

15. $7x^2 - 81 = 31$

16. $\frac{3}{4}x^2 - 3 = 51$

17. $x^2 - \frac{1}{4} = 6$

18. $x^2 + 37 = 199$

In Exercises 19–22, determine the vertex and x-intercepts of the graph. (9.3)

19.

20.

21.

22.

In Exercises 23–26, solve the equation. (9.4)

23. $x^2 - x - 30 = 0$

24. $-x^2 - 8x - 16 = 0$

25. $-x^2 + 3x + 2 = 0$

26. $x^2 + 5x - 2 = 0$

27. *Geometry* The legs of a right triangle are 3 inches and 4 inches. What is the length of the hypotenuse? **(9.1)**

28. *Geometry* The volume of a box with a square base and a height of 14 centimeters is 1400 cubic centimeters. What is the length of an edge of the base? **(9.2)**

29. You are trying to build the world's tallest tower of interlocking toy blocks. (The record is $59\frac{1}{2}$ feet.) When your tower is 30 feet tall, the bag holding the loose blocks is knocked off the top of the tower. How many seconds did it take for the bag to hit the floor? **(9.2)**

30. If the bag of blocks in Exercise 29 is thrown down with an initial velocity of 10 feet per second, how many seconds does it take for it to hit the floor? **(9.4)**

9.5

Problem Solving Using the Discriminant

What you should learn:

Goal 1 How to find the number of solutions of a quadratic equation by using the discriminant

Goal 2 How to use the discriminant in real-life models

Why you should learn it:

You can use the discriminant as a quick source of information about quadratic models.

Goal 1 Solutions of a Quadratic Equation

In the quadratic formula, the expression $b^2 - 4ac$ is the **discriminant**.

$$x = \frac{-b \pm \sqrt{\overset{\text{Discriminant}}{b^2 - 4ac}}}{2a} \quad \textit{Quadratic formula}$$

The discriminant of a quadratic equation can be used to find the number of solutions of the quadratic equation.

The Number of Solutions of a Quadratic Equation

Consider the quadratic equation $ax^2 + bx + c = 0$.

1. If $b^2 - 4ac$ is positive, then the equation has two solutions.
2. If $b^2 - 4ac$ is zero, then the equation has one solution.
3. If $b^2 - 4ac$ is negative, then the equation has no solution.

Example 1   *Finding the Number of Solutions of a Quadratic Equation*

$ax^2 + bx + c = 0$	Discriminant $(b^2 - 4ac)$	Number of Solutions
a. $x^2 - 2x + 3 = 0$	$(-2)^2 - 4(1)(3) = -8$	None
b. $x^2 - 2x + 1 = 0$	$(-2)^2 - 4(1)(1) = 0$	One
c. $x^2 - 2x - 2 = 0$	$(-2)^2 - 4(1)(-2) = 12$	Two ■

In Example 1, note that the number of solutions can be changed by just changing the value of c. A graph can help you see why this occurs. By changing the value of c, you can move the graph of $y = x^2 - 2x + c$ up or down in the coordinate plane. If the graph is moved too high, it won't have an x-intercept and the equation $x^2 - 2x + c = 0$ won't have a solution.

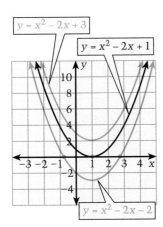

Graphic Check

$y = x^2 - 2x + 3$ *Graph above x-axis (no x-intercepts)*
$y = x^2 - 2x + 1$ *Graph touches x-axis (one x-intercept)*
$y = x^2 - 2x - 2$ *Graph crosses x-axis (two x-intercepts)*

9.5 ▪ *Problem Solving Using the Discriminant*   **479**

Using the Discriminant in Real Life

Rick is a firefighter and is leaning out of a window on the eighth floor. He is trying to throw a grappling hook to a tenth-floor window that is 26 feet above him.

Connections
Physics

Example **2** *Will the Grappling Hook Catch?*

Rick can throw the grappling hook with a maximum speed of 40 feet per second. Can he throw the grappling hook to the window above him?

Solution   You don't know Rick's present height. In the vertical motion model, however, you can let his present height be $s = 0$. Use an initial velocity of $v = 40$ feet per second. To reach the window, Rick must be able to throw the grappling hook to a height of 26 feet.

$$h = -16t^2 + 40t + 0 \quad \textit{Vertical motion model}$$
$$26 = -16t^2 + 40t \quad \textit{Substitute 26 for h.}$$
$$16t^2 - 40t + 26 = 0 \quad \textit{Standard form}$$

Using $a = 16$, $b = -40$, and $c = 26$, the discriminant is

$$b^2 - 4ac = (-40)^2 - 4(16)(26) = -64.$$

Because the discriminant is negative, the equation $16t^2 - 40t + 26 = 0$ has no solution. This means that Rick cannot throw the grappling hook to the window above him. ■

If Rick could throw the hook so it travels just a little faster (41 feet per second) *or* if the window were just a little closer (25 feet), he could throw the hook to the window. Try to see why.

United States Government Payroll

Dollars (in billions)

Year(0 ↔ 1960)

From 1960 to 1990, the total government payroll in the United States (local, state, and federal) can be modeled by $P = 35t^2 + 115t + 3410$, where P is in millions of dollars and $t = 0$ corresponds to 1960.

Real Life
Government

Example 3 *Predicting the Government Payroll*

Judging from the payroll pattern between 1960 and 1990, is it possible that the government payroll will reach 70 billion dollars a year?

Solution In the model for the payroll, P is given in millions of dollars. A payroll of 70 billion dollars would correspond to a P-value of 70,000. Why?

$$P = 35t^2 + 115t + 3410 \qquad \textit{Quadratic model}$$
$$70,000 = 35t^2 + 115t + 3410 \qquad \textit{Substitute 70,000 for P.}$$
$$0 = 35t^2 + 115t - 66,590 \qquad \textit{Standard form}$$

The discriminant of this equation is

$$b^2 - 4ac = 115^2 - 4(35)(-66,590) = 9,335,825.$$

Because the discriminant is positive, the equation has two solutions. Using the quadratic formula, you can find the solutions to be approximately -45 and 42. The solution 42 suggests that, based on the model, the government payroll will reach 70 billion dollars in 2002. ∎

Communicating about **ALGEBRA**

▶ **SHARING IDEAS about the Lesson**

Analyze Consider the equation $x^2 - 4x + c = 0$.

A. Find values of c so that the equation will have no solution, one solution, and two solutions.

B. Give a graphical interpretation of your answers to Part A.

EXERCISES

▶ **CRITICAL THINKING about the Lesson**

1. Write the quadratic formula and circle the part that is called the discriminant.

2. Explain how the discriminant can be used to determine the number of solutions of $ax^2 + bx + c = 0$.

3. Find the discriminant of $3x^2 - 2x - 5 = 0$. How many solutions does this equation have?

In Exercises 4–6, match the discriminant with the graph.

4. $b^2 - 4ac = 3$ 5. $b^2 - 4ac = 0$ 6. $b^2 - 4ac = -2$

a.

b.

c.

Independent Practice

In Exercises 7–12, decide how many solutions the equation has.

7. $2x^2 + 3x - 2 = 0$ 8. $x^2 - 2x + 4 = 0$ 9. $-2x^2 + 4x - 2 = 0$

10. $-\frac{1}{2}x^2 + x + 3 = 0$ 11. $5x^2 - 2x + 3 = 0$ 12. $3x^2 - 6x + 3 = 0$

13. *Spelunking*   You and a friend are *spelunking* (exploring caves) in a section of the Onondaga Cave in Missouri. The two of you are standing beneath a ledge that is 15 feet high. Your friend can throw a grappling hook upward with an initial velocity of 30 feet per second. Will the grappling hook reach the ledge when it is thrown? Explain.

14. *Spelunking, Part II*   While you and your friend are attempting to reach the ledge, some other spelunkers join you. They see the trouble you are having and suggest that your friend stand on a foot-high rock to throw the hook. Would this help? Explain.

Onondaga Cave, in Leasburg, Missouri

15. Geometry Is it possible for a rectangle with a perimeter of 52 centimeters to have an area of 148.75 square centimeters? Explain.

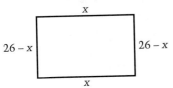

16. Geometry The area of the isosceles triangle is 192 square meters. What is its perimeter?

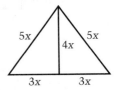

Dunking the Ball **In Exercises 17 and 18, use the vertical motion model:** $h = -16t^2 + vt + s$.

Chun and R.J. are playing basketball. Chun can jump with an initial velocity of 13 feet per second and needs to jump 2.6 feet to dunk the basketball. R.J. can jump with an initial velocity of 15 feet per second and needs to jump 3.6 feet to dunk the ball.

17. Can Chun dunk the ball? Can R.J.? Justify your answers.

18. Suppose that Chun can jump with an initial velocity of 12.5 feet per second and R.J. can jump with an initial velocity of 15.5 feet per second. How, if at all, would this change your answers to Exercise 17?

19. Business as Usual? For the past 30 years, profits of Specialty Aircraft have increased as shown in the graph. The profits can be modeled by

$P = 1.4t^2 + 2.2t + 258,$

where $t = 30$ represents the present year and P is in thousands of dollars. Now, you have been elected president of the company, and the board of directors expects you to increase annual profits by at least 10% per year for five years. Should you follow the previous president's strategies or do you need to make some changes? Explain.

20. Profit or Loss? Your company's income and expenses for the past ten years can be modeled as follows.

$I = 2.3t^2 + 4.8t + 1049$ Income
$E = 6.5t^2 - 54.4t + 546$ Expenses

I and E are measured in thousands of dollars. Describe your company's profit record for the past ten years. How do the next ten years look?

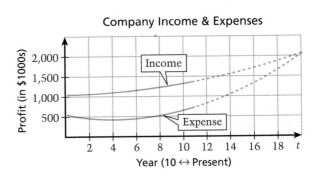

21. *Public School Spending* For 1970 to 1990 in the United States, public school (K–12) spending can be modeled by

$$P = 195t^2 + 3480t + 41{,}540$$

where P is in millions of dollars and $t = 0$ corresponds to 1970. Use the model to predict when annual spending will reach $350 billion.

(Source: U.S. National Center for Education)

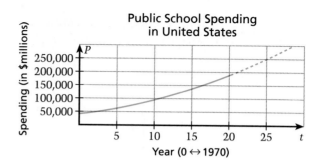

Public School Spending in United States

22. *Computers in the Classroom* For 1980 to 1990, the number of personal computers in grades K–12 (public and private) can be modeled by

$$C = 16t^2 + 96t$$

where C is in thousands of computers and $t = 0$ corresponds to 1980. Use the model to find when 5 million computers will be used in grades K–12.

(Source: Future Computing/Data Inc.)

Numbers of Computers in Classrooms

Integrated Review

23. *College Entrance Exam Sample* If $\frac{1}{x+2} = \frac{1}{2}$, then $x = \boxed{?}$

   a. 2   **b.** 1   **c.** 0   **d.** −1   **e.** −2

24. *College Entrance Exam Sample* If $x = -3$, then $(x + 3)^2 - 3x = \boxed{?}$

   a. −6   **b.** −3   **c.** 0   **d.** 6   **e.** 9

25. *Estimation—Powers of Ten* Which is the best estimate of the time it takes an object to fall 100 feet?

   a. 0.3 second   **b.** 3 seconds   **c.** 30 seconds   **d.** 300 seconds

26. *Estimation—Powers of Ten* Which is the best estimate of distance between Providence, Rhode Island, and San Diego, California?

   a. 250 miles   **b.** 2500 miles   **c.** 25,000 miles   **d.** 250,000 miles

In Exercises 27–30, match the equation with its graph.

27. $y = 3x^2 - 2x + 1$ **28.** $y = \frac{3}{4}x^2 + 2x + 1$ **29.** $y = \frac{3}{4}x^2 - 2x + 1$ **30.** $y = 3x^2 + 2x + 1$

a.

b.

c.

d.

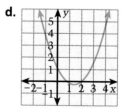

Roller Coaster **In Exercises 31–34, use the following information.**

You are riding on a roller coaster whose path can be modeled by

$$y = 0.005x^2 - 2x + 200$$

where x and y are measured in feet. When $t = 0$ seconds, you are at the point $(0, 200)$.

31. When $t = 4$ seconds, the y-coordinate of your location is 32. What is the x-coordinate of your location?

32. When $t = 4.23$ seconds, the y-coordinate of your location is 18. What is the x-coordinate of your location?

33. Use the Pythagorean theorem to approximate the length of the track between the two points $(x_1, 32)$ and $(x_2, 18)$.

34. What was your average speed between the two points?

Path of Part of a Roller Coaster Ride

$y = 0.005x^2 - 2x + 200$

$(x_1, 32)$

$(x_2, 18)$

Vertical Distance (in feet)

Horizontal Distance (in feet)

Roller coasters may include vertical drops of as much as 190 feet. At the bottom of such drops, the cars may reach a speed of about 72 miles per hour!

Mixed REVIEW

1. Find the quotient of x^2y and xy^2. **(1.3)**

2. Find the sum of $\frac{3}{7}$ and $\frac{1}{2}$. **(1.1)**

3. Evaluate $|x| - \sqrt{x}$ when $x = 9$. **(2.1, 9.1)**

4. Evaluate $|3y + 2| - \frac{1}{2}y$ when $y = -6$. **(2.1)**

5. What is the opposite of $-\frac{6}{7}$? **(2.1)**

6. What is the opposite of $-a^3$? **(2.1)**

7. Sketch the graph of $|3x - 3| - 6 = y$. **(4.7)**

8. Sketch the graph of $y = -\frac{1}{2}x - 2$. **(4.5)**

9. Evaluate $4[(3 \div 2) + \frac{1}{2}]$. **(1.1)**

10. Evaluate $(3x - 2)\frac{1}{2} + 2x$ when $x = 4$. **(1.4)**

11. Is $(4, 6)$ a solution of $2x + 3y = 26$? **(1.5)**

12. Is $(0, 3)$ a solution of $4x - 3y \le 5x + 1$? **(6.5)**

13. Solve $|x + \frac{1}{4}| - 8 < 0$. **(6.4)**

14. Solve $\frac{1}{3}(6x - 1) > 2$. **(6.1)**

In Exercises 15–20, write an equation for the indicated line. (5.2, 5.3)

15. Slope $m = -\frac{1}{2}$, through point $(3, -1)$

16. Slope $m = 5$, through point $(8, -6)$

17. Slope $m = 0$, through point $(-3, 6)$

18. Through two points: $(3, -5)$, $(3, 7)$

19. Through two points: $(44, 28)$, $(33, 17)$

20. Through two points: $(-8, -3)$, $(-5, -5)$

9.6 Graphing Quadratic Inequalities

What you should learn:

Goal 1 How to sketch the graph of a quadratic inequality

Goal 2 How to use quadratic inequalities as real-life models

Why you should learn it:

You can use quadratic inequalities to model many real-life situations, such as those in which the values of a quadratic expression cannot exceed a certain amount.

Goal 1 Sketching a Quadratic Inequality

In this lesson, you will study the following types of **quadratic inequalities.**

$$y < ax^2 + bx + c \qquad y \le ax^2 + bx + c$$
$$y > ax^2 + bx + c \qquad y \ge ax^2 + bx + c$$

The graph of any such inequality consists of the graph of all ordered pairs (x, y) that are solutions of the inequality. The steps used to sketch the graph of a quadratic inequality are similar to those used to sketch the graph of a linear inequality. (See Lesson 6.5.)

Sketching the Graph of a Quadratic Inequality

1. Sketch the graph of the parabola $y = ax^2 + bx + c$. (Use a *dashed* parabola for inequalities with $<$ or $>$ and a *solid* parabola for inequalities with $\le$ or $\ge$.)

2. Test a point inside the U-shape and one outside the U-shape.

3. Only one of the test points will be a solution. Shade the region that contains that test point.

Example 1   *Sketching the Graph of a Quadratic Inequality*

Sketch the graph of $y < 2x^2 - 3x + 4$.

Solution   The parabola $y = 2x^2 - 3x + 4$ has a vertex at $\left(\frac{3}{4}, \frac{23}{8}\right)$. (See graph at left.) Choose a point inside the U-shape, say $(0, 6)$, and a point outside the U-shape, say $(0, 0)$.

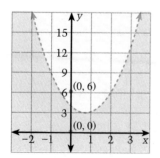

Point	Test the Point.	Conclusion
$(0, 6)$	$6 \overset{?}{<} 2(0)^2 - 3(0) + 4$	Because 6 is *not* less than 4, the ordered pair $(0, 6)$ is not a solution.
$(0, 0)$	$0 \overset{?}{<} 2(0)^2 - 3(0) + 4$	Because 0 *is* less than 4, the ordered pair $(0, 0)$ is a solution.

From this test, the graph must be the region outside the U-shape. ∎

The bridge over the Humber Estuary in England is the longest suspension bridge in the world. Its main suspension cables approximate the parabolic shape given by $y = 0.0001x^2$, where x and y are measured in feet. The vertex of the parabola is at the center of the bridge.

Real Life
Bridge Building

Example 2   *The Humber Estuary Suspension Bridge*

The vertical cables that are suspended from the main cable lie in the region given by

$$y \leq 0.0001x^2.$$

How high are the towers? Sketch a graph of the region containing the vertical cables between the towers.

Solution   The distance between the two towers is 4626 feet. Because the vertex of the parabola $y = 0.0001x^2$ is at the center of the bridge, the x-coordinates of the tower tops must be ± 2313. Substituting either value into the equation gives a y-value of about 535. Thus, the towers are about 535 feet high. The graph of the parabola is shown below. The region that contains the vertical cables lies below the parabola and above the x-axis (the roadbed).

For a package to be accepted for mailing by the United States Postal Service, the sum of the length and girth of the package must not exceed 108 inches.

Connections
Geometry

Area Available (in in.²)

2500, 2000, 1500, 1000, 500

(13.5, 2916)

4 8 12 16 20 24 x
Width of Package (in inches)

Example 3 *Making a Poster*

The outside of a package has a pattern and pictures that you really like. You cut off and discard the square ends of the package. Your plan is to cut apart the sides to make hangings for your bedroom door. The door is 36 by 81 inches. Could there be enough cardboard to completely cover your door?

Solution Because the package was sent through the mail, you know that the sum of its length and girth (the distance around) is at most 108 inches. In the diagram, the girth of the box is $4x$. This means that the length is at most $108 - 4x$.

Verbal Model	Area of hangings	$\leq$	4	$\cdot$	Area of one side of box

Labels Area of hangings = y (square inches)
Area of one side = $x(108 - 4x)$ (square inches)

Inequality $y \leq 4x(108 - 4x)$ **Algebraic model**
$y \leq 432x - 16x^2$

The graph of this inequality is shown at the left. Each point (x, y) in the shaded area represents a solution of the inequality, where y is the area of the cardboard that you intend to use for the hangings. The surface area of your door is $(36)(81) = 2916$ square inches, and the vertex of the parabola is $(13.5, 2916)$. If the ends of the package are 13.5 inches square, you have exactly enough to cover your door. ■

Communicating about ALGEBRA

▶ **SHARING IDEAS about the Lesson**

Extend the Solution Only one shape of package will allow you to completely cover your door.

Find the dimensions of that package. Show how you could cut the unfolded sides of that package into only three rectangular pieces to cover the door.

EXERCISES

Guided Practice

▶ **CRITICAL THINKING about the Lesson**

1. Describe the steps used to sketch the graph of a quadratic inequality.

2. Sketch the graph of $y = x^2 + 3x + 2$.

3. Select a point inside the U-shape and a point outside the U-shape. Determine which of the points is a solution of the inequality $y \leq x^2 + 3x + 2$.

4. Shade the region that contains the test point from Exercise 3 that satisfies the inequality.

Independent Practice

In Exercises 5–8, decide whether the point is a solution of the inequality.

5. $y \geq 2x^2 - x + 9$, $(2, 10)$

6. $y > 4x^2 - 64x + 115$, $(12, -60)$

7. $y < x^2 + 6x + 12$, $(-1, 6)$

8. $y \geq x^2 - 7x + 9$, $(-1, 16)$

In Exercises 9–14, match the inequality with its graph.

9. $y \geq -2x^2 - 2x + 1$

10. $y < -2x^2 + 4x + 3$

11. $y \geq 2x^2 + x + 1$

12. $y \geq 4x^2 - 6x + 5$

13. $y < 2x^2 - x - 3$

14. $y > -4x^2 + 6x - 5$

a.

b.

c.

d.

e.

f.

In Exercises 15–23, sketch the graph of the inequality.

15. $y < -x^2 - 4x - 3$

16. $y \geq x^2 - 3x + 1$

17. $y \geq 8x^2 - 3$

18. $y > -x^2 + 12x - 1$

19. $y \leq 2x^2 + x + 6$

20. $y \geq 3x^2 + 9x - 1$

21. $y > -4x^2 - 8x - 4$

22. $y < -5x^2 - 3x + 6$

23. $y \leq x^2 + 5x + 3$

Diamonds, Diamonds, Diamonds! **In Exercises 24–27, use the following information.**

The price of a diamond is determined by its weight, cut, clarity, and flawlessness. Flawless diamonds with perfect clarity are very rare and very expensive. The equations and their graphs show the wholesale prices of a round-cut diamond with perfect clarity. The five highest grades of flawlessness vary from IF (flawless) to VS2. *(Source: Hook's Gallery)*

Flawlessness	Equation
IF	$y = 40 + 13{,}000x^2$
VVS1	$y = 31 + 10{,}160x^2$
VVS2	$y = 27 + 8670x^2$
VS1	$y = 20 + 6660x^2$
VS2	$y = 16 + 5150x^2$

24. Your aunt tells you that she can get a two-carat diamond at the "wholesale price" of $70,000. She says the diamond is of the highest quality. Describe the region in the coordinate plane that contains the point (2, 70,000). What can you conclude about your aunt's statement?

25. The wholesale price of a $2\frac{1}{2}$-carat diamond with perfect clarity is $55,000. Assume that the price is a fair representation of the flawlessness of the diamond. Which region contains the point $\left(2\frac{1}{2}, 55{,}000\right)$?

a. $y > 31 + 10{,}160x^2$

b. $y < 31 + 10{,}160x^2$

What grade is the diamond?

Wholesale Diamond Prices

Cost (in 1000s of dollars)

Carats

IF
VVS1
VVS2
VS1
VS2

26. You are trying to decide how to cut a large rough diamond. Parts of the diamond have minor inclusions (foreign substances) and fissures (small cracks). Other parts, however, are flawless. Which of the following combinations has the greatest value? Explain.

a. One 3-carat VVS2 and one 1-carat VS1

b. One 2-carat IF and one 2-carat VS1

c. One $1\frac{1}{2}$-carat IF and two $1\frac{1}{4}$-carat VVS2

27. Many famous large diamonds have been found. The Jonker diamond, found in 1934, weighed 726 carats! The rough diamond was cut into 12 flawless stones of perfect clarity, the largest weighing 125 carats. Your uncle says he can get this latter diamond for you at a wholesale price! What price does he have in mind?

28. *Light Reflector*   A cross section of the parabolic light reflector at the right is described by the equation $y = \frac{1}{24}x^2 + 1$. The bulb inside the reflector is located at the point $(0, 7)$. Light bounces off the reflector in parallel rays. This quality allows flashlights to direct light in a narrow beam. In which region is the bulb located?

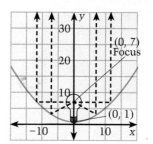

   a. $y > \frac{1}{24}x^2 + 1$ **b.** $y < \frac{1}{24}x^2 + 1$

Glued to the Tube   **In Exercises 29 and 30, use the following information.**

The number, N (in millions), of television sets in use in the world between 1950 and 1990 can be modeled by $N = \frac{1}{2}t^2 + 46$ where $t = 0$ corresponds to 1950.

29. Let A represent the number of television sets in North and South America in 1990. In which region is the point $(40, A)$ located? Explain.

   a. $N < \frac{1}{2}t^2 + 46$ **b.** $N > \frac{1}{2}t^2 + 46$

30. In which region is the point $(30, 500)$ located?

   a. $N < \frac{1}{2}t^2 + 46$ **b.** $N > \frac{1}{2}t^2 + 46$

   If someone told you that in 1980, Americans owned an average of 2.25 television sets each, would you believe them? Explain. (1980 U.S. Population: 225 million)

Integrated Review

In Exercises 31–34, solve the inequality.

31. $9x - 20 > 61$ **32.** $2x + 9 < 3$ **33.** $3x + 5 \le 17$ **34.** $\frac{1}{2}x - 2 \ge 6$

In Exercises 35–38, sketch the graph of the inequality.

35. $y \ge x + 3$ **36.** $y < -x + 1$ **37.** $y > -2x - 4$ **38.** $y \ge 3x - 4$

In Exercises 39–42, sketch the graph of the equation.

39. $y = x^2 + 4x - 5$ **40.** $y = x^2 - 1$ **41.** $y = -\frac{1}{2}x^2 + \frac{3}{2}x - 4$ **42.** $y = -2x^2 - 5x + 3$

Exploration and Extension

In Exercises 43 and 44, shade the region whose points satisfy both inequalities.

43. $\begin{cases} y \le 3x^2 + 5 \\ y > 1 \end{cases}$

44. $\begin{cases} y > x^2 - 1 \\ y \le x + 2 \end{cases}$

9.7

Exploring Data:
Comparing Models

What you should learn:

Goal 1 How to choose a model that best fits a collection of data

Goal 2 How to use models in real-life settings

Why you should learn it:

To be skilled at modeling, you must know characteristics of the different models and be able to recognize those characteristics in real-life settings.

Goal 1 Choosing a Model

You have now studied four basic types of algebraic models.

Type of Model	Equation	Graph
1. Linear	$y = ax + b$	Line
2. Absolute Value	$y = a\|x + b\| + c$	V-Shaped
3. Exponential	$y = C(1 \pm r)^x$	Exponential curve
4. Quadratic	$y = ax^2 + bx + c$	Parabola (U-Shaped)

This lesson will help you understand the differences between these basic types, and will help you choose the type of model that best fits a collection of data.

Example 1   *Choosing a Model*

Name the type of model that best fits each data collection.

a. $(-3, 4), \left(-2, \frac{7}{2}\right), (-1, 3), \left(0, \frac{5}{2}\right), (1, 2), \left(2, \frac{3}{2}\right), (3, 1)$

b. $(-3, 4), (-2, 3), (-1, 2), (0, 1), (1, 2), (2, 3), (3, 4)$

c. $(-3, 4), (-2, 2), (-1, 1), \left(0, \frac{1}{2}\right), \left(1, \frac{1}{4}\right), \left(2, \frac{1}{8}\right), \left(3, \frac{1}{16}\right)$

d. $(-3, 4), \left(-2, \frac{7}{3}\right), \left(-1, \frac{4}{3}\right), (0, 1), \left(1, \frac{4}{3}\right), \left(2, \frac{7}{3}\right), (3, 4)$

Solution   Make scatter plots of the data. Then decide whether the points lie on a line, a V, an exponential curve, or a parabola.

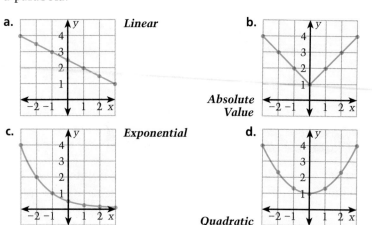

Time, t	Distance, d
0.25 s	0.61 in.
0.50 s	2.45 in.
0.75 s	5.50 in.
1.00 s	9.78 in.
1.25 s	15.28 in.
1.50 s	22.00 in.
1.75 s	29.95 in.
2.00 s	39.12 in.
2.25 s	49.51 in.
2.50 s	61.13 in.
2.75 s	73.96 in.
3.00 s	88.02 in.

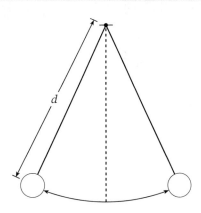

A simple pendulum can be constructed with a string and a weight. The distance, d (in inches), between the fixed point and the weight is related to the time, t (in seconds), it takes for the pendulum to swing through one full period (over and back).

Problem Solving

Make a Graph

Relationship between
Period and Length
of a Pendulum

Example 2   *Finding a Model*

Which type of model best fits the pendulum behavior described above? Find the model.

Solution   Draw a scatter plot for the data, as shown at the left. From the scatter plot, you can see that the pattern is *not* linear or absolute value. If it fits any of the four basic types, it must be exponential or quadratic. If the pattern was exponential, then the pendulum lengths would have to increase by the same percentage (for equal increases in time). This, however, is not true, because $2.45 \div 0.61 \approx 4$, but $5.50 \div 2.45 \approx 2.24$ ($t = 0.25, 0.50, 0.75$).

The only model left to try is a quadratic model. Let's try a simple one: $d = at^2$. To find a, substitute any known value of d and t.

$$d = at^2 \qquad \textit{Simple quadratic model}$$
$$9.78 = a(1^2) \quad \textit{Substitute } d = 9.78 \textit{ and } t = 1.$$
$$9.78 = a \qquad \textit{Solve for } a.$$

At this point, you do not know if the model $d = 9.78t^2$ works for any other values of d and t. However, after testing several values, you can see that the model fits the data. Therefore, the length of a pendulum is related to the period of the pendulum by the quadratic model

$$d = 9.78t^2.$$

The Dutch scientist Christiaan Huygens used this model when he patented the first pendulum clock in 1657. ■

Chamber, n	Volume, v
0	0.787
1	0.837
2	0.889
3	0.945
4	1.005
5	1.068
6	1.135
7	1.207
8	1.283
9	1.364
10	1.450
11	1.541

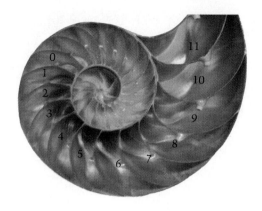

The volumes, v, of 12 consecutive chambers of a nautilus are shown in the table. The chambers are numbered from n = 0 to n = 11.

Problem Solving
Make a graph

Relationship between Position and Volume of Nautilus Chambers

Volume (in cm³) / Number of Chambers

Example 3 Finding a Model

Find a model for the chambered nautilus data above.

Solution From the scatter plot, you can see that the model is not linear or absolute value. To see whether an exponential model fits, find the ratios of consecutive volumes.

$$\frac{0.837}{0.787} \approx 1.064 \qquad \frac{0.889}{0.837} \approx 1.062 \qquad \frac{0.945}{0.889} \approx 1.063$$

Each chamber's volume is about 6.3% larger than the previous chamber. So you can use the exponential model $v = C(1 + r)^n$. In this model, $r = 0.063$ and C is the volume when $n = 0$.

$$v = 0.787(1.063)^n$$

This model was first discovered by the French mathematician René Descartes. ∎

Communicating about ALGEBRA

Cooperative Learning

▶ **SHARING IDEAS about the Lesson**

Work with a Partner and Use a Table Find a model that relates the variables.

The area, A, of an *ellipse* whose radii are r and $r + 1$ is shown in the table. (This model occurred in the writings of Hypatia. She was a Greek mathematician who lived in Egypt.)

Radius, r	1	2	3	4	5	6
Area, A	2π	6π	12π	20π	30π	42π

EXERCISES

Guided Practice

▶ **CRITICAL THINKING about the Lesson**

1. State the four types of algebraic models we have studied. Write an equation for each.

3. Which model has a V-shaped graph?

2. Which model has a U-shaped graph?

4. Describe the graph of each model and sketch an example of each.

Independent Practice

In Exercises 5–8, name the type of model suggested by the graph.

5.

6.

7.

8.

In Exercises 9–14, make a scatter plot of the data. Then name the type of model that best fits the data.

9. $(-1, 16)$, $(0, 4)$, $(1, -2)$, $(2, -2)$, $(3, 4)$, $(5, 34)$

10. $(-3, 2)$, $\left(-2, \frac{5}{2}\right)$, $\left(-1, \frac{7}{2}\right)$, $(0, 5)$, $(1, 7)$, $\left(2, \frac{19}{2}\right)$

11. $(-2, 2)$, $\left(-1, \frac{5}{2}\right)$, $(0, 3)$, $\left(1, \frac{7}{2}\right)$, $(2, 4)$, $\left(3, \frac{9}{2}\right)$

12. $(-4, 5)$, $(-3, 3)$, $(-2, 5)$, $(-1, 7)$, $(0, 9)$, $(1, 11)$

13. $(-2, -3)$, $(-1, 4)$, $(0, 9)$, $(1, 12)$, $(3, 12)$, $(5, 4)$

14. $(-5, 6)$, $(-4, 3)$, $(-2, -3)$, $(-1, -6)$, $(0, -9)$, $(1, -12)$

Cool, Cool Cotton   **In Exercises 15 and 16, use the following information.**

The table gives the cotton consumption, C (in pounds), per American between 1950 and 1990. Let t represent the year, with $t = 0$ corresponding to 1960.

Year, t	−10	−5	0	5	10	15	20	25	30
Pounds of Cotton, C	30.6	27.6	24.6	21.6	18.6	15.6	12.6	13.2	16.2

15. Which of the following models best fits the data?
  a. $C = 24.6 - 0.6t$ **b.** $C = -1.8 + 0.6t$
  c. $C = 0.6|t - 22| + 11.4$

16. Describe the pattern of cotton consumption between 1950 and 1990. What caused this type of pattern?

17. *Stretching a Spring*   Different masses, M (in kilograms), are hung from a spring. The distances, d (in centimeters), that the spring stretches are recorded in the table. Which type of model best fits these data? Find the model. (This model was discovered by the English mathematician Robert Hooke in the late 1600's.)

M	1	2	3	4	5	6	7
d	2.6	5.2	7.8	10.4	13	15.6	18.2

18. *Incompatible Computer Hardware*   The estimated amount of money, A (in millions of dollars), that businesses spent on incompatible hardware between 1984 and 1994 can be modeled by

$$A = 51,000 - 200t + 700t^2,$$

where $t = 4$ corresponds to 1984. Complete the table. Then compute the difference of consecutive A-values.

(Amount in 1985) − (Amount in 1984)
(Amount in 1986) − (Amount in 1985)
(Amount in 1987) − (Amount in 1986)
⋮   ⋮

Describe the pattern given by these differences.

Year, t	4	5	6	7	8	9	10	11	12	13	14
Amount, A	?	?	?	?	?	?	?	?	?	?	?

19. *Population of the Philippines*   In 1970, the population, P, in the Philippine Islands was 38,680,000. Since then, the average annual percent increase has been about 2.7%. Find a model that best fits the population of the Philippines for the years from 1970 on.

20. *Grocery Sales*   The sales of groceries, G (in billions of dollars), in the United States between 1970 and 1990 is given in the table. The year is represented by t, with $t = 0$ corresponding to 1970. Which type of model best fits this data? Find the model.

Year, t	0	5	10	15	16	18	20
Grocery Sales, G	88	154.5	221	287.5	300.8	327.4	354

21. *Buy It through the Mail!*   In 1970, the direct-mail purchases in the United States totaled $2766 million. From 1970 to 1990, the purchases increased about 12% per year. Find a model for the total direct-mail expenditures, D (in millions), from 1970 to 1990. Let $t = 0$ represent 1970.

22. *Surface Area of a Sphere*   The surface area, S, of a sphere with radius r is shown in the table. Find a model that relates. (This model was discovered by mathematicians in early Greece.)

Radius, r	1	2	3	4	5
Area, S	4π	16π	36π	64π	100π

Integrated Review

In Exercises 23–25, find an equation of the line that passes through the two points.

23. $(3, -2)$, $(5, 4)$ **24.** $(-3, -9)$, $(5, 7)$

25. $(2, 3)$, $(-4, 6)$

In Exercises 26–28, solve the equation.

26. $t^2 + t - 30 = 0$ **27.** $\frac{1}{2}x^2 - 35 = 37$ **28.** $3t^2 - 4t = 0$

In Exercises 29 and 30, write an exponential model for the amount A in year t.

29. Initial value: 1000,   4% increase each year   **30.** Initial value: 160,   8% decrease each year

Exploration and Extension

31. *Hey, Teacher, I Know!*   Karl Gauss was one of the most famous mathematicians who ever lived. Read the following story.

One day in math class, during Gauss's early school life, Gauss's teacher wanted to give the students a project that would use up some of the class time. The teacher asked the students to find the sum of the integers from 1 to 100. After only a few seconds, Karl stood up and said, "The sum is 5050!"

To see how Karl may have found the total, consider the following:

$$1 = 1 \qquad n = 1$$
$$1 + 2 = 3 \qquad n = 2$$
$$1 + 2 + 3 = 6 \qquad n = 3$$
$$1 + 2 + 3 + 4 = 10 \qquad n = 4$$
$$1 + 2 + 3 + 4 + 5 = 15 \qquad n = 5$$
$$1 + 2 + 3 + 4 + 5 + 6 = 21 \qquad n = 6$$

Let S be the sum of the first n integers. There is a quadratic model for S of the form $S = \boxed{?}\, n^2 + \boxed{?}\, n$. Can you find it? The numbers 1, 3, 6, 10, 15, and 21 were called triangular numbers by mathematicians in early Greece. Can you guess why?

9 Chapter Summary

What did you learn?

Skills

1. Evaluate square roots
   - exactly for some numbers. **(9.1)**
   - with a calculator for other numbers. **(9.1)**

2. Solve a quadratic equation
   - by finding square roots. **(9.2)**
   - by the quadratic formula. **(9.4)**

3. Find the number of solutions of a quadratic equation
   - by using the discriminant. **(9.5)**
   - by sketching a graph. **(9.3, 9.5)**

4. Sketch the graph of a quadratic equation. **(9.3)**
   - Find vertex and axis of symmetry of a parabola. **(9.3)**

5. Sketch the graph of a quadratic inequality. **(9.6)**

Strategies

6. Use quadratic models for real-life situations. **(9.1–9.7)**

Exploring Data

7. Decide which type of model best fits given data. **(9.7)**

Why did you learn it?

Real-life problems contain several different types of relations and patterns. For some, linear models fit well. For others, absolute value models or exponential models fit well. In this chapter, you have seen that many real-life situations can be modeled with quadratic equations. Some examples are vertical motion problems, Pythagorean theorem problems, parabolic path problems, and area problems.

How does it fit into the bigger picture of algebra?

Quadratic equations contain the square of a variable. This chapter discusses quadratic equations in one variable. For instance, $x^2 - 9 = 0$ is a quadratic equation in x. Quadratic equations in one variable can be solved using square roots. The chapter also discusses quadratic equations in two variables, such as $y = x^2 - 9$. The graph of this equation is a *parabola*. Try to remember the "algebra-geometry" connection between equations in one and two variables. For instance, the equation $x^2 - 9 = 0$ has two solutions which correspond to the two x-intercepts of the graph of $y = x^2 - 9$. The chapter introduced you to several types of real-life problems that can be modeled with quadratic equations. In the last lesson of the chapter, you compared quadratic models to the other types of algebraic models you have studied.

In Exercises 1–8, evaluate the expression. Give the exact value if possible. Otherwise give an approximation to two decimal places. **(9.1)**

1. $\sqrt{25}$

2. $-\sqrt{0.06}$

3. $\sqrt{47}$

4. $\sqrt{-(-0.25)}$

5. $\sqrt{32}$

6. $\sqrt{30^2 - 4(6)(3)}$

7. $\sqrt{\frac{4}{36}}$

8. $-\sqrt{\frac{4}{13}}$

In Exercises 9–12, solve the equation using square roots. **(9.2)**

9. $w^2 - 144 = 0$

10. $8y^2 = 968$

11. $16t^2 - 81 = 0$

12. $4x^2 - 19 = 6$

In Exercises 13–16, match the equation with its graph. **(9.3)**

13. $y = x^2 - 9$

14. $y = -x^2 + 25$

15. $y = -x^2 + 3x - 2$

16. $y = x^2 - x - 20$

a.

b.

c.

d.

In Exercises 17–20, sketch the graph of the equation. Label the vertex. **(9.3)**

17. $-x^2 - 3x + 2 = y$

18. $x^2 = y$

19. $\frac{1}{4}x^2 + 2x - 4 = y$

20. $-6x^2 + 10x + 2 = y$

In Exercises 21–26, solve the equation. **(9.4)**

21. $x^2 - \frac{1}{4}x + \frac{1}{64} = 0$

22. $3x^2 - 4x + 1 = 0$

23. $-\frac{1}{4}x^2 + 3x - 9 = 0$

24. $-x^2 + x - \frac{1}{8} = 0$

25. $-2x^2 + x + 6 = 0$

26. $-\frac{1}{4}x^2 + \frac{1}{4}x + \frac{1}{2} = 0$

In Exercises 27–30, sketch the graph of the inequality. **(9.6)**

27. $x^2 - 3 \geq y$

28. $\frac{1}{2}x^2 + 3x - 4 < y$

29. $-x^2 - 2x + 3 \leq y$

30. $-4x^2 + 2x + 5 > y$

In Exercises 31–34, construct a scatter plot of the data. Then decide which type of model best fits the data. **(9.7)**

31. $(-3, 4), (-2, 1), (-1, 0), (0, 1), (1, 4), (2, 9), (3, 16)$

32. $(-3, -7), (-2, -4), (-1, -1), (0, 2), (1, 5), (2, 8), (3, 11)$

33. $\left(-3, \frac{1}{8}\right), \left(-2, \frac{1}{4}\right), \left(-1, \frac{1}{2}\right), (0, 1), (1, 2), (2, 4), (3, 8)$

34. $(-3, 0), (-2, -2), (-1, -4), (0, -2), (1, 0), (2, 2), (3, 4)$

35. *Flower Garden*   You are planting a triangular garden on the roof of your apartment building. To protect the flowers, you put up a small fence around the garden. How much fencing do you need?

36. *Free Fall*   On September 9, 1979, Kitty O'Neill dove 180 feet from a helicopter into a 30- by 60-foot air cushion for a TV film stunt. How long was O'Neill in the air? (Assume no air resistance and an initial velocity of zero.)
(Source: **Guinness Book of World Records***)*

37. *Atom Smasher*   The main instrument at the Fermi National Accelerator Laboratory is a particle accelerator, or atom smasher. In this circular tunnel, protons are accelerated to speeds that are close to the speed of light. Scientists direct a beam of protons at a target and study the results of the collisions. How far does a proton travel in one trip around the tunnel? (Circumference = $2\pi r$.)

One of the world's largest accelerators lies underground at the Fermi National Accelerator Laboratory at Batavia, Illinois. The circular tunnel encloses an area of 3.27 square kilometers. (Area = πr^2.)

38. *Softball Teams*   For 1965 to 1990, the number, S (in thousands), of youth softball teams in the United States can be modeled by

$$S = 0.075t^2 + 1.18$$

where t is the year, with $t = 0$ corresponding to 1965. Use the model to complete the table. Estimate the year for 60,000 teams.

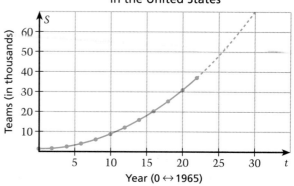

Number of Youth Softball Teams in the United States

Year (0 ↔ 1965)

Year, t	0	5	10	15	20	25
Teams, S	?	?	?	?	?	?

39. *You Could Break a Window Doing That!* Muriel and Connie are playing a game of catch. They decide it would be fun to stand on different sides of a building and throw the ball back and forth. Muriel can throw the ball with a velocity of 14 meters per second. Connie can throw with a velocity of 16 meters per second. Each stands 10 meters from the building. The paths of the ball are:

Muriel: $y = -\dfrac{9.8}{14^2}x^2 + x + 2$

Connie: $y = -\dfrac{9.8}{16^2}x^2 + x + 2$

Might they have broken any windows? Explain.

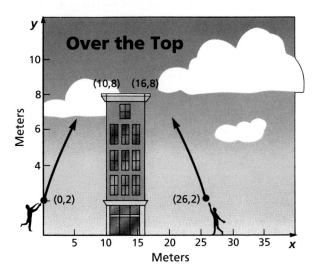

40. *Should Bud Charge More?* Bud sells about 12 dozen muffins a day at $3.60 per dozen. He estimates that he will sell one dozen fewer muffins a day for each $0.20 price increase per dozen.

Price	$3.60	$3.80	$4.00	$4.20	$4.40	$4.60	$4.80	$5.00	$5.20
Dozens Sold	12	11	10	9	8	7	6	5	4

The model that relates the total sales, M (in dollars), with the number of price increases, n, is

$$M = (12 - n)(3.60 + 0.2n) = -0.2n^2 - 1.2n + 43.2.$$

Find the total sales for $n = 0, 1, 2, \ldots, 8$. What should Bud charge to have the greatest sales? Explain.

Nitrogen Oxide **In Exercises 41 and 42, use the following information.**

For 1970 to 1990, the annual amount of nitrogen oxide, A (in thousands of tons), that was released into the air annually in the United States can be modeled by

$$A = 12{,}848 + 697t - 17t^2$$

where t is the year, with $t = 0$ corresponding to 1970. The graph is shown at the right.
(Source: U.S. Environmental Protection Agency)

41. When did the United States begin to reduce the amount of nitrogen oxide it was releasing into the atmosphere?

42. The release of nitrogen oxide increases the production of ozone and contributes to acid rain. Nitrogen oxide is released by burning gasoline, coal, and oil. How do you think the United States has begun to reduce the amount of nitrogen oxide released into the air?

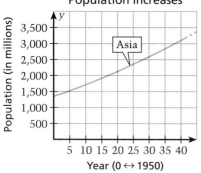

Population Increases

Population (in millions)

3,500
3,000
2,500
2,000
1,500
1,000
500

Asia

5 10 15 20 25 30 35 40
Year (0 ↔ 1950)

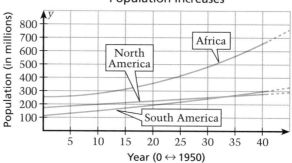

Population Increases

Population (in millions)

800
700
600
500
400
300
200
100

North America

Africa

South America

5 10 15 20 25 30 35 40
Year (0 ↔ 1950)

Earth's Populations   **In Exercises 43–46, match the population model with one of the graphs above.** *(Source: 1989 Demographic Year Book)*

43. $y = 110 + 3.5t + 0.03t^2$

44. $y = 0.23t^2 + 34.8t + 1330$

45. $y = 170 + 2.7t$

46. $y = 0.25t^2 + 254$

47. According to the models, will the population of South America ever exceed the population of Africa?

48. In what year did the population of Asia reach 2000 million?

Breakfast Vendor in Beijing

Market in Ecuador

Market in Morocco

Continent	North America	Africa	South America	Asia (outside former U.S.S.R.)
Area (square kilometers)	21,525,000	30,305,000	17,819,000	27,582,000

49. In 1990, which continent above had the greatest population density? Which was the least densely populated? (The population density is the number of people per square kilometer.)

50. Estimate the population densities of Africa and South America in 2000. Compare the population densities of the two in 1990 and 2000. Which population density is increasing more rapidly?

In Exercises 1–6, evaluate the expression. Give the exact value if possible. Otherwise give an approximation to two decimal places.

1. $-\sqrt{4}$

2. $\sqrt{0.0081}$

3. $\sqrt{\dfrac{4}{25}}$

4. $\sqrt{-9}$

5. $\sqrt{4^2 - 4(3)(-2)}$

6. $\sqrt{8^2 - 4(2)(8)}$

In Exercises 7–12, solve the equation.

7. $\dfrac{1}{2}x^2 - 8 = 0$

8. $-3x^2 + 243 = 0$

9. $x^2 - 8x + 7 = 0$

10. $-2x^2 + 5x + 9 = 0$

11. $x^2 + 9x - 3 = 0$

12. $x^2 + 3x + 3 = 0$

In Exercises 13–16, match the equation or inequality with its graph.

13. $y = x^2 - 2x + 3$ **14.** $y = -x^2 + 3x - 4$ **15.** $y \geq x^2 + 4x - 5$ **16.** $y \leq -x^2 - 2x - 1$

a.

b.

c.

d.

In Exercises 17–20, sketch the graph of the equation or inequality.

17. $y = \dfrac{1}{3}x^2 + 2x - 3$

18. $y = -x^2 + 5x - 6$

19. $y \leq -\dfrac{1}{2}x^2 + 2x + \dfrac{5}{2}$

20. $y \leq x^2 + 7x + 6$

21. *Trying to Fit a Square Peg into a Round Hole*   A round hole has a diameter of 2 inches. You have a square peg with sides of $1\frac{1}{2}$ inches. Will the square peg fit into the round hole? Explain.

22. Henry is standing on a bridge over a creek. He releases a stone 20 feet from the water. How long will it take the stone to hit the water?

23. Henry takes another stone and tosses it straight up with a velocity of 30 feet per second. How long will it take this stone to hit the water?

24. If Henry could throw a stone straight up into the air with a velocity of 50 feet per second, could the stone reach a height of 60 feet above the creek?

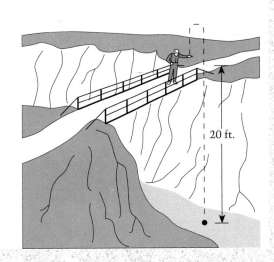

In Exercises 1–6, solve the linear system.

1. $\begin{cases} x + y = 5 \\ 2x + y = 9 \end{cases}$

2. $\begin{cases} \frac{1}{3}x - y = 4 \\ x + 3y = 0 \end{cases}$

3. $\begin{cases} -2x + 16y = 10 \\ x - 4y = -4 \end{cases}$

4. $\begin{cases} 3.2x + 1.1y = -19.3 \\ -32x + 4y = 148 \end{cases}$

5. $\begin{cases} \frac{1}{4}x - \frac{1}{2}y = -\frac{5}{2} \\ -4x + 3y = 5 \end{cases}$

6. $\begin{cases} 1.4x + 2.1y = 17.99 \\ 2.8x - 4.2y = -11.99 \end{cases}$

In Exercises 7–10, match the linear system with its graph.

7. $\begin{cases} 6x + 4y = 24 \\ \frac{1}{2}x + \frac{1}{3}y = 2 \end{cases}$

8. $\begin{cases} -\frac{1}{2}x + 3y = -2 \\ 4x - 24y = -10 \end{cases}$

9. $\begin{cases} -\frac{4}{3}x + \frac{1}{2}y = -4 \\ \frac{2}{3}x - \frac{1}{4}y = 2 \end{cases}$

10. $\begin{cases} x + 2y = -4 \\ 4.5x + 9y = 18 \end{cases}$

a.

b.

c.

d.

In Exercises 11–14, sketch the graph of the system of linear inequalities.

11. $\begin{cases} x \geq 0 \\ y \geq 0 \\ x < 4 \\ y < \frac{3}{2} \end{cases}$

12. $\begin{cases} x \geq 0 \\ y > 1 \\ y < 3 \\ x - y > 3 \end{cases}$

13. $\begin{cases} x > 1 \\ x - y \leq 1 \\ \frac{1}{2}x + y \leq 5 \end{cases}$

14. $\begin{cases} -\frac{1}{4}x + y \leq 2 \\ -4x + y \geq -4 \\ 2x + y \geq -4 \end{cases}$

In Exercises 15–18, simplify the expressions.

15. $\frac{(3w)^2}{2^2 w} \cdot w^{-3}$

16. $\frac{4ab^2}{2a^{-1}} \cdot (a^{-1}b)^4$

17. $\frac{(37p)^0}{p^2} \cdot \frac{(q^2p)^4}{q^2p^2}$

18. $\frac{1}{4}r^2 s^3 t^{-1} \cdot 4r^{-3}t^4$

In Exercises 19 and 20, evaluate the expressions. Write the results in scientific notation *and* in decimal form.

19. $(4.27 \times 10^3) \cdot (2.2 \times 10^2)$

20. $(3.6 \times 10^{-4}) \div (1.4 \times 10^{-3})$

In Exercises 21–26, solve the quadratic equation.

21. $3x^2 - 27 = 0$

22. $-\frac{1}{2}x^2 + 2 = 0$

23. $x^2 - 2x - 63 = 0$

24. $3x^2 + 11x + 6 = 0$

25. $x^2 + 3x - 9 = 0$

26. $5x^2 - 24x - 5 = 0$

In Exercises 27–32, sketch the graph of the equation or inequality.

27. $y = -x^2 + 2x$

28. $y = x^2 - 3x + 2$

29. $y = 3x^2 + 6x + 1$

30. $y \geq \frac{1}{4}x^2 - 2x + 4$

31. $y > x^2 + 4x + 6$

32. $y \leq -2x^2 + 8x - 3$

Fashion Doll Clothes   **In Exercises 33 and 34, use the following information.**

Jan is planning to start a small business, creating fashion doll clothes. She has designed two dresses: Style X (a daytime dress) and Style Y (an evening dress). The table below shows the cost of material, the number of hours of labor, and the profit for each style. The wages for employees is $5 per hour. Jan can spend up to $200 for the cost of material and up to $900 for labor.

33. Let *x* represent the number of dresses of Style X. Let *y* represent the number of dresses of Style Y. Use linear programming to find the number of dresses of each style that must be produced to obtain the maximum profit.

	X	Y
Cost of material ($)	2	4
Number of hours of labor	2	3
Profit ($)	6	10

34. In Exercise 33, what is the objective equation? What is the system of constraints?

Las Bolas Grandes   **In Exercises 35 and 36, use the following information.**

The diameters of *Las Bolas Grandes* of Costa Rica range from a few inches to eight feet. Researchers believe that these granite spheres were carved 1600 years ago.

35. One of the great stone balls has a radius of four feet. What is its volume? Write the result in scientific notation and in decimal form.

36. The ball in Exercise 35 weighs 16 tons. What is the weight in pounds? What is the density of the ball (in pounds per cubic foot)?

37. *Compound Interest*   Your savings account earns 4.8% interest, compounded annually. Another bank in town is offering 5.1% interest, compounded annually. The balance in your account is $567. How much additional interest could you earn in 5 years by moving your account to the bank with the 5.1% interest? How much additional interest could you earn in 10 years?

38. *Depreciation*   A used car was purchased in 1992 for $3700. If the value of the car depreciates 15% each year, what will the value be at the end of 1996?

Model Rocket   **In Exercises 39 and 40, use the following information.**

A model rocket is propelled straight up with an initial velocity of 300 feet per second.

39. How long will it take the rocket to reach an altitude of 1100 feet?

40. Will the rocket reach an altitude of 1500 feet? Explain.

LESSONS

10.1 Adding and Subtracting Polynomials ▪ 508

10.2 Multiplying Polynomials ▪ 515

10.3 Multiplying Polynomials: Two Special Cases ▪ 522

10.4 Factoring: Special Products ▪ 528

10.5 Factoring Quadratic Trinomials ▪ 535

10.6 Solving Quadratic Equations by Factoring ▪ 541

10.7 Solving Quadratic Equations by Completing the Square ▪ 549

This brilliant pattern of colors is formed by ice crystals photographed in polarized light.

Dating Ice Samples

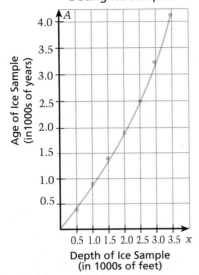

Age of Ice Sample (in 1000s of years) — vertical axis: 0.5, 1.0, 1.5, 2.0, 2.5, 3.0, 3.5, 4.0

Depth of Ice Sample (in 1000s of feet) — horizontal axis: 0.5 1.0 1.5 2.0 2.5 3.0 3.5

To study Earth's climate, scientists are drilling thousands of feet into Greenland's ice sheet at a research site called GISP2. Core samples of ice are removed and analyzed. Samples taken near the surface were formed recently, but samples from great depths were formed thousands of years ago. The *polynomial* model

$$A = \frac{9}{16}(x^3 - 7x^2 + 33x + 12)^2$$

relates the age of the ice, A (in years), with the depth of the core sample, x (in 1000's of feet). The ice crystals undergo changes in size, shape, and orientation with increasing depth. Researchers use polarized light to measure the changes in the ice crystals.

(Source: Popular Science, 1991.)

Depth, x	0.5	1.0	1.5	2.0	2.5	3.0	3.5
Age, A	406	856	1357	1892	2478	3164	4028

10.1

Adding and Subtracting Polynomials

What you should learn:

Goal 1 How to add and subtract polynomials

Goal 2 How to use polynomials as models in real-life settings

Why you should learn it:

You can use polynomials as models for a majority of real-life situations such as the performance of an industry over an interval of time.

Goal 1 Adding and Subtracting Polynomials

An expression whose terms are of the form ax^k, where k is a non-negative integer, is a **polynomial in one variable** or simply a **polynomial.**

The integer k is the **degree** of ax^k. The term ax has a degree of one, and the **constant term** a has a degree of zero. The **degree of a polynomial** is the largest degree of its terms. Polynomials are usually written in **standard form,** which means that the terms are written in descending order, from the largest degree to the smallest degree.

The number a is the **coefficient** of the term ax^k. When a polynomial is written in standard form, the coefficient of its first term is the **leading coefficient** of the polynomial.

Example 1 *Identifying Coefficients of a Polynomial*

Identify the coefficients of $-4x^2 + x^3 + 3$.

Solution Write the polynomial in standard form. Account for each degree, even if you must include zero coefficients.

$$-4x^2 + x^3 + 3 = (1)x^3 + (-4)x^2 + (0)x + 3$$

The coefficients are 1, -4, 0, and 3. The leading coefficient is 1. ■

Polynomials that have only one term are **monomials.** Polynomials that have two terms are **binomials.** Polynomials that have three terms are **trinomials.**

Example 2 *Classifying Polynomials*

Polynomial	Degree	Classified by Degree	Classified by Terms
a. 6	0	Constant	Monomial
b. $-2x$	1	Linear	Monomial
c. $3x + 1$	1	Linear	Binomial
d. $-x^2 + 2x - 5$	2	Quadratic	Trinomial
e. $4x^3 - 8x$	3	Cubic	Binomial
f. $2x^4 - 7x^3 - 5x + 1$	4	Quartic	Polynomial

■

To add two polynomials, add the coefficients of like terms. You can use a horizontal or vertical format.

Example 3 **Adding Polynomials Horizontally**

Add $2x^2 + x - 5$ and $x^2 + x + 6$.

Solution

$$(2x^2 + x - 5) + (x^2 + x + 6)$$
$$= (2x^2 + x^2) + (x + x) + (-5 + 6)$$
$$= 3x^2 + 2x + 1 \quad \blacksquare$$

Example 4 **Using a Vertical Format to Add Polynomials**

Use a vertical format to find the sum.

$$(5x^3 + 2x^2 - x + 7) + (3x^2 - 4x + 7) + (-x^3 + 4x^2 - 8)$$

Solution Align the like terms of the polynomials.

$$
\begin{array}{r}
5x^3 + 2x^2 - x + 7 \\
3x^2 - 4x + 7 \\
-x^3 + 4x^2 \phantom{{}- 4x} - 8 \\
\hline
4x^3 + 9x^2 - 5x + 6
\end{array}
\quad \blacksquare
$$

To subtract a polynomial, you must subtract *each of its terms*.

Example 5 **Subtracting Polynomials Horizontally**

Subtract $2x^2 - x - 4$ from $3x^2 - 5x + 3$.

Solution

$$(3x^2 - 5x + 3) - (2x^2 - x - 4)$$
$$= 3x^2 - 5x + 3 - 2x^2 + x + 4$$
$$= (3x^2 - 2x^2) + (-5x + x) + (3 + 4)$$
$$= x^2 - 4x + 7 \quad \blacksquare$$

One of the most common mistakes in algebra is to forget to subtract *each* term when subtracting one expression from another. Here is an example.

Wrong Signs
↓ ↓

$$(x^2 - 2x + 3) - (x^2 + 2x - 2) \neq x^2 - 2x + 3 - x^2 + 2x - 2$$

Example 6

Example 6 · Using a Vertical Format to Subtract Polynomials

Use a vertical format to find the difference.

$$(-2x^3 + 5x^2 - x + 8) - (-2x^3 + 3x - 4)$$

Solution To subtract each term, you *add its opposite*. One way is to multiply each "subtracted" term by -1 and then add.

$$
\begin{array}{l}
(-2x^3 + 5x^2 - x + 8) \\
-(-2x^3 \qquad + 3x - 4)
\end{array}
\rightarrow
\begin{array}{r}
-2x^3 + 5x^2 - x + 8 \\
2x^3 \qquad - 3x + 4 \\
\hline
5x^2 - 4x + 12
\end{array}
\quad \blacksquare
$$

Goal 2 ## Using Polynomials in Real-Life Modeling

Real Life
Stained Glass

Example 7 · Finding the Area of a Border

You are designing a stained-glass window. The border is made of red glass and is x inches wide. The interior uses other colors of glass. Write a polynomial expression for the amount of red glass you will use. Then use the expression to find how much red glass would be used for a 2-inch border and for a 3-inch border.

Solution

Verbal Model

$$\boxed{\text{Area of border}} = \boxed{\text{Total area}} - \boxed{\text{Area of interior}}$$

Labels
Total width $= 8x$	(inches)
Total height $= 14x + 2$	(inches)
Total area $= 8x(14x + 2) = 112x^2 + 16x$	(sq. in.)
Interior width $= 6x$	(inches)
Interior height $= 12x + 2$	(inches)
Interior area $= 6x(12x + 2) = 72x^2 + 12x$	(sq. in.)

Equation
$$
\begin{aligned}
\text{Area of border} &= (112x^2 + 16x) - (72x^2 + 12x) \\
&= (112x^2 - 72x^2) + (16x - 12x) \\
&= 40x^2 + 4x
\end{aligned}
$$

If the border is 2 inches wide, then the area of red glass is

$$40(2^2) + 4(2) = 168 \text{ square inches.}$$

If the border is 3 inches wide, then the area of red glass is

$$40(3^2) + 4(3) = 372 \text{ square inches.} \quad \blacksquare$$

Lobster pots on a dock at West Tremont, Maine. Maine harvests more lobster than any other state.

Real Life
Fishing Industry

Example 8 *Using Polynomial Models*

The number of pounds of shrimp, S, and lobster, L, consumed in the United States from 1980 to 1990 can be modeled by

$S = 42.8t + 425$ *Shrimp (millions of pounds)*
$L = -1.5t^2 + 20.7t + 194.5$ *Lobster (millions of pounds)*

where $t = 0$ represents 1980. Find a model that represents the total amount, T, of shrimp *and* lobster consumed from 1980 to 1990. Estimate the total amount, T, consumed in 1991.

Solution   The sum of the two polynomial models is

$$(42.8t + 425) + (-1.5t^2 + 20.7t + 194.5) = -1.5t^2 + 63.5t + 619.5.$$

The model for the total consumption of shrimp and lobster is

$$T = -1.5t^2 + 63.5t + 619.5.   \textit{Total (millions of pounds)}$$

Using this model, and substituting $t = 11$, you can estimate the 1991 consumption to be

$$T = -1.5(11^2) + 63.5(11) + 619.5 = 1136.5 \text{ million pounds.}$$

(Source: U.S. National Oceanic and Atmospheric Administration)   ■

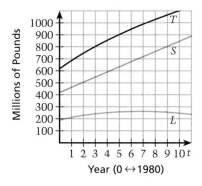

Annual Consumption of Lobster and Shrimp

Millions of Pounds

Year (0 ↔ 1980)

Communicating about ALGEBRA

▶ **SHARING IDEAS about the Lesson**

Use Terminology   To "do" algebra, you must know how to use the language.

A. The prefixes *poly, mono, bi,* and *tri* mean many, one, two, and three, respectively. Explain how these prefixes are used in *polygon, monopoly, binocular,* and *tricycle.*

B. Give an example of two polynomials of degree 3 whose sum is a polynomial of degree 2.

EXERCISES

▶ **CRITICAL THINKING about the Lesson**

1. Describe a polynomial in one variable.

2. Name the terms of $-3x^3 - 2x^2 + 4x - 5$.

3. Name the coefficients in $-7x^3 + 12x - 31$.

4. Write $15y - 6 + 10y^3 - 3y^2$ in standard form.

5. What is the degree of $2x^2 - 4x^3 + 7$?

6. Subtract $(2x^2 - 4x + 1)$ from $(x^2 + 8)$.

Independent Practice

In Exercises 7–10, classify the polynomial by degree and by number of terms.

7. $-5x - 4$

8. -7

9. $16 - 4x + 3x^2$

10. $3x^2 + 6x + 1$

In Exercises 11–16, add the polynomials. (Use a horizontal format.)

11. $x^2 - 3$; $3x^2 + 5$

12. $-3y + 2$; $y^2 + 3y + 2$

13. $2x^2 + 3x + 1$; $x^2 - 2x + 2$

14. $2x^2 - x + 3$; $3x^2 - 4x + 7$

15. $12x^3 + 2x^2 - 4$; $9x^2 + 3x - 8$

16. $-4x^3 - 2x^2 + x - 5$; $2x^3 + 3x + 4$

In Exercises 17–20, add the polynomials. (Use a vertical format.)

17. $2z - 8z^2 - 3$; $z^2 + 5z$

18. $6x^2 + 5$; $3 - 2x^2$

19. $5x^4 - 2x + 7$; $-3x^4 + 6x^2 - 5$

20. $4x^2 - 7x + 2$; $-x^2 + x - 2$

In Exercises 21–24, subtract the second polynomial from the first. (Use a horizontal format.)

21. $z^3 + z^2 + 1$; z^2

22. 10; $u^2 + 5$

23. $2x^2 + 3x - 4$; $x^2 + x - 1$

24. $3x^3 - 4x^2 + 3$; $x^3 + 3x^2 - x - 4$

In Exercises 25–28, subtract the second polynomial from the first. (Use a vertical format.)

25. $10x^3 + 15$; $17x^3 - 4x + 5$

26. $y^2 + 3y^4$; $y^5 - y^4$

27. $-2x^3 + 5x^2 - x + 8$; $-2x^3 + 3x - 4$

28. $3x^2 + 7x - 6$; $3x^2 + 7x$

In Exercises 29–34, perform the indicated operations. Use either a horizontal or vertical format and explain why you chose the method you used.

29. $(6x - 5) - (8x + 15) + (3x - 4)$

30. $(2x^2 + 1) + (x^2 - 2x + 1) - (2x^2 + 8)$

31. $-(x^3 - 2) + (4x^3 - 2x) - (2x^2 + 3)$

32. $-(5x^2 - 1) - (-3x^2 + 5) - (x^2 - x)$

33. $2(t^2 + 5) - 3(t^2 + 5) + 5(t^2 + 5)$

34. $-10(u + 1) + 8(u - 1) - 3(u + 6)$

35.

36.

37. *Chicken or Turkey?*   For 1980 through 1990, the numbers of pounds of chicken, C, and turkey, T, consumed on the average per American can be modeled by

$$C = 0.16t^2 + 0.73t + 49.9$$

$$T = 0.14t^2 - 0.37t + 10.6$$

where $t = 0$ represents 1980. Find a model for the average number of pounds, P, of chicken *and* turkey consumed from 1980 to 1990.

(Source: U.S. Department of Agriculture)

38. *Food Stores*   For 1980 through 1990, the numbers of grocery stores, G (including convenience stores), and specialty food stores, S, in the United States can be modeled by

$$G = 0.086t^2 - 1.55t + 172.5 \quad \text{(in 1000's)}$$

$$S = -0.040t^2 - 0.20t + 73.3 \quad \text{(in 1000's)}$$

where $t = 0$ represents 1980. Find a model that represents the total number of retail food stores, F, from 1980 to 1990.

(Source: National Restaurant Association)

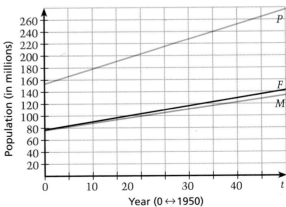

39. *American Men and Women*   For 1950 through 1990, the total population, P, and male population, M, of the United States can be modeled by

$$P = 2451.7t + 153,093.8 \quad \text{(in 1000's)}$$

$$M = 1153.8t + 75,825.8 \quad \text{(in 1000's)}$$

where $t = 0$ represents 1950. Find a model that represents the female population, F, of the United States from 1950 to 1990. *(Source: U.S. Bureau of the Census)*

40. *U.S. Retail Sales* Retail stores are classified as durable-goods stores (car dealers, hardware stores, furniture stores, jewelers) and nondurable-goods stores (department stores, drugstores, restaurants, grocery stores, gas stations, general merchandise stores). For 1980 through 1990, the total sales for retail stores, R, and for durable-goods stores, D, in the United States can be modeled by

$R = -0.21t^2 + 31.6t + 357.4$ (in billions $)
$D = 0.26t^2 + 2.9t + 34.3$ (in billions $)

where $t = 0$ represents 1980. Find a model that represents the sales for nondurable-goods stores, N.

Integrated Review

In Exercises 41–44, simplify the expression.

41. $8y - 2x + 7x - 10y$

42. $\frac{5}{6}x - \frac{2}{3}x + 8$

43. $\frac{1}{2}x + \frac{3}{2}y - 3y + 4x$

44. $-2y + 4x - 4x + 6y$

Discrete Math **In Exercises 45–48, perform the indicated matrix operation.**

45. $\begin{bmatrix} x^2 - 4x & -3x \\ 7x & 2x^2 + 4 \end{bmatrix} + \begin{bmatrix} x^2 + 4x & 2x \\ -7 + 2x & -5x^2 \end{bmatrix}$

46. $\begin{bmatrix} 4 & -6x \\ 5x^2 + x & 2x \end{bmatrix} + \begin{bmatrix} 3x^2 - 1 & 4x \\ 2x & x - 1 \end{bmatrix}$

47. $\begin{bmatrix} 6x - 5 & 10 \\ x^3 & 4y^2 - 5y \end{bmatrix} - \begin{bmatrix} 8 - 14x & 3x \\ -7y^3 & 6y - 2 \end{bmatrix}$

48. $\begin{bmatrix} 7x^3 & x^2 - 3x \\ 2x - 1 & 4 - 2x \end{bmatrix} - \begin{bmatrix} -2x^2 & 2x^2 + x \\ 3 & x^2 + 5x \end{bmatrix}$

Geometry **In Exercises 49 and 50, find the value(s) for x.**

49. Area of shaded region is 260 square units.

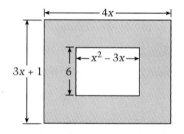

50. Area of shaded region is 84 square units.

Exploration and Extension

51. What must you add to $4x^2 + x - 5$ to get $x^2 + 5x + 1$?

52. What must you add to $x^2 - 7x + 3$ to get $-3x^2 + 2x - 1$?

53. What must you subtract from $3x^2 + 7x - 9$ to get $12x^2 - x + 6$?

10.2

Multiplying Polynomials

What you should learn:

Goal 1 How to multiply two polynomials using the Distributive Properties and the FOIL method

Goal 2 How to use polynomial multiplication in real-life settings

Why you should learn it:

You can model many situations with polynomial expressions that have to be multiplied, such as a rate times a quantity.

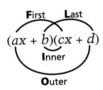

$$\overset{\text{First} \quad \text{Last}}{(ax + b)(cx + d)}$$

Inner

Outer

Goal 1 Multiplying Polynomials

You already know the simplest type of polynomial multiplication—multiplying a polynomial by a monomial.

$$(3x)(2x^2 - 5x + 3) = (3x)(2x^2) - (3x)(5x) + (3x)(3)$$
$$= 6x^3 - 15x^2 + 9x$$

To multiply two binomials, you can use both left and right Distributive Properties.

$$(3x - 2)(2x + 7) = 3x(2x + 7) - 2(2x + 7)$$
$$= (3x)(2x) + (3x)(7) - (2)(2x) - 2(7)$$
$$= 6x^2 + 21x - 4x - 14$$

Product of First terms	Product of Outer terms	Product of Inner terms	Product of Last terms

$$= 6x^2 + 17x - 14$$

With practice, you will be able to multiply two binomials in a single step using the **FOIL pattern.**

Example 1 *Multiplying Binomials (Distributive Property)*

Multiply: $(x - 3)$ by $(x + 2)$.

Solution

$(x + 2)(x - 3)$
$= x(x - 3) + 2(x - 3)$ *Right Distributive Property*
$= x^2 - 3x + 2x - 6$ *Left Distributive Property*
$= x^2 - x - 6$ *Combine like terms.* ■

Example 2 *Multiplying Binomials (FOIL Pattern)*

Multiply: $(3x + 4)(2x + 1)$.

Solution

$$(3x + 4)(2x + 1) = \overset{F}{6x^2} + \overset{O}{3x} + \overset{I}{8x} + \overset{L}{4}$$
$$= 6x^2 + 11x + 4 \qquad ■$$

To multiply two polynomials, remember that *each term of one polynomial must be multiplied by each term of the other polynomial.* This can be done using either a vertical or a horizontal format. In either case, it is best to begin by writing each polynomial in standard form.

Example 3 — Multiplying Polynomials (Vertical Format)

Multiply: $(x - 2)(5 + 3x - x^2)$.

Solution Begin by aligning like terms in columns.

$$
\begin{array}{r}
-x^2 + 3x + 5 \quad \textit{Standard form} \\
\times \qquad\qquad x - 2 \quad \textit{Standard form} \\
\hline
2x^2 - 6x - 10 \quad \leftarrow \quad -2(-x^2 + 3x + 5) \\
-x^3 + 3x^2 + 5x \qquad\quad \leftarrow \quad x(-x^2 + 3x + 5) \\
\hline
-x^3 + 5x^2 - x - 10 \quad \textit{Add like terms.} \quad \blacksquare
\end{array}
$$

Example 4 — Multiplying Polynomials (Horizontal Format)

Multiply: $(4x^2 - 3x - 1)(2x - 5)$.

Solution

$$
\begin{aligned}
(4x^2 &- 3x - 1)(2x - 5) \\
&= 4x^2(2x - 5) - 3x(2x - 5) - (1)(2x - 5) \\
&= 8x^3 - 20x^2 - 6x^2 + 15x - 2x + 5 \\
&= 8x^3 - 26x^2 + 13x + 5 \qquad\qquad \blacksquare
\end{aligned}
$$

Connections
Geometry

Example 5 — An Area Model for Multiplying Polynomials

Use an area model (or algebra tiles) to show that

$$(x + 2)(2x + 1) = 2x^2 + 5x + 2.$$

Solution Think of a rectangle whose sides have lengths $x + 2$ and $2x + 1$. The area of this rectangle is

$$(x + 2)(2x + 1). \qquad \textit{Area = (width)(length)}$$

Another way to find the area is to add the areas of the rectangular parts. There are two squares whose sides are x, five rectangles whose sides are x and 1, and two squares whose sides are 1. The total area of these nine rectangles is

$$2x^2 + 5x + 2. \qquad \textit{Area = sum of rectangular areas}$$

Because each method must produce the same area, you can conclude that

$$(x + 2)(2x + 1) = 2x^2 + 5x + 2. \qquad \blacksquare$$

For many American dairy farmers, the 1980's were not good years. Although milk production per cow increased through computer management and breeding, the price of milk paid to dairy farmers decreased.

Goal 2 | **Polynomial Multiplication in Real Life**

Example 6 | *The Plight of the Dairy Farmer*

Dairies measure milk in 100-pound units. (A gallon of milk weighs about 8 pounds.) For 1980 through 1990, the average annual milk production, M, per dairy cow can be modeled by $M = 3t + 115$, where M is measured in hundreds of pounds and $t = 0$ represents 1980. The prices, p, paid to dairy farmers can be modeled by $p = -0.25t + 14.25$, where p is price in dollars per hundred pounds. Find a model for average annual revenue per cow. What can you conclude from the model?

Solution

Verbal Model

Revenue per cow	=	100 pounds per cow	·	Price per 100 pounds

Labels
Revenue per cow = R
100 pounds per cow = $M = 3t + 115$
Price per 100 pounds = $p = -0.25t + 14.25$

Equation $R = (3t + 115)(-0.25t + 14.25)$
$= -0.75t^2 + 14t + 1638.75$

From the graph, you can see that the average revenue per cow peaked in about 1989. For many dairy farmers, the increased revenue was not sufficient to offset the increasing costs of machinery, fertilizers, and feed. *(Source: U.S. Dept. of Agriculture)* ■

Milk Production

Revenue per Cow (in dollars)

1700 R
1680
1660
1640

0 1 2 3 4 5 6 7 8 9 t
Year (0 ↔ 1980)

Communicating about ALGEBRA

Cooperative Learning

▶ **SHARING IDEAS about the Lesson**

Work with a Partner and Make a Model Construct area models similar to Example 5 for each polynomial product.

A. $(x + 3)(x + 2)$ **B.** $(x + 1)(3x + 1)$

EXERCISES

Guided Practice

▶ **CRITICAL THINKING about the Lesson**

1. Show how the Distributive Properties can be used to multiply $(2x - 3)$ and $(x + 4)$.

2. Multiply: $(x + 1)(x^2 - x + 1)$. Explain your use of the Distributive Property.

3. Multiply: $(x - 3)(2x + 5)$.

4. What does **FOIL** represent?

Independent Practice

In Exercises 5–10, multiply.

5. $(3x - 7)(-2x)$

6. $3x^2(5x - x^3 + 2)$

7. $(-x)(2x^2 - 3x)$

8. $2x(3x^2 - 4x + 1)$

9. $4x^2(5x^3 - 2x^2 + x)$

10. $-x^2(6x^3 - 14x + 9)$

In Exercises 11–16, use the FOIL pattern to multiply.

11. $(3x - 2)(5x + 7)$

12. $(3x + 5)(2x + 1)$

13. $(x - 4)(x + 4)$

14. $(2x - 3)(x + 3)$

15. $(x - 5)(2x + 10)$

16. $(3x - 5)(2x + 1)$

In Exercises 17–22, use an area model (or algebra tiles) to multiply.

17. $(x + 1)(x + 5)$

18. $(x + 2)(x + 6)$

19. $(x + 1)(x + 2)$

20. $(3x + 1)(2x + 2)$

21. $(x + 2)(2x + 3)$

22. $(2x + 1)(x + 3)$

In Exercises 23–28, use the Distributive Property to multiply.

23. $(x - 3)(3x + 1)$

24. $(2x + 1)(3x + 1)$

25. $(3x^2 + x - 5)(2x - 1)$

26. $(2x^2 - 7x + 1)(4x + 3)$

27. $(x^2 + 9)(x^2 - x - 4)$

28. $(x + 3)(x^2 - 6x + 2)$

In Exercises 29–37, multiply.

29. $(x + 3)(x - 4)$

30. $(2x - 1)(x + 9)$

31. $(2x - 5)(x + 6)$

32. $(3x - 4)\left(\frac{1}{3}x + 1\right)$

33. $\left(x + \frac{6}{5}\right)(4x - 5)$

34. $\left(x + \frac{1}{4}\right)\left(x - \frac{5}{4}\right)$

35. $\left(\frac{1}{2}x + 3\right)\left(\frac{1}{2}x - 2\right)$

36. $(-3x^2 + x - 1)(x + 3)$

37. $(x^2 + 4x - 9)(x - 4)$

38. *Area of a Sail* The base of a triangular sail is x feet and its height is $\frac{1}{2}x + 5$ feet. Find an expression for the area, A, of the sail.

39. Use the expression in Exercise 38 to complete the table.

Base, x	5	6	7	8	9	10
Area, A	?	?	?	?	?	?

In recent years, people in Britain were puzzled by the overnight appearance of "crop circles." Many were surrounded by concentric rings. Those shown below appeared in a wheat field in 1987 about three miles from Stonehenge, England.

40. The area (in square feet) of the circular ring of grain shown in the upper right corner of the photo is given by

$A = \pi(4x + 28)(4x - 28)$.

Simplify this expression. Substitute $x = 9$ to obtain the area of this circular ring in square feet.

41. If you doubled the value of x, would the value of A double? Explain.

42. *FOIL Pattern*   Find the area of the rectangle in two different ways: by multiplying length times width *and* by adding the areas of the smaller rectangles. Explain how this is related to the FOIL pattern for finding the product $(x + a)(x + b)$.

43. *College Entrance Exam Sample* $(x + 9)(x + 2) = \boxed{?}$
   a. $x^2 + 18$ **b.** $11x$ **c.** $x^2 + 11$ **d.** $x^2 + 11x + 18$ **e.** $9(x + 2) + 2(x + 9)$

44. *Geometry*   Find an expression for the area of the trapezoid. (Area $= \frac{1}{2}h(b_1 + b_2)$)

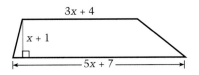

45. *Geometry*   Find an expression for the area of the triangle.

46. *Gross Domestic Product (GDP)* For 1980 through 1990, each American's dollar share, S, of the GDP can be modeled by

$$S = 900t + 11{,}800 \quad \textit{dollar share per American}$$

where $t = 0$ represents 1980. The population, P (in millions), of the United States during the same time can be modeled by

$$P = 228 + 2.2t. \quad \textit{number of Americans}$$

Find a model for the *total* Gross Domestic Product, T, from 1980 to 1990. Then use the three models to complete this table.

Year, t (1980 = 0)	0	5	10
Per capita GDP, S (dollars per American)	?	?	?
Population, P (millions of Americans)	?	?	?
Total GDP, T (millions of dollars)	?	?	?

(Source: Organization for Economic Cooperation and Development, Paris, France)

Integrated Review

In Exercises 47–50, rewrite the product in exponential form.

47. $(-3)(-3)(-3)(-3)$ **48.** $(x)(x)(x)$ **49.** $(-2)(-2)(x)(x)(x)$ **50.** $(4)(4)(y)(y)$

In Exercises 51–54, rewrite the expression as repeated multiplication.

51. $\left(\frac{4}{5}\right)^4$ **52.** $(4.5)^5$ **53.** $(x^2)^3$ **54.** $(y^2)^2$

In Exercises 55–58, simplify the expression.

55. $2(x - 4) + 5x$ **56.** $4(3 - y) + 2(y + 1)$

57. $-3(z - 2) - (z - 6)$ **58.** $(u - 2) - 3(2u + 1)$

In Exercises 59–62, simplify the expression.

59. $\dfrac{x^4}{3x^{-3}}$ **60.** $\dfrac{6x^{-1}}{2x}$ **61.** $\dfrac{5x^2y^0}{xy^3}$ **62.** $\dfrac{x^3y^3}{x^0y}$

Exploration and Extension

In Exercises 63 and 64, multiply.

63. $(x + 1)(2x - 3)(x - 7)$ **64.** $(3x + 7)(x + 4)(2x - 3)$

65. *Patterns* Multiply: $(x - 1)(x + 1)$, $(x - 1)(x^2 + x + 1)$, and $(x - 1)(x^3 + x^2 + x + 1)$. Find a pattern in your results. Use the pattern to guess the result of multiplying $(x - 1)$ and $(x^4 + x^3 + x^2 + x + 1)$. Then verify your guess by multiplying.

1. What is 22% of $4,242.00?
2. What is $\frac{1}{4}$ of $\frac{2}{3}$?
3. What is the reciprocal of x^2y? **(2.7)**
4. What is the reciprocal of $-\frac{1}{2}$? **(2.7)**
5. Solve $6^{x+3} = (3 + 3)^2$. **(8.2)**
6. Solve $3x^2 - 2x - 1 = 0$. **(9.4)**
7. Solve $x^2 + 4x + 4 = 0$. **(9.4)**
8. Solve $y^{x+3} = y^7$ for x. **(8.1)**
9. Evaluate $x^2 - 5x - 7$ when $x = -1$. **(1.3)**
10. Evaluate $|x + 2| + 3x$ when $x = -4$. **(2.1)**
11. Evaluate $(0.9)(3.2)^t$ when $t = 2$. **(1.3)**
12. Evaluate $(7.29)(6.2)^{-t}$ when $t = 1$. **(8.2)**
13. Is 3 a solution of $3x + 2^x \geq 15$? **(1.5)**
14. Is -4 a solution of $-y + 7y^2 - 14 < 18$? **(1.5)**
15. Is $(5, -3)$ a solution of $x + 2 = |-3y|$? **(2.1)**
16. Is $(-4, -1)$ a solution of $2^x < (2^y)^2$? **(8.1)**
17. Write 0.00794 in scientific notation. **(8.4)**
18. Write 3.29×10^4 in decimal form. **(8.4)**
19. Find the slope of $2x - 5y = 10$. **(4.3)**
20. Find the intercepts of $y = 3x - 2$. **(4.3)**

Milestones

LEONHARD EULER (1707–1783)

1650   1700   1750   1800   1850

Euler born

Euler at
St. Petersburg
Academy of Science

— Euler heads Academy of Science, Berlin

When Leonhard Euler entered the University of Basel in Switzerland, he began studying for the clergy but, encouraged by one of his teachers, soon switched to mathematics. He received his master's degree at the age of sixteen. His arrival in Russia in 1727 coincided with the death of Czarina Catherine I and the beginning of a regime unfavorable to scientific pursuits. Later political change brought a more favorable climate for research, and he began teaching at the newly founded St. Petersburg Academy of Science.

Euler made significant contributions to the study of number theory, geometry, and calculus. A prolific writer, he published 866 papers on mathematical topics. He introduced the symbol i for imaginary numbers, e for the base of natural logarithms, and $f(\ )$ for functions. He was one of the first to adopt the use of the symbol π. He was also a pioneer in the field of topology. Although totally blind the last 17 years of his life, he continued his work in mathematics. An unassuming man, he said, "The path that I followed will be of some help perhaps."

Name a significant event in the history of the United States that occurred during Euler's lifetime.

Leonhard Euler

10.3

Multiplying Polynomials: Two Special Cases

What you should learn:

Goal 1 How to use special-product patterns for the product of a sum and difference and for the square of a binomial

Goal 2 How to use special-product patterns in real-life models

Why you should learn it:

You can multiply some polynomials very efficiently if they have a special form.

Goal 1 Using Special-Product Patterns

Some binomial products occur so frequently in algebra that it is worth remembering special patterns for them. For instance, the product $(x + 3)(x - 3)$ is called the *product of the sum and difference of two terms*. This special product has no "middle term."

$$(x + 3)(x - 3) = x^2 - 3x + 3x - 9 \quad \textit{"Sum and difference"}$$
$$= x^2 - 9 \quad \textit{No middle term}$$

Another common type of product is the *square of a binomial*. In its pattern, the middle term is always twice the product of the two terms in the binomial.

$$(2x + 5)^2 = (2x + 5)(2x + 5) \quad \textit{Square of a binomial}$$
$$= 4x^2 + 10x + 10x + 25$$
$$= 4x^2 + 20x + 25 \quad \textit{Middle term is 2(2x)(5).}$$

These two patterns are generalized in the following summary. When you use these special-product patterns, remember that a and b can be numbers, variables, or even variable expressions.

Special Products

Sum and Difference Pattern   **Example**

$$(a + b)(a - b) = a^2 - b^2 \qquad (3x - 4)(3x + 4) = 9x^2 - 16$$

Square of a Binomial Pattern   **Example**

$$(a + b)^2 = a^2 + 2ab + b^2 \qquad (x + 4)^2 = x^2 + 2(x)(4) + 4^2$$
$$= x^2 + 8x + 16$$
$$(a - b)^2 = a^2 - 2ab + b^2 \qquad (x - 6)^2 = x^2 - 2(x)(6) + 36$$
$$= x^2 - 12x + 36$$

You don't need to write the steps that can be performed with mental math.

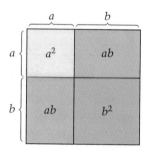

Connections
Geometry

The square-of-a-binomial pattern $(a + b)^2 = a^2 + 2ab + b^2$ can be verified with the area model shown at the left. The two rectangles with areas ab produce the middle term $2ab$.

Example 1 — The Product of the Sum and Difference of Two Terms

Multiply: $(5t - 2)(5t + 2)$.

Solution   This special product represents the sum and difference of two terms. The product has the form $(a - b)(a + b) = a^2 - b^2$.

$$(5t - 2)(5t + 2) = (5t)^2 - 2^2$$
$$= 25t^2 - 4 \qquad \blacksquare$$

Example 2 — Squaring a Binomial

Multiply: $(2x - 7)^2$.

Solution   This special product represents the square of a binomial. The product has the form $(a - b)^2 = a^2 - 2ab + b^2$. Note that the *middle* term of the product is twice the product of the two terms of the binomial.

$$(2x - 7)^2 = (2x)^2 - 2(2x)(7) + 7^2$$
$$= 4x^2 - 28x + 49 \qquad \blacksquare$$

Goal 2   ## Using Special Products in Real-Life Models

Connections
Geometry

Example 3 — Finding an Area

Find an expression for the area of the blue region shown at the left. Then evaluate the expression when x is equal to 2 inches; to 3 inches; and to 4 inches.

Solution

Verbal Model	Area of blue region	$=$	Area of entire square	$-$	Area of green region

Labels   Area of blue region $= A$ (sq. in.)
Area of entire region $= (x + 3)^2$ (sq. in.)
Area of green region $= (x + 1)(x - 1)$ (sq. in.)

Equation $A = (x + 3)^2 - (x + 1)(x - 1)$
$ = (x^2 + 6x + 9) - (x^2 - 1)$
$ = x^2 + 6x + 9 - x^2 + 1$
$ = 6x + 10$

When $x = 2$ inches, $A = 6(2) + 10 = 22$ square inches.
When $x = 3$ inches, $A = 6(3) + 10 = 28$ square inches.
When $x = 4$ inches, $A = 6(4) + 10 = 34$ square inches. $\blacksquare$

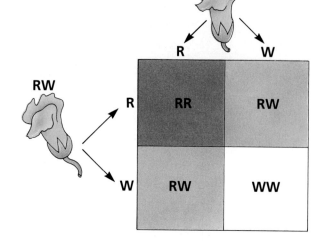

A pink snapdragon has two genes—one white (W) and one red (R)—that determine its color. This Punnett square *illustrates the possible results of crossing two pink snapdragons. Since each parent snapdragon passes along only one gene for color to an offspring (and pollination is at random), the snapdragon offspring will be approximately 25% red (RR), 50% pink (RW), and 25% white (WW).*

Connections
Biology

Example 4 *Using Punnett Squares*

Show how the product of two binomials can be used to model the Punnett square shown above.

Solution Each of the two pink "parent" snapdragons have half red genes and half white genes. You can model the genetic makeup of each parent as $50\% R + 50\% W = 0.5R + 0.5W$. When the two parents are crossed, the genetic makeup of the offspring can be modeled by the product $(0.5R + 0.5W)^2$.

$$(0.5R + 0.5W)^2 = (0.5R)^2 + 2(0.5R)(0.5W) + (0.5W)^2$$
$$= \underbrace{0.25R^2}_{\text{Red}} + \underbrace{0.5RW}_{\text{Pink}} + \underbrace{0.25W^2}_{\text{White}}$$

Thus, 25% of the offspring should be red, 50% should be pink, and 25% should be white. ■

Communicating about ALGEBRA

▶ **SHARING IDEAS about the Lesson**

Extend the Concept Is the trinomial the square of a binomial? Explain your reasoning.

A. $x^2 - 4x + 4$

B. $2x^2 - 6x + 9$

C. $4x^2 + 24x + 36$

EXERCISES

Guided Practice

▶ CRITICAL THINKING about the Lesson

1. **True or False?** The product of $(a - b)$ and $(a - b)$ is $a^2 - b^2$. Explain.

2. Find the missing term:
$(a + b)^2 = a^2 + \boxed{?} + b^2$.

3. Write two expressions for the area of a square whose sides are each $x - 4$.

4. Give an example of each of the three types of special products in this lesson.

Independent Practice

In Exercises 5–10, use an area model (or algebra tiles) to write the square as a trinomial.

5. $(x + 2)^2$
6. $(x + 3)^2$
7. $(2n + 1)^2$
8. $(3a + 2)^2$
9. $(2x + 2)^2$
10. $(3x + 1)^2$

In Exercises 11–16, write the square as a trinomial.

11. $(n + 6)^2$
12. $(x + 4)^2$
13. $(2x + 1)^2$
14. $(2m - 3)^2$
15. $(3t - 2)^2$
16. $(x - 9)^2$

In Exercises 17–22, multiply.

17. $(x + 5)(x - 5)$
18. $(x - 2)(x + 2)$
19. $(2x - 2)(2x + 2)$
20. $(5x - 6)(5x + 6)$
21. $(a + 2b)(a - 2b)$
22. $(4x - 7y)(4x + 7y)$

In Exercises 23–28, write the square as a trinomial.

23. $(x + 6)^2$
24. $(x + 10)^2$
25. $(a - 2)^2$
26. $(2x - 5)^2$
27. $(2x - 5y)^2$
28. $(4s + 3t)^2$

Area Model (or Algebra Tiles) In Exercises 29 and 30, write two different expressions for the area of the figure. Describe the special-product pattern that is represented.

29.

30.

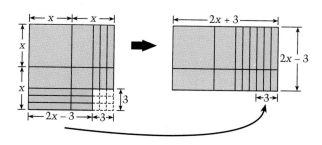

31. *Albino Tigers*   In tigers, the normal color gene, *C*, is *dominant* and the albino color, *A*, is *recessive*. This means that tigers whose color genes are *CC*, *CA*, or *AC* will have normal coloring. A tiger whose color genes are *AA* will be an albino. The Punnett square at the right shows the possible results of crossing two tigers that have recessive albino genes. What percent of the offspring of two such tigers will be the normal color? What percent will be albino? Use the model

$$(0.5C + 0.5A)^2$$
$$= 0.25CC + 0.5CA + 0.25AA$$

to answer the question.

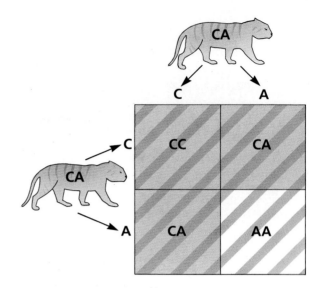

32. *Frizzle-Feathered Chickens*   In chickens, neither the normal-feathered gene, *F*, nor the frizzle-feathered gene, *f*, is dominant. This means that chickens whose feather genes are *FF* will have normal feathers. Chickens with *Ff* or *fF* will have mildly frizzled feathers. Chickens with *ff* will have extremely frizzled feathers. The Punnett square at the right shows the possible results of crossing two chickens with mildly frizzled feathers. What percent of the offspring of two such chickens will have normal feathers? What percent will have mildly frizzled feathers? What percent will have extremely frizzled feathers? Use the model

$$(0.5F + 0.5f)^2$$
$$= 0.25FF + 0.5Ff + 0.25ff$$

to answer the question.

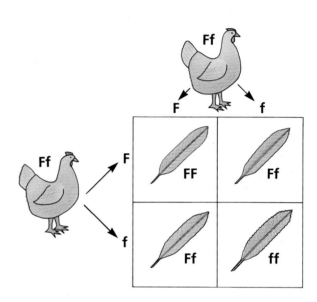

33. *Geometry*   The ratio of the height and width of the smaller rectangle is equal to the ratio of the height and width of the larger rectangle. Find expressions for the perimeters and areas of both.

34. *Geometry*   Find the area of the rectangle and the area of the triangle.

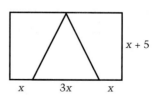

35. *Compounded Interest*   After two years, an investment of $1000 compounded annually at an interest rate, r, will grow to the amount $1000(1 + r)^2$ in dollars. Write this product as a trinomial.

36. *Compounded Interest*   After two years, an investment of $2000 compounded annually at an interest rate of 6% will have a dollar balance of

$$2000(1 + 0.06)^2 = 2000 + 2000(0.12) + 2000(0.0036).$$

Evaluate each side of this equation and compare your results.

37. *Common Errors*   Verify that $(a + b)^2 \neq a^2 + b^2$ by letting $a = 3$, $b = 4$, and evaluating both expressions.

38. *Common Errors*   Verify that $(a - b)^2 \neq a^2 - b^2$ by letting $a = 5$, $b = 4$, and evaluating both expressions.

Integrated Review

In Exercises 39–44, evaluate the expression.

39. $(x + 5)^2$ when $x = 4$
40. $(2x - 4)^2$ when $x = 1$
41. $(-3x + 5)^2$ when $x = 0$

42. $(x + 3)^2$ when $x = -6$
43. $\left(\frac{1}{4}x + 9\right)^2$ when $x = -40$
44. $(6x - 5)^2$ when $x = \frac{1}{3}$

In Exercises 45–50, simplify the expression.

45. $\dfrac{x^2y}{xy^2}$
46. $\dfrac{4x^6y^8}{2y^2}$
47. $\dfrac{9x^5y^3}{3x^2y}$

48. $4x - (x + 5)(x - 5)$
49. $(4 - x)^2 + 8$
50. $(x + 2)^2 - x^2 + 9$

51. *College Entrance Exam Sample*   If $x = -3$, then $(x + 3)^2 - 3x = \boxed{?}$
    a. -6 **b.** -3 **c.** 0 **d.** 6 **e.** 9

52. *College Entrance Exam Sample*   For what positive value of x does $\frac{4}{x} = \frac{x}{16}$?
    a. 2 **b.** 8 **c.** 20 **d.** 32 **e.** 64

53. *Estimation—Powers of Ten*   Which of the following is the best estimate for the capacity of an automobile's fuel tank?
    a. 1.5 gallons   **b.** 15 gallons
    c. 150 gallons   **d.** 1500 gallons

54. *Estimation—Powers of Ten*   Which of the following is the best estimate for the number of fourteen-year-olds in the United States?
    a. 4×10^3 **b.** 4×10^4
    c. 4×10^5 **d.** 4×10^6

Exploration and Extension

55. Find the product of $(a + b)(a + b)(a - b)$ by two methods.
    a. First step: Find the product of the sum and difference of two terms.
    b. First step: Find the square of the binomial. (Compare your results.)
    c. Which method do you prefer? Explain.

56. *Geometry*   Use an area model to find the product: $(a + b + c)^2$.

Factoring: Special Products

What you should learn:

Goal 1 How to factor polynomials that have a monomial factor, that are the difference of two squares, and that are perfect-square trinomials

Goal 2 How to use factoring in real-life models

Why you should learn it:

You can use factoring to help answer questions about polynomial models such as those used for geometric situations.

Goal 1 Factoring Polynomials

In this lesson and in the next lesson, you will learn strategies for factoring polynomials. **Factoring** is the *reverse* process of multiplying.

Part of factoring is being able to find the **greatest common factor** of two or more terms. For example, $2x$ is the greatest common factor of the terms of $(4x^2 + 6x)$. Writing this polynomial as the product $2x(2x + 3)$ illustrates one type of factoring. The factor $2x$ is a **monomial factor.** The Distributive Property is used to "factor out" a monomial factor.

Polynomial	Monomial Factor	Factored Form
$3x + 6$	3	$3(x + 2)$
$5x^2 - 15x$	$5x$	$5x(x - 3)$
$4x^2 + 6x + 8$	2	$2(2x^2 + 3x + 4)$

Each of the special product patterns that you studied in Lesson 10.3 can be used to factor polynomials.

Factoring Special Products

Difference of Two Squares Pattern   **Example**
$a^2 - b^2 = (a + b)(a - b)$ $9x^2 - 16 = (3x + 4)(3x - 4)$

Perfect Square Trinomial Pattern   **Example**
$a^2 + 2ab + b^2 = (a + b)^2$ $x^2 + 8x + 16 = (x + 4)^2$
$a^2 - 2ab + b^2 = (a - b)^2$ $x^2 - 12x + 36 = (x - 6)^2$

Note that *perfect square trinomials* come in two forms. The coefficient of the middle term can be positive or negative.

To recognize the **difference of two squares,** look for coefficients that are squares and for variables that are raised to the second power.

Polynomial	Difference of Squares	Factored Form
$x^2 - 4$	$x^2 - 2^2$	$(x + 2)(x - 2)$
$4x^2 - 25$	$(2x)^2 - 5^2$	$(2x + 5)(2x - 5)$
$25 - 49x^2$	$5^2 - (7x)^2$	$(5 + 7x)(5 - 7x)$

To recognize a **perfect square trinomial,** remember that the first and last terms must be positive and perfect squares, a^2 and b^2, and the middle term must be twice the product of a and b.

Example 1 *Factoring Perfect Square Trinomials*

a. $x^2 - 4x + 4 = x^2 - 2(2x) + 2^2$
$\qquad\qquad\qquad = (x - 2)^2$

b. $16y^2 + 24y + 9 = (4y)^2 + 2(4y)(3) + 3^2$
$\qquad\qquad\qquad\quad = (4y + 3)^2$

c. $9t^2 - 30t + 25 = (3t)^2 - 2(3t)(5) + 5^2$
$\qquad\qquad\qquad\quad = (3t - 5)^2$

Before trying to apply one of the special product patterns for factoring, factor out any common monomial factor.

Example 2 *Removing a Common Monomial Factor First*

a. $3x^2 - 27 = 3(x^2 - 9)$
$\qquad\qquad\quad = 3(x + 3)(x - 3)$

b. $3x^2 - 30x + 75 = 3(x^2 - 10x + 25)$
$\qquad\qquad\qquad\quad = 3(x - 5)^2$

c. $16y^3 + 80y^2 + 100y = 4y(4y^2 + 20y + 25)$
$\qquad\qquad\qquad\qquad\quad = 4y(2y + 5)^2$

Goal 2   **Using Factoring in Real-Life Models**

Connections
Geometry

Example 3 *Finding Dimensions*

You are shopping for a travel kennel. Your new puppy can just barely squeeze through a square opening that is $3\frac{1}{2}$ inches on each side. Are the grille openings in the kennel at the left too large to hold your puppy?

Solution   Let each of the large grille openings be x inches on each side. The grille, then, forms 9 large squares with an area of x^2 each, 12 rectangles with an area of x each, and 4 small squares with an area of 1 each. By factoring,

$$9x^2 + 12x + 4 = (3x + 2)^2$$

you find that each side of the grille is $3x + 2$. By solving the equation $3x + 2 = 11$, you find x to be 3 inches. So your pup will be secure.

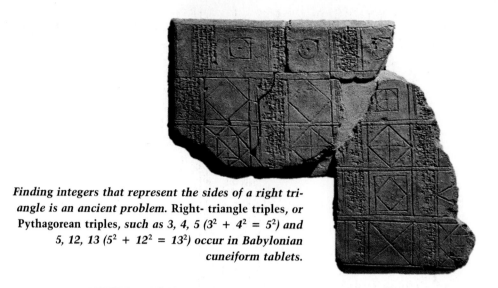

Finding integers that represent the sides of a right triangle is an ancient problem. Right- triangle triples, or Pythagorean triples, such as 3, 4, 5 ($3^2 + 4^2 = 5^2$) and 5, 12, 13 ($5^2 + 12^2 = 13^2$) occur in Babylonian cuneiform tablets.

Example 4 **Right-Triangle Triples**

Here is a technique for finding right-triangle triples.

Solution

1. Choose a positive integer and square it: $7^2 = 49$.

2. Factor into two odd factors or two even factors: $7^2 = (1)(49)$.

3. Write the product as the difference of two squares:

Average of factors
↓   ↓

$(1)(49) = (25 - 24)(25 + 24) = 25^2 - 24^2.$
↑   ↑

Difference between average and either factor

4. Write in Pythagorean form:

$$7^2 = 25^2 - 24^2$$
$$7^2 + 24^2 = 25^2 \qquad \textit{Pythagorean form, } a^2 + b^2 = c^2$$

The triple is $a = 7$, $b = 24$, and $c = 25$. ∎

Communicating about **ALGEBRA**

▶ **SHARING IDEAS about the Lesson**

Recognize Patterns   Factor each polynomial. Explain your steps and reasoning.

A. $9t^2 - 49$

B. $x^2 - 16x + 64$

C. $4y^2 + 36y + 81$

D. $121x^2 - 100$

EXERCISES

Guided Practice

▶ **CRITICAL THINKING about the Lesson**

1. Describe the relationship between multiplying polynomials and factoring a polynomial.

2. Factor out the greatest common monomial factor: $3x^3 - 6x^2 + 9$.

3. Show how the Distributive Property can be used to factor $2x(2x - 3) + 3(2x - 3)$.

4. Give an example of each of the three special-product factoring patterns in the lesson.

Independent Practice

In Exercises 5–10, find the greatest common factor of the three terms.

5. $6x^5, 30x^4, 12x^3$

6. $7x^3, 28x, 14x^4$

7. $24x^3, 32x^2$

8. $99x^6, 45x^3$

9. $16x^2y, 84xy^2, 36x^2y^2$

10. $10xy^2, 25x^3y^2, 80x^2y$

In Exercises 11–19, factor out the greatest common monomial factor.

11. $2x^2 - 4$

12. $3x + 6$

13. $4a - 12$

14. $14z^3 + 21$

15. $24x^2 - 18$

16. $-a^3 - 4a$

17. $21u^2 - 14u$

18. $36y^4 + 24y^2$

19. $4x^2 - 8x + 8$

In Exercises 20–28, factor the expression.

20. $x^2 - 64$

21. $y^2 - 144$

22. $2x^2 + 16x + 32$

23. $9x^2 - 30xy + 25y^2$

24. $4y^2 + 20yz + 25z^2$

25. $u^2 - \frac{1}{16}$

26. $v^2 - \frac{9}{25}$

27. $81 - (z + 5)^2$

28. $3(x - 3)^2 - 12$

In Exercises 29 and 30, use the following information.

A manufacturer of television sets has modeled the revenue, R, for Model TXX to be

$$R = 800x - 0.05x^2 = xp$$

where x is the number of units sold, and p is the price of Model TXX. The graph of the model is shown at the right.

Revenue from Sale of Model TXX

Revenue (in millions of dollars)

Number of Units Sold (in 1000s)

29. Economists use a principle that states that "as the price decreases, the demand increases." Explain how this principle applies to the graph of the price model.

30. If you were the manager of the marketing department, what price would you recommend for each television set? Explain your reasoning.

Right-Triangle Triples **In Exercises 31–33, use the technique described in Example 4 to find the indicated right-triangle triple. (Exercise 33 has two solutions.)**

31. $4^2 + b^2 = c^2$ **32.** $6^2 + b^2 = c^2$ **33.** $8^2 + b^2 = c^2$

34. *A Jade Pi*   The *jade pi* (pronounced "jade bee") at the right has an inside radius of 5 centimeters and an outside radius of 30 centimeters. Find the area of one of the flat surfaces of the pi.

35. *Chemical Reaction*   The rate of change of some chemical reactions can be modeled by

$$kQx - kx^2$$

where Q is the amount of the original substance, x is the amount of the substance formed, and k is a constant of proportionality. Factor this rate-of-change expression.

Early Chinese emperors used ring-shaped disks of jade in ceremonies to appeal to celestial spirits. The circular shape symbolized Heaven.

36. *Marching Band*   Your band is asked to be in a local parade. It is allotted 3200 square feet in the parade and must stay at least x feet from each curb. Your director decides that rows will be 4 feet apart and each row will contain 8 band members. Can all of the 160 members of the band be in the parade?

It takes musicianship, teamwork, and plenty of practice to maintain correct marching ranks, while still producing a well-balanced sound.

37. *Package from Grandma* A week before your birthday you receive this card from your grandmother, a retired math teacher. Will her package fit in your mailbox, which is 9 inches by 5 inches by 4 inches, or will it be returned to the post office, where you will have to pick it up later?

Hello Dear,
Hope you will have a wonderful birthday party. By the way I am sending you a birthday package. Besides the sketch I've drawn, here's some more information!

I hope it fits! Love to all.

Grandma

- Its volume is 161 cubic inches.
- It's 7 inches high.
- Its base area is $25x^2 - 1$.

7 in.

$5x + 1$

Integrated Review

In Exercises 38–43, multiply.

38. $12x(2x - 3)$

39. $7y(4 - 3y)$

40. $t(t^2 + 1) - t(t^2 - 1)$

41. $2z(z + 5) - 7(z + 5)$

42. $(11 - x)(11 + x)$

43. $(6r + 5s)(6r - 5s)$

In Exercises 44–49, solve the equation.

44. $(x + 2)^2 - x^2 = 8$

45. $(x - 1)^2 + 2x = 4$

46. $(x - 4)^2 + 8x = 32$

47. $(x - 6)^2 - x^2 = 0$

48. $(x + 3)(x - 3) + 5 = 0$

49. $(x - 4)(x + 4) = -7$

50. *Up, Up, and Away* The height (in feet) of a bottle rocket is modeled by

$$h = -16t^2 + 57t$$

where t is the time in seconds. Find the height of the rocket after 2 seconds.

51. *Pythagorean Theorem* The lengths of the sides of a right triangle are $a = 5$, b, and $c = 13$. What is b?

Exploration and Extension

Geometry **In Exercises 52 and 53, find the perimeter of the rectangle and square. The lengths of the sides are obtained by factoring the expression for the area.**

52. Area $= x^2 - 49$

53. Area $= x^2 + 6x + 9$

Take this test as you would take a test in class. The answers to the exercises are given in the back of the book.

In Exercises 1 and 2, perform the indicated operation. Use a horizontal format. (10.1)

1. $(x^2 + 2x - 1) + (3x - 4x^2 + 2)$ **2.** $(-2x^2 + 4x - 5) - (3 - 7x + x^2)$

In Exercises 3 and 4, perform the indicated operation. Use a vertical format. (10.1)

3. $(3x^2 - x + 2) + (x^2 - 3x + 2)$ **4.** $(7x^2 - 5x + 10) - (3x^2 + 2x + 5)$

In Exercises 5–8, multiply. (10.2)

5. $(3x + 2)(3x + 5)$ **6.** $(4x - 5)(2x + 10)$

7. $(x + 1)(2x^2 - 3x + 2)$ **8.** $(2x + 1)(5x^2 + 7x - 3)$

In Exercises 9–12, multiply using the FOIL pattern. (10.2)

9. $(x + 2)(x - 3)$ **10.** $(x - 3)(x - 6)$ **11.** $(2x + 3)(4 - x)$ **12.** $(3 + x)(4 + x)$

In Exercises 13–16, use the special-product patterns to multiply. (10.3)

13. $(2x + 3)^2$ **14.** $(4x - 5)^2$ **15.** $(2x - 6)(2x + 6)$ **16.** $(x - 7)(x + 7)$

In Exercises 17–22, factor the polynomial. (10.4)

17. $4x^2 - 49$ **18.** $3x^2 - 108$

19. $x^2 - 2x + 1$ **20.** $7x^2 + 42x + 63$

21. $9x^2 + 12x + 4$ **22.** $x^2 - 169$

23. From 1970 to 1990, the number of pieces, F, of first-class U.S. mail can be modeled by

$F = 50{,}262 + 99.2t^2$ (in millions)

where $t = 0$ represents 1970. The number of pieces, K, of all other types of U.S. mail can be modeled by

$K = 33{,}045 + 140.7t^2$. (in millions)

Find a model for the number of pieces, M, of all types of U.S. mail. *(Source: Statistical Abstract, 1990)* **(10.1)**

24. Three storage cubes have sides of $(x + 1)$, $(x + 3)$, and $(x + 5)$. Write an expression for the total volume of the three cubes. **(10.2)**

25. You are making a tick-tack-toe board for your cousin's birthday. Each square will have a side of x inches, and the board will have a 1-inch-wide border. Write a polynomial for the area of the board. **(10.3)**

26. You want to frame a 16-inch by 20-inch watercolor for your parents' anniversary. The frame is x inches wide on all four sides. Write a polynomial for the area of the framed picture. **(10.2)**

10.5 Factoring Quadratic Trinomials

What you should learn:

Goal 1 How to factor a quadratic trinomial or recognize that it cannot be factored

Goal 2 How to use factoring in real-life models

Why you should learn it:

You can use factoring as an efficient step in solving some types of mathematical problems.

Goal 1 Factoring a Quadratic Trinomial

Let's look at quadratic trinomials of the form $x^2 + bx + c$. Try covering the factored forms in the left column. Can you find the factored form from the trinomial form?

Factored Form	F	O	I	L		Trinomial Form
$(x + 2)(x + 4)$	$= x^2$	$+ 4x$	$+ 2x$	$+ 8$	$=$	$x^2 + 6x + 8$
$(x - 3)(x - 2)$	$= x^2$	$- 2x$	$- 3x$	$+ 6$	$=$	$x^2 - 5x + 6$
$(x - 1)(x + 4)$	$= x^2$	$+ 4x$	$- x$	$- 4$	$=$	$x^2 + 3x - 4$

To see how to factor this type of quadratic trinomial, consider the following.

$$(x + r)(x + s) = x^2 + \overbrace{(r + s)}^{\text{Sum of terms}}x + \overbrace{rs}^{\text{Product of terms}}$$

$$= x^2 + \boxed{b}\,x + \boxed{c}$$

Notice that you must find factors of c whose sum is b. If c is positive, the factors must have *like* signs. If c is negative, the factors must have *unlike* signs.

Example 1 Factoring When c Is Positive

Factor $x^2 + 3x + 2$.

Solution For this trinomial, $b = 3$ and $c = 2$.

$x^2 + 3x + 2 = (x + \boxed{?})(x + \boxed{?})$ *Think: You need factors of 2 whose sum is 3.*

$= (x + 1)(x + 2)$ *2 = (1)(2), 1 + 2 = 3* ∎

Example 2 Factoring When c Is Positive

Factor $x^2 - 5x + 6$.

Solution For this trinomial, $b = -5$ and $c = 6$.

$x^2 - 5x + 6 = (x + \boxed{?})(x + \boxed{?})$ *Think: You need factors of 6 whose sum is −5.*

$= (x - 2)(x - 3)$ *6 = (−2)(−3),*
−2 − 3 = −5 ∎

Example 3 Factoring When c Is Negative

Factor $x^2 - 2x - 8$.

Solution For this trinomial, $b = -2$ and $c = -8$.

$$x^2 - 2x - 8$$
$$= (x + \boxed{?})(x + \boxed{?}) \quad \textit{Think: You need factors of } -8$$
$$\textit{whose sum is } -2.$$
$$= (x + 2)(x - 4) \quad -8 = (2)(-4),\ 2 - 4 = -2 \quad\blacksquare$$

To factor a trinomial whose leading coefficient is not 1, consider the following pattern.

$$ax^2 + bx + c = (\boxed{?}x + \boxed{?})(\boxed{?}x + \boxed{?})$$

Factors of a

Factors of c

The goal is to find a combination of factors of a and c so that the outer and inner products add to the middle term bx.

Example 4 Factoring When Leading Coefficient Is Not 1

Problem Solving
Guess and Check

Factor $6x^2 + 7x - 5$.

Solution For this trinomial, $a = 6$, $b = 7$, and $c = -5$. Use a guess-and-check strategy to find the binomial factors.

Guess	Check
$(x + 1)(6x - 5) = 6x^2 + x - 5$	
$(x - 1)(6x + 5) = 6x^2 - x - 5$	
$(2x + 1)(3x - 5) = 6x^2 - 7x - 5$	
$(2x - 1)(3x + 5) = 6x^2 + 7x - 5$	$\leftarrow$ *Correct factoring.* $\blacksquare$

It is important to remember that *many* quadratic trinomials cannot be factored with integer coefficients. A quadratic trinomial $ax^2 + bx + c$ will factor (using integer coefficients) only if the *discriminant* $b^2 - 4ac$ is a perfect square.

Example 5 Using the Discriminant

Show that $2x^2 + 3x - 6$ cannot be factored.

Solution For this trinomial, $a = 2$, $b = 3$, and $c = -6$. Since the discriminant

$$b^2 - 4ac = 3^2 - 4(2)(-6) = 57$$

is not a perfect square, the trinomial cannot be factored (using integer coefficients). $\blacksquare$

Using Factoring in Real-Life Models

Salaries on the Line

Salary (in 1000s of dollars)

3000

2000

1000

1 2 3 4 5 6 7 8 9 10 *t*

Year (0 ↔ 1980)

For 1980 to 1990, the annual salary, S (in 1000s of dollars), paid by a manufacturer to its assembly-line workers is given by the quadratic model $S = 3t^2 + 130t + 1000$, where $t = 0$ represents 1980.

Example 6 *Finding the Salary per Employee*

In 1980, the above manufacturer had 100 assembly-line workers. Each year the number of workers increased by 3. Find a model for the workers' average annual salary from 1980 to 1990.

Solution Because the number of workers increased by 3 each year, the number of workers in year t is given by the linear model $3t + 100$.

Problem Solving
Write an Equation

Verbal Model	Total salary	=	Number of workers	×	Average salary

Labels
Year = t (0 is 1980)
Total salary = $3t^2 + 130t + 1000$ ($1000s)
Number of workers = $3t + 100$ (workers)
Average salary = W ($1000s per worker)

Equation $3t^2 + 130t + 1000 = (3t + 100)W$

By factoring, you can see that

$$3t^2 + 130t + 1000 = (3t + 100)(t + 10)$$

which means the average salary was $W = t + 10$. From this model, you can see that the average salary was $10,000 in 1980. For the next 10 years, it increased by $1000 each year. ∎

Communicating *about* A L G E B R A

▷ **SHARING IDEAS about the Lesson**

Recognize Patterns Factor each polynomial. Explain your steps and reasoning.

A. $x^2 + 7x + 12$ **B.** $a^2 - 6a + 5$ **C.** $3n^2 + 4n - 4$

EXERCISES

▶ CRITICAL THINKING about the Lesson

1. Factor $x^2 - 4x + 3$. When testing possible factorizations, why is it unnecessary to test $(x - 1)(x + 3)$ and $(x + 1)(x - 3)$?

2. Factor $x^2 + 2x - 3$. When testing possible factorizations, why is it unnecessary to test $(x - 1)(x - 3)$ and $(x + 1)(x + 3)$?

3. What is the discriminant of $ax^2 + bx + c$?

4. If the discriminant of $ax^2 + bx + c$ is 35, can the trinomial be factored with integer coefficients? Explain.

Independent Practice

In Exercises 5–10, choose the correct factorization. (If neither is correct, find the correct factorization.)

5. $x^2 + x - 20$
   a. $(x - 4)(x + 5)$
   b. $(x + 4)(x - 5)$

6. $x^2 + 8x + 16$
   a. $(x + 2)(x + 8)$
   b. $(x + 4)(x + 4)$

7. $x^2 - 10x + 24$
   a. $(x - 6)(x - 4)$
   b. $(x - 12)(x + 2)$

8. $3x^2 - 7x - 6$
   a. $(x - 3)(3x + 2)$
   b. $(x + 3)(3x - 2)$

9. $6x^2 - 7x - 5$
   a. $(6x + 1)(x - 5)$
   b. $(2x + 1)(3x - 5)$

10. $2x^2 - 7x - 9$
    a. $(x - 1)(2x + 9)$
    b. $(2x - 1)(x + 9)$

In Exercises 11–28, factor the trinomial.

11. $x^2 + 3x - 4$

12. $x^2 - 5x + 6$

13. $x^2 + 3x - 18$

14. $y^2 - 16y - 36$

15. $x^2 - 10x + 24$

16. $x^2 + 13x + 22$

17. $x^2 + 15x + 50$

18. $y^2 + 30y + 216$

19. $y^2 - 35y + 300$

20. $t^2 - 4t - 21$

21. $3x^2 + 8x + 5$

22. $6x^2 + 5x - 4$

23. $2x^2 - x - 21$

24. $3x^2 + 11x + 10$

25. $48 - 16y + y^2$

26. $32 + 12x + x^2$

27. $2x^2 - x - 6$

28. $5 + 34x - 7x^2$

In Exercises 29–34, use the discriminant to decide whether the polynomial can be factored with integer coefficients. If it can be factored, then find the factors.

29. $12x^2 - 11x + 3$

30. $2x^2 - 5x - 12$

31. $6x^2 - 10x + 4$

32. $10x^2 - 9x + 6$

33. $14x^2 - 19x - 40$

34. $24x^2 + 3x - 11$

35. *Geometry* The area of a rectangle is given by $A = x^2 + 4x - 5$. Find expressions for possible lengths and widths of the rectangle.

36. *Geometry* The area of a circle is given by $A = \pi(4x^2 + 12x + 9)$. Find an expression for the radius of the circle.

The letters of the alphabet from A to Z (excluding W and X) are represented by nonzero integers from -12 to 12. Copy and complete the table by factoring the polynomials in Exercises 37–42. Then use the table to match the coded words in Exercises 43–46 with one of the pieces of African art.

Letter	A	B	C	D	E	F	G	H	I	J	K	L
Code Number	1	?	?	?	9	?	?	?	2	?	?	?

Letter	M	N	O	P	Q	R	S	T	U	V	Y	Z
Code Number	3	?	?	?	6	?	?	?	11	?	?	?

37. $8x^2 - 35x + 12 = (Ax + B)(Cx + D)$

38. $90x^2 - 143x + 56 = (Ex + F)(Gx + H)$

39. $10x^2 - 57x + 54 = (Ix + J)(Kx + L)$

40. $12x^2 - 43x + 10 = (Mx + N)(Ox + P)$

41. $42x^2 - 89x + 22 = (Qx + R)(Sx + T)$

42. $132x^2 - 199x + 60 = (Ux + V)(Yx + Z)$

43. | 2 | −12 | 4 | −11 | 12 | | 3 | 1 | 7 | 5 |

44. | 8 | 1 | −11 | −12 | 9 | −3 | | 7 | −2 | 4 | 4 | −6 |

45. | −1 | 1 | −2 | −2 | 9 | −11 | −10 | 9 | −3 | | −12 | 9 | 7 | 7 | 9 | −6 |

46. | 3 | 1 | 7 | 1 | 2 | | −10 | 9 | 8 | 5 | −6 | 1 | 8 | 9 |

a. Ivory Coast

b. Central Africa

d. Kenya

c. Central Africa

Algebra Tiles In Exercises 47 and 48, factor the trinomial. Use an area model to illustrate your result. Use the following area model for $x^2 + 3x + 2 = (x + 1)(x + 2)$ as a sample.

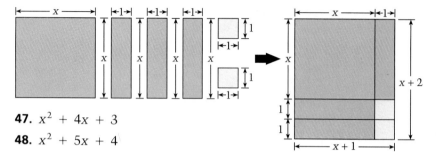

47. $x^2 + 4x + 3$

48. $x^2 + 5x + 4$

49. *Hot Dog Stand* You run a hot-dog stand for the adult softball league. Your revenue, R (in dollars), each week can be given by

$$R = \frac{1}{100}(-40t^2 + 740t + 1200)$$

where t represents the week with $t = 0$ for the first week. In the first week, you sold 12 hot dogs and each week after that the number of sales increased by 8. Find a model for the price of a hot dog over the 8-week season. Use the model to find the price of a hot dog during each week of the season.

50. *Summer Basketball* During the summer, the number, B, of people who played intramural basketball each week is given by the model

$$B = t^2 + 11t + 30$$

where t represents the week, with $t = 0$ for the first week. In the first week, six teams were in the league. Each week, for five weeks, a new team joined the league. Find a model for the average number of members per team for the six-week season. Use the model to find the average number of players on each team during each week.

Integrated Review

In Exercises 51–53, multiply.

51. $-2y(y + 1)$

52. $(x + 4)^2$

53. $(v - 1)(v - 6)$

In Exercises 54–56, solve the equation.

54. $3(x + 2) = 5$

55. $-1(4x - 5) = x$

56. $5(y - 3) = -1(y + 6)$

Exploration and Extension

In Exercises 57–60, factor the polynomial as the product of *linear* factors.

57. $2x^3 - 5x^2 - 3x$

58. $48x^3 - 2x^2 - 20x$

59. $x^4 - 5x^2 + 4$

60. $x^4 - 13x^2 + 36$

10.6

Solving Quadratic Equations by Factoring

What you should learn:

Goal 1 How to use factoring to solve a quadratic equation

Goal 2 How to use factoring with real-life models

Why you should learn it:

You can use factoring to help efficiently solve some quadratic equations.

Problem Solving
Solve a Simpler Problem

Goal 1 Solving by Factoring

The **Zero-Product Property** states that if the product of two factors is zero, then one (or both) of the factors must be zero.

Zero-Product Property

If the product $ab = 0$, then $a = 0$ or $b = 0$.

This property connects factoring to solving equations. For instance, to solve the equation $(x - 2)(x + 3) = 0$, you can use the Zero-Product Property to conclude that either $x - 2 = 0$ or $x + 3 = 0$.

Set first factor equal to 0.
$$x - 2 = 0$$
$$x = 2$$

Set second factor equal to 0.
$$x + 3 = 0$$
$$x = -3$$

The equation $(x - 2)(x + 3) = 0$ has the solutions 2 and -3.

Factoring and the Zero-Product Property allow you to solve a quadratic equation by converting it into two *linear* equations, which you already know how to solve. This is a common strategy of algebra—to break down a problem into simpler parts, each solved by previously learned methods.

Example 1 *Solving a Quadratic Equation by Factoring*

Solve $x^2 - x - 12 = 0$.

Solution

$$x^2 - x - 12 = 0$$
$$(x + 3)(x - 4) = 0 \qquad \textit{Factor.}$$
$$x + 3 = 0 \quad \text{or} \quad x - 4 = 0 \qquad \textit{Zero-Product Property}$$
$$x = -3 \quad \text{or} \qquad x = 4 \qquad \textit{Solve for x.}$$

The equation has two solutions: -3 and 4. Check these solutions in the original equation. ∎

To use the Zero Product Property, the quadratic equation should be written in the standard form, $ax^2 + bx + c = 0$.

Example 2 — Rewriting in Standard Form First

Solve $3x^2 + 5x = 12$.

Solution

$$3x^2 + 5x = 12 \qquad \textit{Rewrite original equation.}$$
$$3x^2 + 5x - 12 = 0 \qquad \textit{Write in standard form.}$$
$$(3x - 4)(x + 3) = 0 \qquad \textit{Factor.}$$
$$3x - 4 = 0 \qquad \textit{Set factors equal to 0.}$$
$$\text{or } x + 3 = 0$$
$$x = \frac{4}{3}$$
$$\text{or } x = -3 \qquad \textit{Solve for x.}$$

The equation has two solutions: $\frac{4}{3}$ and -3. Check these solutions in the original equation. ∎

In Examples 1 and 2, each equation had two solutions. Some quadratic equations have only one solution. This occurs when the quadratic is a perfect square trinomial.

Example 3 — A Quadratic Equation with One Solution

Solve $x^2 - 6x + 11 = 2$.

Solution

$$x^2 - 6x + 11 = 2 \qquad \textit{Rewrite original equation.}$$
$$x^2 - 6x + 9 = 0 \qquad \textit{Write in standard form.}$$
$$(x - 3)^2 = 0 \qquad \textit{Factor.}$$
$$x - 3 = 0 \qquad \textit{Set factor equal to 0.}$$
$$x = 3 \qquad \textit{Solve for x.}$$

The equation has only one solution: 3. Check this solution in the original equation. ∎

Be sure you see that the Zero Product Property can only be applied to a product that is equal to *zero*. For instance, you *cannot* conclude from the equation $x(x - 1) = 6$ that $x = 6$ or $x - 1 = 6$. Instead, you must first write the equation in standard form and then factor the left side.

$$x(x - 1) = 6$$
$$x^2 - x = 6$$
$$x^2 - x - 6 = 0$$
$$(x - 3)(x + 2) = 0$$

From the factored form, the solutions are 3 and -2.

Using Factoring with Real-Life Models

Example 4 *Finding the Dimensions of a Sign*

A triangular sign has a base that is to be 4 feet less than twice its height. A local zoning ordinance restricts the area of signs to no more than 24 square feet. Find the base and height of the largest triangular sign that meets the zoning ordinance.

Solution Since the base is to be 4 feet less than twice the height, let h be the height and label the base as $2h - 4$.

Problem Solving
Write an Equation

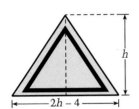

Verbal Model $\frac{1}{2} \times$ Base $\times$ Height $=$ Area

Labels   Height $= h$ (feet)
Base $= 2h - 4$ (feet)
Area $= 24$ (square feet)

Equation $\frac{1}{2}(2h - 4)(h) = 24$
$h^2 - 2h = 24$
$h^2 - 2h - 24 = 0$
$(h + 4)(h - 6) = 0$
$h = -4$ or $h = 6$

The equation has two solutions: -4 and 6. But a negative height makes no sense, so you can conclude that the height of the sign is 6 feet, and the base is $2(6) - 4 = 8$ feet. ■

Communicating about ALGEBRA

▶ **SHARING IDEAS about the Lesson**

Choose a Method You have now studied three ways to solve quadratic equations: by finding square roots, by the quadratic formula, and by factoring. Solve each equation by the method you think is most efficient. Discuss the reasons for your choices and explain how the graphs can be used as a check of the solutions.

A. $x^2 - 3x + 2 = 0$ **B.** $x^2 - 2x - 1 = 0$ **C.** $x^2 - 3 = 0$

    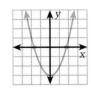

EXERCISES

▶ **CRITICAL THINKING about the Lesson**

1. Use the Zero-Product Property to complete the statement. If $ab = 0$, then $\boxed{?}$.

2. Solve the equation: $(x - 2)(x + 1) = 0$.

3. Solve the equation: $3x^2 + 4x = 0$.

4. Which two numbers satisfy the statement, "The sum of a number and its square is zero."?

5. True or False? If $(5x - 1)(x + 3) = 1$, then $5x - 1 = 1$ or $x + 3 = 1$. Explain.

6. True or False? If $(x + 3)(x - 3) = 0$, then $x + 3 = 0$ or $x - 3 = 0$. Explain

Independent Practice

In Exercises 7–10, solve the equation.

7. $(x + 1)(x + 2) = 0$

8. $(x - 3)(x + 7) = 0$

9. $(x + 3)(x + 4) = 0$

10. $(x + 6)(x - 5) = 0$

In Exercises 11–16, solve the equation by factoring.

11. $x^2 + 5x - 6 = 0$

12. $3x^2 + 11x - 4 = 0$

13. $2x^2 + 5x + 3 = 0$

14. $6x^2 + 13x + 5 = 0$

15. $3x^2 + 7x + 2 = 0$

16. $12x^2 - 5x - 3 = 0$

In Exercises 17–24, match the equation with its solutions.

17. $x^2 - 5x + 6 = 0$ **18.** $x^2 + 5x + 6 = 0$ **19.** $x^2 - 7x + 6 = 0$ **20.** $x^2 + 7x + 6 = 0$

21. $x^2 - 5x - 6 = 0$ **22.** $x^2 + 5x - 6 = 0$ **23.** $x^2 + x - 6 = 0$ **24.** $x^2 - x - 6 = 0$

a. $-1, -6$ **b.** $-2, -3$ **c.** $1, -6$ **d.** $-1, 6$

e. $2, -3$ **f.** $2, 3$ **g.** $1, 6$ **h.** $-2, 3$

In Exercises 25–33, solve the equation by finding square roots, by the quadratic formula, or by factoring.

25. $x(x - 9) = 0$

26. $2y(y + 6) = 0$

27. $y^2 - 7y + 6 = -6$

28. $x^2 - 12 = -3$

29. $x^2 - 8x = -16$

30. $x^2 + 4x + 7 = 3$

31. $4x^2 + 2x = 0$

32. $4y^2 - 18y = 0$

33. $x^2 - 12x + 40 = 4$

In Exercises 34 and 35, multiply both sides of the equation by an appropriate power of ten to obtain integer coefficients. Then solve by factoring.

34. $0.8x^2 + 3.2x + 2.4 = 0$

35. $0.23x^2 - 0.54x + 0.16 = 0$

36. *How to Weigh an Elephant Seal*   The rectangular scale in the photo is 8 feet longer than it is wide. The scale has an area of 33 square feet. What are the dimensions of the scale?

37. *A California Raisin*   During the breeding season, the male elephant seal in the photo lost 38% of his weight. His weight, w (in hundreds of pounds), at the beginning of the season was a solution of $w^2 - 38w + 361 = 0$. What did he weigh at the end of the season?

To weigh this male elephant seal, a biologist at the University of California lured him to cross a special scale by pulling a model female seal named Raisin. *(Source:* Discover, 1991)

The Taj Mahal   **In Exercises 38 and 39, use the following information.**

The Taj Mahal was built by the Indian ruler Shah Jahan as a tomb for his wife who died in 1629. The building is constructed of white marble and sits on a platform of red sandstone. Each corner of the platform has a minaret (tower) *that is 133 feet high.*

38. The platform is about 140 feet wider than the main building. The total area of the platform is about 102,400 square feet. Find the dimensions of the platform and the base of the building. (Assume each is a square.)

39. Which of the following is the best estimate of the dimensions of the entire courtyard shown in the diagram?

a. 640 feet × 1280 feet   **b.** 960 feet by 1280 feet   **c.** 640 feet × 1600 feet

In Exercises 40–45, multiply and simplify.

40. $(2x + 6)(\frac{1}{2}x - 3)$

41. $(x + 9)(4x - 3)$

42. $36 - (x + 2)(x - 3)$

43. $3(x - \frac{1}{3})(3x + 7)$

44. $4(x + 3)(3x - 1) + 1$

45. $5 + (2x - \frac{1}{2})(\frac{1}{2}x + 1)$

In Exercises 46–51, decide whether the number is a solution of the equation.

46. $x^2 - 3x + 4 = 0$; 2

47. $x^2 + 5x + 4 = 0$; -1

48. $\frac{1}{3}x^2 + 2x - 36 = 0$; 6

49. $2x^2 - 3x - 4 = 0$; 2

50. $4x^2 + 3x - 27 = 0$; -3

51. $\frac{1}{2}x^2 - x + 8 = 0$; 4

In Exercises 52–57, use the quadratic formula to solve the equation.

52. $x^2 + 4x + 3 = 0$

53. $x^2 - 7x + 9 = 0$

54. $2x^2 - 5x + 3 = 0$

55. $3x^2 - 11x - 24 = 0$

56. $5x^2 - 16x - 12 = 0$

57. $9x^2 - 17x + 6 = 0$

58. *Height of a Diver*   A diver jumps from a diving board that is 32 feet above the water. The height of the diver is given by

$$\text{Height} = -16(t - 2)(t + 1)$$

where the height is measured in feet, and the time, t, is measured in seconds. When will the diver hit the water? Can you see a quick way to find the answer? Explain.

59. *Balloon Drop*   An object is dropped from a hot-air balloon 1600 feet above the ground. The height of the object is given by

$$\text{Height} = -16(t - 10)(t + 10)$$

where the height is measured in feet, and the time, t, is measured in seconds. When will the object hit the ground? Can you see a quick way to find the answer? Explain.

32 ft

1600 ft

60. *Graphing Calculator*   Sketch $y = x^2 + 5x - 6$ and $y = (x + 6)(x - 1)$ on the same screen. What do you notice?

61. *Graphing Calculator*   Sketch $y = x^2 - 7x - 8$ and $y = (x - 8)(x + 1)$ on the same screen. What do you notice?

Tutoring a Friend   **In Exercises 62–65, you are tutoring a friend and want to create some quadratic equations that can be solved by factoring. Find a quadratic equation that has the given solutions and explain the procedure you used to obtain the equation.**

62. 4 and -3

63. 5 and 5

64. -2 and -5

65. 0 and -1

66. Let a and b be real numbers such that $a \neq 0$. Find the solutions of $ax^2 + bx = 0$.

67. Let a be a nonzero real number. Find the solutions of $ax^2 - ax = 0$.

68. *Ethiopian Weavers*   In every square inch of the cotton fabric used for a shammas, the *warp* (lengthwise threads) intersects the *weft* (crosswise threads) 5000 times. The density (number of threads per inch) of the weft threads is twice that of the warp threads. How many weft threads are in each inch? How many warp threads are in each inch?

These Ethiopian women are wearing a fine cotton fabric known as a shammas, a national costume that is often edged with bright trimming.

Mixed REVIEW

1. Simplify $x^2y^{-1} \div 3x \cdot y^2$. **(8.3)**

2. Simplify $(p^2q^4 \div 2p) \cdot (4p^{-2} \div q^{-2})$. **(8.2)**

3. Find the quotient of $3x^2$ and $9x$. **(8.3)**

4. Find the sum of $2p$ and $-4p$. **(2.6)**

5. Solve $4m + 2n = 3$ for m. **(3.6)**

6. Solve $ab + a = 5$ for a. **(3.6)**

7. Write $2 \cdot x \cdot x \cdot x \cdot x$ in exponential form. **(1.3)**

8. Write 0.00012 in scientific notation. **(8.4)**

9. Evaluate $(2 \times 10^{-3}) \cdot (4 \times 10^4)$. **(8.4)**

10. Evaluate $(3.2 \times 10^6) \div (1.6 \times 10^{-1})$. **(8.4)**

11. Solve $|x + 3| \leq 4$. **(4.8)**

12. Solve $2|3 - x| > 1$. **(4.8)**

13. What are the square roots of 64? **(9.1)**

14. What are the square roots of x^2? **(9.1)**

15. Sketch the graph of $2x + y = 6$. **(4.4)**

16. Sketch the graph of $2|x + 2| + 3 = 0$. **(4.7)**

17. Is -6 a solution of $2^{-x} < -7x$? **(8.2)**

18. Is $(-1, -2)$ a solution of $y = -|2x|$? **(2.1)**

19. Solve the system. $\begin{cases} x - 7y = -17 \\ 3x + y = -7 \end{cases}$ **(7.2, 7.3)**

20. Solve the system. $\begin{cases} 4x + 3y = -1 \\ 5x - 6y = 28 \end{cases}$ **(7.2, 7.3)**

Graphing calculators can be used to obtain a graphic interpretation of polynomial addition or subtraction. In the first graph below, notice that for any x-value, the sum of y_1 and y_2 is equal to y_3. In the second graph, for any x-value, the difference of y_1 and y_2 is equal to y_3.

$y_1 = \frac{1}{2}x,\quad y_2 = x + 1,\quad y_3 = \frac{3}{2}x + 1$

$y_1 = \frac{1}{4}x^2 + 4,\quad y_2 = 3,\quad y_3 = \frac{1}{4}x^2 + 1$

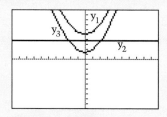

y_3 is the sum of y_1 and y_2.

y_3 is the difference of y_1 and y_2.

TI-81

$\boxed{RANGE}$ (Set range.)
   Xmin = −10
   Xmax = 10
   Xscl = 1
   Ymin = −10
   Ymax = 10
   Yscl = 1
$\boxed{Y=}$ .5 $\boxed{\times}$ $\boxed{X}$ $\boxed{T}$ $\boxed{ENTER}$
   $\boxed{X}$ $\boxed{T}$ $\boxed{+}$ 1 $\boxed{ENTER}$
      1.5 $\boxed{\times}$ $\boxed{X}$ $\boxed{T}$ $\boxed{+}$ 1
:Y$_1$ = .5*X
:Y$_2$ = X + 1
:Y$_3$ = 1.5*X + 1
:Y$_4$ =
$\boxed{GRAPH}$
$\boxed{CLEAR}$ (Clear screen.)

Casio fx-7700G

$\boxed{Range}$ (Set range.)
   Xmin = −10
   max = 10
   scl = 1
   Ymin = −10
   max = 10
   scl = 1
$\boxed{EXE}$ $\boxed{Range}$ $\boxed{SHIFT}$ $\boxed{F5}$ (Cls) $\boxed{EXE}$
$\boxed{MODE}$ $\boxed{SHIFT}$ $\boxed{+}$
$\boxed{Graph}$ .5 $\boxed{\times}$ $\boxed{X,\theta,T}$
   Graph Y = .5*X $\boxed{EXE}$
$\boxed{Graph}$ $\boxed{X,\theta,T}$ $\boxed{+}$ 1
   Graph Y = X + 1 $\boxed{EXE}$
$\boxed{Graph}$ 1.5 $\boxed{\times}$ $\boxed{X,\theta,T}$ $\boxed{+}$ 1
   Graph Y = 1.5*X + 1 $\boxed{EXE}$
$\boxed{SHIFT}$ $\boxed{F5}$ (Cls) $\boxed{EXE}$

Exercises

In Exercises 1–3, let y_3 be the sum of y_1 and y_2. Sketch the graph of all three equations.

1. $y_1 = x - 1$, $y_2 = \frac{1}{2}x + 2$ **2.** $y_1 = x^2 + x$, $y_2 = 1$ **3.** $y_1 = \frac{1}{2}x^2 - 1$, $y_2 = \frac{1}{2}x^2 + 1$

In Exercises 4–6, let y_3 be the difference of y_1 and y_2. Sketch the graph of all three equations.

4. $y_1 = 2x + 1$, $y_2 = x + 1$ **5.** $y_1 = x^2 + 3$, $y_2 = \frac{1}{2}x^2$ **6.** $y_1 = \frac{1}{3}x^2 + x$, $y_2 = 1$

10.7

Solving Quadratic Equations by Completing the Square

What you should learn:

Goal How to solve quadratic equations by completing the square

Why you should learn it:

You can complete the square to help efficiently solve some quadratic equations.

Goal Solving by Completing the Square

In this lesson, you will learn to rewrite a quadratic equation in *completed-square form*. This process is called **completing the square.** To begin, let's look at some trinomials of the form $x^2 + bx + c$ that are perfect squares.

$$x^2 + 6x + 9 = (x + 3)^2 \qquad x^2 - 12x + 36 = (x - 6)^2$$

In each case, the constant term of the left side is the square of half of the coefficient of the x-term.

Perfect Square Trinomial	Square of Binomial
$x^2 + bx + \left(\frac{b}{2}\right)^2$	$\left(x + \frac{b}{2}\right)^2$
(half of b)^2	

Thus, to complete the square for an expression of the form $x^2 + bx$, you must add $\left(\frac{b}{2}\right)^2$ to the expression.

Completing the square can be used to solve a quadratic equation. When using this technique, remember that you must *preserve the equality*. When you add a constant to one side of the equation, be sure to add the same constant to the other side of the equation.

Example 1 *Completing the Square: Leading Coefficient Is 1*

Solve $x^2 - 6x + 7 = 0$ by completing the square.

Solution

$$
\begin{aligned}
x^2 - 6x + 7 &= 0 && \textit{Rewrite original equation.}\\
x^2 - 6x &= -7 && \textit{Subtract 7 from both sides.}\\
x^2 - 6x + (-3)^2 &= -7 + 9 && \textit{Add } (-3)^2, \textit{ or 9, to both sides.}
\end{aligned}
$$

(half of -6)^2

$$
\begin{aligned}
(x - 3)^2 &= 2 && \textit{Binomial squared}\\
x - 3 &= \pm\sqrt{2} && \textit{Find square roots.}\\
x &= 3 \pm \sqrt{2} && \textit{Solve for x.}
\end{aligned}
$$

The equation has two solutions: $3 + \sqrt{2}$ and $3 - \sqrt{2}$. ■

If the leading coefficient of the quadratic is not 1, you should divide both sides of the equation by this coefficient *before* completing the square.

Example 2 · *Completing the Square: Leading Coefficient Is Not 1*

Solve $2x^2 - x - 2 = 0$ by completing the square.

Solution

$2x^2 - x - 2 = 0$	*Rewrite original equation.*
$2x^2 - x = 2$	*Subtract -2 from both sides.*
$x^2 - \frac{1}{2}x = 1$	*Divide both sides by 2.*
$x^2 - \frac{1}{2}x + \left(-\frac{1}{4}\right)^2 = 1 + \frac{1}{16}$	*Add $\left(-\frac{1}{4}\right)^2$, or $\frac{1}{16}$, to both sides.*

$$\left(\text{half of } -\tfrac{1}{2}\right)^2$$

$\left(x - \frac{1}{4}\right)^2 = \frac{17}{16}$	*Binomial squared*
$x - \frac{1}{4} = \pm\dfrac{\sqrt{17}}{4}$	*Find square roots.*
$x = \frac{1}{4} \pm \dfrac{\sqrt{17}}{4}$	*Solve for x.*

The equation has two solutions, $x = \frac{1}{4} + \frac{\sqrt{17}}{4}$ and $x = \frac{1}{4} - \frac{\sqrt{17}}{4}$. As a check, you can use the quadratic formula on the original equation. ∎

You have studied five different methods for solving quadratic equations.

Summary of Methods for Solving $ax^2 + bx + c = 0$

Method	Lesson	Comments
Finding Square Roots	9.2	Efficient way to solve $ax^2 + c = 0$.
Graphing	9.3	Can be used for *any* quadratic equation, but gives only approximate solutions.
Using Quadratic Formula	9.4	Can be used for *any* quadratic equation. Always gives exact solutions.
Factoring	10.5	Efficient way to solve equation *if* quadratic can be factored easily.
Completing the Square	10.6	Can be used for *any* quadratic equation, but is best suited for quadratics with $a = 1$ and b an even number.

A deposit of $6000 was put into a savings account that paid annual interest of r%, compounded yearly. After two years, the balance in the account was $6933.75.

Example 3 *Finding the Annual Interest Rate*

Find the annual interest rate for the above deposit.

Solution

Known Formula	$A = P(1 + r)^t$	
Labels	Number of years $= t = 2$	(years)
	Principal (original deposit) $= P = 6000$	(dollars)
	Balance $= A = 6933.75$	(dollars)
	Annual interest rate $= r$	(decimal form)

Equation

$6933.75 = 6000(1 + r)^2$ *Quadratic model*

$1.156 = (1 + r)^2$ *Divide both sides by 6000.*

$1.075 = 1 + r$ *Take positive square roots.*

$0.075 = r$ *Subtract 1 from both sides.*

The annual interest rate is 7.5%. (Note that the only operation that was necessary to write this equation in completed square form was to divide both sides by 6000.) ■

Communicating about ALGEBRA

▶ **SHARING IDEAS about the Lesson**

Choose a Method Solve each equation by the most efficient method. Explain the reasons for your choices.

A. $x^2 - 6x + 8 = 0$ **B.** $x^2 - 6 = 0$ **C.** $x^2 - 6x = 0$

D. $x^2 - 6x - 8 = 0$ **E.** $2(x - 3)^2 = 12$ **F.** $2x^2 - 6x - 8 = 0$

EXERCISES

Guided Practice

▶ **CRITICAL THINKING about the Lesson**

1. Which is a perfect square trinomial?
   a. $x^2 - 8x + 8$ **b.** $x^2 - 8x + 16$
   c. $x^2 - 8x + 64$

2. Solve $x^2 - 4x = 8$ by completing the square. Solve the same equation by the quadratic formula. Explain the difference in the results.

3. What term must be added to $x^2 + 6x$ to create a perfect square trinomial?

4. Name the five methods for solving a quadratic equation.

Independent Practice

In Exercises 5–10, find the term that must be added to the expression to create a perfect square trinomial.

5. $x^2 - 18x$ 6. $x^2 + 6x$ 7. $x^2 + 12x$

8. $x^2 - 10x$ 9. $x^2 - 7x$ 10. $x^2 - 5x$

In Exercises 11–28, solve the equation by completing the square.

11. $x^2 + 10x - 11 = 0$ 12. $x^2 + 14x - 15 = 0$ 13. $y^2 - 24y + 63 = 0$

14. $y^2 - 8y + 12 = 0$ 15. $t^2 + 3t - \frac{7}{4} = 0$ 16. $y^2 + 9y + \frac{17}{4} = 0$

17. $x^2 - \frac{2}{3}x - 3 = 0$ 18. $x^2 + \frac{4}{5}x - 1 = 0$ 19. $x^2 + x - 1 = 0$

20. $1 + x - x^2 = 0$ 21. $4y^2 + 4y - 9 = 0$ 22. $3x^2 - 24x - 5 = 0$

23. $2x^2 - 6x - 15 = 5$ 24. $5x^2 - 20x - 20 = 5$ 25. $3x^2 + 4x + 4 = 3$

26. $4x^2 + 6x - 6 = 2$ 27. $x^2 + 2x = 2$ 28. $x^2 - 2x = 2$

In Exercises 29–43, use the most convenient method to solve the equation. Explain why you made your choice.

29. $x^2 - 3x - 1 = 0$ 30. $4x^2 - 12 = 0$ 31. $y^2 + 6y - 24 = 0$

32. $4x^2 - 25 = 0$ 33. $x^2 + 7x + 10 = 0$ 34. $u^2 + 5u + 2 = 0$

35. $3x^2 - 5x = 0$ 36. $y^2 + 2y - 26 = 0$ 37. $9z^2 + 10z - 4 = 0$

38. $4x^2 + 4x + 1 = 0$ 39. $7x^2 - 14x = 0$ 40. $4x^2 - 13x + 3 = 0$

41. $8x^2 - 10x + 3 = 0$ 42. $7x^2 - 14 = 0$ 43. $y^2 + 20y + 10 = 0$

44. *Money in the Bank*   At your seventh grade graduation, you and your twin sister each received $200. You each deposited the money in savings accounts that compound interest annually. Two years later your sister's deposit has grown by $28.98. Your account is in a different bank that pays an interest rate that is 1% more than your sister receives. What is your balance after two years?

45. *Splash!*   You and Jared are playing in the surf at the beach. Jared is 5 feet 4 inches tall and is standing at the point where the wave crests, as shown below. Did the wave go over his head? Explain.

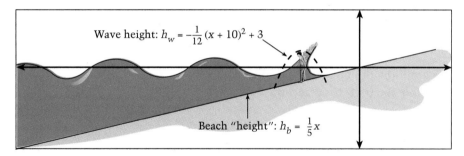

Wave height: $h_w = -\frac{1}{12}(x + 10)^2 + 3$

Beach "height": $h_b = \frac{1}{5}x$

46. *Whale Watching*   At the beach you see an 80-foot whale jump above water. The path followed by the whale is given by the model

$$h = -\frac{1}{400}x^2 + \frac{4}{5}x - 52$$

where h is the height (in feet) above the sea and x is the horizontal distance (in feet) traveled by the whale. Sketch a graph of this equation. For how many horizontal feet did the whale travel over the water before reaching its maximum height?

To attain a maximum thrust, a whale beats its tail down when a wave moves water upward (the front face of the wave) and beats its tail up when the wave moves water downward (the back face of the wave).

47. *Waterfall*   The Vettisfoss waterfall falls over a vertical cliff. The path followed by the water as it flows over the Vettisfoss Falls can be modeled by

$$h = -\frac{1}{30}(x - 10)^2 + 900$$

where h is the height (in feet) above the lower river level, and x measures the horizontal distance (in feet) from the base of the cliff. How far from the base of the cliff does the water hit the river?

48. How long does it take the water to hit the lower river? (Use a vertical motion model. See page 474.)

Vettisfoss Falls, in Norway, is one of the most famous waterfalls in the world. The distance between the lower river and the top of the falls is 900 feet.

Integrated Review

In Exercises 49–54, solve the equation.

49. $x^2 = 16$ **50.** $x^2 + 3 = 7$ **51.** $x^2 + 4 = 29$

52. $\frac{1}{7}x^2 + 8 = 15$ **53.** $2x^2 - 7 = 11$ **54.** $3x^2 - 8 = 100$

In Exercises 55–60, sketch the graph of the equation and find any x-intercepts. Explain how factoring could be used to find the x-intercepts.

55. $y = x^2 - 6x + 8$ **56.** $y = -2x^2 - 8x - 6$ **57.** $y = -x^2 - 2x - 1$

58. $y = x^2 + 8x + 16$ **59.** $y = 2x^2 - x - 10$ **60.** $y = x^2 + 5x - 6$

In Exercises 61–66, factor the expression.

61. $3x^2 - 15x - 18$ **62.** $12x^2 + 46x - 8$ **63.** $140y^2 + 340y + 120$

64. $-18y^2 + 156y + 54$ **65.** $12a^2 + 36a + 24$ **66.** $10x^2 + 15x + 5$

In Exercises 67–70, match the equation with its graph.

67. $y = -3x^2 + 6x - 1$ **68.** $y = 3x^2 - 6x + 4$

69. $y = 3x^2 + 6x + 1$ **70.** $y = -3x^2 - 6x - 4$

a. **b.** **c.** **d.**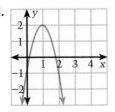

In Exercises 71–74, sketch the graph of the inequality.

71. $y \geq \frac{1}{2}x^2 - 4x + 6$ **72.** $y < \frac{1}{3}x^2 + 2x + 1$

73. $y > -x^2 + 8x - 16$ **74.** $y \leq -x^2 - 4x - 5$

Exploration and Extension

75. *Revenue* The revenue, R, for selling x units of a product is given by

$$R = x\left(50 - \frac{1}{2}x\right).$$

How many units must be sold to produce a revenue of $1218?

76. *Revenue* The revenue, R, for selling x units of a product is given by

$$R = x\left(100 - \frac{1}{10}x\right).$$

How many units must be sold to produce a revenue of $990?

77. *College Entrance Exam Sample* If x and y are positive integers, $x^2 + y^2 = 25$, and $x^2 - y^2 = 7$, then $y = \boxed{?}$.

a. 3 **b.** 4 **c.** 5 **d.** 9 **e.** 16

10 Chapter Summary

What did you learn?

Skills

1. Classify a polynomial by degree and by number of terms. **(10.1)**
2. Add and subtract polynomials. **(10.1)**
3. Multiply polynomials
   - using the Distributive Property. **(10.2)**
   - using the FOIL pattern. **(10.2)**
   - using the sum and difference pattern. **(10.3)**
   - using the square of a binomial pattern. **(10.3)**
4. Factor a polynomial
   - using the difference of two squares pattern. **(10.4)**
   - using the perfect square pattern. **(10.4)**
   - using the guess-and-check strategy. **(10.5)**
5. Solve a quadratic equation
   - by factoring. **(10.6)**
   - by completing the square. **(10.7)**

Strategies

6. Use quadratic models in real-life problems. **(10.1–10.7)**

Exploring Data

7. Recognize sum, difference, and product models in real life. **(10.1–10.7)**

Why did you learn it?

Polynomials were among the first mathematical models to be used. By now, you can see why—they are relatively simple and yet they can model a great variety of real-life situations. In this chapter, you learned that some models are related to each other by addition, subtraction, or multiplication. For instance, a model for the total revenue, R, can be obtained by multiplying the models for the price per unit, p, and the number, x, of units sold. In other words, $R = xp$.

How does it fit into the bigger picture of algebra?

Polynomials are among the most commonly used models for real-life situations. You were already familiar with three types of polynomial models: $y = a$ (constant models), $y = ax + b$ (linear models), and $y = ax^2 + bx + c$ (quadratic models). In this chapter, you learned how to add and subtract polynomials. You also learned how to multiply polynomials and how to "undo" multiplication by a process called *factoring*. This chapter has many connections with the mathematics you studied in Chapter 9. For instance, in Lessons 10.6 and 10.7 you learned two additional methods—factoring and completing the square—for solving a quadratic equation.

In Exercises 1–8, classify the polynomial by degree and by terms. **(10.1)**

1. $x^2 - 1$

2. $3x^2 + 2x - 2$

3. 121

4. $4x$

5. $x^4 - x^2 + 2x + 3$

6. $49x - 2$

7. $8x^3 - 27$

8. $2x^3 + 4x^2 - 5x + 6$

In Exercises 9–20, perform the indicated operation. Use a horizontal format. **(10.1, 10.2)**

9. $(x + 2 - x^2) + (3x^2 + 4x + 5)$

10. $(4x^3 + x^2 - 1) + (2 - x - x^2)$

11. $(15 + 3x - x^2) + (4x^2 - 2x - 10)$

12. $(3x + 2 - x^2) + (4 - x - x^3)$

13. $(x^2 + 3x - 1) - (4x^2 - 5x + 6)$

14. $(x^2 + 9x + 2) - (5 + 8x - 3x^2)$

15. $(3x^2 - 2x + 4) - (-x^3 + 2x - 6)$

16. $(x^3 + 5x^2 - 4x) - (3x^2 - 6x + 2)$

17. $(x - 5)(x - 10)$

18. $(2x + 2)(x + 4)$

19. $(6 + x)(x^2 - 2x + 3)$

20. $(7 - x)(3x^2 + 2x - 6)$

In Exercises 21–32, perform the indicated operation. Use a vertical format. **(10.1, 10.2)**

21. $(6x^2 + 2x - 1) + (x^2 - 2)$

22. $(x - 2) + (4x^2 - 7x + 5)$

23. $(-x^2 - x + 2) + (x^2 + 2x - 4)$

24. $(x^2 + 3x + 5) + (3x^2 - 4x + 6)$

25. $(x^2 - 3) - (4x^2 - 3x + 2)$

26. $(x^2 + 3x - 7) - (-2x^2 + x + 14)$

27. $(x^2 - 4x + 2) - (6x^2 + 4x - 3)$

28. $(10x^2 + 3x - 4) - (5x^2 + 2x - 6)$

29. $(x - 2)(3x^2 + 4x - 1)$

30. $(10 - x)(x^2 + x + 1)$

31. $(2x + 2)(4x^2 - 6x + 2)$

32. $(4 + 3x)(1 - 4x + 6x^2)$

In Exercises 33–36, multiply. **(10.3)**

33. $(x + 15)(x - 15)$

34. $(3x + 2)(3x - 2)$

35. $(x + 2)^2$

36. $(5x - 6)^2$

In Exercises 37–46, use the discriminant to determine whether the polynomial can be factored. If possible, factor the polynomial. **(10.4, 10.5)**

37. $x^2 - 2x - 15$

38. $x^2 + 3x - 70$

39. $x^2 - 64$

40. $4x^2 + 25$

41. $x^2 - 8x + 8$

42. $9x^2 + 12x + 4$

43. $x^2 + 10x + 25$

44. $x^2 - 8x + 16$

45. $4x^2 - 32x + 60$

46. $3x^2 + 21x + 30$

In Exercises 47–54, solve the equation. (10.6)

47. $x^2 - 21x + 108 = 0$ **48.** $x^2 - 8x - 240 = 0$ **49.** $-x^2 + 30x - 200 = 0$

50. $-15x^2 + 45x + 150 = 0$ **51.** $36x^2 - 49 = 0$ **52.** $x^2 + 26x + 169 = 0$

53. $x^2 - 14x + 36 = 0$ **54.** $x^2 + 10x - 3 = 0$

Right-Triangle Triple **In Exercises 55 and 56, find the right-triangle triple. (10.4)**

55. $11^2 + b^2 = c^2$

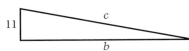

56. $17^2 + b^2 = c^2$

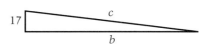

57. *Tossing a Ball* A ball is tossed into the air from a height of 10 feet with an initial velocity of 12 feet per second. Find the time, t (in seconds), for the object to reach the ground by solving the equation

$$-16t^2 + 12t + 10 = 0.$$

58. *Summer Business* Your friend's weekly revenue, R (in dollars), from her tie-dye T-shirt business can be modeled by

$$R = -2t^2 + 37t + 60$$

where t represents the week of sales, with $t = 0$ for the first week. In the first week, 3 T-shirts were sold. After that, the sales increased by 2 T-shirts per week. Did the price of T-shirts remain constant during the 8-week summer season? Explain.

Huffing and Puffing **In Exercises 59 and 60, use the following information.**

Porcupine fish, members of the puffer fish family, range between 10 and 20 inches in length. When in danger, the body of the fish puffs up by taking in water or air. (The tail, which is about 3 inches long, does not puff up.)

Porcupine Fish:
Deflated

59. The volume of a "puffed-up" porcupine fish can be modeled by

$$V = \left(\tfrac{1}{6}\right)\pi(x - 3)^3$$

where x is the total length of the fish in inches. Write the right side of this equation in standard polynomial form.

60. Approximate the volume of an 11-inch porcupine fish.

Inflated

The stopping distance of an automobile traveling at *x* miles per hour is the sum of the distance the car travels during the driver's reaction time *and* the distance the car travels after the brakes are applied. The distance, *R*, in feet, traveled during the driver's reaction time is approximately $R = 1.1x$. The distance, *B*, in feet, traveled after the brakes are applied is $B = 0.14x^2 - 4.43x + 58.4$ approximately.
(These models are based on normal road conditions.)

61. Find a model for the (total) stopping distance, *S* (in feet), of an automobile that is traveling *x* miles per hour.

62. Estimate the total stopping distance for an automobile that is traveling 15 miles per hour; 30 miles per hour; 55 miles per hour.

63. Are stopping distances and speeds related by a linear model? Explain. What does this tell you about the amount of distance you need to allow for stopping when traveling at various speeds?

64. The recommended safe *following distance* on highways under normal road conditions is given by $F = 1.8x$. How many feet should be between cars traveling at 55 miles per hour?

Registered Cars   **In Exercises 65 and 66, use the following information.**

From 1940 to 1990, the number, *C*, of registered cars in the United States can be modeled by $C = 20,500t^2 + 1,460,100t + 25,942,500$, where $t = 0$ represents 1940. **(Source: Motor Vehicle Facts and Figures '90, Federal Highway Administration)**

65. During which year were 129,874,900 cars registered?

66. According to this model, how many cars will be registered in 1995?

Chapter **TEST**

In Exercises 1–12, perform the indicated operations.

1. $(x^2 + 3x - 1) + (4x^2 + 2)$

2. $(x^4 + 3x^2 + 2) + (2x^4 - 3x^2 + 6)$

3. $(5x^2 - 2x + 1) - (7x + 10)$

4. $(5x^3 + 2x - 4) - (4x^3 + 2x^2 - 5x)$

5. $(9x + 2)(9x - 2)$

6. $(5x - 4)(5x + 4)$

7. $(x - 14)^2$

8. $(3x + 5)^2$

9. $(x + 2)(3x + 5)$

10. $(2x - 1)(13x + 5)$

11. $(x - 6)(4x^2 + 3x - 5)$

12. $(4x^3 - 6x + 7)(x + 1)$

In Exercises 13–20, factor the expression.

13. $x^2 - 144$

14. $36x^2 - 25$

15. $x^2 - 12x + 36$

16. $x^2 + 10x + 25$

17. $3x^2 + 2x - 1$

18. $5x^2 - 3x - 2$

19. $x^3 + 2x^2 + x$

20. $2x^2 - 28x + 96$

In Exercises 21–26, solve the equation.

21. $x^2 + 4x + 4 = 0$

22. $x^2 - 7x + 6 = 0$

23. $x^2 - 5x - 150 = 0$

24. $x^2 + 6x - 91 = 0$

25. $12x^2 + 15x + 3 = 0$

26. $4x^2 - 10x - 36 = 0$

In Exercises 27–30, solve the equation by completing the square.

27. $x^2 - 4x + 1 = 0$

28. $x^2 + 6x - 9 = 0$

29. $x^2 + 20x + 3 = 0$

30. $x^2 - 2x - 5 = 0$

31. Find a right-triangle triple such that $5^2 + b^2 = c^2$.

32. The length of a bedroom is 3 feet less than twice its width. The area of the bedroom is 135 square feet. What are the dimensions of the room?

33. A deposit of $5000 was put into a savings account paying an annual interest of r%, compounded yearly. After 2 years, the balance in the account was $5,644.53. What was the rate of interest?

34. The bed of a pond can be modeled by $25y = 2x^2 - 20x + 1$, where x and y are measured in meters and the x-axis matches the water level of the pond. What is the width of the pond?

Using Proportions and Rational Equations

LESSONS

11.1 Problem Solving Using Ratios and Proportions ▪ 562

11.2 Problem Solving Using Percents ▪ 568

11.3 Direct and Inverse Variation ▪ 575

11.4 Exploring Data: Probability ▪ 581

11.5 Simplifying Rational Expressions ▪ 588

11.6 Multiplying and Dividing Rational Expressions ▪ 594

11.7 Dividing Polynomials ▪ 600

11.8 Solving Rational Equations ▪ 607

At the depth at which this photo was taken, the pressure exerted by the ocean is approximately 376 times the pressure at sea level.

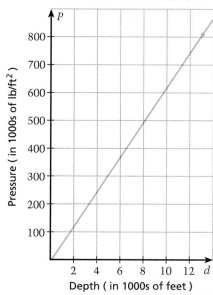

Real Life

Marine Exploration

Underwater Pressure

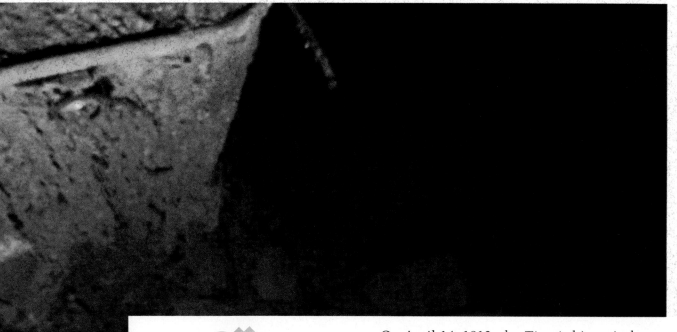

Pressure (in 1000s of lb/ft^2)

Depth (in 1000s of feet)

On April 14, 1912, the *Titanic* hit an iceberg and sank. The ship was considered unsinkable by its builders and owners, but it sank on its first Atlantic crossing. About 1522 of the 2227 passengers perished. For many years, the location of the *Titanic* was not known. In 1985, however, researchers found the wreckage about 500 miles southeast of Newfoundland. The wreckage was found at a depth of 13,000 feet.

Water pressure, P (in pounds per square foot), varies directly with the depth of the water, d, in feet. An equation that relates the two variables is

$$P = 62.4d.$$

The pressure at a depth of 13,000 feet is about 811,200 pounds per square foot. To take the photograph shown here, researchers used a special submarine called *Argo* that could bear such a tremendous pressure.

11.1

Problem Solving Using Ratios and Proportions

What you should learn:

Goal 1 How to solve proportions

Goal 2 How to use proportions to solve real-life problems

Why you should learn it:

You can solve many real-life problems using proportions, such as finding the size of an object from a scale model.

Goal 1 Solving Proportions

In Lesson 2.8, you learned that if two quantities, a and b, are measured in the *same* units, then their ratio is $\frac{a}{b}$. An equation that equates two ratios is a **proportion**. For instance, if the ratio $\frac{a}{b}$ is equal to the ratio $\frac{c}{d}$, then the proportion is the statement of equality

$$\frac{a}{b} = \frac{c}{d}. \qquad a, b, c, \text{ and } d \text{ are nonzero.}$$

This is read as "*a* is to *b* as *c* is to *d*." The numbers a and d are the **extremes** of the proportion. The numbers b and c are the **means** of the proportion.

Properties of Proportions

1. If two ratios are equal, their reciprocals are also equal.

$$\text{If } \frac{a}{b} = \frac{c}{d}, \text{ then } \frac{b}{a} = \frac{d}{c}. \qquad \textit{Reciprocal property}$$

2. The product of the extremes equals the product of the means.

$$\text{If } \frac{a}{b} = \frac{c}{d}, \text{ then } ad = bc. \qquad \textit{Cross-multiplying property}$$

Problems involving proportions often contain a variable. Solving for the variable is called *solving the proportion.*

Example 1 Solving a Proportion

Solve the proportion $\frac{3}{y} = \frac{5}{8}$.

Solution

$$\frac{3}{y} = \frac{5}{8} \qquad \textit{Rewrite original proportion.}$$

$$\frac{y}{3} = \frac{8}{5} \qquad \textit{Reciprocal property.}$$

$$y = 3\left(\frac{8}{5}\right) \qquad \textit{Multiply both sides by 3.}$$

$$y = \frac{24}{5} \qquad \textit{Simplify.}$$

The solution is $\frac{24}{5}$. Check this in the original proportion. ∎

Example 2 Solving a Proportion

Solve the proportion $\frac{x}{x + 4} = \frac{2}{x}$.

Solution

$$\frac{x}{x + 4} = \frac{2}{x} \qquad \textit{Original proportion}$$
$$x(x) = 2(x + 4) \qquad \textit{Cross multiply.}$$
$$x^2 = 2x + 8 \qquad \textit{Simplify.}$$
$$x^2 - 2x - 8 = 0 \qquad \textit{Write in standard form.}$$
$$(x - 4)(x + 2) = 0 \qquad \textit{Factor.}$$
$$x = 4 \text{ or } x = -2 \qquad \textit{Zero-Product Property}$$

The proportion has two solutions: 4 and -2. Check these solutions in the original proportion. ∎

Goal 2 Using Proportions in Real-Life Problems

Mount Rushmore National Memorial is carved out of a granite cliff in the Black Hills of South Dakota. The carvings of George Washington, Thomas Jefferson, Theodore Roosevelt, and Abraham Lincoln are 80 times life size.

Real Life
Sculpture

Example 3 Estimating the Size of a Statue

Estimate the height of the sculpture of George Washington's head. (Assume that an average distance from a man's chin to the top of his head is 9 inches or 0.75 ft.)

Solution Let x represent the height of the sculptured head. You can find x by solving the following proportion.

$$\frac{\text{Height of sculptured head}}{\text{Height of man's head}} = \frac{80}{1}$$

$$\frac{x}{0.75} = \frac{80}{1} \quad \frac{\text{feet}}{\text{feet}}$$

The solution is $x = 60$. The height of the sculptured head of Washington is about 60 feet. ∎

10 ft

640 ft

40 ft
10 ft

One of the
test pits

Excavated
area

One of the most incredible archaeological finds occurred in China in 1974. A life-size army, made of pottery, was buried under a 15-story mound to guard the tomb of the emperor Ch'in Shih Huang Ti (c. 250 B.C.). The army and tomb took 700,000 workers 36 years to build.

Real Life
Archaeology

Example 4   *Estimating the Size of an Army*

To estimate the size of the army, archaeologists excavated 3 test pits and a section at one end of the mound. They found 4 rows containing 320 soldiers in the first 10 feet of the section. (Four similar rows were at the other end of the mound.) In the next 40 feet, they found 316 soldiers, 24 horses, and 6 chariots, which they thought to be representative of the rest of the mound. How many soldiers, horses, and chariots did they estimate to be in the 680-foot portion of the mound between the eight "end rows"?

Solution   Let x represent the total number of soldiers. You can find x by solving the following proportion.

$$\frac{\text{Total number of soldiers}}{\text{Number of soldiers found}} = \frac{\text{Total number of feet}}{\text{Number of feet excavated}}$$

$$\frac{x}{316} = \frac{680}{40}$$

The solution is $x = 5372$. (With the 640 soldiers at the ends, that makes 6012 soldiers.) In a similar way, you can use proportions to estimate that there were 408 horses and 102 chariots! *(Source: National Geographic)* ■

Communicating about A L G E B R A

▷ **SHARING IDEAS about the Lesson**

Explain the Process   Solve each proportion. Explain your solution steps.

A. $\frac{x}{4} = \frac{9}{2}$ **B.** $\frac{5}{x} = \frac{4}{5}$ **C.** $\frac{x}{x+1} = \frac{10}{x+7}$

EXERCISES

Guided Practice

▶ CRITICAL THINKING about the Lesson

1. In the proportion $\frac{a}{b} = \frac{c}{d}$, which numbers are the *extremes*? Which are the *means*?

2. Which of the following are equivalent to $\frac{a}{b} = \frac{c}{d}$?
   a. $ac = bd$ **b.** $ba = dc$ **c.** $ad = bc$

3. Which of the following are equivalent to $\frac{a}{b} = \frac{c}{d}$?
   a. $\frac{a}{b} = \frac{d}{c}$ **b.** $\frac{b}{a} = \frac{d}{c}$ **c.** $\frac{a}{d} = \frac{b}{c}$

In Exercises 4–6, solve the proportion.

4. $\frac{x}{4} = \frac{2}{5}$

5. $\frac{5}{x} = \frac{3}{2}$

6. $\frac{1}{x+1} = \frac{x}{2}$

Independent Practice

In Exercises 7–24, solve the proportion.

7. $\frac{2}{x} = \frac{3}{4}$

8. $\frac{3x}{4x-1} = \frac{1}{x}$

9. $\frac{7x}{x+1} = \frac{5x}{2}$

10. $\frac{8x}{6} = \frac{2x}{x+3}$

11. $\frac{6}{2y} = \frac{5}{8}$

12. $\frac{4}{5} = \frac{7}{y}$

13. $\frac{4}{x} = \frac{6}{8}$

14. $\frac{2}{x} = \frac{6}{3}$

15. $\frac{-3}{x} = \frac{5}{6}$

16. $\frac{4}{x} = \frac{14}{-7}$

17. $\frac{9}{2} = \frac{18}{y}$

18. $\frac{10}{8} = \frac{5}{y}$

19. $\frac{x}{5x+6} = \frac{1}{x}$

20. $\frac{5}{x+1} = \frac{4x}{x}$

21. $\frac{6}{x+2} = \frac{x+1}{x}$

22. $\frac{6}{19x} = \frac{-2}{x^2+2}$

23. $\frac{x+6}{x-2} = \frac{2}{x}$

24. $\frac{x-3}{x} = \frac{2x}{-3}$

25. *Planting Trees*   In 1990, more than 2.1 billion trees were planted in the United States. The states that planted the most acres of trees were Georgia and Alabama. The ratio of Georgia's population to Alabama's population was about the same as the ratio of the numbers of trees planted in Georgia and Alabama, respectively. The 1990 population of Georgia was 6,508,000. What was the 1990 population of Alabama?

(Source: American Forest Resource Alliance)

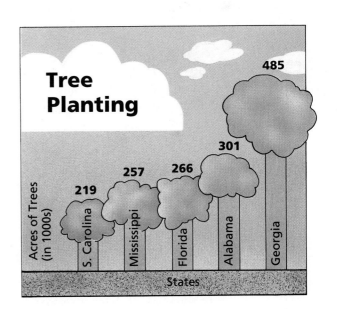

26. *Estimating Whale Populations* To estimate the number, *W*, of blue whales in a portion of the Indian Ocean, researchers marked 200 different whales. Months later the researchers checked 300 whales in the area and found only 15 that were marked. The researchers then assumed that the ratio of 300 to *W* was equal to the ratio of 15 to 200. What did they estimate the blue whale population to be?

Monuments of Stone **In Exercises 27 and 28, use the following information.**

The Chief Crazy Horse Memorial is being carved from Thunderhead Mountain in South Dakota. When completed, it will be the world's largest stone sculpture: 641 feet wide and 563 feet high.

The Stone Mountain Monument in Georgia is a stone carving of Jefferson Davis, Robert E. Lee, and Stonewall Jackson. In 1990, it was the world's largest stone sculpture: 180 feet wide and 90 feet high.

27. The ratio of the sculpture of Chief Crazy Horse to actual size is 140 to 1. Estimate the diameter of the horse's nostril in the sculpture. Assume the diameter of a horse's nostril is 3 inches.

28. The ratio of the Stone Mountain sculpture to actual size is 20 to 1. Estimate the length of a horse's head in the sculpture. Assume that the length of a horse's head is $2\frac{1}{2}$ feet.

29. *Hoosiers* vs. *Boilermakers* The Purdue Boilermakers are playing the Indiana Hoosiers. Estimate the distance the Boilermakers have to travel (from West Lafayette to Indianapolis).

30. *Traveling on Interstate 95* You are driving on Interstate 95 from Philadelphia, Pennsylvania, to Baltimore, Maryland. Estimate the number of miles you will be traveling in Delaware.

In Exercises 31–34, find the reciprocal of the number.

31. $\frac{1}{3}$ **32.** $\frac{4}{5}$ **33.** $\frac{-2}{7}$ **34.** $\frac{7}{6}$

In Exercises 35–38, write the percent in decimal form.

35. 23% **36.** 6.4% **37.** 0.25% **38.** 3%

In Exercises 39–42, write the fraction as a percent.

39. $\frac{3}{4}$ **40.** $\frac{2}{3}$ **41.** $\frac{6}{2}$ **42.** $\frac{1}{5}$

In Exercises 43–46, simplify the fraction.

43. $\frac{6x}{x}$ **44.** $\frac{5xy}{15x^2}$ **45.** $\frac{-2y^2}{14xy}$ **46.** $\frac{-3xy^3}{3x^3y}$

47. *Estimation—Powers of Ten* Which is the best estimate for the length of an adult blue whale (the largest living mammal)?

  a. 10 feet **b.** 100 feet **c.** 1000 feet **d.** 10,000 feet

48. *Estimation—Powers of Ten* Which is the best estimate for the baking temperature of chocolate chip cookies?

  a. 4°F **b.** 40°F **c.** 400°F **d.** 4000°F

Exploration and Extension

49. *Buffon's Needle Experiment* The following experiment was devised by an 18th century French naturalist, Count Buffon.

Place a piece of ruled notebook paper on a flat surface. Cut a thin paper "needle" whose length is the distance between the lines on the paper. Drop the needle from a height of about one foot above the paper. If the needle touches a line, count the drop as a success. If it doesn't, count the drop as a failure. Repeat the experiment 30 or 40 times. Find the ratio of total drops to successes. It should be approximately equal to the ratio of π to 2.

If the needle touches a line, count the drop as a success.

If the needle falls between two lines, count the drop as a failure.

50. If you performed this experiment 3195 times, how many successes would you need to obtain 3.1415929 as the value of π?

11.2

Problem Solving Using Percents

What you should learn:

Goal 1 How to solve percent problems

Goal 2 How to use percents in real-life problems

Why you should learn it:

You can model and solve many real-life problems using percent, such as in presenting survey results.

Goal 1 Solving Percent Problems

Percent means *per hundred*, or *parts of 100*. For example, 30% means 30 parts of 100, which is equivalent to the fraction $\frac{30}{100}$ or the decimal 0.3.

When solving percent problems, we suggest converting percents to decimals *before performing arithmetic operations.*

Verbal Model $\boxed{a}$ is $\boxed{p \text{ percent}}$ of $\boxed{b}$

Labels
Percent = p (decimal form, no units)
Base number = b (assigned units)
Number compared to b = a (*same* units as b)

Equation $a = pb$ (p in decimal form)

Example 1   *Percent Problem: Unknown Number*

What is 30% of 70 feet?

Solution

Labels
Unknown number = a (feet)
Percent = p = 0.3   (decimal form)
Base number = b = 70   (feet)

Equation $a = (0.3)(70)$ *a is p percent of b.*
$a = 21$ feet

Therefore, 21 feet is 30% of 70 feet. ■

Example 2   *Percent Problem: Unknown Base Number*

Fourteen dollars is 25% of what?

Solution

Labels
Number = a = 14   (dollars)
Percent = p = 0.25   (decimal form)
Unknown base number = b (dollars)

Equation $14 = 0.25b$ *a is p percent of b.*
$\frac{14}{0.25} = b$
$\$56 = b$

Therefore, $14 dollars is 25% of $56. ■

Example 3 Percent Problem: Unknown Percent

One hundred thirty-five miles is what percent of 27 miles?

Solution

Labels Number $= a = 135$ (miles)

Percent $= p$ (decimal form)

Base number $= b = 27$ (miles)

Equation $135 = p(27)$ *a is p percent of b.*

$\dfrac{135}{27} = p$

$5 = p$ *Decimal form*

$500\% = p$ *Percent form*

Therefore, 135 miles is 500% of 27 miles. ■

Goal 2 Using Percents in Real-Life Problems

Connections
Sociology

Example 4 Taking a Survey

In 1991, a survey of American "teens" between the ages of twelve and nineteen had the following results.
(*Source: Simmons Market Research Bureau*)

Age Group	Number Surveyed	Number Who Date Regularly
12–14-year-olds	900	207
15–17-year-olds	990	594
18–19-year-olds	650	416

What percent of each age group surveyed said they dated regularly? What information about the survey would you need to know to conclude that the results are representative of *all* American teens?

Solution

Of the 12–14-year-olds, $\frac{207}{900}$, or 23%, said they dated regularly.

Of the 15–17-year-olds, $\frac{594}{990}$, or 60%, said they dated regularly.

Of the 18–19-year-olds, $\frac{416}{650}$, or 64%, said they dated regularly.

To know whether these percents are representative of *all* American teens, you would need to know that the teens used in the survey were chosen from many different backgrounds and many different parts of the country. For instance, if all 2530 teens who were surveyed were from the same city or county, then it would not be fair to form conclusions about a national population. ■

Example 5 *Butterflies and Moths*

Butterflies and moths comprise the insect order *Lepidoptera.* Entomologists (scientists who study insects) have classified about 20,000 species (types) of butterflies and about 140,000 species of moths. Lepidoptera make up 20% of all classified insect species. How many insect species have been classified?

Solution

Verbal Model	Butterfly species + Moth species is p percent of Insect species

Labels Number $= a = 20{,}000 + 140{,}000$ (species)
Percent $= p = 0.2$ (decimal form)
Unknown base number $= b$ (species)

Equation $160{,}000 = 0.2b$ *a is p percent of b.*

$$\frac{160{,}000}{0.2} = b$$

$$800{,}000 = b$$

There are about 800,000 classified species of insects. ■

Example 6 *Finding the Markup Percent*

The wholesale cost of a butterfly net is $18.50. The retail price is $32.95. What is the markup percent (on the cost)?

Solution

Verbal Model	Markup is Markup percent of Cost

Labels Markup $= 32.95 - 18.50 = 14.45$ (dollars)
Markup percent $= p$ (decimal form)
Cost $= 18.50$ (dollars)

Equation $14.45 = p(18.5)$ *a is p percent of b.*

$$\frac{14.45}{18.5} = p$$

$$0.781 \approx p$$

The markup percent on the cost is about 78.1%. ■

Communicating about ALGEBRA

▶ **SHARING IDEAS about the Lesson**

Derive the Meaning The Latin word *centum* means "one hundred." How is "100" related to *centimeter, cent,* and *centennial*? Name some other related "cent" words.

EXERCISES

Guided Practice

▶ **CRITICAL THINKING about the Lesson**

1. In the statement "16 is 10% of 160," what is the base number? Write an equation that represents this statement.

2. Thirty is 15% of what number?

3. What number is 26% of 450?

4. Nineteen is what percent of 10?

Independent Practice

In Exercises 5–22, solve the percent problem.

5. What number is 23% of 90?

6. What number is 71% of 310?

7. 13 is what percent of 50?

8. 48 is 60% of what number?

9. What distance is 6% of 400 meters?

10. How much is 32% of $625?

11. What distance is 21% of 580 miles?

12. How many students is 86% of 950 students?

13. 35 feet is 50% of what length?

14. 54 degrees is 45% of what angle measure?

15. 3 dollars is 2% of what amount?

16. 9 grams is 12% of what weight?

17. 11 people is what percent of 50 people?

18. 13 years is what percent of 20 years?

19. 24 pounds is what percent of 600 pounds?

20. 486 dozen is what percent of 900 dozen?

21. 78 days is what percent of 39 weeks?

22. 52 inches is what percent of 20 feet?

Geometry **In Exercises 23–26, what percent of the region is shaded blue? What percent is shaded yellow?**

23.

24.

25.

26.

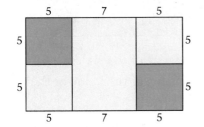

In Exercises 27 and 28, use the following information.

One thousand ten amateur photographers were asked what their favorite subjects were. Each respondent was allowed to choose more than one subject.

(Source: Fuji Photo Film, Inc.)

27. How many of the respondents chose travel and vacations as their favorite subjects?

28. Suppose 1500 amateur photographers had been surveyed. How many would you expect to have chosen travel and vacations?

29. *Recycling Bottles and Jars* About 12% of the glass bottles and jars produced in the United States are recycled. In 1990, an average of 13,698,630 bottles and jars were recycled each day. Find the average number of bottles and jars that were produced each day. How many of these, on average, were *not* recycled? What percent is this of the number produced each day?

30. *Boots* Last year you bought a pair of designer boots for $24.72. Your friend buys the same boots this year for $37.08. Which statements are correct?

  a. You paid $33\frac{1}{3}\%$ less than your friend.

  b. Your friend paid 50% more than you did.

  c. You paid $66\frac{2}{3}\%$ of what your friend paid.

Photographers' Favorite Subjects

- Animals/pets 27%
- Outdoor scenes 39%
- Travel and vacations 48%
- Children 49%
- People they know 54%
- Family celebrations 63%

Could You Lend Me a Day's Worth? **In Exercises 31 and 32, use the following information showing the average numbers of currency bills printed each day in 1991.** *(Source: Bureau of Engraving and Printing)*

Number of Bills Printed per Day

8,714,521   2,498,630

2,129,315   5,023,561   315,616   517,260

31. What percent of the six currency bills printed were $20 bills?

32. What percent of the value of the six types of bills printed was from $20 bills?

33. *Shampoo*   You are shopping at a new store and buy a bottle of shampoo for $2.45. At the store where you usually shop, the price is $1.96. Which statements are correct?
  a. You paid 25% more than your usual price.
  b. You paid 125% more than your usual price.
  c. You paid 125% of your usual price.

34. *Automobile Expenses*   Suppose that a person spent $748 on automobile gasoline in 1991. What would you estimate the total automobile expenses to have been?

35. *Sweater*   A sweater you want is regularly priced at $19.95. The store is having a 20%-off sale. What is the sale price?

36. *Compact Disk Player*   You buy a compact disk player on sale for $107.50. The sale price is 15% less than the original price. What was the original price?

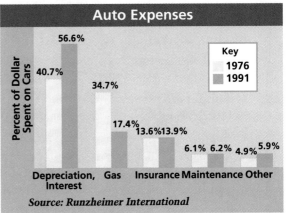

Auto Expenses

Key
1976
1991

Percent of Dollar Spent on Cars

56.6%
40.7%
34.7%
17.4% 13.6% 13.9%
6.1% 6.2% 4.9% 5.9%

Depreciation, Interest   Gas   Insurance   Maintenance   Other

Source: Runzheimer International

Integrated Review

In Exercises 37–39, write the percent in decimal form.

37. 4%

38. 18%

39. 69%

In Exercises 40–42, write the decimal in percent form.

40. 1.34

41. 0.134

42. 0.0134

In Exercises 43–48, solve the equation.

43. $6x = 3$

44. $5x = 2$

45. $108x = 100$

46. $96x = 50$

47. $16x = 9$

48. $110x = 9$

In Exercises 49–54, solve the proportion.

49. $\frac{2}{x} = \frac{x}{8}$

50. $\frac{x}{3} = \frac{3}{x}$

51. $\frac{x + 1}{3} = \frac{1}{4x}$

52. $\frac{3}{x - 6} = \frac{1}{x}$

53. $\frac{2}{2x - 3} = \frac{x}{7}$

54. $\frac{3x + 1}{9} = \frac{10}{3x}$

Exploration and Extension

55. *Say That Again?*   You earn 10% more money at your summer job than your sister does at hers. Does this mean that your sister earns 10% less than you? Explain your answer.

56. *Tennis Shoes*   You buy a pair of tennis shoes on sale for $48. The price is discounted 25% and the sales tax is 7%. Would it cost less to have the discount applied before the sales tax is added or after the sales tax is added? Explain.

1. Write $y - 3 = 2x + 6$ in standard form. **(5.5)**

2. Write $3x - 9 + 2x^2 = 0$ in standard form. **(9.2)**

3. Find the leading coefficient of $3x - 4x^2 + 9$. **(10.1)**

4. Solve the equation in Exercise 2. **(10.6)**

5. Simplify $(x - 1)(x + 2) + 3x - 5$. **(10.2)**

6. Simplify $(xy^2 \div 3xy)(4x^{-2} \div 8x)$. **(8.3)**

7. Solve $8x + 2 = 3(4 - x)$. **(3.3)**

8. Solve $8|x - 2| - 3 = 0$. **(4.8)**

9. Evaluate $y = 3(1.6)^x$ when $x = 4$. **(8.1)**

10. Evaluate $|x + 3| + x^2$ when $x = -2$. **(2.3)**

11. Is 12 a solution of $m^2 - 3m \geq 110$? **(1.5)**

12. Is $(4, -3)$ a solution of $y < -\frac{1}{4}x^2$? **(9.6)**

13. Find the discriminant of $x^2 + 4x - 7$. **(9.5)**

14. Solve $x^2 + 4x - 7 = 0$. **(9.4)**

15. Find the slope of the line $2x + 3y = 6$. **(4.4)**

16. Find the intercepts of the line $3x - y = 16$. **(4.3)**

17. Write $\frac{3}{8}$ in decimal form. **(11.2)**

18. Write 0.92 in percent form. **(11.2)**

19. Evaluate $(3 \times 10^{-6})(6 \times 10^{10})$. **(8.4)**

20. Evaluate $(2.9 \times 10^{-3}) \div (4.6 \times 10^4)$. **(8.4)**

Career Interview

Retailer Melissa Durkee is a retailer specializing in Western wear, boots, Native American jewelry, and accessories.

Q: *How did you get interested in retailing?*

A: I worked part-time as a salesperson through high school and most of college. From my experiences, I knew I wanted to and had the ability to work for myself. I wanted to be my own boss.

Q: *How much math have you learned on the job?*

A: I haven't learned any new math skills per se. However, I am applying my understanding of math in different situations daily. The math skills and the knowledge I learned in school have sharpened my math business sense.

Q: *What math classes did you take in high school?*

A: I took algebra and geometry.

Q: *What would you like to tell kids about math?*

A: Almost every walk of life relies on some application of math to a certain degree. Math often ends up being the tool you'll rely on most in life.

11.3

Direct and Inverse Variation

What you should learn:

Goal 1 How to use direct variation and inverse variation

Goal 2 How to use direct variation and inverse variation in real-life settings

Why you should learn it:

You can solve many real-life problems using the direct variation (increase corresponds to increase) and inverse variation (increase corresponds to decrease) models.

Goal 1 Using Direct and Inverse Variation

Two variable quantities that have the same rate, or ratio, regardless of the values of the variables, have **direct variation.** For example, if you get paid \$5 per hour, then your total pay *varies directly* with the number of hours you work.

Total pay, *p*	\$10	\$20	\$30	\$40
Hours worked, *t*	2	4	6	8
Rate	$\frac{10}{2} = 5$	$\frac{20}{4} = 5$	$\frac{30}{6} = 5$	$\frac{40}{8} = 5$

The variables *p* and *t* are related by the equation $\frac{p}{t} = 5$ or $p = 5t$.

Models for Direct and Inverse Variation

1. The variables *x* and *y* **vary directly** if, for a constant *k*,
$$\frac{y}{x} = k \text{ or } y = kx.$$

2. The variables *x* and *y* **vary inversely** if, for a constant *k*,
$$yx = k \text{ or } y = \frac{k}{x}.$$

In both cases, the number *k* is the **constant of variation.**

Note that two quantities that vary inversely always have the same product.

Example 1 *Solving an Inverse Variation Problem*

The variables *x* and *y* vary inversely. When *x* is 3, *y* is 6. Find an equation that relates *x* and *y*.

Solution

$$\begin{aligned} xy &= k &&\textit{Model for inverse variation} \\ (3)(6) &= k &&\textit{Substitute 3 for x and 6 for y.} \\ 18 &= k &&\textit{Simplify.} \end{aligned}$$

Thus, an equation that relates *x* and *y* is

$$xy = 18 \quad \text{or} \quad y = \frac{18}{x}. \qquad \blacksquare$$

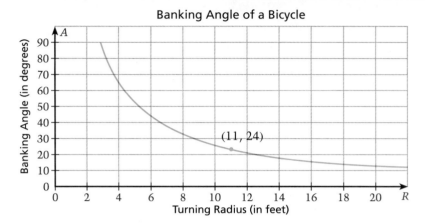

Banking Angle of a Bicycle

(11, 24)

This graph shows the "banking angles" for a bicycle whose speed is 15 miles per hour. The banking angle and the radius of the turn **vary inversely.** As the radius of the turn gets smaller, the bicyclist must lean at greater angles to avoid falling over.

Real Life
Bicycling

Bicycle race in San Rafael, California

Example 2 *Finding a Model for "Banking Angles"*

Find a model that relates the banking angle, A, with the turning radius, R, for a bicyclist whose speed is 15 miles per hour.

a. Use the model to find the banking angle for a turning radius of 8 feet.

b. Does the banking angle increase or decrease as the turning radius decreases?

Solution

a. From the graph, you can see that A is 24° when the turning radius, R, is 11 feet.

$A = \dfrac{k}{R}$ *Model for inverse variation*

$24 = \dfrac{k}{11}$ *Substitute 24 for A and 11 for R.*

$264 = k$ *Solve for k.*

The model is given by

$A = \dfrac{264}{R}$

where A is measured in degrees and R is measured in feet. When the turning radius is 8 feet, the banking angle is

$A = \dfrac{264}{8} = 33°.$

You can use the graph to confirm this result.

b. From the graph, you can see that the banking angle increases as the turning radius decreases. ∎

The first airship, built by Henri Giffard in 1852, had a volume of 8.83×10^4 cubic feet. The Graf Zeppelin II, 1933, was the largest (by volume) rigid airship ever built. Its volume was 7.06×10^6 cubic feet.

Real Life
Aeronautics

Example 3   *Finding a Model of Airship Weight*

The weight that an airship can support varies directly with its volume. Henri Giffard's airship could support a weight of 5650 pounds. Find a model that relates the volume, V (in cubic feet), to the weight, W (in pounds), that an airship filled with hydrogen can support. Use the model to find the weight that the *Graf Zeppelin II* could support. (Both airships were filled with hydrogen.)

Solution

$W = kV$	*Model for direct variation*
$5650 = k(88{,}300)$	*Substitute 5650 for W, 88,300 for V.*
$\dfrac{5650}{88{,}300} = k$	*Divide both sides by 88,300.*
$0.064 \approx k$	*Solve for k.*

The model is $W = 0.064V$. Since the *Graf Zeppelin II* had a volume of 7.06×10^6 cubic feet, it could support a weight of

$$W = 0.064(7{,}060{,}000) = 451{,}840 \text{ pounds.} \blacksquare$$

Communicating about ALGEBRA

▶ **SHARING IDEAS about the Lesson**

Consider an Alternative   Hydrogen is "lighter" than helium.

A. If Giffard's airship had been filled with helium, it could have only supported a weight of 5120 pounds. How much could the *Graf Zeppelin* have supported if it had been filled with helium?

B. Today's airships use helium rather than hydrogen. Since hydrogen can support more weight, why is helium used?

EXERCISES

▶ **CRITICAL THINKING about the Lesson**

1. Give a real-life example of two variable quantities that vary directly.

2. Give a real-life example of two variable quantities that vary inversely.

In Exercises 3–6, classify each equation as direct or inverse variation, or neither.

3. $\frac{x}{y} = 33$

4. $y = 5x + 13$

5. $a = 10b$

6. $ab = 7$

Independent Practice

In Exercises 7–10, state whether the variables have direct variation, inverse variation, or neither.

7. *Speed and Distance*   You are riding your bike at an average speed of 12 miles per hour. The number of miles you ride, d, during t hours is given by $d = 12t$.

8. *Mass and Volume*   The mass, m, and volume, v, of a substance are related by the equation $2v = m$, where 2 is the density of the substance.

9. *Pieces Eaten and Pieces to Eat*   The number of pieces, p, of pizza that Alicia ate for dinner and the number of pieces, q, she can eat for breakfast are related by $p = k + q$.

10. *Waiting Time and People in Line*   The time, t, spent waiting in line for the Super Looper roller coaster, and the number of people, n, in the line are related by the equation $t = kn$.

In Exercises 11—14, the variables *x* and *y* vary directly. Given one pair of values for *x* and *y*, find an equation that relates the variables.

11. $x = 4$, $y = 8$

12. $x = 6$, $y = 24$

13. $x = 18$, $y = 4$

14. $x = 22$, $y = 6$

In Exercises 15–18, the variables *x* and *y* vary inversely. Given one pair of values for *x* and *y*, find an equation that relates the variables.

15. $x = 1$, $y = 4$

16. $x = 10$, $y = 3$

17. $x = \frac{1}{2}$, $y = 7$

18. $x = \frac{3}{4}$, $y = 4$

In Exercises 19–22, find an equation that relates the two variables.

19. *Volume and Pressure*   The volume, V, of a gas at a constant temperature varies inversely with the pressure, P. When the volume is 100 cubic inches, the pressure is 25 pounds per cubic inch.

20. *Time and Typing Speed*   The time, t (in minutes), it takes for Roger to type his 2500-word term paper varies inversely with the number of words per minute, r, he can type.

21. *Pay and A's*   Your great uncle sends you two hamburger gift certificates for each A you receive on your report card. The number, g, of gift certificates he sends varies directly with the number, n, of A's on your report card.

22. *Percent and Correct Answers*   The percent grade, p, on the exam varies directly with the number, n, of correct answers. (There are 20 questions each worth 5 points.)

In Exercises 23 and 24, assume the variables vary directly.

23. If $x = 4$ when $y = 16$, find x when $y = 8$.   **24.** If $c = 6$ when $d = 3$, find c when $d = 5$.

In Exercises 25 and 26, assume the variables vary inversely.

25. If $m = 2$ when $n = 7$, find m when $n = 2$.   **26.** If $q = \frac{1}{2}$ when $r = \frac{1}{3}$, find q when $r = 6$.

27. *Pulse Rate*   Your pulse rate, p, varies directly with the volume, b, of blood pumped from your heart each minute. Each time your heart beats, it pumps approximately 0.006 liter of blood. Find an equation that relates p and b. Take your pulse and find out how much blood your heart pumps per minute.

28. *Weight*   Weight depends on gravity. Neil Armstrong, the first man on the moon, weighed 360 pounds on Earth, including his heavy equipment, but only 60 pounds on the moon, with equipment. If the first woman in space, Valentina V. Tereshkova, had landed on the moon and weighed 54 pounds, with equipment, how much would she have weighed on Earth, with equipment?

29. *Mining Danger*   One of the dangers of coal mining is the methane gas that can leak out of seams in the rock. Methane forms an explosive mixture with air at a concentration of 5 percent or greater. Suppose a steady leak of methane began in a coal mine so that the concentration of methane gas varied directly with time. Twelve minutes after the leak began, the concentration of methane in the air was 2 percent. If the leak continues at the same rate, when could an explosion occur?

30. *Snowshoes*   When a person walks, the pressure, P, on each boot sole varies inversely with the area, A, of the sole. Denise is trudging through deep snow, wearing boots that have a sole area of 29 square inches each. The boot-sole pressure is 4 pounds per square inch. If Denise was wearing snowshoes, each with an area 11 times that of her boot soles, what would be the pressure on each snowshoe? The constant of variation in this problem is Denise's weight. How much does she weigh?

Snowshoeing on Mt. Osceola, N.H.

31. *Oil Spill*   The graph shows the percent, *p*, of oil that remained in Chedabucto Bay, Nova Scotia, after an oil spill. The cleaning of the spill was left primarily to natural actions such as wave motion, evaporation, photochemical decomposition, and bacterial decomposition. After about a year, the percent that remained varied inversely with time. Find a model that relates *p* and *t*, where *t* is the number of years since the spill. Then use your model to find the amount of oil that remained $6\frac{1}{2}$ years after the spill.

Recovery from Oil Spill

32. *Ocean Temperatures*   The graph shows the temperature of the water in the north central Pacific Ocean. At depths greater than 900 meters, the water temperature varies inversely with the water depth. Find a model that relates the temperature, *T*, with the depth, *d*. What is the temperature at a depth of 4385 meters?

Ocean Temperatures

Integrated Review

In Exercises 33–36, solve the proportion.

33. $\frac{a}{20} = \frac{1}{5}$

34. $\frac{3}{x} = \frac{4}{9}$

35. $\frac{3}{8} = \frac{3}{2d}$

36. $\frac{5}{17} = \frac{r}{9}$

In Exercises 37–40, write the percent in decimal form.

37. 50%

38. 10%

39. 120%

40. 3%

Exploration and Extension

41. *Jacket Sale*   A jacket is on sale for $58. The regular price is $70. What is the percent of discount?

42. *Tennis Shoes*   Your friend bought a pair of tennis shoes last week at the regular price. Today in the same store, you found the same kind of shoes at 20% off. You paid $43.96. What did your friend pay?

43. *Photocopies*   Some photocopy machines can reduce and enlarge pictures. If a photocopier reduces a picture 75%, its new length, *l*, and width, *w*, vary directly with its original length, *L*, and width, *W*. Write two equations: one relating *l* and *L* and the other relating *w* and *W*. Then use the equations to find a model that relates the new area, *a*, with the original area, *A*. Is the area reduced by 75%? Explain.

11.4

Exploring Data: Probability

What you should learn:

Goal 1 How to find the probability of an event

Goal 2 How to use probability in real-life settings

Why you should learn it:

You can use probability to anticipate results and to help you make decisions.

Goal 1 Finding the Probability of an Event

The **probability of an event** is a number between 0 and 1 that indicates the likelihood the event will occur. An event that is certain to occur has a probability of 1. An event that is certain to *not occur* has a probability of 0. An event that is **equally likely** to occur or not occur has a probability of $\frac{1}{2}$, or 0.5. For instance, the probability that a tossed coin will land heads up is 0.5.

Probability of 0: event cannot occur	Probability of 0.5: equally likely to occur or not occur	Probability of 1: event must occur

$$
\begin{array}{ccc}
\downarrow & \downarrow & \downarrow \\
0 & 0.5 & 1
\end{array}
$$

Finding the Probability of an Event

The **probability,** P, of an event is the ratio of successful outcomes, called **successes,** to all outcomes of the event, called **possibilities.**

$$P = \frac{\text{Number of successes}}{\text{Number of possibilities}}$$

Example 1   *Finding the Probability of an Event*

a. An algebra class has 17 boys and 16 girls. One student is chosen at random from the class. The probability, P, that the student is a girl is

$$P = \frac{\text{Number of girls}}{\text{Number of students}}$$

$$= \frac{16}{33} \approx 0.485, \quad \text{(a little less than one half)}.$$

b. You are carrying seven cassette tapes in a backpack. On the way to school, you lean against a building and break one of the tapes. The probability that it is one of your two favorites is

$$P = \frac{\text{Number of favorite tapes}}{\text{Number of tapes}} = \frac{2}{7}. \qquad ■$$

Real Life
Parachuting

Example 2   *Finding the Probability of an Event*

You are on a committee to plan the halftime show for a football game. As part of the show, you hire a parachutist to land in the middle of the field. You want the parachutist to land in the center of the field on the square displaying the school emblem. The parachutist will guarantee landing on the field (otherwise the school will not be charged), but will not guarantee landing on the emblem. What is the probability that the parachutist will land on the emblem? (Assume that the landing on the field is sure to occur and that each spot on the field is an equally likely landing space.)

160 ft

80

360 ft   80

Solution   The probability of landing on the emblem is

$$P = \frac{\text{Area of emblem}}{\text{Area of field}}$$

$$= \frac{(80)(80)}{(160)(360)}$$

$$= \frac{6400}{57,600}$$

$$= \frac{1}{9}.$$

There is a 1 in 9 chance that the parachutist will land on the emblem. ■

Real Life
Performing Arts

**Mikhail Baryshnikov and Deirdre
Carberry in a ballet performance.**

Example 3   *Attendance at Performing Arts*

The table shows the results of a survey of 2300 Americans (18 and older). The numbers indicate how many of the 2300 attended at least one performance of the type listed during a year. *Based on this survey,* if an American (18 or older) is chosen at random, what is the probability that the person attended a ballet performance during the past year? What is the probability that the person attended a musical play?
(Source: U.S. National Endowment for the Arts)

Type of Performance	Jazz Concert	Classical Music	Opera	Musical Play	Other Play	Ballet
Number	230	299	69	391	276	92

Solution   The probability that the person attended a ballet is

$$P = \frac{92}{2300} = 0.04. \quad \textit{Probability of attending ballet}$$

The probability that the person attended a musical play is

$$P = \frac{391}{2300} = 0.17. \quad \textit{Probability of attending musical} \quad ■$$

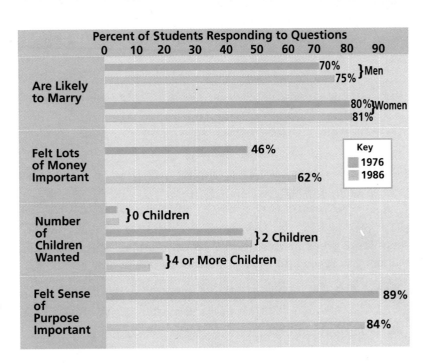

Percent of Students Responding to Questions

| | 0 | 10 | 20 | 30 | 40 | 50 | 60 | 70 | 80 | 90 |

Are Likely to Marry
70% }Men
75%
80% }Women
81%

Felt Lots of Money Important
46%
62%

Key
1976
1986

Number of Children Wanted
}0 Children
}2 Children
}4 or More Children

Felt Sense of Purpose Important
89%
84%

The survey, conducted by the Institute for Social Research at the University of Michigan, shows changes in what high school seniors wanted in 1986 compared to 1976. For instance, more planned to marry and have children. More were interested in having a lot of money, and fewer were interested in finding a sense of purpose.

Real Life
Social Research

Example 4 *Using the Results of a Survey*

In 1986, a randomly selected, female high school senior was asked if she was likely to marry. What is the probability that she said yes? What is the probability that she did not say yes?

Solution From the results of the survey, 81% of the females said they were likely to marry. This means that 19% said they were unlikely to marry or were unsure.

$$Y = \frac{81}{100}$$ *Percent who said* yes
$$= 0.81$$ *Probability of saying* yes

$$N = \frac{19}{100}$$ *Percent who said* no *or were undecided*
$$= 0.19$$ *Probability of saying* no *or of being undecided*

Note that the sum of the two probabilities is one. ∎

Communicating about **ALGEBRA**

Cooperative Learning

▶ **SHARING IDEAS about the Lesson**

Work with a Partner and Explain the Meaning

A. Explain what is meant by an 80% probability of rain.

B. Explain what is meant by a 50% probability of winning.

EXERCISES

Guided Practice

▶ CRITICAL THINKING about the Lesson

1. What is the probability of an event that *cannot* occur? Give an example.

3. How do you find the probability of an event?

2. What is the probability of an event that *must* occur? Give an example.

Marbles in a Jar　**In Exercises 4–6, consider a jar that contains 12 blue marbles, 8 green marbles, and 5 yellow marbles. Without looking at the colors, you reach into the jar and choose one marble.**

4. What is the probability that the marble is blue?

5. What is the probability that the marble is not blue?

6. What is the probability that the marble is not red?

Independent Practice

In Exercises 7–8, find the probability of an event given the number of successes and the number of possibilities.

7. Number of successes: 12
Number of possibilities: 64

8. Number of successes: 2
Number of possibilities: 10

9. *Archaeology*　You are working on an archaeological site during the summer. One day you sift through 16 tables of soil and find artifacts in 3 of the tables. The next day your mother and stepfather visit and watch as you sift through one table of soil. What is the probability that they get to see you find an artifact?

10. *Junior Achievement*　Junior Achievement is an organization that teaches students how the American business system operates. The members manufacture and sell their own products. The probability of a member being a student is 0.95. How many of the 827,000 members are students?

11. *Emily Dickinson*　Emily Dickinson (1830–1886) is one of America's most loved poets, yet during her lifetime, people rarely got the chance to read her poems. In fact, the probability that a particular poem was published during her lifetime is only 0.006. How many of her 1700 poems were published when she was living? From the Dickinson poem at the right, would you guess that the poems published while she was alive were done so with her permission or without her permission?

> *I'm Nobody! Who are you?*
> *Are you—Nobody too?*
> *Then there's a pair of us!*
> *Don't tell! They'd advertise—you know!*
>
> *How dreary—to be—Somebody!*
> *How public—like a Frog—*
> *To tell one's name—the live long June—*
> *To an admiring Bog!*

12. *Baby Sea Turtles*   A sea turtle buries 200 eggs in the sand. After the baby turtles hatch and dig to the surface, they scramble to make it to the relative safety of the ocean. Birds and other predators make the journey tough for the babies. Of the 176 babies that hatched, 125 were eaten by birds, and 39 were eaten by other predators. The rest made it to the ocean. Suppose that just after the eggs were laid, you marked one with an *X*. What is the probability that your egg hatched and the baby turtle made it to the ocean?

Meteorite!   **In Exercises 13 and 14, use the following information.**

The Willamette meteorite was found in the Willamette Valley in Oregon in 1902. It is the largest found in the United States.

13. Earth contains 57,510,000 square miles of land and 139,440,000 square miles of water. What is the probability that a meteorite that hits Earth will fall onto land?

14. What is the probability that a meteorite that hits Earth will fall into water?

Bull's-Eye   **In Exercises 15 and 16, use the following information.**

The bull's-eye of a standard dart board has a radius of about 1 inch. The inner circle has a radius of 5 inches, and the outer circle has a radius of 9 inches. Assume that when a dart is thrown at the board, the dart is equally likely to hit any point inside the outer circle.

15. What is the probability that a dart that hits the dart board lands on the bull's-eye?

16. What is the probability that a dart that hits the dart board lands between the inner and outer rings?

Inner Circle

Outer Circle

Farm Population   **In Exercises 17 and 18, use the table, which shows the number of Americans in thousands who lived on farms in 1988.**

Age group	15 and under	16–19	20–24	25–44	45–64	65 and older
Number	1000	3951	421	1528	1305	697

17. Of all people who lived on a farm in 1988, one is chosen at random. What is the probability that the person was fifteen years old or younger in 1988?

18. In 1988, the United States population was 246,329,000. If a person was chosen at random from the population, what was the probability that the person lived on a farm?

The graph and table show the number of immigrants who have come to the United States during each decade since 1900.

Decade	1901–1910	1911–1920	1921–1930
Number	8,795,000	5,736,000	4,107,000
Decade	1931–1940	1941–1950	1951–1960
Number	528,000	1,035,000	2,515,000
Decade	1961–1970	1971–1980	1981–1990
Number	3,322,000	4,493,000	6,161,000

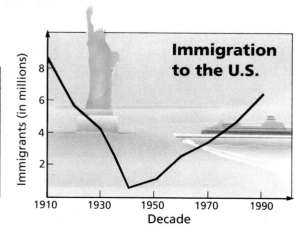

19. What is the probability that a person who immigrated to the United States between 1901 and 1990 came before 1941?

20. What is the probability that a person who immigrated to the United States between 1901 and 1990 came after 1940?

In Exercises 21 and 22, use the information given in Example 4 of this section.

21. In 1986, a randomly selected high school senior was asked if having a lot of money was important. What is the probability that the student said yes?

22. In 1976, what was the probability that a randomly selected high school senior would say that he or she wanted 0 children?

Integrated Review

In Exercises 23–25, simplify the expression.

23. $\frac{2x}{9} \div \frac{x}{3}$

24. $\frac{x^2 - 1}{x} \div \frac{x + 1}{3}$

25. $\frac{32x + x^2}{2} \div \frac{x}{4}$

26. What is 90% of 50?

27. 11 is what percent of 185?

28. 159 is 75% of what number?

Exploration and Extension

In Exercises 29 and 30, use the following information.

The *odds* of an event occurring is the ratio of the number of ways the event can occur to the number of ways the event cannot occur. In reduced form, odds of $\frac{a}{b}$ is read "*a* to *b*."

29. *Raffle Tickets*   There are 600 tickets in a raffle. You buy 12 of them. What are the odds that the winning ticket is one of yours?

30. *Collecting Insects*   Your insect collection has several duplicates: 6 butterflies, 2 crickets, 8 grasshoppers, and 2 walkingsticks. Your cousin asks if he can have one and you agree. What are the odds that your cousin will choose a butterfly? (Assume that each insect is equally likely to be chosen.)

Take this test as you would take a test in class. The answers to the exercises are given in the back of the book.

In Exercises 1–12, solve the proportion. (11.1)

1. $\dfrac{4}{x} = \dfrac{5}{6}$

2. $\dfrac{3}{7} = \dfrac{12}{x}$

3. $\dfrac{a}{3} = \dfrac{5}{27}$

4. $\dfrac{a}{26} = \dfrac{5}{13}$

5. $\dfrac{y}{27} = \dfrac{3}{y}$

6. $\dfrac{2y}{5} = \dfrac{40}{y}$

7. $\dfrac{x}{2x+1} = \dfrac{-1}{x}$

8. $\dfrac{x+4}{x} = \dfrac{-6}{x-4}$

9. $\dfrac{x-3}{-3} = \dfrac{2x-3}{x-3}$

10. $\dfrac{y+2}{5} = \dfrac{4}{y+3}$

11. $\dfrac{y+7}{6} = \dfrac{y+5}{3}$

12. $\dfrac{5}{y-3} = \dfrac{6}{y+2}$

13. How much is $6\frac{1}{2}\%$ of four dollars? **(11.2)**

14. How many students is 75% of 1248 students? **(11.2)**

15. 24 feet is 80% of what length? **(11.2)**

16. 100 bottles is 26% of how many? **(11.2)**

17. 38 grams is what percent of 56 grams? **(11.2)**

18. 17 meters is what percent of 68 meters? **(11.2)**

19. Japan's citizens have four times as much money in their savings accounts as United States citizens have. Belgium's citizens have two times as much as United States citizens. Write a sentence that compares the average Japanese savings account with the average Belgian savings account. **(11.1)**

20. A survey was conducted with 1540 junior and senior high school students. Of the 1540, 55% planned to attend college full-time, 26% planned to work and go to college part-time, 11% planned to go into the armed forces, 7% planned to work, and 1% were undecided. How many planned to attend college either part-time or full-time? How many planned to enter the armed forces? **(11.2)**

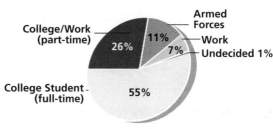

Survey of Students' Goals

College/Work (part-time) 26%
Armed Forces 11%
Work 7%
Undecided 1%
College Student (full-time) 55%

21. The variables a and b vary inversely. When a is 7, b is 35. Find an equation that relates a and b. If a is 5, what is b? **(11.3)**

22. You put $5 into one of 6 pockets of your jeans, but you can't remember which pocket. What is the probability that you will find the money in the first pocket you check? After checking two pockets without success, what is the probability that the $5 will be in the next pocket you check? **(11.4)**

23. You have been mailed a discount catalog in which all regular prices have been discounted 20%. From this catalog you order $60 worth of merchandise but you pay an additional $5 for shipping and handling. What percent did you really save when you consider the $5 charge for shipping and handling? **(11.2)**

11.5 Simplifying Rational Expressions

What you should learn:

Goal 1 How to simplify a rational expression

Goal 2 How to use rational expressions as real-life models

Why you should learn it:

You can use rational expressions as models of real-life situations such as in relating air pressure to altitude.

Goal 1 Simplifying a Rational Expression

A fraction whose numerator and denominator are polynomials is called a **rational expression.** Some examples are

$$\frac{3}{x + 4}, \quad \frac{2x}{x^2 - 9}, \quad \text{and} \quad \frac{6}{x^2 + 1}.$$

The **domain** of a rational expression is the set of all real numbers *except* those for which the denominator is zero. For instance, the domain of the first expression is all real numbers except -4.

A rational expression is **simplified** or **in reduced form** if its numerator and denominator have no factors in common (other than ± 1). To reduce fractions, apply the following property. Be sure you see that this property allows you only to divide out factors, *not* terms.

Simplifying Fractions

Let a, b, and c be nonzero real numbers.

$$\frac{a\cancel{c}}{b\cancel{c}} = \frac{a}{b} \quad \text{Divide out common factor of } c.$$

Example 1 *When and When Not to Divide*

a. $\dfrac{\cancel{2} \cdot x}{\cancel{2}(x + 5)} = \dfrac{x}{x + 5}$ *You CAN divide out the common factor 2.*

b. $\dfrac{3 + x}{3 + 2x}$ *You CANNOT divide out the common term 3.*

c. $\dfrac{\cancel{x}(x^2 + 6)}{\cancel{x} \cdot x} = \dfrac{x^2 + 6}{x}$ *You CAN divide out the common factor x.*

d. $\dfrac{x + 4}{x}$ *You CANNOT divide out the common term x.*

Simplifying a rational expression usually requires two steps. First, factor the numerator and denominator. Then, divide out any *factors* that are common to both the numerator and denominator. Your success in simplifying a rational expression lies in your ability to factor its numerator and denominator.

Example 2 Simplifying a Rational Expression

Simplify $\dfrac{2x^2 - 6x}{6x^2}$.

Solution

$$\dfrac{2x^2 - 6x}{6x^2} = \dfrac{2x(x - 3)}{6x^2}$$ *Factor numerator and denominator.*

$$= \dfrac{\cancel{2x}(x - 3)}{\cancel{2x}(3x)}$$ *Divide out common factor 2x.*

$$= \dfrac{x - 3}{3x}$$ *Simplified form* ∎

Goal 2

Using Rational Expressions in Real Life

Example 3 Areas of Science Laboratories

Rockville High School is building a new science wing. The architect has allocated spaces of x feet by x feet for both the biology and chemistry labs. At the request of the faculty, the principal agrees to increase the length of each lab by 5 feet and increase the width of the chemistry lab by 10 feet. Find an expression for the ratio of the area of the revised chemistry lab to the area of the revised biology lab. Evaluate the ratio when $x = 25$ feet and when $x = 30$ feet.

Problem Solving
Draw a Diagram

Solution

$$\text{Ratio} = \dfrac{\text{Area of Chemistry Lab}}{\text{Area of Biology Lab}}$$

$$= \dfrac{(x + 5)(x + 10)}{x(x + 5)}$$

$$= \dfrac{x + 10}{x}$$ *Divide out common factor.*

When $x = 25$ feet, the ratio is

$$\dfrac{25 + 10}{25} = \dfrac{35}{25} = 1.4$$

which means that the chemistry lab would be 40% larger than the biology lab. When $x = 30$ feet, the ratio is

$$\dfrac{30 + 10}{30} = \dfrac{40}{30} \approx 1.33$$

which means that the chemistry lab would be about 33% larger than the biology lab.

Example 4 ─ An Atmospheric Pressure Model

The air pressure at sea level is about 14.7 pounds per square inch. As the altitude increases, the air pressure decreases. A model that relates air pressure to the altitude is

$$P = \frac{-9.05(x^2 - 65x)}{x^2 + 40x}$$

where P is measured in pounds per square inch and x is measured in 1000's of feet. (This model is valid in Earth's *troposphere*, the portion of the atmosphere closest to Earth.) Suppose you are in an airplane, flying at 40,000 feet. The pressure in the cabin is 14.7 pounds per square inch. What is the pressure outside?

Solution

$$P = \frac{-9.05(x^2 - 65x)}{x^2 + 40x} \qquad \text{\textit{Air pressure model}}$$

$$= \frac{-9.05x(x - 65)}{x(x + 40)} \qquad \text{\textit{Factor.}}$$

$$= \frac{-9.05\cancel{x}(x - 65)}{\cancel{x}(x + 40)} \qquad \text{\textit{Divide out common factor.}}$$

$$= \frac{-9.05(x - 65)}{x + 40} \qquad \text{\textit{Simplified form}}$$

Substitute 40 for x in the model.

$$P = \frac{-9.05(40 - 65)}{40 + 40}$$

$$\approx 2.8 \text{ pounds per square inch} \qquad \blacksquare$$

Communicating about ALGEBRA

▷ **SHARING IDEAS about the Lesson**

Compare Two Expressions

A. Complete the table.

x-values	−2	−1	0	1	2	3	4
$\dfrac{x^2 - x - 6}{x - 3}$	?	?	?	?	?	?	?
$x + 2$	?	?	?	?	?	?	?

B. Write a paragraph describing the equivalence (or non-equivalence) of these two expressions. Support your argument with appropriate algebra from this lesson *and* a discussion of the domains of the two expressions.

EXERCISES

Guided Practice

▶ CRITICAL THINKING about the Lesson

1. What is a rational expression?

2. Define the domain of a rational expression. What is the domain of

$$\frac{2}{x^2 - x - 2}?$$

3. Which is the correct reduced form of $\frac{2x + 6}{x^2 + 5x + 6}$?

a. $\frac{2x}{x^2 + 5x}$ **b.** $\frac{2}{x + 5}$ **c.** $\frac{2}{x + 2}$

4. *True or False?* To simplify a rational expression, you can cancel common factors of the numerator and denominator.

Independent Practice

In Exercises 5–10, find the domain of the rational expression.

5. $\frac{5}{x - 4}$

6. $\frac{10}{x - 6}$

7. $\frac{3}{x^2 - 1}$

8. $\frac{z + 2}{z^2 - 4}$

9. $\frac{x + 4}{x^2 + x - 6}$

10. $\frac{x - 3}{x^2 + 5x - 6}$

In Exercises 11–16, find the missing factor.

11. $\frac{5\boxed{?}}{6x^2} = \frac{5}{2x}$

12. $\frac{3x\boxed{?}}{4x^2} = \frac{3x}{2}$

13. $\frac{x(x + 2)}{2\boxed{?}} = \frac{x}{2}$

14. $\frac{25x^2}{8\boxed{?}} = \frac{5x}{8}$

15. $\frac{3x\boxed{?}}{x^2 - x - 6} = \frac{3x}{x - 3}$

16. $\frac{(1 - z)\boxed{?}}{z^3 + z^2} = \frac{1 - z}{z^2}$

In Exercises 17–28, simplify the expression.

17. $\frac{4x}{12}$

18. $\frac{18y}{36}$

19. $\frac{15x^2}{10x}$

20. $\frac{18y^2}{60y^5}$

21. $\frac{3x}{10x + x^2}$

22. $\frac{x + 2x^2}{2x + 1}$

23. $\frac{y^2 - 16}{3y + 12}$

24. $\frac{x^2 - 25z^2}{x - 5z}$

25. $\frac{3 - x}{x^2 - 5x + 6}$

26. $\frac{y^2 - 7y + 12}{y^2 + 3y - 18}$

27. $\frac{x^3 + 5x^2 + 6x}{x^2 - 4}$

28. $\frac{t^3 - t}{t^3 + 5t^2 - 6t}$

29. *College Entrance Exam Sample* Which expression is equivalent to $\left(\frac{2x^2}{y}\right)^3$?

a. $\frac{8x^5}{3y}$ **b.** $\frac{6x^6}{y^3}$ **c.** $\frac{6x^5}{y^3}$ **d.** $\frac{8x^5}{y^3}$ **e.** $\frac{8x^6}{y^3}$

30. *College Entrance Exam Sample* Which has the same value as $\frac{P}{Q}$?

a. $\frac{P - 2}{Q - 2}$ **b.** $\frac{1 + P}{1 + Q}$ **c.** $\frac{P^2}{Q^2}$ **d.** $\frac{3P}{3Q}$ **e.** $\frac{P + 3}{Q + 3}$

Meteorologists use the term *windchill* factor to estimate the temperature that a person feels when the wind is blowing. The faster the wind blows, the colder you feel. At 0° Fahrenheit, the windchill factor, w, is given by

$$w = \frac{7 - 16x - 23x^2}{(10 - 0.022x + 0.005x^2)(1 + x)}$$

where x is the wind speed in miles per hour.

31. Simplify the expression for the windchill factor.

32. You are driving and see a sign at a bank that gives the temperature as 0°F. On the radio, you hear that the risk of frostbite is high. What is the minimum that the windchill factor could be?

At 0°F, the risk of frostbite is high when the wind is blowing at 15 (or more) miles per hour.

Mail-Order Catalogs   **In Exercises 33–36, use the following information.**

The number of catalogs mailed, C (in billions), in the United States between 1980 and 1990 can be modeled by

$$C = \frac{116 + 68t + 5t^2}{(10 - 0.8t + 0.0592t^2)(2 + t)}$$

where $t = 0$ corresponds to 1980.

33. Simplify the expression for the number of catalogs.

34. How many catalogs were mailed in 1990?

35. What was the average number of catalogs received by an American household in 1990?

36. Sketch a bar graph showing the number of catalogs mailed in 1980, 1982, 1984, 1986, 1988, and 1990.

In 1990, there were about 94 million households in the United States.

Integrated Review

In Exercises 37–42, simplify the expression.

37. $3x^2 \cdot x^4$

38. $\frac{1}{4}x^3 \cdot x^{10}$

39. $xy^3 \cdot y^2$

40. $12xy^3 \cdot \frac{1}{2}x^4y$

41. $\frac{5xy^2}{15x^3y}$

42. $\frac{a^2b^2}{5ab}$

In Exercises 43–48, evaluate the expression.

43. $\dfrac{2x^2 - 1}{x^2 + 3}$, when $x = 1$

44. $\dfrac{3x + 4}{x - 5}$, when $x = -2$

45. $\dfrac{9 + x^2}{(x + 3)(x - 3)}$, when $x = 4$

46. $\dfrac{x + y^2}{x^2 - 1}$, when $x = 2$ and $y = -3$

47. $\dfrac{x^2 + y^2}{x^2 - y^2}$, when $x = -4$ and $y = 2$

48. $\dfrac{3 + x^2}{3 + y^2}$, when $x = 2$ and $y = 1$

Exploration and Extension

49. *Working as a Tutor* You are tutoring a friend in algebra. Your friend needs practice in simplifying expressions. Create some sample problems of the form

$$\frac{ax^2 + bx + c}{dx^2 + ex + f}$$

in which the numerator and denominator have a common factor. Describe the process you used to create numerators and denominators that have a common factor.

50. Solve the proportion.

$$\frac{x^2 + 5x + 6}{x^2 - 2x - 8} = \frac{x^2 - 4x - 5}{x^2 - 8x + 15}$$

Mixed REVIEW

1. Write 4,675,000,000 in scientific notation. **(8.4)**

2. Write 0.000649 in scientific notation. **(8.4)**

3. Write 6.209×10^{-6} in decimal form. **(8.4)**

4. Write 4.255×10^4 in decimal form. **(8.4)**

5. What is the reciprocal of $-m^{-3}$? **(8.3)**

6. What is the opposite of $-m^{-3}$? **(2.1)**

7. What is 7.2% of $69?

8. What is $\frac{4}{9}$ of 36 inches?

9. Solve $4|x - 3| \geq 8$. **(6.4)**

10. Solve $|3x + 2| < 6$. **(6.4)**

11. Simplify $(x^2 y^{-3})^2 \cdot 4x^{-4}y^2 \cdot \frac{1}{8}x$. **(8.2)**

12. Simplify $3(x - 2) + x(-6 - x)$. **(2.6)**

13. Is (5, 6) a solution for $2^y < x^2 + x$? **(6.5)**

14. Is $(-2, 5)$ a solution for $y = 2x^2 - 1$? **(4.2)**

15. Find the square roots of 81. **(9.1)**

16. Solve $5x^2 = 720$. **(9.2)**

17. Evaluate $x^2 - 3\sqrt{x} + 3$ when $x = 4$. **(9.1)**

18. Evaluate $\sqrt{3x} + 2^x$ when $x = 3$. **(9.1)**

In Exercises 19 and 20, write an equation for the indicated line.

19. Slope is $\frac{3}{5}$, contains $(4, -6)$ **(5.2)**

20. Contains $(6, -2)$ and $(27, -2)$ **(5.3)**

11.6

Multiplying and Dividing Rational Expressions

What you should learn:

Goal 1 How to multiply and divide rational expressions

Goal 2 How to use rational expressions in real-life settings

Why you should learn it:

You can use rational expressions to model real-life situations, such as relating boiling points to altitudes.

Goal 1 Working with Rational Expressions

The rule for multiplying rational expressions is the same as the rule for multiplying numerical fractions. That is, *multiply numerators, multiply denominators, and write the new fraction in reduced form.*

$$\frac{a}{b} \cdot \frac{c}{d} = \frac{ac}{bd}$$

To divide one rational expression by another, multiply the first by the reciprocal of the second. Be careful not to confuse the operation. Invert the divisor expression only.

$$\frac{a}{b} \div \frac{c}{d} = \frac{a}{b} \cdot \frac{d}{c}$$

Example 1 *Multiplying Rational Expressions*

Multiply: $\dfrac{4x^3}{3x} \cdot \dfrac{-6x^2}{10x^4}$

Solution

$$\frac{4x^3}{3x} \cdot \frac{-6x^2}{10x^4} = \frac{-24x^5}{30x^5} \qquad \text{\textit{Multiply numerators and denominators.}}$$

$$= \frac{-4 \cdot 6 \cdot x^5}{5 \cdot 6 \cdot x^5} \qquad \text{\textit{Factor, and divide out common factors.}}$$

$$= -\frac{4}{5} \qquad \text{\textit{Simplified form}} \qquad \blacksquare$$

Example 2 *Multiplying Rational Expressions*

Multiply: $\dfrac{x}{5x^2 - 20x} \cdot \dfrac{x - 4}{2x^2 + x - 3}$

Solution

$$\frac{x}{5x^2 - 20x} \cdot \frac{x - 4}{2x^2 + x - 3}$$

$$= \frac{x(x - 4)}{(5x^2 - 20x)(2x^2 + x - 3)}$$

$$= \frac{x(x - 4)}{5x(x - 4)(x - 1)(2x + 3)}$$

$$= \frac{x(x - 4)}{5x(x - 4)(x - 1)(2x + 3)}$$

$$= \frac{1}{5(x - 1)(2x + 3)} \qquad \blacksquare$$

To multiply a rational expression by a polynomial, rewrite the polynomial as a fraction whose denominator is 1. This helps you to avoid confusion in simplifying the product.

Example 3 *Multiplying a Rational Expression by a Polynomial*

Multiply: $\dfrac{3x}{2x^2 - 9x + 10} \cdot (2x - 5)$

Solution

$$\dfrac{3x}{2x^2 - 9x + 10} \cdot (2x - 5) = \dfrac{3x}{2x^2 - 9x + 10} \cdot \dfrac{2x - 5}{1}$$

$$= \dfrac{3x(2x - 5)}{(2x - 5)(x - 2)}$$

$$= \dfrac{3x(\cancel{2x - 5})}{(\cancel{2x - 5})(x - 2)}$$

$$= \dfrac{3x}{x - 2} \qquad \blacksquare$$

Example 4 *Dividing Rational Expressions*

Divide: $\dfrac{3x}{x + 2} \div \dfrac{x - 6}{x + 2}$

Solution

$$\dfrac{3x}{x + 2} \div \dfrac{x - 6}{x + 2} = \dfrac{3x}{x + 2} \cdot \dfrac{x + 2}{x - 6} \qquad \textit{Multiply by reciprocal.}$$

$$= \dfrac{(3x)(x + 2)}{(x + 2)(x - 6)} \qquad \textit{Multiply numerators and denominators.}$$

$$= \dfrac{(3x)(\cancel{x + 2})}{(\cancel{x + 2})(x - 6)} \qquad \textit{Divide out common factors.}$$

$$= \dfrac{3x}{x - 6} \qquad \textit{Simplified form} \qquad \blacksquare$$

Example 5 *Dividing a Rational Expression by a Polynomial*

Divide: $\dfrac{x^2 - 4}{2x^2} \div (x - 2)$

Solution

$$\dfrac{x^2 - 4}{2x^2} \div (x - 2) = \dfrac{x^2 - 4}{2x^2} \cdot \dfrac{1}{x - 2} \qquad \textit{Multiply by reciprocal.}$$

$$= \dfrac{(x + 2)(x - 2)}{2x^2(x - 2)} \qquad \textit{Multiply numerators and denominators.}$$

$$= \dfrac{(x + 2)(\cancel{x - 2})}{2x^2(\cancel{x - 2})} \qquad \textit{Divide out common factors.}$$

$$= \dfrac{x + 2}{2x^2} \qquad \textit{Simplified form} \qquad \blacksquare$$

Using Rational Expressions in Real Life

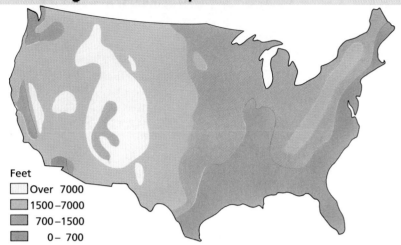

Feet

☐ Over 7000
▨ 1500–7000
▨ 700–1500
▨ 0– 700

*Elevations in the United States
(excluding Alaska and Hawaii)*

Real Life
Cooking

Cooking Time

Cooking Time (in minutes)

T

100
90
80
70
60
50
40
30
20
10

2 4 6 8 10 12 14 *x*

Elevation (in 1000s of feet)

Example 6 *How Long Does It Take to Boil a Potato?*

The boiling point of water is 212°F at sea level. At higher elevations, however, water boils at lower temperatures. A model for the boiling point, *B*, of water at *x* thousand feet is $B = 212 - 1.85x$. The time, *T* (in minutes), required to boil a medium-sized potato is given by the model

$$T = \frac{40(237 - B)}{B - 162}.$$

Write a model for the time, *T*, in terms of the elevation, *x*. Use the model to find the time it takes to boil a potato in Bozeman, Montana (4795 feet), Richwood, West Virginia (2194 feet), and Gary, Indiana (608 feet).

Solution Substitute $212 - 1.85x$ for *B* in the model.

$$T = \frac{40(237 - (212 - 1.85x))}{(212 - 1.85x) - 162} = \frac{40(25 + 1.85x)}{50 - 1.85x}$$

In Bozeman, $T = \dfrac{40(25 + 1.85(4.795))}{50 - 1.85(4.795)} \approx 33$ minutes.

In Richwood, $T = \dfrac{40(25 + 1.85(2.194))}{50 - 1.85(2.194)} \approx 25$ minutes.

In Gary, $T = \dfrac{40(25 + 1.85(0.608))}{50 - 1.85(0.608)} \approx 21$ minutes. ∎

Communicating about **A L G E B R A**

▷ **SHARING IDEAS about the Lesson**

Explain the Process Write each expression in simplified form. Explain your steps.

A. $\dfrac{x^2 - 1}{x} \cdot \dfrac{2x}{x - 1}$ **B.** $\dfrac{x^2 - 4x + 3}{2x} \div \dfrac{x - 1}{2}$ **C.** $\dfrac{2}{x^2 - 4} \cdot (x + 2)$

EXERCISES

▶ **CRITICAL THINKING about the Lesson**

1. Explain the steps used to multiply two rational expressions.

2. Explain the steps used to divide two rational expressions.

3. Multiply $\frac{3x}{2x^2}$ and $-\frac{4x^2}{12x^3}$. Explain your steps.

4. Divide $\frac{4x^2 - 25}{4x}$ by $(2x - 5)$. Explain your steps.

5. What went wrong?

$$\frac{x^2 - 4}{5x} \div \frac{x + 2}{x - 2} = \frac{5x}{x^2 - 4} \cdot \frac{x + 2}{x - 2}$$

$$= \frac{5x}{(x + 2)(x - 2)} \cdot \frac{x + 2}{x - 2} = \frac{5x}{(x - 2)^2}$$

6. What went wrong?

$$(2x + 2) \cdot \frac{x^2 - 2x - 3}{x + 4} = \frac{2x + 2}{1} \cdot \frac{x + 4}{x^2 - 2x - 3}$$

$$= \frac{2(x + 1)}{1} \cdot \frac{x + 4}{(x - 3)(x + 1)} = \frac{2(x + 4)}{x - 3}$$

Independent Practice

In Exercises 7–30, simplify the expression.

7. $\frac{6x}{5} \cdot \frac{1}{x}$

8. $\frac{8x^2}{3} \cdot \frac{9}{16x}$

9. $\frac{3x^2}{2x} \cdot \frac{12x^2}{6x}$

10. $\frac{12x^2}{6x} \cdot \frac{12x}{8x^2}$

11. $\frac{25y^2}{8y} \cdot \frac{8y}{5y}$

12. $\frac{11x^4}{3x} \cdot \frac{3x}{x^2}$

13. $\frac{5 - 4x}{4} \cdot \frac{48}{10 - 8x}$

14. $\frac{4x}{x^2 - 9} \cdot \frac{x - 3}{8x^2 + 12x}$

15. $\frac{3x}{x^2 - 2x - 24} \cdot \frac{x - 6}{6x^2 + 9x}$

16. $\frac{5}{x - 1} \cdot \frac{x - 1}{25(x - 2)}$

17. $\frac{x^2 - 3x}{x^2 - 5x + 6} \cdot \frac{(x - 2)^2}{2x}$

18. $\frac{x + 1}{x^3(3 - x)} \cdot \frac{x(x - 3)}{5}$

19. $\frac{x}{2x^2 - x - 3} \cdot (2x - 3)$

20. $\frac{8}{2 + 3x} \cdot (8 + 12x)$

21. $3(a + 2) \cdot \frac{1}{3a + 6}$

22. $(4x^2 + x - 3) \cdot \frac{1}{(4x + 3)(x - 1)}$

23. $\frac{x}{x + 4} \div \frac{x + 3}{x + 4}$

24. $\frac{7x^2}{10} \div \frac{14x^3}{15}$

25. $\frac{2(x + 2)}{5(x - 3)} \div \frac{4(x - 2)}{5x - 15}$

26. $\frac{3x + 12}{4x} \div \frac{x + 4}{2x}$

27. $\frac{x^2 - 6x + 8}{x^2 - 2x} \div (3x - 12)$

28. $\frac{5x^2 - 30x + 45}{x + 2} \div (5x - 15)$

29. $\left(\frac{x^2}{5} \cdot \frac{x + 2}{2} \right) \div \frac{x}{30}$

30. $\left(\frac{2u^2}{3} \cdot \frac{5}{u} \right) \div \frac{6u^2}{25}$

Service Industry   In Exercises 31–34, use the following information.

The total sales, S, of services in the United States from 1970 to 1990 can be modeled by

$$S = \frac{390(9 + t)}{30 - t} \qquad \text{(billion \$)}$$

where $t = 0$ represents 1970. The total sales of hotels, H, and auto repair services, A, during the same years can be modeled by

$$H = \frac{21(9 + t)}{32 - t} \qquad \text{(billion \$)}$$

$$A = \frac{27(8 + t)}{34 - t}. \qquad \text{(billion \$)}$$

(Source: U.S. Bureau of Economic Analysis)

Paramedical and other health services account for about 28% of the service industries in the U.S.

31. Find the total sales given by each model in 1990.

32. Find a model for the ratio of hotel sales to the total service industry sales. Was this ratio increasing or decreasing from 1970 to 1990? Explain.

33. Find a model for the ratio of auto service sales to the total service industry sales. Was this ratio increasing or decreasing from 1970 to 1990? Explain.

34. Match the models for S, H, and A with their graphs.

a.

b.

c.

Printing and Copying Franchises   In Exercises 35 and 36, use the following information.

In the United States from 1970 to 1990, the number, P, of franchised printing and copying businesses can be modeled by

$$P = \frac{10{,}000 + 5500t}{35 - t}$$

where $t = 0$ represents 1970.

35. The total sales, S (in millions of dollars), of franchised printing and copying businesses from 1970 to 1990 can be modeled by

$$S = \frac{2200 + 400t}{24 - t}.$$

Find a model for the average sales per business.

36. Use the model found in Exercise 35 to complete the table.

Year, t	0	5	10	15	20
Average Sales (in millions of dollars)	?	?	?	?	?

Integrated Review

In Exercises 37–44, simplify the expression.

37. $\dfrac{9}{15} \cdot \dfrac{3}{5}$

38. $\dfrac{4}{7} \cdot \dfrac{8}{5}$

39. $\dfrac{4x^2}{x}$

40. $\dfrac{6x}{3x^3}$

41. $\dfrac{x^2 - 1}{(x + 1)(x + 3)}$

42. $\dfrac{x^2 - 4}{(x - 2)(x + 6)}$

43. $\dfrac{8x}{8x + 24}$

44. $\dfrac{10x}{5x^2 + 20x + 20}$

In Exercises 45–52, solve the equation.

45. $\dfrac{9}{6} = \dfrac{4}{x}$

46. $\dfrac{7}{3} = \dfrac{18}{y}$

47. $\dfrac{16}{2y} = \dfrac{3}{4}$

48. $\dfrac{8}{3x} = \dfrac{12}{18}$

49. $\dfrac{3}{x + 2} = \dfrac{x}{5}$

50. $\dfrac{x - 1}{x + 1} = \dfrac{x - 2}{2}$

51. $\dfrac{x - 4}{9} = \dfrac{4}{x + 1}$

52. $\dfrac{3}{x} = \dfrac{x + 11}{4}$

In Exercises 53–56, find the domain of the expression.

53. $\dfrac{x - 3}{8x^2 + 12x}$

54. $\dfrac{4x}{x^2 - 9}$

55. $\dfrac{x^2 - 3x}{x^2 - 5x + 6}$

56. $\dfrac{x}{2x^2 - 3x - 20}$

Geometry   **In Exercises 57 and 58, find the ratio of the area of the blue region to the total area of the figure.**

57.

58.

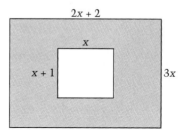

Exploration and Extension

In Exercises 59–62, decide whether the given value of the variable is in the domain of the rational expression.

59. $\dfrac{x - 2}{2x^2 - 2}$, $x = -1$

60. $\dfrac{3 - y}{y^2 - 5y + 6}$, $y = 2, 3$

61. $\dfrac{y^2 - 4}{y^3 + 3y^2 - 10y}$, $y = 0, 2, -5$

62. $\dfrac{x^2 - 7x}{x^3 - 8x^2 + 7x}$, $x = 0, -3, -2$

63. Find *two* different pairs of rational expressions (with first-degree numerators and first-degree denominators) whose product is

$$\dfrac{6x^2 - 39x + 18}{x^2 + 5x - 36}.$$

11.7

Dividing Polynomials

What you should learn:

Goal 1 How to divide a polynomial by a monomial or a binomial

Goal 2 How to use polynomial division in real-life models

Why you should learn it:

You can use polynomial division to provide alternate forms for rational expressions to help you better understand the expressions.

Goal 1 Dividing a Polynomial

To divide a polynomial by a *monomial*, divide each term by the monomial, add the results, and simplify each fraction. For instance, you can divide $2x^2 - 3$ by $6x$ as follows.

$$(2x^2 - 3) \div (6x)$$

$$= \frac{2x^2 - 3}{6x} \qquad \textit{Write in fraction form.}$$

$$= \frac{2x^2}{6x} - \frac{3}{6x} \qquad \textit{Divide each term of } 2x^2 - 3 \textit{ by } 6x.$$

$$= \frac{2x(x)}{3(2x)} - \frac{3}{3(2x)} \qquad \textit{Factor out common factors.}$$

$$= \frac{x}{3} - \frac{1}{2x} \qquad \textit{Simplified form}$$

Example 1 *Dividing a Polynomial by a Monomial*

Divide $12x^2 - 20x + 8$ by $4x$.

Solution

$$(12x^2 - 20x + 8) \div (4x) = \frac{12x^2 - 20x + 8}{4x}$$

$$= \frac{12x^2}{4x} - \frac{20x}{4x} + \frac{8}{4x}$$

$$= \frac{(3x)(4x)}{4x} - \frac{5(4x)}{4x} + \frac{2(4)}{4x}$$

$$= 3x - 5 + \frac{2}{x}$$

To divide a polynomial by a *binomial*, you can use the canceling technique of Lesson 11.6 when the numerator and denominator have common factors.

$$\frac{x^2 - 2x - 3}{x - 3} = \frac{(x + 1)(x - 3)}{x - 3}$$

$$= x + 1$$

For polynomials that do not have common factors, you use **polynomial long division.** To begin, you may need to review the process for long division in arithmetic.

Example 2 — *The Long Division Algorithm*

Use the long division algorithm to divide 6584 by 28.

Solution

Think $\frac{65}{28} \approx 2$

Think $\frac{98}{28} \approx 3$

Think $\frac{144}{28} \approx 5$

$$
\begin{array}{r}
2\,3\,5 \\
28\overline{)6\,5\,8\,4} \\
\underline{5\,6} \\
9\,8 \\
\underline{8\,4} \\
1\,4\,4 \\
\underline{1\,4\,0} \\
4
\end{array}
$$

Multiply 2 · 28.

Subtract and bring down 8.

Multiply 3 · 28.

Subtract and bring down 4.

Multiply 5 · 28.

Subtract to get the remainder.

In this problem, 6584 is the **dividend**, 28 is the **divisor**, 235 is the **quotient**, and 4 is the **remainder**.

$$
\underbrace{\frac{\overbrace{6584}^{\text{Dividend}}}{28}}_{\text{Divisor}} = \overbrace{235}^{\text{Quotient}} + \underbrace{\frac{\overbrace{4}^{\text{Remainder}}}{28}}_{\text{Divisor}} = 235 + \frac{1}{7}
$$

Polynomial long division uses a process that is similar to the algorithm. Note: the divisor and dividend are in standard form.

Example 3 — *Polynomial Long Division*

Divide $(x^2 + 2x + 4)$ by $(x - 1)$.

Solution

Think $\frac{x^2}{x} \approx x$

Think $\frac{3x}{x} \approx 3$

$$
\begin{array}{r}
x + 3 \\
x - 1\overline{)x^2 + 2x + 4} \\
\underline{x^2 - x} \\
3x + 4 \\
\underline{3x - 3} \\
7
\end{array}
$$

Multiply $x(x - 1)$.

Subtract and bring down 4.

Multiply $3(x - 1)$.

Subtract to get the remainder.

The result is written as follows.

$$
\underbrace{\frac{\overbrace{x^2 + 2x + 4}^{\text{Dividend}}}{x - 1}}_{\text{Divisor}} = \overbrace{x + 3}^{\text{Quotient}} + \underbrace{\frac{\overbrace{7}^{\text{Remainder}}}{x - 1}}_{\text{Divisor}}
$$

Using Polynomial Division in Real Life

The cost of removing pollutants from smokestack emission does not vary directly with the percent removed. That is, if it costs C dollars to remove 25% of the pollutants, it would cost more than 2C dollars to remove 50% of the pollutants. As the percent of removed pollutants approaches 100%, the cost tends to become prohibitive.

Real Life
Environment

Example 4 *Cost-Benefit Model for Pollutants*

A utility company burns coal to generate electricity. The cost, C (in dollars), of removing p percent of the smokestack pollutants can be modeled by

$$C = \frac{120,000p}{1 - p}.$$

As a member of the state legislature, you are considering a law that will require companies to remove 90% of their smokestack pollutants. The current law requires 85% removal. How much additional expense would the new law require of the utility company?

Solution   Under the current law, the removal cost is

$$C = \frac{120,000(0.85)}{1 - 0.85} \approx \$680,000. \quad \textit{85\% removal}$$

If the new law is passed, increasing the percentage removal to 90%, the cost to the utility company will be

$$C = \frac{120,000(0.9)}{1 - 0.9} \approx \$1,080,000. \quad \textit{90\% removal}$$

The new law would require the company to spend \$400,000 more to remove an additional 5% of the pollutants. ∎

Cost of Removing Pollutants

Cost (in millions of dollars)

2.4
2.0
1.6
1.2
0.8
0.4

90%
85%
}$400,000

0 20 40 60 80 *p*
Percent of Pollutants Removed

Communicating about ALGEBRA

▷ **SHARING IDEAS about the Lesson**

Examine the Model   Use long division to rewrite the model given in Example 4 as

$$C = \frac{120,000}{1 - p} - 120,000.$$

What happens to C when p gets closer and closer to 1?

EXERCISES

Guided Practice

▶ **CRITICAL THINKING about the Lesson**

1. Match each number with its name: $\frac{5469}{42} = 130 + \frac{9}{42}$.

   a. Dividend **b.** Divisor **c.** Quotient **d.** Remainder

2. Match each expression with its name: $\frac{x^2 + 2}{x - 3} = x + 3 + \frac{11}{x - 3}$.

   a. Dividend **b.** Divisor **c.** Quotient **d.** Remainder

In Exercises 3–6, use long division.

3. Divide 365 by 52.

4. Divide 25,001 by 15.

5. Divide $x^2 + 3x - 1$ by $x + 2$.

6. Divide $3x^3 - 4x - 1$ by $x + 1$.

Independent Practice

In Exercises 7 and 8, simplify the expression.

7. $\dfrac{10x^2}{2x(5x + 2)}$

8. $\dfrac{33x^3(x + 1)}{27x^4(x + 2)}$

In Exercises 9–16, divide.

9. $(6z + 10) \div 2$

10. $(9x + 10) \div 3$

11. $(10z^2 + 4z - 12) \div 4$

12. $(4u^2 + 8u - 24) \div 16$

13. $(7x^3 - 2x^2) \div 14x$

14. $(6a^2 + 7a) \div a$

15. $(m^4 + 2m^2 - 7) \div m$

16. $(x^2 - 8) \div (-x)$

In Exercises 17 and 18, determine the quotient, remainder, and divisor. (The long division is shown.)

17. $\dfrac{x^3 - 27}{x - 3} = \boxed{\text{Quotient}} + \dfrac{\boxed{\text{Remainder}}}{\boxed{\text{Divisor}}}$

$$
\require{enclose}
\begin{array}{r}
x^2 + 3x + 9 \\
x - 3 \enclose{longdiv}{x^3 + 0x^2 + 0x - 27} \\
\underline{x^3 - 3x^2} \\
3x^2 + 0x \\
\underline{3x^2 - 9x} \\
9x - 27 \\
\underline{9x - 27} \\
0
\end{array}
$$

18. $\dfrac{4x^3 + 5x}{2x - 1} = \boxed{\text{Quotient}} + \dfrac{\boxed{\text{Remainder}}}{\boxed{\text{Divisor}}}$

$$
\require{enclose}
\begin{array}{r}
2x^2 + x + 3 \\
2x - 1 \enclose{longdiv}{4x^3 + 0x^2 + 5x + 0} \\
\underline{4x^3 - 2x^2} \\
2x^2 + 5x \\
\underline{2x^2 - x} \\
6x + 0 \\
\underline{6x - 3} \\
3
\end{array}
$$

In Exercises 19–26, divide. Write the result as Quotient $+ \dfrac{\text{Remainder}}{\text{Divisor}}$

19. $(x^2 - 8x + 15) \div (x - 3)$

20. $(t^2 - 18t + 72) \div (t - 6)$

21. $(x^2 + 15x + 50) \div (x + 5)$

22. $(y^2 - 6y - 16) \div (y + 2)$

23. $(x^2 - 4) \div (x - 3)$

24. $(y^2 + 5y) \div (y + 1)$

25. $(4x^2 + 12x - 10) \div (x - 2)$

26. $(5y^2 + 2) \div (y - 1)$

Canoes and Other Boats   **In Exercises 27 and 28, use the following information.**

The number of canoes, C, in the United States from 1980 to 1990 can be modeled by

$$C = 100{,}000(t + 13)$$

where $t = 0$ represents 1980. The total number of recreational boats, B, can be modeled by

$$B = 400{,}000(t + 30).$$

27. Use long division to find a model for the ratio of canoes to boats.

28. Use the model obtained in Exercise 27 to complete the table. Was canoeing becoming more or less popular compared to the total use of recreational boats? Explain.

Year, t	0	2	4	6	8	10
Ratio of *C* to *B*	?	?	?	?	?	?

Traveling and Eating Out   **In Exercises 29 and 30, use the following information.**

From 1975 to 1990, the travel and restaurant industry revenue, T, can be modeled by

$$T = 15(t + 6), \quad \text{(billions of dollars)}$$

where $t = 0$ represents 1975. The restaurant revenue, R, can be modeled by

$$R = 7.5(t + 7), \quad \text{(billions of dollars).}$$

29. Use long division to find a model for the ratio of restaurant revenue to the total travel and restaurant industry revenue.

30. Use the model from Exercise 29 to complete the table. How was the restaurant industry doing compared to the total travel and restaurant industry? Explain your answer.

Year, t	0	3	6	9	12	15
Ratio of *R* to *T*	?	?	?	?	?	?

In Exercises 31–36, simplify by factoring and dividing out common factors.

31. $\dfrac{2z^2 - 9z + 4}{z - 4}$

32. $\dfrac{2x^2 + 4x - 30}{2x - 6}$

33. $\dfrac{6y + 2y^2}{2y}$

34. $\dfrac{12p^2 - 15p}{3p^2}$

35. $\dfrac{2m^2 - 8m - 10}{m + 1}$

36. $\dfrac{2t^2 + 10t + 12}{4t + 12}$

In Exercises 37–42, divide. Use long division *or* factoring and dividing out common factors. Explain why you chose the method you did.

37. $\dfrac{x^2 + 3x + 2}{x - 2}$

38. $\dfrac{a^2 + 4a - 77}{a + 7}$

39. $\dfrac{6y^2 + y - 2}{3y + 2}$

40. $\dfrac{3z^2 - 2z - 2}{3z - 2}$

41. $\dfrac{2b^2 + 21b + 10}{b - 10}$

42. $\dfrac{2c^2 + 19c - 10}{2c - 1}$

43. *Estimation—Powers of Ten*   Which is the best estimate of the ratio of Americans who are thirty-three years old or younger to *all* Americans?

a. 0.005   **b.** 0.05   **c.** 0.5   **d.** 5.0

44. *Estimation—Powers of Ten*   Which is the best estimate of the ratio of Americans who are thirty-three years old or younger to those who are older than thirty-three?

a. 0.001   **b.** 0.01   **c.** 0.1   **d.** 1.0

In Exercises 45 and 46, use $\dfrac{x^2 + 6}{x + 2} = x - 2 + \dfrac{10}{x + 2}$.

45. Complete the table. What happens to the values of

$$\dfrac{x^2 + 6}{x + 2},\ (x - 2),\ \text{and}\ \dfrac{10}{x + 2}$$

as x gets larger and larger?

x	0	20	40	60	80	100
$\dfrac{x^2 + 6}{x + 2}$	?	?	?	?	?	?
$x - 2$	?	?	?	?	?	?
$\dfrac{10}{x + 2}$	?	?	?	?	?	?

46. Which of the graphs shown is the graph of

$$y = x - 2?$$

Which is the graph of

$$y = \dfrac{x^2 + 6}{x + 2}?$$

47. *Age Problem*   You are 14 and your brother is 4. In t years, your ages will be $t + 14$ and $t + 4$. Use long division to rewrite the ratio of your brother's age to your age. Is this ratio getting smaller or larger as the years go by?

Graphs of rational expressions often have **asymptotes**—*lines that resemble the graph in certain regions of the coordinate plane. For instance, consider the graphs of*

$$y_1 = \frac{2x}{x + 5} \quad \text{and} \quad y_2 = 2.$$

Using long division, you can write

$$\underbrace{\frac{2x}{x + 5}}_{y_1} = \underbrace{2}_{y_2} - \underbrace{\frac{10}{x + 5}}_{\substack{\text{Remainder} \\ \text{fraction}}}.$$

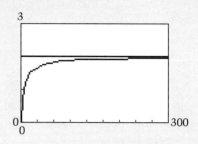

Graphs of y_1 and y_2

The value of the "remainder fraction" becomes very small as the values of x become large. This is why we say that the graph of y_1 resembles the line $y_2 = 2$ when x is large.

A graphing calculator can show how close together two graphs can be.

TI-81

RANGE (Set range.)
  Xmin = 0
  Xmax = 300
  Xscl = 30
  Ymin = 0
  Ymax = 3
  Yscl = 1
Y=   2 × X,T ÷
     (X,T + 5) ENTER
Y=   2
  :Y₁ = 2*X/(X + 5)
  :Y₂ = 2
  :Y₃ =
  :Y₄ =
GRAPH
CLEAR (Clear screen.)

Casio fx-7700G

Range (Set range.)
  Xmin = 0
  max = 300
  scl = 30
  Ymin = 0
  max = 3
  scl = 1
EXE Range SHIFT F5 (Cls) EXE
MODE SHIFT +
Graph   2 × X,θ,T ÷
     (X,θ,T + 5) EXE
  Graph Y = 2 × X ÷ (X + 5) EXE
Graph   2
  Graph Y = 2 EXE
SHIFT F5 (Cls) EXE

Exercises

In Exercises 1 and 2, sketch the graphs of y_1 and y_2. Experiment to find a range setting in which the two graphs resemble each other.

1. $\underbrace{\frac{3x + 10}{x + 4}}_{y_1} = \underbrace{3}_{y_2} - \underbrace{\frac{2}{x + 4}}_{\substack{\text{Remainder} \\ \text{fraction}}}$

2. $\underbrace{\frac{x^2}{x + 1}}_{y_1} = \underbrace{x - 1}_{y_2} + \underbrace{\frac{1}{x + 1}}_{\substack{\text{Remainder} \\ \text{fraction}}}$

11.8

Solving Rational Equations

What you should learn:

Goal 1 How to solve rational equations

Goal 2 How to use rational equations in real-life settings

Why you should learn it:

You can model many real-life problems with rational equations, such as comparing changing quantities.

Goal 1 Solving Rational Equations

In this lesson, you will learn how to solve equations that involve rational expressions. There are two basic techniques: multiplying by the least common denominator (LCD) and cross multiplying.

Multiplying by the least common denominator of each fraction in the equation will work for any rational equation. After multiplying by the least common denominator, simplify each term. The resulting equation will be a polynomial equation, which you can solve using standard techniques.

Example 1 *Multiplying by the LCD*

Solve $\frac{2}{x} + \frac{1}{3} = \frac{4}{x}$.

Solution

$$\frac{2}{x} + \frac{1}{3} = \frac{4}{x} \qquad \textit{LCD is 3x.}$$

$$3x \cdot \frac{2}{x} + 3x \cdot \frac{1}{3} = 3x \cdot \frac{4}{x} \qquad \textit{Multiply each term on both sides by 3x.}$$

$$6 + x = 12 \qquad \textit{Simplify.}$$

$$x = 6 \qquad \textit{Subtract 6 from both sides.}$$

The solution is 6. Check this in the original equation. ∎

Example 2 *Multiplying by the LCD*

Solve $\frac{6}{x} + \frac{x}{2} = 4$.

Solution

$$\frac{6}{x} + \frac{x}{2} = 4 \qquad \textit{LCD is 2x.}$$

$$2x \cdot \frac{6}{x} + 2x \cdot \frac{x}{2} = 2x \cdot 4 \qquad \textit{Multiply each term on both sides by 2x.}$$

$$12 + x^2 = 8x \qquad \textit{Simplify.}$$

$$x^2 - 8x + 12 = 0 \qquad \textit{Standard form}$$

$$(x - 2)(x - 6) = 0 \qquad \textit{Factor.}$$

$$x = 2 \text{ or } 6 \qquad \textit{Zero Product property}$$

The solutions are 2 and 6. Check them in the original equation. ∎

Cross multiplying (see Lesson 11.1) can be used only for equations in which each side is a single fraction.

Example 3   *Cross Multiplying*

Solve $\dfrac{5}{y+2} = \dfrac{y}{3}$.

Solution

$$\dfrac{5}{y+2} = \dfrac{y}{3} \qquad \textit{Rewrite original equation.}$$
$$5(3) = y(y+2) \qquad \textit{Cross multiply.}$$
$$15 = y^2 + 2y \qquad \textit{Simplify.}$$
$$0 = y^2 + 2y - 15 \qquad \textit{Standard form}$$
$$0 = (y+5)(y-3) \qquad \textit{Factor.}$$
$$y = -5 \text{ or } 3 \qquad \textit{Zero Product Property}$$

The solutions are -5 and 3. Check these in the original equation. ∎

Goal 2   # Using Rational Equations in Real Life

Real Life
Retail Business

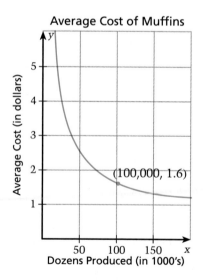

Average Cost of Muffins

(100,000, 1.6)

Dozens Produced (in 1000's)

As your initial investment of $80,000 is distributed over more and more muffins, the average cost per dozen decreases.

Example 4   *Finding the Average Cost Per Unit*

You have invested $80,000 to start a muffin shop in a shopping mall. You can produce a dozen muffins for $0.80. How many dozens must you produce before your average cost per dozen (*including* your initial investment of $80,000) drops to $1.60?

Solution

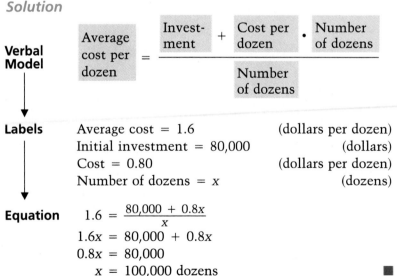

Labels   Average cost = 1.6   (dollars per dozen)
Initial investment = 80,000   (dollars)
Cost = 0.80   (dollars per dozen)
Number of dozens = x (dozens)

Equation $1.6 = \dfrac{80,000 + 0.8x}{x}$

$$1.6x = 80,000 + 0.8x$$
$$0.8x = 80,000$$
$$x = 100,000 \text{ dozens}$$ ∎

Example 5   *Finding a Batting Average*

You have been officially at bat 140 times and have 35 hits. Your batting average is $\frac{35}{140}$ = .250. How many consecutive hits must you get to increase your batting average to .300?

Solution   If you hit safely in each of the next x times at bat, then x will be the number of future hits *and* the future times at bat.

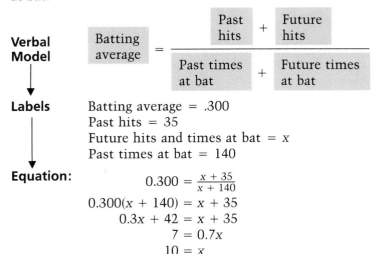

Verbal Model

$$\text{Batting average} = \frac{\text{Past hits} + \text{Future hits}}{\text{Past times at bat} + \text{Future times at bat}}$$

Labels   Batting average = .300
Past hits = 35
Future hits and times at bat = x
Past times at bat = 140

Equation:
$$0.300 = \frac{x + 35}{x + 140}$$
$$0.300(x + 140) = x + 35$$
$$0.3x + 42 = x + 35$$
$$7 = 0.7x$$
$$10 = x$$

You need to get a hit in each of your next 10 times at bat. Check this result by finding the batting average for 45 hits in 150 at bats. ∎

The batting average of a baseball player is the ratio of the number of hits to the number of official times at bat. In 1990, Daryl Strawberry (Mets) had a batting average of .225, and Barry Bonds (Pittsburgh Pirates) had a batting average of .248.

Communicating **about ALGEBRA**

▷ **SHARING IDEAS about the Lesson**

In solving a rational equation, it is possible to obtain a "false solution." This is one reason it is important to check each solution in the original equation. Find the false solutions of the following.

A. $\dfrac{4}{x^2 - 2x} = \dfrac{4}{3x - 6}$ **B.** $\dfrac{4}{x(x + 1)} = \dfrac{3}{x}$

EXERCISES

Guided Practice

▶ **CRITICAL THINKING about the Lesson**

1. What is the least common denominator for $\frac{1}{x}$, $\frac{x}{3}$, and $\frac{2}{3x}$?

In Exercises 2 and 3, solve $\frac{3}{x} = \frac{x}{12}$. Which method do you prefer? Why?

2. Solve the equation by cross multiplying.

3. Solve the equation by multiplying both sides by the least common denominator.

In Exercises 4–6, decide which solution method is better and use that method to solve the equation.

4. $\frac{1}{x} + \frac{x}{3} = \frac{4}{3}$

5. $\frac{16}{x} = \frac{4}{2}$

6. $\frac{x}{9} - \frac{1}{3} = \frac{6}{x}$

Independent Practice

In Exercises 7–12, find the greatest common factor.

7. $3, 12x, 6$

8. $x, -4x, 3x^2$

9. $2x^2, 4x, -2$

10. $3x^2, -6$

11. $4x, 6x^2, 8x^2$

12. $x^3, -5x, 3x^2$

In Exercises 13–18, solve the equation by cross multiplying.

13. $\frac{x}{3} = \frac{5}{2}$

14. $\frac{x}{10} = \frac{12}{5}$

15. $\frac{3}{x} = \frac{9}{2(x+2)}$

16. $\frac{5}{x+4} = \frac{5}{3(x+1)}$

17. $\frac{3}{x+5} = \frac{2}{x+1}$

18. $\frac{7}{x+1} = \frac{5}{x-3}$

In Exercises 19–30, solve the equation by multiplying both sides by the least common denominator.

19. $\frac{1}{2} + \frac{2}{x} = \frac{1}{x}$

20. $\frac{1}{3} - \frac{2}{3x} = \frac{1}{x}$

21. $\frac{x}{3} - \frac{1}{x} = \frac{2}{3}$

22. $\frac{x}{4} - \frac{5}{x} = \frac{1}{4}$

23. $\frac{25}{t} = 10 - t$

24. $x + 4 = -\frac{4}{x}$

25. $\frac{x}{x+4} = \frac{4}{x+4} + 2$

26. $\frac{7}{3x-12} - \frac{1}{x-4} = \frac{2}{3}$

27. $\frac{1}{x-3} + \frac{1}{x+3} = \frac{10}{x^2-9}$

28. $\frac{1}{x-2} + 3 = -\frac{16}{x^2+x-6}$

29. $5 + \frac{6}{x-3} = \frac{x+3}{x^2-9}$

30. $\frac{2}{(x-2)^2} = 1 - \frac{1}{x-2}$

In Exercises 31–42, solve the equation (by the more convenient method).

31. $\frac{3x}{x+1} = \frac{2}{x-1}$

32. $\frac{20-x}{x} = x$

33. $\frac{4}{x} - \frac{x}{6} = \frac{5}{3}$

34. $x + \frac{1}{x} = \frac{5}{2}$

35. $\frac{x+30}{x} = x$

36. $\frac{3}{x+5} = \frac{2}{x+1}$

610 Chapter **11** ▪ *Using Proportions and Rational Equations*

37. $\dfrac{18}{u} = \dfrac{u}{2}$

38. $\dfrac{4}{x+2} - \dfrac{1}{x} = \dfrac{1}{x}$

39. $\dfrac{15}{x} - 4 = \dfrac{6}{x} + 3$

40. $\dfrac{5}{u+8} = \dfrac{1}{4}$

41. $\dfrac{2}{x+3} + \dfrac{1}{x} = \dfrac{4}{3x}$

42. $\dfrac{10}{x+3} - \dfrac{3}{5} = \dfrac{10x+1}{3x+9}$

43. *Batting Average*   After 50 times at bat, a baseball player has a batting average of .160. How many consecutive hits must the player get to raise the batting average to .250?

44. *Bowling Average*   After 12 games, your bowling average is 120. What must your average score be for the next 6 games to increase your overall average to 130?

45. *The Karate Kid, Part 0*   You are interested in attending a karate class at the Y. Membership at the Y is $36 per year. The charge per lesson is $3.50 for members. Write an expression that represents your average cost per lesson for *n* lessons. After completing the course, you figured that your average cost per lesson (including the membership fee) was $6.50. How many karate lessons did you take?

46. *Specialty Dog Food*   You have started a specialty dog food company. Your initial investment was $120,000. Each pound of dog food costs $0.50 to produce. Write an expression that represents your average cost per pound after producing *x* pounds of dog food. You are selling the dog food for $1 per pound. How many pounds must you produce to make your average cost per pound equal to your per-pound selling price? (This is called the *break-even point* for your business.)

By 1990, specialty dog foods and cat foods, produced mainly by small companies, accounted for $1.5 billion of the total $7.5 billion United States pet food market. (Source: Forbes Magazine)

47. *Book Report*   You had 21 days to read a 420-page book for a book report. After finishing half of the book, you realize that you must read twice as many pages a day to finish on time. What was your average daily rate? What must your rate be to finish on time? Use the following model to answer the questions.

$$\dfrac{210 \text{ pages}}{\text{Previous rate}} + \dfrac{210 \text{ pages}}{2 \cdot \text{Previous rate}} = 21 \text{ days}$$

48. *Delivering Newspapers*   You have 40 minutes to deliver 90 newspapers in your neighborhood. After you have delivered half of the papers, you realize that you must begin to deliver them three times as quickly to finish on time. How many papers per minute were you delivering? How many papers per minute must you now deliver to finish on time? Use the following model to answer the questions.

$$\dfrac{45 \text{ newspapers}}{\text{Previous rate}} + \dfrac{45 \text{ newspapers}}{3 \cdot \text{Previous rate}} = 40 \text{ minutes}$$

49. *In Search of Pandora*   Which of the following ratios can be used to find the depth, d, of the *Pandora* wreckage? (See page 561.) Explain your answer and find *Pandora's* depth.

  a. The ratio of the pressure, P, to the depth, d, was 62.4.

  b. The ratio of the *Titanic's* depth, D, to *Pandora's* depth, d, was 118.2.

The **Pandora** *sank on Australia's Great Barrier Reef in 1791. The ship was carrying some of the* **Bounty** *crew members who had been accused of mutiny. The wreckage was found in 1977.*

50. *Finding the Bounty*   The wreck of the *Bounty* was discovered n years before the wreck of the *Pandora*. Find the year in which the *Bounty* was discovered by solving

$$\frac{5}{n + 25} = \frac{3}{n - 7}.$$

Integrated Review

In Exercises 51–53, decide whether the value of x is a solution of the equation.

51. $\frac{x}{5} - \frac{3}{x} = \frac{7}{10}$, $x = 6$ **52.** $\frac{3x}{5} + \frac{x^2}{2} = \frac{4}{5}$, $x = -2$ **53.** $\frac{5}{2x} - \frac{4}{x} = 3$, $x = 0$

In Exercises 54–56, solve the equation.

54. $(2x + 3)(x - 9) = 0$ **55.** $x^2 + x - 56 = 0$ **56.** $t^2 - 5t = 0$

In Exercises 57–62, solve the proportion.

57. $\frac{3}{4} = \frac{2}{x}$ **58.** $\frac{5}{x} = \frac{1}{3}$ **59.** $\frac{1}{x + 1} = \frac{1}{6}$

60. $\frac{1}{2x - 3} = \frac{1}{9}$ **61.** $\frac{1}{3 - y} = -\frac{1}{10}$ **62.** $\frac{5}{u + 8} = \frac{1}{4}$

Exploration and Extension

In Exercises 63–65, solve the equation by either method discussed in this lesson. Do you obtain "false solutions"? Explain.

63. $\frac{1}{x^2 - x} = \frac{1}{2x - 2}$ **64.** $\frac{1}{x(x + 4)} = \frac{2}{x + 4}$ **65.** $\frac{5}{x^2} = \frac{-1}{x}$

11 Chapter Summary

What did you learn?

Skills

1. Solve a proportion. **(11.1)**
2. Solve a percent problem. **(11.2)**
3. Solve a problem involving
   - direct variation. **(11.3)**
   - inverse variation. **(11.3)**
   - probability. **(11.4)**
4. Simplify a rational expression. **(11.5)**
5. Multiply and divide rational expressions. **(11.6)**
6. Divide one polynomial by another polynomial. **(11.7)**
7. Solve a rational equation. **(11.8)**

Strategies

8. Use rational expressions in real-life problems. **(11.1–11.8)**

Exploring Data

9. Use data to find ratios, proportions, and probabilities. **(11.1–11.8)**

Why did you learn it?

Rational expressions occur frequently in real life as ratios, rates, percents, and probabilities. To solve problems involving rational expressions, you must be able to simplify rational expressions, multiply and divide rational expressions, and solve equations that involve rational expressions.

How does it fit into the bigger picture of algebra?

In this chapter, you studied *rational expressions*—fractions whose numerators and denominators are polynomials. The first four lessons in the chapter introduce several types of problems—ratios, proportions, percents, direct variation, inverse variation, and probability—that often involve rational expressions. Using ratio, proportion, and variation techniques in your approach to all kinds of real-life contexts should become almost an instinctive problem-solving tool.

The last four lessons describe techniques for simplifying rational expressions, multiplying and dividing rational expressions, and solving rational equations.

In Exercises 1–6, solve the proportions. **(11.1)**

1. $\dfrac{x}{2} = \dfrac{4}{7}$

2. $\dfrac{5}{x} = \dfrac{6}{11}$

3. $\dfrac{7}{10} = \dfrac{9 + x}{x}$

4. $\dfrac{8x}{4 + x} = 2$

5. $\dfrac{x + 3}{x} = \dfrac{4}{x - 1}$

6. $\dfrac{5}{(x + 6)} = \dfrac{(x - 6)}{x}$

In Exercises 7–12, use the following information. **(11.3)**

The variables a and b vary directly. When a is 6, b is 19. The variables p and q vary inversely. When p is 2, q is 9.

7. Find an equation that relates a and b.

8. What is b when a is 3?

9. What is a when b is 14?

10. Find an equation that relates p and q.

11. What is q when p is 30?

12. What is p when q is 27?

13. *Miniature Horses* The ratio of the weight of an adult miniature horse to the weight of a baby miniature horse is about 8. What does an adult weigh? **(11.1)**

14. *Spiral Sculpture* Before creating his Spiral Jetty, Robert Smithson made a model using a ratio of 1 inch to 50 feet. How long was the coil in the model? **(11.1)**

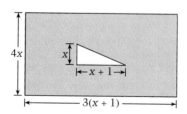

This baby miniature horse is standing on a man's arms. It weighs only 24 pounds.

This environmental sculpture in the Great Salt Lake, by Robert Smithson, is a coil of rocks 1500 feet long.

In Exercises 15 and 16, find the ratio of the area of the blue region to the entire area. **(11.1)**

15.

16.

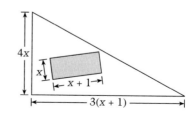

The three-point shot was introduced to college basketball games in 1987. The graph at the right shows the average number of three-point shots attempted per game and the average number of three-point shots made.

17. In 1987, what was the probability that a three-point attempt in a college basketball game was made?

18. What was the probability in 1990?

In Exercises 19–36, simplify the rational expressions.   (11.5, 11.6)

19. $\dfrac{3x}{9x^2 + 3}$

20. $\dfrac{4x^2 - 2x}{8x^2}$

21. $\dfrac{5x^2 + 10x - 5}{25x + 100}$

22. $\dfrac{6x^2}{12x^4 + 18x^2}$

23. $\dfrac{8x^2 - 4x}{16x^3}$

24. $\dfrac{7x^4}{49x^2 + x^2}$

25. $\dfrac{12x^2}{5x^3} \cdot \dfrac{25x^4}{3x}$

26. $\dfrac{2x^3}{4x} \cdot \dfrac{3x^2}{12x^4}$

27. $\dfrac{14x}{x^3} \cdot \dfrac{2x^2}{7x^4}$

28. $\dfrac{2x}{x^2 + 2x + 1} \cdot \dfrac{x + 1}{2x^2 - 2x}$

29. $\dfrac{3x^2 - 3}{x - 1} \cdot \dfrac{4}{x + 1}$

30. $\dfrac{x^2 - 6x - 7}{6x + 30} \cdot \dfrac{2x^2 - 50}{2x - 14}$

31. $\dfrac{3x}{x + 4} \div \dfrac{x^2}{x + 4}$

32. $\dfrac{6x^3 - 6x}{3x^2} \div \dfrac{x + 1}{2x^3}$

33. $\dfrac{x^2 + 5x + 6}{x + 3} \div \dfrac{x + 5}{x^2 + 4x + 3}$

34. $\dfrac{9x^3}{x^3 - x^2} \div \dfrac{x - 8}{x^2 - 9x + 8}$

35. $\dfrac{8x + 4}{32x^2} \div \dfrac{2x^2 + x}{x^3}$

36. $\dfrac{x^2 + 3x + 2}{x^2 + 7x + 12} \div \dfrac{x^2 + 5x + 4}{x^2 + 5x + 6}$

In Exercises 37–48, perform the indicated division.   (11.7)

37. $(12x^2 + 2x - 3) \div 2x$

38. $(8x^2 - 6x + 9) \div 2x$

39. $(9x^2 + 3x + 1) \div 3x$

40. $(4x^2 + 10x - 3) \div 2x$

41. $(3x^2 - 15x - 10) \div 3x$

42. $(6x^2 - 36x + 5) \div 6x$

43. $(3x^2 + 2x - 1) \div (x - 1)$

44. $(x^2 - 4x + 2) \div (x + 2)$

45. $(4x^2 + 9x + 5) \div (2x - 1)$

46. $(6x^2 - 3x - 4) \div (3x + 6)$

47. $(5x^2 + 3x + 6) \div (5x - 2)$

48. $(12x^2 - 8x - 2) \div (4x + 6)$

In Exercises 49–54, solve the equation.   (11.8)

49. $\dfrac{3}{x} + \dfrac{2}{3} = \dfrac{5}{x}$

50. $\dfrac{1}{4} + \dfrac{6}{x} = \dfrac{3}{x}$

51. $\dfrac{x}{5} - \dfrac{6}{x} = \dfrac{1}{5}$

52. $\dfrac{x}{4} + \dfrac{7}{4} = -\dfrac{3}{x}$

53. $\dfrac{x + 2}{2} = \dfrac{4}{x}$

54. $\dfrac{x}{5} = \dfrac{7}{x - 2}$

Comparing Apples and Oranges **In Exercises 55 and 56, use the following information. (11.3)**

The graph at the right shows the per capita consumption of apples and oranges in 1990, the average retail price, and the number of Calories in an average apple and orange. *(Source: United Fresh Fruit and Vegetable Association)*

55. Suppose that the per capita consumption of oranges varies inversely with the retail price. If the price of oranges reaches 75¢, what would be the annual per capita consumption?

56. The number of Calories consumed by eating apples varies directly with the number of apples eaten. If you consumed 558 Calories from apples in one week, how many apples did you eat?

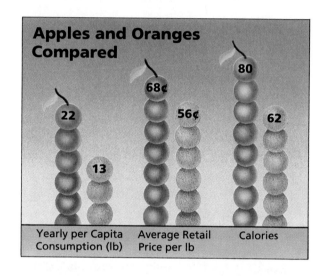

Apple Picking **In Exercises 57 and 58, use the following information. (11.2)**

The graph shows how the 231 million bushels of apples that were picked in 1990 were used. *(Source: International Apple Institute)*

57. What percent of the apples were processed as dried apples?

58. What was the probability that an apple that was picked would be processed for apple juice?

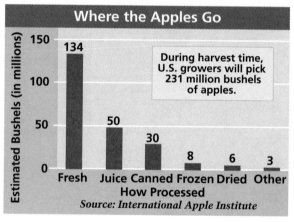

Eating Ethnic **In Exercises 59 and 60, use the following information. (11.2)**

The graph at the right shows the results of a survey of 635 adults. Each person was asked about the types of ethnic restaurants at which they had eaten. *(Source: National Restaurant Association)*

59. How many of the 635 polled have eaten in a Chinese restaurant?

60. Suppose that you took a survey about eating in ethnic restaurants and found that 336 people had eaten in a Mexican restaurant. If your results agreed with those shown, how many people did you survey?

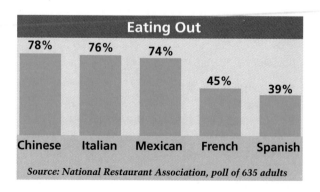

In Exercises 1–4, solve the proportion.

1. $\dfrac{3}{x} = \dfrac{15}{4}$

2. $\dfrac{7}{3} = \dfrac{5}{y}$

3. $\dfrac{x + 2}{5} = \dfrac{-1}{x - 4}$

4. $\dfrac{x + 8}{x} = \dfrac{x + 2}{2}$

5. How much is 22% of 200 gallons?

6. How many is 18% of 4700 people?

7. 37 meters is 74% of what distance?

8. 230 T-shirts is what percent of 500 T-shirts?

9. The variables x and y vary directly. When x is 3, y is 14. Find an equation that relates x and y. If x is 5, what is y?

10. The variables m and n vary inversely. When m is 12, n is 42. Find an equation that relates m and n. If n is 2, what is m?

11. Your cousin's basketball team has 15 members. During the game, each team member played the same amount of time. You walked into the game late. What is the probability that your cousin was playing when you walked in? (There are five team members playing at any given time.)

12. There are 14 plastic forks and 18 plastic spoons in a picnic basket. You grab one utensil. What is the probability that it is a fork? What is the probability that it is a spoon?

In Exercises 13–18, simplify the rational expressions.

13. $\dfrac{3x}{x^2 + 2x}$

14. $\dfrac{x^2 + 2x + 1}{x^2 - 1}$

15. $\dfrac{4x^2}{10x^4} \cdot \dfrac{-3x^2}{6x}$

16. $\dfrac{x^3 + x^2}{x^2 - 9} \cdot \dfrac{x + 3}{4x^3 + x^2 - 3x}$

17. $\dfrac{x + 5}{3x^2} \div \dfrac{4x}{x + 5}$

18. $\dfrac{(x + 5)}{x^3 - x^2 - 6x} \div \dfrac{x^2 - 25}{x^2 + x - 12}$

19. Divide $(3x^2 + x - 1)$ by $(x + 2)$.

20. Divide $(x^2 - 2x + 6)$ by $(x - 3)$.

In Exercises 21 and 22, solve the equation.

21. $\dfrac{6}{x} + \dfrac{1}{2} = \dfrac{4}{x}$

22. $\dfrac{x}{4} - \dfrac{21}{4x} = 5$

23. You have invested $30,000 to start a bagel shop in town. You can produce bagels for $1.20 a dozen. How many dozens must you produce before your average cost per dozen drops to $1.80?

24. You have taken four 100-point tests and your average is 88. What must you average on the remaining two 100-point tests to bring your overall average up to 92?

LESSONS

12.1 Functions and
Relations ▪ 620

12.2 Linear Functions
▪ 626

12.3 Exponential
Functions
▪ 633

12.4 Quadratic Functions
▪ 639

12.5 Rational Functions
▪ 646

12.6 Exploring Data:
Stem-and-Leaf Plots,
Box-and-Whisker
Plots ▪ 652

12.7 Exploring Data:
Measures of Central
Tendency ▪ 658

Functions

*The Ballotini spheres shown here
are tiny glass spheres that are
used in Venetian glass mosaics.*

Many objects occur naturally as spheres or circles. One reason for this is that spheres and circles are each an example of an *optimal design*. For instance, of all solids with a given surface area, the sphere has the greatest volume. Similarly, of all plane figures with a given perimeter, the circle has the greatest area.

As an example, consider a circle that has a circumference of 2π, or 6.283 units. The area of this circle is π, or 3.142 square units. All polygons that have a perimeter of 2π units have an area that is *less* than that of the circle. A model that approximates the area of a regular n-sided polygon whose perimeter is 2π is

$$A \approx \pi \frac{4n^2 - 16}{4n^2 - 3}.$$

Optimization of Area

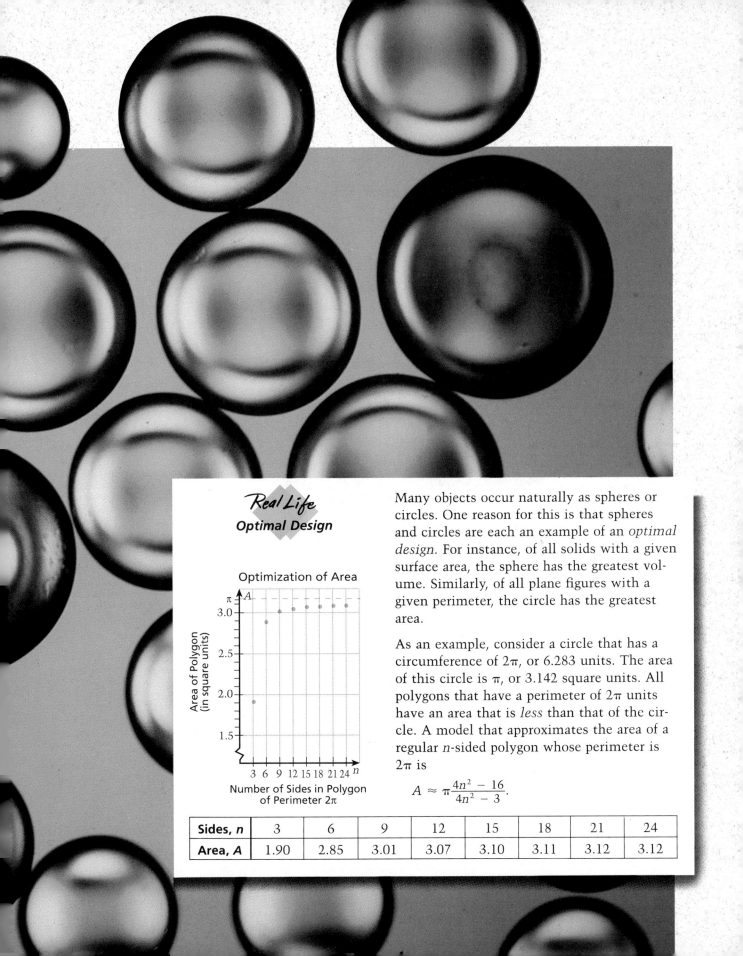

Area of Polygon (in square units)

Number of Sides in Polygon of Perimeter 2π

Sides, n	3	6	9	12	15	18	21	24
Area, A	1.90	2.85	3.01	3.07	3.10	3.11	3.12	3.12

12.1 Functions and Relations

What you should learn:

Goal 1 How to identify functions and use function notation

Goal 2 How to identify real-life relations that are functions

Why you should learn it:

Functions form a foundation for the study of advanced algebra and trigonometry.

Goal 1 Identifying Functions

A **relation** is a set of ordered pairs (x, y). A **function** is a relation in which no two ordered pairs have the same x-value. You can identify a function by checking the graph of the equation.

$y = x^2$ defines a function. (No two points have the same x-value.)

$y = \pm\sqrt{x}$ does not define a function. (Two points have the same x-value.)

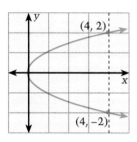

The x-values make up the **domain** (or input) of the function. The y-values are the **range** (or output). There are many ways to define a function: by an equation, a table, a graph, a sentence, or a set of ordered pairs.

Example 1 Identifying Relations That Are Functions

Let $A = \{a, b, c\}$ and let $B = \{1, 2, 3, 4, 5\}$. Which of the following are functions relating the set A to the set B?

a. $\{(a, 1), (b, 4), (c, 4)\}$
b. $\{(a, 1), (b, 2), (c, 3), (b, 4), (a, 5)\}$

c.

Input value	a	b	c	b	a
Output value	1	2	3	4	5

Solution

a. This set of ordered pairs *does* define a function relating A to B. No two ordered pairs have the same first coordinate.

b. This set of ordered pairs *does not* define a function relating A to B. Two of the pairs have the same first coordinate.

c. This is another way of representing the pairs in Part b. ■

The terms "input" and "output" have been used because when a computer is programmed to evaluate a function, it first defines the equation and then prompts the user to input an x-value. Once the x-value has been input, the program computes and outputs the appropriate y-value.

When a function is defined by an equation, it is convenient to name the function. For example, the set of ordered pairs (x, y) that satisfy the equation $y = 3x + 2$ form a function. By naming the function "f," we can use **function notation.**

x–y Notation	**Function Notation**
(x, y) is a solution of $y = 3x + 2$.	$(x, f(x))$ is a solution of $f(x) = 3x + 2$.

The symbol $f(x)$ replaces y and is read as "the value of f at x" or simply as "f of x." When we evaluate $3x + 2$ for a particular value of x, we say we are evaluating f at x. Watch how this notation "works."

x-value	**Value of y, or $f(x)$**
$x = 1$	$f(1) = 3(1) + 2 = 3 + 2 = 5$
$x = 2$	$f(2) = 3(2) + 2 = 6 + 2 = 8$

Up to this point in the text, we have been using parentheses to represent multiplication. The function notation $f(x)$ is a different use of parentheses. Remember that $f(x)$ means the value of f at x. It *does not* mean f times x.

Example 2 *Evaluating a Function*

Evaluate the function $f(x) = x^2 + 2x - 3$ at the given x-values.

a. $x = -2$ **b.** $x = 0$

Solution

a. To find the value of $f(x)$ when $x = -2$, substitute -2 for x in the equation that defines the function.

$$f(x) = x^2 + 2x - 3 \qquad \textit{Equation for f}$$
$$f(-2) = (-2)^2 + 2(-2) - 3 \qquad \textit{Substitute } -2 \textit{ for x.}$$
$$= 4 - 4 - 3 \qquad \textit{Simplify.}$$
$$= -3 \qquad \textit{Simplify.}$$

b. To find the value of $f(x)$ when $x = 0$, substitute 0 for x in the equation that defines the function.

$$f(x) = x^2 + 2x - 3 \qquad \textit{Equation for f}$$
$$f(0) = (0)^2 + 2(0) - 3 \qquad \textit{Substitute 0 for x.}$$
$$= 0 + 0 - 3 \qquad \textit{Simplify.}$$
$$= -3 \qquad \textit{Simplify.}$$

Goal 2   Identifying Functions in Real Life

When (x, y) represents the ordered pairs of a function, we say that y (the second coordinate) *is a function* of x (the first coordinate).

Example 3   *Identifying Relations That Are Functions*

a. The winner of the women's singles U.S. Open Tennis competition from 1987 to 1991 is a function of the year she won. (In no year were there cochampions.)

Year	1987	1988	1989	1990	1991
Winner	Martina Navratilova	Stefi Graf	Stefi Graf	Gabriela Sabatini	Monica Seles

b. In a state that has a sales tax of 8%, the price of a pair of sunglasses is *not* a function of the amount of sales tax. (A given amount of sales tax corresponds to several different prices.)

Sales Tax	$0.08	$0.08	$0.08	$0.08	$0.08	$0.08
Price	$0.94	$0.95	$0.96	$0.97	$0.98	$0.99

Sales Tax	$0.08	$0.08	$0.08	$0.08	$0.08	$0.08
Price	$1.00	$1.01	$1.02	$1.03	$1.04	$1.05

Connections
Geometry

c. The volume of a sphere is a function of the radius of the sphere.

Radius, r	1	2	3	4
Volume, $\frac{4}{3}\pi r^3$	4.2	33.5	113.1	268.1

Communicating about ALGEBRA

▶ **SHARING IDEAS about the Lesson**

A. Let $f(x) = 5x - 7$. Evaluate $f(3)$ and $f\left(\frac{2}{3}\right)$.

B. Let $f(x) = -x^2 + 2x + 4$. Evaluate $f(1)$ and $f\left(-\frac{1}{2}\right)$.

C. Let $f(x) = \frac{1}{x}$. Evaluate $f(2)$ and $f\left(-\frac{3}{4}\right)$.

EXERCISES

Guided Practice

▶ **CRITICAL THINKING about the Lesson**

In Exercises 1–3, state the domain of the function and find the indicated value of the function.

1. Find $f(4)$.
$\{(1, 2), (2, 0), (3, 3), (4, 1)\}$

3. Find $f(3)$.
$\{(1, 0), (2, 1), (3, 2), (4, 3)\}$

4. Evaluate $f(x) = 3x^2 + 2x - 1$ at $x = 1$ and at $x = 2$. Explain your steps.

2. Find $f(2)$.

Independent Practice

In Exercises 5–8, decide whether the graph represents y as a function of x. Explain your reasoning.

5.

6.

7.

8.

In Exercises 9–16, decide whether the information defines a function. If it does, state the domain of the function.

9. $\{(1, 5), (2, 4), (3, 3), (4, 2)\}$

11. $\{(1, 0), (2, 0), (3, 0), (4, 0)\}$

10. $\{(1, 5), (1, 4), (2, 3), (2, 2)\}$

12. $\{(0, 0), (1, 1), (2, 2), (3, 3)\}$

13.

Input value	0	1	2	3	4
Output value	2	4	6	8	10

14.

Input value	0	1	2	1	0
Output value	2	4	6	8	10

15.

Input value	1	3	5	3	1
Output value	1	2	3	4	5

16.

Input value	2	4	6	8	10
Output value	1	1	1	1	1

In Exercises 17–26, evaluate the function at the given *x*-values.

	Function	*x*-values		Function	*x*-values
17.	$f(x) = 10x + 1$	$x = 0, x = 2$	**18.**	$f(x) = 8x - 2$	$x = -1, x = 1$
19.	$f(x) = x^2 + x - 1$	$x = 2, x = 3$	**20.**	$f(x) = 2x^2 - 2x + 1$	$x = 0, x = 2$
21.	$f(x) = 2x^2 - 3$	$x = -1, x = 4$	**22.**	$f(x) = 3x^2 + 5$	$x = 2, x = -4$
23.	$f(x) = 9x^2 - 10x - 1$	$x = -1, x = 1$	**24.**	$f(x) = 6x^2 + 2x - 4$	$x = -2, x = 3$
25.	$f(x) = x^2 - 10x + 10$	$x = -5, x = 5$	**26.**	$f(x) = 2x^2 + 5x - 20$	$x = 4, x = 5$

In Exercises 27 and 28, state the domain of the function. Find $f(0)$ and $f(2)$.

27.

Input values, *x*	0	2	4	6	8	10
Output values, *f(x)*	0	1	2	3	4	5

28.

Input values, *x*	-3	-2	-1	0	1	2	3
Output values, *f(x)*	6	4	2	0	-2	-4	-6

29. Find an equation that defines the function given in Exercise 27.

30. Find an equation that defines the function given in Exercise 28.

31. *Pulse Rates of Mammals*   The table gives typical pulse rates for six different mammals. Are the given mammals a function of the pulse rate? Why or why not?

Pulse rate, *x*	667	315	260	176	67	27
Type of mammal, *y*	Mouse	Rat	Rabbit	Cat	Human	Elephant

32. *Symphony Orchestras*   The number of college and community orchestras in the United States from 1980 to 1988 is given in the table. Is the year a function of the number of college and community orchestras? Why or why not?

Orchestras, *x*	1311	1311	1304	1306	1317	1317	1298	1301	1253
Year, *y*	1980	1981	1982	1983	1984	1985	1986	1987	1988

Spring Semester Tests   **In Exercises 33 and 34, the graph shows the average score on each test in an algebra class from January through June. Is the average score, *y*, a function of the month, *x*? Explain.**

33.

34.

High School and College Students   **In Exercises 35–38, use the following information.**

The graph shows the projected number of students in the United States.
(Source: National Center for Education Statistics)

35. Is the projected high school enrollment a function of the year? Explain.

36. Is the projected college enrollment a function of the year?

37. Let $f(x)$ represent the projected number of high school students in year x. Find $f(1993)$.

38. Let $f(x)$ represent the projected number of college students in year x. Find $f(1993)$.

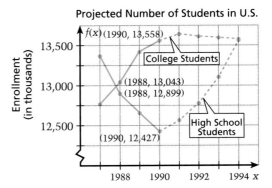

Projected Number of Students in U.S.

Integrated Review

In Exercises 39–42, solve the equation for *y*. Then evaluate *y* when *x* = −2.

39. $2y = 3x - 1$ **40.** $3y - 5 = x$ **41.** $y - 5 = 2x^2$ **42.** $y - 10 = 3x^2 - 2x$

In Exercises 43–46, match the equation with its graph.

43. $y = 2^x$ **44.** $y = -x^2$ **45.** $y = 2x + 1$ **46.** $y = 2 - 2x$

a.   b.   c.   d.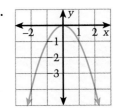

Exploration and Extension

Dog Years vs. Human Years   **In Exercises 47 and 48, use the following information.**

The following *two* equations can be used to find the approximate human age, $f(x)$, that corresponds to a dog's age, x.

For $0.5 < x < 5.5$: $f(x) = 10\sqrt{3x - 1}$

For $5.5 \le x$: $f(x) = 25\sqrt{x - 3}$

(Source: Simon & Schuster's Guide to Dogs)

47. What is the human age of a one-year-old dog?

48. What is the human age of a twelve-year-old dog?

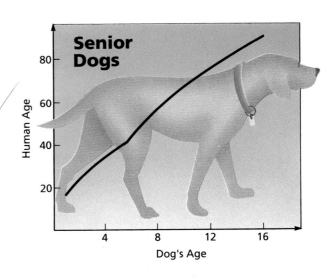

12.2

Linear Functions

What you should learn:

Goal 1 How to use linear functions to solve problems

Goal 2 How to use linear functions to answer questions about real-life situations

Why you should learn it:

You can use linear functions to model many real-life situations, such as those involving distance, rate, and time.

Goal 1 Using Linear Functions

In this and the next three lessons, you will review four of the basic types of models as *functions*.

- Linear function   Lesson 12.2
- Exponential function   Lesson 12.3
- Quadratic function   Lesson 12.4
- Rational function   Lesson 12.5

A **linear function** is a function defined by the equation

$$f(x) = mx + b.$$

The graph of a linear function is a *nonvertical* line whose slope is m and whose y-intercept is b.

Example 1   *An Equation for a Linear Function*

Find an equation of the linear function for which $f(2) = 5$ and $f(6) = 3$.

Solution   Translate the information about the function f.

Function Notation	x-value and y-value	Point on graph
$f(2) = 5$	When $x = 2$, $y = 5$.	$(2, 5)$
$f(6) = 3$	When $x = 6$, $y = 3$.	$(6, 3)$

You need to find an equation for the line that passes through the points $(2, 5)$ and $(6, 3)$. The slope of the line is

$$m = \frac{y_2 - y_1}{x_2 - x_1} = \frac{3 - 5}{6 - 2} = -\frac{1}{2}.$$

Using the procedure you studied in Lesson 5.3, let $m = -\frac{1}{2}$, $x = 2$, and $y = 5$ and solve for b.

$y = mx + b$	*Slope-intercept form*
$5 = \left(-\frac{1}{2}\right)(2) + b$	$m = -\frac{1}{2}$, $x = 2$, $y = 5$
$5 = -1 + b$	*Simplify.*
$6 = b$	*Solve for b.*

The y-intercept is $b = 6$, and the slope-intercept form of the line is $y = -\frac{1}{2}x + 6$. Using function notation, you can write

$$f(x) = -\frac{1}{2}x + 6.$$ ∎

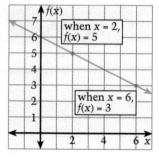

when $x = 2$, $f(x) = 5$

when $x = 6$, $f(x) = 3$

$$f(x) = -\frac{1}{2}x + 6$$

Using Linear Functions as Real-Life Models

Monarch butterflies migrate from the northern United States to Mexico. The trip of about 2400 miles takes about 30 days.

Monarch butterflies winter over in a mountainous region west of Mexico City. During their $4\frac{1}{2}$ month stay, they show little activity.

Real Life
Entomology

Example 2 — A Linear Function to Model Distance

Find a linear function that models the distance traveled by a migrating monarch butterfly. Use the model to find the distance traveled in 20 days of migration.

Solution Because the butterflies travel about 2400 miles in 30 days, their average speed is 80 miles per day.

Verbal Model

Distance traveled	=	Average speed	•	Time

Labels
$$\text{Time} = t \qquad \text{(days)}$$
$$\text{Average speed} = 80 \qquad \text{(miles per day)}$$
$$\text{Distance traveled} = f(t) \qquad \text{(miles)}$$

Function $f(t) = 80t$

After 20 days of migration, the distance traveled is

$$f(t) = 80t \qquad \textit{Linear function}$$
$$f(20) = 80(20) \qquad \textit{Substitute 20 for t.}$$
$$= 1600 \text{ miles} \qquad \textit{Simplify.}$$

Notice that it is not necessary to use x as the variable when writing function notation. Any letter can be used.   ∎

Team	Salary	Percent	Team	Salary	Percent
Atlanta Braves	$14.2	40.1%	Minnesota Twins	$14.2	45.7%
Baltimore Orioles	$ 8.1	47.2%	Montreal Expos	$16.5	52.5%
Boston Red Sox	$22.7	54.3%	New York Mets	$22.2	56.2%
California Angels	$21.9	49.4%	New York Yankees	$20.6	41.4%
Chicago Cubs	$13.8	47.5%	Oakland Athletics	$22.3	63.6%
Chicago White Sox	$11.1	58.0%	Philadelphia Phillies	$14.2	47.5%
Cincinnati Reds	$15.6	56.2%	Pittsburgh Pirates	$15.5	58.6%
Cleveland Indians	$15.4	47.5%	San Diego Padres	$16.7	46.3%
Detroit Tigers	$17.8	48.8%	San Francisco Giants	$22.5	52.5%
Houston Astros	$18.2	46.3%	Seattle Mariners	$12.6	47.5%
Kansas City Royals	$23.6	46.6%	St. Louis Cardinals	$19.6	43.2%
Los Angeles Dodgers	$20.4	53.1%	Texas Rangers	$12.6	51.2%
Milwaukee Brewers	$18.5	45.7%	Toronto Blue Jays	$17.8	53.1%

The table shows the 1990 total team salaries (in millions) of the 26 baseball teams in the American and National Leagues and each team's percent of games won. (Source: Inside Sports)

Real Life
Baseball

Example 3 *Can Money Buy a Win?*

Construct a scatter plot for the data shown in the table.

a. Is the percent of games won by a team a *linear function* of the total salary paid to the team?

b. Can you find a *linear function that approximates* the relationship between the percent of games won by a team and the total salary paid to the team?

Solution Be sure you see that these questions are different.

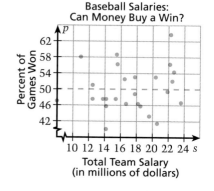

Baseball Salaries: Can Money Buy a Win?

Percent of Games Won

Total Team Salary (in millions of dollars)

a. From the scatter plot, you can see that the points do not all lie on a line. Therefore, the percent of games won by a team is *not* a linear function of the team's total salary.

b. The April 1991 issue of *Inside Sports* claimed that "a correlation exists between payroll and on-field performance," but we can't see it. (See page 258.) It is true that of the eight highest-paid teams, five won more than 50% of their games. Of the eight lowest-paid teams, only two won more than 50% of their games. But it would be hard to argue that a team can win a greater percentage of games by hiring more expensive players. What do you think? ■

Communicating about ALGEBRA

▶ **SHARING IDEAS about the Lesson**

Use Resources Find two quantities whose relationship *can be* approximated by a linear function. Use a scatter plot and the approach discussed in Lesson 5.4.

EXERCISES

▶ CRITICAL THINKING about the Lesson

1. Which type of line *cannot* be the graph of a linear function? Explain.

2. If $f(-3) = 5$, what point must be on the graph of f? Explain.

3. If the point $(1, 5)$ is on the graph of f, what is the value of $f(1)$? Explain.

4. Given that $f(1) = 2$ and $f(3) = -1$, explain how to use this information to find the slope of the graph of f.

Independent Practice

In Exercises 5–8, match the function with its graph.

5. $f(x) = 3x - 5$

6. $f(x) = 2x + 2$

7. $f(x) = -\frac{1}{2}x + 4$

8. $f(x) = -3x - 4$

a.

b.

c.

d.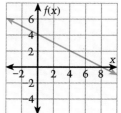

In Exercises 9–14, find the slope of the graph of the linear function f.

9. $f(2) = -3$, $f(-2) = 5$

10. $f(0) = 1$, $f(1) = 0$

11. $f(-3) = -9$, $f(3) = 4$

12. $f(6) = -1$, $f(3) = 8$

13. $f(9) = -1$, $f(-1) = 2$

14. $f(-1) = 1$, $f(1) = 6$

In Exercises 15–26, find an equation for the linear function f.

15. $f(0) = 1$, $f(2) = 1$

16. $f(2) = -2$, $f(-4) = 1$

17. $f(3) = -4$, $f(5) = 2$

18. $f(0) = 5$, $f(-6) = 3$

19. $f(-1) = 1$, $f(-2) = -4$

20. $f(4) = 6$, $f(9) = 1$

21. $f(0) = 4$, $f(-3) = 6$

22. $f(3) = -2$, $f(5) = -2$

23. $f(6) = 2$, $f(9) = -1$

24. $f(2) = 10$, $f(-4) = 16$

25. $f(-5) = 5$, $f(5) = -3$

26. $f(7) = 2$, $f(3) = -8$

In Exercises 27–32, sketch the graph of the linear function.

27. $f(x) = -2x + 4$

28. $f(x) = -x + 3$

29. $f(x) = \frac{1}{2}x + 1$

30. $f(x) = 2x - 3$

31. $f(x) = -\frac{1}{3}x + 2$

32. $f(x) = 3x - 8$

33. *The Goodyear Blimp* The Goodyear blimp traveled about 980 miles from Dover, Delaware, to Kansas City, Kansas, for a football game. It took the blimp 28 days to make the trip. Find a linear function that models the time taken by the blimp. Then use the model to estimate the time it would take the blimp to go from Kansas City to Indianapolis, Indiana (430 miles away).

34. *Go, Verne, Go!*   On February 21, 1990, a garden snail named Verne set a world record at West Middle School in Plymouth, Michigan. Verne completed a 12.2-inch course in 133 seconds. Find a linear function that models the distance Verne traveled. *(Source: Guinness Book of Records)*

35. *Apparent Temperature*   The temperature that a person feels depends on the actual temperature of the air and the humidity. The higher the humidity, the warmer the air feels. The graph at the right shows the *apparent temperature* when the actual temperature is 70°F. Find a linear function that models the apparent temperature. Use the model to find the apparent temperature when the actual temperature is 70°F and the humidity is 90%.

Cost of Raising Children   **In Exercises 36–38, use the following information.**

The table at the right shows the projected average annual costs of raising a child that was born in 1990. In each income group, the cost increases steadily, then jumps. At what ages do the costs jump? Why do you think these jumps occur?

(Source: American Demographics Magazine)

36. Construct a scatter plot for the annual cost for a low-income family. Find a linear function that approximates the annual cost, $f(t)$. (Let $t = 0$ represent 1990.)

37. Construct a scatter plot for the annual cost for a middle-income family. Find a linear function that approximates the annual cost, $f(t)$. (Let $t = 0$ represent 1990.)

38. Construct a scatter plot for the annual cost for a high-income family. Find a linear function that approximates the annual cost, $f(t)$. (Let $t = 0$ represent 1990.)

Year	Age	Low	Middle	High
1990	0	$4,330	$6,140	$8,770
1991	1	$4,590	$6,510	$9,300
1992	2	$4,870	$6,900	$9,850
1993	3	$5,510	$7,790	$11,030
1994	4	$5,850	$8,260	$11,690
1995	5	$6,200	$8,750	$12,390
1996	6	$6,550	$9,220	$12,950
1997	7	$6,950	$9,770	$13,730
1998	8	$7,360	$10,360	$14,550
1999	9	$7,570	$10,690	$15,120
2000	10	$8,020	$11,340	$16,030
2001	11	$8,500	$12,020	$16,990
2002	12	$10,360	$14,190	$19,680
2003	13	$10,980	$15,040	$20,860
2004	14	$11,640	$15,940	$22,110
2005	15	$13,160	$17,950	$24,610
2006	16	$13,950	$19,030	$26,090
2007	17	$14,780	$20,170	$27,650

In Exercises 39–42, construct a scatter plot. Then match the plot with the description.

39. Temperature, T ($°K$), and volume, V, of gas at constant pressure.

V	T
10	200
14	280
15	300
17	340
19	380
20	400
22	440
25	500

40. Average annual salary, S, of chemical workers in year t.

t	S
1972	8,731
1975	11,227
1977	13,839
1980	18,269
1982	20,836
1984	22,665
1985	23,345
1987	25,065

41. The density factor, d, of water at a temperature of T ($°C$).

T	d
0	28.93
2	28.79
4	28.60
6	28.36
8	28.08
10	27.75
12	27.38
14	26.97

42. Atomic radius, r, of various atoms with a nuclear charge of N.

N	r
3	1.52
9	1.36
11	1.86
13	1.43
14	1.17
18	1.54
19	2.31
37	2.44

a. Approximately linear, positive correlation. **b.** Exactly linear.

c. Approximately linear, negative correlation. **d.** Not linear.

Integrated Review

43. Evaluate $y = 6x + 9$ when $x = \frac{1}{2}$.

44. Evaluate $y = 3x - 1$ when $x = -4$.

45. Evaluate $y = 13 + x$ when $x = 0$.

46. Evaluate $y = -\frac{1}{3}x + 1$ when $x = 9$.

In Exercises 47–50, find the equation of the line that passes through the two points.

47. $(2, -5), (-4, 0)$ **48.** $(-1, 7), (0, 2)$ **49.** $(0, 3), (6, 1)$ **50.** $(5, 4), (-3, 1)$

In Exercises 51–54, sketch the line.

51. $y = \frac{1}{2}x + 2$ **52.** $y = 3x$ **53.** $y = -\frac{3}{2}x - 3$ **54.** $y = -\frac{1}{4}x + 1$

Exploration and Extension

55. *NFL Players*   The data in the table show the maximum number, n, of active players allowed on a NFL football team in year t, where $t = 0$ represents 1920. Do you think a linear function could be used to approximate these data? Explain your answer.

t	5	6	8	11	13	15	17	18	19	23	27
n	24	25	30	33	28	33	34	35	32	33	35

t	29	30	31	33	38	44	46	50	52	54	58
n	36	38	36	37	40	47	43	45	48	49	45

1. Write 4,240,000 in scientific notation. **(8.4)**

2. Write 0.00000062 in scientific notation. **(8.4)**

3. Classify $3x^2 + 2x - 1$ by degree and terms. **(10.1)**

4. Find the leading coefficient of $2 + 3x - 4x^2$. **(10.1)**

5. Evaluate $y = 3 + 14(1.2)^t$ when $t = 3$. **(8.6)**

6. Evaluate $y = 3(6.2)^{-t}$ when $t = 2$. **(8.6)**

7. Divide $3x^2 + 2x - 6$ by $x - 2$. **(11.7)**

8. Multiply $4x^2 - 2$ by $4x^2 + 2$. **(10.2)**

9. Find the vertex of $-3|x - 3| + 2 = y$. **(4.7)**

10. Find the vertex of $y = 2x^2 + 3$. **(9.3)**

11. Solve $7 = -3x + x^2$ (quadratic formula). **(9.4)**

12. Solve $x^2 + 8x + 5 = 0$. (Complete the square.) **(10.7)**

13. Is $(-1, 1)$ a solution for $y \leq x^2 - x + 2$? **(6.1)**

14. Is $(7, 2)$ a solution for $y + 2 = \frac{1}{3}(x + 5)$? **(4.2)**

15. Solve $-x^2 - 3x + 4 = 0$. **(10.6)**

16. Solve $3x^2 = 27$. **(9.2)**

17. Find the x-intercepts: $y = 3x^2 + 14x + 8$. **(9.3)**

18. Find the y-intercept: $3x + 2y = -6$. **(4.3)**

19. What is 28 percent of 490?

20. 99 is what percent of 450?

Milestones   UNSOLVED PROBLEMS

| 1700 | 1750 | 1800 | 1850 | 1900 | 1950 | 2000 | 2050 |

Goldbach's conjecture — 1750

Four-color problem posed — 1850

Four-color problem solved — 1950

Canada

Great Lakes

Atlantic Ocean

Four-color map

In the study of mathematics many questions are raised. Some, like the four-color problem posed in 1840, have been solved in this century. The problem was to prove that four colors could be used on any map so that no two regions sharing a border would be the same color. It was solved in 1976 through a lengthy computer analysis.

Some questions raised hundreds of years ago remain unanswered today. An example is a conjecture made by Christian Goldbach in 1742 that every even number greater than 4 can be written as the sum of two odd prime numbers and that every odd number greater than 7 can be written as the sum of three odd prime numbers. While no examples have been found to disprove this conjecture, no one has been able to prove that it is true.

Find an odd number greater than 7 that can be written as the sum of three odd prime numbers in three different ways.

12.3

Exponential Functions

What you should learn:

Goal 1 How to transform the graph of a function

Goal 2 How to use exponential functions as models of real-life problems

Why you should learn it:

You can model many real-life situations using exponential functions, such as college enrollments.

Goal 1 Transforming a Graph

In Chapter 8, you were introduced to graphs that model the exponential function.

Exponential Growth:
$$f(x) = 2^x$$

Exponential Decay:
$$f(x) = \left(\tfrac{1}{2}\right)^x$$

If the graph of a function is shifted about on the coordinate plane, it may then define a different function that is related in a simple way to the original function. Such a shift is one example of a **transformation.** In this lesson, you will learn to graph a function by transforming the graph of a simpler, related function.

In Example 1, note how letters other than f, such as g and h, are commonly used to denote functions.

Example 1   *Vertical Shifts*

a. To sketch the graph of
$$g(x) = 2^x + 3$$
shift the graph of $f(x) = 2^x$ *three units up.*

b. To sketch the graph of
$$h(x) = \left(\tfrac{1}{2}\right)^x - 2$$
shift the graph of $f(x) = \left(\tfrac{1}{2}\right)^x$ *two units down.*

Example 2   *Horizontal Shifts*

a. To sketch the graph of

$$g(x) = 3^{x-2}$$

shift the graph of
$f(x) = 3^x$ *two units to the right.*

b. To sketch the graph of

$$h(x) = 3^{x+2}$$

shift the graph of
$f(x) = 3^x$ *two units to the left.*

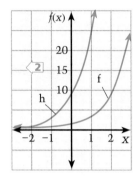

One graph is a **reflection** of another graph in the *x*-axis if the two graphs are mirror images of each other. (The mirror lies on the *x*-axis.)

Example 3   *Reflections*

a. To sketch the graph of

$$g(x) = -2^x$$

reflect the graph of
$f(x) = 2^x$ in the *x*-axis.

b. To sketch the graph of

$$h(x) = -\left(\tfrac{1}{2}\right)^x$$

reflect the graph of
$f(x) = \left(\tfrac{1}{2}\right)^x$ in the *x*-axis.

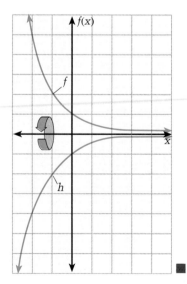

Lake LaCross, Mt. Steel, Olympic National Park

In 1975, 26% of the 9.73 million college students in the United States were enrolled in two-year colleges. By 1990, the percent of college students in two-year colleges had risen to about 38%.

Goal 2

Using Exponential Models in Real Life

Real Life
Education

Example 4 *Graphing an Exponential Function*

The percent of all college students in the United States from 1975 to 1990 who were enrolled in two-year colleges can be modeled by

$$f(t) = 38 - (0.8)^t$$

where $t = 0$ represents 1975. Find a model for the percent of college students who were enrolled in 4-year colleges. Then sketch the graphs of both functions.

Two-year and Four-year College Enrollment

Percent of Total College Enrollment

80
70 4-Year
62%
60
50
40 38%
30 2-Year

2 4 6 8 10 12 14 *T*
Year (0↔1975)

Solution

Verbal Model	% in four-year colleges	=	100%	−	% in two-year colleges

Labels   % in two-year colleges $= 38 - (0.8)^t$ (%)
              % in four-year colleges $= g(t)$ (%)

Equation $g(t) = 100 - (38 - (0.8)^t)$
              $= 62 + 0.8^t$

The graphs of the two models are shown at the left.   ∎

Communicating about ALGEBRA

Cooperative Learning

▶ **SHARING IDEAS about the Lesson**

Work with a Partner and Draw Visual Models Sketch the graphs of the functions. Which shift or reflection is useful for each?

A. $f(x) = 2^x - 4$ **B.** $f(x) = \left(\frac{1}{2}\right)^x + 2$ **C.** $f(x) = 2^{x+1}$

D. $f(x) = \left(\frac{1}{2}\right)^{x-2}$ **E.** $f(x) = -3^x$ **F.** $f(x) = -\left(\frac{1}{3}\right)^x$

EXERCISES

▶ **CRITICAL THINKING about the Lesson**

In Exercises 1 and 2, does the function represent exponential growth or exponential decay? Explain your reasons.

1. $f(x) = \left(\frac{1}{4}\right)^x$

2. $f(x) = 5^x$

In Exercises 3–6, state whether the graph of the function g is related to the graph of $f(x) = \left(\frac{1}{3}\right)^x$ by a vertical shift, a horizontal shift, or a reflection. Use your answer as an aid to sketch the graph of g.

3. $g(x) = \left(\frac{1}{3}\right)^{x-1}$

4. $g(x) = \left(\frac{1}{3}\right)^x - 3$

5. $g(x) = -\left(\frac{1}{3}\right)^x$

6. $g(x) = \left(\frac{1}{3}\right)^x + 4$

Independent Practice

In Exercises 7–18, describe the relationship between the graph of f and the graph of g. (You do not need to sketch the graphs of f and g to answer the question.)

7. $f(x) = \left(\frac{5}{3}\right)^x$, $\quad g(x) = -\left(\frac{5}{3}\right)^x$

8. $f(x) = 7^x$, $\qquad g(x) = 7^x + 7$

9. $f(x) = 15^x$, $\quad g(x) = 15^{x-3}$

10. $f(x) = (2.2)^x$, $\quad g(x) = (2.2)^{x-9}$

11. $f(x) = 16^x$, $\quad g(x) = 16^x - 1$

12. $f(x) = \left(\frac{1}{5}\right)^x$, $\quad g(x) = -\left(\frac{1}{5}\right)^x$

13. $f(x) = 8^x$, $\qquad g(x) = 8^x - \frac{1}{3}$

14. $f(x) = \left(\frac{2}{3}\right)^x$, $\quad g(x) = -\left(\frac{2}{3}\right)^x$

15. $f(x) = 2^x$, $\qquad g(x) = 2^x + 8$

16. $f(x) = \left(\frac{1}{3}\right)^x$, $\quad g(x) = \left(\frac{1}{3}\right)^{x+10}$

17. $f(x) = 7^x$, $\qquad g(x) = -7^x$

18. $f(x) = 4^x$, $\qquad g(x) = 4^{x+2}$

In Exercises 19–24, use a vertical shift to sketch the graph of the function.

19. $f(x) = 2^x + 1$

20. $g(x) = 3^x - 2$

21. $h(x) = \left(\frac{1}{2}\right)^x + \frac{1}{2}$

22. $h(x) = (0.6)^x - 4$

23. $f(x) = 2^x - 5$

24. $f(x) = \left(\frac{1}{3}\right)^x + 10$

In Exercises 25–30, use a horizontal shift to sketch the graph of the function.

25. $f(x) = \left(\frac{1}{2}\right)^{x-1}$

26. $f(x) = \left(\frac{1}{4}\right)^{x+4}$

27. $h(x) = 2^{x+5}$

28. $g(x) = 1.5^{x-2}$

29. $h(x) = \frac{1}{3}(5)^{x-1}$

30. $g(x) = \left(\frac{1}{2}\right)^{x-5}$

In Exercises 31–36, use a reflection to sketch the graph of the function.

31. $h(x) = -3^x$

32. $g(x) = -4^x$

33. $f(x) = -(0.25)^x$

34. $f(x) = -(0.75)^x$

35. $h(x) = -\left(\frac{1}{5}\right)^x$

36. $g(x) = -\left(\frac{4}{3}\right)^x$

In Exercises 37–40, use the following information.

Piano tuners use an *equal temperament* scale to tune pianos. The frequency, $f(n)$, of the nth note is given by the exponential function

$$f(n) = 440 \cdot (\sqrt[12]{2})^n \quad \text{(frequency in vibrations per second)}$$

where n represents the position of the note below or above the note called A-440. (The number $\sqrt[12]{2}$ is approximately 1.0594631, and $(\sqrt[12]{2})^{12} = 2$.)

37. What are the frequencies of the lowest and highest notes on the piano?

38. Which letter, A, B, C, D, E, F, or G, denotes notes with integer frequencies?

39. Two notes harmonize (sound pleasing to the human ear) if the ratio of their frequencies is an integer or a simple rational number. Find examples of notes whose frequencies have the following ratios.

Octave: 2	Fifth: $\frac{3}{2}$	Fourth: $\frac{4}{3}$	
Major third: $\frac{5}{4}$	Minor third: $\frac{6}{5}$	Major sixth: $\frac{5}{3}$	Minor sixth: $\frac{8}{5}$

40. Piano tuners tune piano keys by adjusting the tension on each string. How much tension should there be on the lowest note for a 5-foot string that weighs 0.00235 pounds per foot? The tension, T, weight per foot, W, length, L, and frequency, F, are related by $T = 4WF^2L^2$.

Snowflake   **In Exercises 41 and 42, use the following information.**

In the snowflake sequence below, the snowflakes are numbered from 0 to 5. The perimeter, $f(n)$, of the nth snowflake is given by $f(n) = \left(\frac{4}{3}\right)^n$.

0

1

2

3

4

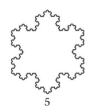
5

41. Find the perimeters of the 6 snowflakes.

42. If the pattern continues, what would be the perimeter of Snowflake 15?

In Exercises 43–46, match the function with its graph.

43. $f(x) = 1.2^{x-1}$ **44.** $f(x) = -1.2^x$ **45.** $f(x) = 1.2^x$ **46.** $f(x) = 1.2^x - 1$

a.   **b.**   **c.**   **d.**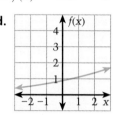

In Exercises 47–52, evaluate the function as indicated.

47. $f(x) = (0.05)^x$, $f(3) = \boxed{?}$

48. $f(x) = \frac{1}{7}(10)^x$, $f(5) = \boxed{?}$

49. $f(x) = 6^x - 12$, $f(2) = \boxed{?}$

50. $f(x) = 21\left(\frac{1}{3}\right)^x$, $f(8) = \boxed{?}$

51. $f(x) = \frac{1}{11}(2^x) + 4$, $f(5) = \boxed{?}$

52. $f(x) = 6\left(\frac{1}{6}\right)^x$, $f(9) = \boxed{?}$

53. *College Entrance Exam Sample*   If $x \neq 0$ and $3x^2 - 12x = 0$, what is x?

    a. -9 **b.** -4 **c.** 3   **d.** 4   **e.** 9

54. *College Entrance Exam Sample*   On a certain map, the distance of 100 miles is represented by 1 inch. What distance is represented by 2.4 inches on this map?

    a. 200.4 mi. **b.** 204.0 mi. **c.** 225.0 mi. **d.** 233.3 mi. **e.** 240.0 mi.

Exploration and Extension

Sweet Tooth   **In Exercises 55 and 56, use the following information.**

For 1982 through 1990, the consumption of sugar in the United States, as a percent, $f(t)$, of the total consumption of sweeteners, can be modeled by

$$f(t) = 75 + 37.25(0.615)^t$$

where $t = 2$ represents 1982.

55. Find a model for the consumption of non-sugar sweeteners as a percent, $g(t)$, of the total consumption of sweeteners.

56. Sketch the graphs of f and g. Does the percent of sugar compared to the percent of nonsugar sweeteners appear to be stabilizing? Explain.

57. Sketch the graph of $f(x) = 2^x$. Does it have an x-intercept? What does this tell you about the number of solutions of the equation $2^x = 0$? Explain.

12.4

Quadratic Functions

What you should learn:

Goal 1 How to sketch the graph of a quadratic function

Goal 2 How to use quadratic functions as models of real-life problems

Why you should learn it:

You can model many real-life situations, such as maximizing the area of a figure, using quadratic functions.

Goal 1 Graphing a Quadratic Function

The graph of a quadratic function

$$f(x) = ax^2 + bx + c \quad \text{Standard form}$$

is a parabola. From Lesson 9.3, you know that the graph opens up if a is positive and opens down if a is negative.

In this lesson, you will learn how to sketch graphs of quadratic functions that are written in *completed square form*.

Completed Square Form

The completed square form of a quadratic function is

$$f(x) = a(x - h)^2 + k. \quad \text{Completed square form}$$

The vertex of the parabola is the point (h, k).

Example 1 Sketching the Graph of a Quadratic Function

a. The graph of

$$f(x) = (x - 2)^2 - 1$$

opens up ($a > 0$) and has its vertex at $(2, -1)$. Some additional points are given by the table.

x	0	1	2	3	4
f(x)	3	0	-1	0	3

b. The graph of

$$f(x) = -(x + 1)^2 + 3$$

opens down ($a < 0$) and has its vertex at $(-1, 3)$. Some additional points are given by the table.

x	-3	-2	-1	0	1
f(x)	-1	2	3	2	-1

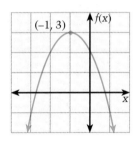

If a quadratic function is given in standard form, you can rewrite it in completed square form. When the leading coefficient is 1, you can complete the square by *adding and subtracting* the square of half the coefficient of x.

Example 2 Completing the Square: Leading Coefficient Is 1

Write the function $f(x) = x^2 - 6x + 5$ in completed square form. Then sketch its graph.

Solution

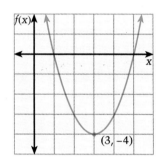

$$f(x) = x^2 - 6x + 5 \qquad \textit{Standard form}$$
$$f(x) = x^2 - 6x + (-3)^2 - (-3)^2 + 5 \qquad \textit{Add and subtract } (-3)^2.$$
$$\text{(half of } -6)^2$$
$$f(x) = (x^2 - 6x + 3^2) - 9 + 5 \qquad \textit{Group the terms.}$$
$$f(x) = (x - 3)^2 - 4 \qquad \textit{Completed square form}$$

From the completed square form, you can see that the vertex of the parabola is the point $(3, -4)$. See the graph at the left. ■

When the leading coefficient is not 1, you must first group the x^2-term and x-term. Then, factor the leading coefficient out of the grouping. Finally, add and subtract the square of half the coefficient of x *inside the grouping*.

Example 3 Completing the Square: Leading Coefficient Is Not 1

Write the function $f(x) = 2x^2 + 4x + 1$ in completed square form. Then sketch its graph.

Solution

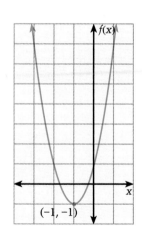

$$f(x) = 2x^2 + 4x + 1 \qquad \textit{Standard form}$$
$$f(x) = (2x^2 + 4x) + 1 \qquad \textit{Group } x^2\text{- and x-terms.}$$
$$f(x) = 2(x^2 + 2x) + 1 \qquad \textit{Factor out leading coefficient.}$$
$$f(x) = 2(x^2 + 2x + 1^2 - 1^2) + 1 \qquad \textit{Add and subtract } 1^2$$
$$\text{(half of 2)}^2 \qquad \textit{inside parentheses.}$$
$$f(x) = 2[(x + 1)^2 - 1^2] + 1 \qquad \textit{Group terms.}$$
$$f(x) = 2(x + 1)^2 - 2(1^2) + 1 \qquad \textit{Distributive Property}$$
$$f(x) = 2(x + 1)^2 - 1 \qquad \textit{Completed square form}$$

From the completed square form, you can see that the vertex of the parabola is $(-1, -1)$. The graph is shown at the left. ■

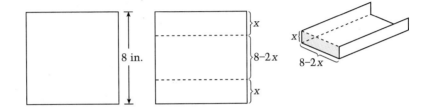

Start with a piece of paper that is 8 inches long. Fold both sides of the paper up by the same amount, x. The resulting "trough" has cross sections with area x(8 − 2x).

Connections
Geometry

Example 4 *Finding the Maximum Area*

Where should the paper described above be folded to obtain the maximum cross-section area?

Solution

Verbal Model

| Area | = | Width | × | Height |

Labels

Height of cross section = x (inches)
Width of cross section = $8 - 2x$ (inches)
Area of cross section = A (square inches)

Function
$A = (8 - 2x)(x)$
$A = -2x^2 + 8x$ *Standard form*
$A = -2(x - 2)^2 + 8$ *Completed square form*

The graph of this equation is a parabola that opens down and has its vertex at (2, 8) This tells you that the maximum cross-section area is 8 square inches and that you can obtain the maximum area by folding up 2 inches of paper on each end. ∎

Communicating about **ALGEBRA**

▶ **SHARING IDEAS about the Lesson**

Use a Pattern   Write each function in completed square form. Then identify the vertex and sketch the graph.

A. $f(x) = x^2 - 4x + 2$ **B.** $f(x) = -x^2 - 2x - 5$

C. $f(x) = 2x^2 - 4x + 7$ **D.** $f(x) = -3x^2 - 6x - 4$

EXERCISES

Guided Practice

▶ **CRITICAL THINKING about the Lesson**

1. Write $f(x) = x^2 - 6x + 6$ in completed square form.

2. What is the vertex of the graph of $f(x) = 3(x + 4)^2 - 3$?

3. Sketch the graph of $f(x) = (x + 1)^2 + 1$. Explain why the vertex is the lowest point on the graph.

4. Sketch the graph of $f(x) = -(x - 1)^2 - 1$. Explain why the vertex is the highest point on the graph.

Independent Practice

In Exercises 5–10, find the vertex of the graph of the function. Is the vertex the lowest or highest point on the graph?

5. $f(x) = -2(x - 1)^2 + 5$

6. $f(x) = -(x - 3)^2 - 5$

7. $f(x) = 3(x - 3)^2 - 2$

8. $f(x) = 4(x - 7)^2$

9. $f(x) = (x + 2)^2 + 6$

10. $f(x) = 9(x + 5) + 9$

In Exercises 11–14, match the function with its graph.

11. $f(x) = (x - 4)^2 + 5$

12. $f(x) = -(x - 1)^2 + 3$

13. $f(x) = -(x + 3)^2 - 3$

14. $f(x) = (x + 2)^2 - 4$

a.   **b.**   **c.**   **d.**

In Exercises 15–20, sketch the graph of the function.

15. $f(x) = (x - 1)^2 - 3$

16. $f(x) = -(x + 7)^2 + 2$

17. $f(x) = -(x + 2)^2 - 7$

18. $f(x) = -(x - 2)^2 + 6$

19. $f(x) = (x - 4)^2 + 2$

20. $f(x) = (x + 8)^2 - 2$

In Exercises 21–28, write the function in completed square form. Then find the vertex of its graph.

21. $f(x) = x^2 - 18x + 79$

22. $f(x) = x^2 + 8x + 11$

23. $f(x) = x^2 - 4x + 16$

24. $f(x) = x^2 + 10x + 33$

25. $f(x) = x^2 + 16x + 62$

26. $f(x) = x^2 - 24x + 151$

27. $f(x) = -x^2 - 6x - 1$

28. $f(x) = -x^2 + 8x - 25$

In Exercises 29–36, write the function in completed square form. Then sketch its graph.

29. $f(x) = x^2 - 10x + 19$

30. $f(x) = x^2 - 8x + 25$

31. $f(x) = x^2 + 8x + 9$

32. $f(x) = x^2 - 20x - 50$

33. $f(x) = 2x^2 + 32x + 121$

34. $f(x) = -3x^2 + 30x - 81$

35. $f(x) = 3x^2 - 12x + 6$

36. $f(x) = 2x^2 - 4x + 5$

Cardboard Play Box   **In Exercises 37 and 38, use the following information.**

You are building a cardboard play box for a kitten from a 48-inch square piece of cardboard. You want to maximize the area of the side of the box.

37. Let $f(x)$ represent the area of the one side of the box. Write an equation for $f(x)$ in completed square form. Sketch its graph.

38. How tall should you make the box? What are the dimensions of its base?

Human Cannonball   **In Exercises 39 and 40, use the following information.**

A human cannonball is shot from a cannon and follows the path given by

$$h(x) = -\frac{1}{100}x^2 + x + 8$$

where $h(x)$ is the height in feet (above ground) and x is the horizontal distance traveled in feet.

39. Write the function in completed square form. Explain how this form can be used to find the maximum height of the human cannonball.

40. The human cannonball lands in a net that is 8 feet above the ground. How many feet does the human cannonball travel?

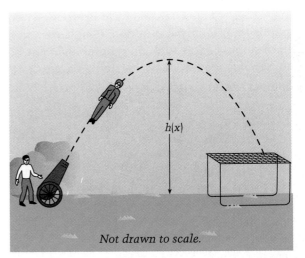

Not drawn to scale.

The human cannonball act originated in 1875 at the Circus d'Hiver in Paris, France. The record distance shot is 175 feet (1940, Ringling Brothers, Barnum & Bailey Circus).

Iron and Steel Production   **In Exercises 41 and 42, use the following information.**

For 1950 through 1990, the United States iron and raw steel production, $f(t)$, as a percent of the world's production can be modeled by $f(t) = 1.7t^2 - 15.3t + 45.2$, where $t = 0$ represents 1950, $t = 1$ represents 1960, and so on.

41. Write the model in completed square form. Sketch its graph from $t = 0$ to $t = 7$.

42. The U.S. percent of world production has been decreasing. According to the model, when will this trend change?

In Exercises 43–48, solve the equation by completing the square.

43. $x^2 + 6x - 7 = 0$

44. $x^2 - 2x - 35 = 0$

45. $x^2 - 4x - 9 = 0$

46. $x^2 + 12x - 16 = 0$

47. $4x^2 - 16x - 5 = 0$

48. $3x^2 + 24x - 131 = 0$

In Exercises 49–54, find the vertex of the graph in two ways: by using shifts from the origin, as in Lesson 9.3, and by the method presented in this lesson. Which do you prefer and why?

49. $y = x^2 - 4x + 11$

50. $y = x^2 + 18x + 90$

51. $y = x^2 + 2x - 2$

52. $y = x^2 - 8x + 22$

53. $y = 3x^2 - 72x + 428$

54. $y = 2x^2 - 4x + 3$

In Exercises 55–60, sketch the graph of the equation. Use any method and explain why you chose the method.

55. $y = x^2 + 2x - 2$

56. $y = x^2 - 14x + 53$

57. $y = x^2 + 10x + 18$

58. $y = x^2 + 2x - 9$

59. $y = 2x^2 - 4x + 18$

60. $y = 4x^2 + 24x + 33$

Homeowners and Renters   **In Exercises 61 and 62, use the circle graphs to answer the question. (Single-person households have one or more single people with *no* children living at home. Female or male households are families with single parents *and* children living at home.)**

61. What is the probability that a randomly chosen homeowner is a female householder?

62. What is the probability that a randomly chosen renter is a female householder?

Exploration and Extension

63. Let *a* and *b* be positive numbers. Which two of the following functions have graphs that do not intersect the *x*-axis? Explain.

   a. $f(x) = -(x - a)^2 + b$ **b.** $f(x) = -(x - a)^2 - b$

   c. $f(x) = (x - a)^2 + b$ **d.** $f(x) = (x - a)^2 - b$

Take this test as you would take a test in class. The answers to the exercises are given in the back of the book.

In Exercises 1 and 2, decide whether the table defines _y_ as a function of _x_. (12.1)

1.

x	a	b	c	a	a
y	1	3	5	7	9

2.

x	g	h	i	j	k
y	9	3	0	4	5

In Exercises 3–8, evaluate the function at $x = -2$, $x = 0$, and $x = 2$. (12.1)

3. $f(x) = 3x + 2$

4. $f(x) = -2x - 4$

5. $f(x) = x^2 - 1$

6. $f(x) = -3x^2 + 5$

7. $f(x) = 4x^2 - 2x + 1$

8. $f(x) = -2x^2 + 4x + 6$

In Exercises 9–11, find an equation for the linear function _f_. (12.2)

9. $f(0) = 3, f(3) = 9$

10. $f(-2) = 6, f(2) = -6$

11. $f(-1) = 4, f(5) = 4$

In Exercises 12–14, how does the graph of _g_ compare to the graph of $f(x) = 3^x$? (12.3)

12. $g(x) = 3^x + 2$

13. $g(x) = 3^x - 4$

14. $g(x) = 3^{x-2}$

In Exercises 15–17, write the function in completed square form. Then sketch its graph. (12.4)

15. $f(x) = x^2 - 4x + 9$

16. $f(x) = -x^2 - 2x - 4$

17. $f(x) = 2x^2 - 4x - 7$

18. The table shows the number of bowling establishments and the number of bowling lanes in use from 1984 to 1988 in the United States. Is the number of bowling lanes, L (in 1000's), a function of the number of bowling establishments, B?

Year	1984	1985	1986	1987	1988
Establishments, B	8351	8275	8149	8031	7923
Lanes, L	155	155	153	151	150

19. While cartwheeling down a sand dune, a golden wheel spider can travel 5 feet per second. Find a linear function that gives the distance traveled as a function of the time. Use the function to find the distance traveled in 12 seconds.

20. A sheet of paper is 20 centimeters wide. When x centimeters of paper are folded up on each side, the area of the cross section is $A = x(20 - 2x)$ square centimeters. How many centimeters should be folded up to obtain a maximum cross-section area?

This is an orb weaver spider from Florida, which specializes in perfect webs.

Rational Functions

What you should learn:

Goal 1 How to sketch the graph of a rational function

Goal 2 How to use rational functions as models of real-life problems

Why you should learn it:

You can use rational functions to model the change in the ratios of two quantities over a period of time.

Hyperbola with asymptotes

Goal 1 Graphing a Rational Function

A **rational function** is a function of the form

$$f(x) = \frac{\text{polynomial}}{\text{polynomial}}.$$

In this lesson, you will study rational functions whose numerators and denominators are first-degree polynomials. Using long division, such a function can be written in the form

$$f(x) = \frac{a}{x - h} + k.$$

Rational Functions Whose Graphs Are Hyperbolas

The graph of the rational function

$$f(x) = \frac{a}{x - h} + k$$

is a **hyperbola** whose **center** is (h, k). The vertical and horizontal lines through the center are the **asymptotes** of the hyperbola.

The center and asymptotes of a hyperbola are used as sketching aids. They are *not* part of the graph.

Example 1 *Sketching the Graph of a Rational Function*

Sketch the graph of $f(x) = \frac{1}{x} + 2$.

Solution Think of the function as

$$f(x) = \frac{1}{x - 0} + 2 = \frac{a}{x - h} + k. \qquad f(x) = \frac{a}{x - h} + k$$

You can see that the center is $(0, 2)$. The asymptotes can be drawn as dashed lines through the center. Construct a table of values to help locate several points on the graph. Choose a few x-values to one side of the x-coordinate of the center. (Because the hyperbola is symmetrical about the center, you need only plot points on one branch.)

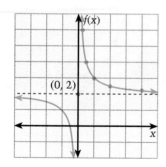

x	0	0.25	0.5	1	2	4
$f(x) = \frac{1}{x} + 2$	Undefined	6	4	3	2.5	2.25

Example 2 — *Graphing a Rational Function*

Sketch the graph of these rational functions.

a. $f(x) = \dfrac{-1}{x + 2} + 1$

b. $f(x) = \dfrac{2}{x - 3} - 2$

Solution

a. The graph of

$$f(x) = \frac{-1}{x + 2} + 1$$

is a hyperbola with center at $(-2, 1)$.

x	−1.5	−1	0
f(x)	−1	0	0.5

b. The graph of

$$f(x) = \frac{2}{x - 3} - 2$$

is a hyperbola with center at $(3, -2)$.

x	3.5	4	5
f(x)	2	0	−1

Polynomial long division can be used to write some rational functions in the form

$$f(x) = \frac{a}{x - h} + k.$$

Example 3 — *Using Polynomial Long Division First*

Sketch the graph of $f(x) = \dfrac{2x + 1}{x + 2}$.

Solution Begin by dividing $2x + 1$ by $x + 2$.

$$
\begin{array}{r}
2 \\
x + 2 \overline{)\, 2x + 1} \\
\underline{2x + 4} \\
-3
\end{array}
$$

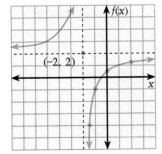

From the form

$$f(x) = 2 - \frac{3}{x + 2} \quad \text{or} \quad f(x) = \frac{-3}{x + 2} + 2$$

you can see that the graph is a hyperbola with center at $(-2, 2)$. Some points on the hyperbola are shown in the table.

x	−1.5	−1	0	2
f(x)	−4	−1	0.5	1.25

In 1970, Americans consumed a per capita average of about 11 pounds of cheese. By 1990, the average consumption had more than doubled.

Connections
Consumer Studies

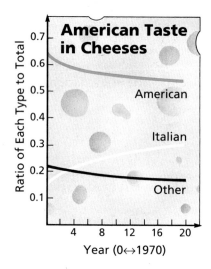

American Taste in Cheeses

American

Italian

Other

Ratio of Each Type to Total

0.7
0.6
0.5
0.4
0.3
0.2
0.1

4   8   12   16   20

Year (0↔1970)

Example 4   *Finding Ratios*

For 1970 to 1990, the per capita consumption of cheese in the United States can be modeled as follows ($t = 0$ represents 1970).

Type of Cheese	Consumption Model
All types:	$C = 10.70 + 0.75t$ (pounds)
American (including cheddar):	$A = 6.75 + 0.34t$ (pounds)
Italian (including mozzarella):	$I = 1.60 + 0.31t$ (pounds)
Other (including cream cheese):	$O = 2.35 + 0.10t$ (pounds)

Use graphs to show how the ratio of each of the three consumptions to the total consumption was changing.

(Source: U.S. Department of Agriculture)

Solution   The three ratios are as follows:

$$\frac{A}{C} = \frac{6.75 + 0.34t}{10.70 + 0.75t} \qquad \frac{I}{C} = \frac{1.60 + 0.31t}{10.70 + 0.75t} \qquad \frac{O}{C} = \frac{2.35 + 0.10t}{10.70 + 0.75t}$$

Notice that each graph is part of a branch of a hyperbola.   ∎

Communicating about **ALGEBRA**

▶ **SHARING IDEAS about the Lesson**

Sketch a Graph   Sketch the graph of each function.

A. $f(x) = \dfrac{1}{x - 1} + 1$

B. $f(x) = -\dfrac{2}{x + 1} + 3$

C. $f(x) = \dfrac{3x + 1}{x - 2}$

D. $f(x) = \dfrac{3x - 1}{x + 1}$

EXERCISES

Guided Practice

▶ **CRITICAL THINKING about the Lesson**

In Exercises 1–4, describe the center and asymptotes of the hyperbola. Explain the steps you used.

1. $f(x) = \dfrac{4}{x+5} - 3$

2. $f(x) = \dfrac{-10}{x-10} + 4$

3. $f(x) = \dfrac{-1}{x-3} + 16$

4. $f(x) = \dfrac{3}{x+1} - 9$

5. Sketch the graph of $f(x) = \dfrac{4}{x}$.

6. Sketch the graph of $f(x) = \dfrac{1}{x+1} + 2$.

Independent Practice

In Exercises 7–12, find the center and asymptotes of the hyperbola.

7. $f(x) = \dfrac{1}{x-5} + 2$

8. $f(x) = \dfrac{1}{x-3} - 8$

9. $f(x) = \dfrac{2}{x-4} + 6$

10. $f(x) = -\dfrac{3}{x+1} + 8$

11. $f(x) = -\dfrac{6}{x+9} - 7$

12. $f(x) = -\dfrac{3}{x+1} - 4$

In Exercises 13–18, match the equation with its graph.

13. $f(x) = \dfrac{1}{x-6} - 1$

14. $f(x) = -\dfrac{1}{x+7} - 1$

15. $f(x) = \dfrac{-2}{x+3} + 7$

16. $f(x) = \dfrac{2}{x-6} + 9$

17. $f(x) = \dfrac{1}{x-9} - 6$

18. $f(x) = \dfrac{1}{x-1} - 7$

a.

b.

c.

d.

e.

f.

In Exercises 19–30, sketch the graph of the function.

19. $f(x) = \dfrac{1}{x + 4} + 2$

20. $f(x) = \dfrac{1}{x + 7} + 3$

21. $f(x) = \dfrac{3}{x - 1} + 4$

22. $f(x) = \dfrac{2}{x - 2} + 9$

23. $f(x) = -\dfrac{2}{x - 5} - 4$

24. $f(x) = -\dfrac{1}{x + 9} + 1$

25. $f(x) = \dfrac{2}{x + 9} - 4$

26. $f(x) = -\dfrac{3}{x - 3} - 2$

27. $f(x) = -\dfrac{1}{x - 7} + 4$

28. $f(x) = \dfrac{2}{x + 8} - 8$

29. $f(x) = \dfrac{5}{x - 5} - 3$

30. $f(x) = \dfrac{4}{x + 4} + 5$

In Exercises 31–36, use polynomial division to help sketch the graph of the function.

31. $f(x) = \dfrac{-2x + 11}{x - 5}$

32. $f(x) = \dfrac{x + 10}{x + 8}$

33. $f(x) = \dfrac{-9x + 16}{x - 2}$

34. $f(x) = \dfrac{9x - 6}{x - 1}$

35. $f(x) = \dfrac{-5x + 19}{x - 3}$

36. $f(x) = -\dfrac{6x - 50}{x + 8}$

Hong Kong **In Exercises 37 and 38, use the following information.**

In 1898, Britain signed a lease with China. In the lease, Britain was allowed control of Hong Kong for a certain number of years. Let t represent any of the years between 1898 and 1997, the year the lease is up. The ratio, $f(t)$, of the years leased to the years yet to lease is given by

$$f(t) = \frac{t - 1898}{1997 - t}.$$

37. Sketch the graph of the function f on the interval $1898 \leq t < 1997$. What is the vertical asymptote of the graph? In this problem, what does it represent?

38. During which year was $f(t)$ equal to 1? What was the significance of this year?

Hong Kong is known for its many shops. Over two million tourists visit Hong Kong each year.

Soaking Crabs **In Exercises 39 and 40, use the following information.**

You and your sister are visiting Christmas Island (near Australia) during the crab migration. The weather is hot, and you decide to set up a crab rescue station. At the rescue station, you soak the crabs in water, then release them. Your sister collects 5 crabs the first day and you collect 20. Each day after that your sister collects 2 more than the day before and you collect 1 more.

39. Create a model that represents the ratio, $f(x)$, of the number of crabs you collect each day to the number of crabs your sister collects. (Let $x = 0$ represent the first day.)

40. Your rescue station is open for 30 days. Sketch a graph of the function f.

In Exercises 41–43, simplify the quotient.

41. $\dfrac{x^2 - 2x - 3}{4} \div \dfrac{x - 3}{2}$

42. $\dfrac{x^2 + 3x - 10}{14} \div \dfrac{x + 5}{2}$

43. $\dfrac{1}{x^2 - 4} \div \dfrac{x + 2}{x - 2}$

In Exercises 44–46, solve the equation.

44. $\dfrac{1}{x^2} = \dfrac{1}{4}$

45. $\dfrac{x - 3}{4} = \dfrac{1}{x}$

46. $\dfrac{1}{x} - \dfrac{5}{x - 5} = 16$

In Exercises 47–50, match the equation with its graph.

47. $f(x) = \dfrac{2x - 3}{x + 1}$

48. $f(x) = x^2 - 4x + 5$

49. $f(x) = \dfrac{1}{3}x$

50. $f(x) = \left(\dfrac{5}{3}\right)^x - 1$

a.

b.

c.

d.
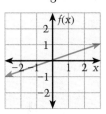

Government Payroll   **In Exercises 51 and 52, use the following information.**

For 1980 through 1990, the total government payroll (in millions of dollars), can be modeled by $T = 1836t + 1954$, where $t = 0$ represents 1980. The total payroll of the states in millions of dollars can be modeled by $S = 431.5t + 4189$.

51. Find a model that represents the ratio of the state payroll to the total government payroll. Then use a graphing calculator to sketch the graph of the model.

52. Estimate the horizontal asymptote of the graph. What does it represent?

Mixed R E V I E W

1. Find the reciprocal of $2x^2y^{-1}$. **(8.2)**

2. Solve $\dfrac{1}{x} - \dfrac{2x}{3} = \dfrac{5}{3}$. **(11.8)**

3. Evaluate $3^n + 4n$ when $n = 3$. **(1.4)**

4. Solve $3|4 - m| \le 3$. **(6.4)**

5. Simplify $(x^2y^{-2})^{-1} \div 3(xy^4)^2$. **(8.2)**

6. What is 69% of 43?

7. Evaluate $(6.7 \times 10^{-3}) \div (2.0 \times 10^5)$. **(8.4)**

8. Find the vertex: $y = x^2 + 6x - 25$. **(9.3)**

9. Solve $512 = 8(1 + p)^2$. **(9.2)**

10. Solve the system: $\begin{cases} 2x - 3y = 4 \\ -2x - 4y = 10 \end{cases}$ **(7.3)**

Exploring Data: Stem-and-Leaf Plots, Box-and-Whisker Plots

What you should learn:

Goal 1 How to construct a stem-and-leaf plot for data

Goal 2 How to construct a box-and-whisker plot for data

Why you should learn it:

Stem-and-leaf plots can help you organize large sets of data, such as the salaries of professional athletes.

Goal 1 Constructing Stem-and-Leaf Plots

A **stem-and-leaf plot** is a technique for ordering data in increasing order or decreasing order. In the following example, the *stem* consists of the tens digits for the data and the *leaves* consist of the units digits.

	Stem-and-Leaf	
Unordered Data	**Plot**	**Ordered Data**
52, 35, 26, 7, 31,	6 │ 0 3 2 4	64, 63, 62, 60
31, 60, 14, 24, 54,	5 │ 2 4 8 0	58, 54, 52, 50
15, 19, 24, 63, 58,	4 │ 1 4 7 5 2	47, 45, 44, 42, 41
41, 23, 39, 8, 12,	3 │ 5 1 1 9 4	39, 35, 34, 31, 31
18, 34, 62, 6, 44,	2 │ 6 4 4 3 6 9 8	29, 28, 26, 26, 24, 24, 23
47, 45, 26, 29, 50,	1 │ 4 5 9 2 8 7 1	19, 18, 17, 15, 14, 12, 11
17, 11, 64, 28, 42	0 │ 7 8 6	8, 7, 6

Stem　　Leaves

Real Life

Golf

Example 1 *Using a Stem-and-Leaf Plot*

The top 15 PGA Senior Tour golf winners for 1990 (through November 1) are shown in the table. Use a stem-and-leaf plot to order the winnings. *(Source: USA Today)*

Solution　To construct a stem-and-leaf plot, consider only the first two digits of each number.

```
9 │ 5
6 │ 4 7 4 8 3
4 │ 6 2 5 3 9
3 │ 1 4 2 4     Key: 9 │ 5 represents $950,000.
```

Now, using the stem-and-leaf plot, order the winnings (in thousands) as follows.

$950	$680	$670	$640	$640
Trevino	M. Hill	Coody	Archer	Dent
$630	$490	$460	$450	$430
Rodriguez	Player	Charles	Douglass	McBee
$420	$340	$340	$320	$310
Crampton	Henning	Nicklaus	D. Hill	Gelberger ■

Winnings in 1000's	
George Archer	$640
Bob Charles	$460
Charles Coody	$670
Bruce Crampton	$420
Jim Dent	$640
Dale Douglass	$450
Al Gelberger	$310
Harold Henning	$340
Dave Hill	$320
Mike Hill	$680
Rives McBee	$430
Jack Nicklaus	$340
Gary Player	$490
Chi Chi Rodriguez	$630
Lee Trevino	$950

Constructing Box-and-Whisker Plots

You already know how to find the *average*, or **mean,** of *n* numbers: Add the numbers and divide the sum by *n*. It is one of the ways to represent the "middle" or "center" of a collection of numbers. (We will say more about measures of *central tendency* in the next lesson.) Another way to represent the middle of a collection of numbers is with a number called the *median*.

> **The Median of a Collection of Numbers**
>
> **1.** The **median** of an odd collection of numbers, arranged *in order,* is the middle number.
> **2.** The **median** of an even collection of numbers, arranged *in order,* is the average of the two middle numbers.

Example 2   *Finding the Median*

a. The median of 2, 4, 4, 5,   6 , 8, 8, 9, 10 is 6.

         Middle

b. The median of 1, 1, 3, 4, 4, 5, 6, 6, 7, 8 is $\frac{9}{2}$. ∎

The median of an ordered collection of numbers roughly partitions the collection into two halves: those below the median and those above. The **first quartile** is the median of the lower half. The **second quartile** is the median of the entire collection. The **third quartile** is the median of the upper half. Quartiles partition an ordered collection into four **quarters.**

Example 3   *Finding the Quartiles*

The 15 golf winnings in Example 1 can be partitioned into quarters by the quartiles 340 (1st), 460 (2nd), and 640 (3rd).

1st Quarter:	310, 320, 340,	$x \leq 340$
2nd Quarter:	420, 430, 450,	$340 \leq x \leq 460$
3rd Quarter:	490, 630, 640,	$460 \leq x \leq 640$
4th Quarter:	670, 680, 950	$640 \leq x$

∎

A **box-and-whisker plot** can be used to present a graphic summary of information shown, like that in Example 3.

310 340   460   640   950

Heights of Females
(18-24 years old)

62.5"   64.5"   66.5"

Heights of Males
(18-24 years old)

67.5"   69.5"   71.5"

The box-and-whisker plots represent the heights of American females and males. (Source: U.S. Center for Health Statistics)

Real Life

Human Heights

Example 4	*Reading a Box-and-Whisker Plot*

Aaron and Ann are twins who will be starting college in the fall. Aaron is 5′10″ tall and Ann is 5′7″ tall.

a. What percent of the men at college are taller than Aaron?

b. What percent of the women at college are taller than Ann?

Solution

a. Aaron is 70 inches tall. For American males between 18 and 24 years of age, this is $\frac{1}{2}$ inch above the median. Less than 50% of the men are taller than Aaron.

b. Ann is 67 inches tall. This is $\frac{1}{2}$ inch above the third quartile. Less than 25% of the women are taller than Ann. ■

Communicating about **ALGEBRA**

▶ **SHARING IDEAS about the Lesson**

The book *Life in America's Small Cities* rated 219 United States towns in several categories. The list shows the "diversions" ratings (on a scale from 0 to 100) for towns in North Carolina, South Carolina, and Georgia (diversions are shopping, dining, theaters, recreation). Make a stem-and-leaf plot *and* a box-and-whisker plot for these data. (High numbers indicate more diversions.)

Brunswick, GA	59	New Bern, NC	29
Greenwood, SC	30	Rocky Mount, NC	33
Hinesville, GA	22	Statesville, NC	30
Myrtle Beach, SC	75	Wilson, NC	36
Rome, GA	28	Greenville, NC	37
Shelby, NC	23	Hilton Head, SC	47
Valdosta, GA	43	Lumberton, NC	24
Goldsboro, NC	25	Orangeburg, SC	26
Havelock, NC	29	Sanford, NC	41
Kinston, NC	38	Sumter, SC	22

EXERCISES

▶ **CRITICAL THINKING about the Lesson**

1. Why might you construct a stem-and-leaf plot for a data collection?

2. Describe the mean and median of a collection of numbers. Give an example in which they are the same. Give an example in which they are different.

3. Copy the data listing shown at the right. Label the first, second, third, and fourth *quarters* of the data collection. Label the first, second, and third *quartiles* of the data collection. Which quartile is equal to the median?

4. Construct a stem-and-leaf plot for the collection. Use your result to construct a box-and-whisker plot.

   55, 43, 12, 38, 49, 17, 32, 12, 39, 51, 44, 25, 46, 29, 20, 51, 24, 32, 13, 54

2, 2, 3, 4, 4, 5, 6, 6, 7, 8, 8, 9

Independent Practice

In Exercises 5–8, find the median of the collection of numbers.

5. 16, 7, 25, 0, 3, 3, 21, 8

6. 150, 156, 160, 149, 150, 152

7. 1, 12, 15, 3, 11, 8, 12, 19, 4, 9, 10, 13, 7

8. 6.35, 4.40, 3.56, 3.56, 4.68

In Exercises 9 and 10, construct a stem-and-leaf plot for the data. Use the result to list the data in increasing order.

9. 48, 10, 48, 25, 40, 42, 44, 23, 21, 13, 50, 17, 18, 19, 21, 35, 33, 25, 50, 13, 12, 46, 57, 41, 13, 59, 31, 48, 26, 15

10. 85, 61, 55, 78, 79, 86, 30, 76, 76, 87, 68, 82, 61, 84, 52, 33, 30, 68, 89, 70, 37, 42, 80

In Exercises 11–14, construct a box-and-whisker plot for the data.

11. 48, 60, 40, 68, 51, 47, 57, 41, 65, 61, 20, 65, 49, 34, 63, 53, 52, 35, 45, 35, 65, 65, 48, 36, 24, 53, 64, 48, 40, 22, 66, 66

12. 167, 191, 190, 154, 188, 174, 192, 166, 180, 155, 157, 161, 163, 172, 169, 167, 182, 184, 158, 160, 176, 192, 174, 161

13.

14.

In Exercises 15–18, create a collection of 16 numbers that could be represented by the box-and-whisker plot. (There are many correct answers.)

15.

10 13   19   27   38

16.

106   124   150 162   193

17.

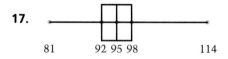

81   92 95 98   114

18.

284 302   325   382 404

19. *Birthdays*   Use a stem-and-leaf plot (months as stems, days as leaves) to write the following birthdays in order (earliest to latest).

10-11	4-14	7-31	12-28	4-15	4-30	2-22	8-21
1-24	9-12	1-3	2-7	4-30	10-17	6-5	1-25
5-10	11-11	12-9	4-1	8-26	12-15	3-17	6-13

20. *Food Drive*   Twelve ninth-grade classes are having a food drive. Use a stem-and-leaf plot to order (from smallest to largest) the number of food items collected per class.

120, 98, 150, 129, 126, 122, 136, 121, 133, 139, 155, 99

Immigration   **In Exercises 21 and 22, use the following information.**

In 1988, 264,500 people immigrated to the United States from Asia and 64,800 immigrated from Europe. The lists show the number of immigrants (in 1000's) from several Asian countries and several European countries. Use a stem-and-leaf plot to write the numbers in decreasing order. *(Source: U.S. Immigration and Naturalization Service)*

21.

Cambodia	9.6	China	28.7	Taiwan	9.7	Hong Kong	8.5
India	26.3	Iran	15.2	Iraq	1.0	Israel	3.6
Japan	3.6	Jordan	4.5	Korea	34.7	Laos	10.7
Lebanon	4.9	Pakistan	5.4	Philippines	50.7	Syria	2.2
Thailand	6.9	Turkey	1.6	Vietnam	25.8		

22.

Czechoslovakia	1.5	France	2.5	Germany	6.8	Greece	2.5
Hungary	1.2	Ireland	5.1	Italy	2.9	Netherlands	1.2
Poland	9.5	Portugal	3.2	Romania	3.9	Soviet Union	2.9
Spain	1.5	Sweden	1.2	Switzerland	0.8	United Kingdom	13.2
Yugoslavia	1.9						

23. *Presidential Election*   In the 1988 presidential election, 91,600,000 Americans voted. The following list shows the percent of this total in the 20 states with the greatest numbers voting. Use a stem-and-leaf plot to order the data in increasing order. Then use the results to construct *two* visual models of the data: a box-and-whisker plot and a bar graph. (Use intervals of width 2, beginning with $1 \leq x < 3$.) Which visual model do you think helps to best present the data? Explain your reasons.

(Source: Committee for the Study of the American Electorate)

California	10.8	Florida	4.7	Georgia	2.0	Illinois	5.0
Indiana	2.4	Maryland	1.9	Massachusetts	2.9	Michigan	4.0
Minnesota	2.3	Missouri	2.3	New Jersey	3.4	New York	7.1
North Carolina	2.3	Ohio	4.8	Pennsylvania	5.0	Tennessee	1.8
Texas	5.9	Virginia	2.4	Washington	2.0	Wisconsin	2.4

24. *Presidential Election*   The following list shows the 20 states that had the greatest percent of their own populations vote in the 1988 presidential elections. Construct *two* visual models of the data: a box-and-whisker plot and a bar graph. (Use intervals of width 2, beginning with $40 \leq x < 42$.) How would you explain the fact that this list is so different from the list given in Exercise 23?

(Source: Committee for the Study of the American Electorate)

Colorado	42	Connecticut	45	Idaho	41	Iowa	43
Maine	46	Massachusetts	45	Minnesota	49	Missouri	41
Montana	45	Nebraska	41	New Hampshire	42	New Jersey	40
North Dakota	45	Ohio	40	Oregon	43	Rhode Island	41
South Dakota	44	Vermont	44	Washington	40	Wisconsin	45

25. Use the information given in Exercises 23 and 24 to find the 1988 population of Washington.

26. Use the information given in Exercises 23 and 24 to find the 1988 population of New Jersey.

27. The heights, in meters, of the world's tallest skyscrapers are given in the list below. Choose one or more of the data-organization techniques discussed in this text to organize the data. Explain why you chose the method you used.

Allied Bank Plaza, Houston	302	Amoco, Chicago	346
Bank of Montreal Tower, Toronto	285	Bank of China, Hong Kong	305
Columbia Seafirst Center, Seattle	291	Citicorp Center, New York City	279
First Interstate World, Los Angeles	310	Empire State, New York City	381
NCNB Plaza, Dallas	281	John Hancock Center, Chicago	344
Scotia Plaza, Toronto	276	Overseas Union Bank, Singapore	280
Texas Commerce Tower, Houston	305	Sears Tower, Chicago	443
Two Prudential Plaza, Chicago	288	World Trade Center, New York City	411

Exploring Data: Measures of Central Tendency

Real Life
Quality Control

Goal 1 Measuring Central Tendency

There are three commonly used measures of **central tendency** for a collection of numbers.

1. The **mean,** or **average,** of *n* numbers is the sum of the numbers divided by *n*.

2. The **median** of *n* numbers is the middle number when the numbers are written in order. (If *n* is even, the median is the average of the two middle numbers.)

3. The **mode** of *n* numbers is the number that occurs most frequently. If two numbers tie for most frequent occurrence, the collection has two modes and is called **bimodal.**

Many collections of numbers that are taken from real life have bar graphs that are *bell-shaped.* For such collections, the mean, median, and mode are approximately equal.

Example 1 *Central Tendency of a Bell-Shaped Distribution*

A tire manufacturer conducted a survey of 118 people who had purchased a particular type of tire. Each person was asked to report the number of miles driven before replacing tires. The responses are shown at the left. Construct a bar graph for these data. Find the mean, median, and mode.

Solution The bar graph is bell-shaped. Most of the tires lasted between 18,000 and 22,000 miles. The median and mode are each 20,000. The mean is more difficult to calculate, but after some effort, you can find that it is also 20,000 miles.

Miles	Number of Responses
14,000	1
15,000	2
16,000	5
17,000	9
18,000	14
19,000	18
20,000	20
21,000	18
22,000	14
23,000	9
24,000	5
25,000	2
26,000	1

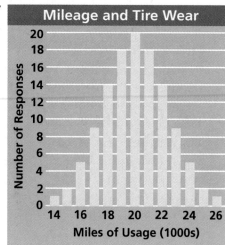

Mean: 20,000 miles
Median: 20,000 miles
Mode: 20,000 miles

Measures of central tendency are part of a field of mathematics called *statistics*. The goal of statistics is to organize large collections of data in ways that can be used to understand trends and make predictions.

Unfortunately, almost any data collection can be organized in several different ways—some of which are not at all representative of the data. Example 2 describes such an *abuse* of statistics.

Real Life
Education

Example 2 *Interpreting Measures of Central Tendency*

Elliot School, a small rural high school, had 28 graduates in 1992. Of the 28, 7 were 17 years old, 19 were 18 years old, 1 was 19 years old, and 1 was 80 years old! (A retired member of the community had decided to go back to high school to obtain a diploma.) The next fall a legislator from a neighboring school district wanted to have Elliot School closed. One reason given was that "the average age of a high school graduate at Elliot is 20 years." Was the legislator's mathematics correct? Was the choice of a measure of central tendency an honest representation of the typical age of an Elliot graduate?

Solution   The legislator's mathematics was correct.

$$\text{Mean} = \frac{7(17) + 19(18) + 1(19) + 1(80)}{28} = \frac{560}{28} = 20$$

The choice of a measure of central tendency, however, was unfair to Elliot School. Both the median and the mode of the ages were 18 years.

In 1988, approximately 10% of the 20,000 public high schools in the United States had enrollments of less than 100 students.

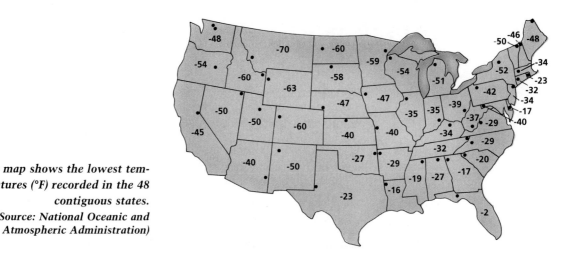

The map shows the lowest temperatures (°F) recorded in the 48
contiguous states.
*(Source: National Oceanic and
Atmospheric Administration)*

Connections
Meteorology

Example 3 *Finding the Mean, Median, and Mode*

Find the mean, median, and mode of the temperatures shown
in the map above. Sketch a box-and-whisker plot for the data.

Solution In increasing order, the low temperatures are:

$$-70, -63, -60, -60, -60, -59, -58, -54, -54, -52,$$
$$-51, -50, -50, -50, -50, -48, -48, -47, -47, -46,$$
$$-45, -42, -40, -40, -40, -40, -39, -37, -35, -35,$$
$$-34, -34, -34, -32, -32, -29, -29, -29, -27, -27,$$
$$-23, -23, -20, -19, -17, -17, -16, -2$$

The median is $-40°F$. There are two modes: $-40°F$ and
$-50°F$, each of which occurs four times. The mean is

$$\frac{-70 - 63 - 60 - 60 - \cdots - 16 - 2}{48} = \frac{-1914}{48} = -39.875°.$$

The box-and-whisker plot for these data is as follows.

-70   -50   -40   -29   -2   ■

Communicating about **ALGEBRA**

▶ **SHARING IDEAS about the Lesson**

Analyze Data At a family reunion, four brothers are comparing their weights. Which of the following have a mean
of 180? A median of 180? A mode of 180?

A. 170, 171, 182, 197   **B.** 165, 178, 180, 197

C. 165, 178, 180, 180   **D.** 172, 180, 180, 188

EXERCISES

Guided Practice

▸ **CRITICAL THINKING about the Lesson**

1. Define the mean, median, and mode of a collection of numbers.

2. Find the mean, median, and mode of the following numbers:

     231, 235, 238, 226, 235, 239, 232

3. Give an example in which the mean of a collection of numbers is *not* representative of a typical number in the collection.

4. The following bar graph and box-and-whisker plot represent the *same* data. Compare these two visual models.

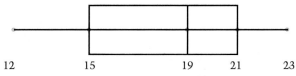

Independent Practice

5. *Hatching Eggs*   You are incubating 55 eggs in science class. Every 20 minutes you record the percent humidity to see that it remains between 60% and 65%. Your friend tells you that the mean, median, and mode of your readings are equal. Do you agree? Explain.

8:30 A.M.	62.5%	10:10 A.M.	63.1%	11:50 A.M.	60.9%	1:30 P.M.	63.9%
8:50 A.M.	62.8%	10:30 A.M.	63.0%	12:10 P.M.	62.6%	1:50 P.M.	62.8%
9:10 A.M.	61.3%	10:50 A.M.	62.8%	12:30 P.M.	63.1%	2:10 P.M.	64.3%
9:40 A.M.	61.0%	11:10 A.M.	61.7%	12:50 P.M.	64.2%	2:20 P.M.	64.5%
9:50 A.M.	63.2%	11:30 A.M.	61.7%	1:10 P.M.	64.0%	2:50 P.M.	64.6%

6. *Urban Lawyers*   The number of lawyers in several large cities is shown in the table. Find the mean and median of these numbers. Are the mean and median equal?

City	Boston	Chicago	Los Angeles	New York	San Francisco	Washington, D.C.
Lawyers	16,400	30,500	27,000	66,200	14,200	12,400

7. *Rain in Wichita*   The bar graph shows the number of days of rain in Wichita, Kansas. Find the mean and median of the data. Construct a box-and-whisker plot for the data.

8. *All the Presidents' Children*   The bar graph shows the number of children of American Presidents. Find the mean, median, and mode of the data. Construct a box-and-whisker plot for the data.

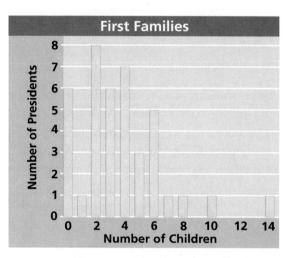

9. *Measuring Frogs*   Your science class is collecting and measuring frogs of different ages. Which measure of central tendency is the most representative of a typical length of the 17 frogs the class has collected? Explain your reasoning.

5.4 in.	4.7 in.	0.2 in.	4.3 in.
6.3 in.	0.9 in.	5.1 in.	4.4 in.
4.0 in.	4.6 in.	6.1 in.	5.5 in.
0.2 in.	5.0 in.	0.5 in.	4.2 in.
6.2 in.			

This is a blue poison dart frog from the savannah of Surinam.

10. *Southeastern Households*   The number of households (in thousands) in each of the southeastern states (including the District of Columbia) is shown below. Which measure of central tendency do you think is most representative of the typical number of households in a south Atlantic state? Explain your reasoning.

Delaware	246	Georgia	2314	Florida	4922
Virginia	2228	West Virginia	708	Washington, D.C.	246
North Carolina	2444	Maryland	1696	South Carolina	1225

11. *Average Salary*   A small town has an adult population of 100. One person is a multimillionaire who makes 5 million dollars a year. The mean annual salary in the town is $74,750. Is this a fair measure of a typical salary in the town? What is the mean salary of the other 99 adults?

12. *Average Age*   Create two different examples, each having 10 ages. Create one example so that the mean age is 14 and the median age is 16. Create the other example so that the median age is 14 and the mean age is 16.

Integrated Review

13. 20 is what percent of 80?

14. What is 50% of 11.3?

15. 7.3 is what percent of 9.5?

16. $\frac{1}{2}$ is 10% of what?

17. What is 27% of 21.4?

18. $\frac{6}{5}$ is 6% of what?

19. *Estimation—Powers of Ten*   Which is the best estimate of the number of calories in an orange?

   a. 6   **b.** 60
   c. 600   **d.** 6000

20. *Estimation—Powers of Ten*   Which is the best estimate of the weight of an adult elephant?

   a. 100 pounds   **b.** 1000 pounds
   c. 10,000 pounds   **d.** 100,000 pounds

21. *In-Line Skates*   At five different stores, a pair of identical in-line skates costs $119, $149, $139, $100, and $125. What is the mean cost?

22. *Protective Gear*   At five different stores, the cost of protective gear for in-line skating is $90, $89, $100, $97, and $115. What is the mean cost?

23. *Riding to School*   You rode your bike to and from school each school day for two weeks and your daily riding times are given below. What was your mean riding time?

   12.50 min   15.00 min   15.75 min   13.00 min   13.00 min
   14.50 min   14.75 min   14.75 min   14.00 min   14.50 min

24. *Practicing a Speech*   You practiced a speech each school day for a week. What was your mean delivery time?

   10.00 min   9.75 min   9.60 min   9.00 min   8.00 min

Exploration and Extension

Study Time   **In Exercises 25 and 26, use the following information.**

In your math class, you were asked to record the number of hours you spend on homework each day for 4 weeks.

Study hours	0.0–0.5	0.5–1.0	1.0–1.5	1.5–2.0	2.0–2.5
Number of days	2	4	1	5	4

Study hours	2.5–3.0	3.0–3.5	3.5–4.0	4.0–4.5	4.5–5.0
Number of days	2	6	3	0	1

25. What measure of central tendency do you think best describes the number of hours you study on a typical day? Explain.

26. Construct a bar graph and a box-and-whisker plot for the data. Which visual model do you think is better? Explain your reasoning.

Graphing calculators can be used to perform statistical computations such as drawing a bar graph or **histogram** of a collection of numbers. The histogram at the right represents how many times each number appears in the following data.

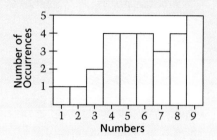

6, 1, 6, 4, 4, 7, 9, 4, 5, 7, 9, 5, 6, 2,
6, 9, 7, 5, 9, 3, 8, 5, 8, 4, 8, 3, 8, 9

TI-81

RANGE (Set range.)
  Xmin = 1
  Xmax = 10
  Xscl = 1
  Ymin = 0
  Ymax = 6
  Yscl = 1
Y= CLEAR
2nd STAT Cursor to DATA
1 (Edit)
Enter coordinates. (Enter 1 for y.)

x1 = 6	x8 = 4	x15 = 6	x22 = 8
y1 = 1	y8 = 1	y15 = 1	y22 = 1
x2 = 1	x9 = 5	x16 = 9	x23 = 8
y2 = 1	y9 = 1	y16 = 1	y23 = 1
x3 = 6	x10 = 7	x17 = 7	x24 = 4
y3 = 1	y10 = 1	y17 = 1	y24 = 1
x4 = 4	x11 = 9	x18 = 5	x25 = 8
y4 = 1	y11 = 1	y18 = 1	y25 = 1
x5 = 4	x12 = 5	x19 = 9	x26 = 3
y5 = 1	y12 = 1	y19 = 1	y26 = 1
x6 = 7	x13 = 6	x20 = 3	x27 = 8
y6 = 1	y13 = 1	y20 = 1	y27 = 1
x7 = 9	x14 = 2	x21 = 8	x28 = 9
y7 = 1	y14 = 1	y21 = 1	y28 = 1

2nd STAT Cursor to DRAW
1 (Histogram) ENTER

Casio fx-7700G

Range (Set range.)
  Xmin = 1
  max = 10
  scl = 1
  Ymin = 0
  max = 6
  scl = 1
EXE Range
MODE × (SD) MODE SHIFT 3 (DRAW)
MODE SHIFT 1 F2 F3 F1
SHIFT Defm 9 EXE
SHIFT F5 (Cls) EXE
SHIFT CLR F2 EXE
Sort values. Enter in order.
1 F1
2 F1
3 F1 F1
4 F1 F1 F1 F1
5 F1 F1 F1 F1
6 F1 F1 F1 F1
7 F1 F1 F1
8 F1 F1 F1 F1
9 F1 F1 F1 F1 F1
Graph EXE

Exercises

In Exercises 1 and 2, construct a histogram for the data.

1. 10, 14, 11, 18, 14, 16, 17, 17, 10, 11, 19,
15, 13, 17, 11, 13, 19, 18, 12, 14, 19, 10,
12, 15, 17, 15, 15, 12, 18, 16, 16, 10, 19

2. 26, 29, 35, 34, 33, 30, 31, 32, 30, 30, 32,
27, 28, 28, 34, 33, 33, 28, 28, 31, 31, 32,
30, 31, 33, 27, 26, 34, 33, 33, 30, 29, 31

12 Chapter Summary

What did you learn?

Skills

1. Identify relations that are functions. **(12.1)**
2. Use function notation to evaluate a function. **(12.1)**
3. Find the domain of a function. **(12.1)**
4. Sketch the graph of
   - a linear function. **(12.2)**
   - a quadratic function. **(12.4)**
   - a rational function. **(12.5)**
5. Transform a graph. **(12.3)**

Strategies

6. Create models of real-life problems. **(12.2–12.5)**
7. Use functions to solve real-life problems. **(12.1–12.5)**

Exploring Data

8. Create stem-and-leaf plots for data. **(12.6)**
9. Create box-and-whisker plots for data. **(12.6)**
10. Use measures of central tendency to describe data. **(12.7)**

Why did you learn it?

Most of the models you studied in earlier chapters *are* functions—we just didn't use that name. This chapter gives you a chance for more practice with four basic types of models: linear, exponential, quadratic, and rational. The chapter also introduces you to transformations, and some function notation and terminology, which helps prepare you for other math courses.

How does it fit into the bigger picture of algebra?

This chapter explores functions. A *function* is a special type of relationship between two variables in which each *input* variable corresponds to exactly one *output* variable. For instance, the area of a circle is a function of its radius, and you can think of the radius of a circle as input and the area of a circle as output. If someone gives you the radius, r, of a circle, you know the area is $A = \pi r^2$.

In Lesson 12.1, you saw that functions can be described in several different ways. In the next four lessons, you studied functions that are described by equations, and how to transform the graph of a function. The last two lessons in the chapter described ways to organize data using stem-and-leaf plots, box-and-whisker plots, and measures of central tendency.

In Exercises 1–4, decide whether the set of ordered pairs defines a function. If it does, state the domain of the function. (12.1)

1. $\{(a, 0), (b, 3), (c, 3), (d, 4)\}$

2. $\{(m, 7), (n, 6), (p, 4), (p, 5)\}$

3. $\{(3, 8), (4, 8), (6, 8), (8, 8)\}$

4. $\{(3, 5), (6, 5), (9, 8), (12, 9)\}$

In Exercises 5–8, find an equation for the linear function, *f*. Then sketch its graph. (12.2)

5. $f(-3) = -6, f(2) = -1$

6. $f(0) = 0, f(5) = -3$

7. $f(-3) = 2, f(1) = 6$

8. $f(3) = 3, f(7) = 2$

In Exercises 9–12, match the function with its graph. (12.3)

9. $g(x) = 1.5^x$

10. $g(x) = 1.5^{x+2}$

11. $g(x) = 1.5^x + 3$

12. $g(x) = -1.5^x$

a.
b.
c.
d.

In Exercises 13–16, describe the relationship between the graph of *f* and the graph of *g*. (12.3)

13. $f(x) = \left(\frac{3}{4}\right)^x, g(x) = \left(\frac{3}{4}\right)^x - 2$

14. $f(x) = 2^x, g(x) = 2^{x-5}$

15. $f(x) = 3.9^x, g(x) = -3.9^x$

16. $f(x) = 5^x, g(x) = 5^{x+2} - 5$

In Exercises 17–20, write the function in completed square form. Then find the vertex of its graph. Does the graph open up or down? (12.4)

17. $f(x) = x^2 + 10x + 27$

18. $g(x) = -3x^2 + 42x - 151$

19. $h(x) = -\frac{1}{3}x^2 - \frac{4}{3}x - \frac{22}{3}$

20. $g(x) = \frac{1}{2}x^2 - 10x + 55$

In Exercises 21–24, match the function with its graph. (12.5)

21. $f(x) = \frac{1}{x+1} - 2$

22. $f(x) = \frac{1}{x-3} + 1$

23. $f(x) = \frac{-2}{x+2} + 3$

24. $f(x) = \frac{-3}{x-1} - 2$

a.
b.
c.
d.

In Exercises 25–30, sketch the graph of the function. (12.5)

25. $f(x) = \dfrac{3x - 8}{x - 4}$

26. $f(x) = \dfrac{2x + 3}{x + 1}$

27. $f(x) = \dfrac{-5x + 12}{x - 2}$

28. $f(x) = \dfrac{-3x - 12}{x + 5}$

29. $f(x) = \dfrac{2x}{x - 2}$

30. $f(x) = \dfrac{-3x - 2}{x + 3}$

In Exercises 31–34, use the following collection of data points. (12.6, 12.7)

40, 60, 49, 43, 37, 69, 75, 67, 56, 70
44, 68, 45, 72, 70, 44, 36, 35, 68, 45
71, 64, 53, 46, 50, 49, 37, 47, 54, 72

31. Construct a stem-and-leaf plot for the data.

32. Find the mean, median, and mode.

33. Construct a box-and-whisker plot for the data.

34. Construct a bar graph for the data using the following intervals. $35 \le x < 45$, $45 \le x < 55$, $55 \le x < 65$, $65 \le x < 75$

35. *The Sands of Time*   Before the 1900's, sailors used a 30-second "hourglass" to determine the speed of a ship. A rope was tied to a log, and the log was thrown into the water to drift freely behind the ship. After 30 seconds, the rope was measured. Let x represent the length of the rope after 30 seconds. Write a linear function that represents the speed of the ship (in feet per second) in terms of x. Use the function to find the speed of a ship for which 100 feet of rope was let out.

36. *Life Span of Animals*   Construct a box-and-whisker plot for the average life spans of the animals shown below. For which animals do the life spans fall between the second and third quartiles?

Bear	22	Cat	11
Chicken	7	Cow	10
Deer	12	Dog	11
Duck	10	Elephant	35
Fox	9	Goat	12
Groundhog	6	Guinea Pig	3
Hamster	2	Hippopotamus	30
Horse	22	Kangaroo	5
Lion	10	Monkey	13
Mouse	2	Parakeet	8
Pig	10	Pigeon	11
Rabbit	7	Rat	3
Sheep	12	Squirrel	8
Whale	45	Wolf	11

For 1970 through 1988, the costs of all local and national advertising (in millions of dollars) are shown in the graphs. In each graph, a different type of function was used as a model. In each model, $t = 0$ represents 1970. *(Source: McCann-Erickson, Inc.)*

Model: f(t) = 5670 + 5655t

Model: f(t) = 266t² + 865t + 19,240

Model: f(t) = 18,230(1.113)ᵗ

$$\text{Model: } f(t) = \frac{1878t + 17{,}133}{-0.03t + 1}$$

37. Use the linear model to predict the total cost of advertising in the year 2000.

38. Use the quadratic model to predict the total cost of advertising in the year 2000.

39. Use the exponential model to predict the total cost of advertising in the year 2000.

40. Use the rational model to predict the total cost of advertising in the year 2000.

41. Which of these models do you think best predicts the total cost of advertising in the year 2000? Explain your reasoning.

In Exercises 1 and 2, use the table.

Variable, x	a	b	c	d	e
Variable, y	2	3	2	1	5

1. Is y a function of x?

2. Is x a function of y?

3. Evaluate $f(x) = 17x - 25$ when $x = -3$ and $x = 2$.

4. Find an equation of the linear function such that $f(-2) = -4$ and $f(3) = 3$.

In Exercises 5–8, match the function with its graph.

5. $f(x) = \left(\frac{1}{4}\right)^x$

6. $f(x) = \left(\frac{1}{4}\right)^x + 1$

7. $f(x) = \left(\frac{1}{4}\right)^{x-2}$

8. $f(x) = -\left(\frac{1}{4}\right)^x - 2$

a.

b.

c.

d.

9. Write $f(x) = x^2 + 6x + 15$ in completed square form. Then sketch its graph.

10. Sketch the graph of $f(x) = \dfrac{1}{x - 4} + 1$.

11. Sketch the graph of $f(x) = \dfrac{3x + 2}{x - 1}$.

In Exercises 12–15, use the following data:
17, 7, 16, 8, 4, 9, 11, 3, 20, 8, 7, 9, 10, 14, 3, 9.

12. Construct a stem-and-leaf plot for the data.

13. Find the quartiles of the collection.

14. Find the mean, median, and mode of the collection.

15. Construct a box-and-whisker plot for the data.

16. The human heart pumps about 2000 gallons of blood each day. Create a model that gives the total amount of blood, $f(x)$ in gallons, pumped in x days. Sketch a graph of the function.

17. Cissy's hair is 5 inches long and is growing at a rate of 4 inches per year. Julie's hair is 12 inches long and is growing at a rate of 3 inches per year. Write a model that gives the ratio of the length of Cissy's hair to the length of Julie's hair. (Let t represent the number of years and let $f(t)$ represent the ratio.) Sketch the graph of f over the interval $0 \le t \le 4$.

18. The table gives the average number of days of rain in each month in Sioux Falls, South Dakota. Construct a bar graph for these data. Find the mean, median, and mode of the data.

Month	Jan	Feb	Mar	Apr	May	Jun	Jul	Aug	Sep	Oct	Nov	Dec
Days of Rain	6	6	9	9	10	11	9	9	8	6	6	6

In Exercises 1–6, classify the polynomial by term and by degree.

1. 436

2. $7x^3 + 25x^2 + 36x - 1$

3. $\frac{1}{2}x^2 + 3x + 4$

4. $5x^4 - 1$

5. $27x - 4$

6. $-17x$

In Exercises 7–12, perform the indicated operation.

7. $3x(x^2 + 3x + 4)$

8. $(x + 2)(2x - 1)$

9. $(4x^2 + 2)(3x + 5)$

10. $\left(\frac{1}{2}x - 3\right)(-x + 2)$

11. $(2x + 4)(2x - 4)$

12. $(2x + 7)^2$

In Exercises 13–18, use factoring to solve the equation.

13. $x^2 - 9x + 5 = -13$

14. $3x^2 + 8x - 4 = 12$

15. $3x^2 + 18x = 0$

16. $-x^2 - 2x + 35 = 0$

17. $4x^2 - 37 = 12$

18. $9x^2 + 30x + 24 = -1$

In Exercises 19–24, solve the equation by any convenient method.

19. $x^2 + 3x - 5 = 0$

20. $x^2 - 6x + 7 = 0$

21. $x^2 - 4x - 13 = 0$

22. $x^2 + 8x - 1 = 0$

23. $2x^2 - 12x + 7 = 0$

24. $3x^2 - 24x + 6 = 0$

In Exercises 25–27, solve the proportion.

25. $\frac{3}{4m} = \frac{5}{2}$

26. $\frac{x+5}{3} = \frac{2}{x}$

27. $\frac{x+5}{x-8} = \frac{1}{3x}$

Geometry   **In Exercises 28–30, what percent of the region is shaded blue?**

28.

29.

30.

31. What is 130% of 24 yards?

32. 40 cm is what percent of 36 cm?

33. $120 is what percent of $840?

34. 4 days is what percent of 180 days?

In Exercises 35–37, the variables *x* and *y* vary directly. Use the given values to find an equation that relates *x* and *y*.

35. $x = 3, \ y = 5$

36. $x = \frac{1}{2}, \ y = \frac{1}{3}$

37. $x = 4.2, \ y = 3.1$

In Exercises 38–40, the variables *x* and *y* vary inversely. Use the given values to find an equation that relates *x* and *y*.

38. $x = 12, \ y = 2$

39. $x = \frac{3}{2}, \ y = 6$

40. $x = 6.3, \ y = 10.1$

Giving Book Reports **In Exercises 41–44, use the following information.**

There are 25 students in your English class. To determine the speaking order for presenting book reports, slips of paper numbered from 1 to 25 are placed in a box. Each student then draws a number to determine his or her speaking order.

41. What is the probability that the number you draw will be odd?

42. What is the probability that the number you draw will be even?

43. Five book reports will be given on each day. What is the probability that you will have to give your report on the first day?

44. What is the probability that you will be the very last person to give his or her book report?

In Exercises 45–56, simplify the expression.

45. $\dfrac{3y}{4} \cdot \dfrac{2}{6y^2}$

46. $\dfrac{8x^3}{3} \cdot 5x^2$

47. $\dfrac{5p^4}{3} \div \dfrac{3p^3}{2}$

48. $\dfrac{(x-2)}{3x} \div \dfrac{4}{15x^2}$

49. $\dfrac{m}{m^2 - 4m + 4} \cdot (m-2)$

50. $\dfrac{3n^2 - 2n - 5}{n+1} \div (n+1)$

51. $(6z^2 + 4z) \div 2z$

52. $(8x^2 + 4x - 7) \div 4$

53. $(y^2 + 6y - 2) \div (y-2)$

54. $(4m^3 + m + 6) \div (m+2)$

55. $\left(\dfrac{1}{3}z^3 + z^2 - 7z\right) \div (z+3)$

56. $(27x^2 + 3x - 2) \div (3x-1)$

In Exercises 57–62, solve the equation.

57. $\dfrac{5}{x+3} = \dfrac{6}{x+1}$

58. $\dfrac{4}{2x+1} = \dfrac{1}{x}$

59. $\dfrac{2}{x} - \dfrac{1}{2} = \dfrac{5}{x}$

60. $\dfrac{4}{x} + \dfrac{29}{30} = \dfrac{x}{5}$

61. $\dfrac{4}{2x+1} = \dfrac{3}{x+1}$

62. $\dfrac{4x^2}{x-1} - \dfrac{4x}{x-1} = \dfrac{-3}{4x-4}$

In Exercises 63–68, evaluate the function at the given value of the variable.

63. $f(t) = 4t + 2,\ t = 4$

64. $f(x) = 2^x + 14,\ x = 3$

65. $f(x) = x^2 + 4x - 3,\ x = -5$

66. $f(t) = -3(t - 7)^2,\ t = 1$

67. $f(x) = \dfrac{3}{x},\ x = 6$

68. $f(t) = \dfrac{6}{t-2} + 4,\ t = -10$

In Exercises 69–72, match the function with its graph.

69. $f(x) = \dfrac{1}{2}(x+2)^2$

70. $f(x) = -\dfrac{4}{3}x + 4$

71. $f(x) = \left(\dfrac{1}{2}\right)^x - 3$

72. $f(x) = \dfrac{1}{x-2} + 3$

a.

b.

c.

d.

In Exercises 73 and 74, the two rectangles are proportional to each other. Find the length represented by *x*.

73.

74.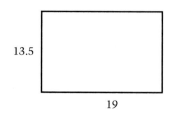

75. *Sweatshirt Sale* Sweatshirt City is having a "20%-off sale" on all college sweatshirts. The sale price is $18.80. What was the original price?

76. *Snack Recipe* A snack recipe calls for 5 cups of bite-sized cereal and $1\frac{1}{2}$ cups of pretzel sticks. Find an equation that relates the amount of cereal, *c*, to the amount of pretzel sticks, *p*.

Basketball Booster Club **In Exercises 77 and 78, use the following information.**

For a $10 membership fee to the Basketball Booster Club, a parent of a high school student receives a $1 discount off the $3 price of a basketball ticket at each basketball game.

77. How many games must a parent attend to average $2.50 per ticket? (Include the $10 membership fee.)

78. After the basketball season, one member of the booster club said that she ended paying more per game than if she had not joined. What is the maximum number of games she attended?

In Exercises 79–82, sketch the graph of the function.

79. $f(x) = \frac{1}{3}x + 4$ 80. $f(x) = 2^{x-1}$ 81. $f(x) = 3x^2 - 2x$ 82. $f(x) = \frac{3x + 1}{x - 2}$

Pilots and Flight Attendants **In Exercises 83 and 84, use the following information.**

In 1980, commercial airlines in the United States employed 31,665 pilots and 54,420 flight attendants. For the next 10 years these numbers increased by an average of 1545 pilots per year and 2900 flight attendants per year. *(Source: Air Transport Association of America)*

83. Create a model that gives the ratio of employed flight attendants to employed pilots for 1980 through 1990. (Let $t = 0$ represent 1980.)

84. Was the ratio of flight attendants to pilots increasing or decreasing from 1980 to 1990? Explain.

The table shows the amount of measurable snow (in inches) that fell in Erie, Pennsylvania, during December 1988. (No snow fell on days not listed.)

Day	1	2	3	8	9	10	11	13
Snowfall	6.4	0.1	0.3	0.1	1.8	8.2	0.7	0.9

Day	15	16	17	18	25	27	28	29
Snowfall	0.2	0.6	2.9	1.1	0.3	0.2	4.0	0.4

85. Use a stem-and-leaf plot to order the recorded snowfall in increasing order.

87. What was the median daily snowfall for the sixteen days of snow?

86. What was the mean daily snowfall for the sixteen days of snow?

88. Construct a box-and-whisker plot for the data. What does this indicate about snowfall in Erie?

Snowblowing   **In Exercises 89 and 90, use the following information.**

Suppose that you lived in Erie during December 1988. On December 1, to test your new snowblower, you cleared the sidewalks around the entire block shown in the diagram.

89. The sidewalk around the block is 3 feet wide. How many square feet of snow did you clear?

90. How many *cubic feet* of snow did you clear? (Use the information given in the above table, and assume that all of the day's snow had fallen before you began clearing.)

Snowblowing for Profit   **In Exercises 91 and 92, use the following information.**

After seeing how well you cleared the sidewalks, three neighbors offered to pay you to snowblow their driveways. Each week after that, one more neighbor became a client. Your weekly earnings, *R*, during an eight-week period can be modeled by

$$R = 2t + 6$$

where $t = 0$ represents the first week.

91. How much did you charge to snowblow each driveway?

92. How much did you earn during the eight weeks?

LESSONS

13.1 The Distance Formula • 676

13.2 Simplifying Radicals • 682

13.3 Operations with Radicals • 689

13.4 Solving Radical Equations • 695

13.5 The Tangent of an Angle • 703

13.6 Formal Use of Properties of Algebra • 710

This montage of Voyager 2 images obtained in 1986 shows the blue-green planet Uranus overlaid with portion of a close-approach image of Miranda, Uranus' moon.

The Moons of Uranus

Voyager 1 and *Voyager 2* were launched by the United States in 1977 to observe Jupiter and Saturn. *Voyager 1* reached Jupiter in 1979 and Saturn in 1980. *Voyager 2* also passed by Jupiter and Saturn and then continued on to observe the outer planets. In 1986, *Voyager 2* transmitted stunning pictures of the rings of Uranus.

To escape Earth's gravitational pull, the *Voyagers* had to be propelled upward from Earth's surface with a velocity of at least

$$v = \sqrt{\frac{2Gm}{r}} \approx 11{,}186 \text{ (meters per second)}$$

where G is the universal gravitational constant, m is the mass of Earth, and r is Earth's radius.

For each of the five moons of Uranus, the graph relates the distance of the moon from Uranus with the time the moon takes to orbit the planet.

13.1

The Distance Formula

What you should learn:

Goal 1 How to find the distance between two points

Goal 2 How to find the midpoint between two points

Why you should learn it:

On maps and other grids, you often need to find the distance or midpoint between two points not on the same grid line.

Goal 1 Finding the Distance Between Points

Suppose you were asked to find the distance between the points $A(2, 1)$ and $B(6, 4)$. How would you do it? One way is to construct a right triangle that has the line segment $\overline{AB}$ as its hypotenuse. The right angle occurs at the point $C(6, 1)$.

Because you know how to find horizontal and vertical distances in a coordinate plane, you can find the lengths of the two legs of the right triangle.

$a = 4 - 1 = 3$ *Length of $\overline{BC}$*

$b = 6 - 2 = 4$ *Length of $\overline{AC}$*

From the Pythagorean theorem, you know that $c = \sqrt{a^2 + b^2}$.

$c = \sqrt{(4 - 1)^2 + (6 - 2)^2}$ *Pythagorean theorem*

$c = \sqrt{25}$ *Simplify.*

$c = 5$ *Simplify.*

By performing this process with two general points (x_1, y_1) and (x_2, y_2), you can obtain the *Distance Formula.*

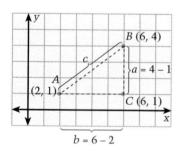

The Distance Formula

The distance, d, between the points (x_1, y_1) and (x_2, y_2) is

$$d = \sqrt{(x_2 - x_1)^2 + (y_2 - y_1)^2}.$$

Example 1   *Finding the Distance Between Two Points*

Find the distance between $(-1, 4)$ and $(2, -3)$.

Solution   Let $(x_1, y_1) = (-1, 4)$ and $(x_2, y_2) = (2, -3)$.

$d = \sqrt{(2 - (-1))^2 + (-3 - 4)^2}$

$ = \sqrt{9 + 49}$

$ = \sqrt{58}$

$ \approx 7.62$

The distance between the points is about 7.62 units.   ∎

So far in the book we have been using only one part of the Pythagorean theorem. *If a triangle is a right triangle,* then the lengths of its sides satisfy the equation $a^2 + b^2 = c^2$. It has another part that is also true. *If the lengths of the sides of a triangle satisfy the equation $a^2 + b^2 = c^2$,* then the triangle is a right triangle. (The second statement is the **converse** of the first statement.)

Connections
Geometry

Example 2 *Deciding Whether a Triangle Is a Right Triangle*

Show that the points $(2, 1)$, $(4, 0)$, and $(5, 7)$ are vertices of a right triangle.

Solution Use the Distance Formula to find the lengths of the three sides.

$$d_1 = \sqrt{(5 - 2)^2 + (7 - 1)^2} = \sqrt{9 + 36} = \sqrt{45}$$
$$d_2 = \sqrt{(4 - 2)^2 + (0 - 1)^2} = \sqrt{4 + 1} = \sqrt{5}$$
$$d_3 = \sqrt{(5 - 4)^2 + (7 - 0)^2} = \sqrt{1 + 49} = \sqrt{50}$$

Because $d_1{}^2 + d_2{}^2 = 45 + 5 = 50 = d_3{}^2$, you can conclude that the triangle is a right triangle.

When you want to use the Distance Formula to find a distance in a real-life problem, the first step is to draw a diagram and assign coordinates to the points. This process is called *superimposing* a coordinate system on the diagram.

Example 3 *Finding the Distance of a Pass*

In a football game, a quarterback throws a pass from the 5 yard line, 10 yards from the sideline. The pass is caught by a wide receiver on the 45 yard line, 40 yards from the same sideline. How long was the pass?

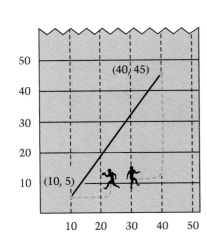

Solution You can begin by superimposing a coordinate system on the football field. The quarterback throws the ball from the point $(10, 5)$. It is caught at the point $(40, 45)$.

$$d = \sqrt{(40 - 10)^2 + (45 - 5)^2}$$
$$= \sqrt{900 + 1600}$$
$$= \sqrt{2500}$$
$$= 50 \text{ yards}$$

The pass was 50 yards long.

Finding the Midpoint of Two Points

The coordinates of the midpoint between two points are the averages of the coordinates of the two points.

The Midpoint Formula

The **midpoint** between (x_1, y_1) and (x_2, y_2) is $\left(\dfrac{x_1 + x_2}{2}, \dfrac{y_1 + y_2}{2}\right)$.

The Pony Express was in operation from April 1860 to October 1861. Its riders were mostly young men, fourteen to eighteen years old, who rode about 70 miles each along the 2000-mile trip from St. Joseph, Missouri, to Sacramento, California. At each Pony Express station, riders were given a fresh horse. The entire trip took between 8 and 15 days, depending on the weather.

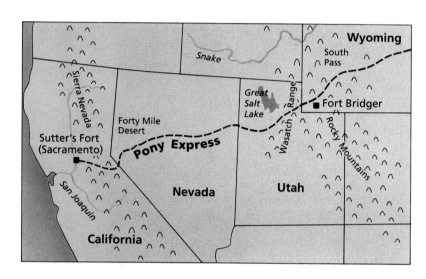

Real Life
Pony Express

Example 4 *Finding the Midpoint Between Points*

Pony Express stations were about 10 miles apart. The latitude-longitude coordinates of 2 former stations in western Nevada are (39.5 N, 117.8 W) and (39.3 N, 118.2 W). These two stations are about 20 miles apart. Estimate the coordinates of the station that was between them.

Solution Let (x_1, y_1) be (39.5, 117.8) and (x_2, y_2) be (39.3, 118.2). The approximate coordinates of the midpoint station would be

$$\text{midpoint} = \left(\frac{39.5 + 39.3}{2}, \frac{117.8 + 118.2}{2}\right) = (39.4, 118.0). \quad \blacksquare$$

Communicating about ALGEBRA

▶ **SHARING IDEAS about the Lesson**

Understand a Formula Explain why either of the two points may be chosen to be (x_1, y_1) when using the Distance Formula or the Midpoint Formula.

EXERCISES

Guided Practice

▶ **CRITICAL THINKING about the Lesson**

1. Plot the points $(3, 6)$ and $(-3, -2)$ in a coordinate plane. Use the scale of the plane to estimate the distance between the two points. Then use the Distance Formula to find the exact distance between the points.

2. Find the midpoint of $(6, -1)$ and $(-4, 5)$. Check your result with a graph.

3. State the converse of the statement. "If a triangle is a right triangle, then the lengths of its sides satisfy the equation $a^2 + b^2 = c^2$."

Independent Practice

In Exercises 4–7, use the coordinate plane to estimate the distance between the two points. Then use the Distance Formula to find the distance between the points. Round the result, if necessary, to two decimal places.

4. $(1, 5), (-3, 1)$ **5.** $(-2, 2), (2, 1)$ **6.** $(-3, -2), (4, 1)$ **7.** $(5, -2), (-1, 1)$

      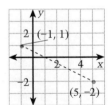

In Exercises 8–15, find the distance between the two points. Round the result, if necessary, to two decimal places.

8. $(1, 0), (9, -4)$ **9.** $(1, -7), (-2, 2)$ **10.** $(3, -1), (0, 3)$ **11.** $(1, -4), (-4, 6)$

12. $(6, 9), (-3, 1)$ **13.** $(-2, 2), (1, 5)$ **14.** $\left(\frac{1}{2}, \frac{1}{4}\right), \left(-\frac{1}{2}, \frac{5}{4}\right)$ **15.** $\left(\frac{1}{2}, \frac{3}{2}\right), (1, 1)$

In Exercises 16–19, decide whether the three points are the vertices of a right triangle.

16. $(4, 0), (2, 1), (-1, -5)$ **17.** $(4, 5), (1, 0), (-1, 2)$

18. $(1, -3), (3, 2), (-2, 4)$ **19.** $(-1, -1), (10, 7), (2, 18)$

In Exercises 20–25, find the midpoint between the two points.

20. $(-4, 4), (2, 0)$ **21.** $(0, 0), (0, 10)$ **22.** $(2, 1), (14, 6)$

23. $(-1, 0), (6, 2)$ **24.** $(-2, 2), (3, -10)$ **25.** $(1, 6), (4, 2)$

Geometry   **In Exercises 26 and 27, find the perimeter of the polygon.**

26.

27.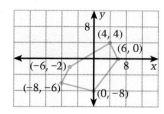

Distance on a Map   **In Exercises 28–30, use the following information.**

Each square on the grid that is superimposed on the map represents a square that is 95 miles by 95 miles.

28. Use the map to estimate the distance between Pierre, South Dakota, and Santa Fe, New Mexico.

29. Use the map to estimate the distance between Wichita, Kansas, and Cheyenne, Wyoming.

30. Use the map to estimate the distance between Oklahoma City, Oklahoma, and Des Moines, Iowa.

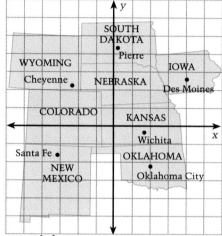

The Spider and the Fly   A spider and a fly are on opposite walls of a rectangular room. The spider asks the fly if it can come over and "visit" the fly. The fly believes that the shortest distance, walking on one of the room's surfaces, is 42 feet. (That is the distance if the spider walks straight up the wall, over the ceiling, and straight down the opposite wall.) So the fly agrees to the visit, *provided* the spider can find a path that is shorter than 42 feet. Use the "unfolded room" and the Distance Formula to explain the fly's fatal miscalculation.

Spider

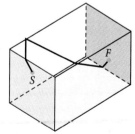

32. *Trapezoid*   A trapezoid is **isosceles** if its two opposite nonparallel sides have the same length. Sketch the polygon whose vertices are (1, 1), (5, 9), (2, 8), and (0, 4). Show that it is a trapezoid by showing that two of the sides are parallel. Then use the Distance Formula to show that the trapezoid is isosceles.

33. *Parallelogram*   Sketch the parallelogram whose vertices are $(1, 4)$, $(7, 11)$, $(1, -3)$, and $(7, 4)$. Use the Distance Formula to show that lengths of opposite sides of the parallelogram are equal.

34. *Diagonals of a Parallelogram*   Sketch the parallelogram whose vertices are $(-1, 5)$, $(-3, 5)$, $(1, -3)$, and $(3, -3)$. Find the midpoint of each diagonal. What do you notice about the midpoints of the diagonals of a parallelogram?

Integrated Review

In Exercises 35–38, evaluate the expression.

35. $\sqrt{a^2 + b^2}$ when $a = 4$ and $b = 9$

36. $c^2 - b^2$ when $c = 13$ and $b = 6$

37. $(x - 2)^2 + (y + 3)^2$ when $x = 4$ and $y = -2$

38. $\sqrt{x^2 + y^2}$ when $x = 1$ and $y = 6$

Geometry   **In Exercises 39–42, the lengths of two sides of a right triangle are given. Find the length of the other side.**

39.

40.

41.

42.

In Exercises 43–48, plot the points. Then find the equation of the line passing through the points.

43. $(3, 1)$, $(2, 11)$

44. $(-1, 6)$, $(5, 3)$

45. $(1, -2)$, $(3, -2)$

46. $(9, 2)$, $(-1, 0)$

47. $(2, 7)$, $(6, -4)$

48. $(8, 0)$, $(8, -5)$

Exploration and Extension

Hero's Formula   **In Exercises 49 and 50, use Hero's Formula to find the area of the triangle. Hero's Formula states that the area of a triangle with sides of lengths *a*, *b*, and *c* is area $= \sqrt{s(s - a)(s - b)(s - c)}$, where $s = \frac{1}{2}(a + b + c)$.**

49.

50.

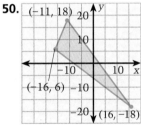

13.2

Simplifying Radicals

What you should learn:

Goal 1 How to simplify radicals by applying their properties

Goal 2 How to use radicals in real-life situations

Why you should learn it:

You can simplify radicals to make computations easier in many real-life problems, such as the period of a swinging pendulum.

Goal 1 Simplifying Radicals

An *expression with radicals* is in **simplest form** if the following are true.

1. No radicands (expressions under radical signs) have perfect square factors other than 1.

$$\sqrt{8} = 2\sqrt{2}$$

2. No radicands contain fractions.

$$\sqrt{\tfrac{3}{4}} = \tfrac{1}{2}\sqrt{3}$$

3. No radicals appear in the denominator of a fraction.

$$\frac{1}{\sqrt{4}} = \frac{1}{2}$$

Properties of Radicals

Let a and b be positive numbers.

1. The square root of a product equals the product of the square roots of the factors.

$$\sqrt{ab} = \sqrt{a} \cdot \sqrt{b} \qquad \textit{Product Property}$$

2. The square root of a quotient equals the quotient of the square roots of the numerator and denominator.

$$\sqrt{\frac{a}{b}} = \frac{\sqrt{a}}{\sqrt{b}} \qquad \textit{Quotient Property}$$

Example 1 *Simplifying Radicals*

Simplify.   **a.** $\sqrt{50}$ **b.** $\sqrt{\tfrac{3}{4}}$

Solution

a.
$$
\begin{aligned}
\sqrt{50} &= \sqrt{25 \cdot 2} & \textit{Perfect square factor}\\
&= \sqrt{25} \cdot \sqrt{2} & \textit{Product Property}\\
&= 5\sqrt{2} & \textit{Simplest form}
\end{aligned}
$$

b.
$$
\begin{aligned}
\sqrt{\tfrac{3}{4}} &= \frac{\sqrt{3}}{\sqrt{4}} & \textit{Quotient Property}\\[4pt]
&= \frac{\sqrt{3}}{2} & \textit{Simplest form}
\end{aligned}
$$

The denominator in Example 1b could be rewritten without radicals because it was the square root of a perfect square. If the radical in a denominator is not the square root of a perfect square, then a different strategy is required.

Example 2 *Simplifying a Radical Expression*

Simplify $\dfrac{1}{\sqrt{2}}$.

Solution   To simplify this expression, multiply the numerator and denominator by $\sqrt{2}$. (This is algebraically justified because it is equivalent to multiplying the original fraction by 1.)

$$\frac{1}{\sqrt{2}} = \frac{1}{\sqrt{2}} \cdot \frac{\sqrt{2}}{\sqrt{2}} \qquad \textit{Multiply by } \frac{\sqrt{2}}{\sqrt{2}} \textit{, or 1.}$$

$$= \frac{1 \cdot \sqrt{2}}{\sqrt{2} \cdot \sqrt{2}} \qquad \textit{Multiply numerators and denominators.}$$

$$= \frac{\sqrt{2}}{\sqrt{2 \cdot 2}} \qquad \textit{Product Property}$$

$$= \frac{\sqrt{2}}{2} \qquad \textit{Simplest form}$$

■

Goal 2   ## Using Radicals in Real-Life Problems

Connections
Geometry

Example 3 *Finding the Area of a Rectangle*

Find the area of a rectangle whose width is $\sqrt{2}$ inches and whose length is $\sqrt{30}$ inches. Give the result in exact form and in decimal form.

Solution

$$\begin{aligned} \text{Area} &= \text{Length} \cdot \text{Width} \\ &= \sqrt{30} \cdot \sqrt{2} \\ &= \sqrt{30 \cdot 2} \qquad \textit{Product Property} \\ &= \sqrt{60} \qquad \textit{Simplify.} \end{aligned}$$

This expression is the exact area, but it is not in simplified form. The simplified form is

$$A = \sqrt{60} = \sqrt{4 \cdot 15} = \sqrt{4} \cdot \sqrt{15} = 2\sqrt{15} \text{ square inches.}$$

The decimal approximation of the area is

$$A = \sqrt{60} \approx 7.746 \text{ square inches.}$$

Try multiplying 2 by $\sqrt{15}$ on a calculator to see if you obtain the same approximation.   ■

Spirals occur in many forms in nature. Some are left-handed (spiraling counterclockwise) and some are right-handed (spiraling clockwise). Trumpet honeysuckle winds to the left and bindweed winds to the right. Some snails occur in both left- and right-handed versions.

Connections
Geometry

Bindweed   **Trumpet Honeysuckle**

Example 4   **Using the Pythagorean Theorem**

The *square root spiral* above is formed by a sequence of right triangles, each with a side whose length is 1. Let r_n be the length of the hypotenuse of the nth triangle. Find r_1, r_2, and r_{15}.

Solution   Each leg of the first triangle is 1 unit. Use the Pythagorean theorem with $a = 1$, $b = 1$, and $c = r_1$.

$$r_1 = \sqrt{a^2 + b^2} = \sqrt{1^2 + 1^2} = \sqrt{2}$$

For the second triangle, the lengths of the legs are $a = 1$ and $b = \sqrt{2}$. Thus, the length of the hypotenuse is

$$r_2 = \sqrt{a^2 + b^2} = \sqrt{1^2 + (\sqrt{2})^2} = \sqrt{3}.$$

By continuing this procedure, you can find a pattern.

$r_0 = \sqrt{1}$	$r_1 = \sqrt{2}$	$r_2 = \sqrt{3}$	$r_3 = \sqrt{4}$
$r_4 = \sqrt{5}$	$r_5 = \sqrt{6}$	$r_6 = \sqrt{7}$	$r_7 = \sqrt{8}$
$r_8 = \sqrt{9}$	$r_9 = \sqrt{10}$	$r_{10} = \sqrt{11}$	$r_{11} = \sqrt{12}$
$r_{12} = \sqrt{13}$	$r_{13} = \sqrt{14}$	$r_{14} = \sqrt{15}$	$r_{15} = \sqrt{16}$ ∎

Communicating about **ALGEBRA**

▶ **SHARING IDEAS about the Lesson**

Extend the Idea

A. Which of the r_n in Example 4 are simplified? Simplify those that are not.

B. Let A_n be the area of the nth triangle. Find a formula for A_n.

C. Find the ratio of A_8 to A_7. Give your answer in simplified form.

EXERCISES

▶ **CRITICAL THINKING about the Lesson**

1. Describe the three conditions that must be true for a radical expression to be in simplest form.

2. Describe the Product Property of radicals in words.

3. Describe the Quotient Property of radicals in words.

4. Explain how the Product Property can be used to simplify $\sqrt{28}$.

5. Explain how the Product Property can be used to multiply $\sqrt{6}$ and $\sqrt{24}$.

6. Describe the steps you would use to simplify $\frac{1}{\sqrt{3}}$.

Independent Practice

In Exercises 7–22, simplify the radical expression.

7. $\sqrt{40}$

8. $\sqrt{18}$

9. $\sqrt{48}$

10. $\sqrt{75}$

11. $\sqrt{\frac{7}{9}}$

12. $\sqrt{\frac{11}{16}}$

13. $\sqrt{\frac{2}{50}}$

14. $\sqrt{\frac{20}{12}}$

15. $\frac{1}{2}\sqrt{80}$

16. $\frac{1}{3}\sqrt{27}$

17. $2\sqrt{\frac{5}{4}}$

18. $18\sqrt{\frac{5}{81}}$

19. $\sqrt{\frac{1}{12}}$

20. $\sqrt{\frac{4}{5}}$

21. $2\sqrt{\frac{1}{2}}$

22. $3\sqrt{\frac{5}{6}}$

In Exercises 23–34, perform the indicated operation. Simplify your result.

23. $\sqrt{5} \cdot \sqrt{15}$

24. $\sqrt{10} \cdot \sqrt{20}$

25. $\sqrt{2} \cdot \sqrt{6} \cdot \sqrt{3}$

26. $\sqrt{2} \cdot \sqrt{3} \cdot \sqrt{5}$

27. $(2\sqrt{13})^2$

28. $(7\sqrt{3})^2$

29. $(\frac{1}{2}\sqrt{8})^2$

30. $(\frac{2}{3}\sqrt{3})^2$

31. $\frac{1}{\sqrt{18}}$

32. $\frac{2\sqrt{5}}{\sqrt{4}}$

33. $\frac{\sqrt{6}}{\sqrt{2}}$

34. $\frac{6}{\sqrt{3}}$

Geometry   **In Exercises 35–38, find the area of the figure. Give both the exact answer in simplified form and a decimal approximation rounded to two decimal places.**

35.

36.

37.

38.

Geometry In Exercises 39 and 40, use the Pythagorean theorem to find *x*.
Express the result as a simplified radical.

39.

40.

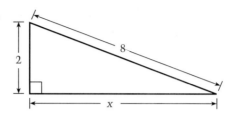

Tsunami In Exercises 41 and 42, use the following information.

A *tsunami* (tsōō nä′ mē′), or tidal wave, is a destructive ocean wave
that is caused by a large storm at sea or by an undersea earthquake.
The speed, *s* (in meters per second), at which a tsunami moves
is determined by the depth, *d* (in meters), of the ocean:

$$s = 3.1\sqrt{d}$$

41. Find the speed of a tsunami in a region of
the ocean that is 60 meters deep. Write
the result in simplified form.

42. Find the speed of a tsunami in a region of
the ocean that is 200 meters deep. Write
the result in simplified form.

At the Top of Delaware In Exercises 43–46,
use the following information.

The northern boundary of Delaware is the arc
of a circle whose center is at New Castle,
Delaware. The radius of the circle is

$$\sqrt{\frac{24{,}200}{18\pi^2}} \text{ miles.}$$

43. Simplify the expression for the radius.

44. On the coordinate plane at the right, the
coordinates of Booths Corner are
(1.5, 3.7). Is Booths Corner in Delaware or
Pennsylvania? Explain.

45. The coordinates of Yorklyn are (−1.6, 3.4).
In which state is Yorklyn? Explain.

46. The coordinates of Naamans Gardens are
(2.1, 3). In which state is Naamans
Gardens? Explain.

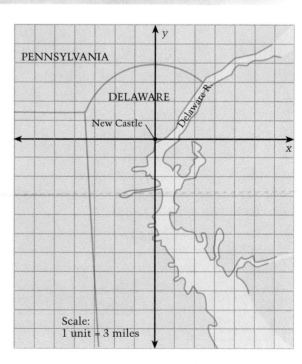

In Exercises 47–52, evaluate the function at the given value of x. Write the result in simplified form.

47. $f(x) = x^2 - 7$, $x = \sqrt{6}$ **48.** $f(x) = 2x^2 + 2$, $x = \sqrt{10}$ **49.** $f(x) = \sqrt{2} \cdot \sqrt{x}$, $x = 8$

50. $f(x) = \sqrt{3} \cdot \sqrt{x}$, $x = 12$ **51.** $f(x) = x^2 - 5$, $x = 2\sqrt{5}$ **52.** $f(x) = x^2 - 10$, $x = 4\sqrt{2}$

In Exercises 53–58, use the quadratic formula to solve the equation. Write the result in simplified form.

53. $\frac{1}{2}x^2 + 6x - 6 = 0$ **54.** $\frac{1}{2}x^2 + 10x + 10 = 0$ **55.** $x^2 + 2x - 1 = 0$

56. $x^2 + 6x - 6 = 0$ **57.** $x^2 - 4x - 5 = 0$ **58.** $x^2 - 3x - 4 = 0$

Geometry   In Exercises 59 and 60, find the ratio of the area of the blue region to the area of the green region. Express the result in simplified form.

59.

60.

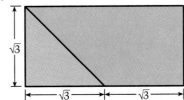

In Exercises 61 and 62, find the distance between the two points.

61. $(0, 9)$, $(\sqrt{12}, 3)$ **62.** $(\sqrt{5}, 5)$, $(0, 10)$

Pendulums and Resonance   In Exercises 63 and 64, use the following information.

The period, T (in seconds), of a pendulum is the time it takes for the weights to swing back and forth. The period is related to the length, L (in feet), of the pendulum by

$$T = 2\pi \sqrt{\frac{L}{32}}.$$

63. A string is pulled taut in a horizontal position. From the string, two pendulums are attached, each one the same weight and length. One is set in motion. Soon its partner will begin to swing with the *same* period. This is called *resonance*. Each pendulum is 1 foot long. What is their period? Write your result in simplified form.

64. Try the experiment described in Exercise 63. Then change the length of one of the pendulums. When one is set in motion, does its partner begin to move?

1. Factor. $x^2 + 8x + 7$. **(10.5)**

2. Factor. $-3x^2 - x - 2$. **(10.5)**

3. Solve. $4x^2 - 6x - 5 = 0$. **(9.4)**

4. Solve. $x^2 + 5x + 2 = 0$. **(9.4)**

5. Evaluate $f(x) = 3x + 2$ when $x = 6$. **(12.1)**

6. Evaluate $f(t) = 300(1.07)^t$ when $t = 0$. **(12.1)**

7. Write 4,230,000,000 in scientific notation. **(8.4)**

8. Write 0.0026 in scientific notation. **(8.4)**

9. Is (3, 4) a solution of $x^2 + y^2 = 5$? **(4.2)**

10. Is (2, 3) a solution of $y \geq 4 \cdot 3^{-x}$? **(8.2)**

11. Sketch the graph of $f(x) = \frac{3}{2}x + 2$. **(12.2)**

12. Sketch the graph of $f(x) = x^2 - 6x - 7$. **(12.4)**

13. Solve. $\frac{1}{x} + \frac{x}{5} = \frac{6}{5}$. **(11.8)**

14. Solve. $\frac{1}{y} + \frac{3}{5} = \frac{2}{y}$. **(11.8)**

15. Find the opposite of $3x^2 - 2$. **(2.1)**

16. Find the reciprocal of $\frac{1}{2}x^2y^{-1}$. **(8.3)**

17. Write $3 \cdot m \cdot m \cdot m \cdot m$ using exponents. **(1.3)**

18. Simplify $4x^2y^{-3}z^4 \div 6x^4yz^{-2}$. **(8.3)**

19. Add $\begin{bmatrix} 3 & 4 \\ -2a & b \end{bmatrix}$ and $\begin{bmatrix} 2b & 3 \\ 4 & 2b \end{bmatrix}$. **(2.4)**

20. Subtract $\begin{bmatrix} 3 & 6 \\ -2 & 5 \end{bmatrix}$ from $\begin{bmatrix} 7 & 9 \\ 6 & -4 \end{bmatrix}$. **(2.4)**

Career Interview

Translation Services

Jose Blanco is the owner and manager of a translation service specializing in English to Spanish translations. "As a small business I need to do my own accounting, payroll, and so on."

Q: *Did you take math classes in high school?*
A: The math courses I took in school have turned out to be the most useful in my daily experiences. I rely on basic algebra and some geometry, which is especially useful when doing page designs.

Q: *Does having a math background help you on the job?*
A: Definitely! I wouldn't be able to survive or be competitive without math skills to figure out or quantify projects properly. I often have to combine my basic math skills and my instincts. Being good with numbers is important.

Q: *How much mental math and estimation do you use?*
A: Lots, and constantly. They are both necessary to make decisions! For example, when negotiating a bid, we don't always have much time; some decisions need to be made on the spot. I rely on estimation and mental math a lot.

Q: *What would you like to tell kids who are in school?*
A: Having a strong number sense will be crucial to you.

13.3

Operations with Radicals

What you should learn:

Goal 1 How to add and subtract radical expressions

Goal 2 How to use radical operations in real-life problems

Why you should learn it:

You can use operations with radicals to solve many problems, such as finding the perimeters of figures on a grid.

Goal 1 Adding and Subtracting Radicals

Two radical expressions are **like radicals** if they have the same radicand. For instance, $\sqrt{2}$ and $3\sqrt{2}$ are like radicals. To add or subtract like radicals, add or subtract their coefficients.

Sum: $\sqrt{2} + 3\sqrt{2} = (1 + 3)\sqrt{2} = 4\sqrt{2}$
Difference: $\sqrt{2} - 3\sqrt{2} = (1 - 3)\sqrt{2} = -2\sqrt{2}$

Two radical expressions that are unlike may simplify to like radicals. (See Example 1b).

Example 1   *Adding and Subtracting Radicals*

a. $2\sqrt{3} + \sqrt{2} - 4\sqrt{3} = -2\sqrt{3} + \sqrt{2}$ *Add like radicals.*
b. $3\sqrt{2} - \sqrt{8} = 3\sqrt{2} - \sqrt{4 \cdot 2}$ *Perfect square factor*
$= 3\sqrt{2} - \sqrt{4} \cdot \sqrt{2}$ *Product Property*
$= 3\sqrt{2} - 2\sqrt{2}$ *Simplify.*
$= \sqrt{2}$ *Subtract like radicals.*

Example 2   *Multiplying Radicals*

a. $3\sqrt{2}(\sqrt{2} + 4\sqrt{6})$
$= (3\sqrt{2})(\sqrt{2}) + (3\sqrt{2})(4\sqrt{6})$ *Distributive Property*
$= 3(\sqrt{2} \cdot \sqrt{2}) + (3)(4)(\sqrt{2} \cdot \sqrt{6})$ *Regroup factors.*
$= 3\sqrt{4} + 12\sqrt{12}$ *Product Property*
$= 3\sqrt{4} + 12\sqrt{4 \cdot 3}$ *Perfect square factor*
$= 3\sqrt{4} + 12\sqrt{4} \cdot \sqrt{3}$ *Product Property*
$= 3(2) + 12(2)\sqrt{3}$ *Simplify.*
$= 6 + 24\sqrt{3}$ *Simplest form*

b. $(3 + 2\sqrt{2})^2$
$= 3^2 + 2(3)(2\sqrt{2}) + (2\sqrt{2})^2$ *Square of binomial*
$= 9 + 12\sqrt{2} + 2^2(\sqrt{2})^2$ *Simplify.*
$= 9 + 12\sqrt{2} + 4(2)$ *Definition of square root*
$= 17 + 12\sqrt{2}$ *Simplest form*

Example 3 **Checking Quadratic Formula Solutions**

Solve $x^2 - 4x + 1 = 0$. Check the solutions.

Solution

$$x^2 - 4x + 1 = 0 \qquad \textit{Rewrite original equation.}$$

$$x = \frac{4 \pm \sqrt{4^2 - 4(1)(1)}}{2(1)} \qquad \textit{Quadratic Formula}$$

$$= \frac{4 \pm \sqrt{12}}{2} \qquad \textit{Simplify.}$$

$$= \frac{4 \pm 2\sqrt{3}}{2} \qquad \textit{Product Property}$$

$$= \frac{2(2 \pm \sqrt{3})}{2} \qquad \textit{Factor numerator.}$$

$$= 2 \pm \sqrt{3} \qquad \textit{Cancel common factors.}$$

Check Here is the check for $2 + \sqrt{3}$.

$$x^2 - 4x + 1 = 0 \qquad \textit{Rewrite original equation.}$$

$$(2 + \sqrt{3})^2 - 4(2 + \sqrt{3}) + 1 \stackrel{?}{=} 0 \qquad \textit{Substitute } 2 + \sqrt{3} \textit{ for x.}$$

$$4 + 4\sqrt{3} + 3 - 8 - 4\sqrt{3} + 1 \stackrel{?}{=} 0 \qquad \textit{Multiply.}$$

$$0 = 0 \qquad \textit{Solution checks.} \qquad ■$$

Connections
Geometry

Example 4 **Finding the Perimeter of a Polygon**

You have purchased an irregularly shaped lot. The vertices of your lot have coordinates $(0, 6)$, $(2, 2)$, $(4, 1)$, $(7, 7)$, and $(6, 9)$. Each unit represents 15 feet. Find the perimeter of your lot.

Solution The lengths of the five sides are as follows.

$$d_1 = \sqrt{(2 - 0)^2 + (2 - 6)^2} = \sqrt{20} = 2\sqrt{5}$$
$$d_2 = \sqrt{(4 - 2)^2 + (1 - 2)^2} = \sqrt{5}$$
$$d_3 = \sqrt{(7 - 4)^2 + (7 - 1)^2} = \sqrt{45} = 3\sqrt{5}$$
$$d_4 = \sqrt{(6 - 7)^2 + (9 - 7)^2} = \sqrt{5}$$
$$d_5 = \sqrt{(0 - 6)^2 + (6 - 9)^2} = \sqrt{45} = 3\sqrt{5}$$

The perimeter, P, of the lot is

$$P = 2\sqrt{5} + \sqrt{5} + 3\sqrt{5} + \sqrt{5} + 3\sqrt{5}$$
$$= 10\sqrt{5} \text{ units.}$$

Because each unit is 15 feet, the perimeter is

$$P = 10\sqrt{5} \cdot 15$$
$$= 150\sqrt{5} \approx 335.4 \text{ feet.} \qquad ■$$

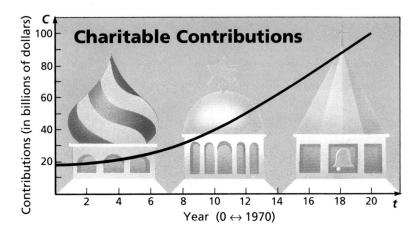

Charitable contributions by individuals account for about 83% of all charitable contributions in the United States. Of that, more than half is given to religious organizations.

Real Life
Philanthropy

Example 5   *Finding the Total Contributions*

For 1970 through 1990, the annual amount, C, given by individuals to religious organizations can be modeled by

$$C = 1.1\sqrt{310 + t^3} \quad \textit{billions of dollars}$$

where $t = 0$ represents 1970. Estimate the total amount given during this 21-year period.

Solution   Use a calculator to find the total.

$$\text{Total} = 1.1\sqrt{310 + 0^3} + 1.1\sqrt{310 + 1^3} + \cdots + 1.1\sqrt{310 + 20^3}$$
$$= 1.1(\sqrt{310} + \sqrt{311} + \cdots + \sqrt{8310})$$
$$\approx 992 \text{ billion dollars} \qquad \blacksquare$$

Communicating about **ALGEBRA**

▶ **SHARING IDEAS about the Lesson**

Extend the Idea   Use the following steps to find the total area of the lot described in Example 4.

A. Plot the vertices of the lot.

$A = (0, 6)$, $B = (2, 2)$, $C = (4, 1)$, $D = (7, 7)$, $E = (6, 9)$

B. Show that $\angle BAE$, $\angle AED$, and $\angle BCD$ are right angles.

C. The area of the lot is the sum of the area of the trapezoid $ABDE$ and the triangle BCD. Compute the area of the lot.

EXERCISES

Guided Practice

▶ **CRITICAL THINKING about the Lesson**

1. Give an example of two radical expressions that are like radicals. Give an example of two that are not.

2. Write $\sqrt{2}$ and $\sqrt{18}$ as like radicals.

In Exercises 3–5, simplify the expression.

3. $3\sqrt{6} + \sqrt{24}$ **4.** $\sqrt{72} - 5\sqrt{2}$ **5.** $\sqrt{3}(5\sqrt{3} - 2\sqrt{6})$

6. Is $3 + \sqrt{6}$ a solution of the equation $x^2 - 6x + 3 = 0$?

Independent Practice

In Exercises 7–18, simplify the expression.

7. $4\sqrt{7} + 3\sqrt{7}$ **8.** $\sqrt{5} + 3\sqrt{5}$ **9.** $9\sqrt{3} - 12\sqrt{3}$

10. $2\sqrt{6} - \sqrt{6}$ **11.** $\sqrt{2} + \sqrt{18}$ **12.** $\sqrt{27} + \sqrt{3}$

13. $4\sqrt{5} + \sqrt{80} + \sqrt{20}$ **14.** $5\sqrt{5} + \sqrt{405} + \sqrt{5}$ **15.** $\sqrt{44} - 2\sqrt{11}$

16. $\sqrt{72} - 9\sqrt{2}$ **17.** $\sqrt{20} - \sqrt{45} + \sqrt{5}$ **18.** $\sqrt{243} + \sqrt{75} - \sqrt{300}$

In Exercises 19–24, simplify the expression.

19. $\sqrt{3}(3\sqrt{2} + \sqrt{3})$ **20.** $\sqrt{6}(5\sqrt{2} + 6)$ **21.** $(\sqrt{5} + 4)^2$

22. $(2\sqrt{3} - 5)^2$ **23.** $(\sqrt{2} + 4)(1 - 5\sqrt{2})$ **24.** $(\sqrt{7} + 3)(\sqrt{7} - 3)$

25. *Geometry* Find the area and perimeter. **26.** *Geometry* Find the area.

In Exercises 27 and 28, evaluate the function.

27. $f(x) = x^2 + 5x - 4$, when $x = \sqrt{10}$ **28.** $f(x) = x^2 - x - 6$, when $x = 2\sqrt{3}$

In Exercises 29 and 30, decide whether the *x*-value is a solution of the equation.

29. $x^2 - 4x - 15 = 0$, $x = 2 - \sqrt{19}$ **30.** $2x^2 + 16x - 21 = 0$, $x = -4 + \sqrt{106}$

31. Swimming Pool   Find the perimeter of the swimming pool. (Each unit in the coordinate system corresponds to 2 feet.) The coordinates of the vertices are as follows.

$A = (0, 0)$ $B = (-2, 2)$
$C = (-2, 4)$ $D = (0, 6)$
$E = (2, 6)$ $F = (7, 1)$
$G = (7, -1)$ $H = (5, -1)$
$I = (3, 1)$ $J = (1, 1)$

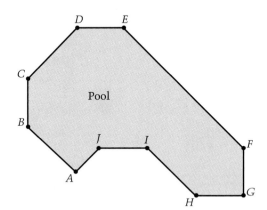

32. The Troublesome T   The puzzle pieces below can be arranged to form the letter "T." Find the total perimeter of all four pieces. (Use the coordinate system to find the vertices of each piece: The piece at the lower left has coordinates (0, 0), (5, 0), (5, 3), and (0, 8).) Copy the pieces, cut out the copies, and form the letter "T." What do you notice about the perimeter of the "T"? Explain how to find the area of all four pieces.

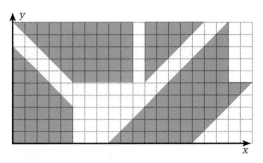

33. U.S. Households   For 1970 through 1990, the number, H (in millions), of households in the United States can be modeled by

$$H = \sqrt{3978 + 241t}$$

where $t = 0$ represents 1970. How many households were there in 1970? How many households were there in 1971? How many households were there in 1972? Create a table that shows that the number of households was "increasing at a decreasing rate."

34. Selling a Puzzle   The Spanish Club at school has its picture taken and sends the picture to a company that makes jigsaw puzzles. The club sells the puzzles to make money for a trip. The number, P, of puzzles sold each week for 20 weeks can be modeled by

$$P = 4\sqrt{6t - 3}$$

where $t = 1$ represents the first week. Use a table *and* graph to describe the sales pattern of the puzzles. If the club made a profit of $4 on each puzzle, what is the total profit made in 20 weeks?

In Exercises 35–38, find the distance between the points. Write the result in simplified form.

35. $(8, \sqrt{5}), (5, 6\sqrt{5})$

36. $(6\sqrt{2}, 5), (\sqrt{2}, 3)$

37. $(\sqrt{2}, 3), (-2\sqrt{2}, 2)$

38. $(3, \sqrt{3}), (4, 4\sqrt{3})$

39. Is 4 a solution of $\sqrt{x + 5} + \sqrt{x} = 5$?

40. Is -2 a solution of
$\sqrt{x + 6} + \sqrt{14 - x} = 20$?

In Exercises 41 and 42, simplify the expression.

41. $\dfrac{\sqrt{243} \times 10^4}{\sqrt{27} \times 10^{-2}}$

42. $\dfrac{\sqrt{112} \times 10^{-1}}{2\sqrt{7} \times 10^3}$

43. *College Entrance Exam Sample*   The expression $\sqrt{a^2 + b^2}$ is equal to

a. $a + b$ **b.** $a - b$ **c.** $(a + b)(a - b)$ **d.** $\sqrt{a^2} + \sqrt{b^2}$ **e.** none of these

Perpendicular Lines   **In Exercises 44 and 45, use the following information.**

Two nonvertical lines are perpendicular if their slopes, m_1 and m_2, are negative reciprocals of each other, or $m_1 \cdot m_2 = -1$. Show that the triangle is a right triangle in two ways. First, use the Distance Formula and the Pythagorean theorem. Second, show that two sides of the triangle are perpendicular. Which method do you prefer? Explain.

44. $(-3, -4), (1, 4), (5, 2)$

45. $(1, -7), (-5, 1), (-2, 2)$

46. *The Shortest Path to Shore*   You are in a boat at the point $(-4, 7)$. The shoreline is given by the equation $y = \frac{5}{3}x$. The shortest distance between you and the shore is along the line that passes through the point $(-4, 7)$ and is perpendicular to the shoreline.

- Find the slope of the shortest path.
- Find an equation of the shortest path.
- Find the point of intersection of the shoreline and the shortest path.
- Find the distance between the point of intersection and the point describing your location.

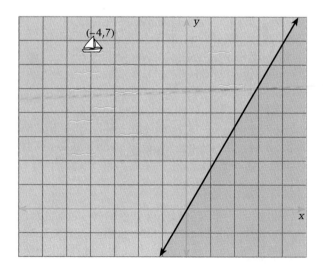

13.4

Solving Radical Equations

What you should learn:

Goal 1 How to solve radical equations

Goal 2 How to use radical equations to solve real-life problems

Why you should learn it:

You can use radicals to solve many real-life problems, such as compensating for inaccuracy of a balance.

Goal 1 Solving a Radical Equation

Solving an equation that contains radicals is somewhat like solving a rational equation—you try to rewrite the equation as a polynomial equation. Then you solve the polynomial equation using the standard procedures. The following property plays a key role.

Squaring Both Sides of an Equation
If $a = b$, then $a^2 = b^2$.

Squaring both sides of an equation often introduces **extraneous solutions** of $a^2 = b^2$ that are *not* solutions of $a = b$. So when you use this procedure, it is critical that you check each solution in the *original* equation.

Before squaring both sides of an equation, you should isolate the radical expression on one side of the equation.

Example 1 *Solving a Radical Equation*

Solve $\sqrt{x} - 8 = 0$.

Solution

$$\sqrt{x} - 8 = 0 \qquad \textit{Rewrite original equation.}$$
$$\sqrt{x} = 8 \qquad \textit{Add 8 to both sides.}$$
$$(\sqrt{x})^2 = 8^2 \qquad \textit{Square both sides.}$$
$$x = 64 \qquad \textit{Simplify.}$$

Check

$$\sqrt{x} - 8 = 0 \qquad \textit{Rewrite original equation.}$$
$$\sqrt{64} - 8 \stackrel{?}{=} 0 \qquad \textit{Substitute 64 for x.}$$
$$8 - 8 = 0 \qquad \textit{Solution checks.}$$

The equation has 64 as its solution. ∎

Try solving the equation $\sqrt{x} + 8 = 0$. You will obtain the same solution, 64. For this equation, however, 64 is extraneous. Try to see why.

Example **2** **Solving a Radical Equation**

Solve $\sqrt{2x - 1} + 1 = 4$.

Solution

$$\sqrt{2x - 1} + 1 = 4 \qquad \textit{Rewrite original equation.}$$
$$\sqrt{2x - 1} = 3 \qquad \textit{Subtract 1 from both sides.}$$
$$(\sqrt{2x - 1})^2 = 3^2 \qquad \textit{Square both sides.}$$
$$2x - 1 = 9 \qquad \textit{Simplify.}$$
$$2x = 10 \qquad \textit{Add 1 to both sides.}$$
$$x = 5 \qquad \textit{Divide both sides by 2.}$$

After checking $x = 5$ in the original equation, you can conclude that the equation has 5 as its solution. ∎

Example **3**   **Solving a Radical Equation**

Solve $x = \sqrt{x + 2}$.

Solution

$$x = \sqrt{x + 2} \qquad \textit{Rewrite original equation.}$$
$$x^2 = (\sqrt{x + 2})^2 \qquad \textit{Square both sides.}$$
$$x^2 = x + 2 \qquad \textit{Simplify.}$$
$$x^2 - x - 2 = 0 \qquad \textit{Write in standard form.}$$
$$(x - 2)(x + 1) = 0 \qquad \textit{Factor.}$$
$$x = 2 \text{ or } x = -1 \qquad \textit{Zero-Product Property}$$

Try checking *each* x-value in the original equation. You will find that $x = 2$ checks, but $x = -1$ *does not* check. Thus, the equation has 2 as its solution. ∎

Example **4**   **Finding the Geometric Mean of Two Numbers**

The **geometric mean** of a and b is $\sqrt{ab}$. If the geometric mean of a and 4 is 12, what is a?

Solution

Geometric mean $= \sqrt{a \cdot 4}$

$$12 = \sqrt{4a}$$
$$12^2 = (\sqrt{4a})^2$$
$$144 = 4a$$
$$36 = a$$

Check

$$12 \overset{?}{=} \sqrt{(36)(4)}$$
$$12 \overset{?}{=} \sqrt{144}$$
$$12 = 12 \quad (\textit{checks})$$

The geometric mean of 36 and 4 is 12. ∎

Solving Radical Equations in Real Life

Balance scales can give inaccurate results if the lengths of the left and right arms, L and R, are not *exactly* the same. Here is a technique that scientists use to be sure of an accurate weight. Let W be the true weight of an object.

1. Place the object on the left side of the scale. Counterbalance the right side with a weight of W_1. By a property of levers, you can write $\frac{W}{W_1} = \frac{R}{L}$.

2. Place the object on the right side of the scale. Counterbalance the left side with a weight of W_2: $\frac{W_2}{W} = \frac{R}{L}$

3. Equate the two expressions for $\frac{R}{L}$ and solve for W. The solution is $W = \sqrt{W_1 W_2}$. Thus, the true weight is the geometric mean of the weights obtained by weighing the object on the left and right sides of the scale.

Connections
Physical Science

Example 5   *Finding an Accurate Weight*

In science class, you weigh a sulfur sample only once—on the left side of a scale: It weighs 92 grams. Your teacher says the actual weight is 95 grams. If 95 grams is correct, what weight would you have obtained on the right side of the scale?

Solution   The actual weight is $W = 95$ grams. On the left side of the scale, you observed the weight to be $W_1 = 92$ grams. Let W_2 be the weight that would be observed on the right side of the scale.

$$W = \sqrt{W_1 W_2} \qquad \textit{W is the geometric mean of } W_1 \textit{ and } W_2.$$
$$95 = \sqrt{92 W_2} \qquad \textit{Substitute 95 for W and 92 for } W_1.$$
$$9025 = 92 W_2 \qquad \textit{Square both sides of the equation.}$$
$$98.1 \approx W_2 \qquad \textit{Divide both sides by 92.}$$

You would have obtained 98.1 grams on the right side.   ■

Communicating about **ALGEBRA**

Cooperative Learning

▷ **SHARING IDEAS about the Lesson**

Work with a Partner and Use Your Own Words   Solve the equations. Explain your steps.

A. $\sqrt{x} - 5 = 0$ **B.** $\sqrt{x} + 5 = 0$

C. $\sqrt{3x + 4} - 2 = 5$ **D.** $x - 2 = \sqrt{8 - x}$

E X E R C I S E S

▶ **CRITICAL THINKING about the Lesson**

1. Describe a strategy for solving a radical equation. Then apply your strategy to solve $\sqrt{2x} - 10 = 0$.

2. Is $x = 25$ a solution of $\sqrt{x} = -5$? Why or why not?

3. One reason for checking a solution in the original equation is that you might have made an error in one of the steps of the solution. Describe another reason.

4. The geometric mean of 12 and x is 6. What is x?

Independent Practice

In Exercises 5–16, solve the equation. (Some of the equations have no solution.)

5. $\sqrt{x} - 10 = 0$

6. $\sqrt{x} - 1 = 0$

7. $\sqrt{-x} - \frac{1}{2} = \frac{3}{2}$

8. $\sqrt{3x} - 4 = 6$

9. $\sqrt{3x + 2} + 2 = 3$

10. $\sqrt{4 - x} - 5 = 1$

11. $4 = 6 - \sqrt{21x - 3}$

12. $10 = 17 + \sqrt{6x + 7}$

13. $\sqrt{\frac{1}{2}x - 5} - 1 = 11$

14. $\sqrt{\frac{1}{9}x + 1} - \frac{2}{3} = \frac{5}{3}$

15. $-5 - \sqrt{10x - 2} = 5$

16. $6 - \sqrt{7x - 9} = 3$

In Exercises 17–24, solve the equation.

17. $x = \sqrt{20 - x}$

18. $x = \sqrt{6 - x}$

19. $\sqrt{-10x - 4} = 2x$

20. $x = \sqrt{100 - 15x}$

21. $\sqrt{77 - 4x} = x$

22. $2x = \sqrt{-13x - 10}$

23. $\frac{1}{2}x = \sqrt{x + 3}$

24. $x = \sqrt{4x + 32}$

25. Find the geometric mean of 8 and 32.

26. Find the geometric mean of 4 and 32.

27. The geometric mean of x and 5 is 15. What is x?

28. The geometric mean of 9 and x is 6. What is x?

Geometry   **In Exercises 29 and 30, find the value of x.**

29.

30.

A ride at an amusement park spins in a circle of radius r, (in feet). The centrifugal force, F (in pounds), experienced by a passenger on the ride can be found by solving the equation

$$t = \sqrt{\frac{\pi^2 wr}{8F}}.$$

t is the number of seconds the ride takes to make one complete revolution and w is the weight, (in pounds), of the passenger.

31. A person who weighs 115 pounds is on a ride that is spinning at a rate of 10 seconds per revolution. The radius of the circular ride is 20 feet. How much centrifugal force does the person feel?

32. You are spinning on ice skates with your arms outstretched. As you pull your arms in toward your body, you are decreasing the radius, r. What effect does this have on t? What effect does it have on the skater? (Assume that the centrifugal force, F, is constant.)

The Speed of Sound   **In Exercises 33 and 34, use the following information.**

The speed of sound near Earth's surface depends on the temperature. An equation that relates the speed, v (in meters per second), with the temperature, t (in degrees Celsius), is $v = 20\sqrt{t + 273}$.

33. Your friend is playing basketball 170 meters from you. You hear the sound of the ball hitting the backboard 0.5 seconds after seeing the ball hit the backboard. What is the temperature?

34. The temperature $-273°C$ is called absolute zero. What is the speed of sound at this temperature?

Rifle Velocity   **In Exercises 35 and 36, use the following information.**

Because of the air resistance, the velocity of a bullet decreases after the bullet is fired. For a 25–06 rifle, the velocity, v (in feet per second), of the bullet after t seconds is given by $v = \frac{3200}{t + 1}$. If the rifle is held horizontally, the distance, h (in feet), the bullet *falls* is related to the time by the equation $t = \frac{1}{4}\sqrt{h}$.

The Winter Olympics Biathlon combines Nordic skiing with rifle shooting.

35. A 25–06 rifle is fired horizontally at a target. The bullet hits the target in $\frac{1}{8}$ second. How fast is the bullet moving when it hits the target?

36. How far did the bullet fall before hitting the target?

In Exercises 37–40, are the given *x*-values solutions of the equation?

37. $x - \sqrt{9} = 0, \quad x = \pm 3$

38. $2x - \sqrt{16} = 0, \quad x = \pm 2$

39. $x = \sqrt{80 - 2x}, \quad x = -10, x = 8$

40. $x = \sqrt{12 - 11x}, \quad x = -12, x = 1$

In Exercises 41–46, write the solutions in simplified form.

41. $4x^2 + 22x + 30 = 0$

42. $3x^2 - 4x + 1 = 0$

43. $x^2 - 3x - 9 = 0$

44. $x^2 + 14x - 12 = 0$

45. $x^2 - 14x + 33 = 0$

46. $10x^2 + \frac{5}{8}x - 2 = 0$

In Exercises 47–50, write the solutions in simplified form. (Multiply first by the least common denominator to "clear" the equation of fractions.)

47. $x^2 + \frac{5}{3}x + \frac{4}{9} = 0$

48. $\frac{1}{21}x^2 - \frac{3}{7}x - \frac{10}{21} = 0$

49. $\frac{1}{6}x^2 + \frac{2}{3}x + \frac{1}{3} = 0$

50. $\frac{1}{4}x^2 + \frac{5}{8}x - 2 = 0$

Exploration and Extension

51. *Orbits of the Sun*   Johannes Kepler (1571–1630), discovered a relationship between the average distance of a planet from the sun and the time, or *period*, it takes the planet to orbit the sun. The following table shows the average distance, *x* (in astronomical units), and the period, *y* (in years), for the six planets that are closest to the sun. Complete the table. Then use the results to write *y* as a function of *x*.

	Mercury	Venus	Earth	Mars	Jupiter	Saturn
Average Distance, *x*	0.387	0.723	1	1.523	5.203	9.541
x^3	?	?	?	?	?	?
Period, *y*	0.241	0.615	1	1.881	11.861	29.457
y^2	?	?	?	?	?	?

The domain of the function $f(x) = \sqrt{x}$ is the set of nonnegative numbers. Some graphing utilities will display an error message when asked to sketch a graph over an interval that contains x-values that are not in the domain. The TI-81 and fx-7700G, however, just ignore such values and draw the graph for values of x that are in the domain. Because of this feature, you can use either of these graphing calculators to explore the domain of a radical function. For instance, the display at the right shows the graph of $f(x) = \sqrt{x}$. Notice that the graph begins at the origin and continues to the right. To the left of the origin, the graph does not exist because negative x-values are not in the domain of f.

Graph of $f(\mathbf{x}) = \sqrt{\mathbf{x}}$

TI-81

$\boxed{RANGE}$ (Set range.)
  Xmin = −10
  Xmax = 10
  Xscl = 1
  Ymin = −10
  Ymax = 10
  Yscl = 1
$\boxed{Y=}$ $\boxed{2nd}$ $\boxed{\sqrt{}}$ $\boxed{X\mid T}$
  :Y₁ = √ X
  :Y₂ =
  :Y₃ =
  :Y₄ =
$\boxed{GRAPH}$
$\boxed{CLEAR}$ (Clear screen.)

Casio fx-7700G

$\boxed{Range}$ (Set range.)
  Xmin = −10
  max = 10
  scl = 1
  Ymin = −10
  max = 10
  scl = 1
$\boxed{EXE}$ $\boxed{Range}$
$\boxed{SHIFT}$ $\boxed{F5}$ (Cls) $\boxed{EXE}$
$\boxed{Graph}$ $\boxed{\sqrt{}}$ $\boxed{X,\theta,T}$
  Graph Y = √ X
$\boxed{EXE}$
$\boxed{SHIFT}$ $\boxed{F5}$ (Cls) $\boxed{EXE}$

Exercises

In Exercises 1–4, use a graphing calculator to sketch the graph of the function. From the graph, describe the domain of the function.

1. $f(x) = \sqrt{2x}$ **2.** $f(x) = \sqrt{x-1}$ **3.** $f(x) = \sqrt{x+2}$ **4.** $f(x) = \sqrt{2x-6}$

In Exercises 5–8, use a graphing calculator to sketch the graph of both functions. Explain how the graph of g is related to the graph of f.

5. $f(x) = \sqrt{x}$, $g(x) = \sqrt{x-3}$ **6.** $f(x) = \sqrt{x}$, $g(x) = \sqrt{x} - 3$

7. $f(x) = \sqrt{x}$, $g(x) = -\sqrt{x}$ **8.** $f(x) = \sqrt{x}$, $g(x) = \sqrt{x+4}$

In Exercises 1 and 2, find the distance between the two points. **(13.1)**

1. $(4, 5), (7, 2)$

2. $(1, -2), (-4, 8)$

In Exercises 3 and 4, decide whether the points are vertices of a right triangle. **(13.1)**

3. $(3, -2), (4, 6), (11, -1)$

4. $(1, 5), (2, 8), (-2, 6)$

In Exercises 5 and 6, find the midpoint between the two points. **(13.1)**

5. $(4, 2), (5, -6)$

6. $(0, 10), (-12, 5)$

In Exercises 7–10, simplify the radical expression. **(13.2)**

7. $\sqrt{98}$

8. $\sqrt{432}$

9. $\sqrt{\dfrac{5}{36}}$

10. $\sqrt{\dfrac{7}{20}}$

In Exercises 11–14, perform the indicated operations. **(13.3)**

11. $5\sqrt{3} + \sqrt{3} - \sqrt{2}$ **12.** $3\sqrt{3}(4\sqrt{3} + \sqrt{6})$ **13.** $\sqrt{2}(8\sqrt{2} - 2\sqrt{10})$ **14.** $(2\sqrt{3} - 3)^2$

In Exercises 15–18, solve the equation. **(13.4)**

15. $\sqrt{x} - 3 = 0$ **16.** $\sqrt{3x - 2} - 6 = 0$ **17.** $x = \sqrt{5x + 6}$ **18.** $x = \sqrt{-3x + 4}$

19. Find the geometric mean of 4 and 9. **(13.4)**

20. The geometric mean of a and 32 is 8. What is a? **(13.4)**

21. Find the perimeter of the polygon. **(13.3)**

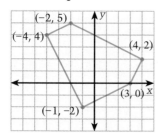

22. Find the area and perimeter of the polygon. **(13.3)**

23. Two infielders position themselves so that second base is at their midpoint. Find the coordinates of second base. **(13.1)**

24. In the baseball stadium whose infield is shown at the right, any ball that is hit farther than 400 feet will be a home run. A batter hits a fly ball to the coordinates $(-245, -285)$. Is it a home run? (Each unit corresponds to 1 foot.) **(13.1)**

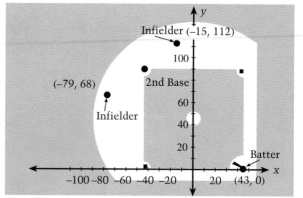

13.5

The Tangent of an Angle

What you should learn:

Goal 1 How to use the tangent of an angle to find the lengths of the sides of a right triangle

Goal 2 How to use the tangent of an angle to solve real-life problems

Why you should learn it:

You can use the tangent of an angle to solve many real-life problems, such as finding distances that cannot be measured directly.

Goal 1 Using the Tangent of an Angle

Angles are measured in degrees. An **acute angle** is an angle whose measure is greater than 0° and less than 90°. A right triangle has two acute angles and one right angle. The acute angles are denoted by A and B. The right angle is denoted by C. The measures of the three sides are denoted by the lowercase form of the same letters.

- The side BC is opposite angle A. Its length is a.
- The side AC is opposite angle B. Its length is b.
- The side AB is opposite angle C. Its length is c.

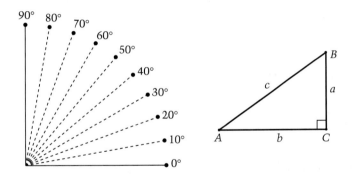

The Tangent of an Acute Angle

Let A and B be the acute angles of a right triangle. The **tangent** of A and the **tangent** of B are as follows:

$$\tan A = \frac{\text{length of side opposite } A}{\text{length of side adjacent to } A} = \frac{a}{b}$$

$$\tan B = \frac{\text{length of side opposite } B}{\text{length of side adjacent to } B} = \frac{b}{a}$$

Example 1 Finding the Tangent of an Angle

Find the tangent of A and the tangent of B for the triangle shown.

Solution
$$\tan A = \frac{a}{b} = \frac{5}{12}$$

$$\tan B = \frac{b}{a} = \frac{12}{5}$$

■

Example **2**

Finding the Lengths of the Sides of a Right Triangle

The tangent of angle A is $\frac{4}{3}$. The length of the side opposite A is 12. What are the lengths of the other two sides?

Solution

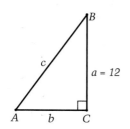

$$\tan A = \frac{a}{b} \qquad \textit{Definition of tangent of A}$$

$$\frac{4}{3} = \frac{12}{b} \qquad \textit{Substitute } \tfrac{4}{3} \textit{ for tan A and 12 for a.}$$

$$4b = 3(12) \qquad \textit{Cross multiply.}$$

$$b = 9 \qquad \textit{Divide both sides by 4.}$$

To find c, use the Pythagorean theorem.

$$c^2 = a^2 + b^2 \qquad \textit{Pythagorean theorem}$$
$$c^2 = 12^2 + 9^2 \qquad \textit{Substitute 12 for a and 9 for b.}$$
$$c^2 = 225 \qquad \textit{Simplify.}$$
$$c = \sqrt{225} \qquad \textit{Find the positive square root.}$$
$$c = 15 \qquad \textit{Simplify.}$$

The lengths of the other two sides are 9 and 15. ∎

To find the tangent of an angle whose degree measure is given, you can use the tangent key, $\boxed{\text{TAN}}$, on a scientific calculator.

Connections

Technology

Example 3

Finding the Lengths of the Sides of a Right Triangle

The measure of angle A is 30°, and b is 8. What is a?

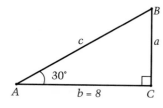

Solution Use a scientific calculator to find the tangent of A. (First set the calculator to *degree mode*.)

Keystrokes	Display
30 $\boxed{\text{TAN}}$	0.577350

Thus, $\tan 30° \approx 0.57735$. You can solve for a as follows.

$$\tan A = \frac{a}{b} \qquad \textit{Definition of tangent of A}$$

$$0.57735 \approx \frac{a}{8} \qquad \textit{Substitute 0.57735 for tan A and 8 for b.}$$

$$8(0.57735) \approx a \qquad \textit{Multiply both sides by 8.}$$

$$4.62 \approx a \qquad \textit{Simplify.}$$

The length of a is about 4.62 units. ∎

The Grand Canyon is one of the most famous natural wonders in the United States. Its area is larger than Rhode Island. In some places, it is one mile deep.

Real Life
Surveying

Example 4   *Finding the Depth of a Canyon*

Suppose that surveyors measure the angle between the horizontal and a point on the canyon floor to be 40°. Using a laser beam, they find the horizontal distance between their surveying equipment and a point above the canyon floor to be 5740 feet. What is the vertical distance to the canyon floor?

Solution   Use a calculator to find $\tan 40° \approx 0.8391$.

$$\tan 40° = \frac{a}{5740}$$

$$0.8391 \approx \frac{a}{5740}$$

$$0.8391(5740) \approx a$$

$$4816.4 \approx a$$

The vertical distance is about 4816 feet. ■

Communicating about **A L G E B R A**

▶ **SHARING IDEAS about the Lesson**

Extend the Idea   Explain how to use the tangent to find the lengths of the sides.

A.

B.

C.

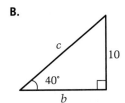

EXERCISES

Guided Practice

▶ **CRITICAL THINKING about the Lesson**

1. What is an *acute* angle? In a right triangle, what is the sum of A and B?

2. Find the tangent of the angle A.

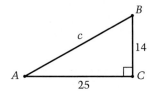

3. Find the lengths b and c.

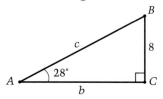

4. Use a calculator to evaluate tan 35°. Round the value to two decimal places.

Independent Practice

In Exercises 5–10, find tan A and tan B.

5.

6.

7.

8.

9.

10.

Technology   **In Exercises 11–16, use a calculator to evaluate the expression. Round the value to two decimal places.**

11. tan 12°

12. tan 48°

13. tan 84°

14. tan 24.5°

15. tan 1.8°

16. tan 64.3°

17. The tangent of angle A in a right triangle is $\frac{2}{3}$. The length of the side opposite A is 8. What are the lengths of the other two sides? Sketch the triangle to scale and label the length of each side.

18. The tangent of angle A in a right triangle is $\frac{7}{2}$. The length of the side adjacent to A is 3. What are the lengths of the other two sides? Sketch the triangle to scale and label the length of each side.

In Exercises 19–24, find the remaining side and angle measurements.

19.

20.

21.

22.

23.

24.
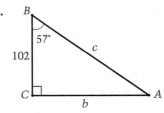

25. *45°-45°-90° Triangle*   Use the triangle to find the exact value of the tangent of 45°.

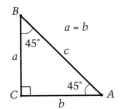

26. *30°-60°-90° Triangle*   Use the triangle to find the exact values of tan 30° and tan 60°.

27. *Airplane Engine*   The cylinders of the airplane engine form equal angles. The distance between the center of the engine and the tip of a cylinder is 28 inches. Find the distance between the tips of two consecutive cylinders.

28. *Air Force Rescue Helicopter*   The blades of the helicopter meet at right angles and are all the same length. The distance between the tips of two consecutive blades is 32.5 feet. Find the measure of the angles in one of the triangles whose legs are consecutive blades. How long is each blade?

In Exercises 29 and 30, find the lengths x and y. Round your results to two decimal places.

29.

30.

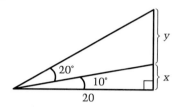

31. *Measuring an Arch*   You are standing 75 feet from the base of a stone arch in Arches National Park, Utah. The angle formed by the ground and your line of sight to the top of the arch is 38°. How high is the arch?

32. *Measuring an Arch*   Use the result from Exercise 31 and the angle shown in the photo to find the thickness of the top of the stone arch.

33. *Hagia Sophia*   Imagine yourself standing 100 feet from the base of one of the four spires of the Hagia Sophia in Istanbul, Turkey—one of the most famous mosques in the world. The angle formed by the ground and your line of sight to the top of the spire is 65°. How tall is the spire?

34. *Hagia Sophia*   You are standing 120 feet from the same spire of the mosque. What is the tangent of the angle formed by the ground and your line of sight to the top of the spire?

Integrated Review

In Exercises 35–40, solve the equation.

35. $a^2 + 4^2 = 8^2$

36. $6^2 + b^2 = 9^2$

37. $4^2 + 5^2 = c^2$

38. $\frac{2}{5} = \frac{a}{3}$

39. $\frac{7}{3} = \frac{4}{b}$

40. $\tan 20° = \frac{3}{b}$

In Exercises 41 and 42, find the slope of the line that passes through the points. Explain how the slope of the line is related to the indicated angle.

41.

42.

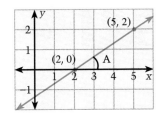

43. *College Entrance Exam Sample*   In a right triangle, the ratio of the legs is 1:2. If the area of the triangle is 25 square units, what is the length of the hypotenuse?

a. $\sqrt{5}$ **b.** $5\sqrt{5}$ **c.** $5\sqrt{3}$ **d.** $10\sqrt{3}$ **e.** $25\sqrt{5}$

Exploration and Extension

44. A line with a positive slope passes through the origin, making an angle of $60°$ with the positive x-axis. Write an equation of the line.

45. A line with a negative slope passes through the origin. The angle between the line and the negative x-axis is $60°$. Write an equation of the line.

Mixed **REVIEW**

1. Simplify $2x(x + 3) - x(4 - x^2)$. **(2.6)**

2. Simplify $(3x \div 4x) + \frac{1}{4}$. **(2.7)**

3. Is 3 a solution of $x^2 - 2x + 4 < 5$? **(1.5)**

4. Is -4 a solution of $|3m + 2| + m > 5$? **(4.5)**

5. Solve $3p^2 - 6q = 0$ for p. **(3.6)**

6. Solve $3m + 3mn - 6x = 0$ for m. **(3.6)**

7. Evaluate $36x^2 + 2x - 6$ when $x = \frac{1}{4}$. **(1.4)**

8. Evaluate $3x + 9$ when $x = \frac{2}{9}$. **(1.4)**

9. Find the mean of 2, 3, 5, 7, and 8.

10. Find the median of 26, 42, 35, 16, and 81.

11. 216 is what percent of 360?

12. 212.5 is 25% of what number?

13. Sketch the graph of $-4x + 5y = -5$. **(4.3)**

14. Sketch the graph of $y = |3x + 2| - 4$. **(4.7)**

15. Sketch the graph of $f(x) = \left(\frac{1}{4}\right)^x + 2$. **(12.3)**

16. Sketch the graph of $f(x) = \frac{x + 2}{x + 1}$. **(12.5)**

17. Sketch the graph of $y < 3x + 2$. **(6.5)**

18. Sketch the graph of $y \geq x^2 - 4$. **(9.6)**

19. Solve the system $\begin{cases} x + 2y = -15 \\ 5x - 4y = 9 \end{cases}$ **(7.3)**

20. Solve the system $\begin{cases} 4x + 2y = 8 \\ 6x - 5y = 28 \end{cases}$ **(7.3)**

Formal Use of Properties of Algebra

What you should learn:

Goal How to use properties of algebra to prove a statement true and to use counter-examples to prove a statement false

Why you should learn it:

You will use the properties of algebra more formally in higher-level mathematics courses.

GOAL ## Using Properties of Algebra

Mathematics evolved over the past few thousand years in many stages. *All* of the early stages were centered around the use of mathematics to answer questions about real life. This is much like the way we wrote *Algebra 1*. We centered the concepts around the real-life use of mathematics.

As mathematical development matured, people began to collect and categorize the different rules, formulas, and properties that had been discovered. This took place independently in many different parts of the world: Africa, Asia, Europe, North America, and South America. The mathematics that we use today is a combination of the work of literally thousands of people.

As the collections and catalogs of rules, formulas, and properties grew, some discrepancies were noticed—some of the rules didn't seem to fit with some of the other rules. This made people wonder which rules were "true," and they tried to see which could be **proved.** After some effort, however, they realized that you can't prove *every* rule—some have to be accepted "on faith." In mathematics, the rules that we accept to be true *without proof* are called **postulates** *or* **axioms.** Many of the rules in Chapter 2 fall into this category.

The Basic Axioms of Algebra

Let a, b, and c be any real numbers.

Name of Axiom	Addition Axioms	Multiplication Axioms
Closure	$a + b$ is a real number.	ab is a real number.
Commutative	$a + b = b + a$	$ab = ba$
Associative	$(a + b) + c = a + (b + c)$	$(ab)c = a(bc)$
Identity	$a + 0 = a, 0 + a = a$	$a(1) = a, 1(a) = a$
Inverse	$a + (-a) = 0$	$a\left(\frac{1}{a}\right) = 1, a \neq 0$

Axiom Relating Addition and Multiplication

Distributive	$a(b + c) = ab + ac$	$(a + b)c = ac + bc$

Once a list of axioms has been accepted, you can add more rules, formulas, and properties to the collection. Some of the new concepts are **definitions.** You don't have to prove a definition, but you do need to check that it is consistent with previous definitions and axioms.

Other new concepts, called **theorems,** do have to be proved. For instance, it is possible (although it is not done here) to use the basic axioms to prove that $c(-b) = -cb$ for all real numbers b and c.

Example 1 | *Proving a Theorem*

Use the definition of subtraction, $a - b = a + (-b)$ and prove that the following theorem is true for all real numbers a, b, and c.

$$c(a - b) = ca - cb$$

Solution

$c(a - b)$	$= c(a + (-b))$	*Definition of subtraction*
	$= ca + c(-b)$	*Distributive Property*
	$= ca + (-cb)$	*Theorem listed above*
	$= ca - cb$	*Definition of subtraction*

Proofs are not easy to write *or* to read. They take a lot of practice. Our reason for listing this proof is simply to point out that when you are proving a new formula, *every* step must be justified by an axiom, a definition, or a previously proved theorem. ∎

Sometimes people propose new rules that *are not* consistent with the axioms, definitions, and theorems in the accepted list. To show that a proposed rule is *inconsistent* or *false*, you need to find only one counterexample.

Example 2 | *Finding a Counterexample*

Assign values to a and b to show that the following "rule" is inconsistent: $a + (-b) = (-a) + b$ for all real numbers a and b.

Solution Almost any choices of a and b will show the inconsistency. For instance, let $a = 1$ and let $b = 2$. Then

$$a + (-b) = 1 + (-2) = -1 \quad \text{and} \quad (-a) + b = -1 + 2 = 1.$$

Because -1 and 1 are not the same number, you have shown one case in which $a + (-b)$ is not equal to $(-a) + b$. Therefore, the proposed rule must be false. (If it were true, it would have to work for any choices of a and b.) ∎

Sometimes people have proposed rules and properties that they believe to be true but are unable to prove. For instance, Christian Goldbach (1690–1764) proposed the following rule, which is called *Goldbach's Conjecture.*

> *Every even number except 2 is equal to the sum of two prime numbers.*

No one has ever been able to prove this statement.

Example 3 *Can a Proof Consist of Examples Only?*

The following list shows that every even number between 4 and 26 is equal to the sum of two prime numbers. Does this prove that *every* even number greater than 2 is equal to the sum of two prime numbers? (Remember that a prime number is a number whose only factors are itself and 1. For instance, the numbers 2, 3, 5, 7, 11, 13, 17, 19, and 23 are prime.)

$4 = 2 + 2$	$6 = 3 + 3$	$8 = 3 + 5$	$10 = 3 + 7$
$12 = 5 + 7$	$14 = 3 + 11$	$16 = 3 + 13$	$18 = 5 + 13$
$20 = 3 + 17$	$22 = 3 + 19$	$24 = 5 + 19$	$26 = 3 + 23$

Solution This list of examples *does not* prove the conjecture. One counterexample is enough to show that the rule is false, but no amount of examples can prove that the rule is true for *every* even integer greater than 2. ∎

Communicating about ALGEBRA

▶ **SHARING IDEAS about the Lesson**

Explain the Consequences The famous French mathematician Pierre de Fermat (1601–1655) conjectured that the formula $2^{(2^n)} + 1$ produces a prime number for every nonnegative integer n. For instance,

$$2^{(2^0)} + 1 = 2^1 + 1 = 3 \qquad 2^{(2^1)} + 1 = 2^2 + 1 = 5$$
$$2^{(2^2)} + 1 = 2^4 + 1 = 17 \qquad 2^{(2^3)} + 1 = 2^8 + 1 = 257$$

are each prime. Later another famous French mathematician, Leonhard Euler (1707–1783), found that

$$2^{(2^5)} + 1 = 2^{32} + 1 = 4,294,967,297 = 641(6,700,417).$$

Explain the consequences to Fermat's conjecture.

EXERCISES

Guided Practice

▶ **CRITICAL THINKING about the Lesson**

1. The **difference** of a and b is defined as the sum of a and the opposite of b. Write this definition symbolically. Does this definition have to be proved? Explain.

2. Prove the property $(a - b)c = ac - bc$. (Use only the basic axioms of algebra, the definition of subtraction, and the fact that $(-b)c = -(bc)$.)

3. A member of your algebra class proposes the following theorem. *The sum of the first n odd integers is n^2.* She gives four examples.

$$1 = 1^2, \quad 1 + 3 = 2^2, \quad 1 + 3 + 5 = 3^2, \quad \text{and} \quad 1 + 3 + 5 + 7 = 4^2$$

Do the examples prove her conjecture? Explain. Do you think the conjecture is true?

4. *The Four-Color Problem* A famous theorem states that any map can be colored with four different colors so that no two countries that share a border have the same color. No matter how the map at the right is colored with *three* colors, at least two countries having a common border must have the same color. Does this map serve as a counterexample to the following proposal? Explain.

Any map can be colored with three different colors so that no two countries that share a border have the same color.

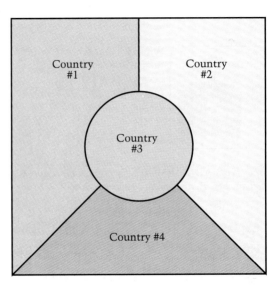

Independent Practice

Proving a Theorem **In Exercises 5 and 6, prove the property. (Use the basic axioms of algebra and the definition of subtraction given in Exercise 1.)**

5. If a and b are real numbers, then $a - b = -b + a$.

6. If a, b, and c are real numbers, then $(a - b) - c = a - (b + c)$.

Finding a Counterexample **In Exercises 7–10, find a counterexample to show that the statement is *not* true.**

7. If a and b are real numbers, then $(a + b)^2 = a^2 + b^2$.

8. If a and b are real numbers, then $(a - b)^2 = a^2 - b^2$.

9. If a, b, and c are real numbers such that $ab = ac$, then $b = c$.

10. If a, b, and c are nonzero real numbers, then $(a \div b) \div c = a \div (b \div c)$.

Mr. Brown's patio is made from 40 square tiles. The tiles have deteriorated and he wants to cover them with a new set.

Betsy: What's the trouble Dad?
Mr.Brown: These blasted tiles won't fit. It's driving me nuts. I always end up with two squares I can't cover.

He chooses new tiles to match his lawn furniture. Unfortunately these tiles only come in rectangles, each of which covers two of his old tiles.
Storekeeper: How many of these do you want?
Mr.Brown: Well, I have to cover 40 squares, so I'll need 20, I guess.

Mr. Brown's daughter drew a plan of the patio and colored it like a checker board. Then she studied it for several minutes.

When Mr. Brown tried to cover his patio with the new tiles he became very frustrated. No matter how hard he tried, he couldn't make them fit.

Betsy: Aha! I see what the trouble is. It's obvious once you realize that each rectangular tile must cover a red square and a white square.
How does this help? Do you know what Betsy means?

*(Source: From **AHA! INSIGHT** by Martin Gardner. Copyright © 1978 by Scientific American, Inc. Reprinted with permission of W.H. Freeman and Company.)*

11. Explain how Betsy solved the problem.

12. How could Betsy prove to her father that the patio could not be covered with the 20 rectangular tiles *without* cutting one of the tiles in half?

13. *Geometry*   Explain how the following diagrams could be used to give a geometrical argument to support the theorem proposed in Exercise 3.

14. Explain how the following diagram could be used to give a *geometrical* proof of the Pythagorean theorem.

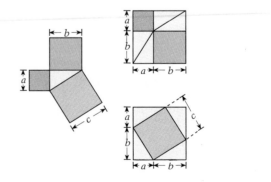

In Exercises 15–18, solve the equation for *a*.

15. $ab - ac = 12$

16. $a^2 - 2a = 12$

17. $ab - b^2 = 12$

18. $\frac{1}{a} + a = 12$

19. *Diagonal of a Rectangle* A rectangular room is 12 feet wide and 14 feet long. How long is the diagonal line segment that connects two opposite ceiling corners of the room?

20. *Height of a Tree* A rock is 20 feet from the base of a tree. The angle formed by the ground and the line segment connecting the rock to the top of the tree is 50°. How tall is the tree?

21. *Estimation—Powers of Ten* Which is the best estimate of the distance between New Orleans, Louisiana, and Chicago, Illinois?

a. 80 miles   **b.** 800 miles   **c.** 8000 miles   **d.** 80,000 miles

22. *Estimation—Powers of Ten* Which is the best estimate of the weight of this book?

a. 4 ounces   **b.** 40 ounces   **c.** 400 ounces   **d.** 4000 ounces

23. *Jumping Jim** Explain how you can "work backward" to solve the following maze.

Jumping Jim is about to begin his grand performance at the circus, but his jealous enemy, Dastardly Dan, has restrung all the trampolines. The number on each trampoline indicates how far Jim will move (horizontally or vertically, but *not* diagonally) when he bounces on the trampoline. Jim begins his routine by leaping onto the trampoline at the upper left. He must get to the Goal at the lower right, where he will take his bow. How can he get there?

3	6	4	3	2	4	3
2	1	2	3	2	5	2
2	3	4	3	4	2	3
2	4	4	3	4	2	2
4	5	1	3	2	5	4
4	3	2	2	4	5	6
2	5	2	5	6	1	GOAL

* Written by Robert Abbott, Mad Mazes, Copyright © 1990, Bob Adams, Inc., Publishers.

Chapter Summary

What did you learn?

1. Find the distance between two points. **(13.1)**

2. Find the midpoint between two points. **(13.1)**

3. Simplify a radical expression. **(13.2)**

4. Multiply and divide radical expressions. **(13.2, 13.3)**

5. Add and subtract radical expressions. **(13.3)**

6. Solve a radical equation. **(13.4)**

7. Find and use the tangent of an angle. **(13.5)**

8. Create models of real-life problems. **(13.1–13.5)**

9. Use properties of algebra formally. **(13.6)**

Why did you learn it?

In this chapter, you learned that the distance between two points in a coordinate plane can involve a radical expression. You also learned that many other real-life models involve radical expressions. Many of you will be going on to other courses in mathematics. Because of this, we included several topics in the chapter that are representative of other courses: geometry, trigonometry, and Algebra 2.

How does it fit into the bigger picture of algebra?

Radicals have many applications in geometry and in other fields. In this chapter, you learned to simplify radicals, multiply, divide, add, and subtract radicals, and solve radical equations.

The chapter also contains material that helps prepare you for other courses in mathematics. There are many applications involving geometry, an introduction to the tangent of an angle (which is part of a branch of mathematics called trigonometry), and an introduction to some of the formal properties of algebra (which is part of Algebra 2).

In Exercises 1–6, find the distance between the points. Then find the midpoint. (13.1)

1. $(-6, 0), (-9, -1)$

2. $(-3, 6), (1, 7)$

3. $(0, 0), (-8, 9)$

4. $(-3, -2), (1, 7)$

5. $(-3, -3), (6, 7)$

6. $(-9, 17), (5, -7)$

In Exercises 7 and 8, show that the points are vertices of a right triangle. (13.1)

7. $(0, 0), (1, 2), (2, -1)$

8. $(-4, 2), (8, 5), (-2, -6)$

In Exercises 9–14, simplify the radical expression. (13.2)

9. $\sqrt{216}$

10. $\sqrt{175}$

11. $\sqrt{18}$

12. $\sqrt{\frac{4}{17}}$

13. $\sqrt{\frac{8}{9}}$

14. $\sqrt{\frac{25}{125}}$

In Exercises 15–20, perform the indicated operations. Write the result in simplified form. (13.3)

15. $\sqrt{5} + 2\sqrt{5} - \sqrt{3}$

16. $3\sqrt{3} - 6\sqrt{3} + \sqrt{2}$

17. $\sqrt{6}(2\sqrt{3} - 4\sqrt{2})$

18. $\sqrt{2}(2\sqrt{2} - 6)$

19. $(3\sqrt{5} - \sqrt{10})^2$

20. $(2\sqrt{3} - 2)(2\sqrt{3} + 2)$

In Exercises 21–26, solve the equation. (13.4)

21. $2\sqrt{x} - 4 = 0$

22. $\frac{1}{3}\sqrt{x} + 2 = 8$

23. $x = \sqrt{-4x - 4}$

24. $\sqrt{3x - 2} = x$

25. $\sqrt{11x + 12} = x$

26. $x = \sqrt{3x}$

27. Find the geometric mean of 6 and 30.

28. Find the geometric mean of 7 and 35.

Geometry **In Exercises 29 and 30, find the perimeter of the polygon. (13.3)**

29.

30.
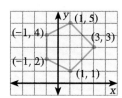

Geometry **In Exercises 31 and 32, find the perimeter and the area of the rectangle. (13.3)**

31.

32.

Geometry   In Exercises 33–36, find the remaining side and angle measurements.

33.

34.

35.

36.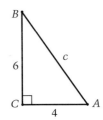

37. *Triangular Numbers*   The numbers 1, 3, 6, 10, 15, . . . are **triangular numbers.** Each triangular number can be represented with a visual model, as shown below. Use the visual model to support the conjecture that the sum of two consecutive triangular numbers is a perfect square.

38. *The Song of Hiawatha*   You are standing at a point that is 10 meters from the base of Minnehaha Falls. The angle formed by the ground and the line connecting the point with the top of the falls is 58°. How high is Minnehaha Falls?

> *In 1855, Henry Wadsworth Longfellow published the narrative poem "The Song of Hiawatha," based on the Native American folklore of a fifteenth-century Mohawk chief. The Minnehaha Falls mentioned in the poem are on Minnehaha Creek in Minneapolis, Minnesota.*

Chemistry   In Exercises 39 and 40, use the following information.

Your chemistry teacher asks you to weigh a magnesium sample as an exercise in accurate measurement. You are asked to weigh the sample once on each side of the scale and find the geometric mean of the two weights.

39. On the left side, the sample weighs 36 grams. On the right side, the sample weighs 40 grams. What is the true weight of the sample?

40. Using a scale *different* from the one used in Exercise 39, you weigh the sample on the left side and find the weight to be 37 grams. What would the sample weigh on the right side of this scale?

Sonar Fishing   **In Exercises 41–44, use the following information.**

You are fishing in a boat and use a sonar device that detects schools of fish. The device
indicates that a school of fish is 70 feet from
your boat. The angle between the water's surface and the direction of the fish is 30°.

41. Write an equation that relates a and b
with the acute angle A.

42. Solve the equation for b.

43. Substitute the expression for b into the
equation $a^2 + b^2 = 70^2$, and solve for a.

44. How deep should you set your fishing
lines to be at the same depth as the fish?

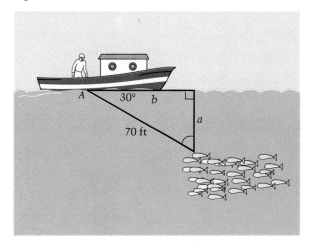

ZOTOK   **In Exercises 45–48, use the following information.**

In the game of *ZOTOK*, there are three countries: South Zotok (purple), West Zotok (yellow), and East Zotok (orange). Green controls
West Zotok and Pink controls East Zotok. Each unit on the x-axis and
y-axis corresponds to 100 miles. A piece can move to any coordinate
point (x, y) that is within the piece's range.

45. Can any of Green's pieces be hit by any of Pink's missiles? Explain.

46. Can any of Pink's pieces be hit by any of Green's missiles? Explain.

47. Which of Green's pieces can be hit by Pink's fighter
planes in *two* moves?

48. Which of Pink's pieces can be hit by Green's fighter
planes in *two* moves?

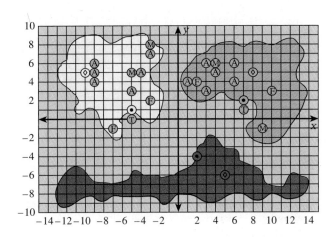

LEGEND		
(A) Armored Unit:	200 miles
(T) Navy Transport:	300 miles
(M) Missile:	700 miles
(F) Fighter Plane:	500 miles
(◇) Capital City	
(•) Port City	

In Exercises 1 and 2, show that the three points are the vertices of a right triangle.

1. $(-6, -4), (0, -4), (-6, 0)$

2. $(5, 2), (-5, 0), (1, 22)$

In Exercises 3–6, simplify the radicals.

3. $\sqrt{500}$

4. $\sqrt{384}$

5. $\sqrt{\frac{1}{8}}$

6. $\sqrt{\frac{25}{27}}$

In Exercises 7–10, perform the indicated operations.

7. $4\sqrt{3} - \sqrt{2} - \sqrt{3}$

8. $6\sqrt{6} + \sqrt{6} + \sqrt{2}$

9. $3\sqrt{5}(2\sqrt{5} - 6\sqrt{10})$

10. $(4\sqrt{5} + 1)^2$

In Exercises 11—14, solve the equation.

11. $\sqrt{y} + 6 = 10$

12. $\sqrt{2m + 3} - 6 = 4$

13. $n = \sqrt{9n - 18}$

14. $p = \sqrt{-3p + 18}$

15. Find the area and perimeter.

$3\sqrt{5} + 4\sqrt{2}$

$2\sqrt{2}$

16. Find the perimeter of the parallelogram.

In Exercises 17 and 18, find the length of each side of the triangle.

17.

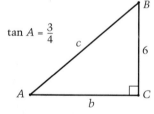

$\tan A = \frac{3}{4}$

18.

19. Find a counterexample to the statement:

If a, b, and c are numbers, c ≠ 0, and a < b, then $\frac{a}{c} < \frac{b}{c}$.

20. The ratio of the length of a rectangular box to the width of the box is the same as the ratio of the width to the height. The length is 6 feet and the height is 3 feet. What is the width?

21. You are standing 134 feet from the Gateway Arch in St. Louis, Missouri. The angle formed by the ground and your line of sight to the top of the arch is 78°. What is the height of the Gateway Arch?

Table of Squares and Approximate Square Roots

n	n^2	$\sqrt{n}$	$\sqrt{10n}$	n	n^2	$\sqrt{n}$	$\sqrt{10n}$
1	1	1.000	3.162	51	2601	7.141	22.583
2	4	1.414	4.472	52	2704	7.211	22.804
3	9	1.732	5.477	53	2809	7.280	23.022
4	16	2.000	6.325	54	2916	7.348	23.238
5	25	2.236	7.071	55	3025	7.416	23.452
6	36	2.449	7.746	56	3136	7.483	23.664
7	49	2.646	8.367	57	3249	7.550	23.875
8	64	2.828	8.944	58	3364	7.616	24.083
9	81	3.000	9.487	59	3481	7.681	24.290
10	100	3.162	10.000	60	3600	7.746	24.495
11	121	3.317	10.488	61	3721	7.810	24.698
12	144	3.464	10.954	62	3844	7.874	24.900
13	169	3.606	11.402	63	3969	7.937	25.100
14	196	3.742	11.832	64	4096	8.000	25.298
15	225	3.873	12.247	65	4225	8.062	25.495
16	256	4.000	12.649	66	4356	8.124	25.690
17	289	4.123	13.038	67	4489	8.185	25.884
18	324	4.243	13.416	68	4624	8.246	26.077
19	361	4.359	13.784	69	4761	8.307	26.268
20	400	4.472	14.142	70	4900	8.367	26.458
21	441	4.583	14.491	71	5041	8.426	26.646
22	484	4.690	14.832	72	5184	8.485	26.833
23	529	4.796	15.166	73	5329	8.544	27.019
24	576	4.899	15.492	74	5476	8.602	27.203
25	625	5.000	15.811	75	5625	8.660	27.386
26	676	5.099	16.125	76	5776	8.718	27.568
27	729	5.196	16.432	77	5929	8.775	27.749
28	784	5.292	16.733	78	6084	8.832	27.928
29	841	5.385	17.029	79	6241	8.888	28.107
30	900	5.477	17.321	80	6400	8.944	28.284
31	961	5.568	17.607	81	6561	9.000	28.460
32	1024	5.657	17.889	82	6724	9.055	28.636
33	1089	5.745	18.166	83	6889	9.110	28.810
34	1156	5.831	18.439	84	7056	9.165	28.983
35	1225	5.916	18.708	85	7225	9.220	29.155
36	1296	6.000	18.974	86	7396	9.274	29.326
37	1369	6.083	19.235	87	7569	9.327	29.496
38	1444	6.164	19.494	88	7744	9.381	29.665
39	1521	6.245	19.748	89	7921	9.434	29.833
40	1600	6.325	20.000	90	8100	9.487	30.000
41	1681	6.403	20.248	91	8281	9.539	30.166
42	1764	6.481	20.494	92	8464	9.592	30.332
43	1849	6.557	20.736	93	8649	9.644	30.496
44	1936	6.633	20.976	94	8836	9.695	30.659
45	2025	6.708	21.213	95	9025	9.747	30.822
46	2116	6.782	21.448	96	9216	9.798	30.984
47	2209	6.856	21.679	97	9409	9.849	31.145
48	2304	6.928	21.909	98	9604	9.899	31.305
49	2401	7.000	22.136	99	9801	9.950	31.464
50	2500	7.071	22.361	100	10000	10.000	31.623

PROPERTIES

Basic Properties	**Addition** **Multiplication** **Commutative** $a+b=b+a$ $ab=ba$ **Associative** $(a+b)+c=a+(b+c)$ $(ab)c=a(bc)$ **Identity** $a+0=a,\ 0+a=a$ $a(1)=a,\ 1(a)=a$ **Inverse** $a+(-a)=0$ $a\cdot\frac{1}{a}=1,\ a\neq0$ **Distributive** $a(b+c)=ab+ac$ or $(a+b)c=ac+bc$
Properties of Equality	**Addition** If $a=b$, then $a+c=b+c$. **Subtraction** If $a=b$, then $a-c=b-c$. **Multiplication** If $a=b$, then $ca=cb$. **Division** If $a=b$, and $c\neq0$, then $\frac{a}{c}=\frac{b}{c}$.
Properties of Exponents	**Product of Powers** $a^m\cdot a^n=a^{m+n}$ **Power of a Power** $(a^m)^n=a^{m\cdot n}$ **Power of a Product** $(a\cdot b)^m=a^m\cdot b^m$ **Quotient of Powers** $\frac{a^m}{a^n}=a^{m-n},\ a\neq0$ **Power of a Quotient** $(\frac{a}{b})^m=\frac{a^m}{b^m},\ b\neq0$ **Negative Exponent** $a^{-n}=\frac{1}{a^n},\ a\neq0$ **Zero Exponent** $a^0=1,\ a\neq0$
Properties of Radicals	**Product Property** $\sqrt{ab}=\sqrt{a}\cdot\sqrt{b}$ **Quotient Property** $\sqrt{\frac{a}{b}}=\frac{\sqrt{a}}{\sqrt{b}}$
Properties of Proportions	**Reciprocal** If $\frac{a}{b}=\frac{c}{d}$, then $\frac{b}{a}=\frac{d}{c}$. **Cross-multiplying** If $\frac{a}{b}=\frac{c}{d}$, then $ad=bc$.
Properties of Matrices	**Equal Matrices** If $\begin{bmatrix} a & b \\ c & d \end{bmatrix}=\begin{bmatrix} 2 & 4 \\ 7 & 5 \end{bmatrix}$ then $a=2, b=4, c=7,$ and $d=5$. **Adding Matrices** $\begin{bmatrix} a & b \\ c & d \end{bmatrix}+\begin{bmatrix} 2 & 4 \\ 7 & 5 \end{bmatrix}=\begin{bmatrix} a+2 & b+4 \\ c+7 & d+5 \end{bmatrix}$
Order of Operations	1. Parentheses 4. Addtion/Subtraction 2. Exponents 5. Left-to-Right 3. Multiplication/Division

Special Products and their Factors	**Product** **Factors**
	Sum and Difference Pattern $(a+b)(a-b)$ $\longleftrightarrow$ a^2-b^2
	Square of a Binomial Pattern $(a+b)^2$ $\longleftrightarrow$ $a^2+2ab+b^2$
	                            $(a-b)^2$ $\longleftrightarrow$ $a^2-2ab+b^2$
	
	FOIL The product $(a+b)(c+d)$ can be written:
	     $a\cdot c\ +\ a\cdot d\ +\ b\cdot c\ +\ b\cdot d$
	     First Outer Inner Last

A Problem-Solving Plan	**Ask** yourself what you need to know to solve the problem. Then **write a verbal model** that will give you what you need to know. **Assign labels** to each part of your verbal model. Use the labels to **write an algebraic model** based on your verbal model. **Solve** the algebraic model. **Answer** the original question. **Check** that your answer is reasonable.
Summary of Equations of Lines in Two Variables	**Slope-intercept Form** $y = mx + b$ **Point-slope Form** $y - y_1 = m(x - x_1)$ **Standard form** $Ax + By = C$ **Intercept Form** $\dfrac{x}{a} + \dfrac{y}{b} = 1$ **Slope of a Line through Two Points** $m = \dfrac{(y_2 - y_1)}{(x_2 - x_1)}$
Algebraic Models	**Linear** $f(x) = mx + b$ **Quadratic** $f(x) = ax^2 + bx + c$ or $f(x) = a(x - h)^2 + k$ **Exponential** $f(x) = C(a)^x$ **Rational** $f(x) = \dfrac{a}{x - h} + k$
Quick Graphs as Graphic Check of Solutions	The solution of a linear equation involving one variable, x, can be checked graphically with the following steps. 1. Write the equation in the form $ax + b = 0$. 2. Sketch the graph of $y = ax + b$. 3. The solution of $ax + b = 0$ is the x-*intercept* of $y = ax + b$.
Approximating the Best-Fitting Line	To approximate the best-fitting line for a set of ordered pairs, use the following steps. 1. **Sketch a Scatter Plot:** Sketch a scatter plot for the data. 2. **Sketch the Line:** Sketch the line that appears to most clearly follow the pattern given by the points. There should be about as many points above the line as below the line. 3. **Locate Two Points on the Line:** Locate two points on the line and approximate the x- and y-coordinates of each point. 4. **Find an Equation of the Line:** Use the technique described in Lesson 5.3 to find an equation of the line that passes through the two points in step 3.
Models for Direct and Inverse Variation	1. The variables x and y vary directly if, for a constant k, $\dfrac{y}{x} = k$ or $y = kx$. 2. The variables x and y vary inversely if, for a constant k, $yx = k$ or $y = \dfrac{k}{x}$. In both cases, the number k is the constant of variation.

TRANSFORMATIONS

Using Transformations to Solve Equations, Inequalities and Systems

Transformations that Produce Equivalent Equations

1. Add or subtract the same number to *both* sides.
2. Multiply or divide *both* sides by the same nonzero number.
3. Interchange the two sides.

Solving Equations Using Two or More Transformations

1. If the variable is on both sides of the equation, collect variables on the side with the greater variable coefficient.
2. Simplify both sides of the equation (if needed).
3. Use inverse operations to isolate the variable.
4. Check your solution in the original equation.

Transformations that Produce Equivalent Inequalities

1. Add or subtract the same number to *both* sides.
2. Multiply or divide *both* sides by the same *positive* number.
3. Multiply or divide *both* sides by the same *negative* number and reverse the inequality.

Solving a System of Linear Equations

To decide which method to use—graphing, or transformations (substitution or linear combinations)—consider the following.

1. The *graphing* method is useful for approximating a solution, checking a solution, and for providing a visual model of the problem.
2. To find an exact solution, use either *substitution* or *linear combinations*.
3. For linear systems in which one variable has a coefficient of 1 or -1, *substitution* may be more efficient.
4. In other cases, the *linear combinations* method is usually more efficient.

Using Transformations to Graph Related Functions

Quadratic Functions

When a quadratic function is written in the form $f(x) = (x - h)^2 + k$ (by completing the square), the vertex of the parabola has coordinates (h, k).

- The function can be graphed by translating (shifting) the graph of $f(x) = x^2$ vertically by k units and horizontally by h units.
- If k is positive, the vertical shift is upward; if k is negative, the vertical shift is downward.
- If h is positive, the horizontal shift is to the right; if h is negative, the horizontal shift is to the left.
- The function $f(x) = -x^2$ can be graphed by reflecting the graph of $f(x) = x^2$ in the x-axis.

Exponential Functions

An exponential function can be written in the form $f(x) = a^{(x-h)} + k$.

- The function can be graphed by translating (shifting) the graph of $f(x) = a^x$ vertically by k units and horizontally by h units.
- If k is positive, the vertical shift is upward; if k is negative, the vertical shift is downward.
- If h is positive, the horizontal shift is to the right; if h is negative, the horizontal shift is to the left.
- The function $f(x) = -a^x$ can be graphed by reflecting the graph of $f(x) = a^x$ in the x-axis.

absolute value of a real number (64, 217) The distance between the origin and the point representing the real number. For example: $|3| = 3$, $|-3| = 3$, or $|0| = 0$.

acute angle (699) An angle whose measure is greater than 0° and less than 90°.

addition property of equality (124) See Properties on pages 722-724.

additive identity (71) See Axioms on pages 722-724.

algebraic expression (8) A collection of numbers, variables, operations, and grouping symbols.

algebraic model (34) An algebraic expression or equation used to represent a real-life situation.

approximate (2) To express a numerical value to different degrees of accuracy. For example, $\frac{3}{7} = 0.42857$ can be approximated as 0.43.

associative axiom (706) See Axioms on pages 722-724.

asymptotes (606, 646) Lines that resemble the graph of a rational expression in certain regions of the coordinate plane.

axis of symmetry of a parabola (465) The vertical line passing through the vertex of a parabola and dividing the parabola into two parts that are mirror images of each other.

bar graph (50, 51) A graph that organizes a collection of data by using horizontal or vertical bars to display how many times each number occurs in the collection.

base of an exponent (14, 400) The number or variable that is used as a factor in repeated multiplication. For example, in the expression 4^6, 4 is the base.

best-fitting line (255) A line that best fits the data points on a scatter plot.

bimodal (658) A collection of numbers that has two modes.

binomial (508) A polynomial that has only two terms.

box-and-whisker plot (619, 652) A plot used to present a graphic summary of information. The quartiles and extreme values of a set of data displayed using a number line.

budget variance (315) The difference between budgeted expense and actual expense.

Cartesian plane (211) The x, y coordinate plane is often called the Cartesian plane because René Descartes first introduced it in 1637.

circle graph (327) A circle partitioned into sectors used to show the relative size of different portions of a whole.

closure axiom (706) See Axioms on pages 722-724.

coefficient (97, 508) In a term that is the product of a number and a variable, the number is the coefficient of the variable.

commutative axiom (706) See Axioms on pages 722-724.

completed-square form (549, 639) A quadratic equation in the form "perfect square $= k$", $k \geq 0$; a quadratic function in the form $f(x) = a(x - h)^2 + k$. The vertex of the parabola is the point (h, k).

completing the square (549) A process which can be used to solve any quadratic equation.

compound inequality (305) Two inequalities connected by *and* or *or*.

compound interest (432) Interest paid on the original principal and on interest that becomes part of the account.

conjecture (322) A statement that you think is true but that has not been proved true.

constant of variation (575) The constant k in the relationships of variation.

constant term (508) A monomial without a variable. For example, in $x^2 + 2x + 5$ the number 5 is the constant term.

constraints (387) The system of linear inequalities in a linear programming problem.

coordinate plane (160) A plane formed by two real number lines intersecting at a right angle.

counterexample (707) An example given to disprove a proposed axiom, or theorem.

cross-multiplying property (562) See Properties of Proportions on pages 722-724.

data (49) The facts, or numbers, that describe something.

definition (707) A statement or meaning of a word. A definition does not have to be proved but must be checked to be sure it is consistent with previous definitions and axioms.

degree of a monomial (508) The integer k is the degree of ax^k.

denominator (9) The divisor in a quotient expressed in fraction form. For example, 2 is the denominator of $\frac{5x}{2}$.

difference (3, 75, 709) The result obtained when numbers or expressions are subtracted. The difference of a and b is defined as $a - b$.

difference of two squares (522) See Special Products on pages 722-724.

direct variation (575) A function whose equation has the form $y = kx$ or $\frac{y}{x} = k$.

discriminant (479) The expression $b^2 - 4ac$, for a quadratic equation $ax^2 + bx + c = 0$.

distance formula (672) The distance, d, between any two points, (x_1, y_1) and (x_2, y_2), is given by $d = \sqrt{(x_2 - x_1)^2 + (y_2 - y_1)^2}$.

distributive property (95, 706) See Properties pages 722-724.

division property of equality (124) See Properties pages 722-724.

domain, or input, of a function (620) The x-values of a function $y = f(x)$.

domain of a rational expression (588) The set of all real numbers, except those for which the denominator is zero.

equal matrices (81) Matrices are equal if the entries in corresponding positions are equal.

equally–likely outcome (581) An event that is as likely to happen as not to happen.

equation (27) A statement formed when an equality symbol is placed between two equal expressions.

equivalent equations (122) Equations with the same solution set.

equivalent expressions (77) Expressions that have the same value for each number represented by the variable.

evaluate an algebraic expression (8) To find the value of an algebraic expression by replacing each variable in the expression by a number.

exponent (14, 400) The number or variable that represents the number of times the base is used as a factor. For example, in the expression 4^6, 6 is the exponent.

exponential decay (401) A situation in which the original amount is repeatedly multiplied by a change factor less than one.

exponential equation (402) An equation in which the variables appear as exponents.

exponential form of a power (14) The expression 4^6 is the exponential form of $4 \cdot 4 \cdot 4 \cdot 4 \cdot 4 \cdot 4$.

exponential growth (401) A situation in which the original amount is repeatedly multiplied by a change factor greater than one.

factors (9) The numbers and variables that are multiplied in an expression. For example, 4 and x are factors of $4x$.

FOIL pattern (515) A method used to multiply two binomials in a single step. Find the sum of the products of the **F**irst terms, **O**uter terms, **I**nner terms, and **L**ast terms.

formula (10) An algebraic expression that represents a relationship in real-life situations.

frequency distribution (51) A table that organizes a collection of data by counting how many times each number occurs in the collection.

function (619) A special type of relationship between two values in which each input value corresponds to exactly one output value. A relation in which no two ordered pairs (x, y) have the same x-value.

general form of a linear equation (264) A linear equation in the form $Ax + By = C$.

geometric mean (692) The geometric mean of a and b is $\sqrt{ab}$.

geometric sequence (405) A sequence in which each term after the first is the product of the preceding term and a constant, r. The constant is called the common ratio.

graph of an equation (183) A visual model of an equation.

greatest common factor (528) The greatest monomial factor that can be factored from the terms of a polynomial.

half-plane (320) In a plane, the region on either side of a boundary.

histogram (664) A bar graph that shows a frequency distribution.

horizontal shift of a graph (634) See Transformations on pages 722-724.

hyperbola (646) The graph of a rational function $f(x) = \dfrac{a}{(x - h)} + k$, whose center is (h, k).

hypotenuse (454) In a right triangle, the side opposite the right angle.

identity axiom (706) See Axioms on pages 722-724.

inequality (29) An open sentence formed when an inequality symbol is placed between two expressions.

integers (62) The set of numbers {..., $-3, -2, -1, 0, 1, 2, 3,...$}.

intercept form of an equation of a line (269) See Equations on pages 722-724.

inverse axiom (706) See Axioms on pages 722-724.

inverse operations (122) Two operations that "undo" each other. For example, addition and subtraction are inverse operations. Multiplication and division are inverse operations.

inverse variation (575) A function defined by an equation of the form $xy = k$ or $y = \dfrac{k}{x}$.

irrational number (453) A real number that cannot be expressed as the quotient of two integers. For example, the square roots of numbers that are not perfect squares $\sqrt{2}, \sqrt{3}, \sqrt{5}$, and $\sqrt{6}$. When expressed as a decimal, it neither repeats nor terminates.

leading coefficient (458, 508) The coefficient of the first term in a polynomial written in standard form.

like terms (97) Terms in which the variable factors are the same.

line plot (51) A graph that organizes a collection of data by using an X each time a number occurs in the collection.

linear combination method (360) A method of solving systems of equations that involves adding multiples of the given equations.

linear function (626) A function defined by the equation $f(x) = mx + b$.

linear model (235) An equation of a line that is used to represent a real-life situation.

linear programming (387) A type of optimization process for finding the maximum or minimum value of an objective quantity by using a system of constraints.

literal equation (154) An equation which uses more than one letter as a variable. For example, $3x + y = 4$ is a literal equation.

matrix (81) A rectangular arrangement of numbers into rows and columns.

mean (658) The sum of a set of numbers divided by the number of numbers in the set.

measures of central tendency (619, 658) The mean, median, and mode of a distribution.

median (658) The middle number of an odd collection of numbers; the average of the two middle numbers in an even collection of numbers.

mental math (3) When operations are performed in one's head without other aids such as paper and pencil or calculator.

mode (658) The number that occurs most frequently in a collection of numbers. If two numbers tie for most frequent occurrence, the collection is said to be bimodal.

modeling (34) Writing algebraic expressions or equations to represent real-life situations.

monomial (508) A polynomial with only one term.

multiplication property of equality (124) See Properties on pages 722-724.

multiplicative identity (89) See Axioms on pages 722-724.

negative correlation (258) Data points on a scatter plot that approximate a line with a negative slope.

negative numbers (62) Numbers represented by points to the left of the origin on the real number line. Numbers less than 0.

numerator (9) The dividend in a quotient expressed in fraction form. For example, $5x$ is the numerator of $\frac{5x}{2}$.

numerical expression (4) A collection of numbers, operations, and grouping symbols.

objective quantity (387) In linear programming, the quantity or expression to be maximized or minimized.

odds (586) The ratio of the number of ways an event can occur to the number of ways the event cannot occur.

opposites (64) Two points on the real number line that are the same distance from the origin but on opposite sides of the origin. For example, 3 and -3 are opposites.

optimal design (618) The most desirable or satisfactory design.

optimization (387) Finding the minimum or maximum value of a quantity.

order of operations (20, 21) See Procedures on pages 722-724.

ordered pair (160) A pair of real numbers used to locate each point in a coordinate plane.

origin of the coordinate plane (160) The point in the coordinate plane at which the horizontal axis intersects the vertical axis. The point (0, 0).

origin of the real number line (62) The point that represents 0 on the real number line.

parabola (465) The graph of a quadratic equation.

percent (2, 258) Another way of expressing hundredths, or a number divided by 100, usually denoted by the symbol %.

perfect squares (453) Numbers whose square roots are integers or quotients of integers.

perfect square trinomial (536) A trinomial that factors into the square of a binomial.

perimeter of a polygon (12) The sum of the lengths of the sides of the polygon.

picture graph (327) Stylized versions of bar graphs.

point-slope form of the equation of a line (270, 272) See Equations on pages 722-724.

polynomial (508) The sum or difference of monomials. Monomials are also polynomials.

positive correlation (258) Data points on a scatter plot that approximate a line with a positive slope.

positive numbers (62) Numbers represented by the points to the right of the origin on the real number line. Numbers greater than 0.

postulate, or axiom (706) The rules in mathematics that are accepted to be true without proof.

power (14, 400) The result of repeated multiplication. For example, in the expression $4^2 = 16$, 16 is the second power of 4.

power of a power property (400) See Properties on pages 722-724.

power of a product property (400) See Properties on pages 722-724.

power of a quotient property (413) See Properties on pages 722-724.

probability (581) The ratio of successful outcomes to the total number of outcomes of the event.

probability of an event (581) A number between 0 and 1 that indicates the likelihood the event will occur.

problem–solving plan (46) See Procedures on pages 722-724.

product (3, 89) The result obtained when numbers or expressions are multiplied. The product of a and b is $a \cdot b$, or ab.

product property of radicals (678) See Properties on pages 722-724.

program (19) An ordered list of instructions for a calculator or computer.

properties of addition (69) See Properties on pages 722-724.

properties of multiplication (89) See Properties on pages 722-724.

properties of opposites (64) See Properties on pages 722-724.

proportion (562) An equation that equates two ratios. For example, $\frac{a}{b} = \frac{c}{d}$, where a, b, c, and d, are nonzero real numbers.

Pythagorean theorem (454) For any right triangle, the sum of the squares of the lengths of the legs, a and b, equals the square of the length of the hypotenuse, c. For example, $a^2 + b^2 = c^2$.

quadrant (160) In the coordinate plane, one of the four parts into which the axes divide the plane.

quadratic equation (458) An equation in x that can be written in the standard form $ax^2 + bx + c = 0, a \neq 0$.

quadratic formula (472) See Formulas on pages 722-724.

quartile (653) The values in a collection of numbers that separate the data into four equal parts.

quotient (3, 101) The result obtained when numbers or expressions are divided. The quotient of a and b is $\frac{a}{b}$, where a and b are real numbers, and $b \neq 0$.

quotient of powers property (413) See Properties on pages 722-724.

quotient property of radicals (678) See Properties on pages 722-724.

radicand (452, 678) The number or expression under a radical symbol.

range, or output, of a function (620) The y-values of a function $y = f(x)$.

rate of a to b (109) The relationship $\frac{a}{b}$ of two quantities a and b that are measured in different units.

rate of change (200) A relationship such as distance over time often described by using a slope.

ratio of a to b (109) The relationship $\frac{a}{b}$ of two quantities a and b that are measured in the same units.

rational equation (607) An equation that involves rational expressions with the variable occurring in the denominator(s).

rational expressions (561) Fractions whose numerators and denominators are polynomials.

rational numbers (109) Any number that can be written in the form $\frac{a}{b}$, where a and b are integers and $b \neq 0$.

real number line (62) A horizontal line that pictures real numbers as points.

real numbers (62) The set of numbers consisting of the positive numbers, the negative numbers, and zero.

reciprocal (101) If $\frac{a}{b}$ is a non-zero number, then its reciprocal is $\frac{b}{a}$.

reciprocal property (562) See Properties on pages 722-724.

reflection of a graph (634) See Transformations on pages 722-724.

relation (620) A set of ordered pairs (x, y).

round-off error (148) The error produced when a decimal result is rounded in order to provide a meaningful answer.

scatter plot (160) The plot, or graph, of the points that correspond to the ordered pairs in a collection.

scientific notation (419) Uses the powers of ten to express decimal numbers. Numbers in scientific notation are written $c \times 10^n$, where $1 \leq c < 10$ and n is any integer.

set (62) A well-defined collection of objects.

similar triangles (125) Two triangles are similar if their corresponding angles are congruent.

simple interest (432) The amount paid or earned for the use of money for a unit of time.

simplest form of a radical expression (678) See Procedures on pages 722-724.

simplified, or reduced form, of a rational expression (588) See Procedures on pages 722-724.

slope of a line (197, 272) The ratio of the vertical change to the horizontal change; the ratio of the change in y to the corresponding change in x.

slope-intercept form (205, 272) See Procedures on pages 722-724.

solution of a system of equations (346) An ordered pair that is a solution of each of the equations in the system.

solution of a single-variable equation (27) A number that, when substituted for the variable in an equation, results in a true statement.

solving a proportion (562) Finding the value for the variable in a proportion.

solving an equation (28, 122) Finding all the solutions of an equation.

speed (65) The absolute value of the velocity of an object; expressed as the rate: distance over time.

square matrix (83) A matrix that has the same number of rows and columns.

square root (452) If $b^2 = a$, then b is a square root of a.

stacked bar graph (52) A bar graph that displays more than one collection of data simultaneously.

standard form of a polynomial (508) A polynomial in which the terms are written in descending order, from the greatest degree to the smallest degree.

standard form of the equation of a line (264) See Equations on pages 722-724.

statistics (659) A field of mathematics that organizes large collections of data in ways that can be used to understand trends and make predictions.

stem-and-leaf plot (619, 652) See Procedures on pages 722-724.

substitution method (353) A method of solving a system of equations in which one variable is written in terms of other variables in one equation and the resulting expression is substituted into the other equation.

subtraction property of equality (124) See Properties on pages 722-724.

subtraction rule (75) See Procedures on pages 722-724.

sum (3, 68) The result obtained when numbers or expressions are added. The sum of a and b is $a + b$.

system of equations (346) A set of equations in the same variables.

system of inequalities (381) A set of inequalities in the same variables.

tangent of angle A (699) See Formulas on pages 722-724.

terms (9, 75) In an expression such as $3x + 2$, $3x$ and 2 are called terms.

theorem (454, 707) A statement that can be proven to be true.

time-line graph (327) A graph used to represent events that occur in a given sequence in time.

transformations (633) See Transformations on pages 722-724.

trinomial (508) A polynomial that has only three terms.

unit analysis (91) A technique that can be used to decide the unit of measure assigned to a product.

variable (8) A letter that is used to represent one or more numbers.

velocity (65) The speed and direction in which an object is traveling.

verbal model (34) An expression that uses words to represent a real-life situation.

vertex of a parabola (465) The lowest point of a parabola that opens up and the highest point of a parabola that opens down.

vertex of convex polygons (linear programming) (381) The corner points of the graph of a system of constraints.

vertical shift of a graph (633) See Transformations on pages 722-724.

whole numbers (2) The set of numbers $\{0, 1, 2, 3, 4, ...\}$.

x-axis (160) The horizontal axis in the coordinate plane.

x-coordinate (160) The first number of an ordered pair, the horizontal coordinate.

x-intercept (190) The value of x when $y = 0$.

y-axis (160) The vertical axis in the coordinate plane.

y-coordinate (160) The second number of an ordered pair, the vertical coordinate.

y-intercept (190) The value of y when $x = 0$.

zero-product property (541) See Properties on pages 722-724.

CHAPTER 1

■ *1.1 Communicating About Algebra p. 4*
A. Possible estimates:
$[400 \div 8] - 3 = 47, [420 \div 7] - 3 = 57,$
$[420 \div 6] - 3 = 67$
B. $0.4 \cdot 1 \cdot 20 = 8, 0.5 \cdot 1 \cdot 17 = 8.5, 0.5 \cdot 1 \cdot 18 = 9$
A–B: If the difference between the calculator result and the estimate could be due to rounding alone, the answer is reasonable. Note that the closer the rounded numbers used for the estimate are to the actual numbers, the closer the estimate will be to the actual result.

■ *1.1 Guided Practice p. 5*
1. California **2.** Accept any reasonable answer such as one that involves population or climate. **3.** 59,000 **4.** c
5. Accept any reasonable answers that involve operating on rounded numbers. **6.** 7300

■ *1.1 Independent Practice pp. 5–6*
7. 13 **9.** 1 **11.** 24 **13.** 4 **15.** 12 **17.** 24 **19.** 3 **21.** 13
23. 2 **25.** 6 **27.** 5 **29.** 17.73 **31.** 2.31 **33.** 185.63 **35.** 16 ft^2 **37.** 20 in.^{2} **39.** 37.5 yd^2 **41.** $5,500,000

■ *1.1 Integrated Review p. 7*
43. 1.2 **45.** 75% **47.** $\frac{8}{25}$ **49.** 0.44 **51.** 25% **53.** 36

■ *1.2 Communicating About Algebra p. 10*
A. True **B.** True **C.** False, $x = 7$ **D.** True **E.** True
F. False, $b = 7$

■ *1.2 Guided Practice p. 11*
1. r divided by the product of 3 and s **2.** $6x + y$ **3.** 24
4. 7 **5.** 7 **6.** 16; $x = 6$ and $y = 1$, $x = 0$ and $y = 4$, among others

■ *1.2 Independent Practice p. 11*
7. 9 **9.** 7 **11.** 18 **13.** 36 **15.** 3 **17.** 6 **19.** 4 **21.** 40.07
23. 51.30 **25.** 5390 **27.** 144 km

■ *1.2 Integrated Review p. 12*
29. 17 **31.** 48 **33.** 51.9 **35.** 1.53 **37.** 6 **39.** 4
41. $30 - [(36 \div 3) + 6]$ **43.** $P = a + b + c$ **a.** 9
b. 12 **c.** 15 **45.** Increases by 3 units

■ *1.2 Mixed Review p. 13*
1. 36 **3.** $24.50 **5.** 36 **7.** 1 **9.** 3 **11.** 7 **13.** 2
15. $x + x + x + x$ or $4x$ **17.** 11.88 **19.** 3

■ *1.3 Communicating About Algebra p. 16*
A. 85,486.5 ft^2 **B.** 509,645,864 km^2
C. 148,816,592 km^2 **D.** 360,829,272 km^2

■ *1.3 Guided Practice p. 17*
1. Eighteen to the third power, eighteen cubed **2.** Base
3. Exponent **4.** 5832 **5.** x^2 is the area of a square with side x. **6.** y^3 is the volume of a cube with edge y.

■ *1.3 Independent Practice pp. 17–18*
7. 2^3 **9.** 9^y **11.** 3^4 **13.** a^6 **15.** $(2x)^3$ **17.** 81 **19.** 24
21. 40 **23.** 100 **25.** 4 **27.** 28,561 **29.** 177,147
31. 1331 in.^{3} **33.** 139.7 cm^2 **35.** $\approx$8411.67 m^3

■ *1.3 Integrated Review p. 18*
37. 10.49 **39.** 47.61 **41.** 3

■ *1.4 Communicating About Algebra p. 22*
A. 40, 60; 40 **B.** 33, 17, 13, 21; 17
C. 13, 3, 11; 13 **D.** 3, 12; 3

■ *1.4 Guided Practice p. 23*
1. Exponent operation **2.** Leftmost operation
3. $4 + (16 \div 8) - 2$ **4.** 39, 63, $3 + (4 \cdot 9)$

■ *1.4 Independent Practice pp. 23–24*
5. 5 **7.** 10 **9.** 11 **11.** 24 **13.** 4 **15.** b **17.** 18 **19.** 36
21. 44 **23.** 5 **25.** Calc. 1; 16 $\boxed{-}$ [(4 $\boxed{\div}$ 2) $\boxed{\times}$ 5] $\boxed{=}$
27. Calc. 2; 10 $\boxed{+}$ (15 $\boxed{\div}$ 5) $\boxed{+}$ 16 $\boxed{=}$
29. Calc. 1; (12 $\boxed{\div}$ 3) $\boxed{+}$ (16 $\boxed{\div}$ 4) $\boxed{=}$
31. No, the department did not follow the correct order of operations. **33.** $(1248 + 741 + 402) \div 3 = 797$

■ *1.4 Integrated Review pp. 24–25*
35. $2x + 3x + 4x$, 116.1 cm **37.** 16.82 units^2 **39.** $2\pi r^2$
41. $4.3 + (6.9 \div 2.3)$ **43.** $6.2 \div 3.1 + (4.7 \cdot 5.3)$

■ *1.4 Mid-Chapter Self-Test p. 26*
1. 0.625 **2.** 20% **3.** $\frac{3}{4}$ **4.** 4 **5.** 8 **6.** $\frac{1}{3}$ **7.** 19 **8.** 18
9. 9 **10.** $3\frac{1}{2}$ **11.** $1\frac{1}{3}$ **12.** 20 **13.** 4 **14.** 321 **15.** 4.26
16. 0.595 **17.** 32 m^2 **18.** x^3 **19.** $2x + 350$, 500 ft
20. 708.75 in.^{2} **21.** 56.52 m^2

■ *1.5 Communicating About Algebra p. 29*
A. Only 2 and 3 are. **B. 1.** b **2.** c **3.** a

■ *1.5 Guided Practice p. 30*
1–6. An equation has "=," an inequality has "<," "≤," ">," or "≥," and an expression has none of these.
1. Equation **2.** Expression **3.** Expression **4.** Equation
5. Inequality **6.** Inequality
7. $13 + 4x = 2x + 1$ **8.** b
    left   right

■ *1.5 Independent Practice pp. 30–31*
9. Yes **11.** Yes **13.** No **15.** 3 **17.** 7 **19.** 4 **21.** 20 **23.** 3
25. 3 **27.** It is. **29.** It is. **31.** It is not.

33. 20: number of ft^2 needed for each station,

x: number of computers,

400: total number of ft^2 available

35. 18: dollar cost of a tank of gas,

x: number of times you can fill the tank,

y: dollar amount left,

65: dollar amount available

■ *1.5 Integrated Review p. 31*

37. 11 **39.** 32 **41.** 3 **43.** 7 **45.** 25 **47.** 25 **49.** 144

■ *1.6 Communicating About Algebra p. 35*

A. 30x, (mg per oz) × oz = mg **B.** 30

■ *1.6 Guided Practice p. 36*

1. Subtraction **2.** $8 - x$ **3.** Yes **4.** Write a verbal model, assign labels, and write an algebraic model.

5. $x + 5 = 12$ **6.** $4n < 36$ **7.** $m - 5 < 20$

8. $10 \div y = 5$

■ *1.6 Independent Practice pp. 36–37*

9. $x + 12$ **11.** $\frac{1}{2}m$ **13.** $11 + r \div 7$ **15.** d **17.** e **19.** b

21. $s + 16 = 36$ **23.** $25 - y = 10.5$

25. $8 + 12 + (x + 4) + 8 + 6 + 2x$

27. Correct **29.** Incorrect **31.** b **33.** a

■ *1.6 Integrated Review pp. 37–38*

35. x^7 **37.** y^6 **39.** 4 **41.** 165 **43.** It is. **45.** It is.
47. It is not.

■ *1.6 Mixed Review p. 38*

1. 15 **3.** 35 **5.** 57 **7.** Yes **9.** 6 **11.** No **13.** 2, 4
15. $160.45

■ *1.7 Communicating About Algebra p. 41*

A. Sales tax is too much. **B.** Area is too big.

C. Interest is too much. **D.** Time is too little.

■ *1.7 Guided Practice p. 42*

1.

Profit per box	•	Number of boxes to be sold	=	Amount of money needed

2. Profit per box = 1.50 (dollars)
Number of boxes to be sold = x
Amount of money needed = 1800 (dollars)

3. $1.50x = 1800$ **4.** $x = 1200$ **5.** 1200

6. Multiply $1.50 by 1200.

■ *1.7 Independent Practice pp. 42–44*

7. 20

9. Time to walk home = t (hours)
Your walking speed = 4 (miles per hour)
Distance from home = 1 (miles)

or

Time to walk home = t (minutes)
Your walking speed = $\frac{4}{60} = \frac{1}{15}$ (miles per minute)
Distance from home = 1 (miles)

11. $t = \frac{1}{4}$ hr or $t = 15$ min **13.** $150

15. Extra cost = 150 (dollars)
Number of contributors = y
Suggested contribution = $0.75

17. $y = 200$ **19.** 6

21. Hours available for:
driving = 6
uncle's car speed = 50 (miles per hour)
greatest distance to and from
grandmother's home = x (miles)

23. $x = 300$ round trip

25.

Number of weeks worked	•	Amount you saved each week	=	Price of stereo with compact disk player

27. $12m = 432$ **29.** 18 minutes

31. Travel time = 18 (minutes)
Rate of travel = x (miles per minute)
Distance from robbery site to
gas station = 12 (miles)

or

Travel time = $\frac{18}{60} = \frac{3}{10}$ (hours)
Rate of travel = x (miles per hour)
Distance from robbery site to
gas station = 12 (miles)

33. $x = \frac{2}{3}$ miles per min, or $x = 40$ miles per hour

■ *1.7 Integrated Review p. 45*

35. $412 + 613 + 510 + 620 + x \geq 2500$, 345

■ *1.8 Communicating About Algebra p. 51*

A. 318, 64, 32, 24 **B.** 23 million, 32 million, 42 million
C. $3\frac{2}{3}$

■ *1.8 Guided Practice p. 52*

1. Facts or numbers that describe something

2. Yes, because a table *is* an organized set of data.

3. It is an organized set of data that tells how often each datum occurs.

4. Sometimes it helps when the numbers in the data are small and occur at various frequencies.

■ *1.8 Independent Practice pp. 52–53*

5. List the records down the left hand column and list the events across the top, or list the events down the left hand column and list the records across the top.

7. 1987, first **9.** Numbers sold are added cumulatively

11. b

13.

Number	Tally	Frequency
0	I	1
1	I	1
2	II	2
3	II	2
4	II	2
5	II	2
6	III	3
7	IIIII	5
8	II	2
9	I	1
10	II	2
11	I	1
12	II	2
13	I	1
14		0
15	I	1
16		0
17	I	1
18	I	1

15. 12 hours should have 2 X's, 13 hours should have 1 X. **17.** $-23°C$ to $-18°C$

■ 1.8 Integrated Review p. 54
19. $W + L + W + L = 120$ or $2W + 2L = 120$
21. The closer the length is to the width, the greater is the area; b, the length is equal to the width.

■ 1.8 Chapter Review pp. 56–58
1. 0.125 **3.** $\frac{3}{4}$ **5.** 0.10 **7.** $\frac{13}{2}$ **9.** 16 **11.** 0 **13.** 2
15. 1.5125 **17.** 25 **19.** 7 **21.** 5.2 **23.** x^5 **25.** 2 **27.** 2
29. 4 **31.** $\frac{3}{2}$ **33.** 4 **35.** 4 **37.** Yes **39.** No
41. 4: dollar amount saved each week
x: number of weeks you must save
y: dollar amount left
15.90: dollar cost of disk
43. $x^2 + 6$ **45.** $x \div 2 > 7$ **47.** $x^3 - y = 60$
49. $180x + 200y$ **51.** Just 1 **53.** s^2, 81 in.² **55.** 33
57. Decreasing

CHAPTER 2 ————————————

■ 2.1 Communicating About Algebra p. 65
A. False. Zero is an integer and is neither positive nor negative.
B. True. The absolute value of a real number is a distance from zero, and distance is represented by a positive number.
C. False. If a is negative, then $-a$ is positive.
D. True. Every negative number is to the left of every positive number on the number line.
E. True. One number has to be to the left of the other on the number line.

■ 2.1 Guided Practice p. 66
1. Five is less than six, 5 is to the left of 6
2. $2 > -3$ **3.** Location of numbers on the real number line verifies that only the first one is false.
4. -10 **5.** 6 **6.** -2

■ 2.1 Independent Practice pp. 66–67
7. 4 **9.** 2 **11.** 4.5 **13.** $\frac{3}{4}$ **15.** $-1.9, -\frac{1}{2}, 0, \frac{1}{2}, 3.1, 4$
17. -6 **19.** 2.4 **21.** 9 **23.** 0 **25.** 5 **27.** $\frac{4}{5}$ **29.** 3.2 **31.** 0
33. Sun **35.** Libya, Ireland **37.** Chile, Ireland, Mexico
39. -12 ft per second, 12 ft per second

■ 2.1 Integrated Review p. 67
41. 11 **43.** $-\frac{11}{4}$ or $-2\frac{3}{4}$ **45.** 7 **47.** 4 **49.** 4 **51.** 8

■ 2.2 Communicating About Algebra p. 70
A.

■ 2.2 Guided Practice p. 71
1. False **2.** True
3. No

4. Any number added to 0 is that identical number.

■ 2.2 Independent Practice pp. 71–72
5. 4 **7.** $\frac{1}{2}$ **9.** 1 **11.** 1 **13.** -2 **15.** 7 **17.** -15 **19.** -8
21. -13 **23.** -6 **25.** -7.2 **27.** 3.1 **29.** $x - 5$
31. $x - 4$ **33.** 22
35. $+1$, ion;
0, atom; 0, atom; -1 ion
37. Yes, profits and losses total a profit of $182.92.
39. 5:00 P.M.

■ 2.2 Integrated Review pp. 72–73
41. 16 **43.** 7 **45.** 4 **47.** 81 **49.** 3 **51.** a, c, d
53. No. You can use one stroke (a hole in one) on the final hole to finish the round two over par to win the round and tie overall. You can score two to finish the round three over par to tie the round. Otherwise, your sister wins both round and overall.

	Sister	You
1st round	$+6$	$+8$
2nd round	$+4$	$+3$
3rd round	$+3$	?

■ 2.2 Mixed Review p. 74

1. 24 **3.** 37.5% **5.** s^5 **7.** 3 **9.** Yes **11.** 24 **13.** 43.56
15. $-8, -5, -2, 0, 1, 3, 4$ **17.** 125 in.^{3}

■ 2.3 Communicating About Algebra p. 77

A. Equivalent **B.** Not equivalent for any number but 0
C. Not equivalent for any number

■ 2.3 Guided Practice p. 78

1. True **2.** True **3.** $-x, -3$ **4.** Yes; $4 - 3 = 1$ and
$3 - 4 = -1$ **5.** 0 **6.** Yes; $-(6 - 3) = -(3) = -3$,
$-6 + 3 = -3$

■ 2.3 Independent Practice pp. 78–79

7. -5 **9.** 3 **11.** $\frac{3}{2}$ **13.** -6 **15.** 2 **17.** -10 **19.** 3.5
21. -1 **23.** 1 **25.** -5 **27.** 5 **29.** 5.7 **31.** 1.04 **33.** 6.8
35. 1 **37.** 16 **39.** 11 **41.** -1
43. $780, lose; income is $500 and expenses are $280
more than that
45. $-2\%, 7\%, 1\%, 0\%, -3\%, 1\%, 5\%, -7\%, -2\%$

■ 2.3 Integrated Review p. 80

47. $-5, -3, -2\frac{1}{2}, -1.25, 1, 2\frac{1}{2}, 4.3$
49. $-2\frac{1}{2}, -1.25, 1, 2\frac{1}{2}$ **51.** 4 **53.** -8 **55.** 18 **57.** 24

■ 2.4 Communicating About Algebra p. 83

$$\boxed{9}\ \boxed{6}\ \boxed{7}\ \boxed{12}$$
$$\boxed{4}\ \boxed{15}\ \boxed{14}\ \boxed{1}$$

■ 2.4 Guided Practice p. 84

1. 3, 2 **2.** -3 **3.** $a = 1, b = 3, c = -1, d = 0$
4. $\begin{bmatrix} 2 & -2 & -4 \\ 0 & -2 & -4 \end{bmatrix}, \begin{bmatrix} -4 & 2 & -4 \\ 4 & -4 & 4 \end{bmatrix}$

■ 2.4 Independent Practice pp. 84–86

5. Can **7.** Cannot **9.** $\begin{bmatrix} 8 & -4 \\ -1 & 2 \end{bmatrix}$

11. $\begin{bmatrix} 3 & -2 & 2 \\ 5 & 5 & -2 \end{bmatrix}$ **13.** $\begin{bmatrix} 1.3 & 4.7 & -13.8 \\ 17.5 & 3.2 & -9.2 \end{bmatrix}$

15. $\begin{bmatrix} 3 & -10 \\ 4 & 0 \end{bmatrix}$ **17.** $\begin{bmatrix} -9 & -3 \\ 5 & -17 \\ 2 & 3 \end{bmatrix}$

19. $a = 5, b = 3, c = 20, d = -4$

21.

	New releases	Regular selections
Comedy	25	215
Drama	30	350
Horror	25	180

; 25

23. 1987: All teams played 15 regular season games
1989: All teams played 16 regular season games.

25. Burritos: $39, Tacos: $14, Cheeseburgers: $104

■ 2.4 Integrated Review p. 86

27. $\begin{bmatrix} 8 & 9 \\ 2 & 0 \end{bmatrix}$ **29.** $1\frac{1}{4}$ **31.** 27

■ 2.4 Mid-Chapter Self-Test p. 88

1. -4 **2.** $-\frac{1}{2}$ **3.** 6 **4.** $-\frac{3}{2}$ **5.** 4 **6.** $-3\frac{1}{3}$ **7.** 2 **8.** -4
9. $\frac{1}{4}$ **10.** 10.6 **11.** 3.4 **12.** -7.7 **13.** 5.4 **14.** 0
15. $5 - x, 1$ **16.** $3\frac{1}{2} + x, 4\frac{1}{2}$ **17.** $-2y + 2, 4$
18. $|r| - r - 3, 7$ **19.** 3, 3 **20.** $2s - \frac{13}{2}, -\frac{21}{2}$
21. $\begin{bmatrix} 0 & 12 & 7 \\ 5 & 8 & 12 \\ 0 & 8 & 1 \end{bmatrix}$ **22.** $\begin{bmatrix} -1 & -5 & 0 \\ 8 & -8 & -1 \\ 6 & 10 & 3 \end{bmatrix}$

23. -15 feet per second, 15 feet per second **24.** 63°F

25.

	Income ($)	Expenses ($)
Bowlathon	384	192
Car Wash	150	10
Sub Sale	400	200

; yes, $32 over

26.

	Feet	Meters
Sears Tower	1454	443
World Trade Center	1350	411
Empire State Building	1250	381
Amoco Building	1136	346
John Hancock Center	1127	344

■ 2.5 Communicating About Algebra p. 91

A. yards, down **B.** baskets, dollars, basket

■ 2.5 Guided Practice p. 92

1. False **2.** False **3.** True **4.** True **5.** No **6.** Feet

■ 2.5 Independent Practice pp. 92–93

7. -48 **9.** -28 **11.** $-x$ **13.** $-48a$ **15.** 30 **17.** 42
19. 9 **21.** $-8x^3$ **23.** -30 **25.** $-48x$ **27.** $168x^2$
29. $-\frac{1}{10}a^3$ **31.** 70.62 **33.** 353.01 **35.** 30 **37.** -28
39. -20 **41.** -14 **43.** -34
45. $T - 10, 72°$

Temperature					
	Number of days later				
Current	1	2	3	4	5
82°	80°	78°	76°	74°	72°

47. c, $16\frac{1}{2}$ feet, no **49.** a, 48 km

■ 2.5 Integrated Review p. 94

51. 2.5 **53.** -5 **55.** 3 **57.** -4
59. $a = 7, b = 10, c = 8, d = 5$

■ 2.6 Communicating About Algebra p. 97

$-2y = -2(2x - 3) = -4x + 6$ by the Distributive
Property.

■ 2.6 Guided Practice p. 98

1. Not true, $2(4 + 6) = 2(4) + 2(6)$
2. True, application of Distributive Property
3. True, application of Distributive Property
4. Not true, $(3 - 2)16 = 3(16) - 2(16)$
5. Distributive Property **6.** $x - 5$ **7.** $3x - 6$ **8.** $x + 1$

■ **2.6 Independent Practice pp. 98–99**

9. $3y + 18$ **11.** $28 - 7x$
13. $-2x - 10$ **15.** $8x + x^2$
17. $-y^2 + 9y$ **19.** $a^2 - 2a$
21. $40 - 12x$ **23.** $-20s - 15$
25. $6x^2 + 9x$ **27.** $-24x + 18x^2$
29. $18x + 2x^2$ **31.** $12y - 5y^2$
33. $-16y^2 - 56y$ **35.** $-12a^2 + 16a$
37. $3 + x$ **39.** $11x^2 + 4$
41. $-3x - 5$ **43.** $8x + 24$
45. $-5x^2 + 6x$ **47.** $1.06x + 15.9 \leq 42$
49. a and b   **51.** $x + (x - 7) + x + (x - 7)$, $4x - 14$
53. $a(b + c) = ab + ac$

■ **2.6 Integrated Review pp. 99–100**

55. $3.6x - 4.32$ **57.** $-12.2 + 64.6x$
59. $-8.61x^2 + 167.69x$ **61.** $3x = 12, 4$
63. $5y + 3 = 8, 1$ **65.** $3z = 27, 9$

■ **2.6 Mixed Review p. 100**

1. $3 \div (4 - 1)$ **3.** 19   **5.** $1\frac{7}{8}$ **7.** 250   **9.** $\frac{1}{5}$ **11.** No
13. No   **15.** 9   **17.**

$-2\frac{1}{2}$ $-\frac{4}{3}$ $\frac{15}{38}$

$\leftarrow$ | | | | | | | $\rightarrow x$
-3 -2 -1 0 1 2

■ **2.7 Communicating About Algebra p. 103**

A. Product of a number and its reciprocal is 1.
B. Using the division key; fewer keys to press

■ **2.7 Guided Practice p. 104**

1. False, dividing 8 by 2 is not the same as multiplying 8 by -2 **2.** True by definition of reciprocal   **3.** $\frac{1}{22}$
4. $-\frac{1}{17}$ **5.** $\frac{5}{4}$ **6.** $-\frac{2}{7}$ **7.** 0   **8.** Yes, 0

■ **2.7 Independent Practice pp. 104–105**

9. $16 \cdot \frac{1}{4}$ **11.** $2x \cdot 9$ **13.** $\frac{4}{9} \cdot \frac{1}{6}$ **15.** $48 \cdot 2$ **17.** 2
19. 18   **21.** 184   **23.** -2 **25.** -2 **27.** -90 **29.** $\frac{1}{21}$
31. $\frac{x}{12}$ **33.** $245x$ **35.** $-105x$ **37.** $3x - 9$ **39.** $4 - \frac{1}{8}x$
41. 2   **43.** 9   **45.** $\frac{105}{2}$ **47.** 10   **49.** 48   **51.** \$13.86
53. $\frac{1}{1,400,000}$ second
55. FM, the frequency is 90,000,000.

■ **2.7 Integrated Review p. 106**

57. -6 **59.** 12   **61.** 5   **63.** -20 **65.** 135   **67.** -2
69. -12 **71.** $\frac{1}{4}$ **73.** $\frac{1}{8}$

■ **2.8 Communicating About Algebra p. 109**

A. π, $\frac{355}{113}$, 3.1416, $\frac{22}{7}$ **B.** $\frac{355}{113}$

■ **2.8 Guided Practice p. 110**

1. A rate compares two quantities measured in different units. A ratio compares two quantities measured in the same units.   **2.** Rate   **3.** Ratio, π **4.** Rate, ratio

■ **2.8 Independent Practice pp. 110–113**

5. $146\frac{2}{3}$ **7.** \$4.25   **9.** ≈ 106.7 km per hour
11. \$1.66, \$0.13   **13.** ≈ 4.6, better   **15.** 4, 13
17. 965,000 colas drunk for breakfast per day
19. 33 new consumer products introduced per day
21. \$1,232,877 spent on sun care products per day
23. 56 house fires started by arson per day
25. 68 animals treated with acupuncture per day
27. $\frac{36}{35}$ **29.** $\frac{1}{15}$, no   **31.** $\frac{1}{9}$ **33.** $\frac{2}{3}, \frac{4}{7}, \frac{1}{2}, \frac{4}{9}, \frac{2}{5}$
35. $\frac{1}{4}$ **37.** e   **39.** a   **41.** g   **43.** b

■ **2.8 Integrated Review p. 113**

45. -1 **47.** -7 **49.** $2x$ **51.** 8   **53.** 2   **55.** -21

■ **2.8 Chapter Review pp. 115–116**

1. 1

$\leftarrow$ ● | | | | ● $\rightarrow x$
-4 -3 -2 -1 0 1

3.

-5 5

$\leftarrow$ | ● | | | ● | $\rightarrow x$
-6 -4 -2 0 2 4 6

5. 1.1   **7.** 4   **9.** 1   **11.** -1 **13.** -13.6 **15.** 28   **17.** $\frac{3}{4}$
19. $-\frac{1}{12}$ **21.** -3 **23.** 9   **25.** $7y + 3$ **27.** $2x - 8$
29. $\begin{bmatrix} -1 & 2 \\ 10 & -3 \\ 8 & -3 \end{bmatrix}$
31.

	Nov	Dec	Jan	Feb	Mar	Apr
High	64	57	56	59	61	63
Low	45	45	40	43	44	45

33. January through September   **35.** c, 20 feet per second
37. 10 A.M.   **39.** Atom   **41.** Ion   **43.** Elk Island: 64,
Wood Buffalo: 3280.6, Wind Cave: 87.1, Yellowstone:
778.9   **45.** Elk Island   **47.** 298
49. a and b; in **a** the number who have not worked for pay is subtracted from 1500, in **b** the fraction who have worked for pay is multiplied by 1500.
51. $\approx 5.9\%$ **53.** a, $(1.06)^{18} \approx 2.85$ **55.** $3\frac{5}{11}$ **57.** 140

CHAPTER 3

■ **3.1 Communicating About Algebra p. 125**

A. $\frac{3}{2}$ **B.** Yes, because it checks; no
C. 5, to isolate the variable
D. Transformation gives $x = -135$.

■ **3.1 Guided Practice p. 126**

1. True   **2.** True   **3.** False, the number must be nonzero.
4. Addition and subtraction, multiplication and division
5. Divide both sides by 2, add 5 to both sides, subtract 2 from both sides, multiply both sides by 4
6. See page 124.   **7.** Equivalent   **8.** Not equivalent

■ **3.1 Independent Practice pp. 126–128**

9. Subtract 31   **11.** Divide by -2 **13.** 9   **15.** 16   **17.** -12

19. 10 **21.** -3 **23.** 15 **25.** 10 **27.** -8 **29.** 16 **31.** 16
33. -80 **35.** 0 **37.** -100 **39.** 11 **41.** 10 **43.** 8 **45.** -6
47. -1 **49.** a, 6 **51.** $2\frac{1}{7}$ ft **53.** $4\frac{2}{7}$ ft **55.** a, $1\frac{1}{2}$
57. $1.90x = 95$ or $\frac{x}{95} = \frac{100}{190}$, 50

■ 3.1 Integrated Review p. 128
59. -12 **61.** -4 **63.** 12 **65.** -16 **67.** -18 **69.** 55
71. 1 **73.** $\frac{3}{4}$ **75.** -4 **77.** 15

■ 3.2 Communicating About Algebra p. 131
A. $2(x - 3) = 5$
$2x - \cancel{6} = 5$
$2x = \cancel{8} 11$
$x = \cancel{4} \frac{11}{2}$

Should have multiplied $2x(-3)$

B. $5 - 3x = 10$
$-3x \cancel{2x} = \cancel{10} 5$
$x = \cancel{5} -\frac{5}{3}$

Should not have subtracted 3 from 5, because 5 is not a coefficient of x.

C. $\frac{1}{4}x - 2 = 7$
$x - \cancel{28} = 28$
$x = \cancel{30} 36$

Should have multiplied $4(-2)$.

■ 3.2 Guided Practice p. 132
1. Subtract 1 from both sides. **2.** It is.
3. 8 was added to, instead of subtracted from, the right side. **4.** Either, but using **b** is more efficient.

■ 3.2 Independent Practice pp. 132–134
5. No **7.** Yes **9.** No **11.** 10 **13.** 4 **15.** 4
17. $-2\frac{1}{2}$ or $-\frac{5}{2}$ **19.** -6 **21.** 9 **23.** 1 **25.** 6 **27.** 8
29. 17 **31.** $\frac{7}{12}$ **33.** 3
35. $32x + 285 = 357, 2\frac{1}{4}$ **37.** $\frac{7}{8}$ second
39. 6 and 8, $3\frac{3}{7}$ **41.** 2 m

■ 3.2 Integrated Review p. 134
43. 24 **45.** 4 **47.** 0 **49.** 20.07

■ 3.3 Communicating About Algebra p. 137
A. $-3x + 5 = 9x - 19$
$-3x + 3x + 5 = 9x + 3x - 19$ Add $3x$ to both sides.
$5 = 12x - 19$ Simplify.
$5 + 19 = 12x \quad 19 + 19$ Add 19 to both sides.
$24 = 12x$ Simplify.
$\frac{24}{12} = \frac{12x}{12}$ Divide both sides by 12.
$2 = x$ Simplify.

Check:
$-3x + 5 = 9x - 19$
$-3(2) + 5 \stackrel{?}{=} 9(2) - 19$
$-1 = -1$
B. Write $-(3y - 6)$ as $-3y + 6$; to combine like terms

■ 3.3 Guided Practice p. 138
1. False; it is best to collect the variables on the side with the larger variable coefficient, if you want to avoid a negative coefficient in the single variable term.
2. True; subtract x from both sides and $0 = x$ is the result.
3. Use the Distributive Property, $81 - 9x = 4x - 10$
4. Add $9x$ to both sides, see explanation in Exercise 1, $81 = 13x - 10$
5. Add 10 to both sides, $91 = 13x$
6. $x = 7 \quad (9 - 7)9 \stackrel{?}{=} 4(7) - 10$
$(2)9 \stackrel{?}{=} 28 - 10$
$18 = 18$

■ 3.3 Independent Practice pp. 138–139
7. Subtract x from both sides. **9.** Add 18 to both sides.
11. Use the Distributive Property. **13.** -27 **15.** $\frac{1}{2}$
17. $\frac{1}{2}$ **19.** -1 **21.** 1 **23.** -1 **25.** $\frac{5}{6}$ **27.** 2 **29.** 5
31. $-4\frac{1}{3}$ or $-\frac{13}{3}$ **33.** $\frac{1}{2}$ **35.** $-\frac{10}{13}$
37. 15 or more **39.** a **41.** c

■ 3.3 Integrated Review p. 139
43. $-x + 2$ **45.** $4 + 6x$ **47.** $46x$ **49.** Yes **51.** No
53. No

■ 3.3 Mixed Review p. 140
1. $\frac{1}{20}$ **3.** 9 **5.** $-2 - 2x$ **7.** $3^2 \cdot x^3$ **9.** $-\frac{7}{2}$
11. 3 is, 4 is not
13. $w + 3\frac{1}{2}w + w + 3\frac{1}{2}w$ or $9w$
15. $3x - 2 < 12$

■ 3.4 Communicating About Algebra p. 143
A. $1\frac{7}{10}$ in. **B.** $\frac{15}{17}$ **C.** No, yes

■ 3.4 Guided Practice p. 144
1. Rate of 1st runner = 10 (km per hour)
Time after 2nd runner starts = t (hours)
Distance advantage of 1st runner = 7 (km)
Rate of 2nd runner = 15 (km per hour)
2. $10t + 7 = 15t$
3. $t = 1\frac{2}{5}$; From the instant the 2nd runner started running, each runner ran $1\frac{2}{5}$ hours. **4.** 21 km

■ 3.4 Independent Practice pp. 144–145
5.

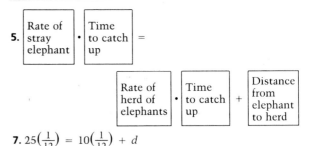

7. $25\left(\frac{1}{12}\right) = 10\left(\frac{1}{12}\right) + d$

9.

Population of western region in 1988	$+$	Rate of western increase	$\cdot$	Time	$=$

Population of midwest region in 1988	$+$	Rate of midwest increase	$\cdot$	Time

11. $50{,}679{,}000 + 982{,}000y = 58{,}878{,}000 + 222{,}000y$

13.

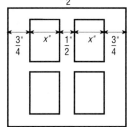

15. Cover width $= 6\frac{1}{2}$ (inches)

Margin width $= \frac{3}{4}$ (inch)

Space between pictures $= \frac{1}{2}$ (inch)

Picture width $= x$ (inches)

17. $x = 2\frac{1}{4},\ 2\frac{1}{4}$ in.

19. Money you currently have $= 60$ (dollars)

Money you save each week $= 5$ (dollars)

Time $= w$ (weeks)

Money sister currently has $= 135$ (dollars)

Extra money she spends each week $= 10$ (dollars)

21. $w = 5$, 5 weeks

23. Greenville temperature $= 69$ (°F)

Rate of temperature increase $= 2$ (°F per hour)

Time $= h$ (hours)

Waterloo temperature $= 84$ (°F)

Rate of temperature decrease $= 3$ (°F per hour)

25. $h = 3$, 3 hours

■ *3.4 Integrated Review p. 146*

27. feet   **29.** liters   **31.** inches   **33.** hours per day

■ *3.4 Mid-Chapter Self-Test p. 147*

1. 6   **2.** 28   **3.** 13   **4.** $\frac{5}{2}$ or $2\frac{1}{2}$ **5.** 5   **6.** -37 **7.** $\frac{58}{15}$ or $3\frac{13}{15}$

8. 8   **9.** $\frac{1}{2}$ **10.** 6   **11.** $\frac{8}{3}$ or $2\frac{2}{3}$ **12.** $\frac{11}{3}$ or $3\frac{2}{3}$

13.
$$0 = 5x + 7$$
$$-7 = 5x$$
$$-\frac{7}{5} \text{ or } -1\frac{2}{5} = x$$

14. Correct   **15.** Correct   **16.** c   **17.** a and c   **18.** b

19. 30 ft   **20.** c

■ *3.5 Communicating About Algebra p. 150*

A. 0.44, 0.28, 5.26   **B.** $0.44 + 0.28x = 5.26$;
$x \approx 17.21$, 18 minutes

■ *3.5 Guided Practice p. 151*

1. Examples vary; see page 148.   **2.** b, Nonwhole numbers are not meaningful; b is least objectionable.
3. Multiply both sides by 10.   **4.** b

■ *3.5 Independent Practice pp. 151–152*

5. -367.8 **7.** 63.6   **9.** 14.6   **11.** 5.36   **13.** -44.67
15. 110.26   **17–28.** See page 148 for example of check.
17. 8.65   **19.** 1.83   **21.** -1.1 **23.** 3.56   **25.** 0.31   **27.** 0.89
29. 1.33   **31.** -0.21 **33.** 8.44   **35.** -1.41 **37.** 10.33
39. \$30.61   **41.** a   **43.** ≈ 90.4 in.

45.

Rate of cold water	$\cdot$	Time cold water is on	$=$	Rate of hot water	$\cdot$	Time hot water is on

47. $12.3t = 7.8(t + 2)$ **49.** \$394.74

■ *3.5 Integrated Review p. 152*

51. 12   **53.** 1   **55.** $-\frac{8}{5}$ or $-1\frac{3}{5}$ **57.** 2   **59.** $-\frac{4}{7}$

■ *3.6 Communicating About Algebra p. 156*

A. $h = \frac{3V}{s^2}$ **B.** 480 ft

■ *3.6 Guided Practice p. 157*

1. False   **2.** b, c; Each uses more than one letter as a variable.   **3.** $m = \frac{9 - 3n}{4}$ **4.** $r = \frac{I}{Pt}$

■ *3.6 Independent Practice pp. 157–158*

5. $h = \frac{2A}{b}$ **7.** $L = \frac{V}{WH}$ **9.** $C = \frac{S}{1 + r}$
11. $r = \frac{A - P}{Pt}$ **13.** $b_1 = \frac{2A}{h} - b_2$ **15.** $n = \frac{L - a}{d} + 1$
17. ≈ 0.26 ft   **19.** 15 in.   **21.** 150 pounds   **23.** \$282.59, \$292.88, \$74.03   **25.** \$159.49

■ *3.6 Integrated Review p. 158*

27. 2   **29.** 6   **31.** -1 **33.** ≈ -0.09

■ *3.6 Mixed Review p. 159*

1. ≈ -12.27 **3.** $\frac{7}{8}$ **5.** $3x^2 - 14x + 2$ **7.** $2x - 16$ **9.** 1
11. 9   **13.** $24 = 7n + 3$ **15.** $(x + 6)\frac{1}{4}$

■ *3.7 Communicating About Algebra p. 162*

A.

B. As latitude increases, temperature decreases.
C. $\approx 39.0°$

■ 3.7 Guided Practice p. 163

1. b **2.** 3, 7 **3.** $A(2, 3)$, $B(-1, 4)$, $C(0, 0)$, $D(3, 0)$, $E(-2-2)$, $F(2, -3)$ **4.** Below, right

5.

■ 3.7 Independent Practice pp. 163–165

7. $A(2, 4)$, $B(1, 2)$, $C(-2, 3)$, $D(-1, 0)$, $E(0, -1)$, $F(4, -2)$

9.   **11.**

13. 1990, 5 **15.** c **17.** inches, inches

19.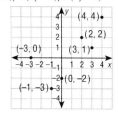

21. Some points might be considered as clustering around (38, 1.9); cities with similar January climates

23.   **25.**

■ 3.7 Integrated Review p. 165

27. $x = 4 - 2y$ **29.** $a = \frac{1}{2}(-16 - 3b)$ or $-8 - \frac{3}{2}b$
31. $n = -m - \frac{4}{5}$ **33.** 7 **35.** -1

■ 3.7 Chapter Review pp. 168–170

1. 14 **3.** 2 **5.** 3 **7.** -8 **9.** $\frac{1}{2}$ **11.** $-\frac{62}{7}$ or $-8\frac{6}{7}$ **13.** 1.57
15. 2.61 **17.** 0.43 **19.** $y = \frac{1}{3}(4x - 2)$ **21.** $b = \frac{2A}{h}$
23. 12 **25.** Flour: $6\frac{1}{4}$, raisins: $\frac{5}{6}$ **27.** $148\frac{1}{2}$ **29.** $x + 20$, 5 mL **31.** 1975, 1976–1988 **33.** $405 billion, $255 billion, $660 billion, yes **35.** $205 billion, $265 billion

■ 3.7 Cumulative Review for Chapters 1–3 pp. 172–173

1. 11 **3.** 9 **5.** -7.8 **7.** 100.6 **9.** $\frac{2}{9}$ **11.** $-\frac{39}{7}$ **13.** $\frac{17}{5}$
15. $p > -\frac{15}{11}$ **17.** $\frac{4}{9}$ **19.** 1.41 **21.** $t > 0.15$
23. $\begin{bmatrix} 14 & 15 & 32 \\ 50 & -41 & -35 \end{bmatrix}$ **25.** $3n - 27$ **27.** $\frac{1}{2}(n + 27) = 37$
29. $|n| < \frac{36}{5}$ **31.** 400 **33.** $\frac{4}{3}$ **35.** 2 **37.** 20%

CHAPTER 4

■ 4.1 Communicating About Algebra p. 179

A.
B. It is 0; it is $y = 0$. **C.** $x = 0$
D. $(0, 0)$ **E.** $x = -4$
F. The x-coordinate is 1 for all points on the line $x = 1$.

■ 4.1 Guided Practice p. 180

1. 2 **2.** -3 **3.** False. The graph of $x = 4$ consists of all points with x-coordinate 4; this is a vertical line.
4. True **5.** $(-4, 6)$ **6.** $y = -2$, $x = 3$

■ 4.1 Independent Practice pp. 180–182

7. c **9.** d **11.** $(6, -1)$ **13.** $(-4, -5)$ **15.** Yes **17.** No
19. $x = 2$ **21.** $y = -72$ **23.** $y = -6$, $x = 10$
25. $y = -15$, $x = -21$ **27.** $y = 12$, $x = -5$
29. $y = 0$, $x = 3$
31. The TV was off from noon until 1 P.M., the TV was on from 1–2 P.M. on Channel 4, the TV was off from 2–4 P.M., the TV was on from 4–6 P.M. on Channel 7, the TV was on from 6–6:30 P.M. on Channel 6, the TV was off from 6:30–8 P.M., the TV was on from 8–9 P.M. on Channel 8, the TV was on from 9–11 P.M. on Channel 7, the TV was on from 11–11:30 P.M. on Channel 6, and the TV was off from 11:30 P.M. to midnight.
33. Channel 7; each of its segments is longer than any other segment. **35.** ≈ 0.6, ≈ 0.6, ≈ 0.6, ≈ 0.6 **37.** All entries are 1572. **39.** The total number of college/urban orchestras was 1572 for each year. **41.** Water temp.

■ 4.1 Integrated Review p. 182

43. $y = \frac{1}{5}(10 - 2x)$ **45.** $y = \frac{1}{2}(14 + 5x)$
47. $y = \frac{1}{7}(5x - 19)$ **49.** No **51.** Yes

■ 4.2 Communicating About Algebra p. 185

A.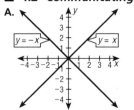
They bisect the 4 quadrants of the plane.

B. 11, 9, 7, 5, 3, 1, −1,

$y = -2x + 5$

C. 2; if two points are plotted and a line drawn, the remaining points will be on the line.
D. Multiples of 4, so that y would be an integer.

■ 4.2 Guided Practice p. 186

1. A number pair that makes the equation true. **2.** The collection of all points (x, y) that are solutions of the equation. **3.** c, d **4.** $y = \frac{3}{2}x + \frac{5}{2}$ Add 6x to both sides to isolate the y-term on the left side. Multiply each side by $\frac{1}{4}$ to get a y-term with a coefficient of 1.

■ 4.2 Independent Practice pp. 186–188

5. a **7.** a **9.** $(0, -4)$, $(2, 0)$ **11.** $(0, -3)$, $(1, 3)$

13.

15.

17.

19.

21. b **23.** a **25.** $-40°C = -40°F$

27.

29. a

31.

■ 4.2 Integrated Review p. 188

33.

35.

37. $(-4, 7)$ **39.** $(-10, -12)$ **41.** $x = 6$, $y = -3$
43. $x = 8$, $y = 21$

■ 4.3 Communicating About Algebra p. 192

A. −19, no **B.** 615, no **C.** 0, 0; same, found the point where each occurs; $(0, 0)$. **D.** Horizontal lines, vertical lines, and lines that pass through the origin have only one point as an intercept instead of the two needed to do a quick graph.

■ 4.3 Guided Practice p. 193

1. True **2.** 2; only 1 line can be drawn between 2 points.
3. Set $y = 0$ and solve for x. **4.** Set $x = 0$ and solve for y.
5. x-intercept **6.** -4; $y = 6x - 4 = 6 \cdot 0 - 4 = -4$

■ 4.3 Independent Practice pp. 193–194

7. c **9.** d **11.** 2, 3 **13.** -4, -1 **15.**

17.

19.

21. 4 **23.** 3 **25.** -7
27. -12 **29.** -2 **31.** 26
33. -4 **35.** 5

37.

39.

41.

43.

45.

47.

49.

51.

19. 2   **21.** $-\dfrac{3}{4}$

23. undefined   **25.** 0

27. $-\dfrac{3}{5}$

29. Rises to right
31. Vertical
33. Falls to right
35. 3 inches per minute

37. Form the vertices of a triangle **39.** $\dfrac{1}{3}$ dollar per year
41. All, increase **43.** $-\dfrac{2600}{3}$ feet per minute
45. 0 symphony orchestras per year **47.** 13,670 people per year **49.** San Diego

■ *4.3 Integrated Review p. 194*
53. No **55.** $y = 9 - 3x$ **57.** $y = -3x - \dfrac{2}{3}$

■ *4.3 Mixed Review p. 196*
1. 7 **3.** $y = 2(x - 1)$ **5.** 3.2 **7.** 1 **9.** $7x^2 - 4x - 3$
11. No **13.** $\begin{bmatrix} -3.9 & 11.0 \\ 4.1 & 10.0 \end{bmatrix}$ **15.** No **17.** Yes **19.** Yes

■ *4.4 Communicating About Algebra p. 200*
A. 45 mph **B.** $-6°F$ per hour

■ *4.4 Guided Practice p. 201*
1. Did not use same order of subtraction for numerator and denominator. **2.** Rise **3.** Run **4.** Denominator becomes zero, so slope is undefined. **5.** Zero **6.** b, if the slope is interpreted as steepness; c, if the slope is interpreted as a number. **7.** True **8.** Answers vary; for example, miles per hour

■ *4.4 Independent Practice pp. 201–203*
9. a: -1, b: 1 **11.** a: -2, b: undefined

13.   **15.**   **17.** $\dfrac{5}{4}$

■ *4.4 Integrated Review p. 203*
51. $y = -\dfrac{1}{2}(14 - 9x)$ **53.** $y = 6 + 2x$ **55.** $\dfrac{16}{3}, -\dfrac{4}{3}$
57. 3, -14

■ *4.4 Mid-Chapter Self-Test p. 204*
1. $(-1, 2)$ **2.** $y = -6, x = 4$
3. $y = 27 - 18x$
4. $y = \dfrac{4}{3}(4 - x)$

5. $y = \dfrac{12}{5}x - 4$ **6.** $y = \dfrac{1}{4}(3 - 3x)$; Tables vary.

7. Yes **8.** No
9.   **10.**

11. c **12.** b **13.** -3 **14.** 3 **15.** $\frac{2}{3}$ **16.** -6

17. \$1.47 per pound **18.** $\approx$533 people per square mile

19.

20. \$103.33 per month

■ *4.5 Communicating About Algebra p. 207*

A. Cost that is independent of the number of books printed; cost per book printed
B. \$3.50, \$2.25
C. Yes, the cost that is independent of the number of books printed would be spread among more books.

■ *4.5 Guided Practice p. 208*

1. Yes; slope of line does not change **2.** Slope, y-intercept **3.** Parallel **4.** $-\frac{3}{2}, \frac{1}{2}$

■ *4.5 Independent Practice pp. 208–210*

5. $y = -\frac{5}{7}x$ **7.** $y = -\frac{3}{4}x + 3$ **9.** $y = -10$
11. $-2, 1$ **13.** $-8, -4$ **15.** $-2, -4$

17. $y = 2x - 3$

19. $y = -x$

21. $y = -\frac{1}{2}x + 1$

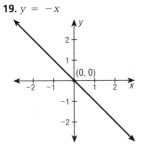

23. $y = \frac{3}{4}x + \frac{1}{2}$

25. $y = 3$

27. $y = -\frac{1}{3}x + 3$

29. d **31.** a

33. -3; $\left(\frac{2}{3}, 0\right)$, $(0, 2)$; $\left(-\frac{2}{3}, 0\right)$, $(0, -2)$

35. 6, $\left(-\frac{4}{3}, 0\right)$, $(0, 8)$; $\left(\frac{1}{3}, 0\right)$, $(0, -2)$

37. $\frac{3}{4}$ ft **39.** You **41.** b

43.

-1, rate of weight loss in pounds per week; 148, Mark's weight in pounds before he starts his weight-loss program

■ *4.5 Integrated Review p. 210*

45. $\frac{1}{6}$ **47.** 0 **49.** $(0, 4)$, etc. **51.** $(0, 0)$, etc.

53.

55.

■ *4.6 Communicating About Algebra p. 213*

A. a **B.** c **C.** b

■ *4.6 Guided Practice p. 214*

1. $x = 4$ **2.** $y = 9x - 36$
3. 4
4. True. The x-intercept of $y = ax + b$ is the value of x when $y = 0$; this value of x is the solution of $ax + b = 0$.

■ *4.6 Independent Practice pp. 214–215*

5. d **7.** c **9.** $y = 9x + 8$ **11.** $y = -3x - 11$ **13.** 2
15. -4 **17.** -6 **19.** $\frac{1}{2}$ **21.** $-\frac{4}{9}$ **23.** 4 **25.** -2 **27.** $\frac{1}{2}$
29. 65 **31.** 1985

■ 4.6 Integrated Review p. 215

33. 4 **35.** 1 **37.** 4 **39.** −5 **41.** −13, −9, −5, −1, 3, 7, 11 **43.** d

■ 4.6 Mixed Review p. 216

1. −9 **3.** 9 **5.** Dollars **7.** $2x − 1$ **9.** 44 **11.** $a = \frac{b}{2}$
13. Yes **15.** ≈ −12.11 **17.** $x − 6 \le 10$ **19.** $3(−10) − 1$

■ 4.7 Communicating About Algebra p. 219

A. Graph of $y = |x| − 1$ is 1 unit down from graph of $y = |x|$.
B. Graph of $y = |x − 2|$ is 2 units to the right of graph of $y = |x|$.
C. Graph of $y = −|x|$ opens down while graph of $y = |x|$ opens up.
D. $y = 2|x|$

■ 4.7 Guided Practice p. 220

1. True **2.** Highest; the vertex is (0, 0) and $y \le 0$.
3. $(−4, −2)$ **4.** Complete a table of values that contains the coordinates of the vertex and of points to the right and left of the vertex. Then plot the points and draw the graph.

■ 4.7 Independent Practice pp. 220–222

5. c **7.** d **9.** b **11.** c **13.** $(0, −6)$ **15.** $(0, −3)$ **17.** $(2, 0)$
19. $(−3, −2)$ **21.** $(9, 10)$ **23.** $(2, 8)$ **25.** c **27.** a
29. −3, −1, 1, 3, 1, −1, −3
31. $\frac{1}{2}$, −1, $−\frac{5}{2}$, −4, $−\frac{5}{2}$, −1, $\frac{1}{2}$

33.   **35.**

37.   **39.**

41.   **43.**

45.   **47.**

49.

51. True, both have vertex (3, 4).
53. 56 ft from the other corner

■ 4.7 Integrated Review p. 222

55. −5 **57.** −2 **59.** −6 **61.** $3\frac{1}{2}$

■ 4.8 Communicating About Algebra p. 225

A. To pass certification, the scale must weigh from 159 to 161 oz.
B. To be eligible for one of the 13 weight classes on the wrestling team, your weight must be from 103 to 275 lb.
C. To obtain a bonus, the pizza delivery driver must deliver the pizza in 20 to 40 minutes.

■ 4.8 Guided Practice p. 226

1. 1, −3 **2.** $y = |x + 1| − 2$ **3.** $x + 1 = 32$, $x + 1 = −32$ **4.** 82.5 ft, 90 and −90

■ 4.8 Independent Practice pp. 226–227

5. −1, −7 **7.** −3, 15 **9.** 4, −10 **11.** $|x + 1| = 3$
13. $|4 − x| = −5$ **15.**

17. 8, −6 **19.** $\frac{9}{4}$, $−\frac{15}{4}$
21. −8, −2 **23.** $−\frac{7}{3}$, 7
25. 13, 5 **27.** $\frac{7}{2}$, $\frac{1}{2}$ **29.** $\frac{13}{3}$, −5
31. $\frac{9}{2}$, $−\frac{11}{2}$ **33.** $−\frac{19}{12}$, $−\frac{35}{12}$ **35.** 10 ft
37. 13 ft **39.** $|x − 183| = 7$, 176 lb, 190 lb

■ 4.8 Integrated Review p. 227

41. −1 **43.** 26 **45.** −28 **47.** $x = 5$ **49.** 6, −3
51.

1. $(0, -3)$ **3.** $(-6, 4)$

5. Yes **7.** No

9.

11. Tables vary.

13. c **15.** d **17.** 5 **19.** $-\frac{4}{3}$ **21.** $\frac{1}{4}$, -3

23.

25. 2 **27.** 8

29. Tables vary.

31. Tables vary.

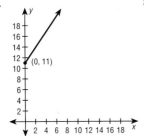

45. 0.42 million of boats per year **47.** 30 ft **49.** $\frac{15}{14}$

CHAPTER 5

■ *5.1 Communicating About Algebra p. 238*

A. $y = 0.45x + 1.25$

B. A seven-minute call to the second number

C. A 12-minute call to the first number

■ *5.1 Guided Practice p. 239*

1. Slope-intercept form **2.** y-intercept **3.** -1, 0

4. $y = -7x - \frac{2}{3}$ **5.** 32,307,400 **6.** $y = 1.50x + 11$

7.

8. $29

■ *5.1 Independent Practice pp. 239–240*

9. $y = 3x - 2$ **11.** $y = -x + 3$ **13.** $y = \frac{3}{2}x + 3$

15. $y = 2x + 2$ **17.** $y = -\frac{2}{3}x + 2$

19. a: $y = 2x + 3$, b: $y = 2x$, c: $y = 2x - 4$

21. $y = 0.25x + 30$

23. 36.25, 42.50, 48.75, 55.00

25. $P = 38{,}400t + 3{,}122{,}000$

27. $y = -50t + 200$, as time increases the distance from home decreases

29. $y = 7{,}500{,}000x$; 2,737,500,000 gallons per year

■ *5.1 Integrated Review p. 241*

31. -3, 6 **33.** -2, 2

35. $\frac{3}{2}$, 3 **37.** Horizontal

39. Vertical **41.** Horizontal

43. Yes **45.** $y = 3$ **47.** $y = 10x$

■ *5.2 Communicating About Algebra p. 244*

A. 415 million **B.** 520 million **C.** 1989

D. No, extending the graph to the left would decrease the number of vacation trips to zero around 1962.

■ *5.2 Guided Practice p. 245*

1.

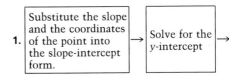

2. $\frac{1}{3}$, -2, 4, b **3.** $y = -2x + 5$ **4.** $y = 7$

5. $y = \frac{1}{2}x - 6$ **6.** $y = 9x - 6$ **7.** $y = 6000x + 86{,}000$

8. 146,000

■ 5.2 Independent Practice pp. 245–247

9. $y = 2x + 12$ **11.** $y = -x + 2$

13. $y = -2x - 9$ **15.** $y = \frac{1}{2}x - 4$

17. $y = 3x - 1$ **19.** $y = 0 \cdot x + 5$

21. $y = \frac{2}{3}x + 6$ **23.** $y = -2x - 2$

25. $y = \frac{1}{2}x + 2$ **27.** $y = -\frac{1}{3}x + 1$

29. $y = 1{,}100{,}000x + 10{,}534{,}000$

31. $m = 2n + 14$ **33.** $y = \frac{1}{2}x$

35. $C = 0.46 + 0.31(t - 1)$

■ 5.2 Integrated Review p. 247

37. 4 **39.** 2 **41.** 5 **43.** 0 **45.** $y = -2x + 2$

■ 5.2 Mixed Review p. 248

1. $-\frac{1}{3}$ **3.** 16 ft² **5.** 11 **7.** $x + 4$ **9.** No **11.** 5 **13.** 18

15.   **17.**

19. $y = 2x + 3$

■ 5.3 Communicating About Algebra p. 251

A. The store sold 255 more jeans per year. **B.** 5455

C. $x = \frac{y - 2650}{255}$, 1995 **D.** \$186,940

■ 5.3 Guided Practice p. 252

1. See page 250. **2.** To write the equation of a line you need to know the slope and one of the points on the line.
3. 4 **4.** $y = 4x - 5$ **5.** $y = 25x + 300$ **6.** 550

■ 5.3 Independent Practice pp. 252–254

7. $y = x - 1$ **9.** $y = 3x + 13$ **11.** $y = 3x + 2$

13. $y = \frac{1}{2}x - 1$ **15.** $y = -4x$ **17.** $y = -2x - 1$

19. $y = x$ **21.** $y = 3$ **23.** $y = \frac{1}{2}x + 5$

25. $y = -\frac{2}{3}x - 4$

27. $y = 19x$

29. $y = -\frac{13}{1500}x + 60,\ -\frac{13}{1500}$

31. $y = 1350x + 3710$

33. $y = 773{,}000x + 47{,}231{,}000$

■ 5.3 Integrated Review p. 254

35. -2 **37.** $\frac{1}{3}$

    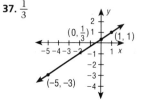

39. $y = -2x + 3$ **41.** $y = x - 7$

■ 5.4 Communicating About Algebra p. 258

A.   **B.** Positive

C. See scatter plot. **D.** (2, 2,067,475), (6, 4,001,450)
E. $y = 483{,}493.75x + 1{,}100{,}487.5$ **F.** \$8,836,387.50

■ 5.4 Guided Practice p. 259

1. Scatter plot **2.** Best-fitting **3.** 17 **4.** $y = 17x + 73.7$
5. 87.3°F **6.** 0.96

■ 5.4 Independent Practice pp. 259–261

7. Suggest **9.** Do not suggest **11–13.** Best-fitting lines vary.

11. $y = \frac{1}{2}x - 1$, positive   **13.** $y = -\frac{2}{3}x + 1$, negative

15. $y = -\frac{3}{2}x + \frac{29}{2}$, negative **17.** $y = 4x - 165$, 175

                           19. $y = -x + 113$, 73°F

■ 5.4 Integrated Review p. 261

21. Negative   **23.** Negative

25. $y = \frac{3}{2}x + \frac{5}{2}$ **27.** $y = -\frac{2}{3}x + \frac{22}{3}$

■ 5.4 Mid-Chapter Self-Test p. 263

1. $y = -\frac{1}{3}x + 4$

2. $y = 2x - 3$

3. $C = 0.40x + 35$ **11.** $y = \frac{12}{5}x$; 960 cm²

4. $y = 3x + 10$

5. $y = -\frac{2}{3}x$

6. $y = 3$

7. $A = 8.14t + 55.54$

8. $y = -\frac{4}{7}x + \frac{23}{7}$

9. $y = -\frac{4}{5}x + 4$

10. $y = 7x$, 70 pounds

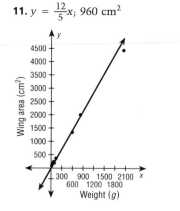

5.5 Communicating About Algebra p. 266

A. $4x + 3y = 12$ **B.** $y = -\frac{4}{3}x + 4$

C.

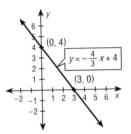

D. $\left(\frac{3}{4}, 3\right), \left(2, 1\frac{1}{3}\right)$

E. Any size greater than 3 ft^3 and less than 4 ft^3.

5.5 Guided Practice p. 267

1. Slope-intercept form   **2.** Standard form
3. $x + 2y = 10$
4. $y = -\frac{2}{3}x + 3$, $2x + 3y = 9$
5. $1.25x + 2y = 10$ **6.** 5 lb, 4 lb, 2.5 lb, 1 lb, 0 lb

5.5 Independent Practice pp. 267–268

7. $3x - y = 6$ **9.** $4x - 3y = 18$
11. $x = 3$ **13.** $3x + y = 4$
15. $x + 3y = -6$ **17.** $x + 8y = 3$
19. $x = -1, y = 3$ **21.** $x + y = -1$
23. $y = -1$ **25.** $-2x + 3y = 8$
27. $x + 2y = -4$ **29.** $3p + 4c = 24$
31. $4x + 6y = 48$ **33.** $x + y = 60$

5.5 Integrated Review p. 269

35. $y = -2x + 7$ **37.** $y = \frac{1}{3}x - 2$

39.

41.

43. Best-fitting lines vary; $-8x + y = 4$

5.6 Communicating About Algebra p. 273

A. The number of feet per second the parachutist is traveling, because the parachutist is traveling downward.
B. The height at which the parachutist jumped
C. 1560 ft   **D.** 12:16:48

5.6 Guided Practice p. 274

1. Point-slope form   **2.** 2, 2, -3 **3.** $y = 2x - 7$
4. $y = -\frac{1}{2}x + 3$ **5.** a   **6.** $y = 124t$ **7.** About 2:25 P.M.
8. 124, number of feet climbed per hour

5.6 Independent Practice pp. 274–275

9. $y = \frac{1}{3}x + \frac{8}{3}$ **11.** $y = -x + 1$
13. $y = \frac{1}{2}x - \frac{3}{2}$
15. $y + 2 = -\frac{4}{3}(x - 3)$ or $y - 2 = -\frac{4}{3}(x - 0)$
17. $y - 0 = \frac{3}{5}(x - 5)$ or $y + 3 = \frac{3}{5}(x - 0)$
19. $y = 639.2x$, 11:36 A.M.

5.6 Integrated Review pp. 275–276

21. Slope-intercept form, because the slope and y-intercept are given. $y = \frac{2}{3}x + 4$
23. Slope-intercept form, because the slope and y-intercept are given. $y = 2x - 3$
25. Point-slope form, because the slope and a point are given. $y + 4 = x - 1$
27. b   **29.** c

5.6 Mixed Review p. 276

1. $-\frac{1}{8}$ **3.** $b = \frac{4 - 3a}{2}$ **5.** No   **7.** No   **9.** $y = -\frac{4}{5}x + \frac{8}{5}$
11. $y = 5x - 3$

5.7 Communicating About Algebra p. 280

A. No, the y-intercept is negative.   **B.** 2,345,000
C. 292,500

5.7 Guided Practice p. 281

1. $y = 0.02x + 1000$ **2.** $1500   **3.**

4. 0.02, commission rate   **5.** 1000, base pay   **6.** $50,000

5.7 Independent Practice pp. 281–282

7. $y = 0.15x + 750$ **9.**

11. 750, base pay
13. $y = \frac{5}{4}x + 7\frac{1}{2}$
15. $7\frac{1}{2}$, weight at birth
17. 12
19. $2x + y = 84$
21. 44, 34, 24, 14, 4

23. $y = -\frac{2}{3}t + 58$ **25.**

27. $y = \frac{35}{4}x + 90$

29. b **31.** a

■ 5.7 Chapter Review pp. 285–288

1. $y = 2x - 6$ **3.** $y = -\frac{1}{3}x - 1$

5. $y = -\frac{3}{2}x + 3$ **7.** $y = \frac{5}{4}x + 5$

9. $-4, 3$ **11.** $y = -3000x + 32{,}000$

$y = -4x + 3$

13. $y = 3x - 19$ **15.** $y = -x - 1$

17. $y = 4$ **19.** $y = \frac{1}{5}x - 4$

21. $y = \frac{-3}{4}x + 3$ **23.** $y = 4x + 6$

25. $y = 3x + 5$ **27.** $A = 32{,}000t + 288{,}000$

29. $y = 3x + 5$ **31.** $y = -\frac{2}{3}x - 2$

33. $y = -x + 2$ **35.** $y = \frac{1}{2}x - 6$

37. $-\frac{1}{3}$ **39.** -1

41. $x = -1$ **43.** $y = 6$

45. $R = 150t - 400$ **47.** $y = \frac{4}{5}x + 1$

49.   **51.** $y = -\frac{3}{5}x + 1$

$y = 813x + 68{,}838$

53. $-3x + 4y = 2$ **55.** $10x + 5y = 30$

57. 6, 4, 2, 0   **59.** 0; 170,000; 340,000; 510,000; 680,000; 850,000; 1,020,000   **61.** 170,000 per year

63. Those without networks

CHAPTER 6

■ 6.1 Communicating About Algebra p. 295

A. b, Add the same number to both sides

B. a, Divide both sides by the same positive number

C. b, Multiply (or divide) both sides by the same negative number and reverse the inequality sign.

D. a, Meaning of '<' or '>'

■ 6.1 Guided Practice p. 296

1. $x \geq 4$ **2.** All real numbers less than or equal to negative two.   **3.**

4. $x \leq 1$ **5.** Yes, no; $4.78 < 5$ and 6 is not < 6 **6.** $x > 2$

7. When you multiply a true inequality such as $3 > -3$ by -1, the inequality becomes false; to make the inequality true, you must reverse the inequality sign.

8. $x \leq 4$

■ 6.1 Independent Practice pp. 296–297

9.

11.

13.

15. $x < 2$

17. $x < 9$ **19.** $x \leq -14$

21. $x \geq -\frac{3}{2}$ **23.** $x \leq -3$

25. $-\frac{1}{3} \leq x$ **27.** $x < -\frac{1}{2}$

29. $x \geq 11$ **31.** $x < 12$

33. $x \leq -2$, d   **35.** $x < 8$, e

37. $x \leq 4$, f   **39.** $x > -\frac{4}{3}$, h

41. $x \geq 2$, i

43. $E \geq -282$

45. $V < 95$

■ 6.1 Integrated Review p. 297

47. 6, -10 **49.** -6, 12   **51.** $t = 5w + 15$

53. $y = \frac{3}{2}x - 7$

■ 6.2 Communicating About Algebra p. 300

A. $\frac{2}{r} \leq \frac{1}{5}$, $r \geq 10$ mph   **B.** $10L \geq 100$, $L \geq 10$ inches

C. $7.50x - (48 + 3.50x) \geq 300$; $7.50x$ is the income, $48 + 3.50x$ is the total cost, and the difference is the profit; $x \geq 87$

■ 6.2 Guided Practice p. 301

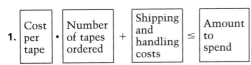

1. $\boxed{\begin{array}{c}\text{Cost}\\\text{per}\\\text{tape}\end{array}} \cdot \boxed{\begin{array}{c}\text{Number}\\\text{of tapes}\\\text{ordered}\end{array}} + \boxed{\begin{array}{c}\text{Shipping}\\\text{and}\\\text{handling}\\\text{costs}\end{array}} \leq \boxed{\begin{array}{c}\text{Amount}\\\text{to}\\\text{spend}\end{array}}$

2. Cost per tape = 3   (dollars)
Number of tapes ordered = x
Shipping and handling cost = 2   (dollars)
Amount to spend = 20   (dollars)
3. $3x + 2 \leq 20$ **4.** $x \leq 6$

■ 6.2 Independent Practice pp. 301–303

5. $m > -37.8°F$ **7.** $x < 2500$ ft **9.** $5 + 0.8x \leq 13$, 10
11. $4 \geq 0.48 + 0.22(t - 1)$, 17 minutes **13.** 1981 to 1990
15. 2 **17.** $x \leq 18$ ft

■ 6.2 Integrated Review p. 303

19. $x \leq 5$ **21.** $x < -1$ **23.** $x < 2$ **25.** $x \geq -2$ **27.** c

■ 6.2 Mixed Review p. 304

1. $\frac{3}{16}$ **3.** $-\frac{1}{6}$ **5.** $b = a - \frac{7}{3}$ **7.** $b = -2$ **9.** No
11. $-2x + 4$ **13.** 4, 0 **15.**

17.

19. $y = \frac{1}{2}x + \frac{3}{2}$

■ 6.3 Communicating About Algebra p. 307

A. a, Subtract the same number from the sides
B. b, Divide the sides by the same positive number
C. b, Multiply (or divide) the sides by the same negative quantity and reverse the inequalities
D. a, Subtract the same number from the sides and divide the sides by the same positive number

■ 6.3 Guided Practice p. 308

1. c **2.** a **3.** d **4.** b
5. $0 \leq x < 4$

6. $x < 4$ or $x \geq 4$ (all real numbers)

■ 6.3 Independent Practice pp. 308–310

7. $-2 < x \leq 8$ **9.** $1 < x < 7$
11. $-12 \leq x \leq -2$ **13.** $x < -7$ or $x \geq 8$
15. As is.

17. $-3 < x < 5$

19. $-2 < x \leq 5$

21. $4 < x < 7$

23. $0 \leq x < 4$

25. $1 < x < 4$, No

27. $0 < x < \frac{3}{2}$, Yes

29. $0.96 \leq x \leq 550,000$ **31.** a **33.** $2 \leq x \leq 3$

■ 6.3 Integrated Review p. 310

35. e **37.** $x > -1$ **39.** 8, -6 **41.** 5, -6 **43.** $\frac{19}{5}$, -3

■ 6.3 Mid-Chapter Self-Test p. 312

1. c **2.** a **3.** b **4.** $-5 \leq x \leq 3$
5. $-4 < x < \frac{1}{3}$ **6.** $-6 \leq x < 1$
7. $1 < x \leq 4$ **8.** $x < -\frac{7}{3}$ or $x \geq \frac{7}{3}$
9. $x \leq 6$ or $x \geq 9$
10. $5 < x < 8$

11. $-3 \leq x \leq 2$

12. $x < -1$ or $x \geq 0$

13. $-4 \leq x \leq 3$

14. $-\frac{11}{3}$

15.

16.

17. $x \geq 52$
18. $2\frac{1}{2} < x < 7\frac{1}{2}$
19. $1.96x + 0.69 \leq 3.00$, $x \leq 1\frac{5}{28}$
20. $1 < x < 9$

■ 6.4 Communicating About Algebra p. 315

A. $|x - 1| < 4$ **B.** $|x + 2| \geq 1$

6.4 Guided Practice p. 316

1. True, $|x + 1| < 3$ is equivalent to the compound inequality $-3 < x + 1 < 3$.
2. True, $|x| \geq 5$ is equivalent to the compound inequality $x \leq -5$ or $x \geq 5$.
3. $-3 < x < 5$ **4.** $x < -12$ or $x > 6$ **5.** a **6.** b

6.4 Independent Practice pp. 316–318

7. d **9.** b **11.** f **13.** $-3 < x < 7$
15. $x < -1$ or $x > 2$ **17.** $x \geq 6$ or $x \leq 2$
19. $-17 < x < 1$

21. $-1 < x < 9$

23. $x \leq 6$ or $x \geq 18$

25. $x < -18$ or $x > 16$

27. $x \leq 2$ or $x \geq 2$ (all real numbers)

29. $-5 \leq x \leq 4$

31. $|x - 2| \leq 8$
33. $|x + 4| < 2$ **35.** $|x| \geq 4$
37. $|x - 14{,}000| < 1000$ **39.** $|x - 80| \leq 20$
41. c–d, orange-red **43.** b, green **45.** $|x - 1080| \leq 1020$

6.4 Integrated Review p. 318

47. $-2 < x < 7$ **49.** $3 \leq x \leq 13$
51. $-\frac{1}{3} < x < \frac{3}{2}$

53.

55.

57.

6.4 Mixed Review p. 319

1. 0.35 **3.** \$0.24 **5.** $-\frac{3}{4}$ **7.** $y = \frac{1}{4}(-20 - 3x)$ **9.** 21
11. $5x - \frac{15}{2}$ **13.** $\frac{19}{37}$ **15.**

17. Yes
19. $-\frac{1}{2}$, 3

6.5 Communicating About Algebra p. 322

A. below

B. above

C. When y is less than the expression involving x, the graph is below the line; when y is greater than the expression involving x, the graph is above the line.

6.5 Guided Practice p. 323

1. $ax + by < c$, $ax + by \leq c$, $ax + by > c$, $ax + by \geq c$ **2.** half plane **3.** Both are. **4.** Both are.
5. Both are. **6.**

• Write the inequality in slope-intercept form.
• Sketch the line (here, solid) of the corresponding equation.
• Test a point (here, the origin) to find whether it is a solution of the inequality.
• Shade the correct half-plane.

6.5 Independent Practice pp. 323–325

7. Only (1, 3) is. **9.** Both are.
11.

13.

15. c **17.** d **19.**

21.

23. $y \le -2x + 2$ **25.** $y < 2x$
27. $0 \le x + y \le 6$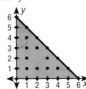

29. $3x + 2y \le 42$

■ 6.5 Integrated Review p. 325
31. $x > \dfrac{8}{3}$ **33.** $x \le -2$ **35.** $-3 < x \le -1$
37. $-3 \le x \le \dfrac{13}{2}$ **39.** Is not. **41.** Is.
43.

45.

47.

49.

■ 6.6 Communicating About Algebra p. 329
A. 9% **B.** 14.4 million **C.** 12.6 million **D.** 7.2 million

■ 6.6 Guided Practice p. 330
1. No **2.** $\dfrac{1}{2}$ **3.** Out of the box **4.** Bored: 180, moved: 95, redecorated: 80, purchased: 75, other: 70

■ 6.6 Independent Practice pp. 330–332
5. c **7.** b **9.** 7:00 A.M., 12 noon, 6:00 P.M. **11.** Answer depends upon choice. **13.** 60% **15.** 13% **17.** Coal
19. ≈5 million barrels more **21.** 13%

23.

Lighting ≈ 14 %
Refrigeration ≈ 25 %
Water heating ≈ 21 %
Other ≈ 16 %
Air-Conditioning ≈ 16 %
Cooking ≈ 9 %

25. $22,050

6.6 Integrated Review pp. 332–333

27. 7% **29.** 14 **31.**

33.

35.

37. b

6.6 Chapter Review pp. 335–338

1.

3.

5. $x \geq -\frac{1}{3}$

7. $x \leq 21$ **9.** $x > \frac{13}{3}$ **11.** $-\frac{5}{6} < x < -\frac{1}{3}$

13. $8 \leq x \leq 88$ **15.** $x \geq \frac{5}{4}$ or $x < 1$

17. $x \leq \frac{1}{2}$ or $x \geq \frac{7}{2}$ **19.** $x < -16$ or $x > 20$

21. $x \geq 16$

23. $-\frac{5}{3} < x < 1$

25. $-\frac{15}{4} < x < \frac{25}{4}$

27. b **29.** a **39.**

31. $|x - 7\frac{1}{2}| \leq 2\frac{1}{2}$

33. $|x - 2\frac{1}{2}| < 3\frac{1}{2}$

35. Only $(-4, -3)$ is.

37. Only $(-2, 1)$ is.

41.

43. $1 \leq h \leq 40$ or $12 \leq h \leq 480$ **45.** $3 \leq p \leq 12$
47. $0.10d + 0.05n \leq 24.50$ **49.** $1.35x + 0.90y \leq 18.00$
51. Nigeria **53.** 41 barrels
55. $0 \leq x \leq 50$ **57.** ≈ 45, $\approx 87\%$
    $50 \leq x \leq 150$
    $150 \leq x \leq 300$
    $x \geq 300$

6.6 Cumulative Review for Chapters 1–6 pp. 340–343

1. $y = 4$; $x = -3$ **3.** $y = 6.2$; $x = 7$
5. -3; 2

7. $-\frac{3}{2}$; 7

9. $-\frac{7}{6}$ **11.** $-\frac{3}{2}$ **13.** c **15.** d
17. $y = 3x - 3$ **19.** $y = -5x - 9$ **21.** $y = \frac{3}{4}x + 6$
23. $y = 2.5x - 14.1$
25. $-5, -4, -3, -4, -5, -6$

27. $-6, -4, -2, -4, -6, -8$

29. $-3, -6$ **31.** $-4, 4$ **33.** c **35.** a

37. $-2 < x < 6$; c **39.** $x < -12$ or $x > -4$; a

41.

43.

45.

47. $y = 3x + 20$ **49.** An increase of $3 for each week

51.

53. An average increase of $10 per ticket each year

55. First Adding Machine, a **57.** Slide Rule, d **59.** 351

61. 6 or 7 **63.** 680 miles per day **65.** $3\frac{1}{4} < w < 8\frac{3}{4}$

67. $y = -|x - 1| - 2$

CHAPTER 7

■ 7.1 Communicating About Algebra p. 348

A. Find an ordered pair (a, b) that satisfies each equation.

B. It is not. **C.** $(5, 2)$

■ 7.1 Guided Practice p. 349

1.

2. $(3, 2)$

3. $4(3) - 2(2) = 12 - 4 = 8,$
$-3(3) + 6(2) = -9 + 12 = 3$; for example:
$4(3) - 2(-2) = 12 + 4 = 16 \neq 8,$
$-3(3) + 6(-2) = -9 - 12 = -21 \neq 3$

4. $(2, 3)$, $3 = 2 + 1$ and $3 = -2 + 5$

5. $(4, 2)$, $2 = -\frac{1}{2}(4) + 4 = -2 + 4$ and
$2(4) - 6 = 8 - 6$

6. $(2, 1)$, $3(2) - 1 = 6 - 5 = 5$ and
$-2 + 2(1) = -2 + 2 = 0$

■ 7.1 Independent Practice pp. 349–351

7. Only $(2, -1)$ is. **9.** Only $(-3, 1)$ is.

11. Only $\left(\frac{3}{2}, 1\right)$ is. **13.** $(2, 0)$ **15.** $(-1, -1)$

17. $(1, 2)$

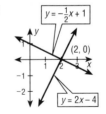

19. $(2, 0)$

21. (3, 1)

23. (3, 6)

25. (1, −2)

27. (8,6)

29. (0, 4)

31. (−3, 2)

33. (2, 3)

35. (2, 1)

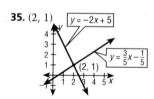

37. Amount in 5% fund = x (dollars)

Amount in $7\frac{1}{2}$% fund = y (dollars)

Total invested = 12,000   (dollars)

Total interest = 850   (dollars)

$2000 at 5%; $10,000 at $7\frac{1}{2}$%

39. 1968

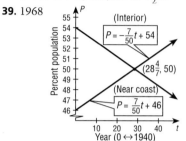

■ *7.1 Integrated Review p. 351*

41. Is not.   **43.** Is not.

45.   **47.**

49. $-x + y = 4$ **51.** $-8x + 7y = -33$ **53.** $-\frac{1}{2}$ **55.** $\frac{1}{4}$

57. $y = -3x + 5$, -1 **59.** $y = \frac{2}{5}x + \frac{4}{5}$, $-\frac{2}{5}$

■ *7.2 Communicating About Algebra p. 355*

A. $2394.24, $1760.90   **B.** 60%

■ *7.2 Guided Practice p. 356*

1. $y = -x + 9$ **2.** 5   **3.** 4, (5, 4)   **4.** Algebraically: Substitute the solution into the original equations and simplify. Graphically: Graph the equations and see if their intersection agrees with the solution.

■ *7.2 Independent Practice pp. 356–358*

5. (1, 1)   **7.** (1, 2)   **9.** (7, 4)   **11.** (1, 9)   **13.** $\left(\frac{5}{2}, -\frac{3}{2}\right)$

15. (1, −1)   **17.** (0, 0)   **19.** (5, 5)   **21.** $\left(\frac{1}{2}, 3\right)$ **23.** $\left(\frac{20}{3}, \frac{40}{3}\right)$

25. $\left(-\frac{5}{3}, -1\right)$ **27.** (100, 50)

29. Number of people over 12 = x

Number of people 12 and under = y

Total number of people = 6

Total price = 61.70   (dollars)

4 of people over 12, 2 of people 12 and under

31. 100,000   **33.** (−146, 4)

35. Meters uphill = x

Meters downhill = y

Rate uphill = 180   (meters per minute)

Rate downhill = 250   (meters per minute)

Total meters = 1557

Total time = 7.6   (minutes)

882 uphill, 675 downhill

37. $y = -\frac{2}{3}x + \frac{8}{3}$ **39.** $y = \frac{9}{2}x - 12$ **41.** $y = \frac{3}{4}x - \frac{7}{2}$

43. $8y$ **45.** $15x - 3y - 42$ **47.** $2x^2 + 8x - y + 5$

49. $(3, 2)$

51. $(-6, -2)$

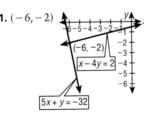

■ **7.2 Mixed Review p. 359**

1. $3x + 10$ **3.** $2\frac{1}{6}$ **5.** $n = \frac{1 - 2m}{2m + 4}$ **7.** $\frac{2}{5}$ **9.** $x < 1\frac{3}{4}$
or $x > 2\frac{1}{4}$ **11.** $\frac{2}{3}$ **13.** Yes **15.** $4x + y = -10$
17. $-3x + 2y = 1$ **19.** $-x + 4y = -36$

■ **7.3 Communicating About Algebra p. 362**

Archimedes' solution compares the volume of the crown to the volumes of equal weights of gold and silver. The system solution compares the volume and weight of the crown with the volume and weight of a gold and silver compound.

■ **7.3 Guided Practice p. 363**

1. $(2, 1)$ **2.** $(1, -1)$ **3.** $(2, -1)$ **4.** $(1, 1)$; linear combination, because x-coefficients are opposites. **5.** $(2, 0)$; substitution, because both equations are solved for y.
6. $(2, 1)$; substitution, because a y-coefficient is 1.

■ **7.3 Independent Practice pp. 363–365**

7. $(2, 0)$ **9.** $(-1, -1)$ **11.** $(8, 4)$ **13.** $(2, 1)$ **15.** $(5, 1)$
17. $(3, -4)$ **19.** $(4, -1)$ **21.** $\left(-\frac{49}{12}, -\frac{11}{2}\right)$ **23.** $(40, 40)$
25. $\left(\frac{13}{3}, -2\right)$ **27.** $\left(13, \frac{5}{8}\right)$ **29.** $x + 3y = 1$, 1 inch

31. Air speed $= x$ (mph)
Wind speed $= y$ (mph)
Ground speed against wind $= 300$ (mph)
Ground speed with wind $= 450$ (mph)
75 mph, 375 mph

33. No

■ **7.3 Integrated Review pp. 365–366**

35. d, $\left(-\frac{1}{3}, -\frac{2}{3}\right)$ **37.** b, $\left(\frac{12}{7}, -\frac{23}{14}\right)$ **39.** e, $\frac{2}{7}$
41. $\left(\frac{9}{2}, \frac{1}{4}\right)$ Substitution, because an x-coefficient is 1.
43. $\left(\frac{21}{5}, \frac{6}{5}\right)$ Linear combination, because no coefficient is 1.
45. $\left(\frac{44}{21}, \frac{73}{21}\right)$ Substitution, because an x-coefficient is 1.
47. $\left(-\frac{10}{11}, \frac{36}{11}\right)$ Linear combination, because no coefficient is 1.

49. Winter solstice: $2x + 3y = 30$, summer solstice: $2x + y = 10$; $(0, 10)$, the point of intersection is the top of the post.

■ **7.4 Communicating About Algebra p. 369**

A. $s = r + 50$, $2r + 1.5s = 1825$; No
B. $r = 500$, $s = 550$; substitution, 1st equation is already solved for s

■ **7.4 Guided Practice p. 370**

1.

| Number of gallons of regular unleaded | $\cdot$ | Cost per gallon of regular unleaded | $+$ | Number of gallons of premium unleaded | $\cdot$ | Cost per gallon of premium unleaded |

| cost per gallon of regular unleaded | $+ \; 0.20 \; =$ | cost per gallon of premium unleaded | $=$ | Total cost |

2. Number of gallons of regular unleaded $= 15$
Cost per gallon of regular unleaded $= x$ (dollars)
Number of gallons of premium unleaded $= 10$
Cost per gallon of premium unleaded $= y$ (dollars)
Total cost $= 35.50$ (dollars)
3. $15x + 10y = 35.50$, $y = x + 0.20$
4. $(1.34, 1.54)$; $1.34, $1.54

■ **7.4 Independent Practice pp. 370–371**

5. 80: $333\frac{1}{3}$ gal, 86: $166\frac{2}{3}$ gal **7.** 10 **9.** $0.90, $2.00
11. 8m by 3m **13.** $-273.2°$C

■ **7.4 Integrated Review p. 372**

15. It is. **17.** It is not. **19.** $\left(-\frac{4}{3}, 1\right)$
21. $(3, 5)$ Substitution, because a y-coefficient is 1.
23. $(-6, -29)$ Substitution, because a y-coefficient is 1.
25. $(-3, 3)$ Linear combination, because no coefficient is 1.
27. $\left(14, -\frac{5}{4}\right)$ Substitution, because an x-coefficient is 1.
29. $(5, 0)$ Linear combination, because no coefficient is 1.
31. b

■ **7.4 Mid-Chapter Self-Test p. 373**

1. $(-3, -4)$ **2.** $(-1, 7)$ **3.** $(-2, 3)$ **4.** $(9, -8)$ **5.** $\left(-\frac{5}{6}, 5\right)$
6. $\left(\frac{1}{2}, \frac{1}{2}\right)$ **7.** $(3, 4)$

8. $(-3, -4)$

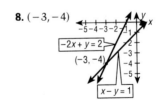

9. $(1, 2)$ **10.** $(-3, -2)$ **11.** $(6, 8)$ **12.** $(1, -5)$ **13.** $(-1, 3)$
14. $(4, -2)$ **15.** $\left(-\frac{1}{2}, -1\right)$ **16.** $\left(4, \frac{15}{7}\right)$ **17.** $\left(\frac{1}{2}, -\frac{1}{3}\right)$
18. $(-1, 4)$ **19.** $\left(-\frac{1}{2}, \frac{1}{2}\right)$ **20.** $\left(\frac{2}{9}, -\frac{2}{3}\right)$ **21.** \$5000 in 4%,
\$3000 in 5% **22.** 2, 3 **23.** 40 3-point, 6 5-point
24. 20 11-inch, 60 12-inch

■ 7.5 Communicating About Algebra p. 376
Measure the height and shadow length of something else and compare them to the height and shadow length of one of the statues.

■ 7.5 Guided Practice p. 377
1. 2 parallel lines **2.** 1 line **3.** 2 intersecting lines
4. 2 parallel lines **5.** 2 intersecting lines **6.** 1 line

■ 7.5 Independent Practice pp. 377–379
7. b **9.** f **11.** e
13. No solution

15. Many solutions

17. No solution

19. No solution

21. Many solutions

23. No solution

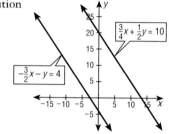

25. Sample answer: $y = 4x - 2$,
$3y = 12x - 6$
27. $y = -\frac{1}{2}x + 4$, $y = -\frac{1}{2}x - 4$
29. Many solutions: $n = 8$, no solution: $n \neq 8$
31. Many solutions: $n = -6$, no solution: $n \neq -6$
33. Horizontal and vertical lines
35. Male: $y = 89 + 1.1x$
Female: $y = 91 + 1.3x$
37. Married couples with children and single-person households; the 1st type is decreasing to 25% and the 2nd type is increasing to 25%.
39. $y = [(x + 10)2 - 18]\frac{1}{2} - x$. The equations represent the same line, so there are many solutions; any number may be chosen.

■ 7.5 Integrated Review p. 379
41. $(15, 7)$ **43.** $(4, 3)$ **45.** $(-1, -1)$ **47.** $(4, 1)$
49. $\left(\frac{8}{11}, \frac{43}{11}\right)$ **51.** $\left(2\frac{3}{4}, -\frac{3}{4}\right)$

■ 7.5 Mixed Review p. 380
1. 3 **3.** $\begin{bmatrix} 4 & 2 \\ 6 & 14 \end{bmatrix}$ **5.** $b = \frac{1}{4}(6 - 3a)$
7. Yes **9.** $y = -12x + 24$ **11.** Yes **13.** 3 **15.** -5
17. $\frac{8}{13}$ **19.** $y = \frac{1}{4}x - 3$

■ 7.6 Communicating About Algebra p. 383
A. II **B.**   **C.**

■ 7.6 Guided Practice p. 384
1. False, "any" should be "each." **2.** Point of intersection of 2 lines in the system

3. It is. $x + y \leq 2$, $1 + 0 \leq 2$;
$x - y > 0$, $1 - 0 > 0$; $y \geq -2$, $0 \geq -2$.
4. It is not. $x + y \leq 2$,
$4 + 3 \leq 2$; false
5. It is. $x + y \leq 2$, $1 + (-1) \leq 2$;
$x - y > 0$, $1 - (-1) > 0$; $y \geq -2$,
$-1 \geq -2$.
6. It is not. $x - y > 0$,
$-1 - 2 > 0$; false.

■ *7.6 Independent Practice pp. 384–386*

7. c **9.** d **11.** e

13.   **15.**

17.   **19.**

21.   **23.**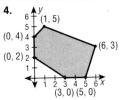

25. (0, 12), (9, 3), (5, 0), (0, 0)
27. (1, 4), (3, −2), (−2, −1)
29. $x \geq 2$
   $y \geq 1$
   $x \leq 5$
   $y \leq 7$

31. $y \geq 0$
   $y \leq \frac{3}{2}x$
   $y \leq -x + 5$

33. $0.25x + 0.15y \leq 45$,
   $x \geq 80$, $y \geq 120$

35. $x \geq 0$
   $y \geq 0$
   $y \leq -x + 3$

37. $y \leq x + 3$, $y \leq -x + 9$, $y \geq x - 3$,
$y \geq -x + 3$ **39.** $x \geq 0$, $x \leq 19$, $y \geq 0$,
$-\frac{2}{19}x + y \leq 6$

■ *7.6 Integrated Review p. 386*

41.   **43.**

45.   **47.**

■ *7.7 Communicating About Algebra p. 389*
0, 1200

■ *7.7 Guided Practice p. 390*

1. They define region of possible answers. **2.** It is evaluated at vertices formed by constraints. **3.** Find the minimum or maximum value of some quantity.

4.

5. $C = 14$ **6.** $C = 51$

■ *7.7 Independent Practice pp. 390–392*

7.   **9.**

11. $C = 0$, $C = 19$ **13.** $C = 12$, $C = 49$
15. $C = 0$, $C = 12$ **17.** $C = 27$, $C = 50$
19. $C = 0$, $C = 24$ **21.** $C = 6$, $C = 29$
23. A: 1200L, B: 1400L, maximum profit: $1420
25. A: 200, B: 50, maximum profit: $11,500

27.

29.

31.

33.

35.

37.

39. $(4, -3)$

41. $(-1, 4)$

7.7 Chapter Review pp. 394–396

1. Any point on the line $3x + 8y = 4$

3. $(-3, -1)$ **5.** $(4, 0)$

7. $(-3, 1)$ **9.** Any point on the line $x + 3y = 6$
11. No solution   **13.** $(20, 6)$ **15.** Any point on the line
$5x - 2y = 4$ **17.** No solution   **19.** $(0, 5)$ **21.** $(-1, -2)$
23. $(2, -3)$ **25.** $(2, 6)$ **27.** $\left(\frac{8}{3}, -\frac{16}{3}\right)$ **29.** $(27, 3)$

31.   **33.**

35.

37. $C = -1$, $C = 18$ **39.** $C = 0$, $C = 22$
41. $7\frac{1}{2}$ **43.** $y = -3x + 84$, $y = 3x + 65$ **45.** $71,875
47. The plane is off course.   **49.** Doubtful.

CHAPTER 8

8.1 Communicating About Algebra p. 402
A. 2, 4, 6; 2, 4, 8

B. 2^x; for $x > 2$, $y = 2^x$ pays more.   **C.** $768

8.1 Guided Practice p. 403
1. No, the bases are not the same.
2. a^{30}, Power of a Power   **3.** No, $a^5 \cdot a^3 = a^{5+3} = a^8$
4. No, $(-3b)^4 = (-3)^4 b^4 = 81b^4$ **5.** a^7 **6.** 1.90
7. y is doubled.   **8.** growth, growth, decay, decay

8.1 Independent Practice pp. 403–404
9. 4^5 or 1024   **11.** $(-9)^8$ or 43,046,721   **13.** x^6
15. $(2x + 3)^6$ **17.** 21^4 or 194,481   **19.** $25a^2$ **21.** $16a^3$
23. $(-3xy)^6$ or $729x^6y^6$ **25.** $3^2(-4)^4a^6$ or $2304a^6$
27. $18x^5$ **29.** $-a^5b^3$ **31.** $8x^5y^3$ **33.** $16a^{12}$ **35.** x^{10}
37. $-8t^5$ **39.** $a^7b^5c^6$ **41.** $-108x^7y^8$ **43.** 128   **45.** 32
47. 78,125   **49.** $(5 \cdot 2)^5$ **51.** 6

$$\overbrace{}^{n \text{ times}}$$
53. $(a^m)^n = a^m \cdot a^m \cdot a^m \ldots$
$$= a^{nm}$$
$$= a^{mn}$$

55. 85.18   **57.** 191.10   **59.** 8,629,188.75
61. $49,333,333\frac{1}{3}$ ft^3 **63.** 2   **65.** $\frac{1}{4}$ **67.** growth
69. decay

8.1 Integrated Review p. 405
71. 11   **73.** 65   **75.** $x = 6$, $y = 8$
77. $60 + 120 + 60 + 120 = 360$

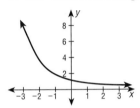

1. True, the base determines whether the term is positive or negative. **2.** 1, reciprocals **3.** 5 does not have a negative exponent. **4.** $\frac{12}{c}$, no **5.** (0, 1); no

7. $\frac{1}{x^9}$ **9.** $\frac{3}{x^2}$ **11.** $\frac{x^5}{4}$ **13.** $\frac{x^6}{y^7}$ **15.** $\frac{6}{x^2y^4}$ **17.** $\frac{x^{10}}{2y^{12}}$ **19.** $\frac{1}{16}$
21. $\frac{1}{4}$ **23.** 1 **25.** $\frac{1}{15,625}$ **27.** 1 **29.** $\frac{1}{27}$ **31.** $\frac{1}{25y^2}$ **33.** 1
35. $\frac{1}{16x^2y^2}$ **37.** $\frac{8}{a^9}$ **39.** $5a^4$ **41.** $32y^5$ **43.** Yes **45.** Yes
47. 1,112,968; 1,025,000; 943,985 **49.** About 8000 years
51. $700,000.00; $633,067.45, $572,534.85

53. 64 **55.** $\frac{4}{9}$ **57.** 7 **59.** a^{10} **61.** $-t^6$ **63.** m^5n^5

1. $\frac{1}{35}$ **3.** 55.5 **5.** $a = -\frac{5}{6}b + \frac{5}{3}$ **7.** 2
9. $y = -\frac{3}{2}x + 3$ **11.** $-x + 14$ **13.** -1
15. Yes **17.** Yes **19.** $\left(-\frac{2}{7}, \frac{11}{7}\right)$

A. Personal choice.
$$\left(\frac{a^{-2}}{b^5}\right)^{-3} = \frac{(a^{-2})^{-3}}{(b^5)^{-3}}$$
$$= \frac{(b^5)^3}{(a^{-2})^3}$$
$$= \frac{b^{15}}{a^{-6}}$$
$$= a^6b^{15}$$

1. No, the bases are not the same. **2.** x **3.** Subtract
4. Reciprocals, their product is 1.

5. 36 **7.** -1 **9.** 32 **11.** $\frac{1}{49}$ **13.** $\frac{125}{27}$ **15.** $\frac{16}{25}$ **17.** $\frac{16}{x^4}$
19. $\frac{1}{x^6}$ **21.** $\frac{1}{x^2}$ **23.** $\frac{10}{y}$ **25.** $6x^3y^4$ **27.** $\frac{7y^2}{3x^5}$ **29.** Yes
31. ≈ 3.05 **33.** 1.1837

35. x^{15} **37.** x^8 **39.** $\frac{1}{x^8}$ **41.** x^5y, 96 **43.** $36x^2y^4$, 576
45. x^3y^2, 200 **47.** r^2s^2, 144

A. 5.475%
B. 15,625; 78,125; 390,625; 1,953,125; 9,765,625; 48,828,125; 244,140,625; 1,220,703,125; 6,103,515,625; 3.0517578×10^{10}; 1.5258789×10^{11}; 7.6293945×10^{11}; 15 or greater **C.** 1.147791×10^{-5}

1. b **2.** 5 **3.** 6.2×10^4 **4.** 1×10^{-3}; one thousandth

5. 1,090,000 **7.** 6.21 **9.** 0.00852 **11.** 0.0867
13. 9.3×10^7 **15.** 1.637×10^9 **17.** 4.35×10^{-4}
19. 4.392×10^{-3} **21.** 1800 **23.** 8000 **25.** 3,600,000
27. 4,984,000,000,000; 4.984×10^{12} **29.** 3,098,100; 3.0981×10^6 **31.** 0.00000000000000000000011574317; $1.1574317 \times 10^{-22}$ **33.** 4×10^{-23} **35.** 4.8×10^6
37. $\approx 3.3 \times 10^8$ **39.** $\approx 4.8 \times 10^{-24}$ **41.** $\approx 1 \times 10^{25}$
43. 4.47×10^{14} **45.** $\approx 4.4 \times 10^7$ **47.** $\approx 308

49. $(9.1 \times 10^4)^4$, $(9.1 \times 10^{10})^2$, $(9.1 \times 10^5)^4$, $(9.1 \times 10^2)^{10}$
51. ≈ -14 **53.** 2.7×10^8

1. 0.2 **3.** $-5, 1$ **5.** $27x^7$ **7.**

9. x^{-3} or $\frac{1}{x^3}$ **11.** $-\frac{2}{3}$ **13.** 9

1. q^5 **2.** x^7 **3.** n^{10} **4.** $-t^6$ **5.** $-24s^5$ **6.** $\frac{5}{x^5}$
7. $\frac{1}{4b^2}$ **8.** 4 **9.** $\frac{2x}{y}$ **10.** $\frac{1}{p^5}$ **11.** $\frac{4q^7}{3}$ **12.** $\frac{4wz^4}{y^4}$
13. 36 **14.** $\frac{1}{4}$ **15.** $\frac{9}{16}$ **16.** $\frac{4}{25}$ **17.** 61.4656 **18.** 729
19. 10,079,000 **20.** 0.0005006 **21.** 3.78965×10^6
22. 1.79×10^{-6} **23.** $\approx 6.8 \times 10^{-2}$ **24.** $\approx 1.3 \times 10^2$
25. 381.51 **26.** ≈ 33.49 in.^{3}
27. 16, 8, 4, 2, 1

28. $\approx 38.81\%$

■ *8.5 Communicating About Algebra p. 428*
≈0.165

■ *8.5 Guided Practice p. 429*
1. • Write a verbal model.
  • Assign labels to the model.
  • Write an algebraic model.
  • Solve the algebraic model.
  • Answer the question.

2.

| Number of flowers to visit | = | Number of flowers per pound of honey | • | Number of pounds of honey |

3. Number of flowers to visit = n

Number of flowers per pound
of honey = $\dfrac{(45 \text{ to } 64) \times 10^6}{2.2}$

Number of pounds of honey = 500

4. $n = \dfrac{(45 \text{ to } 64) \times 10^6}{2.2} \cdot 500$

5. 1.0×10^{10} to 1.5×10^{10}
6. 1.0×10^{10} to 1.5×10^{10}

■ *8.5 Independent Practice pp. 429–430*
7. 2.6×10^3 seconds **9.** Louisiana: ≈\$18.00, Gadsden:
≈\$340.00 **11.** ≈6.497×10^9, ≈7.094×10^9,
≈7.197×10^9, ≈7.100×10^9, ≈7.091×10^9
13. 2.5×10^{-9} cm^3 **15.** ≈5.42×10^{-4} second **17.** ≈71

■ *8.5 Integrated Review p. 431*
19. $24y^5$ **21.** $\dfrac{4}{b^4}$ **23.** $42x^2y^9$ **25.** $\dfrac{y^2}{25x^6}$ **27.** 6.5×10^{-7}
29. 2,650,000,000,000,000 **31.** 2.562×10^4

■ *8.6 Communicating About Algebra p. 434*
For the first 3 years plan B pays more. After 3 years, the
increases of plan A are greater than the \$1000 of plan B.
Each increase after that is greater than the previous one,
so choose plan A.
A. Exponential **B.** Linear

■ *8.6 Guided Practice p. 435*
1. True **2.** \$1628.89 **3.** $1 + r$ **4.** % the amount
increases

■ *8.6 Independent Practice pp. 435–436*
5. \$140.26 **7.** \$362.54 **9.** c **11.** a
13. $P = 9{,}580{,}000(1.0194)^t$ **15.** a
17. $y = 334{,}000(1.034)^x$ **19.** $y = 17.46t + 266$,
$y = 266(1.062)^t$; no

■ *8.6 Integrated Review p. 437*
21. $-\dfrac{3}{8}$ **23.** 64 **25.** 20.01 **27.** 4.62×10^{-3}
29. 6.75×10^7 **31.** c

■ *8.7 Communicating About Algebra p. 441*
A. Both decrease, but $y = 0.9^x$ decreases less rapidly.

B. ≈1006.6 pounds

■ *8.7 Guided Practice p. 442*
1. Base of power < 1. a, d **2.** 4% **3.** $E = 75{,}000(0.98)^t$
4. ≈2800, no

■ *8.7 Independent Practice pp. 442–443*
5. ≈36 **7.** 1240, ≈1215, ≈1191, ≈1167, ≈1144, ≈1121,
≈1098, ≈1076

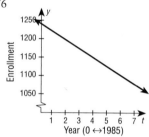

9. $D = 18.8(0.97)^t$; ≈ 13.9 million

■ *8.7 Integrated Review p. 443*
11. d **13.** b **15.** Voyager 1

■ *8.7 Chapter Review pp. 446–448*
1. b^9 **3.** a^9 **5.** $16m^5$ **7.** $128x^3y^2$ **9.** 1 **11.** 1 **13.** p^2
15. 4 **17.** $\dfrac{1}{4p^9q^3}$ **19.** $\dfrac{6a^5}{b^4}$ **21.** $18pq^6$ **23.** $81w^8$
25. 0.006667 **27.** 0.000000981 **29.** 768,000
31. 5.88×10^{-2} **33.** 2.33×10^{-8} **35.** 7.95×10^3
37. $\dfrac{1}{27}$ **39.** 6 **41.** $\dfrac{2}{5}$ **43.** 2×10^6 **45.** 5×10^{-9}
47. 9×10^{-13} **49.** ≈\$4.425 $\times 10^9$, ≈\$6460
51. $125m^3$, $\dfrac{125}{8}m^3$ **53.** 1,482,200,000,000 **55.** ≈0.220
57. 48% **59.** 1988–1990 **61.** b **63.** d **65.** 400
67. No, because the outer portion of A would then be
visible beyond the circumference of B.

CHAPTER 9 ─────────

■ *9.1 Communicating About Algebra p. 454*
A. 7.21 **B.** 0.76 **C.** 0.56, −3.56

■ 9.1 Guided Practice p. 455

1. True

2. a. True, -1
 b. True, 0
 c. True, 25 has 5 and -5
 d. False

3. 5, -5, ± 5 **4.** 8 and -2 **5.** 9, $\frac{1}{4}$, 0.01

6. Yes, no, no; An irrational number cannot be represented by a fraction.

■ 9.1 Independent Practice pp. 455–457

7. 8, -8 **9.** None **11.** $\frac{2}{3}$, $-\frac{2}{3}$ **13.** 0.4, -0.4 **15.** -16

17. 3.32 **19.** 10 **21.** 6 **23.** 6.48 **25.** 0.2 **27.** $\frac{9}{18}$ or $\frac{1}{2}$

29. $-\frac{1}{8}$ **31.** 3 **33.** $\sqrt{-23}$ is undefined **35.** 7.12, -5.12

37. -11.24, -2.76 **39.** 5.2 **41.** 4

43. ≈ 360 ft by ≈ 360 ft **45.** $\sqrt{3}$ in. or ≈ 1.73 in.

47. ≈ 11.2 ft **49.** ≈ 362.8 ft

■ 9.1 Integrated Review p. 457

51. miles **53.** $9a^2$ **55.** $4x^4y^2$ **57.** 3, -3 **59.** 2

■ 9.2 Communicating About Algebra p. 460

113 feet per second

■ 9.2 Guided Practice p. 461

1. b, d **2.** As is, -3 **3.** As is, $\frac{1}{2}$

4. $-x^2 - 8x + 4 = 0$, -1 **5.** $\pm\sqrt{17}$ **6.** 0

7. No real solution **8.** $\pm\sqrt{6}$

■ 9.2 Independent Practice pp. 461–463

9. ± 3 **11.** ± 10 **13.** ± 11 **15.** ± 3 **17.** ± 4 **19.** ± 4

21. ± 4.24 **23.** ± 2.45 **25.** ± 3.16 **27.** ± 0.58

29. 2 seconds **31.** ≈ 5.59 seconds **33.** 5 ft **35.** 1978 and 1986, 1974 and 1990 **37.** 0.10 mm, 0.22 mm, 0.15 mm

39. ≈ 1.36 seconds

■ 9.2 Integrated Review p. 463

41. 49 **43.** -40 **45.** 8 **47.** 8 **49.** 36

■ 9.2 Mixed Review p. 464

1. $\frac{1}{a^4}$ **3.** $p = \frac{2+q}{1+q}$ **5.** -30 **7.** 5 **9.** 1.299×10^9

11. Yes **13.** $y = \frac{5}{2}x + 4$ **15.** $2x^2 + 4x$ **17.** $-3, 9$

19. 7.92×10^{-2}

■ 9.3 Communicating About Algebra p. 467

A. The axis of symmetry $x = 0$, is the same; the graphs all open upward.

B. The axis of symmetry $x = 0$, is the same; the graphs all open downward.

■ 9.3 Guided Practice p. 468

1. $y = -x^2 + 4x - 3$ **2.** parabola **3.** if $a > 0$, graph opens up; if $a < 0$ graph opens down. **4.** True; $x = \frac{-b}{2a}$ is a vertical line **5.** $(-1, -4)$ **6.** $x = \frac{1}{2}$

■ 9.3 Independent Practice pp. 468–469

7. Up $(0, 4)$ **9.** Down, $(0, 0)$ **11.** Down, $\left(-\frac{1}{10}, \frac{201}{20}\right)$

13. $x = -\frac{1}{3}$, $\left(-\frac{1}{3}, \frac{11}{3}\right)$ **15.** $x = -\frac{1}{2}$, $\left(-\frac{1}{2}, 9\right)$

17. $x = -\frac{7}{4}$, $\left(-\frac{7}{4}, -\frac{217}{8}\right)$

19.

$\left(-\frac{1}{2}, \frac{7}{4}\right)$

21.

$\left(\frac{3}{2}, \frac{-9}{2}\right)$

23.

$\left(\frac{1}{4}, \frac{29}{8}\right)$

25.

$\left(\frac{1}{8}, \frac{95}{16}\right)$

27.

$\left(\frac{1}{5}, \frac{-9}{5}\right)$

29.

$\left(\frac{-5}{6}, \frac{61}{12}\right)$

31.

$(-3, -4)$

33.

$\left(-3, \frac{17}{2}\right)$

35.

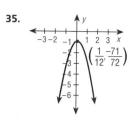

$\left(\frac{1}{12}, \frac{-71}{72}\right)$

37. No. At 72 ft, the 50° shot-put is on the ground while the 45° shot-put is in the air; at 72.8 ft the 40° shot-put is on the ground while the 45° shot-put is in the air. **39.** Yes, $\approx 45°$ **41.** It decreased gold production.

9.3 Integrated Review p. 470
43. ± 4 **45.** ± 5 **47.** ± 2 **49.** b **51.** f **53.** d **55.** -24 **57.** 12 **59.** 6

9.4 Communicating About Algebra p. 474
In ≈ 15.8 seconds

9.4 Guided Practice p. 475
1. False **2.** See top of page 474. **3.** $a = -1, b = 9, c = 1$
4. $1, -2$ **5.**

6. They are the same.

9.4 Independent Practice pp. 475–477
7. $-3x^2 + 5x - 9 = 0$ **9.** $x^2 + 3x - 9 = 0$ **11.** 17
13. 64 **15.** $3, \frac{1}{4}$ **17.** $-\frac{1}{2}, -3$ **19.** $\frac{-1 + \sqrt{11}}{5} \approx 0.46,$

$\frac{-1 - \sqrt{11}}{5} \approx -0.86$ **21.** $\frac{-10 + \sqrt{70}}{6} \approx -0.27,$

$\frac{-10 - \sqrt{70}}{6} \approx -3.06$ **23.** $25, -25$ **25.** $\frac{3 + \sqrt{11}}{2} \approx 3.16,$

$\frac{3 - \sqrt{11}}{2} \approx -0.16$ **27.** None

29. $4, -5$ **31.** $\frac{1}{2}, -\frac{3}{2}$
33. ≈ 8.1 seconds; yes, the rock would be traveling at ≈ 90 mph and could do a lot of damage to whatever it hit.
35. 2.2 seconds **37.** 1.45 hours
39. 1994

9.4 Integrated Review p. 477
41. 2 **43.** Is. **45.** Is not.

47.

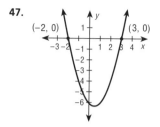

(−2, 0)   (3, 0)

9.4 Mid-Chapter Self-Test p. 478
1. ± 8 **2.** ± 11 **3.** ± 0.08 **4.** $\pm \frac{7}{10}$ **5.** $\pm \frac{1}{9}$ **6.** ± 0.1 **7.** 2
8. 1 **9.** 2.83 **10.** 1.5 **11.** 0.32 **12.** 7.07 **13.** ± 9 **14.** ± 5
15. ± 4 **16.** $\pm \sqrt{72} \approx \pm 8.49$ **17.** $\pm \frac{5}{2}$
18. $\pm \sqrt{162} \approx \pm 12.73$ **19.** $(0, -4); 2, -2$ **20.** $(1, 4);$
$-1, 3$ **21.** $(0, 2); 2, -2$ **22.** $(0, -3); 1, -1$ **23.** $6, -5$
24. -4 **25.** $\frac{3 + \sqrt{17}}{2} \approx 3.56, \frac{3 - \sqrt{17}}{2} \approx -0.56$
26. $\frac{-5 + \sqrt{33}}{2} \approx 0.37, \frac{-5 - \sqrt{33}}{2} \approx -5.37$ **27.** 5 in.
28. 10 cm **29.** ≈ 1.37 seconds **30.** ≈ 1.09 seconds

9.5 Communicating About Algebra p. 481
A. $c > 4, c = 4, c < 4$
B. Graph has 0, 1 or 2 x-intercepts.

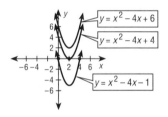

$y = x^2 - 4x + 6$

$y = x^2 - 4x + 4$

$y = x^2 - 4x - 1$

9.5 Guided Practice p. 482
1. $x = \frac{-b \pm \sqrt{b^2 - 4ac}}{2a}$

2. If the discriminant is negative, there is no solution. If the discriminant is 0, there is one solution. If the discriminant is positive, there are two solutions.
3. 64, 2 **4.** b **5.** c **6.** a

9.5 Independent Practice pp. 482–484
7. 2 **9.** 1 **11.** None **13.** No, the discriminant is negative. **15.** Yes, the discriminant is positive.
17. Yes, the discriminant is positive; no, the discriminant is negative.
19. You need to make some changes. In 5 years the profit from the model would be $2050 thousand; the board of directors expects a profit of $2551 thousand in 5 years.
21. 2001–2002

9.5 Integrated Review p. 484
23. c **25.** b **27.** b **29.** d

■ *9.5 Mixed Review p. 485*

1. $\frac{x}{y}$ **3.** 6 **5.** $\frac{6}{7}$ **7.**

9. 8 **11.** Yes

13. $-\frac{33}{4} < x < \frac{31}{4}$ **15.** $x + 2y = 1$ **17.** $y = 6$
19. $x - y = 16$

■ *9.6 Communicating About Algebra p. 488*

13.5 in. by 13.5 in. by 54 in.

■ *9.6 Guided Practice p. 489*

1. • Sketch the graph of the parabola.
• Test 2 points, 1 inside and 1 outside the U-shape.
• Shade the region containing the point that is a solution.

2–4.

3. Points vary. (0, 0) is a solution.

■ *9.6 Independent Practice pp. 489–491*

5. Is not. **7.** Is. **9.** d **11.** a **13.** c

15.

17.

19.

21.

23.

25. b, VVS2 **27.** ≈$200 million

29. a, The number in the Americas will be less than the number in the world.

■ *9.6 Integrated Review p. 491*

31. $x > 9$ **33.** $x \le 4$ **35.**

37.

39.

41.

■ *9.7 Communicating About Algebra p. 494*

$A = \pi(r)(r + 1)$

■ *9.7 Guided Practice p. 495*

1. See page 492 for examples. **2.** Quadratic **3.** Absolute value **4.** See page 492 for a graph of each model.

■ *9.7 Independent Practice pp. 495–497*

5. Quadratic **7.** Absolute value

9. Quadratic

11. Linear

13. Quadratic

15. c

17. Linear, $d = 2.6M$ **19.** $P = 38,680,000(1.027)^t$
21. $D = 2,766,000,000(1.12)^t$

■ *9.7 Integrated Review p. 497*

23. $3x - y = 11$ **25.** $x + 2y = 8$ **27.** ± 12

■ *9.7 Chapter Review pp. 499–502*

1. 5 **3.** 6.86 **5.** 5.66 **7.** $\frac{1}{3}$ **9.** ± 12 **11.** $\pm\frac{9}{4}$ **13.** d **15.** c

17.

19.

21. $\frac{1}{8}$ **23.** 6 **25.** $-\frac{3}{2}, 2$ **27.**

29.

31. Quadratic

33. Exponential

35. ≈ 10.24 ft
37. 6.41 km **39.** Yes; Connie can throw over the building, but Muriel can't. **41.** 1991 **43.** South America
45. North America **47.** No **49.** Asia, North America

■ *9.7 Cumulative Review for Chapters 7–9*
pp. 504–505

1. (4, 1) **3.** $\left(-3, \frac{1}{4}\right)$ **5.** (4, 7) **7.** c **9.** b
11.

13.

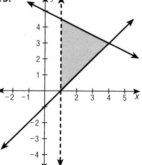

15. $\frac{9}{4w^2}$ **17.** q^6
19. 9.394×10^5; 939,400 **21.** 3, -3 **23.** 9, -7
25. $\dfrac{-3 + \sqrt{45}}{2}, \dfrac{-3 - \sqrt{45}}{2}$

27.

29.

31.

33. 60 Style X and 20 Style Y dresses

35. 2.68×10^2 ft^3; 268 ft^3 **37.** $10.31, $26.28
39. 5 seconds

CHAPTER 10

■ 10.1 Communicating About Algebra p. 511
A. Polygon refers to something with *many* sides; **monopoly** refers to ownership of something by *one*; **binocular** refers to something with *two* telescopes; **tricycle** refers to a vehicle with *three* wheels.
B. $(x^3 + x^2) + (-x^3 - 1)$

■ 10.1 Guided Practice p. 512
1. See page 508. **2.** $-3x^3, -2x^2, 4x, -5$
3. $-7, 0, 12, -31$ **4.** $10y^3 - 3y^2 + 15y - 6$ **5.** 3
6. $-x^2 + 4x + 7$

■ 10.1 Independent Practice pp. 512–514
7. Linear, binomial   **9.** Quadratic, polynomial
11. $4x^2 + 2$ **13.** $3x^2 + x + 3$
15. $12x^3 + 11x^2 + 3x - 12$ **17.** $-7z^2 + 7z - 3$

19. $2x^4 + 6x^2 - 2x + 2$ **21.** $z^3 + 1$
23. $x^2 + 2x - 3$ **25.** $-7x^3 + 4x + 10$
27. $5x^2 - 4x + 12$ **29.** $x - 24$
31. $3x^3 - 2x^2 - 2x - 1$ **33.** $4t^2 + 20$
35. $2x^2 - 2x$
37. $P = 0.3t^2 + 0.36t + 60.5$
39. $F = 1297.9t + 77,268$

■ 10.1 Integrated Review p. 514
41. $5x - 2y$ **43.** $\frac{9}{2}x - \frac{3}{2}y$ **45.** $\begin{bmatrix} 2x^2 & -x \\ -7 + 9x & -3x^2 + 4 \end{bmatrix}$

47. $\begin{bmatrix} 20x - 13 & 10 - 3x \\ x^3 + 7y^3 & 4y^2 - 11y + 2 \end{bmatrix}$ **49.** 5 units

■ 10.2 Communicating About Algebra p. 517
A.

B.

■ 10.2 Guided Practice p. 518
1. $(2x - 3)(x + 4) = 2x(x + 4) - 3(x + 4)$
$= 2x^2 + 8x - 3x - 12$
$= 2x^2 + 5x - 12$
2. $x^3 + 1$ **3.** $2x^2 - x - 15$
4. F: Product of the First terms
   O: Product of the Outer terms
   I: Product of the Inner terms
   L: Product of the Last terms

■ 10.2 Independent Practice pp. 518–520
5. $-6x^2 + 14x$ **7.** $-2x^3 + 3x^2$
9. $20x^5 - 8x^4 + 4x^3$ **11.** $15x^2 + 11x - 14$
13. $x^2 - 16$ **15.** $2x^2 - 50$
17. $x^2 + 6x + 5$

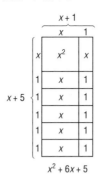

19. $x^2 + 3x + 2$

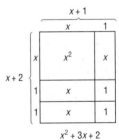

21. $2x^2 + 7x + 6$ **23.** $3x^2 - 8x - 3$

25. $6x^3 - x^2 - 11x + 5$ **27.** $x^4 - x^3 + 5x^2 - 9x - 36$
29. $x^2 - x - 12$ **31.** $2x^2 + 7x - 30$
33. $4x^2 - \frac{1}{5}x - 6$ **35.** $\frac{1}{4}x^2 + \frac{1}{2}x - 6$
37. $x^3 - 25x + 36$ **39.** $18\frac{3}{4}, 24, 29\frac{3}{4}, 36, 42\frac{3}{4}, 50$
41. No; if $x = 18$, $A = 4400\pi \neq 2(512)\,\pi$ **43.** d
45. $A = \frac{1}{2}(6x - 5)(x + 4) = 3x^2 + \frac{19}{2}x - 10$

■ 10.2 Integrated Review p. 520
47. $(-3)^4$ **49.** $(-2)^2 x^3$ **51.** $\frac{4}{5} \cdot \frac{4}{5} \cdot \frac{4}{5} \cdot \frac{4}{5}$
53. $x^2 \cdot x^2 \cdot x^2$ **55.** $7x - 8$ **57.** $-4z + 12$ **59.** $\frac{1}{3}x^7$
61. $\frac{5x}{y^3}$

■ 10.2 Mixed Review p. 521
1. \$933.24   **3.** $\frac{1}{x^2 y}$ **5.** -1 **7.** -2 **9.** -1 **11.** 9.216
13. Yes   **15.** No   **17.** 7.94×10^{-3} **19.** $\frac{2}{5}$

■ 10.3 Communicating About Algebra p. 524
A. Yes, $(x - 2)^2$
B. No, the coefficient of x^2 is not a perfect square.
C. Yes, $4(x + 3)^2$

■ 10.3 Guided Practice p. 525
1. False, $(a - b)(a - b) = a^2 - ab - ab + b^2$
$$= a^2 - 2ab + b^2$$
$$\neq (a - b)^2$$
2. $2ab$ **3.** $(x - 4)^2, x^2 - 8x + 16$
4. $(x - 3)(x + 3) = x^2 - 9$;
   $(x + 3)^2 = x^2 + 6x + 9$;
   $(x - 3)^2 = x^2 - 6x + 9$

■ 10.3 Independent Practice pp. 525–527
5. $x^2 + 4x + 4$ **7.** $4n^2 + 4n + 1$

 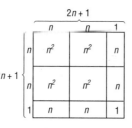

9. $4x^2 + 8x + 4$

11. $n^2 + 12n + 36$ **13.** $4x^2 + 4x + 1$
15. $9t^2 - 12t + 4$ **17.** $x^2 - 25$
19. $4x^2 - 4$ **21.** $a^2 - 4b^2$
23. $x^2 + 12x + 36$ **25.** $a^2 - 4a + 4$
27. $4x^2 - 20xy + 25y^2$ **29.** $(x + 2)^2, x^2 + 4x + 4$; square of a binomial   **31.** 75%; 25%
33. Large: $P = 5w, A = \frac{3}{2}w^2$.

     Small: $P = \frac{10}{3}w, A = \frac{2}{3}w^2$
35. $1000 + 2000r + 1000r^2$ **37.** $49 \neq 25$

■ 10.3 Integrated Review p. 527
39. 81   **41.** 25   **43.** 1   **45.** $\frac{x}{y}$ **47.** $3x^3 y^2$ **49.** $24 - 8x + x^2$
51. e   **53.** b

■ 10.4 Communicating About Algebra p. 530
A. $(3t)^2 - 7^2 = (3t + 7)(3t - 7)$
B. $x^2 - 2(8x) + 8^2 = (x - 8)^2$
C. $(2y)^2 + 2(18y) + 9^2 = (2y + 9)^2$
D. $(11x)^2 - 10^2 = (11x + 10)(11x - 10)$

■ 10.4 Guided Practice p. 531
1. Each is the reverse process of the other.
2. $3(x^3 - 2x^2 + 3)$
3. $2x(2x - 3) + 3(2x - 3) = (2x - 3)(2x + 3)$
4. $4x^2 - 25 = (2x - 5)(2x + 5)$
   $x^2 + 14x + 49 = (x + 7)^2$
   $x^2 - 16x + 64 = (x - 8)^2$

■ 10.4 Integrated Practice pp. 531–533
5. $6x^3$ **7.** $8x^2$ **9.** $4xy$ **11.** $2(x^2 - 2)$
13. $4(a - 3)$ **15.** $6(4x^2 - 3)$
17. $7u(3u - 2)$ **19.** $4(x^2 - 2x + 2)$
21. $(y + 12)(y - 12)$ **23.** $(3x - 5y)^2$
25. $\left(u + \frac{1}{4}\right)\left(u - \frac{1}{4}\right)$ **27.** $(4 - z)(14 + z)$
29. The graph of the linear model shows that the lower the price is, the greater the number of TV sets sold.
31. $a = 4, b = 3, c = 5$ **33.** $a = 8, b = 15, c = 17$, or $a = 8, b = 6, c = 10$ **35.** $kx(Q - x)$ **37.** You will have to pick it up at the post office.

■ 10.4 Integrated Review p. 533
39. $28y - 21y^2$ **41.** $2z^2 + 3z - 35$ **43.** $36r^2 - 25s^2$
45. $\pm\sqrt{3}$ **47.** 3   **49.** ± 3 **51.** 12

■ 10.4 Mid-Chapter Self-Test p. 534
   1. $-3x^2 + 5x + 1$ **2.** $-3x^2 + 11x - 8$

3. $4x^2 - 4x + 4$ **4.** $4x^2 - 7x + 5$
5. $9x^2 + 21x + 10$ **6.** $8x^2 + 30x - 50$
7. $2x^3 - x^2 - x + 2$ **8.** $10x^3 + 19x^2 + x - 3$
9. $x^2 - x - 6$ **10.** $x^2 - 9x + 18$
11. $-2x^2 + 5x + 12$ **12.** $x^2 + 7x + 12$
13. $4x^2 + 12x + 9$ **14.** $16x^2 - 40x + 25$
15. $4x^2 - 36$ **16.** $x^2 - 49$
17. $(2x + 7)(2x - 7)$ **18.** $3(x + 6)(x - 6)$
19. $(x - 1)^2$ **20.** $7(x + 3)^2$
21. $(3x + 2)^2$ **22.** $(x + 13)(x - 13)$
23. $M = 83{,}307 + 239.9t^2$
24. $(x + 1)^3 + (x + 3)^3 + (x + 5)^3$
25. $(3x + 2)^2$ **26.** $(2x + 16)(2x + 20)$

■ 10.5 Communicating About Algebra p.537
A. $(x + 4)(x + 3)$ **B.** $(a - 5)(a - 1)$ **C.** $(3n - 2)(n + 2)$

■ 10.5 Guided Practice p. 538
1. $(x - 1)(x - 3)$ Since c is positive, its factors must have the same sign.
2. $(x + 3)(x - 1)$ Since c is negative, its factors must have opposite signs.   **3.** $b^2 - 4ac$
4. No. The discriminant must be the square of an integer.

■ 10.5 Independent Practice pp. 538–540
5. a   **7.** a   **9.** b   **11.** $(x + 4)(x - 1)$
13. $(x + 6)(x - 3)$ **15.** $(x - 6)(x - 4)$
17. $(x + 10)(x + 5)$ **19.** $(y - 15)(y - 20)$
21. $(3x + 5)(x + 1)$ **23.** $(2x - 7)(x + 3)$
25. $(y - 12)(y - 4)$ **27.** $(2x + 3)(x - 2)$
29. Cannot factor   **31.** $2(3x - 2)(x - 1)$
33. $(7x + 8)(2x - 5)$ **35.** $x + 5$, $x - 1$
37. A = 1, B = −4, C = 8, D = −3
39. I = 2, J = −9, K = 5, L = −6
41. Q = 6, R = −11, S = 7, T = −2
43 a. Ivory Mask   **45. c.** Patterned Vessel
47. $(x + 3)(x + 1)$
49. $P = -\frac{1}{20}t + 1$; $1.00, 95¢, 90¢, 85¢, 80¢, 75¢, 70¢, 65¢

■ 10.5 Integrated Review p. 540
51. $-2y^2 - 2y$ **53.** $v^2 - 7v + 6$ **55.** 1

■ 10.6 Communicating About Algebra p. 543
A. 1, 2; Factoring, easily factored
B. $1 + \sqrt{2} \approx 2.41$, $1 - \sqrt{2} \approx -0.41$; quadratic formula, not factorable
C. $\sqrt{3} \approx 1.73$, $-\sqrt{3} \approx -1.73$; square roots, no x term
A–C. x-intercepts are solutions.

■ 10.6 Guided Practice p. 544
1. $a = 0$ or $b = 0$ **2.** 2, −1   **3.** 0, $-\frac{4}{3}$ **4.** 0, −1
5. False. The product of any number and its reciprocal is 1; so neither factor has to equal 1.
6. True. A product cannot equal 0, unless one of the factors is 0.

■ 10.6 Independent Practice pp. 544–545
7. −1, −2   **9.** −3, −4   **11.** −6, 1   **13.** $-\frac{3}{2}$, −1
15. $-\frac{1}{3}$, −2   **17.** f   **19.** g   **21.** d   **23.** e   **25.** 0, 9   **27.** 3, 4
29. 4   **31.** 0, $-\frac{1}{2}$ **33.** 6   **35.** $\frac{8}{23}$, 2   **37.** 1178 pounds
39. b

■ 10.6 Integrated Review p. 546
41. $4x^2 + 33x - 27$ **43.** $9x^2 + 18x - 7$
45. $x^2 + \frac{7}{4}x + \frac{9}{2}$ **47.** Is.   **49.** Is not.   **51.** Is not.
53. $\frac{7 + \sqrt{13}}{2} \approx 5.30$, $\frac{7 - \sqrt{13}}{2} \approx 1.70$
55. $\frac{11 + \sqrt{409}}{6} \approx 5.20$, $\frac{11 - \sqrt{409}}{6} \approx -1.54$
57. $\frac{17 + \sqrt{73}}{18} \approx 1.42$, $\frac{17 - \sqrt{73}}{18} \approx 0.47$
59. In 10 seconds. One of the factors must equal zero; The factor $(t - 10)$ will give a positive answer.
61. They are the same graph.

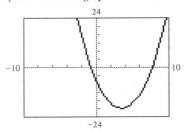

■ 10.6 Mixed Review p. 547
1. $\frac{xy}{3}$ **3.** $\frac{x}{3}$ **5.** $m = \frac{-2n + 3}{4}$ **7.** $2x^4$ **9.** 80
11. $-7 \le x \le 1$ **13.** 8, −8   **15.**

17. No   **19.** $(-3, 2)$

■ 10.7 Communicating About Algebra p. 551
A. 4, 2; factoring, easy to factor
B. $\pm\sqrt{6}$; find square root, no x term
C. 0, 6; factoring, easy to factor
D. $3 + \sqrt{17}$, $3 - \sqrt{17}$; completing the square, $a = 1$ and b is even
E. $3 + \sqrt{6}$, $3 - \sqrt{6}$; find square root, no x term
F. 4, −1; factoring, easy to factor

■ 10.7 Guided Practice p. 552
1. b   **2.** $2 + \sqrt{12}$, $2 - \sqrt{12}$; no difference   **3.** 9   **4.** See chart on page 550.

■ 10.7 Independent Practice pp. 552–553
5. 81   **7.** 36   **9.** $\frac{49}{4}$ **11.** 1, −i1   **13.** 21, 3   **15.** $\frac{1}{2}$, $-\frac{7}{2}$
17. $\frac{1}{3} + \frac{\sqrt{28}}{3}$, $\frac{1}{3} - \frac{\sqrt{28}}{3}$ **19.** $-\frac{1}{2} + \frac{\sqrt{5}}{2}$, $-\frac{1}{2} - \frac{\sqrt{5}}{2}$

21. $-\frac{1}{2} + \frac{\sqrt{10}}{2}, -\frac{1}{2} - \frac{\sqrt{10}}{2}$ **23.** $5, -2$

25. $-\frac{1}{3}, -1$ **27.** $-1 + \sqrt{3}, -1 - \sqrt{3}$

29. $\frac{3}{2} + \frac{\sqrt{13}}{2}, \frac{3}{2} - \frac{\sqrt{13}}{2}$

31. $-3 + \frac{\sqrt{132}}{2}, -3 - \frac{\sqrt{132}}{2}$

33. $-5, -2$ **35.** $0, \frac{5}{3}$

37. $-\frac{5}{9} + \frac{\sqrt{244}}{18}, -\frac{5}{9} - \frac{\sqrt{244}}{18}$

39. $0, 2$ **41.** $\frac{3}{4}, \frac{1}{2}$ **43.** $-10 + \frac{\sqrt{360}}{2}, -10 - \frac{\sqrt{360}}{2}$

45. No, the crest is 3 ft above sea level; Jared had 2 ft of his body below sea level and 3 ft 4 in. of his body above sea level.

47. ≈ 174 ft

■ *10.7 Integrated Review p. 554*

49. ± 4 **51.** ± 5 **53.** ± 3 **55.** $(2, 0), (4, 0)$

57. $(-1, 0)$

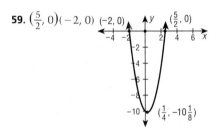

59. $\left(\frac{5}{2}, 0\right)(-2, 0)$

61. $3(x - 6)(x + 1)$ **63.** $20(7y + 3)(y + 2)$

65. $12(a + 1)(a + 2)$ **67.** d **69.** b

71.

73.

■ *10.7 Chapter Review pp. 556–558*

1. Quadratic, binomial   **3.** Constant, monomial

5. Quartic, polynomial   **7.** Cubic, binomial

9. $2x^2 + 5x + 7$ **11.** $3x^2 + x + 5$

13. $-3x^2 + 8x - 7$ **15.** $x^3 + 3x^2 - 4x + 10$

17. $x^2 - 15x + 50$ **19.** $x^3 + 4x^2 - 9x + 18$

21. $7x^2 + 2x - 3$ **23.** $x - 2$

25. $-3x^2 + 3x - 5$ **27.** $-5x^2 - 8x + 5$

29. $3x^3 - 2x^2 - 9x + 2$ **31.** $8x^3 - 4x^2 - 8x + 4$

33. $x^2 - 225$ **35.** $x^2 + 4x + 4$

37. $(x - 5)(x + 3)$ **39.** $(x - 8)(x + 8)$

41. cannot factor   **43.** $(x + 5)^2$

45. $4(x - 5)(x - 3)$ **47.** $9, 12$ **49.** $10, 20$ **51.** $\pm\frac{7}{6}$

53. $7 + \frac{\sqrt{52}}{2}, 7 - \frac{\sqrt{52}}{2}$ **55.** $11, 60, 61$ **57.** 1.25 seconds

59. $\frac{\pi}{6}x^3 - \frac{3\pi}{2}x^2 + \frac{9\pi}{2}x - \frac{9\pi}{2}$

61. $S = 0.14x^2 - 3.33x + 58.4$

63. No, it is related by a quadratic model since the x term is squared. The distance needed to stop increases quadratically with an increase in speed.

65. 1984

CHAPTER 11 ———————

■ *11.1 Communicating About Algebra p. 564*

A. 18; multiply both sides by 4, simplify

B. $\frac{25}{4}$; reciprocal property, multiply both sides by 5, simplify

C. $5, -2$; cross multiply, simplify, write in standard form, factor, Zero Product Property

■ *11.1 Guided Practice p. 565*

1. a and d are extremes; b and c are means **2.** c **3.** b

4. $\frac{8}{5}$ **5.** $\frac{10}{3}$ **6.** $-2, 1$

■ *11.1 Independent Practice pp. 565–566*

7. $\frac{8}{3}$ **9.** $0, \frac{9}{5}$ **11.** $\frac{24}{5}$ **13.** $\frac{16}{3}$ **15.** $\frac{-18}{5}$ **17.** 4 **19.** $6, -1$

21. $1, 2$ **23.** -2 **25.** $\approx 4{,}039{,}000$ **27.** 420 in. or 35 ft

29. between 60 to 70 mi

■ *11.1 Integrated Review p. 567*

31. 3 **33.** $-\frac{7}{2}$ **35.** 0.23 **37.** 0.0025 **39.** 75% **41.** 300%

43. 6 **45.** $\frac{-y}{7x}$ **47.** b

■ *11.2 Communicating About Algebra p. 570*

100 are in a meter, 100 are in a dollar, occurs every 100 years; century, centavo, centurion

■ *11.2 Guided Practice p. 571*

1. $160, 16 = 0.10(160)$ **2.** 200 **3.** 117 **4.** 190%

■ *11.2 Independent Practice pp. 571–573*

5. 20.7 **7.** 26% **9.** 24 m **11.** 121.8 mi **13.** 70 ft

15. 150 dollars **17.** 22% **19.** 4% **21.** 28.6%

23. $13.3\%, 86.7\%$ **25.** $25\%, 75\%$ **27.** ≈ 485

29. 114,155,250; 100,456,620; 88% **31.** 26.2%
33. a and c **35.** $15.96

■ *11.2 Integrated Review p. 573*
37. 0.04 **39.** 0.69 **41.** 13.4% **43.** $\frac{1}{2}$ **45.** $\frac{25}{27}$ **47.** $\frac{9}{16}$
49. 4, -4 **51.** $-\frac{3}{2}, \frac{1}{2}$ **53.** $\frac{7}{2}, -2$

■ *11.2 Mixed Review p. 574*
1. $-2x + y - 9 = 0$ **3.** -4 **5.** $x^2 + 4x - 7$ **7.** $\frac{10}{11}$
9. 19.6608 **11.** No **13.** 44 **15.** $-\frac{2}{3}$ **17.** 0.375
19. 1.8×10^5

■ *11.3 Communicating About Algebra p. 577*
A. 409,480 pounds **B.** Hydrogen is flammable.

■ *11.3 Guided Practice p. 578*
1. Examples vary; distance and rate when time is constant, circumference and diameter of a circle.
2. Examples vary; rate and time when distance is constant, distance from the fulcrum of a lever and weight
3. Direct **4.** Neither **5.** Direct **6.** Inverse

■ *11.3 Independent Practice pp. 578–580*
7. Direct **9.** Neither **11.** $y = 2x$ **13.** $y = \frac{2}{9}x$
15. $xy = 4$ **17.** $xy = \frac{7}{2}$ **19.** $VP = 2500$ **21.** $g = 2n$
23. 2 **25.** 7 **27.** $b = 0.006p$ **29.** 30 minutes
31. $pt = 114$, $\approx 17.5\%$

■ *11.3 Integrated Review p. 580*
33. 4 **35.** 4 **37.** 0.5 **39.** 1.20

■ *11.4 Communicating About Algebra p. 583*
A. Of all days on record with comparable meteorological conditions, rain occurred on 80% of the days.
B. Of all the time in a comparable situation, a person won 50% of the time.

■ *11.4 Guided Practice p. 584*
1. 0; The sun sets in the morning.
2. 1; The sun rises in the morning.
3. Find the ratio of successful outcomes to all outcomes.
4. 0.48 **5.** 0.52 **6.** 1

■ *11.4 Independent Practice pp. 584–586*
7. 0.1875 **9.** $\frac{3}{16}$ **11.** 10, without **13.** $\frac{1917}{6565}$ **15.** $\frac{1}{81}$
17. $\frac{500}{4451}$ **19.** $\frac{9583}{18,346}$ **21.** $\frac{31}{50}$

■ *11.4 Integrated Review p. 586*
23. $\frac{2}{3}$ **25.** $2(32 + x)$ **27.** 5.9%

■ *11.4 Mid-Chapter Self-Test p. 587*
1. $\frac{24}{5}$ **2.** 28 **3.** $\frac{5}{9}$ **4.** 10 **5.** 9, -9 **6.** 10, -10 **7.** -1
8. $-8, 2$ **9.** 0 **10.** $-7, 2$ **11.** -3 **12.** 28 **13.** $0.26
14. 936 **15.** 30 **16.** ≈ 385 **17.** 67.9% **18.** 25%

19. $j = 2b$ **20.** 1247, 169 **21.** $ab = 245$, 49 **22.** $\frac{1}{6}, \frac{1}{4}$
23. $13\frac{1}{3}\%$

■ *11.5 Communicating About Algebra p. 590*
A. 0, 0; 1, 1; 2, 2; 3, 3; 4, 4; $\frac{0}{0}$, 5; 6, 6
B. $\frac{x^2 - x - 6}{x - 3}$ is undefined at $x = 3$; the two expressions are equivalent for all values of x except $x = 3$.

■ *11.5 Guided Practice p. 591*
1. A fraction whose numerator and denominator are polynomials **2.** The set of all real numbers except those for which the denominator is zero; all real numbers except 2 and -1. **3.** c **4.** True

■ *11.5 Independent Practice pp. 591–592*
5. All real numbers except 4 **7.** All real numbers except 1 and -1 **9.** All real numbers except 2 and -3 **11.** $3x$
13. $(x + 2)$ **15.** $(x + 2)$ **17.** $\frac{x}{3}$ **19.** $\frac{3x}{2}$ **21.** $\frac{3}{10 + x}$
23. $\frac{y - 4}{3}$ **25.** $\frac{-1}{x - 2}$ **27.** $\frac{x(x + 3)}{x - 2}$ **29.** e
31. $\frac{7 - 23x}{10 - 0.022x + 0.005x^2}$ **33.** $C = \frac{58 + 5t}{10 - 0.8t + 0.0592t^2}$
35. ≈ 145

■ *11.5 Integrated Review pp. 592–593*
37. $3x^6$ **39.** xy^5 **41.** $\frac{y}{3x^2}$ **43.** $\frac{1}{4}$ **45.** $\frac{25}{7}$ **47.** $\frac{5}{3}$

■ *11.5 Mixed Review p. 593*
1. 4.675×10^9 **3.** 0.000006209 **5.** $-m^3$ **7.** $4.97
9. $x \geq 5$ or $x \leq 1$ **11.** $\frac{x}{2y^4}$ **13.** No **15.** 9, -9 **17.** 13
19. $-3x + 5y + 42 = 0$

■ *11.6 Communicating About Algebra p. 596*
A. $2(x + 1)$; multiply numerators and denominators, divide out common factors
B. $\frac{x - 3}{x}$; multiply by reciprocal, divide out common factors
C. $\frac{2}{x - 2}$; multiply, divide out common factors

■ *11.6 Guided Practice p. 597*
1. Multiply numerators, multiply denominators, and divide out the common factors.
2. Multiply the first by the reciprocal of the second, and divide out the common factors.
3. $\frac{-1}{2x^2}$, See Exercise 1. **4.** $\frac{2x + 5}{4x}$, See Exercise 2.
5. When you divide, you multiply the first fraction by the reciprocal of the second fraction.
6. The first was multiplied by the reciprocal of the second. The multiplication dot was mistaken for a division sign.

■ *11.6 Independent Practice pp. 597–599*
7. $\frac{6}{5}$ **9.** $3x^2$ **11.** $5y$ **13.** 6
15. $\frac{1}{(x + 4)(2x + 3)}$ **17.** $\frac{x - 2}{2}$ **19.** $\frac{x}{x + 1}$

769

21. 1 **23.** $\frac{x}{x+3}$ **25.** $\frac{x+2}{2(x-2)}$ **27.** $\frac{1}{3x}$
29. $3x(x+2)$
31. S: \$1131 billion; H: 50.75 billion; A: \$54 billion
33. $\frac{A}{S} = \frac{9(8+t)(30-t)}{130(9+t)(34-t)}$, decreasing
35. $\frac{S}{P} = \frac{2(11+2t)(35-t)}{5(24-t)(20+11t)}$

■ 11.6 Integrated Review p. 599
37. $\frac{9}{25}$ **39.** $4x$ **41.** $\frac{x-1}{x+3}$ **43.** $\frac{x}{x+3}$ **45.** $\frac{8}{3}$ **47.** $\frac{32}{3}$
49. $-5, 3$ **51.** $8, -5$
53. All real numbers except 0 and $-\frac{3}{2}$.
55. All real numbers except 2 and 3. **57.** $\frac{1}{6}$

■ 11.7 Communicating About Algebra p. 602

$$-p+1 \;\overline{\Big)\; 120{,}000p}$$
$$\frac{-120{,}000 + \frac{120{,}000}{-p+1}}{\begin{array}{l}120{,}000p - 120{,}000\\ \hline 120{,}000\end{array}} \; ; \; C \text{ gets larger}$$

11.7 Guided Practice p. 603
1. a. 5469 **b.** 42 **c.** 130 **d.** 9
2. a. x^2+2 **b.** $x-3$ **c.** $x+3$ **d.** 11
3. $7+\frac{1}{52}$ **4.** $1666+\frac{11}{15}$ **5.** $x+1-\frac{3}{x+2}$
6. $3x^2-3x-1$

11.7 Independent Practice pp. 603–604
7. $\frac{5x}{5x+2}$ **9.** $3z+5$ **11.** $\frac{5}{2}z^2+z-3$
13. $\frac{1}{2}x^2-\frac{1}{7}x$ **15.** $m^3+2m-\frac{7}{m}$
17. Quotient = x^2+3x+9
Remainder = 0
Divisor = $x-3$
19. $x-5$ **21.** $x+10$
23. $x+3+\frac{5}{x-3}$ **25.** $4x+20+\frac{30}{x-2}$
27. $\frac{C}{B} = \frac{1}{4} - \frac{17}{4t+120}$ **29.** $\frac{R}{T} = \frac{1}{2}+\frac{1}{2t+12}$

■ 11.7 Integrated Review p. 605
31. $2z-1$ **33.** $3+y$ **35.** $2m-10$
37. $x+5+\frac{12}{x-2}$ **39.** $2y-1$ **41.** $2b+41+\frac{420}{b-10}$
37–42. Use long division, so you won't have to take time looking for factors that may not exist. **43.** c

■ 11.8 Communicating About Algebra p. 609
A. 2 **B.** 0

■ 11.8 Guided Practice p. 610
1. $3x$ **2.** $6, -6$ **3.** $6, -6$ **4.** $1, 3$ **5.** 8 **6.** $-6, 9$

11.8 Independent Practice pp. 610–612
7. 3 **9.** 2 **11.** $2x$ **13.** $\frac{15}{2}$ **15.** 4 **17.** 7 **19.** -2
21. $3, -1$ **23.** 5 **25.** -12 **27.** 5 **29.** 2
31. $-\frac{1}{3}, 2$ **33.** $-12, 2$ **35.** $6, -5$ **37.** $6, -6$ **39.** $\frac{9}{7}$

41. $\frac{3}{5}$ **43.** 6 **45.** $\frac{36+3.50n}{n}$, 12
47. 15 pages per day; 30 pages per day
49. b, $\frac{13{,}000}{d} = 118.2, \approx 110$ ft

■ 11.8 Integrated Review p. 612
51. Yes **53.** No **55.** $-8, 7$ **57.** $\frac{8}{3}$ **59.** 5 **61.** 13

■ 11.8 Chapter Review pp. 614–616
1. $\frac{8}{7}$ **3.** -30 **5.** 3 or -1 **7.** $a = \frac{6}{19}b$ **9.** $\frac{84}{19}$ **11.** $\frac{3}{5}$
13. 192 lb **15.** $\frac{23}{24}$ **17.** $\frac{70}{183}$ **19.** $\frac{x}{3x^2+1}$ **21.** $\frac{x^2+2x-1}{5(x+4)}$
23. $\frac{2x-1}{4x^2}$ **25.** $20x^2$ **27.** $\frac{4}{x^4}$ **29.** 12 **31.** $\frac{3}{x}$
33. $\frac{(x+1)(x+2)(x+3)}{x+5}$ **35.** $\frac{1}{8}$
37. $6x+1-\frac{3}{2x}$ **39.** $3x+1+\frac{1}{3x}$
41. $x-5-\frac{10}{3x}$ **43.** $3x+5+\frac{4}{x-1}$
45. $2x+\frac{11}{2}+\frac{21}{2(2x-1)}$ **47.** $x+1+\frac{8}{5x-2}$
49. 3 **51.** $6, -5$ **53.** $-4, 2$ **55.** 9.7 lb **57.** 2.6% **59.** 495

CHAPTER 12

■ 12.1 Communicating About Algebra p. 622
A. $8, -3\frac{2}{3}$ **B.** $5, 2\frac{3}{4}$ **C.** $\frac{1}{2}, -\frac{4}{3}$

■ 12.1 Guided Practice p. 623
1. 1, {1, 2, 3, 4} **2.** 4, {1, 2, 3, 4} **3.** 2, {1, 2, 3, 4}
4. 4, 15; substitute 1 and 2 in equation for f and simplify.

■ 12.1 Independent Practice pp. 623–625
5. Yes, No 2 ordered pairs have the same first coordinate.
7. No, Two ordered pairs have the same first coordinate.
9. Yes, {1, 2, 3, 4} **11.** Yes, {1, 2, 3, 4}
13. Yes, {0, 1, 2, 3, 4}
15. No **17.** 1, 21 **19.** 5, 11 **21.** $-1, 29$ **23.** 18, -2
25. 85, -15 **27.** {0, 2, 4, 6, 8, 10}; 0, 1 **29.** $f(x) = \frac{1}{2}x$
31. Yes, No 2 ordered pairs have the same first coordinate. **33.** Yes, No 2 ordered pairs have the same first coordinate. **35.** Yes, No 2 ordered pairs have the same first coordinate. **37.** $\approx 13{,}100$

■ 12.1 Integrated Review p. 625
39. $y = \frac{3}{2}x - \frac{1}{2}, -3\frac{1}{2}$ **41.** $y = 2x^2+5, 13$
43. c **45.** b

■ 12.2 Communicating About Algebra p. 628
Answers vary. For example, height above sea level of a city and the average daily temperature of that city's outdoor air; someone's present salary for work and the number of past years that someone has worked at the same company.

12.2 Guided Practice p. 629

1. Vertical line **2.** $(-3, 5)$; when $x = -3$, $y = 5$ **3.** 5; when $x = 1$, $y = 5$ **4.** Use the points $(1, 2)$, $(3, -1)$; and the slope formula.

12.2 Independent Practice pp. 629–631

5. c **7.** d **9.** -2 **11.** $\frac{13}{6}$ **13.** $-\frac{3}{10}$
15. $f(x) = 1$ **17.** $f(x) = 3x - 13$
19. $f(x) = 5x + 6$ **21.** $f(x) = -\frac{2}{3}x + 4$
23. $f(x) = -x + 8$ **25.** $f(x) = -\frac{4}{5}x + 1$

27.

29.

31.

33. $f(m) = \frac{1}{35}m$ where $m = $ distance; $12\frac{2}{7}$ days
35. $f(x) = \frac{1}{10}x + 63$; $72°F$
37. $f(t) = 4900 + 800t$

39. b **41.** c

12.2 Integrated Review p. 631

43. 12 **45.** 13 **47.** $y = -\frac{5}{6}x - \frac{10}{3}$
49. $y = -\frac{1}{3}x + 3$
51.   **53.**

12.2 Mixed Review p. 632

1. 4.24×10^6 **3.** Quadratic, trinomial
5. 27.192 **7.** $3x + 8 + \frac{10}{x - 2}$ **9.** $(3, 2)$
11. $\frac{3 + \sqrt{37}}{2}, \frac{3 - \sqrt{37}}{2}$ **13.** Yes **15.** -4, 1
17. $\left(-\frac{2}{3}, 0\right)$ **19.** 137.2

12.3 Communicating About Algebra p. 635

A.

B.

C.

D.

E.

F.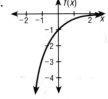

12.3 Guided Practice p. 636

1. Decay, $0 < \frac{1}{4} < 1$ **2.** Growth, $5 > 1$
3. Horizontal shift

4. Vertical shift

5. Reflection

6. Vertical Shift

■ 12.3 Independent Practice pp. 636–637

7. Reflection **9.** Horizontal shift **11.** Vertical shift
13. Vertical shift **15.** Vertical shift **17.** Reflection

19.

21.

23.

25.

27.

29.

31.

33.

35.

37. 27.5, ≈ 4186.0

39. Answers vary.
  Octave: C ($n = 3$) to C ($n = -9$)
  Fifth: $G(n = -2)$ to $C(n = -9)$
  Fourth: $F(n = -4)$ to $C(n = -9)$
  Major Third: $E(n = -5)$ to $C(n = -9)$
  Minor Third: $G(n = -2)$ to $E(n = -5)$
  Major Sixth: $A(n = 0)$ to $C(n = -9)$
  Minor Sixth: $C(n = 3)$ to $E(n = -5)$

41. $f(0) = 1$
  $f(1) = \dfrac{4}{3} \approx 1.33$
  $f(2) = \left(\dfrac{4}{3}\right)^2 \approx 1.78$
  $f(3) = \left(\dfrac{4}{3}\right)^3 \approx 2.37$
  $f(4) = \left(\dfrac{4}{3}\right)^4 \approx 3.16$
  $f(5) = \left(\dfrac{4}{3}\right)^5 \approx 4.21$

■ 12.3 Integrated Review p. 638

43. d **45.** a **47.** 1.25×10^{-4} **49.** 24 **51.** 6.91 **53.** d

■ 12.4 Communicating About Algebra p. 641

A. $f(x) = (x - 2)^2 - 2$, vertex $(2, -2)$

B. $f(x) = -(x + 1)^2 - 4$, vertex $(-1, -4)$

C. $f(x) = 2(x - 1)^2 + 5$, vertex $(1, 5)$

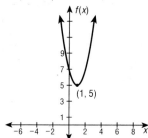

D. $f(x) = -3(x + 1)^2 - 1$, vertex $(-1, -1)$

■ *12.4 Guided Practice p. 642*

1. $f(x) = (x - 3)^2 - 3$ **2.** $(-4, -3)$

3. The graph opens upward and the vertex is the point where the graph reverses direction from downward to upward.

4. The graph opens downward and the vertex is the point where the graph reverses direction from upward to downward.

■ *12.4 Independent Practice pp. 642–643*

5. $(1, 5)$, highest **7.** $(3, -2)$, lowest **9.** $(-2, 6)$, lowest
11. c **13.** b

15.

17.

19.

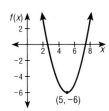

21. $f(x) = (x - 9)^2 - 2$, $(9, -2)$
23. $f(x) = (x - 2)^2 + 12$, $(2, 12)$
25. $f(x) = (x + 8)^2 - 2$, $(-8, -2)$
27. $f(x) = -(x + 3)^2 + 8$, $(-3, 8)$
29. $f(x) = (x - 5)^2 - 6$

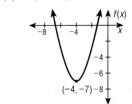

31. $f(x) = (x + 4)^2 - 7$

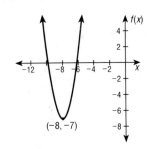

33. $f(x) = 2(x + 8)^2 - 7$

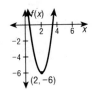

35. $f(x) = 3(x - 2)^2 - 6$

37. $f(x) = -2(x - 12)^2 + 288$

39. $h(x) = -\frac{1}{100}(x - 50)^2 + 33$. The vertex is $(50, 33)$, so the maximum height is 33 ft.
41. $f(t) = 1.7(t - 4.5)^2 + 10.775$

41.

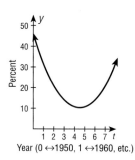
Year (0 ↔1950, 1 ↔1960, etc.)

■ 12.4 Integrated Review p. 644
43. $-7, 1$ **45.** $2 + \sqrt{13}, 2 - \sqrt{13}$
47. $2 + \frac{1}{2}\sqrt{21}, 2 - \frac{1}{2}\sqrt{21}$

49–54. The method in this lesson; each method enables you to easily find the x-coordinate of the vertex, but the method learned in this lesson enables you to find the y-coordinate of the vertex more easily.
49. $(2, 7)$ **51.** $(-1, -3)$ **53.** $(12, -4)$
55–60. Used the method in this lesson to find the vertex for the reason given in Exercises 49–54, then plot pairs of points that were the same horizontal distance from the vertex in order to easily draw a symmetric curve.

55. **57.**
59.

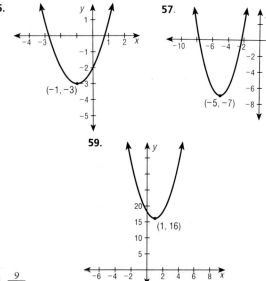

61. $\frac{9}{100}$

■ 12.4 Mid-Chapter Self-Test p. 645
1. No **2.** Yes **3.** $-4, 2, 8$ **4.** $0, -4, -8$ **5.** $3, -1, 3$
6. $-7, 5, -7$ **7.** $21, 1, 13$ **8.** $-10, 6, 6$
9. $f(x) = 2x + 3$ **10.** $f(x) = -3x$
11. $f(x) = 4$ **12.** Vertical shift
13. Vertical shift   **14.** Horizontal shift
15. $f(x) = (x - 2)^2 + 5$ **16.** $f(x) = -(x + 1)^2 - 3$
17. $f(x) = 2(x - 1)^2 - 9$ **18.** Yes **19.** $f(x) = 5x, 60$ ft
20. 5

■ 12.5 Communicating About Algebra p. 648
A. **B.**

C. **D.**

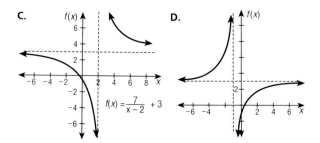

$f(x) = \dfrac{7}{x - 2} + 3$

■ 12.5 Guided Practice p. 649
1–4. $f(x) = \dfrac{a}{x - h} + k$ is a hyperbola whose center is (h, k) and whose asymptotes are the vertical and horizontal lines through the center.
1. $(-5, -3)$; $x = -5, y = -3$ **2.** $(10, 4)$; $x = 10, y = 4$
3. $(3, 16)$; $x = 3, y = 16$ **4.** $(-1, -9)$; $x = -1, y = -9$
5. **6.**

■ 12.5 Independent Practice pp. 649–650
7. $(5, 2)$, $x = 5, y = 2$ **9.** $(4, 6)$, $x = 4, y = 6$
11. $(-9, -7)$, $x = -9, y = -7$ **13.** c **15.** d **17.** b
19.

21.

23.

25.

27.

29.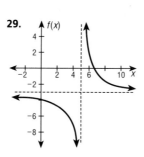

31. $f(x) = \dfrac{1}{x-5} - 2$

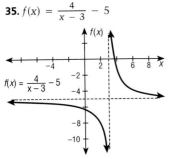

33. $f(x) = -\dfrac{2}{x-2} - 9$

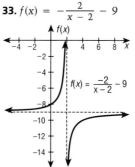

35. $f(x) = \dfrac{4}{x-3} - 5$

37. 1997, the year the lease is up

37.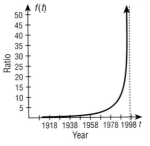

39. $f(x) = \dfrac{20+x}{5+2x}$

■ *12.5 Integrated Review p. 651*
41. $\dfrac{x+1}{2}$ **43.** $\dfrac{1}{(x+2)^2}$ **45.** 4, -1 **47.** b **49.** d

■ *12.5 Mixed Review p. 651*
1. $\frac{1}{2}x^{-2}y$ **3.** 39 **5.** $\dfrac{1}{3x^4y^6}$ **7.** 3.35×10^{-8} **9.** 7, -9

■ *12.6 Communicating About Algebra p. 654*

7	5
5	9
4	137
3	003678
2	223456899

■ *12.6 Guided Practice p. 655*
1. To arrange data in increasing or decreasing order.
2. The mean is the average of a collection of numbers, the median is the middle number of an ordered collection of numbers. Answers vary; they are the same in 4, 5, 6 and they are different in 1, 4, 10.
3. Bottom boxes: 1st, 2nd, 3rd, 4th quarters; top boxes: 1st, 2nd, 3rd quartiles; 2nd

5	1145
4	3469
3	2289
2	0459
1	2237

4.

■ *12.6 Independent Practice pp. 655–656*
5. 7.5 **7.** 10
9. 10, 12, 13, 13, 13, 15, 17, 18, 19, 21, 21, 23, 25, 25, 26, 31, 33, 35, 40, 41, 42, 44, 46, 48, 48, 48, 50, 50, 57, 59
11.

13.

15. Answers vary; 10, 11, 12, 13, 13, 14, 15, 16, 22, 23, 24, 25, 29, 32, 35, 38
17. Answers vary; 81, 84, 87, 90, 94, 94, 94, 94, 96, 96, 97, 97, 99, 104, 109, 114

19. 1-3, 1-24, 1-25, 2-7, 2-22, 3-17, 4-1, 4-14, 4-15, 4-30, 4-30, 5-10, 6-5, 6-13, 7-31, 8-21, 8-26, 9-12, 10-11, 10-17, 11-11, 12-9, 12-15, 12-28

21. 50.7, 34.7, 28.7, 26.3, 25.8, 15.2, 10.7, 9.7, 9.6, 8.5, 6.9, 5.4, 4.9, 4.5, 3.6, 3.6, 2.2, 1.6, 1.0

■ 12.6 Integrated Review p. 657

23. 1.8, 1.9, 2.0, 2.0, 2.3, 2.3, 2.3, 2.4, 2.4, 2.4, 2.9, 3.4, 4.0, 4.7, 4.8, 5.0, 5.0, 5.9, 7.1, 10.8 The box-and-whisker plot is better in showing how the data is clustered or spread out, while the bar graph is better in showing specific relationships among the data.

2.65 4.9
2.3   10.8

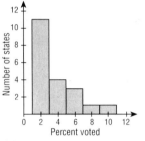

25. 4,580,000

■ 12.7 Communicating About Algebra p. 660

Mean of 180: A, B, D; median of 180: D; mode of 180: C, D

■ 12.7 Guided Practice p. 661

1. See page 658. **2.** Mean: 233.7, median: 235, mode: 235
3. Answers vary; a mean of 34 for the collection 1, 2, 99
4. The graph shows the frequency of each number, the plot shows the median and quartiles.

■ 12.7 Independent Practice pp. 661–663

5. No; the mean and the median are 62.9, the mode is 62.8.
7. Mean: 7.25; median: 7.5

5   6   7.5 8   11

9. Median of 4.6 since the mode is the smallest length and the mean is smaller than most of the lengths
11. No; $25,000

■ 12.7 Integrated Review p. 663

13. 25% **15.** 76.8% **17.** 5.778 **19.** b **21.** $126.40
23. 14.175 min

■ 12.7 Chapter Review pp. 666–668

1. Yes $\{a, b, c, d\}$ **3.** Yes $\{3, 4, 6, 8\}$
5. $f(x) = x - 3$ **7.** $f(x) = x + 5$
9. b **11.** d **13.** shift 2 units down **15.** Reflection

17. $f(x) = (x + 5)^2 + 2$, $(-5, 2)$; opens upward
19. $h(x) = -\frac{1}{3}(x + 2)^2 - 6$, $(-2, -6)$; opens downward
21. c **23.** d **25.**

(4, 3)

27.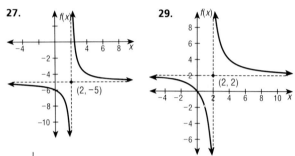

(2, −5)   (2, 2)

31.
```
7 | 001225
6 | 047889
5 | 0346
4 | 0344556799
3 | 5677
```

33.

35   44   51.5   68   75

35. $f(x) = \frac{x}{30}$, $3\frac{1}{3}$ ft per second
37. $175,320 million **39.** ≈$452,524 million
41. Quadratic model; it appears to be the best fit for the given points.

■ 12.7 Cumulative Review for Chapters 7–12 pp. 670–673

1. Monomial, 0 **3.** Trinomial, 2 **5.** Binomial, 1
7. $3x^3 + 9x^2 + 12x$ **9.** $12x^3 + 20x^2 + 6x + 10$
11. $4x^2 - 16$ **13.** 3, 6 **15.** 0, −6 **17.** $-\frac{7}{2}, \frac{7}{2}$
19. $\frac{-3 + \sqrt{29}}{2}, \frac{-3 - \sqrt{29}}{2}$ **21.** $2 + \sqrt{17}, 2 - \sqrt{17}$
23. $3 + \frac{\sqrt{88}}{4}, 3 - \frac{\sqrt{88}}{4}$ **25.** $\frac{3}{10}$ **27.** $-4, -\frac{2}{3}$
29. 37.5% **31.** 31.2 yards **33.** 14.3% **35.** $5x = 3y$
37. $3.1x = 4.2y$ **39.** $xy = 9$ **41.** $\frac{13}{25}$ **43.** $\frac{1}{5}$ **45.** $\frac{1}{4y}$
47. $\frac{10p}{9}$ **49.** $\frac{m}{m - 2}$ **51.** $3z + 2$ **53.** $y + 8 + \frac{14}{y - 2}$
55. $\frac{1}{3}z^2 - 7 + \frac{21}{z + 3}$ **57.** −13 **59.** −6 **61.** $\frac{1}{2}$ **63.** 18
65. 2 **67.** $\frac{1}{2}$ **69.** b **71.** d **73.** 18 **75.** $23.50 **77.** 20

79.

81.

83. $\dfrac{54,420 + 2900t}{31,665 + 1545t}$

85.

0	1122334679
1	18
2	9
4	0
6	4
8	2

87. 0.65 inches   **89.** 3876 ft^2 **91.** \$2 per week

CHAPTER 13

■ *13.1 Communicating About Algebra p. 678*

In the distance formula, squaring a positive difference gives the same result as squaring a negative difference. In the midpoint formula, addition of coordinates is commutative.

■ *13.1 Guided Practice p. 679*

1. 10   **2.** $(1, 2)$ **3.** If the lengths of the sides of a triangle satisfy the equation $a^2 + b^2 = c^2$, then the triangle is a right triangle.

■ *13.1 Independent Practice pp. 679–681*

5–7. Estimates may vary.   **5.** 4.12   **7.** 6.71   **9.** 9.49
11. 11.18   **13.** 4.24   **15.** 0.71   **17.** No   **19.** Yes   **21.** $(0, 5)$
23. $\left(\frac{5}{2}, 1\right)$ **25.** $\left(\frac{5}{2}, 4\right)$
27. $10 + 2\sqrt{20} + \sqrt{68} + \sqrt{136}$ **29.** ≈ 460 mi.
31. The shortest path is 40 ft.
33. $d_1 = \sqrt{(7 - 1)^2 + (11 - 4)^2} = \sqrt{85}$,
$d_3 = \sqrt{(7 - 1)^2 + (4 - (-3))^2} = \sqrt{85}$;
$d_2 = \sqrt{(7 - 7)^2 + (11 - 4)^2} = 7$,
$d_4 = \sqrt{(1 - 1)^2 + (4 - (-3))^2} = 7$

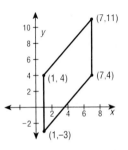

■ *13.1 Integrated Review p. 681*

35. $\sqrt{97}$ **37.** 5   **39.** 24   **41.** 60   **43.** $y = -10x + 31$
45. $y = -2$ **47.** $y = -\frac{11}{4}x + \frac{25}{2}$

■ *13.2 Communicating About Algebra p. 684*

A. $r_1, r_2, r_4, r_5, r_6, r_9, r_{10}, r_{12}, r_{13}, r_{14}; r_0 = 1$,
$r_3 = 2, r_7 = 2\sqrt{2}, r_8 = 3, r_{11} = 2\sqrt{3}, r_{15} = 4$
B. $A_n = \frac{1}{2}(1)(r_{n-1})$ **C.** $\frac{2\sqrt{14}}{7}$

■ *13.2 Guided Practice p. 685*

1–3. See page 682.
4. $\sqrt{28} = \sqrt{4 \cdot 7} = \sqrt{4} \cdot \sqrt{7} = 2\sqrt{7}$
5. $\sqrt{6} \cdot \sqrt{24} = \sqrt{6 \cdot 24} = \sqrt{144} = 12$
6. $\frac{1}{\sqrt{3}} = \frac{1}{\sqrt{3}} \cdot \frac{\sqrt{3}}{\sqrt{3}} = \frac{\sqrt{3}}{\sqrt{3 \cdot 3}} = \frac{\sqrt{3}}{3}$

■ *13.2 Independent Practice pp. 685–686*

7. $2\sqrt{10}$ **9.** $4\sqrt{3}$ **11.** $\frac{\sqrt{7}}{3}$ **13.** $\frac{1}{5}$ **15.** $2\sqrt{5}$ **17.** $\sqrt{5}$
19. $\frac{\sqrt{3}}{6}$ **21.** $\sqrt{2}$ **23.** $5\sqrt{3}$ **25.** 6   **27.** 52   **29.** 2   **31.** $\frac{\sqrt{2}}{6}$
33. $\sqrt{3}$ **35.** $10\sqrt{2}, 14.14$ **37.** $12\sqrt{6}, 29.39$ **39.** $3\sqrt{2}$
41. $6.2\sqrt{15}$ **43.** $\frac{110}{3\pi}$ **45.** Delaware

■ *13.2 Integrated Review p. 687*

47. -1 **49.** 4   **51.** 15   **53.** $-6 \pm 4\sqrt{3}$ **55.** $-1 \pm \sqrt{2}$
57. $5, -1$ **59.** $\frac{\sqrt{2}}{2}$ **61.** $4\sqrt{3}$

■ *13.2 Mixed Review p. 688*

1. $(x + 7)(x + 1)$ **3.** $\frac{3 \pm \sqrt{29}}{4}$ **5.** 20   **7.** 4.23×10^9
9. No   **11.**

13. $x = 1$ or $x = 5$
15. $-3x^2 + 2$ **17.** $3m^4$ **19.** $\begin{bmatrix} 2b + 3 & 7 \\ -2a + 4 & 3b \end{bmatrix}$

■ *13.3 Communicating About Algebra p. 691*

A. See page 690.
B. $(\sqrt{20})^2 + (\sqrt{45})^2 = (\sqrt{65})^2, (\sqrt{45})^2 + (\sqrt{5})^2 = (\sqrt{50})^2$,
$(\sqrt{45})^2 + (\sqrt{5})^2 = (\sqrt{50})^2$
C. 30 unit^2 or 6750 ft^2

■ *13.3 Guided Practice p. 692*

1. $3\sqrt{5}, \sqrt{5}; 2\sqrt{5}, \sqrt{2}$ **2.** $\sqrt{2}, 3\sqrt{2}$ **3.** $5\sqrt{6}$ **4.** $\sqrt{2}$
5. $15 - 6\sqrt{2}$ **6.** Yes

■ *13.3 Independent Practice pp. 692–693*

7. $7\sqrt{7}$ **9.** $-3\sqrt{3}$ **11.** $4\sqrt{2}$ **13.** $10\sqrt{5}$ **15.** 0   **17.** 0
19. $3\sqrt{6} + 3$ **21.** $21 + 8\sqrt{5}$ **23.** $-6 - 19\sqrt{2}$

25. $34 + 18\sqrt{17}$, $6\sqrt{17} + 18$ **27.** $6 + 5\sqrt{10}$ **29.** Yes
31. $20 + 24\sqrt{2}$ feet

33.

Year	# Households (in millions)	Increase from previous year
1970	≈ 63.07	
1971	≈ 64.95	1.88
1972	≈ 66.78	1.83
1973	≈ 68.56	1.78

■ *13.3 Integrated Review p. 694*
35. $\sqrt{134}$ **37.** $\sqrt{19}$ **39.** Yes   **41.** 3×10^6 **43.** e

■ *13.4 Communicating About Algebra p. 697*
A. 25; add 5 to both sides, square both sides
B. No solution; subtract 5 from both sides, square both sides, see that 25 is a false solution
C. 15; add 2 to both sides, square both sides, subtract 4 from both sides, divide both sides by 3
D. 4, -1; square both sides, add $x - 8$ to both sides, factor, set each factor equal to zero, solve each factor for x

■ *13.4 Guided Practice p. 698*
1. Isolate the radical, then square both sides, 50.
2. No, it does not check.   **3.** You could have a false solution.   **4.** 3

■ *13.4 Independent Practice pp. 698–699*
5. 100   **7.** -4 **9.** $-\frac{1}{3}$ **11.** $\frac{1}{3}$ **13.** 298   **15.** No solution
17. 4   **19.** No solution   **21.** 7   **23.** 6   **25.** 16   **27.** 45
29. 26   **31.** 28.38 lb   **33.** 16°C   **35.** $2844\frac{4}{9}$ ft per second

■ *13.4 Integrated Review p. 700*
37. 3, yes; -3, no   **39.** 8, yes; -10, no   **41.** $-\frac{5}{2}$, -3
43. $\frac{3 + 3\sqrt{5}}{2}$, $\frac{3 - 3\sqrt{5}}{2}$ **45.** 11, 3   **47.** $-\frac{4}{3}$, $-\frac{1}{3}$
49. $-2 + \sqrt{2}$, $-2 - \sqrt{2}$

■ *13.4 Mid-Chapter Self-Test p. 702*
1. $3\sqrt{2}$ **2.** $5\sqrt{5}$ **3.** No   **4.** Yes   **5.** $\left(\frac{9}{2}, -2\right)$ **6.** $\left(-6, \frac{15}{2}\right)$
7. $7\sqrt{2}$ **8.** $12\sqrt{3}$ **9.** $\frac{\sqrt{5}}{6}$ **10.** $\frac{\sqrt{35}}{10}$ **11.** $6\sqrt{3} - 2$
12. $36 + 9\sqrt{2}$ **13.** $16 - 4\sqrt{5}$ **14.** $21 - 12\sqrt{3}$ **15.** 9
16. $\frac{38}{3}$ **17.** 6   **18.** 1   **19.** 6   **20.** 2   **21.** $10\sqrt{5}$
22. $3\sqrt{2} + 4\sqrt{3}$, $2\sqrt{3} + 4\sqrt{2} + 2\sqrt{6}$ **23.** $(-47, 90)$
24. Yes

■ *13.5 Communicating About Algebra p. 705*
A. Solve $\tan 50° = \frac{a}{10}$ for a, substitute for a in $a^2 + 10^2 = c^2$ and solve for c
B. Solve $\tan 40° = \frac{10}{b}$ for b, substitute for b in $10^2 + b^2 = c^2$ and solve for c.

C. Solve $a^2 + b^2 = 2^2$ for a in terms of b, substitute for a in $\tan 45° = \frac{a}{b}$ and solve for b, substitute for b in $a^2 + b^2 = 2^2$ and solve for a.

■ *13.5 Guided Practice p. 706*
1. An acute angle is an angle whose measure is greater than 0° and less than 90°. 90°   **2.** $\frac{14}{25}$ **3.** 15,17   **4.** 0.70

■ *13.5 Independent Practice pp. 706–708*
5. $\frac{4}{5}, \frac{5}{4}$ **7.** $\frac{\sqrt{3}}{3}$, $\sqrt{3}$ **9.** ≈ 0.36, ≈ 2.75
11. 0.21   **13.** 9.51   **15.** 0.03   **17.** $12, 4\sqrt{13}$

19. $b \approx 12.8$, $B = 52°$, $c \approx 16.2$ **21.** $a \approx 4.6$, $c \approx 12.9$,
$B = 69°$ **23.** $a \approx 57.6$, $c \approx 73.1$, $A = 52°$
25. 1   **27.** ≈ 24.3
29. $x \approx 7.28$, $y \approx 6.72$ **31.** ≈ 58.6 ft   **33.** ≈ 214.5 ft

■ *13.5 Integrated Review pp. 708–709*
35. $4\sqrt{3}$, $-4\sqrt{3}$ **37.** $\sqrt{41}$, $-\sqrt{41}$ **39.** $\frac{12}{7}$
41. 1, Slope is the tangent of the angle.   **43.** b

■ *13.5 Mixed Review p. 709*
1. $x^3 + 2x^2 + 2x$ **3.** No   **5.** $\sqrt{2q}$, $-\sqrt{2q}$ **7.** $\frac{-13}{4}$
9. 5   **11.** 60%   **13.**

15.

17.

19. $(-3, -6)$

Euler found a counterexample to Fermat's conjecture; so Fermat's conjecture was false.

■ *13.6 Guided Practice p. 713*

1. $a - b = a + (-b)$ No; a definition needs to be consistent with other definitions and with axioms, but is accepted as true rather than having to be proved true.

2. $(a - b)c = (a + (-b))c$ Def. of subtraction
$\qquad\quad = ac + (-b)c$ Distributive axiom
$\qquad\quad = ac + (-bc)$ $(-b)c = -bc$
$\qquad\quad = ac - bc$ Def. of subtraction

3. No; in order to prove her conjecture she would need to give *every* example (to avoid a counterexample) which would be impossible.

4. Yes; the map cannot be colored as proposed.

■ *13.6 Independent Practice pp. 713–714*

5. $a - b = a + (-b)$ Def. of subtraction
$\qquad\quad = -b + a$ Commutative axiom

7–9. Counterexamples vary.

7. $(3 + 4)^2 \overset{?}{=} 3^2 + 4^2$ **9.** $0 \cdot 1 = 0 \cdot 2$
$\qquad 49 \neq 25$ $1 \neq 2$

11. She drew a plan of the patio and colored it like a checkerboard.

13. Each additional *L*-shape contains the next odd number of dots; the dots can be lined up in a square form.

■ *13.6 Integrated Review p. 715*

15. $\dfrac{12}{b-c}$ **17.** $b + \dfrac{12}{b}$ **19.** $2\sqrt{85}$ ft or ≈ 18.4 ft   **21.** b

■ *13.6 Chapter Review pp. 717–719*

1. $\sqrt{10}$; $\left(-\dfrac{15}{2}, -\dfrac{1}{2}\right)$ **3.** $\sqrt{145}$; $\left(-4, \dfrac{9}{2}\right)$

5. $\sqrt{181}$; $\left(\dfrac{3}{2}, 2\right)$ **7.** $(\sqrt{5})^2 + (\sqrt{5})^2 = (\sqrt{10})^2$ **9.** $6\sqrt{6}$

11. $3\sqrt{2}$ **13.** $\dfrac{2\sqrt{2}}{3}$ **15.** $3\sqrt{5} - \sqrt{3}$ **17.** $6\sqrt{2} - 8\sqrt{3}$

19. $55 - 30\sqrt{2}$ **21.** 4   **23.** No solution   **25.** 12   **27.** $6\sqrt{5}$

29. $6\sqrt{10}$

31. $12\sqrt{3} + 4$
$\quad\ 27 + 6\sqrt{3}$

33. $a = \sqrt{3}$ **35.** $b \approx 2.97$
$\quad\ c = 2$ $c \approx 7.60$
$\quad\ B = 30°$ $B = 23°$

37. $1 + 3 = 4 = 2^2$, $3 + 6 = 9 = 3^2$,
$\quad\ 6 + 10 = 16 = 4^2$, $10 + 15 = 25 = 5^2$

39. ≈ 37.9 g   **41.** $\tan 30° = \dfrac{a}{b}$ **43.** $a = 35$

45. No; Green's closest piece, an armored unit at $(-3, 7)$, to one of Pink's missiles is ≈ 707 miles away from its location at $(4, 6)$.

47. $M(-3, 8)$, $M(-5, 5)$, $A(-3, 7)$, $A(-4, 5)$, $A(-5, 3)$, $F(-3, 2)$, $T(-5, 0)$, Port City$(-5, 1)$

A

Abscissa, 160
Absolute value
  equations, 217-218, 223-228
  evaluating expressions, 64-67
  graph, 217-218, 223-228
  inequalities, 313-319
Addition
  decimals, 4, 6-7
  identity element, 71, 710
  integers, 68-73
  like terms, 97, 129-136
  number line, 68
  opposites, 76-78
  polynomials, 508-514
  properties, 69, 124
  radicals, 689-694
  real numbers, 68-73
  rules, 69
  solving equations, 122-172
  transforming equations, 122-172
  transforming inequalities, 293
  whole numbers, 3-6, 13
Addition property
  equations, 124
  inequalities, 293
Additive identity property, 71, 710
Algebra tiles, 516, 522
Algebraic definition, 3
Algebraic expression, 8-13, 33-37,
  42-45, 77, 97, 99, 101, 127-128,
  132-134, 139-140, 158-159, 172,
  292
Angle(s)
  acute, 703
  tangent of, 703-706
Applications *See also* Geometry *and*
  Problem Solving
  advertising, 6, 286, 425, 586
  aeronautics, 577
  agriculture, 168, 266-267, 302,
  351, 385, 391, 439, 500, 513, 517,
  585
  air traffic, 40, 396, 707
  animal studies, 32, 141, 144, 146,
  178, 309, 328, 411, 418, 437, 443-
  444, 476, 526, 545, 553, 557, 566,
  570, 585-586, 624, 627, 630, 645,
  661-662
  archaeology, 564, 584
  architecture, 209, 402, 487, 524,
  566, 589, 657, 708
  astronomy, 66, 227, 301, 309, 423-
  424, 426, 429-430, 448, 585, 700
  banking, 7, 10-11, 17, 127, 145,
  156-157, 171, 246, 281, 297, 410,
  432, 435, 551-552

biology, 108, 113, 305, 423, 430,
  434, 494, 525-526
broadcasting, 105, 286
business, 70, 72-73, 83, 85-86, 90,
  110, 202, 215, 283, 286, 292, 297,
  300, 325, 369, 375, 389, 403, 433,
  436, 442, 483, 496, 531, 537, 570,
  584, 592, 598, 645, 658
chemistry, 69, 72, 153, 169, 317,
  362, 365, 367, 371, 408, 410, 414,
  416, 422-423, 425, 497, 500, 532,
  596, 697
communication, 210, 238, 246,
  302
construction, 3, 25, 73, 105, 209,
  355, 436, 457, 460
consumer, 31, 37, 73, 240, 247,
  253, 268, 281, 287, 301, 332, 357,
  371, 572-573, 580, 638, 648
design, 143, 145, 268, 402, 488,
  510
earth science, 16, 145, 162, 164-
  165, 171, 187, 318, 430, 456
economics, 13, 107-108, 139, 150,
  152, 165, 173, 328, 357, 427, 429,
  433, 469, 495, 520
education, 279-280, 484, 589, 625,
  635, 654, 659
engineering, 428
entertainment, 31, 42, 51, 79, 85,
  137, 165, 181, 194, 202, 246, 286,
  301, 317, 331, 383, 385, 395, 440,
  485, 491, 582
environmental science, 34, 128,
  169, 240, 328, 331, 338, 423, 456,
  462, 501, 572, 580, 602
finance, 18, 22, 24, 76, 94, 106,
  108, 111, 132, 137, 139, 152, 169,
  171-172, 192, 247, 315, 337, 346-
  347, 350, 385, 404, 415, 432, 442,
  554, 572, 608, 611, 630, 662
fitness, 49, 54, 246, 297
geology/mining, 462, 469, 490,
  579
government, 44, 50, 82, 107, 112,
  161, 164, 481, 651, 657
home economics, 105, 128, 168,
  221, 231, 596, 662, 693
law enforcement, 39, 43
library science, 81, 110, 261
medicine, 25, 213, 348, 369, 436
meteorology, 53, 63, 92, 133, 145,
  162, 182, 261, 269, 292, 297, 395,
  431, 506, 592, 630, 662
music, 80, 103, 181, 532, 624, 637
nutrition, 278, 392
oceanography, 336, 566, 580, 585,
  686

paleontology, 336, 410
physics, 10-11, 37, 40, 65, 67, 90-
  91, 93, 103, 110-113, 127, 132,
  155, 158, 202, 219, 222, 240, 246,
  273, 318,364, 369, 396, 423, 428,
  431, 460, 463, 474, 480, 482, 491,
  496, 501, 557, 577-578, 590, 687,
  699
physiology, 131, 188, 257, 625
population, 141-142, 145, 203,
  216, 237, 240, 245, 254, 287, 302,
  378, 409, 422, 429-430, 435, 442-
  444, 459-460, 469, 476, 496, 502,
  513, 565, 585-586, 625
psychology, 441
publishing, 143, 185, 194, 207,
  375, 386, 520, 584, 598
retailing, 22, 24, 28, 31, 43, 52,
  73, 85, 90, 93-94, 98, 110-111,
  150, 202, 251, 254, 265, 269, 274,
  337, 368, 391, 395, 417, 421, 430,
  436, 496, 501, 513-514, 540, 557
social studies, 82, 112, 145, 161,
  170, 179, 260, 287, 427, 650, 654,
  656, 678, 680, 690, 705
sociology, 569, 583, 586-587
space exploration, 423, 426
sports, 11, 24, 37, 71-72, 85, 90,
  93, 96, 99, 110 144, 152, 165, 168,
  195, 200, 210, 215, 227, 232, 246,
  256, 260, 274, 276, 282, 287, 298,
  301, 317, 322, 324, 357-358, 370,
  417, 422, 447, 454, 467-468, 483,
  500, 540, 546, 553, 566, 576, 579,
  582, 604, 609, 611, 622, 628, 631,
  645, 652, 677, 702
technology, 166, 189, 195, 222,
  262, 288, 311, 315, 351
testing, 41, 97, 317, 358, 442, 624
travel, 243-244, 275, 447, 476,
  529, 546, 572, 604
Approximation(s)
  decimal, 148-153, 168, 171
  irrational square root, 453
  repeating decimals, 2, 7
Area formula(s)
  circle, 24, 37, 619
  rectangle, 3, 10-11, 54, 95, 99,
  128, 516, 683
  square, 16, 24
  triangle, 6, 157
  trapezoid, 25, 157
Arithmetic sequence, 157-159
Average, 107-108
Automatic grapher *See* Graphing
  calculator
Axioms
  associative, 710

Axioms (contd.)
  closure, 710
  commutative, 710
  identity, 71, 89, 710
  inverse, 710
Axis(es)
  coordinate, 160-163
  horizontal, 160-163
  symmetry, 465-466, 468, 477, 515
  vertical, 160-163

B

Bar graph, 1, 5, 13, 50, 52, 54, 79, 170, 658, 664
Base of a power, 14, 19
BASIC programs, 19, 87, 166, 262, 311, 315
Binomials
  difference, two squares, 528-533
  FOIL algorithm, 515
  multiplying, 522-524, 528-533
  product, sum /difference, 522-523
  radicals, 689-694
  squares of, 522-524
Biographical/historical note
  abacus, 196
  Ada, programming language, 304
  adding machine, 196
  Aiken, Howard, 412
  analytical engine, 196
  Babbage, Charles, 196, 304, 412
  Brahmagupta, 74
  Byron, Augusta Ada, 304
  calculating through the centuries, 196
  Catherine I, 521
  computers, 196, 304, 412
  Descartes, Rene, 211, 494
  Diophantus, 74
  ENIAC, 412
  Euler, Leonhard, 521, 712
  Fermat, Pierre de, 712
  Gauss, Karl, 497
  Goldbach, Christian, 632, 712
  Hopper, Grace, 412
  Huygens, Christiaan, 493
  Khowarizmi, Mohammed ibn-Musa al-, 74
  knotted cord, 196
  Lindemann, Ferdinand, 109
  mathematical symbols, 521
  Mark I, 412
  Mauchley, John, 412
  origins of algebra, 74
  Pascal, Blaise, 196
  Pythagoras, 454
  Rhind papyrus, 74
  Shockley, William, 412
  unsolved problems, 632

von Neumann, John, 412
Wright, Frank Lloyd, 457
Boundary line, half-plane, 320
Box-and-whisker plot, 653-657, 660, 662-663

C

Calculator
  best-fitting line, 262
  change sign key, 70, 91, 99
  exponential key, 403, 409, 420, 422
  fractions, 76
  graphing, 166, 189, 195, 222, 311, 326, 352, 438, 546, 548, 664, 701
  negative key, 70, 91
  order of operations, 20-22
  polynomial expression, 9, 11-13, 78, 548
  polynomials, 549-554
  powers key, 15, 17-19, 22-23, 25, 91
  rational numbers, 109
  real numbers, 70
  reciprocal key, 70, 91, 103
  scientific key, 403, 409, 420, 422
  solving equations, 195
  square root key, 453-457
  tangent key, 704, 706
  using, 4-6, 9, 11-13, 15, 17-19, 22-23, 25, 70, 91, 109, 166, 189, 195, 222, 262, 288, 403, 409, 420, 422, 438
Career interviews
  counselor, 248
  medical technologist, 25
  pediatrician, 359
  picture framer, 146
  printer, 464
  retailer, 574
  translation services, 688
Central tendency, measures of, 653, 658-663
Chapter Review See Reviews
Chapter Summary, 55, 114, 167, 229, 284, 334, 393, 445, 498, 555, 613, 665, 716
Chapter Test See Tests
Circle, 6, 12
  area, 24
  diameter, 6
  radius, 12
Circumference, 6, 12
Closed half-plane, 320, 381-391
Closed interval, 292-297
Coefficient, 97, 124-140, 148-153, 168, 171, 264, 640
College Entrance Exam See Tests
Common denominator, 607, 610

Common monomial factoring, 528-533, 535
Commutative properties, 706
Completing the square, 549-554
Compound interest, 17, 432, 527, 551
Compute mentally, See Mental Math
Computer(s) See also Algebra biographical/historical notes and BASIC programs
  exponents, 19
  graphing, 166
  grouping symbols, 4-6, 9, 11-13, 140
Computer program(s)
  add and subtract matrices, 87
  best-fitting line, 262
  budget variance, 315
  evaluate expressions, 19
  make, scatter plot, 166
  sketch, inequality, 311
Constant
  term, 9, 75
  variation, 575-580
Converse, 677
Conversions, 2, 7, 140
Coordinate graph, 160-163, 183-188, 193-194, 208, 214
Coordinate plane, 160, 163
Counterexample, 711-715
Critical thinking, 5, 11, 17, 23, 30, 36, 42, 52, 66, 71, 78, 84, 92, 98, 104, 110, 126, 132, 138, 144, 151, 157, 163, 180, 186, 193, 201, 208, 214, 220, 226, 239, 245, 252, 259, 267, 274, 281, 296, 301, 308, 316, 330, 349, 356, 363, 370, 377, 384, 390, 403, 409, 416, 422, 429, 435, 442, 455, 461, 468, 475, 482, 489, 495, 500, 512, 518, 525, 531, 538, 544, 552, 565, 571, 578, 584, 591, 597, 603, 610, 623, 629, 636, 642, 649, 655, 661, 679, 685, 692, 698, 706, 713
Cube
  surface area, 16
  volume, 16, 18, 24, 140
Cumulative Review See Reviews
Cylinder
  volume, 157, 173

D

Data analysis, 49-51, 81-83, 107-109, 160-162, 166, 255-258, 262, 327-329, 387-389, 439-441, 492-494, 581-583, 652-654, 658-660, 664
Decimal(s)
  adding, 4, 6-7

approximation, 148-153, 168, 171
dividing, 4, 6-7
equations, 148-153, 168, 171
forms of rational numbers, 2, 7
fraction form, 2, 7, 140
multiplying, 4, 6-7
percent form, 2, 7
powers of ten, 419-424
rounding, 2, 12
scientific notation, 419-420, 422
subtracting, 4, 6, 7
Degree, 508
Denominator, 9
    least common, 607, 610
    rationalizing, 682-687
Diameter, 6
Difference See also Subtraction
    definition, 3
    of squares, 528-533
Dimensions, array, 81-82
Direct variation, 575, 577-580
Discrete mathematics See also Prob-
    ability, Sets, and Statistics
    linear programming, 375, 387-392
Discriminant, 479-485, 536
Distance
    between two points, 676-681, 694
    rate time formula, 10, 125
Distributive Property
    dividing polynomials, 710
    factoring, 528-533, 535
    multiplying polynomials, 515-520
    simplifying expressions, 95-100
Division
    algorithm, 601
    common factors, 588
    negative numbers, 102
    polynomial by a binomial, 601-
    606
    polynomial by a monomial, 600,
    603
    powers, 413
    property of, 124
    quotient, 3-6, 13
    radical expressions, 682-683, 685-
    687
    real numbers, 101-106
    rule of exponents for, 413-418
    rules for, 101
    scientific notation, 420-424, 426-
    431
    solving equations, 122-172
    whole numbers, 3-6, 13
Division property
    equality, 124
    exponents, 413-418
    powers, 413
    radicals, 682
Domain, 375, 588, 599, 620, 623-
    624, 701
Draw a diagram/picture See Prob-
    lem-solving strategies

Equation(s) See also Linear equa-
    tions, Quadratic equations, Ra-
    tional equations, and Solving
    equations
    absolute value, 217-218, 223-228
    decimal coefficients, 124-140
    equivalent, 122, 126
    fractional coefficients, 124-140
    functions, 620-644
    graphs, linear, 176-188, 193-194,
    201, 208, 214, 236
    integer coefficients, 264
    of a line, 134, 176,
    literal, 134-159, 165, 168, 171
    no solution, 140
    one variable, 28, 31-32, 35, 37, 39,
    41, 43-44, 98, 122-172
    polynomial, 541-545, 547
    properties of equality, 124-172
    radical, 695-700
    roots of, 458-463, 695-700
    sides of, 122-172
    solution of, 27, 30, 122, 130, 134,
    137
    standard form, linear, 190, 264-
    269
    standard form, polynomial, 508
    standard form, quadratic, 458, 461
    systems, linear, 346-380
    transforming, 122-172
    translating problems into, 127-
    128, 132-134, 139-140, 172
Error analysis, 100, 131, 527
Estimation See also Problem-solving
    strategies
    fitting a line, 255-262, 438
    graphs, 346-351
    probability of an event, 581-586
    problem solving, 213, 219, 221-
    222, 225-228, 563-564, 566, 628,
    680
    reasonableness, 4
    sums, 5, 6
Evaluating an expression, 4-6, 8-13,
    15, 17-23, 99, 102, 129, 134, 140,
    158-159, 172
    using a calculator, 4-6, 9, 13, 15,
    17-19, 22-23, 25, 78
    using a computer, 19
Event, 581-586
Expand binomial squares, 522-524
Exploration and Extension, 7, 13,
    18, 25, 32, 38, 44, 54, 67, 73, 80,
    86, 94, 100, 106, 113, 128, 134,
    140, 146, 153, 159, 165, 182, 188,
    195, 203, 210, 216, 222, 228, 241,
    247, 254, 261, 269, 276, 283, 297,
    303, 310, 318, 325, 333, 351, 358,
    366, 372, 380, 386, 392, 405, 411,
    418, 424, 431, 437, 444, 457, 463,

470, 477, 485, 491, 497, 514, 520,
527, 533, 540, 547, 554, 567, 573,
580, 586, 593, 599, 605, 612, 625,
631, 638, 644, 651, 657, 663, 681,
687, 694, 700, 709, 715
Exploring data See Data analysis
Exponent(s)
    expressions, 14-20, 140, 159, 400-
    418
    meaning, 14
    negative, 406-411
    properties, 400-405, 413-418
    zero, 406-411
Exponential form of a power, 17,
    159
Exponential graph, 441, 438, 444,
    633-635, 638
Expression(s) See also Rational ex-
    pressions
    algebraic, 8-13, 33-37, 42-45, 77,
    97, 99, 101, 127-128, 132-134,
    139-140, 158-159, 172, 292
    equivalent, 77
    evaluating, 4-6, 8-13, 15, 17-23,
    99, 102
    exponents, 400-418
    mixed, 4-6, 9, 13, 99, 128, 172
    numerical, 4-6, 12-13
    radical, 676-694
    simplifying, 4-6, 8-11, 14, 139-
    140, 159, 407, 414, 416, 418
    terms of, 9, 75, 97
    value of, 4-6, 8-11, 128, 159, 172
Extraneous roots, 695-700
Extremes of a proportion, 562

Factor
    greatest common, 528-533, 535
    monomial, 9, 528-533, 535
    negative, 90
Factoring
    applications, 531-533, 537-543,
    545-547
    complete the square, 549-554
    difference of two squares, 528-533
    perfect square trinomials, 528-533
    polynomials, 528-533, 535-547
    quadratic trinomials, 535-547
    solving equations, 541-545, 547
Find a pattern See Problem-solving
    strategies
FOIL algorithm, 515
Formula(s) See also Area formula(s)
    arithmetic sequence, 157-159
    centrifugal force, 699
    chemical reaction, 532
    circumference, 6
    compound interest, 17, 157, 432,
    527, 551
    discount, 157

Formula(s) (contd.)
  distance between two points, 672
  distance/rate/time, 10, 40, 42-45, 125
  exponential change/growth/decay, 401, 439, 633
  geometric sequence, 157-159, 405
  Hero's, 681
  horsepower, 155
  markup, 157
  midpoint, 678-681
  of a line, 134
  perimeter, rectangle, 6, 13, 99, 134, 154, 157
  perimeter, triangle,12, 99
  period, 687
  Pythagorean distance, 455, 677
  quadratic, 472
  simple interest, 10, 156-157
  slope, 197, 236
  speed, sound, 699
  speed, tidalwave, 686
  surface area, cube, 16, 18
  surface area, sphere, 16, 497
  Table of, 722
  temperature, 10, 131
  transforming, 134, 154-159
  true weight, 697
  velocity, 674
  velocity, bullet, 699
  volume, circular cylinder, 157, 173
  volume, cube, 16
  volume, rectangular prism, 157
  volume, pyramid, 17,156
  windchill factor, 592
Fractional equations, 124-140
Fractions See also Mixed expressions
  decimal form, 2, 7, 140
  percent form, 2
Frequency distribution, 50-51, 53, 658
Function
  calculators, 639-643
  completed square form, 639-644
  definition, 620
  domain, 620, 623-624, 701
  exponential, 633-638
  graphs, 620, 623-625, 629, 635-636, 638-643, 645, 650, 701
  linear, 620-622, 624, 627-630
  long division, 647, 650
  notation, 621
  quadratic, 621-625, 639-644
  range, 620
  rational, 646, 701
  standard form, 639-641
  transformations, 633-634
  trigonometric, 703-704
  values, 620, 622-624
  vertex, 639-642

G

General linear equation, 190, 264-269
Geometric mean, 696
Geometric sequence, 157-159, 405
Geometry See also Area formula(s) and Volume
  acute angle, 703
  circle graph, 7, 329-332, 404
  circumference, circle, 6, 12
  parallel lines, 179, 206
  perimeter, 6, 12-13, 54, 99, 128, 134, 140, 154, 157-158, 171, 690
  perpendicular lines, 694
  problem solving, 6, 24-25, 37, 125, 127-128, 134, 140, 154, 156-158, 171, 173, 358, 371-372, 376, 425, 447, 478, 483, 510, 513, 523, 525-526, 529-530, 533, 538, 543, 545, 557
  Pythagorean theorem, 454-455, 677-678, 684, 694, 704
  right triangle, 454-455, 530-531, 677-678, 684, 694, 704
  similar figures, 125, 127, 147, 209
  surface area, 16, 18, 497
Glossary, 724
Graph(s)
  absolute value, 217-218, 223-228
  automatic grapher, 166, 189, 195, 222, 262, 311, 326, 352, 438
  bar, 1, 5, 13, 50, 52, 54, 79, 170, 658, 664
  box-and-whisker plot, 653-657, 660, 662-663
  checking a solution, 211-213, 224, 242, 249-250, 271, 293-295, 306-308, 313, 346, 354, 361
  circle, 7, 329-332, 404
  coordinate, 160-163
  discrete domain, 375
  equations, 176-188, 193-194, 208, 214, 236
  exponential decay/growth, 401, 408, 410, 425, 43-434, 437, 439-444, 633-636, 638
  functions, 620, 623-625, 629, 635-636, 638-643, 645-648, 650, 701
  horizontal shifts, 633-634, 636
  hyperbola, 646-650
  interpreting, 177, 185, 283, 329
  linear equations, 176-188, 193-194, 201, 208, 214, 236
  linear inequalities, 292, 320-322, 326
  line plot, 51
  misleading, 187
  number line, 292-297, 303, 306, 308, 310-311, 313-316, 320-326
  ordered pairs, 160-163

  parabola, 465-471, 473, 475-477, 479, 481, 484, 493, 546, 639-644
  picture, 327-329, 331
  point, 62
  quadratic equations, 459-460, 467-469, 474, 476-477, 492-497, 543, 545-547
  quadratic functions, 639-644
  quadratic inequalities, 486-487, 489, 491
  quick (using intercepts), 190-191
  reflections, 634
  relations, 646-650
  scatter plot, 160-166, 170, 255, 257-258, 493-495, 499, 628, 630-631
  sketching/drawing, 178-180, 185, 191-195, 206, 237, 255, 266, 268, 271, 282, 292, 320-322, 326, 346-351, 355, 369, 374, 381-383, 410, 441, 444
  stem-and-leaf plot, 652-657
  systems, inequalities, 381-383, 387
  systems, linear equations, 346-353, 355, 361, 369, 374, 378-379
  technology, using, 166, 189, 195, 222, 262, 311, 326, 352
  time line, 327, 330-331, 333
  transformations, 633-634
  using a, 185, 236, 256, 258
  vertical shifts, 633-634, 636
Graphical model, 13, 50, 52, 54, 79, 170, 185, 237, 260, 268, 320-322, 327-332, 346-351, 355, 369, 374, 381-383, 387, 410, 441, 444, 465-471, 473, 475-477, 479, 481, 484, 493, 546, 576, 580, 620, 623-625, 628-631, 633-636, 638-644, 645-650, 652-658, 660, 662-664, 701
Graphing calculator, 166, 189, 195, 222, 262, 311, 326, 352, 546, 548, 606
Graphing method, 178-180, 185, 191-195, 199, 206, 347, 361
Gravitational force, 460
Greatest monomial factor, 528
Grouping symbols, 4-6, 9, 11-13, 140
Growth factor, 401, 408, 410, 425, 43-434, 437, 439-444, 633-636, 638

H

Half plane, 320, 381-391
Histogram, 664
Horizontal axis, 160, 163
Horizontal line
  equation, 176-180, 201
  slope, 176-180, 201
Hyperbola, 646-650

Identity property
  addition, 71, 710
  multiplication, 1, 89, 710
''If-then'' form of a statement, 677
Inequality *See also* Solving
  inequalities
  absolute value, 313-319
  compound, 305-310
  equivalent, 293, 295, 307, 314
  graph of quadratic, 381-391
  graph of systems of linear, 381-
    383, 387
  graph on a number line, 292-297,
    303, 306, 308, 310-311, 313-316,
    320-326
  problems, 28, 30, 41, 292, 297-
    303, 305, 307, 309-310, 315, 317-
    318, 381-383, 385-389, 391-392
  quadratic, 486-491
  reversing, 293-294, 306
  sketching, 292, 320-322, 324
  slope-intercept form, 321
  solutions, 29-30, 292-319, 381-387
  standard form, 320
  symbols, 29
  transformations, 293-297
  two variables, 292-297, 303, 306,
    308, 310-311, 486-491
Integer(s)
  addition, 68-73
  coefficient, 264
  division, 101-106
  multiplication, 89-94
  negative, 62
  positive, 62
  subtraction, 75-80
Integrated Review *See* Reviews
Intercepts, 190, 205, 236-247, 249-
  262
  finding, 190-193
Interest
  compound, 17, 432, 527, 551
  simple, 10, 156-157
Intersection
  half-planes, 381-391
Inverse operations, 122, 126, 129
Inverse variation, 575-580
Inverse, 706
Irrational numbers, 453-457

L

Least common denominator, 607,
  610
Like terms, 97, 129-136
Line(s)
  boundary, 383
  fitting to data, 255-262, 438

  graphing, 176-188, 193-194, 208,
    214, 237, 255, 266, 268, 271, 282
  horizontal, 176-180, 201
  intersecting, 346-397
  parallel, 179, 206
  perpendicular, 694
  slope of, 197-202, 347, 694
  vertical, 176-180, 210
  x-intercept, 190
  y-intercept, 190, 205, 236-247,
    249-262
Linear combination method, 360-
  366
Linear equation(s) *See also* Systems
  of linear equations
  fit to data, 255-262, 438
  given two points, 249-254
  graph, 176-188, 193-194, 208, 214
  slope and point, 242-247, 270
  slope and y-intercept, 236-241,
    347
  slope-intercept form, 205-206,
    236-247, 249-262, 264, 347
  standard form , 190, 264-269
  two variables, 183-188, 193-194,
    208, 214, 236-254, 270
Linear equation model, 237-240,
  243-244, 251, 265-266, 272-273,
  277-278, 433, 492, 531, 537, 627-
  630
Linear function, 620-622, 624, 627-
  630
  graph, 620, 623-625, 629
Linear graph, 176-188, 193-194, 208,
  214
Linear inequality
  graph, 292, 320-322, 311, 326
  slope-intercept, 321
  standard form, 320
Linear inequality model, 298-300,
  322
Linear programming, 387-392
  contraints, 387
Linear systems, 346-397
Linear term, 148-153, 168, 171, 264
List all possibilities *See* Problem-
  solving stategies
Literal equations, 134-159, 165, 168,
  171

M

Maintaining skills *See* Reviews *and*
  Tests
Math in other disciplines *See*
  Applications *and* Careers
Mathematical model, 33-35, 37, 46,
  68, 70, 73, 133, 137-138, 141, 144,
  147, 150, 168, 187-188, 192, 225,
  237-240, 243-244, 251, 258, 265-
  266, 272-273, 277-280, 298-299,
  322, 348, 350-351, 367-369, 376,

  426, 433, 441, 474, 480, 484-485,
  488, 492-497, 511, 516-517, 523,
  525, 531, 537, 543, 553, 563, 569,
  575-577, 582, 589, 596, 598, 608-
  609, 627-630, 635, 640-641, 643,
  645-648, 683, 691, 697, 705
Matrix (matrices)
  adding, 82-87
  entries, 81-82
  equal, 81
  square, 82
  subtracting, 82-87
  writing a table, 81
Maximum value of interval, 467,
  639, 641-643
Mean, 653, 658-663
Means of a proportion, 562
Measure(s)
  central tendency, 653, 658-663
Median, 653, 658-663
Mental math, 3, 5, 28, 30, 42-45, 67,
  73, 84
Metric system, table of, 722
Mid-Chapter Self-Test *See* Tests
Midpoint, 678-681
Milestones *See*
  Biographical/historical note
Minimum value of interval, 467,
  639, 641-643
Mixed expression(s), 4-6, 9, 13, 99,
  128, 159, 172
Mixed Review *See* Reviews
Mixtures, 153, 169, 268, 278, 281-
  282, 365, 367-368, 370, 385, 389,
  391
Mode, 658-663
Model(s)
  absolute value, 225, 315, 492
  choosing, 492-497
  comparing, 219, 238, 492-497
  estimating/forcasting, 244, 251
  exponential, 492, 494
  graphing, 13, 50, 52, 54, 79, 170,
    185, 237, 260, 268, 320-322, 327-
    332, 346-351, 355, 369, 374, 381-
    383, 387, 410, 441, 444, 465-471,
    473, 475-477, 479, 481, 484, 493,
    546, 576, 580, 620, 623-625, 628-
    631, 633-636, 638-644, 645-650,
    652-658, 660, 662-664, 701
  interpreting, 225, 441
  linear, 68, 70, 73, 133, 137-138,
    141, 144, 147, 150, 168, 187-188,
    192, 225, 237-238, 240, 243-244,
    251, 258, 265-266, 272-273, 277-
    280, 433, 492, 531, 537, 627-630
  mathematical, 33-35, 37, 46, 68,
    70, 73, 133, 137-138, 141, 144,
    147, 150, 168, 187-188, 192, 225,
    237-240, 243-244, 251, 258, 265-
    266, 272-273, 277-280, 298-299,
    322, 348, 350-351, 367-369, 376,

Model(s)
mathematical (contd.)
426, 433, 441, 474, 480, 484-485,
488, 492-497, 511, 516-517, 523,
525, 531, 537, 543, 553, 563, 569,
575-577, 582, 589, 596, 598, 608-
609, 627-630, 635, 640-641, 643,
645-648, 683, 691, 697, 705
polynomials, 511, 516-518, 525
quadratic, 492, 640-641, 643, 645-
648
translating between, 315
variation, 575-577, 598, 608-609
verbal, 33-35, 39-46, 237-238, 265,
277, 298, 300, 322, 347, 362, 367-
369, 426, 523, 543, 568, 570, 608-
609, 627, 635, 641, 648
vertical motion, 474, 480, 485,
553
visual, 1, 6-7, 13, 39, 47, 48-50,
52-54, 63, 67, 71-72, 79-81, 83-86,
88, 92, 99, 106-107, 112, 145-146,
159-162, 164-165, 170, 173, 178,
180-185, 187, 200, 210, 219, 237,
240, 253, 260, 266, 268-269, 278-
280, 282, 287-288, 298, 300, 307,
320-322, 327-332, 346-351, 355,
369, 374, 381-383, 387, 404, 408,
410, 441,465-471, 473, 475-477,
479, 481, 484, 490, 493-497, 516-
518, 520, 523, 525, 539, 546, 620,
623-625, 628-631, 633-636, 638-
650, 652-654, 656-657
Modeling real-life situations, 34-38,
237, 243, 251, 265, 272, 278, 307,
315, 322, 348, 355, 362, 383, 408,
414, 426, 459, 467, 474, 480, 487,
493, 510, 517, 529, 543, 563, 569,
576, 582, 589, 596, 608, 627, 635
Monomial(s)
degree of, 508
dividing polynomial by, 600, 603,
605
factor, 9
multiplying polynomial by, 515
powers of, 14-19
Multiplication
binomials, 515, 522-524, 528-533
binomials with radicals, 689-694
difference of two squares, 528-533
FOIL algorithm, 515
geometric models, 516-517, 523,
525
identity element, 1, 89, 710
polynomial by a monomial, 515
polynomials, 515-520, 522-527
radical expressions, 682-683, 685-
687
real numbers, 89-94
scientific notation, 420-424, 426-
431
solving equations,122, 124-172

squares of binomials, 522-524
whole numbers, 3-6, 13
Multiplication method for solving a
system, 360-366
Multiplication property
equality, 124
exponents, 400-405
negative one, 89
one, 89
order, 89
zero, 89
Multiplicative inverse, 710

Negative exponent(s), 406-411
Negative number(s)
absolute value, 64-67
set of, 62-63
square roots, 452-458
Negative rate of change, 402, 439,
633
Notation
function, 621
scientific, 419-444
Number(s)
absolute value, 64-67
comparing, 29
integers, 62-63, 66-67
irrational, 453-457
opposite , 64
rational, 109
real, 62-63
reciprocal, 101
square, 452
whole, 2-6, 13
Number line
addition, 68
coordinate, point, 163
graphing inequalities, 292-297,
303, 306, 308, 310-311, 313-316,
320-326
origin, 62
Numerator, 9
Numerical coefficient, 97, 124-140,
148-153, 168, 171, 264, 288
Numerical expression, 4-5, 12-13,
99, 128, 159, 172

Open half-plane, 320, 381-391
Open interval, 292-297
Operations
inverse, 122, 126, 129
order of, 20-22
Opposite(s)
number, 64
property of, 64
sum, 76-78
Order

operations, 20-22
properties, 109
rational numbers, 109
real numbers, 62-63
symbols, 4-5, 9
terms in a polynomial, 508-512
Ordered pairs
coordinates, 160-163
graph of, 160-163
Ordinate, 160
Origin, 160
Outcome, equally-likely, 581-586

Parabola(s)
axis of symmetry, 465-466, 468,
477, 515
graphing calculator, 546, 548
maximum point, 639, 641-643
minimum point, 639, 641-643
Parallel lines, 179, 206
Pattern(s) See also Problem-solving
strategies
difference of two squares, 528-533
factoring trinomials, 538-533,
535-547
perfect square trinomial, 528-533
Percent(s)
decimal form, 7, 140
discount/markup, 94, 150, 152
problems, 188, 569-570
of a region, 571
unknown base, 568
unknown number, 7, 568
unknown percent, 569
Perfect square(s)
recognizing, 452
trinomial, 528-533
Perimeter, 6, 12-13, 24, 54, 99, 128,
134, 140, 154, 157-158, 171
Perpendicular lines, 694
Pi (π), 6
Plane, coordinate, 160, 163
Point(s)
coordinates, 160-163
distance between two, 676-681,
694
number line, 62
plotting, 160, 163
Polynomial(s)
addition and subtraction, 508-514
classifying, 508
degree of, 508
difference of two squares, 528
division, binomial, 601-606
division, monomial, 600, 603, 605
evenly divisible, 594-599
factoring, 528-533, 535-547
greatest monomial factor, 528
linear equations, 176-188, 193-
194, 208, 214

long division, 600-606
monomial factors, 508-529, 530-531
multiplication, monomials, 515
multiplication, polynomials, 515-520, 522-527
perfect square trinomials, 528-533
quadratic, 535-547, 549-554
recognizing factors, 528-533, 535-547
simplifying, 528-531
square of a binomial, 522, 525, 530-531
sum/difference, binomials, 522, 525, 530-531
Polynomial equation(s), 176-188, 193-194, 208, 214, 541-545, 547, 549-554
Positive number(s)
absolute value, 64-67
set of, 62-63
Positive rate of change, 401-402, 439, 633
Positive square root, 452-458
Power(s)
monomial, 14-19
power, 400
product, 400
quotient, 413
Principal, 10, 155-157, 305-310
Principal square root, 452-458
Prism
surface area, 16, 18
volume, 157
Probability
equally-likely outcome, 581-586
of an event, 581-586
odds, 586
of one, 586
solving problems, 567, 581-586
Problem solving See also
Applications
absolute value, 219, 221-222, 225-228, 315, 317-318
age, 605, 663
approximating solutions, 213, 219, 221-222, 225-228, 563-564, 566, 628, 680
average, 24, 41, 107, 110, 168, 171, 200, 608-609, 611
cost/income/value, 3, 6, 43, 137, 139, 150, 152, 165, 169, 171-173, 194, 202, 238, 240, 246-247, 253-254, 260, 263, 267-268, 277, 281, 325, 357, 369, 404, 427, 531, 573, 580, 608, 691
decimals, 150, 152-153, 168
discount/markup/tax, 94, 111, 150, 152, 157, 357, 570, 622
distance/rate/time, 10-11, 39-40, 42-45, 52, 110-111, 364, 369-370, 424, 460, 578, 627

equations, one variable, 28, 31-32, 35, 37, 39, 41, 43-44, 98, 125, 127-128, 131-134, 137-139, 141-146, 150-153, 176-179, 181-182
equations, two variables, 154-158, 183-185, 187-188, 192, 194-195, 200, 202-203, 207, 209-210, 213, 215-216, 219, 221-222, 225, 227-228, 237-238, 240-241, 243-244, 246-247, 251, 253-254, 265-266, 268-269, 272-273, 275, 277-283, 346-348, 350-351, 353-355, 357-358, 360-362, 364-371, 374-376, 378-379, 627-630
exponential, 401, 403-404, 408-410, 414-418, 421-423, 425-437, 439-444, 494, 635, 637-638
frequency, 50-51, 53, 103, 105, 319, 637, 658
geometry, 3, 6, 11-13, 16-18, 24-26, 37, , 54, 71-72, 95, 99, 125, 127-128, 134, 140, 145-146, 154, 156-159, 171, 173, 281, 307, 358, 371-372, 376, 425, 447, 453-457, 461, 478, 483, 494, 510, 513, 518-519, 523, 527, 576, 578, 580, 599, 622, 637, 641, 677, 680, 681, 683, 690, 693, 714
inequalities, one variable, 297-302, 305, 307, 309-310, 315, 317-318
inequalities, two variables, 322, 324-325
interest, 7, 11, 156-159, 281, 432, 527, 551-552
investment, 11, 157, 346-347, 350, 608
linear programming, 387-392
matrices, 81-83, 85-86, 94, 112
mean/median/mode, 653, 658-663
mixture, 153, 169, 268, 278, 281-282, 365, 367-368, 370, 385, 389, 391
number, 38, 159, 379, 401
percent, 11, 17, 22, 24, 94, 96, 99, 128, 150, 152-153, 169, 188, 194, 240, 268, 281, 332, 357, 370, 432-434,437, 439-444, 569-570, 572-573, 579, 583, 587, 654, 661
polynomials, 511-514, 517, 529, 531-533, 537-543, 545-547
predicting, 213, 481
probability, 567, 581-586
proportion/variation, 209-210, 426-428, 440, 563-567, 576-580, 648, 650
quadratic equations, 459-460, 467-468, 474, 476-477, 492-497, 543, 545-547, 550-554, 640-641, 643, 648, 650
quadratic inequalities, 486-488, 490-491

radicals, 677-678, 680-684, 686-687, 691, 693-694, 697, 699-700
rate/ratio, 108-113, 125, 127, 143, 147, 161, 173, 178, 181-182, 200, 202-203, 209-210, 246, 251, 253-254, 273, 279-280, 376, 414-415, 426-428, 567, 581-586, 589-590, 592-593, 648, 684, 703-709
rational expressions, 589-590, 592-593, 596, 608-609, 611-612
scale, 37, 112-113, 676
scientific notation, 421-423, 426-437, 439-444
statistics, 658-663
systems, equations, 346-348, 350-351, 353-355, 357-358, 360-362, 364-371, 374-376, 378-379
trigonometry, 703-709
velocity, 480, 482, 674, 699
weight/measure, 225
weighted averages, 367-368, 370, 385, 389
work, 111, 133, 138, 611
Problem-solving plan, 39-41, 46, 132-133, 137-138, 141-145, 150, 169, 369
Problem-solving strategies
checking solution, 40-41
compare/choose method, 543, 551, 678
draw a diagram/picture, 48, 71-72, 112, 145-146, 253, 307, 467, 589, 635, 681, 714
estimate, 4, 213, 219, 221-222, 225-228, 563-564, 566, 628, 676
find/recognizing a pattern, 1, 18, 47, 106, 162, 183, 530, 537, 637, 641, 684
guess/check/revise, 22, 47, 536
make a matrix, 81-83, 85-86, 94, 112
make/use, graph, 13, 50, 52, 54, 79, 170, 185, 237, 260, 268, 320-322, 327-332, 346-351, 355, 369, 374, 381-383, 387, 410, 441, 444, 465-471, 473, 475-477, 479, 481, 484, 493, 546, 576, 580, 620, 623-625, 628-631, 633-636, 638-644, 645-650, 652-658, 660, 662-664, 701
make/use, table, 1, 6-7, 13, 39, 47, 49, 53-54, 67, 79-81, 83-86, 88, 92, 99, 106-107, 112, 159-162, 164-165, 173, 178, 181-184, 187, 240, 266, 268-269, 278-280, 282, 287-288, 404, 408, 410, 490, 493-497, 518, 520, 539, 585-586, 590, 620, 622-624, 628, 630-631, 642, 645-647, 658, 693, 700
models, 13, 48, 50, 52, 54, 68, 70-73, 79, 112, 133, 137-138, 141, 145-147, 150, 160-162, 164-165,

Problem-solving strategies
model (contd.)
168, 170, 181-183, 185, 187-188,
191-192, 194-195, 200, 202-204,
207, 209-210, 213, 215-216, 219,
221-222, 225-228, 237-241, 243-
244, 247, 251, 253, 256-258, 260,
265-266, 268, 272-273, 275, 277-
280, 298, 300, 307, 315, 320-322,
327-332, 346-351, 355, 369, 374,
381-383, 387, 410, 441, 444, 465-
471, 473, 475-477, 479, 481, 484,
493, 516-517, 523, 546, 563, 567-
570, 575-577, 582, 589, 596, 598,
608-609, 620-625, 627-631, 635-
633, 638-644, 645-650, 652-658,
660, 662-664, 701
unit analysis, 91, 164
work backward, 711
Product(s) *See also* Multiplication
binomials, 515, 522-524, 528-533
polynomials, 515-520, 522-533
powers, 400
properties, 89
whole numbers, 3-6, 13
Property
adding like terms, 97, 135-136
addition, 69
addition, of equality, 124
additive identity, 71, 710
associative, of addition, 710
associative, of multiplication, 710
commutative, addition, 89, 710
commutative, multiplication, 89
cross-multiplying, 562
discriminant, 479-485
distributive, 95-96, 130, 132, 136,
710
division, equality, 124
multiplication, equality, 124
multiplication, zero, 89
multiplicative identity, 89, 710
negative exponents, 406-411
opposites, 64, 77, 89
power, 400
power, power, 400
power, product, 400
power, quotient, 413
product, of radicals, 678
quotient, powers, 413
subtraction, equality, 124
zero exponent, 406
zero product, 541
Proportion(s) *See also* Variation
applications, 125, 127, 147
estimating, 563-564, 566
direct variation, 575, 577-580
inverse variation, 575-580
problem solving, 209-210, 426-
428, 440, 563-567, 576-580, 648,
650
properties, 562

similar triangles, 125, 127, 147
solving, 562-567
Pyramid volume, 18, 156, 401
Pythagoras, 454
Pythagorean distance formula, 676-
681, 694
Pythagorean theorem, 454, 530, 533
Pythagorean triples, 530

Q

Quadrants, 160
Quadratic equation(s)
axis of symmetry, 465-466, 468,
477, 515
discriminant, 479-485, 536
finding x-intercept, 473, 475
graphs, 465-471, 473, 475-477,
479, 481, 484, 493, 546
problem solving, 486-488, 490-491
roots, 458-463, 695-700
solutions, 458-463, 472-477, 541-
545, 549-554
solving, calculator, 461, 471
solving, completing the square,
549-554
solving, factoring, 541-545, 547
solving, quadratic formula, 472-
477
standard form, 458, 461
Quadratic function(s), 621-625, 639-
644
Quadratic inequality
graphing, 486-487, 489, 491
solving, 486-491
Quadratic polynomial, 508, 535-547
Quadratic trinomials *See* Factoring
Quartile, 653
Quotient(s) *See also* Division
polynomials, 600-606
powers of, 413
property of radicals, 682
property of square roots, 682
whole numbers, 3-6,13

R

Radical, 452
Radical expression(s)
addition/subtraction, 689-694
multiplication, binomials, 689-
694
multiplication/division, 682
problem solving, 677-678, 680-
681, 683-684, 686-687, 691, 693-
694, 697, 699-700, 703-709
rationalizing, denominator, 682-
687
simplifying, 682-687

Radicand, 452
Range, 620
Rate(s), 107-109, 197, 200, 251, 277
Ratio(s)
equal, 125, 127, 147
trigonometric, 703-706
using, 109, 125, 127, 143, 147,
173
Rational equations, 607
Rational expression(s)
comparing, 590
cross multiplying, 608, 610
dividing, 595-599
dividing, polynomial, 595, 597
domain, 588, 599
false solutions, 609
graphing calculator, 606
LCD, 607, 610
multiplying, 594-599
multiplying, polynomial, 595, 597
problem solving, 589-590, 592-
593, 596, 598, 608-609,
611-612
simplifying, 588-593
solving equations, 607-612
Rational number(s), 109
decimal forms, 2, 7
properties, 594
Rationalizing, denominators, 682-
687
Real number(s)
addition, 68-73
division, 101-106
multiplication, 89-94
number line, 62
reciprocal, 101
set of, 62
subtraction, 75-80
Reciprocal(s)
opposite of a number, 101
problem solving, 123, 131-132
property, 562
Rectangle
area, 3, 6-7, 9, 54, 95, 99
perimeter, 6, 13, 54, ,99, 128, 134,
140, 154, 157-158, 171
Rectangular array, 81-87
Rectangular solid(s)
surface area, 16, 18
volume, 16, 18, 24, 140
Relation(s)
graphs, 646-650
Relative frequency, 50-51, 53, 103,
105, 319, 637, 658
Reviews
Chapter Review, 56-58, 115-118,
168-170, 230-232, , 285-288, 335-
338, 394-396, 446-448, 499-502,
556-558, 614-616, 666-668, 717-
719
Cumulative Review, 172-173,
340-343, 504-505, 670-673

INDEX

Integrated Review, 7, 12, 18, 24, 31, 37, 67, 72, 80, 86, 94, 99, 106, 113, 128, 134, 139, 146, 152, 158, 165, 182, 188, 194, 203, 210, 215, 222, 227, 241, 247, 254, 261, 269, 275, 282, 297, 303, 310, 318, 323, 325, 332, 351, 358, 365, 372, 379, 386, 392, 405, 411, 418, 424, 431, 437, 443, 457, 463, 470, 477, 484, 491, 497, 514, 520, 527, 533, 540, 546, 554, 567, 573, 580, 586, 593, 599, 605, 612, 625, 631, 638, 644, 651, 657, 663, 681, 687, 694, 700, 708-709, 715

Mixed Review , 38, 74, 100, 140, 159, 196, 216, 248, 276, 304, 319, 359, 380, 412, 424, 464, 485, 521, 547, 574, 593, 632, 651, 688, 709

Right triangle
   Pythagorean theorem, 454, 530, 533
   trigonometric ratios, 703-704
   triplets, 530-532, 707

Root(s) *See also* Solution(s)
   extraneous, 695-700
   quadratic equations, 458-463, 695-700

Round-off error, 148-153, 168, 171

Rounding numbers
   decimals, 2, 12, 140
   quotients, 2

Rule(s)
   adding integers, 69
   dividing rational expressions, 594
   multiplying rational expressions, 594
   order of operations, 20-22
   simplifying products, 90
   subtracting integers, 75
   transforming equations, 122
   transforming inequalities, 293

S

Scale, 37, 112-113, 680

Scatter plot, 160-166, 170, 255, 257-258, 493-495, 499

Science *See* Applications *and* Formula(s)

Scientific notation, 419-444

Scientific notes, 69, 103, 105, 117, 272, 317-318, 336, 364-367, 396, 408, 437, 456, 493, 506, 524, 560, 564, 570, 590, 592, 602, 627, 645, 662, 684, 686

Selected Answers, 733

Sequence
   arithmetic, 157-159
   geometric, 157-159, 405

Set(s)
   integers, 62-63, 66-67

irrational numbers, 453-457
rational numbers, 109
real numbers, 62-63
whole numbers, 2-6

Sides
   equation, 122-172
   inequality, 293-297
   triangle, 704

Similar figures, 125, 127, 147

Similar terms, 97, 129-136

Similar triangles, 125, 127, 147

Simple interest, 10, 156-157

Simplest form
   radical expressions, 682
   polynomials, 528-531

Simplifying
   expressions, 4-5, 8-11, 14, 77, 97, 99, 101, 139-140, 159, 407, 414, 416, 418
   polynomials, 528-531
   radical expressions, 682-687
   sides of an equation, 122-172
   sums/differences, radicals, 682-687, 689-694

Simultaneous equations *See* Systems of linear equations

Slope
   horizontal line, 176-180, 201
   interpreting, 200-202
   line, 176-180, 197, 201, 205
   negative, 197
   parallel lines, 206
   perpendicular, 690
   positive, 197
   vertical lines, 176-180, 201
   zero, 197

Slope-intercept form of a linear equation, 205-206, 236-247, 249-262

Solution(s) *See also* Root(s)
   linear equations, 122, 176-188, 193-194, 208, 214, 236
   linear inequalities, 292, 320-322, 326
   quadratic equations, 458-463, 472-477, 541-545, 549-554
   quadratic inequalities, 486-491
   system, equations, 346-355, 361, 369, 374, 378-379
   system, inequalities, 381-387

Solving equations
   absolute value, 217-218, 223-228
   factoring, 124-140
   fractional coefficients, 124-140
   like terms, 97, 129-136
   more than one way, 130, 134, 137
   one transformation, 122-128, 140, 159,168
   one variable, 176-182
   properties, equality, 124-172
   quadratic, 458-463, 472-477, 541-545, 549-554

radical, 695-700
systems, linear, 346-380
transformations, 122-172
two or more transformations, 129-172
two variables, 183-228
variables on both sides, 135-142, 145, 147, 149-153, 165, 168, 171

Solving inequalities, 29-30, 172
   absolute value, 313-319
   properties of inequalities, 292-297
   quadratic, 486-491
   systems, linear, 381-387
   variable on both sides, 293-297

Solving problems *See* Problem solving strategies

Sphere, surface area, 16, 497

Square(s)
   binomials, 522-524
   difference of two, 528-533
   of a number, 452
   perfect, trinomial, 528-533

Square root(s)
   approximating, 453
   evaluating with a calculator, 453
   finding, 452, 458
   principal, 452
   product property, 682
   quotient property, 682
   rational, 452-455
   variable expressions, 458-461

Stacked bar graph, 52

Standard form
   linear equation, 190, 264-269
   polynomial equation, 190
   quadratic equation, 458, 461

Statistics
   analyzing data, 653, 658-663
   bar graph, 1, 5, 13, 50, 52, 54, 170
   box-and-whiskers, 653-657, 660, 662-663
   fitting a line to data, 255-262, 438
   frequency distribution, 50-51, 53, 103, 105, 319, 637, 658
   measures of central tendency, 653, 658-663
   scatter plot, 160-166, 170, 255, 257-258, 493-485, 499
   stacked bar graph, 52
   stem-and-leaf plot, 652-657
   table, 1, 6-7, 13, 39, 47, 49, 53-54, 159-162, 164-165, 173

Substitution method in transform-ing equations, 353-358, 361

Subtraction *See also* Difference
   decimals, 4, 6-7
   definition, 3
   integers, 75-76
   polynomials, 508-514
   property, equality, 124
   radicals, 689-694
   real numbers, 75-80

INDEX

Subtraction (contd.)
  rules, 75
  transforming equations,122-123, 125-172
  whole numbers, 3-6,13
Sum *See also* Addition
  definition, 3
Surface area
  cube, 16, 18
  sphere, 16, 497
Symbol(s)
  absolute value, 64
  approximately equal to, 2
  braces, 62
  equality/inequality, 27, 29, 62
  grouping, 4-6, 9, 11-13, 20-21
  pi, 6, 521
  plus/minus, 62
  square root, 452
  Table of, 722-723
  translating words into, 33-37, 42-45, 127-128, 132-134, 139-140, 172, 292
Symmetry
  axis of, 465-466, 468, 477, 515
  parabola, 465-466, 477, 515
System, inequalities, 381-387
System, linear equations
  adding/subtracting, 360-366
  graphing, 346-351, 361
  infinitely many solutions, 375-377
  no solutions, 374-377
  linear combination, 360-366
  problem solving, 346-348, 350-351, 353-355, 357-358, 360-362, 364-371, 374-376, 378-379
  solution of, 374-377
  substitution, 353-358, 361
System, linear inequalities
  graphing, 381-383, 387

T

Table of
  formulas, 722-723
  metric system, 722-723
  squares/approximate square roots, 721
  symbols, 722-723
Tangent
  angle, 703-704
  function, 706
Technology *See* Calculator, Computer, *and* Computer programs
Temperature, 10, 131, 145, 160, 164-165
Term(s)
  coefficient of, 97, 124-140, 148-153, 168, 171, 264

constant, 9, 75
  expression, 9, 75, 97
  like or similar, 97, 129-136
  polynomial, 97, 129-136
  sequence, 157, 405
Tests
  Chapter Test, 59, 119, 171, 233, 289, 339, 397, 449, 503, 559, 617, 669, 720
  College Entrance, 32, 53, 97, 134, 153, 210, 215, 310, 365, 405, 411, 437, 484, 519, 527, 554, 592, 638, 694, 709
  Mid-Chapter Self-Test, 26, 88, 147, 204, 263, 312, 373, 425, 478, 534, 587, 645, 702
Transformation(s)
  equations, 122-172
  formulas, 134, 154-159
  graphs, 633-634
Translating expressions
  verbal to algebraic, 33-37, 42-45, 127-128, 132-134, 139-140, 172, 292
Translations, 633-643, 636
Triangle(s)
  area, 6, 7, 157, 159
  perimeter, 12, 24, 99
  right, triplets, 532, 703
  similar, 125, 127, 147
  trigonometric, 703-704
Trigonometric ratios
  tangent, 703-706
Trinomial(s)
  factoring, 528-533, 535-547
  perfect square, 528-533
  quadratic, 535-547
Two-dimensional slides, 633-643, 636

V

Value(s)
  expression, 4-5, 8-13, 102, 128, 134, 140, 158-159, 172
  function, 620, 622-624
  trigonometric ratios, 703-706
  variable, 8-11
Variable
  domain, 588, 599, 620, 623-624, 694
  restrictions, fractions, 588, 599
  values, 4-5, 8-13
Variance, 315
Variation *See also* Proportion(s)
  constant of, 575
  direct, 575, 577-580
  inverse, 575-580
  model, 575-577, 598, 608-609
Verbal model, 34-35, 39-46, 237-238, 265, 277, 298, 300, 322, 426, 523,

543, 568, 570, 608-609, 627, 635, 641, 648
Vertex (vertices)
  parabola, 217-218, 224
Vertical axis, 160, 163
Vertical line
  equation of, 176-180, 201
  slope of, 176-180, 201
Visual model, 1, 6-7, 13, 39, 47, 48-50, 52-54, 63, 67, 71-72, 79-81, 83-86, 88, 92, 99, 106-107, 112, 145-146, 159-162, 164-165, 170, 173, 178, 180-185, 187, 200, 210, 219, 237, 240, 253, 260, 266, 268-269, 278-280, 282, 287-288, 298, 300, 307, 320-322, 327-332, 346-351, 355, 369, 374, 381-383, 387, 404, 408, 410, 441,465-471, 473, 475-477, 479, 481, 484, 490, 493-497, 516-518, 520, 523, 525, 539, 546, 620, 623-625, 628-631, 633-636, 638-650, 652-654, 656-657
Volume
  cube, 16, 18, 24, 140
  circular cylinder, 157, 173
  prism, 157
  pyramid, 18, 156

W

Weighted average, 367-368, 370, 385, 389
Whole number(s), 2-6, 13
  addition, 3-6, 13
  product, 3-6, 13
  quotient, 3-6, 13
  subtraction, 3-6, 13

X

x-axis, 160, 163
x-intercept
  line, 190
  parabola, 360-366

Y

y-axis, 160, 163
y-intercept, 190, 205, 236-247, 249-262

Z

Zero
  absolute value, 64-67
  exponent property, 406
  identity for addition, 71, 710
  product property, 541
  reciprocal, 101
  square root, 452

INDEX

Appreciation to the following art/photo production staff:

Leslie Concannon, Pam Daly, Irene Elios, Julie Fair, Martha Friedman, Susan Geer, Aimee Good, Carmen Johnson, Judy Kelly, Maureen Lauran, Mark MacKay, Helen McDermott, Penny Peters, Nina Whitney, Bonnie Yousefian.

ILLUSTRATION CREDITS

Calligraphy by **Jean Evans**
Illustration by **Pat Rossi and Associates**, p. 331 by **Cyndy Patrick**
Technical Illustration by **Tech-Graphics**

PHOTO CREDITS

vi: *l*, C.S. Gray (The Image Works); *c*, Del Mulkey (Photo Researchers, Inc.); *r*, Luis Castaneda (The Image Bank). vii: *t*, Michel Tcherevkoff (Image Bank); *b*, Geraldine Prentice (Tony Stone Worldwide). viii: *t*, IKAN /Voigtmann (Peter Arnold, Inc.); *b*, Barrie Rokeach. ix: *t*, David Madison/Duomo; *b*, Peter Saloutos (The Stock Market). x: *t*, Murray and Associates (The Stock Market); *b*, Roger Ressmeyer (Starlight). xi: *t*, Y. Arthus Bertrand (Photo Researchers, Inc.); *b*, Alfred Pasieka (Peter Arnold, Inc.). xii: *t*, Woods Hole Oceanographic Institution; *b*, Manfred P. Kage (Peter Arnold, Inc.). xiii: NASA.

CHAPTER 1 0-1: Michel Tcherevkoff (The Image Bank). 6: The Arents Collections, The New York Public Library; Astor, Lenox and Tilden Foundations. 10: Alan Carey (The Image Works). 16: Dana Hyde (Photo Researchers, Inc.). 17: Mark Boulton (Photo Researchers, Inc.). 18: Stephan Johnson (Tony Stone Worldwide). 22: Richard Hutchings (Photo Researchers, Inc.). 25: Susan Doheny/©D.C. Heath. 26: Wesley Bocxe (/Photo Researchers, Inc.). 28: Bobbie Kingsley (Photo Researchers, Inc.). 31: Dion Ogust (The Image Works). 32: *b*, Zig Leszczynski (Animals Animals); *t*, John Garrett (Tony Stone Worldwide). 34: Will McIntyre (Photo Researchers, Inc.). 35: Jess Koppel (Tony Stone Worldwide). 38: Robert Tringali, Jr. (SportsChrome East/West, Inc.). 39: Bob Daemmrich Photography. 42: Kay Chernush (The Image Bank). 43: Mimi Forsyth (Monkmeyer Press). 43: Roger Dollarhide (Monkmeyer Press). 44: John Coletti (The Picture Cube). 45: Tony Stone Worldwide. 46: 1963 M.C. Escher/Cordon Art-Baarn-Holland. 48: 1955 M.C. Escher/Cordon Art-Baarn-Holland. 57: F.K. Schleicher © Vireo

CHAPTER 2 60-61: Geraldine Prentice (Tony Stone Worldwide). 65: Roger Ressmeyer (Starlight). 67: Tony Stone Worldwide. 70: Leonard Lessin (Peter Arnold, Inc.). 74: The British Museum (The Bridgeman Art Library, London). 76: John Neubauer (Monkmeyer Press). 79: Parker Brothers. 83: Giraudon (Art Resource). 86: Tony Freeman (PhotoEdit). 93: *b*, Frank Pedrick (The Image Works); *t*, Stephen Dalton (Animals Animals). 96: (SportsChrome East/West, Inc.). 105: Steve Maslowski (Photo Researchers, Inc.). 106: Tom & Pat Leeson (DRK). 108: Robert Frerck (Odyssey, Chicago). 116: Steve Kaufman (Peter Arnold, Inc.). 117: Scott Camazine (Photo Researchers, Inc.). 118: Don Griffin for H.A Perry Foundation.

CHAPTER 3 120-121: IKAN /Voigtmann (Peter Arnold, Inc.). 131: Sybil Shackman (Monkmeyer Press). 133: *b*, R.L. Kelly (Photo Researchers, Inc.); *t*, Larry Nicholson (Photo Researchers, Inc.). 137: Luis Castaneda (The Image Bank). 139: James H. Karales (Peter Arnold, Inc.). 141: Gunter Ziesler (Peter Arnold, Inc.). 144: Miriam Austerman (Animals Animals). 146: Susan Doheny/ © D.C. Heath. 147: Richard Hutchings (Photo Researchers, Inc.). 150: Roy Schneider (The Stock Market). 158: M.A.X. Mayer (The Stock Market).

CHAPTER 4 173-174: Barrie Rokeach. 178: F. Prenzel (Animals Animals). 192: John M. Burley (Photo Researchers, Inc.). 195: Lori Adamski-Peek (SportsChrome East /West, Inc.). 196: *t*, Culver Pictures; *b*, Vincent De Florio (Art Resource). 200: J.F. Causse (Tony Stone Worldwide). 207: Charles Gupton (Stock Boston). 211: North Wind Picture Archives. 215: Craig Milvin (SportsChrome East/West, Inc.). 221: *l*, Los Angeles County Museum of Natural History Foundation; *r*, Courtesy of the Southwest Museum, Los Angeles, Photo #22420. 222: Roger Ressmeyer (Starlight). 225: Maryland Department of Agriculture. 226: Julie Fair. 227: John Beatty (Tony Stone Worldwide). 228: *l*, Clyde H. Smith (/Peter Arnold, Inc.); *r*, Len Rue, Jr (Monkmeyer Press). 232: Lawrence Migdale

CHAPTER 5 234-235: David Madison/Duomo. 237: Spencer Grant (Stock Boston). 243: Paul Conklin (Monkmeyer Press). 247: James Foote (Photo Researchers, Inc.). 248: Susan Doheny/© D.C. Heath. 251: Bob Daemmrich (Stock Boston). 256: Mitchell B. Reibel (SportsChrome East/West, Inc.). 265: Brent Jones. 272: Pat Russo (SportsChrome East/West, Inc.). 275: Susan A. Anderson/© DC Heath. CLUE is a registered trademark of Waddingtons Games Ltd., England and is used with the kind permission of Waddingtons Games Ltd and their licensees Parker Brothers, Division of Tonka Corporation, Beverly, MA 01915, USA. 276: David Johnson (SportsChrome East/West,Inc.). 277: Peter Menzel (Stock Boston). 282: Frank Cezus (Tony Stone Worldwide). 288: Wayne Eastep (The Stock Market)

CHAPTER 6 290-291: Peter Saloutos (The Stock Market). 292: Robert Frerck (Odyssey, Chicago). 297: Raj Rama(LGI). 299: Larry Lefever (Grant Heilman Photography, Inc.). 301: *r*, Peter Menzel (Stock Boston); *l*, Fundemental Photographs. 302: Jay Freis (The Image Bank). 304: Culver Pictures. 309: Christie's, New York. 315: Steve Goldberg (Monkmeyer Press). 317: David Sutherland (Tony Stone Worldwide). 318: Bruce Iverson (Photomicrography). 322: Don Kincaid. 324: Pintos by Bev Doolittle © The Greenwich Workshop, Inc., Trumbull, CT . 336: Ralph Oberlander (Stock Boston). 339: Grant LeDuc (Monkmeyer Press)

CHAPTER 7 344-345: Murray and Associates (The Stock Market). 348: Richard Pasley (Stock Boston). 357: Herb Kawainui Kane. 359: Susan Doheny/© D.C. Heath. 362: North Wind Picture Archives. 365: Kentshire Gallery (Envision). · 368: Steve Kaufman (Peter Arnold, Inc.). 370: Steven E. Sutton (Duomo). 376: George Holton (Photo Researchers, Inc.). 386: Courtesy of the author. 389: Charles Gupton (Tony Stone Worldwide).

CHAPTER 8 398-399: Roger Ressmeyer (Starlight). 402: David Sailors (The Stock Market). 404: Chahokia Mounds Historic Site. 408: Michael Springer (Gamma Liaison). 410: Jim Brandenburg (Minden Pictures). 411: Field Museum of Natural History (Neg. #GEO84564c), Chicago. 412: Bettmann Archives. 414: Tom & Pat Leeson (Photo Researchers,Inc.). 416: Eastcott/Momtiuk (Image Works). 417: David Madison (Duomo). 418: *r*, Charles Peake (Animals Animals); *l*, Robert A. Tyrrell (Animals Animals). 423: Cary Wolinsky (Stock Boston). 427: Nancy Simmerman (Tony Stone Worldwide). 428: *b*, Claudio Ferrer (Tony Stone Worldwide); *t*, H. Guckel, Center for Applied Microelectronics, University of Wisconsin. 430: Oscar Miller (Science Photo Library/Photo Reseachers, Inc.). 431: Ralph Wetmore (Tony Stone Worldwide) . 434: © Lennert Nilsson, *Being Born* (Bonnier Fakta). 437: Frans Lanting (Minden Pictures). 440: Louis Psihoyos (Matrix). 441: Bob Evans (Peter Arnold Inc.). 449: Barbara Cerva (DDB Stock Photo)

CHAPTER 9 450-451: Y. Arthus Bertrand (Photo Researchers, Inc.). 456: Peter Menzel. 457: Ezra Stoller (Esto). 462: Breck P. Kent. 464: Susan Doheny/© D. C. Heath. 467: Wide World Photo. 474: Grant LaDuc (Monkmeyer Press). 476: John Elk III (Stock Boston). 482: Frank Oberle (/Photographic Resources, Inc.). 485: Steve Goldberg (Monkmeyer Press). 487: Simon Jauncey (Tony Stone Worldwide). 490: R. Weldon (Gemological Institute of America). 494: Scott Camazine (Photo Researchers, Inc.). 497: Roger Dollarhide (Monkmeyer Press). 500: Fermilab Photography. 502: *c*, Hugh Rogers (Monkmeyer Press); *l*, Susan Van Etten (Tony Stone Worldwide); *r*, Frans Lanting (Minden Pictures).

CHAPTER 10 506-507: Alfred Pasieka (Peter Arnold, Inc.). 511: Robert Frerck (Tony Stone Worldwide). 517: Larry Lefever (Grant Heilman Photography, Inc.). 519: Spooner (Gamma Liaison). 521: Culver Pictures. 530: Michael Holford. 532: *b*, Mimi Forsyth (Monkmeyer Press); *t*, British Museum, London (Bridgeman Art Library). 537: Rick Brown (Stock Boston). 539: *bl*, Photograph by Eliot Elisofon, National Museum of African Art, Eliot Elisofon Archives, Smith-

sonian Institution; *br*, Photograph by Franko Khoury, National Museum of African Art, Eliot Elisofon Archives, Smithsonian Institution; *tl*, Photograph by Smithsonian Institution Staff, National Museum of African Art, Eliot Elisofon Archives, Smithsonian Institution; *tr*, Peabody Museum, Harvard University. Photograph by Hillel Burger. 545: *b*, Rameshwar Das (Monkmeyer Press); *t*, Chip Deutsch (Discover Magazine). 547: Ilene Perlman (Stock Boston). 551: Gabe Palmer (The Stock Market). 553: Paolo Koch (Photo Researchers, Inc.). 557: *b*, Zig Leszczynski (Animals Animals); *t*, W. Gregory Brown (Animals Animals). 558: Terry Farmer (Tony Stone Worldwide).

CHAPTER 11 560-561: Woods Hole Oceanographic Institution. 563: Don L. Crawford (Tony Stone Worldwide). 564: Joe Carini (The Image Works). 566: *l*, Mark C. Bernsau (The Image Works); *r*, Nancy Fix (Stock Boston). 569: Richard Hutchings (Photo Researchers, Inc.). 570: *t*, Pat & Tom Leeson (Photo Researchers, Inc.); *bl*, Ray Coleman (Photo Researchers, Inc.); *br*, John Serrao (Photo Researchers, Inc.). 574: Susan Doheny © D.C. Heath. 576: Frank Pedrick (The Image Works). 577: *l*, The Bettmann Archive; *r*, Culver Pictures. 579: Craig Blouin (New England Stock). 582: Martha Swope. 585: Jose Luis G. Grande (Photo Researchers, Inc.). 592: *t*, C.S. Gray (The Image Works); *b*, Mark Antman (The Image Works). 602: M. Siluk (The Image Works). 604: Philip & Karen Smith (Tony Stone Worldwide). 609: Carol Lee (Tony Stone Worldwide). 611: Ulrike Welsch (Photo Researchers, Inc.). 612. Jim Brandenburg (Minden Pictures). 614: *l*, Tom Nebbia; *r*, Gianfranco Gorgoni (Contact). 617: Steven Mark Needham (Envision)

CHAPTER 12 618-619: Manfred P. Kage (Peter Arnold, Inc.). 622: Nancy Ploeger (Monkmeyer Press). 627: Patti Murray (Animals Animals). 634: Del Mulkey (Photo Researchers, Inc.). 635: Bob Daemmrich (Tony Stone Worldwide). 638: Obremski (The Image Bank). 645: E.R. Degginger. 648: Steven Mark Needham (Envision). 650: Paul Conklin (Monkmeyer Press). 654: Mimi Forsyth (Monkmeyer Press). 659: Joe Devenney (The Image Bank). 661: Stacy Pick (Stock Boston). 662: Michael Dick (Animals Animals). 667 : *b*, Zig Leszczynski (Animals Animals); *t*, Peabody Museum of Salem. Photo by Mark Sexton

CHAPTER 13 670-671: NASA. 684: Susan Doheny © D.C.Heath. 695: Luis Castaneda (The Image Bank). 695: Steven E. Sutton (Duomo). 701: Peter Chapman (Stock Boston). 703: George Hall (Check Six). 704: Grant LaDuc (Monkmeyer Press). 706: Michael Holford. 714: Edna Douthat (Photo Researchers, Inc.). 716: Richard Pasley (Stock Boston)

In appreciation to the following editorial staff at Larson Texts:

Richard Bambauer, Linda Bollinger, Laurie Brooks, Patti Jo Campbell, Jordan Feidler, Linda Kifer, Deanna Larson, Patricia Larson, Timothy Larson, Amy Marshall, John Musser, Scott O'Neil, Louis Rieger, Paula Sibeto, Kristin Smith, and Evelyn Wedzikowski